ICE manual of
construction law

Institution of Civil Engineers

ICE manual of construction law

Edited by

Sir Vivian Ramsey
Technology and Construction Court, London, UK
Ann Minogue
Ashurst LLP, London, UK
Jenny Baster
Arup, London, UK
Michael P. O'Reilly
Adie O'Reilly LLP, Lincoln, UK

ice | **manuals**

Published by Thomas Telford Limited, 40 Marsh Wall, London E14 9TP, UK
www.thomastelford.com

Distributors for Thomas Telford books are
USA: Publishers, Storage and Shipping Corp., 46 Development Road, Fitchburg, MA 01420
Australia: DA Books and Journals, 648 Whitehorse Road, Mitcham 3132, Victoria

First published 2011

ISBN: 978-0-7277-4087-8

Future titles in the ICE Manuals series from Thomas Telford Limited

ICE manual of geotechnical engineering
ICE manual of highway design and management
ICE manual of structural design

Currently available in the ICE Manual series from Thomas Telford Limited

ICE manual of bridge engineering – second edition. 978-0-7277-3452-5
ICE manual of construction materials – two volume set. 978-0-7277-3597-3
ICE manual of health and safety in construction. 978-0-7277-4056-4

www.icemanuals.com

A catalogue record for this book is available from the British Library

Typeset by Newgen Imaging Sytems Pvt. Ltd., Chennai, India
Printed and bound in Great Britain by Latimer Trend & Company Ltd, Plymouth

DCLG (2000) *Tree Preservation Orders: A Guide to the Law and Good Practice*. DCLG, London, UK. Available for download: www.communities.gov.uk/publications/planningandbuilding/tposguide

DCLG (2009) *Tree Preservation Orders: A Guide to the Law and Good Practice – Addendum May 2009 (including model TPO)*. Available for download: www.communities.gov.uk/publications/planningandbuilding/tposguideaddendum

DCLG (2010) *Planning Policy Statement 5 (PPS5): Planning for the Historic Environment*. TSO, London, UK. Available for download: www.communities.gov.uk/publications/planningandbuilding/pps5

Department of Environment and Department of National Heritage (1994) *Planning Policy Guidance 15 (PPG15): Planning and the Historic Environment*. Available for download: http://webarchive.nationalarchives.gov.uk/+/http://www.communities.gov.uk/publications/planningandbuilding/ppg15 [Note this publication is replaced by DCLG, 2010]

ODPM (2005) *Planning Policy Statement 9 (PPS9): Biodiversity and Geological Conservation*. TSO, London, UK. Available for download from: www.communities.gov.uk/publications/planningandbuilding/pps9

ODPM (2006) *Planning for Biodiversity and Geological Conservation: A Guide to Good Practice*. ODPM Publications, London, UK. Available for download: www.communities.gov.uk/publications/planningandbuilding/planningbiodiversity

Referenced circulars

DCLG Circular 11/95: The Use of Conditions in Planning Permissions. DCLG, London, UK. Available for download: www.communities.gov.uk/publications/planningandbuilding/circularuse

DCLG Circular 05/2000: Planning appeals procedures (including inquiries into called in planning applications). DCLG, London, UK. Available online: www.communities.gov.uk/documents/planningandbuilding/pdf/circularplanningappeals.pdf

DCLG Circular 02/06: (Communities and Local Government): Crown Application of the Planning Acts. TSO, London, UK. Available for download: www.communities.gov.uk/publications/planningandbuilding/circularcommunities

DCLG Circular 02/2008: Standard Application Form and Validation. TSO, London, UK. Available online: www.communities.gov.uk/documents/planningandbuilding/pdf/circularstandardvalidation.pdf

DCLG Circular 04/08: Planning-Related Fees. TSO, London, UK. Available for download: www.communities.gov.uk/publications/planningandbuilding/743603

DCLG Circular 03/09: Costs Awards in Appeals and Other Planning Proceedings. TSO, London, UK. Available for download: www.communities.gov.uk/publications/planningandbuilding/circularcostsawards

ODPM Circular 03/05: Changes Of Use Of Buildings And Land – The Town and Country Planning (Use Classes) Order 1987. TSO, London, UK. Available for download: www.communities.gov.uk/publications/planningandbuilding/circularchanges

ODPM Circular 05/2005: Planning Obligations. TSO, London, UK. Available for download: www.communities.gov.uk/publications/planningandbuilding/circularplanningobligations

ODPM Circular 06/05: Biodiversity and Geological Conservation – Statutory Obligations and Their Impact Within the Planning System. TSO, London, UK. Available for download from: www.communities.gov.uk/publications/planningandbuilding/circularbiodiversity

ODPM Circular 08/2005: Guidance on Changes to the Development Control System. TSO, London, UK. Available online: www.planning-applications.co.uk/circular0805.pdf

Referenced legislation, regulations and standards

Ancient Monuments and Archaeological Areas Act 1979

Conservation of Habitats and Species Regulations 2010

Directive 85/337/EEC of 27 June 1985 on the assessment of the effects of certain public and private projects on the environment. *OJ*, **L175**, 05/07/1985, pp.40–48 (*EIA Directive*)

Directive 2001/42/EC of the European Parliament and of the Council of 27 June 2001 on the assessment of the effects of certain plans and programmes on the environment. *OJ*, **L197**, 21/07/2001, pp.30–37 (*SEA Directive*)

Environmental Assessment of Plans and Programmes Regulaions 200

Environmental Impact Assessment (England and Wales) Regulations 1999

Environmental Protection Act 1995

Hedgerows Regulations 1997

Housing, Town Planning etc. Act 1909

Infrastructure Planning (Applications: Prescribed Forms and Procedures) Regulations 2009

Infrastructure Planning (Compulsory Acquisition) Regulations 2010

Infrastructure Planning (Environmental Impact Assessment) Regulations 2009

Infrastructure Planning (Examination Procedure) Rules 2010

Local Government Act 1972

Local Government Act 2003

Planning Act 2008

Planning and Compensation 1991 Act

Planning and Compulsory Purchase Act 2004

Planning (Listed Buildings and Conservation Areas) Act 1990

Planning (Listed Building and Conservation Areas) Regulations 1990

Town and Country Planning Act 1990

Town and Country Planning (Appeals) (Written Representations Procedure) (England) Rules 2009

Town and Country Planning (Demolition – Description of Buildings) Direction 1995

Town and Country Planning (Determination by Inspectors) (Inquiries Procedure) (England) Rules 2000

Town and Country Planning (Enforcement Notices and Appeals) Regulations 2002

Town and Country Planning (Fees for Applications and Deemed Applications) (England) Regulations amended in 2008

Town and Country Planning (General Development Procedure) Order 1995

Town and Country Planning (General Development Procedure) (Amendment)(England) Order 2006

Town and Country Planning (General Permitted Development) Order 1995

Town and Country Planning (Hearings Procedure) (England) Rules 2000

Town and Country Planning (Inquiries Procedures) (England) Rules 2000

Town and Country Planning (Minerals) Act 1981

Town and Country Planning (Use Classes) Order 1987

Referenced cases

Pyx Granite Co Ltd v. Minister of Housing and Local Government [1958] 1 QB 554

Further reading

Carroll, B. and Turpin, T. (2009) *Environmental Impact Assessment Handbook: A practical Guide for Planners, Developers and Communities, 2nd Edition*. Thomas Telford Ltd, London, UK

Duxbury, R. (2009) *Telling and Duxbury's Planning Law and Procedure, 14th Edition*. Oxford University Press

Moore, V. (2010) *A Practical Approach to Planning Law, 11th Edition*. Oxford University Press

Useful websites

Department for Communities and Local Government (DCLG); www.communities.gov.uk/planningandbuilding/about/planning

Infrastructure Planning Commission; www.infrastructure.independent.gov.uk

National Policy Statement; www.nationalpolicystatements.org.uk

Planning Inspectorate; www.planning-inspectorate.gov.uk

Planning Portal; www.planningportal.gov.uk

Royal Town & Country Planning Institute (RTPI); www.rtpi.org.uk

Chapter 2

Financing the project

John Scriven Allen & Overy LLP, London, UK
Mark O'Neill Allen & Overy LLP, London, UK

doi: 10.1680/mocl.40878.0021

Projects can be funded by different types of external finance depending on the type of project, for instance a Build Own (Operate) Transfer project (BOT), a Public Private Partnership (PPP) project, or a property development. Funding may be equity and mezzanine funding, institutional funding, bank lending, bond issues and/or grant funding. The funders want the project to be constructed to deliver the income stream required to pay interest and repay principal on the loans and pay dividends on the share capital. As far as possible, funders want the risks borne by the project company to be distributed to other parties involved in the project, for instance the contractors who build and operate the facility, or to be covered by insurance. Funders will not want to take a credit risk on the contractors and will look for adequate guarantees and bonding. Funders will also be looking for a viable security package which will include rights to step into the project contracts and rights to call a default on the funding arrangements if covenants, including those relating to the carrying out of the project, are breached.

CONTENTS

2.1 Types of project finance

2.1.1 Introduction

Most major projects rely on external financing to fund the construction of the works. There are different types of financing and the choice largely depends on the type of project. Bank finance and, for large projects, bond financing may be used for infrastructure, and commercial property may be funded by an investing institution. The security of lenders for the repayment of the debt is usually dependent on the project revenues generated from the completion of construction. However, in some property financings, the sponsors of the project will be looking to the sale of the assets to repay the loans and there may be substantial security in the value of the assets at any given stage of completion.

2.1.2 Public Private Partnerships and other project financed schemes

As of July 2010, the UK Private Finance Initiative (PFI) is continuing under the coalition government, but there are likely to be far fewer projects. The Building Schools for the Future programme, which involved an elaborate structure of partnerships between the public and private sector, has been terminated, but it is possible that some kind of project financing may be used in a future schools programme. There are a number of waste projects still under negotiation and a small number of major hospital projects still proceeding. However, worldwide, project financing will continue to be the major source of funding for infrastructure projects, and there are current schemes, for instance, in the Middle East, Asia, Africa and South America as well as North America and Europe.

In a typical infrastructure project, a government entity enters into a project or concession agreement with a special purpose project company under which the project company has the right to build and then operate the facility or the obligation to provide services to the public sector, usually for a fixed period of time. The project company raises equity share capital and borrows from lenders in order to finance the construction of the facility. The revenues which the company receives from operating the facility or as a service charge paid by the government entity need to be sufficient to meet both the interest and the principal due on the debt of the project company used to build the facility, to cover its working capital and operation and maintenance costs and to provide a return for its equity investors. At the end of the concession or project period the facility is usually transferred back to the government entity.

Crucial to the viability of the project is the revenue stream generated by the commercial operation of the facility once it is built. Where the project company is supplying a service such as a road, hospital, schools or water-treatment services to a government entity under a project agreement, the offtake and payment arrangements will be within the main project agreement between the project company and the government entity. In some projects, such as electricity projects, there may also be separate offtake agreements with other entities which may be private or government entities. In other projects, for instance, an LNG (liquified natural gas) project, there may be a long-term offtake agreement with a commercial purchaser or, as in the refinery sector, there may be no long-term agreements but a reliance on the 'spot' market. Finally, in some projects (often referred to as concessions) the project company generates its revenue stream by charging members of the public a tariff, for instance, for the use of a road or bridge or for water services, on the basis that the tariffs are regulated by a concession agreement or a legal regulatory framework.

Whatever the nature of the project, the purpose of the construction arrangements will be to construct a facility which, under the relevant project agreement, offtake agreements or tariff regime, will generate the necessary income to cover operational costs, repay the lenders and provide a return to the equity sponsors.

A project agreement with a government entity for the provision of services is likely to contain detailed provisions in relation to the design and construction standards and the timing of the completion, but in concession arrangements the government may give the project company a freer hand in relation to design and construction. In all cases the project company and its lenders will seek to ensure that the construction risks are passed down from the project company to the contractor or contractors. In UK PPP project agreements, the construction provisions very much resemble those in a design and build contract with design criteria and other requirements in an 'Authority Requirements' document and detailed design in a 'Project Company Proposals' document for which the project company takes responsibility.

In any event, the project agreement is likely to include a requirement that the construction be completed by a specified date with a termination right on the part of the government entity for prolonged delay. Where the services are being provided to a government entity, there may also be liquidated damages for delay payable to that government entity, though this is now rare and usually relates to disruption to removal decanting arrangements. The way in which the obligations of the project company under the concession agreement are passed down to the contractor is discussed in section 2.3.5, in Back-to-back construction contracts, below. (Further discussion of BOT and PPP schemes is included in the chapter *Public-private sector partnerships*.)

2.1.3 Property development

Having identified a site, a developer sponsoring a commercial property development project may arrange that the project company enter into agreements for lease with one or more long-term tenants. This is known as pre-letting. The agreements for lease will specify the development obligations of the project company, for instance, the specification of the building and timing of completion and, for the project company, will remove the letting risk where completion is achieved by the agreed long-stop date and the development obligations are satisfied.

Alternatively, the developer may build on a more speculative basis and will be responsible for letting the project after the financial close of the project. The letting risk will then need to be accepted by the funder, whether this is a bank or an institutional investor which will eventually own the property. A bank in this situation will usually need the professional advice of valuers and letting agents on the letting risk. Whether the development is fully pre-let, partially pre-let or entirely speculative, a lender funding the development will need a valuation of the development on a completed basis to ensure that it is comfortable with the anticipated level of bank debt as against the completed value.

2.2 Range of financing options
2.2.1 Equity and mezzanine funding

A proportion of the funding for any project is normally provided by equity investors in the project (often called sponsors). The level of this funding, which would typically range from 10% to 15% (but higher for property developments), will depend on the nature of the project and its associated risks and amount of the senior funding that is available. Part or all of this funding will take the form of equity share capital which confers on the holders rights of control in relation to the project company. In addition, some of the funds may be provided by the sponsors or other investors in the form of subordinated loans (often referred to as sub-debt or 'mezzanine' financing). The mezzanine financing normally carries a relatively high rate of interest and may be treated for tax purposes in some jurisdictions as equity share capital. The mezzanine financing will, in any event, be 'subordinated', that is, will rank behind the senior lenders in relation to payment of interest and principal and on a winding-up. Equity and mezzanine finance may not be required until the end of the construction period but would be secured by a letter of credit given to the project company at financial close.

2.2.2 Funding for property development, including grant funding

The equity sponsor in a property development project is usually referred to as a developer. A developer, as the word implies, applies its skill in identifying suitable development sites and letting opportunities and ultimately selling the completed developments in the market. The developer will usually require funding for the acquisition of the site and the construction of the development. Some developers may have the option of bank funding, but this funding may have limitations. The loan to value ratio required by the bank may mean that the developer has to provide substantial equity or subordinated loans itself in order to obtain the bank funding. Where this is possible, a developer will need to find an ultimate purchaser of the property to repay the bank loan and realise the property's investment value.

An institutional investor may be an alternative to bank funding. A development funding/sale arrangement, or forward funding arrangement, between an institutional investor and a developer, provides the developer with funding and the institutional investor with a long-term investment. Although institutional investor acquires the land, two types of development arrangement are possible, one where the developer enters into the various contracts with the construction parties, and the other where the institutional investor enters into those contracts itself as principal and the developer acts as a project manager. These two arrangements are discussed in more detail in section 2.4.

Grants from heritage or lottery funds may also be available. While these are outright transfers of funds, rather than loans, the grant document will provide that they are conditional upon adherence to the terms of the grant documentation. This will typically provide detailed obligations in relation to the development, for disbursement of the grant against certified payments and the ability of the grant body to monitor the development and ensure that the obligations under the grant agreement are being adhered to. Breach of the grant agreement may result in a repayment obligation which the project company will not be in a position to fulfil and particular care should be taken to ensure that there are reasonable 'cure' periods for default before a repayment obligation arises.

2.2.3 Bank finance

Particularly in relation to PPP and similar schemes, bank finance remains the most common type of financing. Bank financing is available for both large and small projects, the smaller loan facilities being provided by a single bank and larger ones being provided by a syndicate of banks, with one or more banks acting as arrangers and leaders of the syndicate. The arranger may also underwrite the loan by committing to provide all the finance required for financial close, while aiming to sell a portion of the loan to other banks by syndicating the transaction following financial close. Since the credit crunch in July 2007, banks have been reluctant to underwrite finance and syndicate following financial close and so, where a number of banks are required, lead arrangers will endeavour to organise a 'club' of banks to take up loans on financial close.

In PFI projects there are likely to be an increasing number of funding competitions, which was used for the Treasury Building GOGGS project and more recently for Advance St. Luke's mental healthcare project in Middlesbrough and the Southmead Hospital project in Bristol which closed in February 2010. In these cases the consortia bidding for a project do not include financing in their bids, but the funders are selected following the appointment of the preferred bidder under a process monitored by the government authority. Legal, technical and financial advisers are appointed by the public authority to act for the prospective funders, and they will report on the project documentation and help prepare funding terms before the funders are selected. Prospective funders will then bid competitively on the finance terms, thus enabling the authority to obtain the most advantageous finance (which will be reflected in the authority payments under the project

agreement) available at the relevant time. As in the Southmead project, there may be 'pathfinder' banks who will be involved in the project before the final round of the funding competition in which a greater number of banks are invited to participate.

2.2.4 Bond finance

Bonds are transferable securities issued to a number of investors who would typically hold a portfolio of investment assets. The interest rate on the bonds will often be priced at a margin over the yield of government securities for a similar term, and this can result in a more attractive rate of interest (which may be index linked) than bank financing. However, the commercial and legal arrangements for a bond issue are more complex than for a bank loan, and a bond issue will therefore be appropriate only for larger projects. The market for project bonds in the UK developed strongly until 2007, and most of the larger UK PFI hospital and accommodation projects up to that time were financed by bond issues. Since then the capacity of the 'monoline' guarantors which guarantee bond issues (see section 2.6.1) and their lower credit ratings have meant that monoline guarantees for bond issues are no longer viable. To date there have been very few 'unwrapped' (i.e. not guaranteed) bond issues for projects in the UK, though this market may develop particularly if the bonds become more available to private investors. However, unwrapped bonds have been used recently in other markets.

2.3 The funders' requirements

2.3.1 Introduction

In their risk analysis of the project documents, the lenders or other funders will seek to ensure that each risk has been clearly accepted by one of the other parties involved in the project. They will want the risks to be borne by the project company to be minimized by passing risks to others. This might involve increased costs, for example, of insurance or a higher construction price than might otherwise be the case and which the project company and the sponsors may consider to be uneconomic. Where a risk is to be borne by another party, such as the construction contractor, the funders will want to be satisfied that the party concerned has resources to bear the additional costs which could arise if that risk is realized.

2.3.2 The project company

The project company bears the risks associated with the project which can neither be covered by insurance nor be passed on to the other parties in the project under the project contracts.

Limited recourse financing means that the lenders' recourse is limited to the project company and its assets. This means that lenders will not be able to claim repayment of their loans from the sponsors (who will normally be the shareholders of the project company). A risk borne by the project company is therefore a risk borne by the lenders. However, the risks taken by the lenders will be reduced to the extent of the equity in the project company, subordinated loans or any direct guarantees which the shareholders give to the lenders.

Guarantees by shareholders in relation to particular risks or undertakings to inject further funds into the project company in specified circumstances, often referred to as 'sponsor support', are not normally given in projects for infrastructure and energy but they are more common in property development. In property development, the guarantees can cover completion and also overruns and interest. For example, one or more of the shareholders may agree to additional equity or subordinated loans, up to a defined limit, equal to the amount of any cost overruns borne by the project company in achieving completion. Whether or not lenders require this type of sponsor support will depend on the current financing market and on the lenders' assessment of the risks taken by the project during its various stages.

2.3.3 Security, step-in rights, direct agreements and collateral warranties

A key issue for lenders will be the nature of the security (the rights they have over assets to support repayment) given by the project company. Where a project company defaults on its repayment obligations, the lenders will wish to be able to take over the project and dispose of it to a third party. This will involve taking over all the assets and contracts of a project company necessary to carry out the project, and also usually over the shares of the project company. In the UK, the lenders will be able to take a fixed and floating charge over the shares in, and the assets and undertaking of, the project company. A floating charge will, for a number of larger projects within specified categories, entitle them to appoint an administrative receiver of the company and block an appointment of an administrator. Property developments do not normally benefit from these arrangements.

Where the security of the lenders is dependent on the project revenues available from completion, the lenders enforcing security will want to maintain the integrity of the contract structure so that the project is completed and can produce the revenue necessary for the repayment of the lenders' debt. Direct agreements with step-in rights are an important way of achieving this. The step-in rights permit the lenders to take over the contract in two circumstances. The first is where the contractor would otherwise have been entitled to terminate the contract and the second is where there is an event of default under the loan agreements which entitles the lenders to enforce their security.

In the case of a termination right, the contractor will be required to give a period of notice before terminating, allowing the lenders to step into the contract. Where the step-in right is contained in a collateral warranty given for a property transaction, lenders will normally be required to assume all the obligations of the project company, past, present and future. This will not necessarily be the case in relation to a project financing where there may be limits on the recovery by the contractor in relation to liabilities incurred before step-in. Collateral warranties given in a property development will usually provide

for a permanent novation of the liabilities to a lender. A direct agreement in a project finance transaction will do this, but will also allow for the possibility of a temporary step-in by a company controlled by the lenders as an additional obligor, with a permanent novation to a third party or a sale of the project by the lenders at a later stage. The notice periods given by contractors to the lenders in collateral warranties tend to be fairly short (typically 21 days) but those in project financing direct agreements can extend for much longer periods.

The step-in and novation arrangements in relation to a collateral warranty given in a property development will be much less complex than those in a direct agreement in project financing. However, collateral warranties in a property development will also contain duties of care and obligations in favour of lenders in relation to the performance of the underlying contract as well as other provisions, for instance, in relation to a copyright licence. These provisions will allow lenders to assign the benefit of a collateral warranty to a purchaser of the property following an insolvency. This may be particularly relevant where the contracting parties (building contractors and professional consultants) are under an obligation to provide warranties to purchasers and tenants, but do not do so because they have outstanding claims against the project company. The extent to which the lenders can assign the warranties will therefore be an important issue both for lenders and the contracting parties. However, where the insolvency occurs before the completion of construction and the contractor is not permitted to complete the work, the duty of care or direct obligation on the part of the construction contractor in favour of the lenders may be of limited value. The position may be different for a duty of care given by the consultants whose obligations are not principally to supply a completed project but to provide advice over a period of time.

For further information on collateral warranties, novation and insolvency, see the chapters *Collateral warranties* and *Insolvency in construction*.

2.3.4 The funders' technical adviser

The funders will usually engage a technical adviser to advise on the technical content of the project contracts and to advise generally on commercial and technical issues in relation to the project. This may be an in-house adviser employed by the lending bank or an institutional investor or may be an external consultant. In some project financings (for instance, energy financings), where the project company employs a separate overall technical adviser as well as the consultants providing services in relation to the project, this technical adviser may report to the funders separately after it has completed its work for the project company. In property financings, the funders will normally appoint a project monitor to overview the development and attend site meetings. The technical advisers will often have a role after financial close monitoring compliance with the project undertakings by the project company in the financing documentation (see section 2.5.3).

2.3.5 Construction contract issues

2.3.5.1 General

Like the project company, the funders will want to minimize the risks to them arising from the three principal construction issues of money, time and quality. In relation to money and time, they will therefore focus on the risks assumed by the project company, and in relation to quality they will wish to ensure that the project fulfils its commercial requirements. These requirements may be contained in a project agreement with a government entity, an offtake agreement with a commercial entity or, in the case of a property development, in an agreement for lease.

In commercial property development, the structure may be a traditional Joint Contracts Tribunal (JCT) contract under which the employer supplies the design to the contractor or a design and build contract (although here the nature of the design obligations may be less absolute than in a project financing). Construction management or management contracting structures may also be used in commercial property developments and exceptionally in project financings. Under these structures the project company bears the risk of non-performance of the individual sub-contractors (called 'trade' or 'work' contractors) and the risk of the coordination of design and of construction. These structures will therefore be less attractive to funders than traditional or design and build structures. However, the advantages to the project company in terms of flexibility in the timing of design and construction in using these structures may make it worthwhile for the sponsors of the project company to provide additional sponsor support to the lenders to cover the increased risks.

Where construction management or management contracting structures are used in project financings, for instance power projects, the sponsors may be required to enter into documentation designed to achieve a 'virtual' turnkey under which the sponsors undertake to put the project company in the same position in which it would have been if there had been a turnkey contract. Virtual turnkey structures may also be used where a turnkey contract is split for tax reasons, but in this case the relevant undertakings are given by one or more of the contractors who will, therefore, seek to manage the risks involved.

For a more detailed discussion of different types of construction contracts, see the chapter *The construction contract*.

2.3.5.2 Key issues in the construction contract

Key issues for the funders in the construction contract will include the following.

Design

Responsibility for design will be a key issue in the choice of the contract structure discussed above. Even where there is a design and build contract, there is likely to be some reliance by the contractor on information or concept design provided by the project company. The funders will wish to identify those design elements for which the project company is responsible under the construction contract and to understand the recourse which the project company has to third parties in respect of them.

Performance tests and completion

In many project financings, there will be performance or completion tests under the construction contract. These will test the ability of the project to fulfil the performance criteria required for generating the income necessary to repay the loans or other funding. They will need to be appropriately defined, and the funders' technical adviser may have a role in certifying or reporting on the carrying out of these tests.

Defects liability

The liability of the contractor for defects and the responsibility of the contractor for latent defects after the expiry of the defects liability period will be important to the funders. In particular, unless this is clearly agreed between the parties, funders will want to avoid any implication that the final certificate is conclusive that the works have been performed in accordance with the contract, which could exclude any claims for defects after the issue of the certificate. Similarly, they are likely to resist an 'exclusive remedies' clause having the same effect.

Payment systems

The funders will want to ensure that payments to the contractor are consistent with the value of work performed at any time. The payment system will need to be looked at together with the provisions for retention or retention bonds. The loan agreement or institutional development agreement may contain provisions requiring the funders' technical adviser to check that the amounts are properly due. Alternatively, the funders may be content with a collateral warranty from the certifying consultant.

Time and money events

The funders will want to reduce to a minimum the circumstances entitling the contractor to additional time for completion or additional payment under the contract. In relation to those risks retained by the project company, they will want to ensure that the project company has adequate funding to meet liabilities arising as a result of these risks. They will also want to ensure that the rights of the project company to liquidated damages are safeguarded in the case of a breach of contract or acts of 'prevention' by the project company.

Delay

Where the contractor is responsible for delays, lenders will wish to ensure that the liquidated damages cover at least the debt service obligations of the project company which, if there had been no delay, would have been covered by the project's revenues. Institutional investors will similarly want their loss of investment return to be covered by liquidated damages (though they may not be successful in this). Particularly where a project agreement can be terminated for prolonged delay in completion, the lenders may also expect there to be a right on the part of the project company to terminate the construction contract before that time, allowing the project company to employ a replacement contractor to complete the works within the longstop time allowed under the project agreement. In property transactions, where an agreement for lease could be terminated for prolonged delay, the funders will commonly seek the right to step into the shoes of the project company, by perhaps appointing a receiver, with a view to taking control of the development to achieve the deadline set by the agreement for lease.

Back-to-back construction contracts

In certain BOT projects where the scope of the project company obligations and its entitlement to payment for services provided are defined in a project agreement, such as a PFI transaction in the UK, the funders will wish to ensure that the obligations and liability of the project company in relation to the construction of the facility are passed down to the construction contractor on a 'back-to-back' basis. The obligations will include design responsibilities and the requirement to achieve completion by a specified date on the basis that the definition of completion and the determination as to whether it is achieved is the same under the construction contract as under the concession agreement. The entitlement to extensions of time for completion may be dependent upon time granted by the authority under the project agreement. However, entitlement to additional money cannot be dependent upon certification or payment under the project agreement, since these 'pay when paid' provisions will be ineffective under the provisions of the Housing Grants, Construction and Regeneration Act 1996 (the Act) (see *Midland Expressway v. Carillion Construction and others [2005] 2963 TCC* and further provisions are contained in the Local Democracy, Economic Development and Construction Act 2009 (as of July 2010, not yet in force)). Although the PFI project agreement may be excluded from the operation of the Act, the exclusion will not apply to the construction contract. There should however be scope for the payment to be dependant upon the legal entitlement of the project company under the project agreement, provided the construction contractor can establish this and obtain payment independently of any determination or payment under the project agreement. There is now a possibility that the Secretary of State may disapply certain provisions of the Act to certain types of transactions, thus allowing the possibility that the prohibition on 'pay when paid' provisions will be disapplied in the case of project finance transactions.

Since the 'pay when paid' provisions are ineffective under the Act, contractor parent company loans (called 'parallel loans') may be requested to cover any mismatch of funding resulting from a claim for money being paid to a contractor before the project company recovers from the government authority under the project agreement. This may be resisted by the contractor and will not be appropriate unless the contractor is also a sponsor.

The provisions of the contract in relation to a wide variety of provisions such as the scope of the construction obligations, indemnities, defects, subcontracting, changes and *force majeure* will reflect, usually on a word-for-word basis, those of the project agreement. It will be important that not only are the words the same in appropriate cases but that their interpretation and the determination of issues are the same. This may entail consistent dispute mechanisms, including adjudication, in accordance with the provisions of the Act. To the extent this is not practicable or not permitted by the relevant authority, the contractor will seek provisions ensuring that the project company represents its position in any dispute in which it has an interest.

In some respects, however, the provisions of the construction contract which are equivalent to those in the project agreement may need to be more onerous than the project agreement, for instance, to reflect project company risks inherent in the project agreement obligations (e.g. life-cycle risks). Similarly, time extensions may not necessarily be back to back. This is because, although the government entity grants a time extension to the project company in certain circumstances, thus relieving the project company of any liability for delay damages payable to the government entity and termination for default, it will generally not cover the loss of revenue which would otherwise be covered by liquidated damages payable by the contractor. While in some cases these losses will be covered by business interruption insurance for insured risks, there may be categories of uninsured events where the contractor may be asked to share or bear the risks in order to deal with the loss of revenue (and therefore debt service) which results from the extension of time. It may also not be appropriate to pass down all limitations of liability since the way the authority recovers loss from the project company under the project agreement (for instance through deductions under a payment mechanism) will be different from the way in which the project company recovers loss under the construction contract.

As mentioned above, where the authority has the right to terminate the project agreement for prolonged delay in completion of construction, the funders will wish the project company to have the right to terminate the construction contract before that time on the basis of an adjudicated 'look forward' test to allow the appointment of a replacement contractor to complete the works before the longstop date arrives.

Bonds and guarantees

The funders will not wish to take any credit risk in relation to the contractor, so will assess the nature and terms of any advance payment, performance, retention or other bonds or guarantees given by banks or other institutions on behalf of the contractor to support its obligations. Where the contractor is a subsidiary, funders will usually require a parent company guarantee. Funders will also wish to satisfy themselves as to the creditworthiness of all parties giving bonds and guarantees and may need provisions in the construction contract to cover credit rating downgrades of these parties which require the contractor to provide alternative security in the event of a downgrade.

In international and power projects, there may be a requirement for an on-demand bond which would give the project company access to immediate funds on the default or insolvency of the project company, but this would be unusual in a UK PPP project. A proven default bond can only be enforced when the quantum of the claim, for instance, in relation to additional completion costs, has been agreed or determined under the disputes resolution provisions of the contract. A bond in a UK PPP project may be enforceable following an adjudication award or it may provide that it may be called 'on demand' following an adjudication award. However, the prohibition in the Insolvency Act 1986 on proceedings against a company in administration without the leave of the court may prevent the decision of an adjudicator being made, and this can prevent the payment obligation under a bond arising in these circumstances. To deal with this, it will be necessary to have alternative mechanisms to ensure that liability under the bond arises, such as determination by an expert or referee under the construction contract, or there could be a separate adjudication under the bond, or the bond could be on-demand upon the insolvency of the contractor.

Bonds and guarantees are covered in more detail in *Bond, parent company guarantees and other security*.

Limits on the liability of the contractor

Funders will wish to analyse any limits on the liability of the contractor, for instance in relation to the type of loss recoverable – it is normal for contracts for process plants to exclude recovery of consequential loss – or any monetary limits on liability. This will be particularly relevant in the context of UK PPP projects where the project company may be exposed to losses resulting from the 'liquid market' retender provisions in the project agreement with the public sector entity on a default by the project company (see the chapter *Public-private sector partnerships*).

Consultants' agreements

The funders and their advisers will wish to ensure that the duties of the consultants are adequate, particularly in relation to the definition of the services provided by each of them and the coordination and interface between them. They would expect there to be an appropriate degree of skill, care and diligence, defined by reference to the type of project, and that the consultants will be wholly responsible for the default of sub-consultants. They will also wish to ensure that the level of professional indemnity insurance is adequate and in line with market practice (also see the chapter *Professional indemnity insurance*).

In property development projects, consultants giving collateral warranties will frequently seek to limit their liability to funders and others by use of mechanisms such as 'net contribution' clauses – which require the contribution made by other consultants to the relevant loss to be taken into account – and by taking into account set-offs and counterclaims that the consultant may have against the employer. These are standard requirements of the insurance market in relation to collateral warranties, and 'net contribution clauses' may also be requested in relation to consultants' appointments (see the chapters *Collateral warranties* and *The consulting engineer's appointment*).

2.4 Institutional funding structures

Institutions investing in property may enter into agreements with developers under which the developer is the principal party involved in making the arrangements for the construction of a development. The funds for construction would be provided by the institutional investor who will usually be the owner of the land during the development phase.

The developer may be the contracting party in employing consultants and entering into the construction contract. Alternatively, the developer may be the facilitator or manager of the contractual arrangements entered into by the institutional investor as principal directly with the contractor and consultants. Where the developer acts as principal, it has primary liability to the contractor, and it may take responsibility for some cost overruns. In this structure, the developer will seek reimbursement of direct expenditure (which may include the price of the site), together with a share in the profits resulting from the completed development. Where the developer is a manager on behalf of the institutional investor, the investor will enter into the contractual arrangements and the developer is likely to receive a fee on an ongoing basis but with a smaller profit share.

In either case, the developer's profit share will be calculated by reference to the value of the property when completed and let, which in turn will be calculated by reference to the yield. The multiple of the yield which results in the price will depend on the nature of the property. This will reflect the risks inherent in the market for that type of property at the time. Usually, the profit share of the developer will increase proportionately as the target return of the institutional investor is exceeded.

Even though the developer may be acting as principal in employing the contractor and consultants, the institutional investor will retain the ability to control the activities of the developer through an approval and monitoring regime. This will include approval of the forms of contract and selection of contractors. The developer will be responsible to the institutional investor for ensuring that the development is carried out in accordance with the relevant design plans and specifications. The institutional investor and its advisers will closely control the payment of development costs and will wish to ensure that they are all in accordance with the relevant contracts. There may also be arrangements for the institutional investor to make payments directly to the contractor and consultants.

Where a developer acts as principal, the institutional investor will require collateral warranties containing step-in rights with the contractor and consultants. These would be triggered under the development agreement between the institution and the developer in the event of default or insolvency of a developer. Unlike banks, an institutional investor may not be reticent in exercising step-in rights since it will often have, or can usually acquire, the expertise to carry out and complete the development following the termination of the development agreement.

2.5 Bank financing
2.5.1 Term, interest rate, prepayment and drawdown

Interest on loans taken out to finance the project will commonly be rolled up or capitalized during the construction phase, reflecting the fact that the property will not be revenue generating. The principal may be repaid in one lump sum or in instalments over the period of a loan. A lump sum repayment may be appropriate in the case of a property development where the principal is repaid on the sale of the property or a refinancing. The interest rate is usually a margin or 'spread' over base rate or the London Interbank Offered Rate (LIBOR), the size of the margin reflecting the market for that type of lending. LIBOR is effectively a floating rate basis for the payment of interest, so lenders will frequently require that the risk of changes in interest rate is hedged, perhaps with an interest rate swap or, alternatively, that a fixed interest rate is used. Whether interest is charged at a fixed rate or a floating rate is combined with an interest rate swap to convert the floating rate to a fixed rate, prepayments will, depending on interest rate movements, cause a cost to the project company reflecting the breakage costs of termination of the funders' fixed rate or swap arrangements. While there will be fees payable to the bank for making the loan facilities available, there may also be fees on prepayments. These will be greater if the prepayments are made earlier in the term of the loan.

The loan will be drawn down over the period of construction and, as referred to above, the lenders are likely to require that drawdown can only be made to pay the costs of construction as and when these are incurred under the relevant agreements.

Lenders may also require the proceeds of drawings to be paid directly to contractors and consultants to ensure that the proceeds are used for the purposes for which they were drawn.

There will be conditions precedent to the first and subsequent drawdown. These will include, in relation to the initial drawdown, completion of all necessary documentation and receipt by the lenders of satisfactory reports in relation to the technical aspects of the project. Subsequent drawdowns will frequently require the provision of invoices to verify costs and a confirmation from the lenders' project monitor or technical adviser that the payment is appropriate.

2.5.2 Financial covenants in the loan documentation

There is likely to be an ongoing requirement for the project company to have income which is greater by a specified ratio than the requirements of debt service (the debt service cover ratio). The projected revenue of the project during the life of the loan will also need to be greater by a specified ratio than the total amounts to be repaid under the loan agreement (the loan life cover ratio). There may also be a requirement to maintain specific funds in reserve accounts to cover the inability of the project company to meet expenditure should the revenue be insufficient. These might include a debt service reserve for payment of amounts due under the loan agreement; a maintenance reserve for periodic maintenance, replacement and refurbishment; a capital expenditure reserve where capital expenditure is forecast; tax reserves and other contingency reserves. In property development financings there may be a loan to value covenant. For these purposes, the value during the construction phase will be calculated on the basis of an assumption as to completion of works and, possibly, lettings. This is commonly tested only at the start of the development on the assumption that the loan facility is fully drawn.

2.5.3 Project undertakings in the loan documentation

The loan agreement is likely to contain a large number of detailed undertakings on the part of the project company in relation to the way in which the project is carried out. These undertakings typically include an obligation not to alter the project contracts without the consent of lenders, an obligation to enforce those contracts and also rights for the lenders' technical adviser to inspect the progress of the project, to be provided with a wide variety of information and to monitor progress payments and the state of completion of the project. More specifically, there is also likely to be a list of 'reserved discretions' where the project company is obliged to act in accordance with the instructions of lenders in relation to the exercise by it of specified rights provided for under the construction contract. These can include matters such as variations, the settlement of claims and the rights of suspension or termination available to the project company.

For the project company, it may be important whether the consent in relation to the various reserved discretions can be given by an agent bank on behalf of a syndicate of banks or whether a majority consent of the syndicate of banks is required, since the process of obtaining consents can be time consuming.

Breach of the undertakings is likely to give rise to an event of default which, after appropriate cure periods, will entitle the lenders to accelerate repayment, call a default and enforce a security and take over the project from the project company and its shareholders.

2.6 Bond financing
2.6.1 Types of project bond issue

As mentioned in section 2.1 above, Bond finance, above, financing by means of a bond issue is confined to large projects, particularly in the PFI sector, although since the 'credit crunch' in 2007 bond financings are less viable. Although there are examples of bond issues in the property sector, they are not at all common. The costs of the additional arrangements required for a bond issue mean that it is unlikely to be economic where the project cost is significantly less than £100,000,000. However, since the interest rate applicable to bond financing is usually a margin over the relevant government securities for an equivalent term, the interest rate was for many years more competitive than bank financing. In the first years of project finance, bank financing tended to be for under 20 years, typically 15 years (although much shorter for property development financing), and long-term financing was more easily available at that time from bond issues to make the annual payments more economic. Longer-term bank financing has in the past few years been available particularly in UK PPP transactions, though this has been harder to obtain since the credit crunch.

Most bond issues for UK projects have been 'wrapped', that is, guaranteed by a 'monoline' insurer with the effect that the purchasers of the bonds rely largely on the credit risk of the insurer rather than the commercial viability of the project. The credit risk of the insurers, reflected in their credit rating by rating agencies, has come under increasing scrutiny since the credit crunch and, following downgrading of their credit ratings, monoline insurers have ceased to underwrite new business. Where a bond issue is guaranteed, the offering circular sent to prospective bond holders will contain not only extensive details in relation to the guarantor but also much of the information in relation to the project which would be required in the case of a bond issue which is not guaranteed (an 'unwrapped' bond issue). To date, there have been few unwrapped project bond issues for UK projects.

2.6.2 Offering circular and listing

Whether or not the bond issue is guaranteed, a financial institution, called the arranger, will be required to issue an offering circular to prospective bondholders, although it is likely to disclaim responsibility in relation to the project details supplied to it. The bonds are likely to be listed on the London Stock Exchange or another international stock exchange, and the offering circular issued to prospective bond holders will need to fulfil the applicable statutory and regulatory requirements as to its contents and manner of issue. The offering circular will need to contain full details of the terms and conditions of the bonds which will cover most of the terms included in a loan agreement.

2.6.3 Role of the guarantor, arranger and bond trustee

Where the issue is unwrapped, the institution issuing the offering circular will also underwrite the subscription for the bonds. In this case, the underwriting institution will also take the lead in negotiating the terms and conditions of the bonds and, together with its professional advisers, commenting on the project contracts. Where the issue is guaranteed, this role will be undertaken by the guarantor.

In addition to the financial institution issuing the information memorandum, which may be the underwriter or arranger and/or the guarantor, there will also be a requirement for a trustee to exercise rights on behalf of the bond holders and to hold the security rights on their behalf.

Where there is a guarantor, the collateral deed between the project company and the guarantor will address similar matters to those covered in a loan agreement, in addition to the terms of the bond conditions. The degree of control over the carrying out of the project exercised by a guarantor will therefore be greater than that exercised by a trustee on behalf of the bond holders in relation to an unwrapped bond and will be similar to that in a loan agreement. In the case of an unwrapped bond, the arranger and underwriter will negotiate the terms and conditions of the bond, which will reflect the principal terms to be found in a credit agreement, but the ability on the part of the bond trustee to intervene in the carrying out of the project, for instance in relation to reserved discretions, will be somewhat less than that of a bank lender or the insurer of a wrapped bond.

2.6.4 Verification

The offering circular will need to be verified by the project company's directors, although where the issue is characterised as one of international securities under the Financial Services Act, the personal liability of the directors in relation to the contents of the offering circular may be reduced, with the project company being the party primarily liable.

2.6.5 Rating

The bond issue will need to be rated by a rating agency in order to be marketable and the rating agency will need to review the technical aspects of the project together with the contract documentation. The rating agency is likely to pay particular attention to credit risk issues, in particular the credit risk in relation to the contractor and the bonds and guarantees given by third parties on its behalf as security for any claims against it. In the case of a guaranteed bond issue, the rating of the bonds issued will reflect the credit risk of the guarantor. However, there will also need to be a 'shadow' rating which assesses the project as if the bond issue were not guaranteed. The ability of the monoline insurer to guarantee the project, and its guarantee fee, will be dependent on this 'shadow' rating.

2.6.6 Timing

The timetable for a bond issue will reflect the requirements of the additional parties referred to above. The project contracts and the terms and conditions of the bonds will need to be largely agreed before a preliminary information memorandum is issued to prospective bond holders. As mentioned above, the information memorandum will need to be carefully verified. There should be very few changes between this version and the final preliminary offering circular issued prior to the launch of the bonds. On the day of the launch of the bond issue, the bonds are priced by reference to an interest rate and/or a sale discount on the nominal value. Where the price of services under the project contracts reflects the pricing of the bonds, these contracts will need to be simultaneously entered into to reflect this pricing on the basis that they are conditional only upon financial close. Financial close will typically take place a week or more after the launch of the bonds, when the moneys are subscribed by the bond holders. A feature of a bond issue compared with a bank financing is that the total proceeds to the bond issue will be available on financial close and will be held by the project company in secured accounts or lent under guaranteed investment contracts (GICs) to be drawn down as and when required for construction. Compared with a bank financing, funding for expected variations will be more complicated and provision for funding variations will need to be specifically made at the outset for instance by the provision for variation bonds.

References

Referenced legislation, regulations or standards

Financial Services Act 2010
Housing Grants, Construction and Regeneration Act 1996
Insolvency Act 1986
Local Democracy, Economic Development and Construction Act 2009

Referenced cases

Midland Expressway v. Carillion Construction and others [2005] 2963 TCC

Further reading

Allen, G. (2001) *The Private Finance Initiative* – Research Paper 01/117. House of Commons Library, London, UK. Available online: www.parliament.uk/documents/commons/lib/research/rp2001/rp01–117.pdf

Delmon, J. (2009) *Private Sector Investment in Infrastructure*, Second Edition. The World Bank and Kluwer Law International

Vinter, G. D. (2006) *Project Finance, Third Edition*. Thomson, Sweet & Maxwell

Websites

Joint Contracts Tribunal (JCT); www.jctltd.co.uk

Chapter 3

Public sector projects

David **Marks** CMS Cameron McKenna LLP, London, UK
Chris **Fellowes** Mayer Brown LLP, London, UK

doi: 10.1680/mocl.40878.0031

The procurement of supplies, works and services in the public sector must comply with certain key principles of fairness, equal treatment, transparency and non-discrimination. These requirements are set out in a number of Directives issued by the European Union to its Member States, including the UK. The UK has implemented these Directives by way of statutory instruments which are generally referred to as the Procurement Regulations. There are certain procurements in the public sector that are either excluded from the Procurement Regulations or, for which certain elements of the Procurement Regulations do not apply.

There are a number of different procurement procedures in the public sector, categorised as open, restricted, negotiated and competitive dialogue procedures, each set out detailed requirements in respect of the advertisement for bids, assessment of bids, award of contracts and notification to unsuccessful bidders. Failure to comply with the Procurement Regulations could lead to an unsuccessful bidder successfully challenging the award of a contract. Such challenges could lead to the Court issuing an injunction preventing a contract being entered into, declaring a contract that has been entered 'ineffective' and/or awarding damages to the unsuccessful bidder.

CONTENTS

3.1 Introduction

This chapter explores the procurement of construction projects in the public sector since these are subject to a form of regulated procurement. Here the 'public' sector means work carried out wholly or partly with public funds and should not be confused with the activities of public limited companies (PLCs), who by and large must only satisfy their own shareholders and are part of the 'private' sector. Public–private partnerships using a combination of public and private sector funds, such as those developed under the Private Finance Initiative (PFI) are discussed separately in the chapter *Financing the project*.

For completeness, reference is also made in this chapter to procurement by utilities. Certain procurements by utilities are also regulated, depending on the activity performed by the procuring entity, and irrespective of whether the utility is state or privately owned.

This chapter will consider a range of issues:

- why should the approach to public sector projects be different? (section 3.2);

- what constitutes the public sector for these purposes? (section 3.3);

- the substantive procurement law rules, principally deriving from EC Directives. (section 3.4);

- some problem areas in the application of procurement law. (section 3.5).

3.2 Why should public sector projects be different?

In substance, there should be no difference between public and private sector projects. The underlying principles of contract law are the same and so too are the client's motivations. The difference is that the public sector must be seen to be accountable to the taxpayer. This arises in a number of ways as detailed below.

The way in which projects and services are procured

Public sector contracts must be seen to be awarded fairly and without discrimination. The award process must be both transparent and accountable.

The expenditure of the public funds involved

Public accountability is of paramount importance. Taxpayers, in a democracy, are entitled to know that their money is being spent in accordance with approved policies and that adequate safeguards are in place to prevent the misappropriation of funds. The need for good audit control and the provision of a clear audit trail are therefore central themes in a project procurement strategy.

Maximizing value for money

Value for money does not necessarily mean lowest price. General principles of good practice are supported by the Treasury and mean seeking the optimum combination of price and quality for each specific project or service. In addition, the Local

Government Act 1999 imposes a legal duty to achieve 'best value' on local government.

The public sector is therefore subject to a rigorous accountability discipline which is a proxy for the profit or self-interest motive of the private sector. A substantial body of legislation and regulation has developed to ensure that these objectives are met.

Those working with the public sector for the first time are frequently confused by (if not contemptuous of) the apparent bureaucracy involved as a result. However, it does need to be understood that the obligations imposed on the public sector involve employees and consultants in a different level of responsibility, transparency and accountability than is conventionally the case in the private sector. Failure to comply with the letter of the law may render individuals or the client body as a whole liable to actions at civil law, or to possible criminal prosecution. In the local government context, central government would have powers to step in.

Much of the legislation, particularly in relation to larger projects, has derived from the European Community's (EC) aim to achieve a common market in goods and services. Breaches of the law may result in the European Commission taking infringement action against the responsible member state. Breaches of EC procurement rules also create rights of action by interested parties in national courts. The EC rules are the foundation of most of the substantive law on procurement in the UK. A further gloss to this set of rules derives from the World Trade Organisation's Government Procurement Agreement (GPA).

3.3 What constitutes the public sector?

Outside the utility sectors, contracting authorities which are subject to regulated procurement are defined in the EC rules as:

> the State, regional or local authorities, bodies governed by public law, associations formed by one or several of such authorities or bodies governed by public law.

For example, Directive 2004/18/EC (Article 1(9)) on the coordination of procedures for the award of public works contracts, public supply contracts and public service contracts. The GPA is much narrower in scope, being confined to named central government agencies and sub-central government agencies.

The entities in the UK affected by EC procedures on regulated procurement include a wide range of organizations including:

■ central government;

■ local authorities (including police and fire authorities);

■ utilities (many of which have now been privatized but most of which are still subject to a regulated procurement regime specific to certain utility activities);

■ a range of entities, corporations and other bodies which are in effect controlled by the public sector.

These categories will be considered briefly in turn.

3.3.1 Central government

There is a persistent drive for government to become a 'best practice' client quite independently of the policy drivers behind the EC rules. This has given rise to a considerable volume of procurement guidance and administrative advice, generally from the Office of Government Commerce (including the Achieving Excellence in Construction suite of procurement guides, for example, *Initiative in Action* (PG01), *Project Organisation – rules and responsibilities* (PG02) and *Procurement and Contract Strategies* (PG06)) but also echoed by the various spending ministries (e.g. Department of Health), aimed at providing a modern framework to guide those involved in commissioning construction work and placing contracts. These documents consolidate and build on other literature such as the *Guide to the Appointment of Consultants and Contractors* (GACC). The construction industry has also been the subject of a study designed to identify ways of increasing competition. The industry was the first to be subject to analysis under the Kelly Programme. This resulted in a set of proposals for the strategic management of public sector procurement in the construction market (e.g. in relation to embedding early supplier engagement and sharing market intelligence), see *First Kelly Market Proposal*.

3.3.2 Local government

Local authorities, like other public bodies, are subject to the procurement rules. The Local Government Act 1972 requires local authorities to draw up standing orders relating to the making of contracts for the supply of goods and materials or the execution of works. The detail of these regulations and the thresholds above which they will apply is for the individual authority to decide.

The thresholds for the application of the EC procurement rules are quite high (as detailed in section 3.4.5), but it is usually appropriate for local authority standing orders to require competition at a lower threshold since the use of competitive and transparent procedures is essential for realising the local authorities' objectives.

One particular objective is the duty imposed on local authorities by the Local Government Act 1999 to secure 'best value' in carrying out their functions (Local Government Act 1999 s. 3(1)). An authority must 'make arrangements to secure continuous improvement in the way in which its functions are exercised, having regard to a combination of economy, efficiency and effectiveness'. Best value requirements therefore apply across the whole range of a local authority's activities and competitive processes are a necessary tool for demonstrating compliance.

3.3.3 Utilities

Utilities in the water, energy and transport sectors can also be subject to regulated procurement obligations by virtue of the EC rules. This is the case irrespective of whether the utility is owned in the private or the public sector. For this purpose, utilities are defined not by reference to their ownership but to specific activities, and only procurements related to such activities are regulated.

The regulated procurement regime applicable to utilities is much more flexible than that applying to the general public sector. The rationale for regulating the procurement of utilities, irrespective of ownership, is that utilities perform functions in the general interest. They also do so under governmental or regulatory supervision through statutory or licensing regimes. The public hand is therefore much in evidence and might be in a position to influence expenditure policy.

Many of the utilities covered by this special regime used to be in public ownership. In the UK, many of these companies have been privatized and the sectors in which they operate are now subject to considerable competition. Where a previously regulated sector enters a truly competitive environment, the rationale for regulating procurement by participating entities is no longer present. These areas are progressively being taken outside the scope of the EC utilities procurement regime (e.g. telecommunications activities which are now no longer subject to the EC utilities procurement rules). As a result of recent changes to the utilities rules there is now also a specific mechanism which allows for member states or individual companies to apply for particular sectors to be removed from the scope of the rules on the grounds that the market is sufficiently competitive. In the UK, exemptions have been granted to utilities for the exploration for and exploitation of oil and gas, the supply of electricity and gas, and electricity generation. The position of utilities is referred to at times in this chapter for the sake of completeness.

3.3.4 Other bodies

A range of other bodies which are in effect controlled by the public sector will also be covered by government procurement policy or the EC procurement regime. Such activities will include, for example, many higher education establishments or cultural institutions. The detailed position will depend on whether the entity carries out a function in the general interest, not of a commercial nature, and whether it is primarily financed, or controlled, by the public sector.

A procurement compliance obligation can also be placed on certain purely private bodies where the public sector is subsidizing a project to the extent of more than half the project's value (Public Contracts Regulations 2006, 34(a)). The public sector funding body has an obligation to impose on the recipient a contractual obligation that the recipient will follow the EC procurement rules in procuring the project. By this contractual device, the procurement compliance obligation can be made to follow the public funds. This factor commonly arises in relation to Lottery-funded projects.

3.4 Substantive procurement rules
3.4.1 Introduction

This discussion of the substantive procurement rules is intended to provide the reader with an understanding of the broad framework of the rules. It is necessarily an overview of an increasingly complex subject, more detail can be found in the chapter *Procurement route*.

This section will cover the following:

- the main legal sources
- the role of the EC
- EC directives
- scope: works, supplies or services and value thresholds
- special rules: concessions, subsidized contracts, design contests
- types of procedure
- notices and time limits
- Frameworks, e-auctions and dynamic purchasing systems
- prequalification and selection
- enforcement.

3.4.2 The main legal sources

The bulk of the substantive rules in the UK on regulated procurement derive from EC obligations and in particular from EC directives. The EC directives have been implemented by detailed national regulations in the form of statutory instruments. These rules do, however, co-exist with a miscellany of domestic common law rules affecting procurement procedures. Such common law rules include the following:

- A tendering procedure can create an implied contract between contracting entity and bidders that the process will be run fairly. This rule applies both to public and private sector procedures (see the chapter *Tender process*).

- A public authority's actions can be challenged in the courts if it acts unreasonably when taking decisions, including decisions on the conduct of procurement procedures.

- A public authority can be responsible for a misfeasance in public office which is actionable by interested parties.

The common law rules can be particularly relevant in those situations where the EC-inspired rules do not apply.

However, it is the EC-inspired rules which have imposed some system on an otherwise disorderly patchwork of national law rules.

3.4.3 The role of the EC

A key objective of the EC Treaty is the facilitation of trade within the Community. Achievement of this objective required the creation of a single internal market in which the free movement of goods, persons, services and capital is ensured for all member state nationals. An associated objective was to combat national preference by opening up public sector procurement to all EC nationals.

A high priority was given to opening up public procurement because of the huge sums at issue. The European Commission estimates that EU public procurement markets in 2008 were worth over €2155 billion, more than 17% of total EU Gross Domestic Product (European Commission, 2010). In turn, public sector construction output has historically constituted a significant component of the total value of public sector procurement, and the economic significance of the construction industry ensured that it received considerable attention.

The EC's approach has been to establish a legal framework founded on the following key principles:

- non-discrimination on grounds of nationality; and

- transparency and fairness of process.

EC rules have therefore concentrated purely on the demand side of the market, by forcing purchasing authorities into a consistent procurement framework. The EC's policy is part of a market integration strategy and, while much of the EC procurement regime reflects the Treasury's concerns for best practice and value for money, this is not always the case, and there are a number of areas where there is a mismatch between EC and Treasury objectives.

For example, post-tender negotiations with bidders are generally prohibited under the EC public sector rules for fear of unfairness between bidders, notwithstanding the possible value for money advantages of such negotiations to the purchaser.

3.4.4 EC directives

EC rules to regulate procurement issues have been introduced through EC legal instruments called 'directives'. These are highly flexible in terms of their implementation. Directives specify the objectives to be achieved and the time frame within which they must be brought into force, but allow individual member states considerable freedom to determine the precise form in which these objectives are imposed within their own legal system. The EC has therefore adopted directives to regulate a procurement by the general public sector and by utilities. **Table 1** summarizes the current EC directives and UK regulations in the procurement area and the corresponding UK rules which came into force on 31 January 2006.

The texts for both the general public and utilities sectors have a number of common features to promote principles of non-discrimination and transparency, including:

- the reiteration of the basic principle in Article 12 of the EC Treaty prohibiting discrimination against other member state nationals;

- a qualifying value threshold for contracts above which contracts are to be advertised by specific procedures a distinction between open, restricted, negotiated and competitive dialogue procedures;

General public sector	Utilities (water, energy and transport)[a]
EC: Directive 2004/18/EC[b] (This consolidated and updated three earlier directives for works, services and supplies: Directive 93/37/EEC, Directive 93/36/EEC and Directive 92/50/EEC) Directive 2007/66/EC (Remedies Directive)	EC: Directive 2004/17/EC[c] (This updated an earlier utilities directive: Directive 93/38/EEC) Directive 2007/66/EC (Remedies Directive)
UK: The Public Contracts Regulations 2006 SI 2006/5 (This consolidated and updated three separate regulations for works, supplies and services implementing the old EC directives: the Public Works Contracts Regulations 1991, the Public Services Contracts Regulations 1993 and the Public Supply Contracts Regulations 1995) The Public Contracts and Utilities Contracts (Amendment) Regulations 2007 The Public Contracts and Utilities Contracts (CPV Code Amendments) Regulations 2008 The Public Contracts (Amendment) Regulations 2009	UK: The Utilities Contracts Regulations 2006 SI 2006/6 (This updated the utilities regulations implementing the old utilities directive: the Utilities Contracts Regulations 1996) The Utilities Contracts (Amendment) Regulations 2009
Enforcement Directive 89/665[d]	Directive 92/13[e]

[a] Postal services will have to be switched from the public sector rules from January 2009.
[b] OJ L134/114, 30.04.2004
[c] OJ L134/1, 30.04.2004
[d] OJ L395/33, 30.12.89. UK implementation is integrated in the Public Contracts Regulations 2006.
[e] OJ L76/14, 23.3.92. UK implementation is integrated in the Utilities Contracts Regulations 2006.

Table 1 EC directives and UK regulations affecting procurement

- the publication of tender notices in the Official Journal of the European Union in the prescribed form;
- the promotion of EC as opposed to national standards;
- minimum time limits for publication and response;
- the publication of award notices;
- selection on the basis of lowest price or the most economically advantageous tender; and
- the preservation of compliance records by the contracting authority.

A number of distinctions need to be understood when dealing with the procurement directives:

(a) The sector – does it concern the provision of certain utilities functions (i.e. water, energy or transport)?
(b) The nature of the contract – does it concern works, supplies (goods) or services?
(c) What kind of directive? – some directives lay down rules on how tendering procedures should operate, others deal with methods of enforcing their compliance.

It should be remembered that the EC directives are complemented by the general internal market provisions of the EC Treaty itself, for example, the free movement of goods, the free provision of services and the freedom of establishment. These general EC principles can be relied on even in situations where the EC directives themselves do not apply.

3.4.5 Scope: works, supplies or services and value thresholds

The EC rules make a distinction between procurements of works, supplies and services. The distinction is important because each type of procurement is subject in some respects to a different set of rules. Notably, the value thresholds above which the rules apply vary with the type of procurement at issue.

The scheme of the EC directives is designed to define procurements as either works, supplies or services in a seamless way, thereby preventing certain types of contract from falling outside the regime. The definitions themselves are somewhat circular and there can be occasional difficulties in determining the true nature of a procurement.

In a project for the construction of a building, the procurement is likely to be for work. However, if one were to dissect the construction process it would involve the provision of building materials (supplies) which are processed (services) yet which give rise to a finished building (work). The project will have involved the appointment of construction professionals such as the design team, a quantity surveyor and a project manager (services). It is important to have an understanding of where each discipline begins and ends.

Work is defined as:

> the outcome of any works which is sufficient of itself to fulfil an economic and technical function.
>
> (Public Contracts Regulations 2006, Regulation 2(1))

Work is therefore defined by reference to an end result rather than to an individual input. The nature of 'works' in turn refers to the construction of new buildings and works, restoring and common repairs (Ibid, Schedule 2), including:

- site preparation
- building of complete constructions or parts thereof; civil engineering
- building installation
- building completion.

The rules apply if the procurement is a 'public works contract'. This has a very wide meaning and includes contracts:

> under which a contracting authority engages a person to procure *by any means* the carrying out for the contracting authority of a work corresponding to specified requirements.
>
> (Ibid, Regulation 2(1)) [emphasis added]

This broad definition involving procurement of works 'by any means' was designed to cover increasingly complex project structures.

In relation to *supplies*, a 'public supply contract' is a purchase or hire of goods. In the case of hire, the contracting authority need not become the owner at the end of any hire period. Where installation services are also involved, the contract remains a supply procurement if the value attributable to the goods themselves is equal to or greater than the value attributable to the installation services. An issue of this kind could arise, for example, in relation to the procurement of a standard type of escalator and it will often be difficult to determine whether the procurement should be a supply or a service (or in some cases even a work).

In relation to *services*, a 'public services contract' is a contract for the provision of services but specifically excludes contracts covered by the rules on works and supplies. One peculiarity of the services rules is the distinction between Part A and Part B services. The full rigours of the rules apply to Part A services (which include the procurement of services from construction professionals such as architects, surveyors, engineers and project managers) whereas the procurement of Part B services is only subject to certain requirements on use of standards, record keeping and the publication of an award notice. Part B services include, for example, the provision of certain transport, legal, education and health services and any other service not explicitly listed in Part A.

Certain procurements are excluded from the rules altogether, for example, if secret or requiring special security measures.

Having identified the nature of the procurement, consideration can be given to whether the procurement is likely to exceed the value thresholds at which the procurement rules begin to apply. The thresholds as set in the UK are shown in **Table 2**.

The thresholds have to be considered before a procedure is launched and the exercise requires some informed speculation.

	General public sector Supplies		Services	Works
Entities subject to WTO GPA	£101 323[i]		£101 323[a]	£3 927 260[b]
	(€125 000)		(€125 000)	(€4 845 000)
Other public sector contracting authorities	£156 442		£156 442	£3 927 260[b]
	(€193 000)		(€193 000)	(€54 845 000)
	Utilities Supplies		Services	Works
All sectors	£313 694		£313 694	£3 927 260
	(€387 000)		(€387 000)	(€4 845 000)

* The conversion rates for non € currencies such as £ sterling are as set on 1 January 2010. The level of the thresholds is adjusted every two years by the European Commission.
[a] With the exception of the following services which have a threshold of £156 442 (€193 000): Part B (residual) services; research and development services; certain telecommunications services; and subsidized services contracts under regulation 34.
[b] Including subsidized works contracts under regulation 34.
[i] OGC *Information Note 13/09* 1 December 2009.

Table 2 Procurement value thresholds

If elements of the project are budgeted to exceed relevant value thresholds, they should be advertised under the rules. On the other hand, contracts should not be split up artificially to bring each below the thresholds. There are some special rules on how the thresholds are applied to each of supplies, services and works.

The services and supplies rules require the cumulation of similar supplies or services over a twelve-month period for the application of the thresholds. If the contract is for supplies or services over a number of years, then the value over the duration of the contract is taken into account. In the case of a hire contract whose duration is indefinite, the monthly hire charge is normally multiplied by a factor of 48 (Public Contracts Regulations 2006, 8(9)(c)).

Since 'work' is defined by reference to an outcome which is 'sufficient of itself to fulfil an economic and technical function' the cumulation for the purposes of the works threshold is of expenditure to achieve that outcome rather than of similar works.

There are important and highly practical provisions for dealing with small works, services or supplies packages within an overall project whereby these small packages (frequently 'small lots') do not need to be procured by call for competition. In the case of works, a small lot for these purposes is capped at €1m (£810 580 (OGC, 2009)) and where the small lots, taken together, are less than 20% (Public Contracts Regulations 2006, 8(12)(b)) of the expected value of the works. The corresponding value for services is €80 000 (£64 846 (OGC, 2009)) instead of €1 m.

3.4.6 Special rules: concessions, subsidized contracts, design contests

The rules have particular regimes for a number of types of procurement including concessions, subsidized contracts and design contests.

Special rules on concessions only appear in the Public Contracts Regulations in relation to works contracts (The Commission has published an explanatory communication on concessions OJ C121/29.04.2000). (The use of concessions under the Public Finance Initiative is discussed in greater detail in the chapter *Financing the project*.) A 'public works contract concession' is a public works contract

under which the consideration given by the contracting authority consists of or includes the grant of a right to exploit the work or works to be carried out under the contract.
(Public Contracts Regulations 2006, Regulation 2(1))

A concession therefore involves some form of revenue exploitation risk on the part of the contractor. Typical examples would be toll roads or bridges.

Under the special regime, the concession award is subject to a call for competition. Following award the successful concessionaire then itself becomes subject to obligations to adhere to the procurement rules when letting sub-contracts. There are however important exceptions which can allow the concessionaire to reserve sub-contracts for members of its own consortium.

The favourable treatment of consortium sub-contracts is of considerable practical importance in such projects and can affect the level of private sector interest. A construction contractor may be less inclined to join a consortium to bid for the concession if it had to bid subsequently for sub-contracts as well. There are no similar rules affecting services concessions or anywhere in the utilities regime.

There are also special rules on subsidized contracts in relation to public works and services procurements. Where a contracting authority provides more than half (Ibid, Regulation 34(a)) of the funding for a project to an entity which is not itself a contracting authority with procurement obligations, the contracting authority is bound to include in the funding arrangements a contractual requirement that the recipient adheres to the procurement rules when procuring the project and ensure that the recipient does so comply or recover the contribution. The subsidized contract rules apply to works and to services procurements.

By this method, the procurement obligation is made to follow the public funds. However, the obligations of the recipient are contractual and are owed to the contracting authority rather than generally. It is common for a failure to adhere to the rules to be an event of default in the funding documentation which would trigger repayment of the funding. This mechanism is particularly important in many Lottery-funded projects. This rule on subsidized contracts does not apply in all situations but is confined to certain civil engineering projects and building work for hospitals, sports, recreation and leisure facilities, school and university buildings and buildings for administrative purposes.

There is also a special regime under the services rules for design contests, such as architectural competitions. The procedure is not commonly used in practice. It is more usual for contracting authorities to procure the appointment of an architect or a design team for a project and they may require design concepts as an important part of that appointment process rather than to procure a design.

3.4.7 Types of procedure

There is an important difference between the types of procedure available under the rules. A distinction is made between open, restricted, negotiated and competitive dialogue procedures.

Open procedures do not involve any form of prequalification exercise. Because bids are invited from all comers, adjudication can be very burdensome. As a procedure, it is probably best adapted for a standardized procurement need, such as for generic supplies. It is largely inappropriate for use with complex works projects or for the appointment of construction professionals.

Restricted procedures involve a prequalification and short-listing exercise. This keeps the number of bidders low and thereby helps to contain bid costs for both procurer and bidder. The rules specify that the minimum number of bidders that should be invited to tender is 5 (Ibid, Regulation 16(9)(b)).

Negotiated procedures are perhaps best described by reference to open and restricted procedures. As a matter of principle, negotiation is not possible as part of open or restrictive procedures in general public sector procurement. General public sector procurement permits negotiation in only very narrowly defined circumstances, some with and some without a call for competition. Where the negotiated procedure involves a call for competition, at least three (Ibid, Regulation 17(11)(b)) candidates, if suitable, should be invited to bid. In the utilities sector, a negotiated procedure can be used as of right, rather than as an exception. The utilities rules therefore offer much greater procedural flexibility than the general public sector rules.

In the general public sector rules, the rare situations where a negotiated procedure is possible are set out in detail. Because negotiated procedures are very much the exception, the exceptions are interpreted strictly. They therefore have to be treated with some caution. The following is a summary of the exceptional circumstances where a negotiated procedure *without* a call for competition is possible:

- if an open or restricted procedure is discontinued as a result of irregular tenders or because no acceptable tenders were made, and all operators who submitted a tender in the discontinued process are invited to negotiate the contract;

- in the absence of tenders, suitable tenders or applications in response to an open or restricted procedure;

- for technical or artistic reasons or for reasons connected with the protection of exclusive rights, the contract can only be performed by one contractor;

- in case of extreme urgency;

- the products are manufactured purely for research, experiment, study or development (supplies only);

- provision of additional comparable supplies (generally not for a period of over three years) (supplies only);

- for the purchase or hire of goods quoted on a commodity market (supplies only);

- to take advantage of advantageous terms for the purchase of goods in a closing down sale or other type of sale (supplies only);

- when the rules of a design contest require the contract to be awarded to one of the successful contestants, provided all successful contestants are invited to negotiate the contract;

- for additional works or services not included in the initial project but which have become necessary through unforeseen circumstances for the performance of that contract; and

  - the additional works or services cannot be technically or economically separated from the main contract without great inconvenience to the contracting authority, or

  - although separable, are strictly necessary for the main contract's completion however, the value of the additional works or services cannot exceed 50% of the amount of the main contract (works and services only)

- repeat works or services but where this prospect was referred to in the contract notice for the original contract, the value of the consideration for the repeat works or services was taken into account in determining the estimated value of the original contract and within three years of the conclusion of the original contract (works and services only).

Situations where a negotiated procedure with a call for competition is possible include:

- if an open or restricted procedure is discontinued as a result of irregular tenders or because no acceptable tender were made

- for works contracts carried out solely for research or testing purposes and on a not-for-profit basis

- where the nature of the works, services, or supplies, or the risks attaching to them, do not permit prior overall pricing

- if specifications for a service contract cannot be established with sufficient precision to enable an open or restricted process to be run.

Negotiated procedures can be used as of right in the utilities sectors. The inability to engage in negotiations except in limited circumstances is a severe constraint in the general public sector rules. Indeed, compliance with this requirement is often difficult to achieve in practice. The reform of the procurement directives resulting in Directive 2004/18/EC therefore introduced a new award procedure called *competitive dialogue*. This is the procedure under which most PFI/PPP contracts will be tendered (although its remit is wider). It represents a compromise to the European Commission's opposition to the routine use of the negotiated procedure for PFI/PPP contracts in the UK. PFI/PPP contracts must therefore normally comply with the competitive dialogue procedure under which there is less flexibility for negotiation with the contracting authority.

The competitive dialogue procedure is available for 'particularly complex contracts'. More specifically, it is available where the contracting authority cannot in advance define the technical specification required or specify the 'legal or financial make-up of the project'.

The basic principle of the competitive dialogue procedure is that it allows the contracting authority to hold discussions with bidders in order to develop the desired technical solution before submission of final, priced bids. A minimum number of three (Ibid, Regulation 17(11)(b)) candidates should be invited to participate in the procedure. The contracting authority conducts a dialogue with these candidates in order to identify potential solutions. During this dialogue the contracting authority must ensure that there is no discriminatory treatment between the candidates, for example, in relation to availability of information. The contracting authority also must not divulge a proposed solution or other confidential information of one candidate to the others without that candidate's permission. During the dialogue phase the contracting authority can narrow down the field of tenderers by applying evaluation criteria (including on price).

The contracting authority compares the proposed solutions and identifies which are capable of meeting its needs. It then invites the candidates to submit tenders based on 'any' solution presented during the dialogue. There is no further negotiation with the tenderers on these bids. Tenders may however be 'clarified, specified and fine-tuned' at the request of the contracting authority but without changing the 'basic features of the tender'.

3.4.8 Frameworks, e-auctions and dynamic purchasing systems

Framework agreements are agreements with one or more contractors setting out the terms and conditions under which specific call-offs can be made throughout the term of the agreement. The public contracts rules require that framework agreements are advertised and awarded in compliance with the standard tendering procedures. The specification contained in the framework should also be detailed enough to cover all the works, services or supplies to be awarded under it (e.g. in the case of a construction project, the individual projects involved, when it is envisioned they will take place and the different categories of work being procured).

A framework agreement can be entered into with a single contractor or with a number of contractors. In relation to frameworks concluded with a single contractor, the contractor's tender can be supplemented before a call-off upon the request of the contracting authority (Ibid, Regulation 19(5)) but the contract must be awarded within the limits of the terms laid down in the original framework agreement (Ibid, Regulation 19(5)). In general, frameworks should be limited to four years' duration.

In relation to frameworks concluded with a number of operators (at least three) there are essentially two options. The first option is to award call-offs simply by reapplying the original evaluation criteria. The second option is to run a mini-competition between all the framework contractors capable of meeting the particular need (i.e. not just those whom the contracting authority wants to invite). The public sector regulations contain basic rules for the operation of mini-competitions. A more flexible regime for framework agreements exists under the utilities rules.

E-auctions for the purposes of the procurement rules are on-line auctions where selected bidders submit offers electronically against the contracting authority's specification. E-auctions can be used at the conclusion of any of the available procurement procedures. In particular that means e-auctions can be used at the mini-competition stage of a framework or for call-offs under a dynamic purchasing system. There are however two important limits on the use of e-auctions. First, e-auctions cannot be used for the award of service contracts where the subject matter is a product of 'intellectual endeavour' such as a design contract. Second, e-auctions can only be used to evaluate elements which can be automatically evaluated by reference to figures or percentages.

Dynamic purchasing systems can be set up under an open procedure. This is essentially a form of on-line framework agreement – with the difference that suppliers must be able to enter and exit the framework on an ongoing basis. The system is available for the purchase of 'commonly used' goods, works or services.

3.4.9 Notices and time limits

The EC rules achieve equality of opportunity and transparency by requiring most calls for competition to be published in the *Official Journal of the European Union* (commonly OJ or OJEU). There are various types of call for competition envisaged by the rules and notices must be submitted in the set format as published by the European Commission (Commission Regulation (EC) No. 1564/2005).

The main types are:

- *prior information notice* (PIN): a contracting authority is to send, at the beginning of the financial year, a PIN covering supplies or services contracts for which it expects to invite offers during its financial year where the anticipated value of similar supplies or services is €750 000 (£607 935) (OGC, 2009) or more. For works, the obligation to publish a PIN provides for this to be done as soon as possible after the decision authorising the programme of the works;

- *contract notices*: the same format is used for notices for open, restricted, negotiated and competitive dialogue procedures. There are separate forms of design contest notice and simplified contract notice on a dynamic purchasing system;

- *qualification system notice*: these are envisaged only in the utilities rules. Qualification systems allow considerable flexibility and help to accelerate short-listing;

- *contract award notice*: there is a requirement for a contract award notice in the relevant format to be despatched to the OJEU within 48 days of the award.

The contract notice is an important step in the procurement process. Any national publication of the procurement opportunity cannot be earlier or more extensive than the contract notice. The despatch of this notice to the OJEU triggers the start of procedural time limits. However, the notice defines the scope of the procurement and needs to be prepared with care. Should the procurement as conducted not relate to the procurement as described in the notice, it is likely that the procedural rules will have been breached and it may be necessary to relaunch the process.

A contract notice should give sufficient information for potential contractors to identify the commercial opportunity. At the same time it is sensible for a contracting authority not to limit its freedom of action by describing the project too prescriptively, particularly if tender documentation is still being developed at that stage, as will often be the case.

The OJEU is required to publish the notice within five days (Directive 2004/18/EC, Article 36(3)) of despatch if transmitted by electronic means and within twelve days (Ibid, Article 36(3)) of despatch in most other cases. Since the date of publication is outside the contracting authority's control, the minimum procedural time limits run from the date of despatch, not the date of publication.

The rules set out minimum *time limits* for most stages of the relevant procedure. The rules relating to the public sector are illustrated in **Table 3**. Special time limits apply when documents are notified electronically to the OJEU.

There are a number of situations where shorter time periods can be used. This is possible, for example, where adherence to the nominal minimum periods is made impractical for reasons of urgency. In such cases a restricted procedure can be 'accelerated' by substituting periods as low as 15 and 10 days for 37 and 40 days respectively.

Procedure		Normal limit (days)	Electronic notification to OJEU	Electronic access to contract documents
Open	Minimum time from sending notification until tender return date	52	−7	−5
	With PIN (usual)	36		
	With PIN (minimum)	22		
Restricted	Minimum time from despatch of notice to receipt of requests to be selected to tender	37	30	
	If urgent (minimum)	15	10	
	Minimum time from despatch of invitation to tender until tender return date	40	35	
	If urgent (minimum)	10		
	With PIN (usual)	36	31	
	With PIN (minimum)	22		
Negotiated Procedure	Minimum time from despatch of notice until receipt of requests to be invited to negotiate	37	30	
	If urgent (minimum)	15	10	
Competitive Dialogue	Minimum time from despatch of notice selected until receipt of requests to be to participate	37	30	

Source: (Ibid, Article 38)

Table 3 Time limits for procurement procedures

Where there has been a contract notice there is some visibility as to whether the time limits are being adhered to. Where an accelerated procedure is being used, the pro forma notices provide for the justification for the acceleration to be given on the face of the notice.

3.4.10 Prequalification and selection

The rules set out the framework as to how prequalification and selection processes are to be conducted.

Prequalification is addressed in considerable detail in the general public sector rules. The rules list reasons why contractors may be ineligible to tender, for example in the case of insolvency or arrears of taxes. A contracting authority can add to these reasons provided that they are objective, non-discriminatory and are set out in the contract notice. The rules contain an obligation to exclude candidates or tenderers who have been convicted for participation in a criminal organisation, corruption, fraud, or money laundering. Contracting authorities must exclude such persons where they have 'actual knowledge' of the relevant convictions.

The general public sector contracting authority is, however, limited as to the information it can otherwise request from candidates as part of a prequalification exercise. It can only request certain specific information on economic and financial standing and technical capacity. For economic and financial standing this is limited to statements from bankers, published accounts and statement of turnover of business in the previous three years. For technical capacity the prescribed areas include issues such as similar activities in the previous five years, quality control certification, technical facilities or staff qualifications. Utilities have greater flexibility in their choice of prequalification criteria.

The pro forma contract notices provide for the prequalification basis to be set out on the face of the notice.

As for *selection* of the successful bidder, the rules provide that only one of two possible criteria are possible: either the lowest price or the 'most economically advantageous' tender. If the most economically advantageous criterion is used, the contracting authority is required to indicate in the contract notice or contract documents the relative weighting given to each of the evaluation criteria. The weightings can be expressed as ranges. This requirement can only be avoided where weighting is not objectively possible. Relevant evaluation criteria could include a range of issues including (but not limited to) timing, quality, aesthetics, price and technical merit. The 'most economically advantageous' tender criterion provides the opportunity for considering broader value for money issues in addition to price. This more holistic approach is also more open to subjective judgments and thereby to abuse.

The contract notice pro forma provide for the selection criteria to be set out on the face of the notice, but this can be provided to bidders with the contract documents, that is, as part of the invitation to tender.

3.4.11 Enforcement

Legal protest about the conduct of a procurement procedure is only one manifestation of how these rules are enforced. Rules relating to procedural transparency should be considered equally important in achieving compliance. Contracting authorities have obligations to maintain an audit trail and records can be called for by the European Commission. Furthermore, procuring entities have obligations to notify participants with reasons as soon as they are excluded from the procurement process, even if this is before the award decision is made. These are important incentives for contracting authorities to adhere to the procedure they have set for themselves and in particular to apply the stated selection criteria. It should also be borne in mind that most contracting authorities are subject to the disclosure requirements of the Freedom of Information Act 2000. Guidance from the Office of Government Commerce suggests that disclosure under requests pursuant to the Freedom of Information Act can extend beyond what is required under the procurement rules.

The rules also provide for formal legal remedies in case of breach (or the general public sectors Directive 89/665, OJ L395/33 30.12.89. UK implementation is integrated in the Public Contracts Regulations 2006.). The UK implementation provides for injunction and compensatory remedies. Under these rules there is a statutory minimum 10 day standstill period (commonly referred to as the 'Alcatel period') between the announcement of the successful bidder and the entry into contract.

The objecting party can be any contractor who is potentially affected. The objector has to inform the contracting authority of the breach before commencing proceedings. The UK regulations provide that proceedings have to be brought promptly and in any event within three months of the grounds for bringing the proceedings first arising.

However, the CJEU decision in *Uniplex* found that the word 'promptly' is contrary to EU law as it prevents claimants knowing the exact time limits that apply. The CJEU further held that time should begin to run from the date the claimant knew or ought to have known of the breach rather than the date of the breach itself (Case C-406/08 *Uniplex (UK) Ltd v. NHS Business Services Authority*). Furthermore, under the Public Contracts (Amendments) Regulations 2009 and the Utilities Contracts (Amendments) Regulations 2009 a court can declare a contract 'ineffective' after it has been entered into where there has been a serious breach of procurement rules as defined in the regulations. One such serious breach is where a contracting authority has entered into a contact without having complied with the requirements as to the advertisement of the intended procurement when it was obliged to do so. Such a declaration can be avoided by the contracting authority publishing a 'voluntary transparency notice' in the Official Journal – if the contract is not entered into within 10 days of publication and no challenge is made during that period. The Courts will not declare contracts to be 'ineffective' if 'overriding reasons relating to a general interest require that the effects of the contract should be maintained'. If the Court declares a contract to be ineffective then the contract will be brought to an end. Consequently, the contracting authority would have to re-tender the contract and the previously successful bidder would (if it so wished) have to re-bid the contract. The Courts can also award financial penalties or 'contract shortening' where the duration of the contract is shortened. Any objecting party has six months to bring an ineffectiveness claim but this can be reduced to 30 days where the contracting authority has published a 'contract award notice' or has otherwise notified the objecting party of the conclusion of the contract and a summary of the relevant reasons.

These remedies sit alongside remedies generally available under the common law.

The rules do occasionally throw up high profile cases. *Harmon CFEM Facades (UK) Ltd v. The Corporate Officer of the House of Commons* [1999] All ER(D) 1178 involved the procurement of Portcullis House in Westminster which provides office accommodation for MPs. There was evidence of national preference and a departure from the stated tender procedures. The selection criterion was based on 'best value for money' which the court interpreted to mean, in the absence of greater clarity, the lowest price. The lowest priced bidder did not win and protested. The objector successfully recovered damages for tender costs and loss of profit, albeit on a discounted basis, since it could show that it had a real chance of winning. Interestingly the claims were both statutory under the then prevailing procurement regulations, and under common law including for misfeasance in public office. Overall, recovery of damages will be more difficult to demonstrate if the selection criterion is the more complex 'most economically advantageous' tender. The UK enforcement rules are therefore at their most potent when they are used to threaten an injunction to halt or to rectify the procurement procedure at any time before contract award. However, the potential threat of 'ineffectiveness' which came into place in December 2009 also gives an objecting party certain rights to bring contracts that have been entered into in breach of procurement rules to an end. The 10 day standstill provision improves the potential for seeking injunctions.

Other recourse of a more informal nature is also possible. It is possible to bring irregularities to the attention of the European Commission who can bring infringement proceedings against member states before the European Court. It is also possible for the European Commission to secure 'interim measures', that is, an injunction against member states. There are also information gathering procedures which the European Commission can invoke against member states.

Pressure can also be put on national authorities who might prefer to resolve matters quickly rather than be subject to unwelcome oversight from outside. This sensitivity can be exploited between national authorities and the European Commission as well as between local and central government authorities.

3.5 Some problem areas in the application of procurement law
3.5.1 Introduction

The purpose of this section is to highlight some additional themes which commonly occur in relation to construction projects and which are worth identifying and discussing in greater detail. This section covers the following problem areas, although these are by no means the only problems which arise from this increasingly complex legal area:

- typical breaches of the rules
- negotiations
- construction management
- speculative work and the Lottery
- reopening a deal.

3.5.2 Typical breaches of the rules

The rules are complex and contracting authorities should not underestimate the possibility of making mistakes. Where the contracting authority does make mistakes, these become opportunities for objectors and threats to the contracting authority. Practical experience suggests that the following types of breach are not uncommon.

Mismatch between the project described in the contract notice and the project as let

In an ideal world, the full tender documentation is in place before the contract notice is issued. In reality this rarely happens. The problem does give rise to practical difficulties. Where the thinking moves on after the contract notice is issued, the contracting authority may want to approach the project in a manner materially different from the way in which it was previously described.

Often the problem can be avoided by drafting the notice in a less prescriptive manner. Alternatively, there may be time to reissue the contract notice, suitably amended. In any event, it is important to address the problem sooner rather than later.

Time limits

A disrespect for the limits will be a very public breach of the rules. All parties involved in the procurement will be aware of the time limits and the contract notice itself may betray a departure from the rules.

If there is to be a protest it is most likely to come from a party which needs time for a particular procedural step.

No contract notice – no competition

This would be a radical breach since not even a flawed competition would be run. The contracting authority will only be relatively safe from protest if it is able to maintain secrecy in relation to the breach. However, under the new Remedies regulations this would be a ground for ineffectiveness.

Post-tender negotiations

This theme will be considered in more detail in Section 3.5.3. However, it is one of the most common breaches of the general public sector procurement rules.

Losing the papers

It is not uncommon for the contracting authority to mislay a bid, particularly where an open procedure is used (most commonly in the procurement of generic supplies). Administrative error is all too frequent and can be particularly embarrassing for the contracting authority. In one anecdotal example the objector secured by way of apology a different (and better) contract but without competition.

Misapplication of the prequalification or selection criteria

Contracting authorities have strong incentives to adhere to their stated procedure and criteria. As already seen, those eliminated from a procedure can ask for written reasons. It is important that the reasons given by the contracting authority relate to criteria stated in the competition itself and reflect its own internal file. Discrepancies will be hard to explain away. Even so, the more holistic selection criterion of 'most economically advantageous' tender is more open to subjectivity and potential abuse.

Wrong procedure

The procedure might be wrong because a negotiated procedure or competitive dialogue procedure is used when it is not justified. This will also be a very public breach of the rules since the type of procedure will be clear from the contract notice.

The procedure might also incorrectly classify the procurement as work, a supply or a service. It will be particularly serious if a procurement is deliberately misclassified in order to take advantage of a procedural advantage. An example might be where the procurement is erroneously and deliberately construed as a Part B service (to which the full rigours of the rules do not apply) rather than as a Part A service or another type of procurement altogether.

Extending a contract

There is frequently the temptation to relet a follow-on contract to an incumbent provider without further competition. While there is some scope for doing so under the rules, it will not generally be possible and much will be depend on the detailed circumstances. Follow-on contracts will be fresh procurements which will usually need to be advertised.

3.5.3 Negotiations

The general public sector rules, unlike the utilities rules, do not generally permit negotiations between the contracting authority and bidders. It has already been seen that the rules severely limit the use of negotiations with bidders. The public sector rules provide that negotiations with bidders are only permitted where the conditions are satisfied for use of either the competitive dialogue procedure or the negotiated procedure. Both the public and the utilities regimes limit the scope of negotiations with the winning bidder.

Under the public sector regime the European Courts have endorsed the following statement as an accurate reflection of the position in relation to the open and restricted procedures:

> The Council and the Commission state that in open and restricted procedures all negotiations with candidates or tenderers on fundamental aspects of contracts, variations in which are likely to distort competition, and in particular on prices, shall be ruled out; however, discussions with candidates or tenderers may be held but only for the purpose of clarifying or supplementing the content of their tenders of the requirements of the contracting authorities and provided this does not involve discrimination.

Clarification is therefore acceptable even if negotiation is not. The borderline between the two will often be difficult to determine. As already noted, post-tender negotiation which goes beyond mere 'clarification' is probably one of the most frequent technical breaches of the procurement rules.

The concern about post-tender negotiation in procurement procedures relates to fairness and transparency. It is feared that post-tender negotiations lead to inequality of opportunity between bidders, notwithstanding the potential value for money opportunities which negotiations could offer. For this reason there is always a restriction on negotiation with the winning bidder. This limit is reflected in the provisions governing the use of the competitive dialogue procedure. After selecting the best tender the contracting authority may request the bidder:

> to clarify aspects of that tender or confirm commitments contained in the tender provided that this does not have the effect of modifying substantial aspects of the tender or of the call for tender and does not risk distorting competition or causing discrimination.

However, in practice, post-tender negotiations can easily stray from 'clarifications' to 'changes' to the procurement. In this regard, there is concern that not only should the tenderers that currently remain in the procurement process be asked to resubmit tenders on the basis of this change but also, should tenderers who have been excluded earlier from the procurement process have the same opportunity? Of course, a substantive 'change' could mean that the procurement process needs to start again.

3.5.4 Construction management

Although not so much a problem area it is important to understand the procurement implications of construction management compared with other forms of construction procurements.

The procurement route for construction management differs from more traditional procurement. In construction management the client will let individual contract packages and these are coordinated by the construction manager. The construction manager appointment is one for services. However, in contrast to more traditional construction procurement, no single works contractor takes overall responsibility for the works packages. The client therefore does not deal with one head contractor. **Figure 1** illustrates the procurement differences.

Under the traditional route the client lets one contract, which for a contracting authority would be subject to a regulated procurement procedure. The subcontracts will not be the client's procurement concern.

Under the construction management route the number of individual procurements proliferate. The contracting authority appoints a construction manager (a services procurement) who then coordinates the procurement of each package. The procurement of each package is in the name of the contracting authority. Under the cumulation rules all the packages would need to be taken together for the application of the works value threshold. Particularly helpful will be the small lots rules which dispense with the advertising requirements, that is, where individual works packages are worth less than €1m (£810580 (OGC, 2009)) and which in aggregate are worth less than 20% of the overall project value.

3.5.5 Speculative work and the Lottery

The advent of the Lottery has thrown up a number of procurement law difficulties. A particular problem is the position of a service provider who does speculative work to help an applicant develop its funding application.

In many situations, the entity which is seeking Lottery funding is already a contracting authority for the purposes of the procurement rules. Such an entity will already be used to the compliance obligations which the rules place on it. This will be the case for many theatres, museums and galleries. Even if such a body has charitable status, it is often the case that a majority of the relevant governing body is appointed by central or local government. Outside this 'public' environment there is generally less familiarity with the rules.

Lottery funding is treated as public money. Thus, if it is used to fund a works or a services project, that project can become a 'subsidized contract' for the purposes of the works or services rules. As already seen, where the subsidy runs to more than half the value of the procurement, the funding body must impose on the recipient the obligation to apply the procurement rules and makes the procurement obligation follow the public money. This principle is usually implemented through the funding agreement. Non-compliance with the procurement rules would usually be an event of default which could trigger the requirement to repay the funding received. This is a very strong compliance incentive. Where the Lottery fund applicant is already in the public sector it will be a contracting authority in its own right and will be subject to the procurement rules in any event, irrespective of the contractual obligation which might be imposed in the funding mechanism. Such a clause in the funding agreement is not necessary in this case.

A practical difficulty arises where early conceptual or design work is done, for example, by an architect for a private Lottery fund applicant such as a gallery or a theatre. The architect might be devoting considerable time on a speculative basis to help with the gallery's Lottery funding application and expects to be paid for past and future services if the application is successful.

This can give rise to a number of complications. If the gallery is successful with its application, the funding agreement will impose the obligation to adhere to the procurement rules on pain of repayment. The architect may therefore have to compete for the appointment in which he or she had already invested heavily. If the architect does not continue in the process there can be copyright issues as to whether the gallery can move forward with the architect's initial design or whether the gallery will have to start again. This could also cause difficulty for the continuing validity of the applicant's Lottery submission.

The gallery could have avoided this difficulty by advertising the architect's appointment in anticipation of receiving the Lottery funding and being subject to the procurement obligation. The appointment would have related to the entire design and supervision process and any payment to the architect would have been made conditional on the award of Lottery funding.

See the chapter *Intellectual property* for further details on copyright issues.

3.5.6 Reopening a deal

This is an area where there is little guidance other than the general principles behind the procurement rules and behind the EC Treaty.

One category of situations is readily dealt with. This is where, for example, a services contract is advertised to be for one year but with the option on the part of the contracting authority to extend for a further year. The option to extend was part of the original scope advertised and the exercise of that option is simply the implementation of the procurement in one of the forms in which it was originally conceived. Thus it does not involve reopening the deal at all. There can be many permutations of this example.

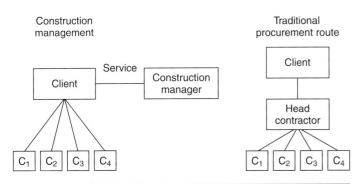

Figure 1 Construction management and traditional procurement

A more complex situation is where the parties to the procurement are in dispute and in settlement of their differences the scope of what the provider does is modified. A number of issues arise:

- Did the extension of the scope beyond the original contract fall within the scope of the original competition? If it did not, arguably the extension is a separate procurement. If it is a separate procurement, does one of the exceptions for running a negotiated procedure without a call for competition apply (e.g. procuring from the same provider additional services or works not exceeding 50% of the value of the original contract, subject to certain detailed conditions)?

- Could it be argued that whatever the contracting authority is now procuring, it has the same economic value as the procurement originally entered into with the provider? Even if, materially, the new arrangement might involve a new procurement, financially it might not.

When approaching problems of this kind it is important to recognize that the revised deal is not a question of post-tender negotiation because once a contract has been entered into the competitive procurement is at an end. This is a post-contractual as opposed to a post-tendering situation. It is therefore important to draw a line under the initial procurement process which gave rise to the contract and to focus on how the rules apply to the new situation.

Because of all the uncertainties involved in this situation, it can be particularly important to make provision for some flexibility in the original contract. The case of a one-year extension to a one-year contract is a simple example. The more complex the contract, the more likely subsequent difficulties are to materialize. The drafting of the contract could devise a range of change mechanisms to deal with such problems. In such a situation the parties will be better placed to argue that the triggering of the mechanisms foreseen in the contract were part of the original procurement and that the restructuring of the arrangement is simply the natural outworking of that original procurement.

3.5.7 Changes to an existing public contract

The question of at which point amendments made to an existing public contract are to be treated as a new award of a public contract has for some time been a grey area in European procurement law. The case of *Pressetext v. Austria* is one of the key cases in this area. In determining the effect of any amendments to an existing contract, the Court in its judgement stated the following key principle should be considered:

> In order to ensure transparency of procedures and equal treatment of tenderers, amendments to provisions of a public contract during the currency of the contract constitute a new award of a contract … when they are materially different in character from the original contract and, therefore, are such as to demonstrate the intention of the parties to renegotiate the essential terms of that contract.

The Court stated that an amendment to a public contract may be regarded as 'material' when:

- it introduces conditions which, had they been part of the initial award procedure, would have allowed for the admission of tenderers other than those initially admitted, or would have allowed for the acceptance of a tender other than the one initially accepted;

- it extends the scope of the contract considerably to encompass services not initially covered;

- it changes the economic balance of the contract in favour of the contractor in a manner which was not provided for in the terms of the initial contract.

In *Pressetext*, the Court provided guidance on a number of scenarios relating to changes to an existing public contract:

- A price change could amount to a breach of the principles of equal treatment and transparency, unless such changes were minimal and did not shift the economic balance of the contract in favour of the Contractor.

- The substitution of a subcontractor would be a material change unless specifically provided for in the contract. Further clarification was given in April 2010 in the case of *Wall v. Stadt Frankfurt am Main*, in which the substitution of a subcontractor was found to be a material amendment despite being provided for in the contract on the basis that the initial award was made in specific contemplation of the participation by the first subcontractor.

- An agreement to waive the right to terminate for three years was not a material change on the basis that neither party would have considered terminating during such time, that three years was not excessive in comparison to the time necessary to re-tender, and that it was not evident that the waiver risked distorting competition.

References

EC (2000) Commission interpretative communication on concessions under Community law. *OJ* **C121**, 29/04/2000. p.2

EC Treaty: *European Union consolidated versions of the treaty on European Union and of the treaty establishing the European Community. OJ* **C321**, 29/12/2006. p.E1–E331

European Commission (2010) *Public Procurement Indicators 2008* (Working Document, 27 April 2010). European Commission, Brussels. http://ec.europa.eu/internal_market/publicprocurement/docs/indicators2008_en.pdf

First Kelly Market Proposals; www.ogc.gov.uk/the_kelly_programme_first_kelly_market_proposals.asp

Office of Government Commerce (2007) *Initiative in Action*, Achieving Excellence in Construction Procurement Guide(PG01). OGC, London, UK. www.ogc.gov.uk/documents/CP0061AEGuide1.pdf

Office of Government Commerce (2007) *Project Organisation – rules and responsibilities*, Achieving Excellence in Construction Procurement Guide (PG02). OGC, London, UK. www.ogc.gov.uk/documents/CP0062AEGuide2.pdf

Office of Government Commerce (2007) *Procurement and Contract Strategies*, Achieving Excellence in Construction Procurement Guide (PG06). OGC, London, UK. www.ogc.gov.uk/documents/CP0066AEGuide6.pdf

Office of Government Commerce (2009) *Information Note 13/09* 1 December 2009. OGC, London, UK. www.ogc.gov.uk/documents/Thresholds_from_January_2010.pdf

PACE Central Advice Unit (1998) *GACC: Guide to the Appointment of Consultants and Contractors. Second edition, Rev. 2.* HMSO, London, UK. www.ogc.gov.uk/documents/PACE_-_GACC.pdf

Referenced legislation, regulations or standards

Agreement on Government Procurement 1994. World Trade Organisation. www.wto.org/english/tratop_e/gproc_e/gp_gpa_e.htm

Commission Regulation (EC) No. 1564/2005 of 7 September 2005 establishing standard forms for the publication of notices in the framework of public procurement procedures pursuant to Directives 2004/17/EEC and 2004/18/EEC of the European Parliament and of the Council. *OJ* **L257**. 01/10/2005. p.1

Directive 89/665 of 21 December 1989 on the coordination of the laws, regulations and administrative provisions relating to the application of review procedures to the award of public supply and public works contracts. *OJ* **L395**, 30/12/89. p.33

Directive 92/13 of 25 February 1992 coordinating the laws, regulations and administrative provisions relating to the application of Community rules on the procurement procedures of entities operating in the water, energy, transport and telecommunications sectors. *OJ* **L76**, 23/03/1992. pp.14–20

Directive 93/37/EEC of 14 June 1993 concerning the coordination of procedures for the award of public works contracts. *OJ* **L199**, 09/08/1993. pp.54–83

Directive 2004/17/EC of the European Parliament and of the Council of 31 March 2004 coordinating the procurement procedures of entities operating in the water, energy, transport and postal services sectors. *OJ* **L134**, 30/04/2004. p.1

Directive 2004/18/EC of the European Parliament and of the Council of 31 March 2004 on the coordination of procedures for the award of public works contracts, public supply contracts and public service contracts. *OJ* **L134**, 30/4/2004, pp.114–240

Directive 2007/66/EC (Remedies Directive) of the European Parliament and of the Council of 11 December 2007 amending Council Directives 89/665/EEC and 92/13/EEC with regard to improving the effectiveness of review procedures concerning the award of public contracts. *OJ* **L335**, 20/12/2007. pp.31–46

Local Government Act 1972. HMSO, London, UK.
Local Government Act 1999. TSO, London, UK.
Freedom of Information Act 2000. TSO, London, UK.
The Public Contracts and Utilities Contracts (Amendment) Regulations 2007. TSO, London, UK.
The Public Contracts and Utilities Contracts (CPV Code Amendments) Regulations 2008. TSO, London, UK.
The Public Contracts (Amendment) Regulations 2009. TSO, London, UK.
Public Contracts Regulations 2006. TSO, London, UK.
The Utilities Contracts (Amendments) Regulations 2009. TSO, London, UK.

Referenced cases

Case C-406/08 *Uniplex (UK) Ltd v. NHS Business Services Authority*

Harmon CFEM Facades (UK) Ltd v. The Corporate Officer of the House of Commons [1999] All ER(D) 1178

Case C-454/06 *Pressetext v. Austria*

Case C-91/08 *Wall v. Stadt Frankfurt am Main*

Websites

Department of Health procurement; www.dh.gov.uk/ProcurementAndProposals/Procurement/fs/en

EC public procurement guidelines; http://ec.europa.eu/internal_market/publicprocurement/guidelines_en.htm

EC Public Procurement Legislation; http://ec.europa.eu/internal_market/publicprocurement/legislation_en.htm

EU Treaties; http://eur-lex.europa.eu/en/treaties/index.htm

Office of Government Commerce (OGC) procurement strategy; www.ogc.gov.uk/documentation_and_templates_procurement_strategy_.asp

OGC Achieving Excellence in Construction Guides; www.ogc.gov.uk/ppm_documents_construction.asp

Official Journal of the European Union; http://eur-lex.europa.eu/en/index.htm

Chapter 4

Public–private sector partnerships

Nicholas Downing Herbert Smith, London, UK
Miranda Ramphul Herbert Smith, London, UK

doi: 10.1680/mocl.40878.0047

This chapter gives brief examples of various public-private partnerships arrangements and then focusses on the principles and aims of the Private Finance Initiative (PFI). In particular, it covers the construction aspects of PFI projects including the various documents involved, risk transfer, design development, compliance monitoring and interface with the operational aspects.

CONTENTS

4.1 Introduction

Public-private partnerships (PPP) as a term of art has developed since the election, of the then Labour government, in 1997. The notion of a partnership in this sense is not a legal one: it relates to the sharing of risk and reward between the public and private sectors in the delivery of public sector investment or exploitation of public sector assets. HM Treasury uses the following description:

In the broadest sense, PPPs can cover all types of collaboration across the interface between the public and private sectors to deliver policies, services and infrastructure. Where delivery of public services involves private sector investment in infrastructure, the most common form of PPP is the Private Finance Initiative.

Examples of PPP arrangements include the following:

■ Concessions: these are financially free-standing projects where the private sector is responsible for the design and construction, operation, maintenance and financing of an asset, recouping its costs through charges levied on the ultimate end users. Examples include the Second Severn Bridge and the Birmingham Northern Relief (M6) Toll Road. Concessions may also involve the public sector paying the private sector a fee for availability.

■ Strategic Infrastructure Partnerships: these are often used where authorities in the same regional area identify facilities in the same sector which alone are too low in capital value to attract private investment but, bundled together, are more attractive. This approach is suitable where there is uncertainty over the phases of the works. Examples include the NHS Local Investment Finance Trust (LIFT) programme, which is used in the health sector for projects involving the refurbishment of primary care facilities. Under this structure, one or more primary care trusts (PCTs) from a geographical region collaborate to identify facilities required which can be bundled together to provide sufficient capital and efficiencies. They then select a private sector entity (which may, itself, be a joint venture between private sector companies) to form a special purpose vehicle joint venture with it (LiftCo). The

Building Schools for the Future programme uses a similar structure to bundle projects involving the rebuilding or remodelling of state secondary schools together.

■ Public Delivery Organisation: under this model, the public sector authority selects a public delivery organisation partner to manage the procurement and integration of the assets and services to provide a service to the public sector. This approach is suitable where there is uncertainty over the long term requirements and flexibility is required. An example is the MOD's Military Flying Training System programme.

■ Wider Markets Initiative: this was established by HM Treasury in 1998 to encourage the use of public sector assets through the development of new, non-statutory goods and services which are sold on a commercial basis. An example is the Congestion Charge in London where Transport for London (TfL) has entered into a contract with a private sector consortium to levy and administer congestion charges within inner London, with net revenues reverting to TfL.

■ Alliancing: this involves the use of a binding partnering contract between the public and private sectors, featuring a more robust approach to partnering, including profit and risk sharing arrangements and sanctions for failing to achieving set targets, but subject to the principles of the partnering philosophy which places emphasis on trust, teamwork, co-operation, communication and a joint approach to risk identification and problem solving. The risks are generally retained by the public sector under this model.

■ Private Finance Initiative (PFI): the procurement of capital projects by the public sector was transformed during the 1990s by the advent of the PFI.

This model seeks to involve the private sector in the provision of public services with the result that the role of the public sector moves from being an owner and provider to an enabler and purchaser. It is based on the belief that the public sector should focus on its core functions, leaving the private sector to perform those functions which it can perform more cost effectively and efficiently.

The extent to which a particular project is a PFI project or some other form of PPP will ultimately depend on the nature of the project itself and the risk and reward allocation between the public and private sectors. Underpinning all PPP transactions is the political desire to bring together the best of the private and public sectors to facilitate the delivery of badly needed capital investment or the achievement of other public sector objectives.

This chapter will focus on the principles and aims of the PFI. The remainder of this introductory section sets out the basic principles of the PFI, the forms it can take and introduces the standardised contract documentation.

4.1.1 Basic structure of the Private Finance Initiative

In a PFI transaction, the key contract is a form of concession agreement between the public sector and the private sector (often called the project agreement). The private sector party will usually be a special purpose vehicle entity (the project company), typically including construction contractors and facility management providers as shareholders. These shareholders are usually the principal subcontractors of the project company, although equity-only investors may also be involved.

The project company will also secure finance for the project on a non-recourse basis. Its shareholders will usually invest only a limited proportion of equity into the project company. Given the non-recourse financing structure, the lenders will require a series of direct agreements with the public sector and the principal subcontractors of the project company which will enable them to take over the project if it is in jeopardy.

The focus on the provision of a service to the public sector rather than the purchase by it of a capital asset is at the heart of the PFI. The private sector has the responsibility for providing, maintaining and operating an asset, with the public sector defining a standard of service to be delivered and leaving the private sector to determine the means of delivery. The public sector will prescribe a set of outputs (the 'what'), which in turn drive the specification for the underlying asset, and the private sector will be responsible for devising the technical solutions (the 'how'). Since the private sector bears the responsibility and risk of determining how to deliver the required output, the public sector is able to transfer to the private sector risks which would otherwise have been borne by the public sector.

Once the asset is constructed and the services are being delivered, the public sector will make periodic payments (often referred to as a 'unitary payment') to the private sector during the contract period, which in many PFI projects runs for 25 or 30 years. The private sector is generally responsible for the up-front financing of the project, either by obtaining debt financing or, particularly for smaller projects, on a corporate finance basis where the private sector raises the required funds based on the strength of the balance sheet of the contractor or its parent company. Obviously the use of such corporate finance has an impact on various elements of the project documentation.

The standard guidance is based on the typical project finance approach to PFI, although it does recognise the role that corporate finance may play and outlines the changes that will be required to the standard drafting.

As the private sector provides the financing for the construction period, the public sector has to justify reimbursing the cost of capital incurred by the private sector, which is inevitably higher than the public sector's cost of capital. The justification for this is made up of a number of elements.

The additional cost of capital may be offset by the ability of the private sector to construct and operate the asset more cheaply and efficiently than would be the case if there were to be a traditional procurement of the asset and a separate contract for its operation. For example, significant cost savings and efficiencies can be made by avoiding the mistake often made by the public sector of having assets over-engineered in an attempt to address every eventuality. The cost of private sector capital can also be mitigated if the private sector is free to generate revenue from the asset in addition to providing the service to the public sector. This additional third-party revenue can assist in minimising the level of unitary payment which the public sector is required to pay.

Ultimately, however, the extra cost of private sector capital can only be justified if the private sector bears certain risks inherent in the project. The fundamental risk which is at the heart of the PFI is performance, namely delivery of the completed asset and related services to a requisite standard. The public sector, as the customer, is purchasing a service and will pay for that service provided it is delivered. In this way, the private sector is accepting the risk that it will only be able to repay the finance which it has raised to fund the project and make a profit, if the asset and services are delivered to the appropriate standard.

Under the PFI, responsibility for the performance of the asset throughout the contract period is with the private sector, as is long-term maintenance and achieving the lowest overall life-cycle costs for the assets and related services. This is in marked contrast to assets procured on a traditional basis where a lack of public sector capital has often meant that assets have not been subject to sufficient periodic maintenance and have fallen into a state of disrepair.

Critics of PFI turn to factors which require the public sector to provide funding for certain projects, arguing that such funding undermines the principles of PFI. For example, the Government has used public sector models such a Credit Guarantee Finance, which involves the splitting of funding and risk-taking. Under this form of financing, the Government acts as funder, raises the finance through the issue of Government bonds, and the private financiers guarantee the payment of interest and principal by the private sector to the Government. In this way, the public sector is able to benefit from lower financing costs without having to take on project risk. However, this form of finance has had limited take-up. More recently, as a result of the global recession with private finance being in short supply, HM Treasury has had to intervene to prevent certain projects from stalling. It has established the Infrastructure Finance Unit to act a as lender of last resort to PFI projects unable to obtain private finance.

4.1.2 Standardisation of contracts

The first PFI projects were negotiated on a case by case basis even though many of the issues were the same in all projects. This inevitably led to project teams wrangling over the same issues, often coming up with different conclusions and incurring significant costs in the process. To address these concerns the Treasury Taskforce (established by the Labour Government in 1997) carried out a widespread consultation process which resulted in the issue of guidance on the *Standardisation of PFI Contracts* in July 1999.

The second and third editions of the guidance were published in 2002 and 2004 respectively and an Addendum, dealing with various issues, was issued in December 2005. The fourth edition of the *Standardisation of PFI Contracts (SoPC4)* was published in March 2007 (with updates published in 2008 and 2009). The objectives of the guidance remain the same as in 1999: to promote standardisation through achieving a common understanding of the risks, to allow consistency of approach and consistency of pricing across similar projects and to reduce the time and costs involved in getting a project to financial close. The standard provisions in SoPC4 take three forms: first, standard drafting of a whole subject with guidance notes; secondly, standard drafting of parts of the subject with the rest of the subject being dealt with in explanatory notes; and thirdly, a guidance note explaining how a subject should be dealt with in broad terms with a recommended approach to the issue. One of the interesting changes introduced in the third edition, and retained in SoPC4, is the fact that significant parts of the drafting are now mandatory with no amendment allowed. The first two editions of SoPC4 were generally used as guidance and as a starting point for negotiations. However, any project which does not now follow the standard wording will require express permission to deviate and derogations will only be allowed in exceptional circumstances.

Although SoPC4 does not contain drafting relating specifically to design and construction issues, it does cover a number of areas which have a major impact on design and construction. For example, it sets out the consequences of a delay in service commencement if that delay is caused by various types of event.

In addition to this generic guidance, sector specific guidance based on the Treasury's standardised documentation has also been produced for areas such as health, schools, housing, local government, waste management, leisure and culture, and street lighting.

4.1.3 Facilitating projects

Since the inception of the PFI in 1992, various bodies have been created to help facilitate PFI transactions. The first such body was the Private Finance Panel, which was created in 1993.

The PFI was reappraised by Sir Malcolm Bates, a founder member of the Private Finance Panel, following the election of 1997. This led to the creation of the Treasury Taskforce, which replaced the Private Finance Panel as a focal point for the PFI across Government. The Treasury Taskforce was set-up with a limited life-span and was replaced by Partnerships UK (PUK) following its launch in June 2000. PUK is not an arm of HM Treasury; instead it is a PPP, with ownership in the hands of the private and public sectors.

Although it is part privately owned, PUK works solely for the public sector. Its stated mission is 'to support and accelerate the delivery of infrastructure renewal, high-quality public services and the efficient use of public assets through better and stronger partnerships between the public and private sectors'.

PUK offers help-desk support to the public sector on PFI/PPP projects. In addition, it offers more intensive support to individual projects which are particularly large, complex, innovative, politically sensitive and/or likely to prove a useful precedent. PUK also played a key role in the Partnerships for Health programme and is still involved in the Partnerships for Schools programmes. Where it is involved in an individual project, it works in partnership with awarding authorities and shares responsibility for the procurement of the project. It does not usually act as an adviser, but rather as a PPP developer, for example, by assisting the awarding authority in the management of the project through helping with project evaluation and implementation, being represented on the project board and having an involvement in major decisions.

As part of the Pre-Budget Report delivered on 9th December 2009, the then Chancellor of the Exchequer announced the establishment of Infrastructure UK (IUK) which will replace PUK.

HM Treasury also has a role. Within it there exists: the Infrastructure Finance Unit referred to in section 4.1.1; the Operational Taskforce, which provides free expert advice and support to public sector partners; the Project Review Group, which oversees the approval for local authority PFI projects; the Major Project Review group, which is a panel providing commercial, independent expert advice to ministers on deliverability and affordability of the largest and most complex projects; and the Office of Government Commerce, which is responsible for improving value for money and is also in charge of the gateway process by which a PFI project is reviewed at six key stages through its programme and, at each gateway, the project is analysed so as to provide assurance that it can progress successfully to the next stage.

In the local authority sector, the PPP Programme (known as the 4Ps) was established in 1996. On 18th August 2009 it became Local Partnerships, a joint venture between the Local Government Association and PUK. It provides general assistance on local government PFI projects and also conducts gateway reviews for the local authority sector. One of its aims is to distribute detailed information about the processes involved in progressing PPP projects. It is also responsible for nine key sectors, including corporate property and regeneration, schools, housing and sustainable communities, culture and sports, transport and regeneration and waste management.

4.1.4 Stages of PFI project

There are numerous stages in a PFI transaction, but these fall broadly into three main phases, as follows.

Feasibility and value for money

The feasibility phase commences with the establishment of a business need and concludes with the preparation of the business case and the decision to proceed with the project. The aim of this phase is to establish the initial viability and scope of the procurement. The result of the feasibility phase will be the production of what is generally called the Outline Business Case (OBC). The objective of an OBC is to consider the specific characteristics of the project and determine whether the decision that the PFI procurement route offers the best value for money can be confirmed. At this stage in the process, it is accepted that firm costs for the PFI solution will not be provided, but rather reasoned argument and examples to show whether PFI is likely to offer the best value for money solution. The project has to go through the gateway process mentioned in section 4.1.3, so if a business case has not been demonstrated the project will not be permitted to continue unchecked with the risk of failure later.

Procurement

Following the introduction of the procurement rules in the UK at the end of January 2006, the competitive dialogue procedure is now used for complex projects such as PFI projects. The negotiated procedure, which was generally used pre-January 2006 for PFI projects, should now only be used for PFI projects in exceptional circumstances.

Under the competitive procedure a dialogue is carried on with pre-qualified bidders with the aim of refining the awarding authority's requirements. This dialogue may take place in various stages with a reducing number of bidders. However, by the end of the process and before selection of the preferred bidder all material points must be agreed; the scope for negotiations once a preferred bidder has been selected is extremely limited. (Also see the chapters *Public sector projects* and *Procurement route* for further detail on procurement)

Contract term

The third phase is the actual lifespan of the project. Most projects comprise a construction phase, during which assets are created or upgraded, and an operational phase during which the assets are used to deliver the required service.

During the contract term there may be a refinancing. This process has developed as the PFI market has matured. There are opportunities for the investors providing the equity capital in a PFI project to secure benefits by refinancing a project, where the construction phase has been completed, on more favourable terms than the debt finance provided at the beginning of the project as the delivery risks of the project will have been dealt with. Also, in the debt markets, it is now possible (subject to the recent global economic downturn) to borrow for longer periods at fixed rates of interest, which are lower than when the early PFI contracts were awarded. In most case, in improving the terms of the debt finance, payments to the investors of equity capital will be made earlier in the contract period. The resulting benefit to the equity investors can significantly improve the returns on their investments as their initial investment tends to be small relative to the debt being refinanced. As a result, SoPC4 recommends that the gain to the investors on a refinancing be shared 50:50 between the awarding authority and the project company.

4.1.5 Aim of this chapter

The remainder of this chapter focuses on the construction aspects of PFI transactions. It assumes that the project in question is a PFI project involving the construction of an asset (as opposed to a refurbishment) and services are sold to the public sector as purchaser and user, with the private sector financing the initial design and construction by a mixture of project finance debt and sponsor equity and the awarding authority paying a unitary payment for a prescribed contract period from the date the asset is complete and the services to be delivered are operational.

In this chapter, the construction subcontractor is the construction contractor engaged by the project company and references to SoPC4 means the Standardisation of PFI Contracts Version 4 published by the Treasury in March 2007 (with updates published in 2008 and 2009).

4.2 Risk transfer

The key aspect of risk allocation in a PFI transaction is that the risks should be borne by the party who is best able to manage them. The public sector is required to demonstrate that the price being paid for the private sector to bear a particular risk represents value for money. If the risk in question is one with which the private sector is unfamiliar or one which is outside its control (e.g. certain change of law risks) the price which the private sector requires for bearing that risk may be excessive. The price charged by the private sector to assume a particular risk will reflect not only its assessment of the probability of the risk materialising but also the consequences which this may have on the private sector's ability to perform its obligations. This is a critical issue as the public sector's obligation is to pay by reference to the level of performance achieved. The public sector is generally entitled to make deductions from the unitary payment for under-performance. In the final analysis, the public sector must achieve a performance regime which genuinely reflects the concept of payment against performance and the private sector must have the incentive to bear the risks inherent in the project, in each case for a price which is value for money. The value for money test is critical as it must be applied wherever public money is involved in a PFI project.

In terms of the design and construction phase in a PFI project, although it is a relatively short period when compared with the operational period, this is disproportionate to its importance. The design and construction of the facility has to be completed and the risks associated with the phase need to be overcome before the project can generate the income necessary to discharge the project debt and create a profit for the project company.

The key risks which are applicable to the design and construction phase of a PFI transaction are considered next.

4.2.1 Design risk

As will be apparent from section 4.4 of this chapter, the awarding authority will state in the output specification its requirements for the services to be provided under the project agreement. It is the responsibility of the project company to propose a design solution which will enable it to achieve completion of the design and construction of the facility and deliver a service to the standards described in the output specification. After completion, the awarding authority will pay for the services rendered provided that they are compatible with the output specification. If there is non-compliance with the output specification, the awarding authority is entitled to reduce the amount payable to the project company provider by making deductions from the unitary payment for poor performance as well as for what is commonly described as unavailability.

As a consequence of this principle of payment against performance, the project company should be given the responsibility to determine the design solution for the facility. It will usually be inappropriate to allow the awarding authority to make deductions from payment when unavailability is attributable to design decisions made by the awarding authority. The responsibility given to the project company on design matters also extends to the maintenance and operation of the facility. It may be to the project company's advantage to design the facility in a way which ensures the efficient and economic operation of the facility and its planned maintenance (i.e. routine maintenance and minor repairs) and reduces life-cycle costs (i.e. major repairs and replacements of elements of the facility during the operational period).

4.2.2 Planning risk

The transfer of the risk of securing appropriate planning consents to the project company can be difficult to achieve in practice. In particular, project financiers are not willing to advance funds until a detailed planning consent has been obtained. Accordingly, the project agreement is unlikely to be signed until, or will be made conditional upon, receipt of a satisfactory planning permission.

Because the planning application will be inextricably linked to the proposed design solution offered by the project company, it is not uncommon for the detailed planning application to be made once a preferred bidder has been selected. The construction subcontractor engaged by the project company to design and construct the facility is unlikely to be prepared to finalise its fixed price for the construction works until planning issues have been resolved, since it would otherwise inherit the risk of having to absorb what may be significant design changes in order to comply with the finalised planning permission.

There may also be advantages in the awarding authority assisting in the planning application (e.g. providing support at a public enquiry or where local pressure groups may object). In effect, the planning process means that the planning risk is shared between the awarding authority and the project company since the project will be delayed if satisfactory planning permission is not secured.

This should not be confused in any way with the discharge of detailed planning conditions or the obtaining of, and compliance with, building regulations and other similar approvals. The responsibility for securing such approvals and complying with all relevant conditions is a responsibility which is invariably placed on the project company, who will in turn ensure that appropriate obligations are passed on to the construction subcontractor. In particular, the construction subcontract will probably impose an obligation on the construction subcontractor to secure requisite approvals without delaying the programme and to ensure that the time and cost risk of any variations arising from the planning process is placed squarely with the construction subcontractor. (Also see the chapter *The planning system*.)

4.2.3 Service commencement risk

In the context of PFI transactions, service commencement is the point at which service delivery is ready to commence. It is a key milestone in PFI because:

(a) the project company will not receive any payment until it starts providing the services in accordance with the awarding authority's requirements (meaning that it must have completed the construction of the facility so that it is ready for operational use). SoPC4 does set out exceptions to this rule: for example, where the awarding authority wishes to make a capital contribution to the project or has some other form of co-financing proposal. The guidance is that any such contributions should be kept 'to a modest size' since they might alter the risk transfer balance and incentives of the project. Either way, the awarding authority should not make any payments towards advisers' fees or working capital; and

(b) the project agreement between the awarding authority and the project company will usually provide for a date by which the services are to be available (liability for damages in the event of late service commencement is dealt with in section 4.3 of this chapter) and/or a longstop date giving the awarding authority the ability to terminate if service commencement has not been achieved by that date.

The project agreement between the awarding authority and project company will address the time and cost consequences to the project company should it fail to achieve service commencement by the originally programmed date, following the occurrence of certain types of event. In particular, provision will be made for the following:

- *Compensation events* – SoPC4 defines a compensation event as a breach by the awarding authority of any of its obligations under the project agreement, although it recognises that it may be appropriate to add other events including those which are sector specific; the project company will be entitled to an extension of time in order to avoid liability for damages for late service delivery (if applicable) and/or to the longstop date in order to prevent a right for the awarding authority to terminate from arising, and to recover from the awarding authority compensation for additional costs incurred as a result of consequential delays (including additional finance costs).

- *Relief events* – these are events which are best managed by the project company and the mandatory SoPC4 definition includes fire and other insured risks, riot, failures by statutory undertakers and strikes; the project company will be given an extension of time but no compensation will be payable by the awarding authority and the period of the concession will not be extended.

- *Force majeure events* – the SoPC4 mandatory definition covers war, civil war, armed conflict, terrorism, nuclear, chemical or biological contamination and pressure waves caused by devices travelling at supersonic speeds; they are events which are beyond the control of either party and may give rise to an extension of the contract term and eventually to a right of termination.

4.2.4 Cost risk

The awarding authority will need to give attention to the financial parameters applicable to a proposed project even before bids are requested and then to the various bids received during the tender process. If it does not, there is a risk that time and costs will be wasted on bids which do not constitute value for money or are unbankable. The gateway reviews are aimed to deal with this.

During the tender stage of the project, it is also essential for the project company to undertake a thorough appraisal of, and assess the risks inherent in, the various options it is considering before deciding on the basis of its bid as PFI transactions require the provision of a service in return for the payment of pre-agreed sums which are calculated, in part, by reference to the budgeted construction and associated finance costs. The payment for services will therefore not be increased if the budgets are exceeded. In effect, the construction cost is fixed and the risk of cost overruns is placed with the project company.

4.2.5 Quality risk

Issues of quality manifest themselves in similar ways to other risks mentioned in this section. In particular, the project agreement between the awarding authority and the project company will ensure that commencement of the income stream is dependent on achieving service commencement to the requisite standards. 'Payment against performance' will be achieved

thereafter through the implementation of detailed compliance monitoring procedures during the operational period and deductions for poor performance and unavailability.

4.2.6 Change of law risk

Changes in law occurring after financial close are outside the control of the project company. However, the awarding authority will want the project company to anticipate and, in any event, manage any additional costs associated with a change in law. The degree to which a change of law will affect the project company's ability to provide the required service within the anticipated costs will vary from project to project. Accordingly, the precise allocation of risk between the awarding authority and the project company will depend on where the risk can be managed most effectively.

The project company usually bears the risk of a generally applicable change of law which affects construction costs, since such a change is regarded as foreseeable over a typical build period.

During the operational period, where changes of law are of a generally applicable nature, the project company bears the revenue cost effect because it is protected through the combined effects of benchmarking or market testing of the service cost and indexation of the unitary payment, and usually shares (up to a cap) unforeseeable capital expenditure required.

Where the change of law is discriminatory or sector specific (as distinct from being generally applicable), the awarding authority bears the risk in both construction and operational periods.

4.2.7 Project obsolescence risk

The proposals of the project company embodied in the contractual documentation may not represent the best technical solution for the awarding authority's needs. For example, if the awarding authority expresses its requirements for an IT system by reference to a specific technical specification such as a number of computers of a certain type configured in a specific way, rather than by way of a service provision requirement expressed in output terms (see section 4.4 of this chapter), the solution offered by the project company may have an element of obsolescence built into it at the outset.

The awarding authority may not be too concerned if this is the case provided that the standards of service are well defined and understood by the users of the asset and have been delivered satisfactorily by the project company. In these circumstances, the awarding authority may initially be indifferent as to how the service is provided, but ultimately the disadvantage of this approach is that the awarding authority will be unable to take advantage of the benefits offered by advances in technology which might in the longer term have provided the awarding authority with better value for money.

The awarding authority may approach its requirement for improving technological standards in different ways where this is a topic of importance to it (e.g. in hospital projects where reliance is placed on specialised equipment). It may require technological standards to be enhanced in line with industry benchmarks or it may be able to create incentives for the project company to ensure that the system is kept up to date by placing the residual value risk with the project company.

4.3 Contractual matrix

Construction contracts are well known for their complexity. In part, this is because the construction of buildings, facilities and infrastructure involves bringing together resources, skills and experience, which are seldom found within one organization. The fragmentation of the industry into discrete sectors has had a direct impact on contractual arrangements and represents one of the principal reasons for the proliferation of interlinking contracts which need to reflect the interplay of the various parties involved in the design and construction process.

In the context of PFI transactions, the contractual arrangements are invariably more complex than would be found in traditional methods of procurement. This is due to the need to overlay traditional procurement techniques with contractual structures which are geared towards the delivery of services and the means by which PFI transactions are generally financed.

In the context of design and construction, the principal contracts are illustrated in **Figure 1**.

4.3.1 Project agreement

The project agreement is the principal agreement in a PFI transaction. It describes the rights and obligations of the awarding authority and the project company throughout the life of the project.

The project agreement will make the project company responsible for procuring the delivery of services (including by undertaking the design and construction of the facility in question).

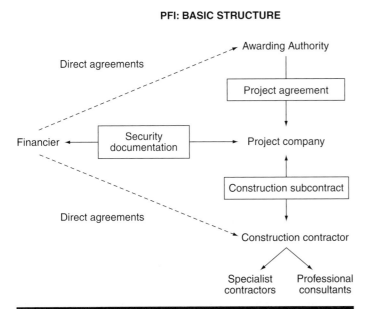

PFI: BASIC STRUCTURE

Figure 1   Principal contracts in PFI transactions

The project agreement will allocate responsibility between the awarding authority and the project company for the key risks applicable to the design and construction phase as well as the ongoing risks applicable to the service delivery phase. It will also set out the project company's obligation to deliver a facility that meets the requirements of the output specification.

Depending on how the payment mechanism responds to construction defects and the quality of the working environment of occupied areas, undertakings of a more general nature, concerning the overall standard and quality of the facility to be provided before the operational period can commence, may also be included in the documentation. These undertakings might extend to compliance with specified standards of design and quality of workmanship and materials. The quality of environmental clean-up works may also have to be addressed, whether in relation to the site of the project or land which may be sold when it becomes surplus to requirements once the new facility is operational.

Consideration will need to be given as to whether the project agreement needs to impose express design and construction obligations in relation to the execution of capital works during the operational period (particularly as a result of a service variation). It is common practice to deal with this through a service variation and, at the time such variation is instructed, to deal with any consequential effect on the project. The project agreement will also address a variety of commercial issues, such as force majeure, payment and performance, changes in law, termination, and compensation payable following termination.

4.3.2 Construction subcontract

Sitting below the project agreement will be the construction subcontract for the design, construction and completion of the asset, and the facility operating and management (FM) subcontracts for the provision of the services and maintenance of the facilities (see the chapter *Facilities management contracts*).

The construction subcontract is likely to be awarded for a lump sum fixed price. It will be a design and build contract so as to impose single-point responsibility on the construction subcontractor covering all aspects of the design and construction of the facility.

The project company and its financiers will want to ensure that the completion and pricing risks which have been assumed under the project agreement are passed through to the construction subcontractor on terms which are no less onerous than those found in or assumed by the project company under the project agreement. The key is to ensure as far as possible that the financial exposure of the project company to the construction subcontractor is as limited as possible. One example of how this is achieved is through equivalent project relief (EPR) clauses, which seek to minimise the risk of inconsistent determinations of entitlements to payment/relief under the project agreement (arising from, say, compensation events) and the relevant subcontract. However, such clauses have met with judicial resistance when they deal with determinations under the Housing Grants, Construction and Regeneration Act 1996 (HGA) (see section 4.8 of this chapter).

In any event, the contractual obligations placed on the construction subcontractor may in some instances be more stringent than (or at least different to) the equivalent obligations found in the project agreement. Two examples are given below.

First, late completion of construction will give rise to delayed service commencement and a delay in the start of payments from the awarding authority to the project company. Accordingly, SoPC4 makes the point that liquidated damages under the project agreement will be inappropriate in the absence of special circumstances, which would make such damages represent value for money, as the project company will pass the risk of incurring such liquidated damages through to the awarding authority in the form of an increased unitary payment. The circumstances which justify liquidated damages will be confined to instances where the awarding authority suffers losses in excess of the unitary payment which the awarding authority would have paid if completion had been achieved on time after taking into account the cost of securing the services. Examples of this include the education sector, where it can be essential for completion to occur prior to the commencement of an academic year, and government office buildings, where vacant possession of the existing premises must be given by a specified date and this can only be achieved if the new facility is ready for occupation on the due date.

The approach under the project agreement should be contrasted with the position under the construction subcontract which will invariably provide for the payment of liquidated damages for delayed completion. Such damages will often be secured to the financiers as they represent lost income needed to service the project debt. Most construction subcontractors will accept liability for liquidated damages provided they are fixed at an appropriate rate. In agreeing the rate, the project company must not overlook the fact that liquidated damages operate as a cap on the construction subcontractor's liability for late completion.

Secondly, the project company and its financiers may require more stringent standards of quality from the construction subcontractor than are contained in the warranties on design and construction set out in the project agreement. The principal justification for this is the fact that income generated during the operational period is, to a greater or lesser extent, dependent on performance, which in turn is dependent on quality and suitability of design and construction. For example, more stringent standards in the construction subcontract are likely to be required if the payment mechanism in the project agreement allows deductions from the unitary payment for unavailability due to defects, particularly if those deductions are not dependent on proving breach of the project agreement. In such circumstances, fitness for purpose obligations might be imposed on the construction subcontractor.

The awarding authority will check that sufficient risk arising from the project agreement has been allocated to the principal subcontractors by the project company in order to deliver a robust project. In addition to ensuring that the completion and pricing risks under the project agreement are passed through to the construction subcontractor, SoPC4 provides some examples of reasons for the awarding authority to review the terms of the construction subcontract. First, if the project agreement requires the project company to pay liquidated damages to the awarding authority for late completion, the awarding authority will need to ensure that the project company is sufficiently robust to meet such an obligation (taking account of the terms of the subcontract and the claims of the project company's financiers). Secondly, if the awarding authority has the benefit of a collateral warranty it will need to ensure that the terms of the subcontract are satisfactory.

Other relevant issues for the construction subcontract include the process of certification of completion and extensions of time (and how these processes and entitlements interrelate with those contained in the project agreement) and the integration of the construction subcontractor with the project company and FM subcontractor during the testing and commissioning phase of the project.

4.3.3 Security documentation

While it will be rare for parent company guarantees and performance bonds to be appropriate in a PFI transaction in order to support the design and construction obligations owed to the awarding authority by the project company under the project agreement, it is not uncommon for the financiers to insist on the provision of a guarantee or a bond (or both) in respect of the construction subcontractor's obligations under the construction subcontract.

If the construction subcontractor can offer a guarantor of substance, it is likely that a guarantee will be considered by the project company and its financiers to be preferable to a performance bond. Most performance bonds are capped at or around 10% of the contract sum and will expire at practical completion or once the defects liability period obligations under the construction subcontract have been discharged. By contrast, a parent company guarantee is likely to be as extensive as the construction subcontractor's liability under the construction subcontract, and therefore will not be subject to a 10% cap and will be enforceable throughout a limitation period expiring twelve years after completion, assuming that the subcontract is executed as a deed. (See the chapter *Bonds, parent company guarantees and other security*.)

4.3.4 Professional consultants and specialist contractors

The awarding authority may already have technical expertise in-house which can be utilised for the purposes of preparing the output specification, reviewing the project company's proposals in response to the output specification and compliance monitoring. However, these resources are often supplemented by professional consultants specifically engaged for the project in hand.

On the private sector side, the professional consultants responsible for the design of the facility will be instructed by the construction subcontractor, rather than the project company. This structure is driven by the requirement for the construction subcontractor to offer single point responsibility for the whole design and construction process. However, in some instances the project company may engage the professional consultants during the early stages of the procurement process when preparing the initial response to the invitation to submit outline proposals and for the purposes of briefing the construction subcontractor. However, much depends on the nature of the consortium comprising the project company.

As regards detailed design and construction, the construction subcontractor will employ specialist subcontractors in a similar way to the manner in which they are engaged under design and build contracts awarded on traditionally procured projects.

4.3.5 Early works agreements

SoPC4 contains guidance regarding early works agreements, providing that they should be avoided where possible. There are a variety of reasons for this, including the potential for breaches of EU procurement law and regulation and the principle that, in the ordinary course of events, the awarding authority should not be under any obligation to make payments prior either to financial close or to commencement of services.

SoPC4 acknowledges that early works agreements may sometimes be justifiable where particular programming issues apply: the example provided is where a school wishes to avoid facility handovers in term-time. In such circumstances, the guidance provides some ground rules for undertaking such early works, including that such works should be planned well in advance and as part of the overall procurement strategy. Consideration should be given to whether it is appropriate for the bidder to undertake such works or whether the awarding authority should independently commission a third party to undertake them. The works proposal should also offer demonstrable savings of a general nature (rather than specifically related to the bidder's preferred solution) so that they will be of value whether or not the project agreement is signed. The guidance states further that the works should only include items that the procuring authority wishes to have done in any event (such as certain surveys, making safe, access roads etc.).

4.3.6 Ancillary construction contracts

The awarding authority's requirement for collateral warranties and direct agreements containing step-in rights are considered in more detail in section 4.8 of this chapter.

4.4 Design and technical documentation

Attached to the project agreement will be two sets of technical documents, the first being the output specification prepared on behalf of the awarding authority and the second being the detailed proposals which are prepared by the project company, mainly through its construction subcontractor, to meet the requirements of the output specification.

4.4.1 Output specification

PFI philosophy allows the project company to choose between the provision of a facility which is expensive to build but cheap to maintain, or cheap to build but expensive to maintain. It reflects an intrinsic consequence of the transfer of design risk to the project company and the payment mechanism found in PFI transactions. It also means that the awarding authority has no real interest in, and (if it wishes to maximise risk transfer) should not become involved with, design issues such as the type of structural frame for, or mechanical and electrical services to be used in, the facility. The awarding authority's interest is limited to securing the required outputs (e.g. the specified ambient temperature being subject to agreed tolerances).

It needs to be recognised that it will not be possible for this theoretical approach to be followed in all cases. There will be occasions when the awarding authority's requirement is so specific that certain elements of the output specification ought to be very similar to a traditional performance specification. In practice, therefore, the output specification may constitute a combination of pure output requirements coupled with specific performance requirements for certain elements. Some sector specific guidance recognises different approaches for different sectors.

The fact that there may be performance specifications included as part of the output specification does not mean that the awarding authority or its consultants should consider, for example, that it needs to approve the type of construction of the facility's car park because constant repairs would be disruptive to occupational use. Rather, the approach should be to ensure that the payment mechanism is sufficiently sensitive so that deductions for poor performance or unavailability can be made if the car park is constantly under repair and cannot be used.

This does not suggest that the awarding authority should not consider and specify its requirements as regards operational implications of design solutions. For example, it would be perfectly in order for minimum redecoration cycles to be included as an output requirement, particularly for areas where regular redecoration would be disruptive to operational use.

The awarding authority's involvement in design should therefore be restricted to what might be described generally as business or user requirements. These requirements will vary depending on the type of project. For example, in the case of an accommodation project, the interests of the awarding authority should centre around the architectural or aesthetic appearance of the building, visitor reception areas and other occupied areas, the location of fixed areas (e.g. service risers) which directly affect occupation, the location of business units (including their adjacencies to one another), the location of partitions, quality of finishes, signage, room and workplace configuration and other operational issues.

However, as the output specification represents the means by which the awarding authority describes its user requirements to the project company, it is the awarding authority's responsibility to ensure that these requirements are adequately defined. If they are not, and alterations to the output specification become necessary, such alterations are likely to impact on the nature or scope of the project, and may give rise to variations which can only be implemented at extra cost to the awarding authority.

The concept of variations should not be treated in exactly the same way as it is in conventional forms of procurement. For example, the awarding authority's requirements may change throughout the life of the project but if flexibility has been addressed properly in the output specification a variation may not necessarily arise even if it is subsequently discovered that the facility needs to be adapted. For example, the *Waste Management Procurement Pack* highlights the point that key landfill diversion performance standards in the output specification will increase during the waste project's contract period to reflect the requirements of documents such as the EU Landfill Directive, Waste Strategy (and so on). The output specification will therefore need to be drafted with sufficient flexibility to allow this, without use of the variation procedure.

A key point here is the difference between *design criteria*, which are the primary concern of the output specification (albeit translated into user requirements); and *ongoing performance requirements*. Specific wording, including a scheme for evaluating performance and the financial consequences of failure, is likely to be required where the latter are intended; such a scheme would normally be found in the payment mechanism and related clauses. *London Bus Services Ltd v. Tramtrack Croydon Ltd* [2007] EWHC 107 highlights the difficulties that can arise. The case concerned a concession agreement to build and run the tram service in Croydon. The performance specification set out requirements in relation to 'fleet size and tram capacity', which set out maximum numbers of passengers and seating requirements 'for the purposes of fleet size determination' (paragraph 3.11). In addition, under the rubric 'Design' the specification provided that the system should be 'capable…of providing for a 33% increase in passengers carrying capacity above that initially required' elsewhere in the specification. The issue between the parties was who should pay for increased capacity to deal with overcrowding: if such increased capacity was within the specification then it was a 'service change' and the service provider paid; otherwise it was a 'service parameters change' and London Buses (effectively, the awarding authority) paid.

The Court of Appeal found that the provisions dealing with capacity were design obligations not ongoing performance requirements: Longmore LJ said 'I cannot read paragraph 3.11 as intended to secure the result that if any time during service standing passengers exceed 5 per square meter then [the service provider] was in breach of contract. This is a paragraph dealing with the number of trams required to comply with the requirements as to frequency and journey times and with capacity, not with the conditions actually encountered in

service.' Neither would increased density of standing passengers over that set out in paragraph 3.11 trigger an obligation to add capacity. 'The very absence of determinative criteria [as to how "over-crowding" was to be measured and when the service provider would be in breach] is at least an indication that this paragraph is dealing with the planning and design stage, not providing a trigger mechanism for the imposition of an obligation to provide enhanced capacity'. The court would have expected to see such criteria before translating a design obligation into a performance requirement. On the question of how the need for increased capacity should be categorised within the contractual framework (i.e. whether it was a service change or a service parameters change), the court concluded that this would need to be re-pleaded at a future date.

The case serves as another reminder of the precision and care that needs to be taken when output specifications are drafted: the awarding authority needs not only to translate design into user requirements but also to consider those requirements in light of conditions likely to be encountered in service and specify the consequences of failing to provide them.

4.4.2 Preparation and development of the output specification and project company's proposals

The preparation of a specification in output terms involves a huge conceptual leap for the authors of the document (as well, it might be noted, as for the construction subcontractor, who may not be used to dealing with client specifications that are not specific and certain). In order to prepare such a specification, a thorough and detailed analysis of the user requirements will be needed and this can only be done effectively if a clear understanding of the awarding authority's business and operational needs has been acquired.

These needs have to be converted into outputs by concentrating on the use to which the facilities, equipment and services will be put rather than inputs, such as the physical specification of the facility. For example, a hospital for 1000 patients does not constitute an output whereas the delivery of a level of patient care is an output; the specification of a particular system of telephones and computer technology does not constitute an output whereas the delivery of an effective communication and information service is an output; and the specification of a certain type of heating system does not constitute an output requirement, whereas specifying the temperature requirements for different areas of a facility *is* an output.

In preparing an output specification, just as much consideration should therefore be given to what information to omit as to what to include. Sufficient information to enable the FM subcontractor to understand the business or user requirements of the awarding authority will be essential. Requirements which are unnecessarily prescriptive or onerous will be detrimental to the objectives of PFI procurement, including best value for money and risk transfer.

If the output specification constitutes a clear and concise definition of user requirements, an opportunity will be created for the FM subcontractor to propose the most innovative, cost effective and flexible solutions. In particular, FM subcontractors will be given the freedom to consider how best to deliver the required service without being unnecessarily constrained by input requirements promulgated by the awarding authority which may not represent the most cost-effective and technically effective solution. Care should be taken to ensure that any project constraints (e.g. operational policies of the awarding authority) do not unnecessarily restrict the opportunity for innovation.

To enhance the potential for maximizing flexibility, the output specification might also be prepared so as to identify core requirements which cannot be changed while allowing other, less essential, needs to be discussed and negotiated with the FM subcontractor prior to financial close with a view to maximizing efficiencies.

Typically, output specifications will address the facility to be delivered plus maintenance, furniture and equipment, energy and cleaning/waste management, and other 'soft services' (such as security, catering and caretaking). Consideration should also be given to providing high-level information regarding the structure of the organization, including the overall size of the various business departments and how they fit together. If the awarding authority has a mission statement, consideration should be given to its incorporation into the output specification in order to provide an indication of the ethos of the organization. As much information as is possible should be provided about future plans and likely changes to the organization and the way in which work is undertaken. Information about requirements for location may be considered for inclusion. Information regarding the existing environment and working practices and how these may be subject to change in the future should be provided.

One of the key responsibilities of the project company is to propose a design solution which enables the awarding authority to carry out its business to the standards and quality expected of it. In addition, the project company will be required, as owner and manager of the facility, to provide support services to the awarding authority in a cost-effective fashion.

Because of its nature, the output specification is likely to be capable of a number of different interpretations. The scope for this will be much greater than would be the case with a conventional performance specification. During the pre-contract period, the awarding authority and the project company will therefore need to engage in discussions to ensure that the project company's interpretation of the output specification accords with that of the awarding authority. This will continue while the project company develops and finalises its design proposals for incorporation into the project agreement.

It is important to emphasise that in agreeing the interpretation of the output specification, the awarding authority is not expected to accept responsibility for the technical competence

or accuracy of the project company's design proposals. To do so would transfer the design risk back to the awarding authority. However, it is not uncommon for the project company to suggest a limited form of sign-off to provide it with the comfort of knowing that the design proposals have encapsulated the awarding authority's business or user requirements: awarding authorities should only be interested in details relating to 'occupied areas' and the sign-off itself should confirm solely that the business function can be carried out. Accordingly, the protocol makes it clear that this does not mean that there is a transfer of design risk back to the awarding authority.

In return for the awarding authority agreeing to provide a limited form of sign-off in respect of the project company's proposals, it is usually accepted by the project company that it will carry out and complete the construction in accordance with the output specification, together with an obligation to deliver the project company's proposals.

4.4.3 Design development

Although the parties to a PFI transaction will endeavour to settle as much of the design proposals as is possible prior to signature of the project agreement, it is unrealistic to expect all areas of design which impact on business or user requirements to be finalised at that stage. This may be due to the project company's need to minimise design costs before financial close, but it may also be attributable to the needs of the awarding authority. For example, the awarding authority may not be in a position to confirm some aspects of its business or user requirements until much closer to service commencement, particularly where the awarding authority's requirements are technology driven, the design and construction period is lengthy or one of its key requirements is flexibility.

The project agreement will therefore need to cater for the development and finalisation of the outstanding areas of design after signature of the project agreement, but this should always be limited to those aspects of the design in which the awarding authority has a legitimate interest. The procedures for this are often critical. For the awarding authority, they will represent the means by which its essential business or user requirements are to be crystallised and incorporated into the facility. For the project company, there will be a concern to ensure that the process does not impact adversely on its ability to achieve completion within budget and on programme. For example, it will want to be assured that the business or user requirements do not result in redesign or reconstruction of any part of the facility, such as having to modify or relocate service cores in the facility. Time and cost implications would preclude this even if any reworking were technically feasible.

The design development procedure is sometimes structured as an iterative process. This will allow for meetings and discussions on draft design submissions before they are presented formally to the awarding authority for sign-off. This is very different from the procedures for review and sanction found in traditionally procured design and build contracts where design proposals are presented for sign-off without much, if any, prior consultation and are simply checked for compatibility with a performance specification. Notwithstanding the benefits of iterative procedures, some sectors have adopted the traditional 'ABC' procedures. The NHS Executive has adopted such procedures as has the *School Standard Form PFI Agreement (non-BSF) August 2004*. Here, design data is submitted to the awarding authority for review and the project company may only start construction works after the awarding authority has either returned the data within 10 days marked 'no comment' or allowed 10 days to elapse without making comment. There is also scope for the parties to agree that if the 10 day period lapses with no comment having been made in relation to certain specified classes of data, then the project company is to assume that objection has been made to it. In either case, the grounds on which the awarding authority can object are carefully prescribed, and relate to the awarding authority's obligation to provide educational services at a certain level, or the rights and obligations of the awarding authority under the project agreement.

A clear distinction needs to be made in the project agreement between matters properly falling within the ambit of design development and variations. The design development procedure should not be used by the awarding authority as a back-door method of securing variations to the output specification at no extra cost. By the same token, however, it is the project company's responsibility to ensure that an appropriate allowance has been included within its budgets and programme for all work necessary to deliver a completed facility on a turnkey basis. A variation should only arise where the awarding authority changes its output specification as this will inevitably lead to a change in the nature or scope of the construction works.

The provisions in the project agreement governing variations are different from the provisions commonly found in traditional procurement methods and there will usually be restrictions on the types of variation which the awarding authority can request. SoPC4 suggests that a number of grounds on which it would be reasonable for the project company to refuse to implement a change; for example, if the change is inconsistent with good industry practice, if it would materially and adversely affect the provider's ability to deliver the services or if it would materially and adversely affect the nature of the project including its risk profile. The project agreement may also contain provisions that limit the number or size of the variations which may be made during the construction period or the time at which any such variation can be requested by the authority.

In the light of these considerations, it is usually sensible to make provision for any variations that might arise during design development to be identified before they are implemented. In this way, the awarding authority and the project company provider can determine in advance whether a variation has arisen and whether, and under what terms, it is to be carried out. The parties may agree that the most economic or practical way in which to implement a variation may be achieved by having it carried out on a 'retrofit' basis.

4.5 Compliance monitoring
4.5.1 Need for compliance monitoring

HM Treasury has, in its publications on PFI, repeatedly stated that monitoring is the awarding authority's responsibility in a PFI transaction, even though service provision is delivered and performance monitored by the private sector provider. It provides a means: to assure the awarding authority and the taxpayer that all the obligations of both contracting parties are being met; of overseeing service changes; of carrying out negotiations for new services; and so on. The role will continue throughout both the construction and the operational phases.

Compliance monitoring during design and construction under a PFI transaction is nevertheless different from supervision carried out for a traditionally procured project. In a traditional project, the client has paid the capital cost of the works to the contractor by completion and its remedies for defects are framed as claims for damages or (if the defects arise during the first year or so after handover) securing repairs (and in respect of which the client will hold a sum of money as retention or a bond until the obligations during the defect correction period have been discharged).

By contrast, in a PFI transaction the awarding authority does not start making payments until the project company has completed the facility and started providing services. It does not therefore need to have the contractual power to issue instructions to the project company on the progress or quality of the work, including for the remedying of what may appear to be defective work. Indeed, there is a danger that such powers could undermine the payment mechanism because the project company might not be prepared to put its income stream at risk if it is obliged to comply with such instructions. There is therefore a tension between the approach that an awarding authority might prefer to make, and that suggested by the legal framework.

4.5.2 Scope of compliance monitoring

Compliance monitoring ought, as a result, to be addressed in the project agreement at a much higher level than would be found in a design and build contract and in a less invasive manner. The project agreement may allow the awarding authority the right to inspect design information (as seen above) as well as manufacturing, fabrication and construction activities, whether carried out on or off site. The monitoring procedures may also provide for access to minutes of site and design team meetings, copies of significant instructions issued to the construction subcontractor and, perhaps, any formal challenges to the validity of such instructions made by the construction subcontractor.

Where it is possible that the project company will require guidance from the awarding authority on its further interpretation of the output specification, the compliance monitoring procedures will need to establish the means by which those interpretations are settled and whether and to what extent they are to be contractually binding.

The awarding authority will also want to be kept informed of progress as this may have an impact on the design development procedure described in section 4.4 and on its arrangements for decant to the new facilities following completion. For example, certain standard project agreements, such as ones for schools, give the awarding authority the right on reasonable notice to inspect the state and progress of the works (and to ascertain whether they are being properly executed) as well as the operation and maintenance of the project, and to monitor compliance by the project company with its obligations under the project agreement.

Some standard forms also cater for opening up: the form for schools, for example, gives a right to the awarding authority to request the project company to open up and inspect the works where it 'reasonably believes' that they are 'defective'. The form goes on to state expressly that the exercise of any such rights will not affect the obligations of the project company under the project agreement (that is, effectively, that the risk profile of the project should not change as a result). A similar approach is taken in the standard form project agreement published by the NHS Executive.

4.5.3 Quality management systems

In most instances, the project company will be required by the project agreement to establish and implement a quality management system. By way of example, in the standard form of project agreement published by the NHS Executive the project company is required to have in place a design quality plan, a construction quality plan and a services quality plan for each service. The awarding authority or its representative or perhaps the independent certifier will be given the power to audit the management system and carry out inspections to determine whether the system is adequate and being implemented correctly. If it is, the awarding authority can more safely assume that the construction works are being undertaken in accordance with good industry practice.

4.5.4 Remedies for defects

It is sometimes suggested that more detailed compliance monitoring by awarding authorities is required in order to establish the existence of defects that manifest themselves prior to completion. However, this is not necessarily the case in PFI transactions. The tests to determine whether the criteria which trigger service commencement and the start of the unitary charge have been satisfied should be sufficiently comprehensive to establish whether or not the requisite standards have been achieved.

Defects which are discovered after service commencement may be dealt with in different ways. In some project agreements, such as the standard form of project agreement published by the

NHS Executive, there is no defects correction clause except for that relating to thermal and energy efficiency assessment post completion. This is because it is assumed that the rectification of defects will be addressed sufficiently in the performance monitoring regime. In addition, awarding the authority a right to step in for the purpose of remedying the breach if certain pre-conditions are satisfied (such as there being an immediate and a serious threat to the health or safety of any user, events that are prejudicial to the awarding authority performing its business function or where the project company has accrued warning points for repeat defaults which exceed the threshold measured within the set timeframe).

In practice, the construction subcontract will invariably contain defects liability provisions in the traditional way. The project company's income could be at risk if defects manifest themselves and there needs to be a strong incentive placed on the construction subcontractor to ensure that defects are remedied. In order to avoid arguments about whether the retention monies should be charged to the project company's financiers, the use of retention bonds, which are assigned by way of security to the financiers, can be a useful device.

Where a defect gives rise to unavailability and, hence, a deduction from the unitary payment, the amount of the deduction will vary depending on the type of facility and the impact which the defect has on its use by the awarding authority. If a defect in a building prevents the operation of certain business units, it may be appropriate for other areas of the building to be treated as unavailable if they are occupied by related business units which are dependent on the operation of the unit directly affected by the defect in question. For example, a defect in the ITU of a hospital may render unavailable both the ITU and the operating theatres. It may also be appropriate for the amount of the deduction to vary from area to area (e.g. storage areas may attract a lower rating than core business areas).

The question of whether deductions from the unitary payment for unavailability due to defects are the sole remedy for the awarding authority can represent an area of significant debate. In the absence of an exclusive remedies clause, the project company can find that there is liability in damages for breach of the project agreement in addition to deductions being made from the income stream.

If the payment mechanism is not sufficiently sensitive to respond to the existence of defects, a claim for damages for breach of the project agreement may represent the principal remedy for the awarding authority. However, project agreements typically exclude the project company's liability for consequential loss and/or contain a damages cap. As an alternative, the awarding authority may be able to require the project company to repair the defect by specific performance or through the operation of 'self-help' procedures. The project agreement may permit such damages or the costs of 'self-help' to be deducted from the unitary payment.

The project company will seek to ensure that any income which is lost as a result of defects can be recovered from the construction subcontractor. The allocation of liability for deductions as between the project company and its subcontractors is usually dealt with in an Interface Agreement (see section 4.6.7). However, the pass-through of liability may not, in all cases, be possible. For example, the ability to make deductions from unitary payments will last throughout the period of the concession, whereas the project company's ability to sue the construction subcontractor for damages may be subject to a limitation period which expires 6 or 12 years after completion, depending on whether or not the construction subcontract has been executed as a deed.

4.6 Service commencement

4.6.1 Significance

The provisions in the project agreement governing the certification of service commencement are of fundamental importance to both parties to the project agreement as well as the project company's financiers. The issue of the requisite certificate will signify that the contracted services are ready for delivery, including confirmation that the asset from which the services will be provided is physically ready.

It will be important to the project company and its financiers that there is an unbreakable link between the criteria which have to be met to achieve service commencement or availability and the issue of the certificate of practical completion under the construction subcontract. In this way, the project company is best placed to ensure that lost income for late service delivery can be recouped through the recovery of liquidated damages if the construction subcontractor is in culpable delay.

The project agreement will describe what is meant by service commencement and the means by which the project company provider is to demonstrate that the requirements for the same have been satisfied. In addition, the project company's financiers may insist on high standards for completion as the construction subcontractor will be released from any further liability for liquidated damages following completion and the financiers will be anxious to know that the income to be generated by the facility will be reliable and consistent.

4.6.2 Certification of service commencement

SoPC4 suggests that, although the method of demonstration that the requirements of the output specification have been achieved differs in each project, the pre-conditions to certification of service commencement may take the form of:

- a completion inspection of the facility and services;
- completion of acceptance trials for new services; and
- other performance tests or inspections.

In the majority of projects, the principal parties to a PFI transaction, including the financiers, will be keen to ensure that the criteria required to be achieved prior to certification are made as objective as possible. Complete objectivity may not be possible in all cases (e.g. where the awarding authority is the best judge as to whether the requisite standards have been achieved), but even in these instances the parties are likely to insist on as much objectivity as is possible. However, it is worth noting that this approach is not followed in all respects in the Department of Health's Standard Form of Project Agreement, where it is suggested that, in addition to passing specified tests satisfactorily, the construction works must be completed in all respects in accordance with the project agreement and this is required in order to permit certification.

While the matters which must be demonstrated by the project company in order to trigger completion will vary depending on the type of project, these will usually involve the successful completion of specified tests to establish that the requisite standards of service or performance have been achieved.

As suggested by SoPC4, the project agreement should also address other procedural issues, such as the programme for the carrying out of the tests, the ability of the awarding authority to witness the tests and to review and retain copies of the test results, responsibility for providing facilities and resources for undertaking and witnessing the tests and the consequences arising if the tests are failed.

4.6.3 Independent certifier

There are differing views on who should be responsible for issuing the certificate under the project agreement to signify service commencement and trigger the income stream. SoPC4 suggests that in most cases there will be either a joint assessment by the awarding authority and the project company or an assessment by an independent third party, although there will be cases where the awarding authority is the best judge.

As in the case of the Department of Health's Standard Form of Project Agreement published by the NHS Executive, it may be agreed that the certificate should be issued by an independent certifier or tester who is appointed jointly by the awarding authority and the project company. Similarly, the Building Schools for the Future standard PFI agreement provides for the independent certifier route. The attraction of appointing an independent certifier is that it gives both parties, and the financiers, confidence that the decision on whether to certify will be made impartially and promptly.

By acknowledging that the independent certifier is, in effect, an expert, owing an equal duty of care to the awarding authority and the project company, the parties may consider it appropriate for the independent certifier's decision on whether the criteria for service commencement have been achieved to be treated as a final and binding decision of an expert which is not open to subsequent challenge under the dispute resolution procedure.

The role of the independent certifier can be perceived as being one attracting a high risk, particularly where the certifier has to make some sort of value judgment about the criteria triggering service commencement. Accordingly, it is likely that fees payable to the certifier will include a premium for this perceived risk unless the role is ring-fenced in an appropriate manner. For example, where the criteria are entirely objective, it may not be necessary for the certifier to be appointed throughout the entire length of the design and construction period or to review in detail the proposed design solutions or inspect quality of work on site. The certifier's role may be restricted to auditing the project company's quality management system and carrying out periodic checks to see that it is being implemented properly, acquiring a sufficient understanding of the output specification and the project company's proposals to understand the criteria and to establish whether the appropriate requirements have been achieved and the relevant tests have been passed.

Where service commencement is not to be judged by wholly objective criteria, it may be necessary for the role of the independent certifier to be expanded to enable the certifier to form an opinion about the general quality of work. However, it is unlikely that the role of the independent certifier should include extensive on-site inspection and the review of detailed design proposals or the provision of early warning regarding potential issues which may result in the completion certificate being withheld. This is, perhaps, inconsistent with the risk transfer embodied within PFI philosophy. There is a danger that the independence of the certifier might be compromised because, in practice, the independent certifier becomes inextricably linked with the project company's design and construction and the independent certifier's review becomes something not dissimilar to progressive acceptance. In addition, the awarding authority may be paying twice for the transfer of the design and construction risk – that is, to both the project company provider and the independent certifier.

Where it is decided that the certificate under the project agreement is also to operate as the practical completion certificate under the construction subcontract, the independent certifier's appointment may become tripartite with the construction subcontractor added as an additional client, or the independent certifier may be asked to sign a collateral warranty in favour of the construction subcontractor. The key FM subcontractor and the project company's financiers may, also, each require a collateral warranty from the independent certifier.

4.6.4 Risk transfer

The issue of the certificate triggering service commencement should not represent an acceptance of the means of service delivery as this may impair risk transfer. The certificate should, so far as possible, merely confirm the date on which the facility was ready.

4.6.5 Outstanding work

Flexibility is usually introduced into the project agreement by allowing the certificate to be issued notwithstanding the existence of minor outstanding works which need to be completed or minor defects which need to be repaired. Such snagging

matters should not inconvenience the use of the facility by the awarding authority. The precise arrangements for rectification of snagging matters will vary from project to project, but the project agreement will usually have to establish the means by which the project company is incentivised to complete the snagging exercise. The difficulty often faced is that the existence of snagging matters will not, by itself, give rise to payment deductions for unavailability, but can nevertheless cause annoyance to the occupants or users of the facility.

4.6.6 Post-occupation commissioning

The awarding authority and the project company's financiers are likely to require as much as is possible of the commissioning process to be concluded by the time service commencement is certified.

However, it may not be technically or practically feasible for this preferred position to be achieved in all cases. For example, it may not be possible for the facility's mechanical and electrical services to be tested under full load or fine-tuned until the awarding authority has installed its equipment or has decanted its operations into the new facility; or, where the awarding authority is to provide equipment for installation into the new facility, it may be necessary for the commissioning of this equipment and the new facility to be co-ordinated. In addition, it may be sensible to allow a period for the project company to train and commission the 'soft' service provision.

In these circumstances, the project agreement needs to prescribe the procedures for post-occupation commissioning. Many of the issues mentioned above on testing procedures will apply on a similar basis. An extra layer of complexity will be added if a fully integrated commissioning programme is required for the commissioning of the awarding authority's equipment along with the new facility.

One of the key issues, to be addressed in the project agreement will be the consequences (if any) on payment if problems or delays are encountered during post-occupation commissioning. The precise consequences will, of course, vary from project to project, and the legal documentation will have to be adapted accordingly. For example, it may be appropriate for the commencement of payment to be postponed until the expiry of a fixed period after completion, during which it is anticipated that the commissioning process will be concluded and/or relaxed arrangements may be settled for payment deductions if there is interim unavailability as a result of prolonged commissioning. However, this should be considered with caution as the additional financing cost of effectively deferring the commencement of the income stream is likely to be factored into the cost of the project and will be reflected in the unitary payment.

From a practical perspective, one of the greatest difficulties arises where equipment is supplied by the awarding authority and the project company and the performance of their respective equipment is dependent on the proper functioning of the equipment supplied by the other party. In this case, procedures allowing for accurate traceability of the source of any problems encountered are necessary so that the payment arrangements can operate fairly depending on the source of the problems encountered.

4.6.7 Interface Agreement

An Interface Agreement (also sometimes known as a Co-ordination Agreement) is an agreement which provides a contractual relationship between the construction subcontractor, FM subcontractors and other key subcontractors such as ICT subcontractors. The project company and its financiers are also parties to the document.

The Interface Agreement allows the subcontractors to warrant to each other the performance of their obligations under their respective subcontracts, agree on interface issues such as those identified sections 4.5.4, 4.6.5 and 4.6.6, design development, rights of access and their liabilities for the same.

The key purpose of Interface Agreements, though, is to protect the cash-flow of the project company and recover deductions which may be applied against it at project agreement level due to a defaulting subcontractor. Accordingly, it is common for Interface Agreements to allow the project company, acting in good faith, to pass on a deduction it suffers under the project agreement as a result of a breach by a subcontractor under its subcontract to that defaulting subcontractor. If that subcontractor considers is has been wrongly allocated the deduction, it can then seek to recover the deduction from one of the other subcontractors party to the Interface Agreement and dispute resolution provisions are included to deal with any dispute which may arise in this respect.

In some Interface Agreements, the project company may be entitled to allocate deductions against the subcontractor it feels is most able to bear the loss. However, this will be strongly resisted by FM subcontractors as they will perceive that the project company will invariably select them as the deduction can easily be taken from their monthly payment, whereas it may be more difficult to recover the deduction from the construction subcontractor whose fees are likely to have been largely paid by service commencement.

4.7 Direct agreements and collateral warranties

4.7.1 Direct agreements

The purpose and effect of direct agreements in favour of the project company's provider's financiers is dealt with in *Financing the project* (this volume). For current purposes, it is sufficient to appreciate that the financiers will require the ability to take over the construction subcontract where the project company defaults. It creates an opportunity for the financiers to complete the construction works and to minimise disruption to the income stream. The direct agreement will allow the financiers either to appoint a replacement company as the project company or to assume itself the responsibilities of the project company.

In parallel with the direct agreements for the financiers, it has become increasingly common for the awarding authority to be given an opportunity to take over the construction subcontract or to appoint a replacement project company if the project agreement is terminated for the project company's default prior to completion. Similar arrangements may also exist in relation to the principal maintenance contracts.

Where such rights exist for the awarding authority, they are invariably subordinated to the step-in rights of the financiers. It is only if the financiers fail to exercise these rights in accordance with the terms of the relevant direct agreement that the awarding authority is given the opportunity to step in.

The project company's financiers may insist that the awarding authority cannot step in to the construction subcontract until they have been paid out in full. In other words, the benefit of the construction subcontract has to stay with the project company to enable the financiers to pursue the construction subcontractor for any losses due to the subcontractor's default. The awarding authority will need to ascertain the extent of these claims and losses as it would not wish to step in only to find that the construction subcontractor is, or subsequently becomes, insolvent. SoPC4 does in fact note the incidence of projects closing with subordination provisions in place, stating that in general there should be no conflict between the interests of the Senior Lenders and those of the awarding authority. It goes on to warn however that blanket subordination provisions which prevent the authority from exercising its rights until the senior debt is fully paid out might preclude the awarding authority from stepping in where continuity of service will otherwise be disrupted. HM Treasury suggests that this situation should be avoided and provides drafting to achieve this (see chapter 31.7 SoPC4 for further details).

Where step-in rights are capable of being exercised, the direct agreement will contain procedures for the construction subcontract to be transferred formally (usually by way of novation) from the project company to a replacement entity selected by the awarding authority, or to the authority itself. There will usually be an intermediary stage in the process under which the awarding authority can step in to the construction subcontract on a temporary basis. This step-in period will end if the construction subcontract has not been formally transferred before the end of a specified period or whenever the awarding authority decides to step out (see the chapter *The construction contract* for further discussion on novations).

If the construction subcontract is to be transferred formally, the financiers will have to release the construction subcontract and any associated parent company guarantee or performance bond from the security package.

4.7.2 Collateral warranties

At first sight, it does appear unnecessary for the construction subcontractor to provide, and, also, to procure that any designers it has appointed provide, a collateral warranty to the awarding authority since the latter's position as occupier or user in the PFI context is very different from an occupier who is a building owner or a tenant under a full repairing and insuring lease. Provision of such a collateral warranty may however, be justified. For example, because the project company will often be a special purpose vehicle with no track record, its assets will be limited to the project assets and income, all of which will be charged to secure the debt owed to the project company's financiers. Also, the payment mechanism may not be sufficiently sensitive to enable deductions from the unitary payment to be made regardless of the nature of, or reasons for, a construction defect or other inadequacy in the facility. While there may be contractual remedies available against the project company under the project agreement, it may be more efficient for the awarding authority to claim directly against the construction subcontractor rather than against the project company.

Collateral warranties are commonly required on Road PFI Projects and Schools PFI projects. Despite the reasons provided above, it is generally accepted, as suggested by SoPC4, that collateral warranties in PFI projects should not grant rights to the awarding authority which are exercisable prior to termination.

Many of the issues usually associated with collateral warranties relating to traditionally procured projects apply equally to collateral warranties in the PFI context (see the chapters *The construction contract* and *Collateral warranties* for further detail).

The rules embodied in the Contracts (Rights of Third Parties) Act 1999 apply to both the project agreement and the construction subcontract. These rules may obviate the need for a collateral warranty to be given by the construction subcontractor to the awarding authority. It is likely, however, that in practice the Act will be excluded.

4.8 Part II of the Housing Grants, Construction and Regeneration Act 1996 (HGA)

4.8.1 Application to the project agreement

Although it applies to contracts which provide for the carrying out of construction operations, Part II of the HGA does not apply to the project agreement in a PFI transaction where the awarding authority has the characteristics described in Article 4 of the Construction Contracts (England and Wales) Exclusion Order 1998. For example, the HGA does not apply to a project agreement where the awarding authority is a Minister of the Crown or a body whose accounts are subject to audit by the Audit Commission.

The status of the project agreement under the Exclusion Order has to be recited in order to confirm the applicability, or otherwise, of the HGA to the project agreement (see paragraph 4(2)(a) of the Exclusion Order).

4.8.2 Application to the construction subcontract

Although the legislation will not apply to the project agreement if the requirements of the Exclusion Order are met, the HGA will apply to the construction subcontract and the FM subcontract as it is not possible for the parties to these subcontracts to override the operation of the statutory code. Accordingly, the project company will need to ensure that the terms of the construction subcontract governing payment and dispute resolution comply with the legislation.

For example, section 113 of the HGA currently renders 'ineffective' any provision in a construction contract which makes payment conditional on the payer receiving payment from a third party, unless that third party is insolvent. Such provisions are commonly known as 'pay-when-paid'. Where the project company is financing the construction costs directly from the loan it receives from its financiers, this does not create a problem. The difficulty arises where the construction subcontractor is entitled to additional payment as a consequence of the occurrence of compensation events. This will arise, for example, where the awarding authority wishes to implement a variation and it is agreed that it will pay the capital cost of the extra work. Where the compensation event is an awarding authority's risk, the project company and its financiers will be concerned to ensure that the construction subcontract has what is, in effect, a pay-when-paid provision so that the project company provider does not find itself in default under the finance documentation because it has mismatched its income from the awarding authority with its payment obligations under the construction subcontract. However, any such arrangement conflicts with section 113 of the HGA and runs the risk of being rendered ineffective.

In order to resolve this difficulty, construction subcontracts have attempted to circumvent section 113 of the HGA by, for example, providing that the construction subcontractor's entitlement to compensation in relation to the awarding authority's risks is conditional on a corresponding entitlement of the project company to payment being established under the project agreement: such provisions are known as 'equivalent project relief' (EPR) provisions. This structure (sometimes called 'pay-when-certified' or 'entitled-when-entitled') attempts to achieve compliance with the HGA by making it clear that the construction subcontractor's underlying entitlement to payment does not arise until the project company has established its own entitlement to payment from the awarding authority, as opposed to a provision which simply requires the construction subcontractor to wait for payment of a sum already due until the project company is put in funds by the awarding authority.

However, the courts have seriously undermined such arrangements. In *Midland Expressway v. Carillion Construction Ltd and Others* (2006) 106 Con LR 154, Jackson J applied a purposive interpretation to the HGA and held that the 'practical consequence' of the EPR clause considered in the case (which was fairly typical) was that the construction subcontractor would not be paid for an awarding authority-instigated variation unless and until the project company had received a corresponding sum from the awarding authority. The distinction between 'entitled-when-entitled' and 'pay-when-paid' was ignored, Jackson J stating that the 'contracting parties cannot escape the operation of section 113 by the use of circumlocution'.

The breadth of the court's approach to interpreting the HGA calls into question the enforceability of a variety of other provisions that might have been used to avoid the problem. Examples of alternative approaches include a provision in the construction subcontract stating that if, for any reason, the 'pay-when-certified' provisions are rendered unenforceable, in circumstances where the project company does not have available funds to meet the contractor's entitlement to additional compensation, a 'parallel loan agreement' between the project company and the subcontractor will take effect. Under such an arrangement, the construction subcontractor is required to make a loan to the project company of the amount necessary to place the project company in sufficient funds to meet the construction subcontractor's entitlement to compensation. In this way, the risk of the project company defaulting on its payment obligations under the construction subcontract, and thereby being in breach of the finance documentation due to lack of funds, is avoided (or at least reduced). It seems doubtful that arrangements such as these would survive an approach such as that taken by Jackson J above.

The provisions of the HGA have been altered by the Local Democracy, Economic Development and Construction Act 2009 (LDEDCA Act) which received Royal Assent on 12th November 2009. This Act amends aspects of the HGA which affect construction contracts, but unfortunately the opportunity to harmonise subcontracts with PFI project agreements was not seized. Instead, the LDEDCA Act now prohibits pay-when-certified clauses (adding to the current prohibition on pay-when-paid clauses). Also, rather than making it clear that construction subcontracts sitting under PFI project agreements are also excluded from the effects of the HGA, the LDEDCA instead only introduces a minor amendment to enhance the Secretary of State's power to create an exclusion order; now, an order excluding a contract from parts of the effects of the HGA can be made on a project specific basis. The LDEDCA Act is likely to come into force in 2011.

4.9 Dispute resolution
4.9.1 Procedures

The dispute resolution provisions in PFI transactions do not normally distinguish between disputes arising from the initial building works and disputes arising from the subsequent provision of services. This is because, for example, the defective execution of the initial building works could ultimately become manifest as a problem with the provision of services. Alternatively, questions could arise as to whether a dispute arose from the initial building works or the performance of ongoing building maintenance, so-called 'hard services'.

To accommodate the range of disputes which might arise over the life of a PFI project, the dispute resolution provisions included in project agreements normally contain an 'escalating' procedure. There is commonly a liaison procedure, involving a committee composed of operational managers from the awarding authority and the project company which meets regularly to discuss any issues that arise, which seeks to prevent issues from becoming fully fledged disputes. Any matters upon which the liaison committee cannot agree are passed up to the respective chief executives of the awarding authority and the project company. They may be able to settle disputes by taking a more strategic view of the issues than the operational managers involved.

Disputes which cannot be settled by the respective chief executives are then escalated again for determination by an independent third party. Usually this will be done by the appointment of an adjudicator, who may be selected from a standing panel (or on an ad hoc basis), using an expedited procedure. The decision is normally binding on the parties and must be implemented. However, either party may normally challenge such a decision, provided they do so within a specified time from the decision. If the decision is challenged the dispute is reheard, either by the courts or by arbitration.

However, the parties must normally comply with and implement the decision until it is altered, if at all, by the courts or an arbitrator. If the decision is not challenged within the requisite time it becomes permanent and cannot subsequently be reopened by either party. See Section 4: *Construction disputes* for further information.

4.9.2 Joinder

One contentious issue in the negotiation of most PFI transactions is that of the joinder and consolidation of disputes between the awarding authority and the project company, on the one hand, with similar disputes between the project company and its subcontractors, on the other.

As the project company has normally negotiated its subcontracts back to back with the project agreement, there should be a corresponding default by one of its subcontractors for most defaults by it under the project agreement. Conversely, there should be a corresponding claim by the project company against the awarding authority for many claims by a subcontractor against the project company. It is these related disputes that project companies may wish to have heard together to protect them from the consequences of inconsistent decisions concerning related disputes. These consequences could be severe. For example, one arbitrator could find that the project company has no right to additional payment, while another arbitrator determines that the same circumstances entitle the subcontractor to additional payment from the project company. As this could affect the project company's ability to repay its funding, this issue is also of concern to the project company's financiers.

This is further complicated by the fact, as discussed above, that the exemption of PFI transactions from Part II of the HGA only applies to the project agreement. As a result, the construction subcontract must include provision for the adjudication of disputes under the construction subcontract. This also applies to disputes arising in relation to the FM subcontract. As an adjudicator's decision normally relates to entitlement to payment, there is again a risk that the project company may have to pay money to its subcontractor not provided for by its funding model, nor reimbursed by the awarding authority.

The structure of a PFI transaction is designed to enable the awarding authority to deal with one party only. This is lost if the joinder and consolidation of disputes is allowed, as the awarding authority finds itself dealing with the subcontractors as well as the project company. As a result of the complication and additional expense resulting from the joinder of disputes, SoPC4 recommends that joinder be resisted wherever possible by awarding authorities, although the required drafting permits the project company to include a subcontractor's submissions in its case to the body hearing the dispute. This has been followed in the dispute resolution procedure contained in the standard form of project agreement published by the NHS Executive where it is noted that joinder provisions have not been included so as to prevent the awarding authority from becoming embroiled in concurrent disputes running between the project company and its subcontractors.

One way to resolve this issue is to have provisions within the Interface Agreement (see section 4.6.7 of this chapter) whereby disputes which affect the project company and/or the construction subcontractor and/or the FM subcontractor are heard together in a period which dovetails, as far as is practical, with any connected dispute between the awarding authority and the project company under the project agreement.

References

HM Treasury (2007) *Standardisation of PFI Contracts Version 4(SoPC4)*. TSO, London, UK. www.hm-treasury.gov.uk/ppp_standardised_contracts.htm

Defra (2007) Waste Strategy for England.TSO, London, UK. www.defra.gov.uk/environment/waste/strategy/

Referenced legislation, regulations and standards

Construction Contracts (England and Wales) Exclusion Order 1998. TSO, London, UK
Contracts (Rights of Third Parties) Act 1999. TSO, London, UK
Housing Grants, Construction and Regeneration Act 1996. HMSO, London, UK
EU Landfill Directive – Council Directive 99/31/EC of 26 April 1999 on the landfill of waste. *OJ* **L182**, 16/07/1999. pp.1–19
Local Democracy, Economic Development and Construction Act 2009. TSO, London, UK

Referenced cases

London Bus Services Ltd v. Tramtrack Croydon Ltd [2007] EWHC 107
Midland Expressway v. Carillion Construction Ltd and Others (2006) 106 Con LR 154

Websites

Defra. WIDP Residual Waste Procurement Pack; www.defra.gov.uk/environment/waste/localauth/funding/pfi/guidance.htm
HM Treasury; www.hm-treasury.gov.uk
Local Government Association; www.lga.gov.uk Major Project Review group; www.ogc.gov.uk/programmes_projects_major_projects_review_group.asp
Project Review Group; www.hm-treasury.gov.uk/ppp_projectreview_group.htm
Office of Government Commerce; www.ogc.gov.uk/index.asp
OGC procurement policy and application of EU rules; www.ogc.gov.uk/procurement_policy_and_practice_procurement_policy_and_application_of_eu_rules.asp
Operational Taskforce; www.hm-treasury.gov.uk/ppp_operational_taskforce.htm
Local Partnerships; www.localpartnerships.org.uk/

Chapter 5

doi: 10.1680/mocl.40878.0067

Facilities management contracts

Ian Griffiths Thring Townsend Lee & Pembertons LLP, Bristol, UK

This chapter gives a definition of facilities management and introduce its various key components. The reasons for the development of facilities management over the past decade is briefly outlined. The key considerations and risks of facilities management as a means of outsourcing are reviewed. Attention is given to the need for contractual flexibility, change control, service definition, pricing, benchmarking and termination issues. A review of standard form approaches to some of these issues is made.

CONTENTS

5.1 Introduction

5.1.1 Definitions

There is no shortage of definitions proffered of facilities management in publications, university course syllabi and professional societies. This profusion of attempts to define facilities management is, perhaps, characteristic of relatively new professions and sectors within the global economy exploring the boundaries of their influence.

Facilities management is defined by CEN, the European Committee for Standardisation as:

> *The integration of processes within an organisation to maintain and develop the agreed services which support and improve the effectiveness of its primary activities.*

Construct IT Centre of Excellence attempts to define facilities management as follows:

> *Facilities management is the means by which the clients' capital investment is not only protected, but made to work in support of the core business*

This definition suggests the very strong link between facilities management and outsourcing, or at least the recognition that the discipline is separate from but important to the core operational functions and business of client organisations.

The definition offered by the British Institute of Facilities Management (BIFM) is:

> *Facilities management is the practice of co-ordinating the physical workplace with the people and work of an organisation*

Of the three definitions given above the latter is possibly the most restrictive in that it tends to emphasise the building or buildings housing the client's workforce or products. Facilities management often covers the services provided in respect of all assets of the client organisation, whether it relates to IT equipment, fleets of vehicles, aircraft or engineering installations or reception facilities.

5.1.2 Development of facilities management

Facilities management is sometimes viewed as the poor relation of the construction industry. This may be due to the ignorance of what facilities management is (hence the number of definitions), or the perception that it only relates to building management. It may be that professions within construction and engineering are trained on the premise of erecting the built environment rather than maintaining it and related services effectively.

Facilities management has, however, been viewed as the fastest growing sector in the construction industry in the UK over the last decade. It would be more correct to state that in the economic conditions of the last two years it is the slowest shrinking sector. In the UK alone British Institute of Facilities Management estimates the sector is worth between £40 billion and £95 billion (BIFM website). A much larger estimate of £174.4 billion was made of the UK facilities management market in its 'broadest scope' in 2006 by the University of Salford Centre for Facilities Management (Moss et al., 2006).

Whilst facilities management, as we know it today, first developed from initiatives in the 1970s and 1980s to outsource non-core services as a means of cost cutting, the key driver for growth has been its integral role within Private Finance Intitatives (PFIs) and Public-Private Partnerships (PPPs).

PFI has taken the emphasis away from the construction of a facility for the public sector to a contractual requirement on the private sector to provide services in relation to the infrastructure built on a long-term basis. Facilities management, like PFI should be service driven. It has been argued that in differentiating facilities management from the core business of the client organisation, a clear mandate is given to it to add value to the client.

Apologists for the profession of facility management highlight the numerous management skills to be demonstrated by those in the profession. Facilities management, they argue, includes:

- property management
- health and safety and risk management
- financial management
- human resources management
- asset management
- utilities supply
- building services engineering
- domestic services.

As detailed in the chapter *Public-private sector partnerships* the PFI model shifted the public sector focus from that of an owner to a purchaser of services. The belief that the public sector should focus on its core operation leaving the private sector to manage the facilities in which the public sector organisation is housed more efficiently has provided an enormous boost to the development of the profession of facilities management. This factor has also resulted in the close association between facilities management and outsourcing, almost to the point where they are erroneously viewed as being synonymous.

Many of the issues and challenges facing the provision and procuring of facilities management on an outsourcing basis will also apply to in-house facilities management services as these also tend to be arranged on a long-term basis and also require sufficient definition of the nature and quality of the service to be provided. All facilities management arrangements will need a system of change control to allow flexibility where the services require variation.

5.1.3 Hard and soft facilities management

Facilities management services are frequently divided into the two categories 'hard FM' and 'soft FM'. Hard FM relates to the maintenance and management of the asset or facility and soft FM characterises the management of support services.

Examples of hard FM include buildings, other facilities, estates, water supply, electricity, engineering and telecommunication systems. Soft FM would encompass services such as catering, cleaning, waste management, security and laundry.

Whilst the differentiation in classifying hard and soft FM services remains, more organisations are offering an integrated approach and offering to provide the entirety of the FM services. The need to tender such services separately is lessening as the original reluctance of building and engineering contracting firms to countenance soft FM services has given way to specialised facilities companies taking a larger share in the market and building surveying and consultancy organisations being prepared to take on the role and subcontract various service aspects to others.

This can be seen in those tendering for the increasing outsourcing of facility management contracts of student accommodation and the recent development of the concept of 'workplace management'. Workplace management is described as a combination of traditional facilities management with more strategic services, the aim being to improve the performance of the workforce.

The influence of PFI and PPP on the growth of facilities management has already been noted. This influence continues as PPP is an evolving service innovation. One of its effects is the altering of the role given to the buildings which house the service provision where these assets are perceived in life cycle cost design terms.

Given the aim of such projects is to achieve a stated level of day to day services to the employees or to the visitors to the building, the emphasis is placed on utility and functionality of all required services in a tangible and measurable form. This emphasis on cohesive service provision will continue to influence the way in which facilities management is viewed and how it will develop.

5.1.4 Standard form contracts

Most facilities management agreements and outsourcing agreements are documented in bespoke contracts. PFI and PPP have seen an increasing standardisation in their approach to project documentation. The NHS LIFT SPA version 5 is an example of such standardisation (see the chapter *Public-private sector partnerships*).

On non PFI projects, even where a high level of unique drafting is required, the use and incorporation of standard form contracts can be useful in providing a coherent framework to the contract and allows the parties better to understand the balance of risk between them.

The standard forms to which we shall refer in this chapter are outlined below:

5.1.4.1 CIOB Facilities Management Contract

This contract, now in its third edition, was published in 2008. As its title would suggest it was purposely drafted as a facilities management contract and offers a basic framework for such contracts. The contract is published by the Chartered Institute of Building (CIOB). Initially, it was published originally in 1999 in association with law firm Cameron McKenna, now CMS Cameron McKenna LLP.

5.1.4.2 GC/Works/10 (2000)

GC/Works/10 is another form of contract specifically drafted for use in facilities management. This contract is part of the well-known GC/Works suite of contracts. The provisions of the contract will be very familiar to anyone who has used another of the GC/Works contract form. The contract is designed either for the engagement of a full service facilities management contractor or a managing agent who will subcontract various services.

5.1.4.3 TPC 2005

This standard form Term Partnering Contract (TPC) is published by the Association of Consultant Architects (ACA) and was drafted by law firm Trowers & Hamlins.

It is based on the approach developed in the PPC 2000 standard form of contract for project partnering and retains its key features including a multi-party approach, risk registers, processes for continuous improvement and supply chain partnering.

The intention is that the TPC 2005 can be used for any type of term works and services, not simply facilities management in any jurisdiction although certain provisions, including those on Transfer of Undertakings (TUPE) and references to the Housing Grants, Construction and Regeneration Act 1996 are restricted to the UK.

5.1.4.4 NEC3 Term Service Contract (NEC3 TSC)

As with the GC/Works/10 and TPC 2005, the NEC3 TSC is part of a much larger suite of contracts. The NEC3 is published by the Institution of Civil Engineers. The NEC3 suite of contracts has benefited in recent years from the endorsement of the Office of Government Commerce (OGC).

Many of the features of the NEC3 contracts including pricing flexibility and provisions to promote real time management of the contract such as early warning notices, risk registers and time limits on compensation event claims lend themselves to the concept of a term service agreement. Indeed, many users of the NEC had adapted the contract to suit their facilities management needs before the NEC3 TSC was published.

5.2 Services and service levels
5.2.1 Services and specification

The schedule to the facilities management contract setting out the service description is likely to be the most important part of the contract. The usual risks of service failure apply to facilities management contracts as apply to other service agreements or works contracts, namely unclear specifications, a lack of adequate supplier capability or supplier corner cutting to increase profitability.

Added to these risks is the variable of the term or duration of the contract. This affects the need for flexibility in the potential range of services to be offered and the need for change control mechanisms in the contract. The fact that a facilities management contract is for maintenance together with its duration brings another key component – the need to address the quality of the service provided.

Construction projects are monitored during their construction phase. The design services and construction works follow a path generally mapped out in a programme document. In simplistic terms, if the services are not performed at all or are performed badly, it is often picked up by those engaged on the project when it affects them, such as the project manager and

members of the design team, or by the obvious inadequacy of the plant, building or IT system as it is being built.

Service inadequacy is more difficult to detect, much less measured without the singular goal of construction and the input of other contributing constructors unless the inadequacy affects operations elements of plant or a building. Facility management contracts must also, therefore, provide for the level and quality of the service supplied to be measured.

An important consideration is that the service and service level schedules should be consistent in terminology and in the use of defined terms. Too often, service schedules are appended from past or other projects and often differing standard form contracts without sufficient regard for the differences in terminology, drafting ethos or procedure to that reflected in the contract terms.

5.2.1.1 Service schedule examples in standard forms

Normally standard form construction or engineering contracts provide no assistance in determining how such schedules are to be set out but a few of the facilities management standard form contracts provide useful guidance. The model forms and commentary publications of the GC/Works/10 (2000) form of contract provide a very useful sample cleaning specification. Example specifications are also provided in some standardised PPP contracts such as the "Example LIFT Specifications".

The GC/Works/10 Model Form and Commentary publication (which accompanies the GC/Works/10) highlights that a specification should contain

■ the contractor's services

■ the service hours for each service to be provided

■ the set up procedures required of the contractor

■ a site description of where the services are to be performed

■ requirements and information relating to site access, security or in relation to the occupation of the employer's premises.

The Example LIFT Specification also includes a list of exclusions to the specifications and lists categories of periods within which items are rectified depending on the category of urgency. A traffic light system of continuous improvement indicators is included within the Example LIFT Specifications also.

5.2.1.2 'Input' and 'output' services specification

To ensure flexibility in the contract it is best to set out the specifications in an 'output' format as encouraged by the Office of Government Commerce.

The traditional 'input' form of specification prescribes the way in which the service is to be performed by the contractor in a detailed fashion. Conversely, an output specification would not describe how performance standards are to be met. Such an approach puts the responsibility on the contractor to propose how it would achieve the appropriate performance standard. It is the contractor after all who has the expertise and it may fetter the ability of the contractor to provide innovation in the delivery of its services if a prescriptive input specification is used. The other likely benefits in using an output approach to specification and allowing the contractor to outline how it will meet the performance requirements set by the employer are:

- lower tender prices
- time and cost saving for the employer in putting together the tender documents
- less opportunity for the service schedules to contradict any separately produced employer requirements document created earlier in the tender process. Employer requirement documents are sometimes used in public procurement contracts where the specification is developed alongside the preferred or successful bidder.

The key disadvantages to the employer of using an output specification approach as opposed to an input specification are:

- a loss of control over services provision
- greater difficulty in assessing contractor performance.

Even if the employer decides to adopt an output specification approach, it is open to him to be more prescriptive on key service areas such as access and security, front of house or customer facing services where he considers that greater control is required.

Where an output specification is used, care should be taken to ensure that the service schedule is anything less than a comprehensive description of the services to be provided.

5.2.2 Service levels or key performance indicators

There is a great deal of literature on the methodology of setting service levels which are also known as key performance indicators ('KPIs'). KPIs are generally to be seen as a tool to be used as part of the overall business plan of an organisation or its outsourced projects. Service levels or KPIs sit behind each of the objectives of the procurement or business plan.

Usually KPIs are set out in percentage terms of a specific quantity or value. They can also be shown in terms of:

- an upper limit
- a lower limit
- a single value
- a value range
- a key date by which a task is to be completed.

As with the balance required in deciding where input and output specifications are to be used in the service schedule, there is a need for compromise in setting KPIs. Employers are often tempted to include too many KPIs. This can create ambiguity

between various service areas or it might simply not reflect the areas truly important to the employer. Such an approach could make the KPIs meaningless. On the other hand, too few KPIs may not present a complete view of the services and allow the contractor to focus on areas covered by the KPIs to the detriment of the services overall. It is considered better to err on the side of less rather than more. Ten to Twenty KPIs is regarded as a rule of thumb.

The quantity of KPIs set by the employer and agreed with the contractor is not the only consideration. The performance levels need to be set at a high enough level to provide a good service to the employer throughout the contract term and to demonstrate progress in meeting its long-term goals. There are invariably financial repercussions if the KPIs are not met. KPIs will need to be set at an achievable level in order for the contractors to agree to them. Performance is generally measured over a performance period of a month or a quarter.

Contractors should ensure that its performance is measured only in respect of services and areas where it has control. Areas of service retained by the employer should be excluded as should the occurrence of an event stated to be at the employer's risk, an instruction to vary the services together with acts or omissions on the employer's part which adversely affect the contractor's service provision.

Point systems are the usual mechanism for determining the financial consequences for performance failures against KPIs. Points accrued by the contractor would be aggregated for the payment period. This amount would constitute part of a calculation to determine whether a deduction should be made from the next scheduled payment to the contractor.

5.2.2.1 Describing KPIs

There are three main ways in which KPIs are described:

- **Continuous KPIs:** Such KPIs measure whether a state of ongoing acceptable performance is being achieved by the contractor. Such KPIs do not measure the achievement of a particular event. An example of such a KPI would be the number of operational hours of a lift by a lift subcontractor over a performance period.
- **Event KPIs:** The classic example of such a KPI would be the telephone calls answered by a maintenance team during the performance period. This relates to whether separate events are performed.
- **Sample KPIs:** This type of KPI assesses whether a sample service or service item meets the required level.

The standards to be achieved are determined in various ways. Inexperienced employer organisations could use external benchmarking consultants to give guidance on the usually applicable standards. There may be recognised standards in a particular market or sector which can be applied. The contractor may offer standardised services where such services are relatively commoditised. The standard offered by lift subcontractors, for example, often apply over many sites and many different customers particularly where a managing agent or estate building surveyor is subcontracting such services over a large portfolio.

In situations where there is simply not enough information to collate meaningful service levels, the parties could agree to measure performance of a service over the equivalent period to a period later to be used as a performance period and determine the appropriate standard from the results obtained. Determining standards on this basis requires a contractual mechanism to guard against slippage. It may be necessary to allow an initial period where KPIs and service charges do not apply but there must be a provision agreed at contract signature allowing either for the level to be set or for that particular service to be dispensed with and the price adjusted accordingly.

5.2.2.2 Treatment of KPIs achievement and failure in the standard forms

GC/Works/10 2000

This contract sets out two options for what is termed 'price adjustment in relation to performance'. The first option sets out the right the employer would have in common law to abatement of the amount to be paid to the contractor for inadequately performed services. The second option allow for adjustments to be made to the amount payable in accordance with any point system set out in a contract document entitled the 'Schedule of Prices and Rates'. The contractor accrues service points or credits if his provision of services is deficient.

Both options in the GC/Works/10 contract are expressly stated to be without prejudice to any other rights or remedies of the employer.

The GC/Works/10 Model Forms and Commentary Publication expect that its users will weigh the points accrued depending on the significance of the failure in accordance with the contract. Such a weighting is common to many bespoke outsourcing contracts. It is the employer's intention to concentrate the contractor's efforts on those services or service elements the employer considers key to its objectives. The example of a failure to empty a bin is given. In an office this may result in one performance point being accrued. Failure to empty a bin in a hospital's intensive care unit may mean the accrual of 20 points.

CIOB Facilities Management Contract

In this standard form, there is simply the statement that where the contractor fails to achieve the performance standards described in the specifications the employer is entitled to make an abatement of the amount resulting from use of a penalty points system in the specification document (if in existence). Again, this mechanism for payment deductions is without prejudice to the other rights and remedies of the employer.

TPC 2005

Whilst the TPC 2005 includes provisions on incentives and targets the consequences of failing to reach or in exceeding such targets are left wholly for the parties to set out. The purpose of KPIs according to the contract is that 'the success of the partnering relationships and the performance of the Partnering Team members shall be kept under review'.

We can assume that attaining or failing to attain the targets will affect the continuation of the partnering team members and any extension to the services but in order to use these provisions as a means to deduct from payments further drafting will be required.

NEC3 TSC

This contract differentiates between service levels and key performance indicators. There are two separate optional clauses for low service damages (Option X17) and key performance indicators (Option X20).

The low services damages are the employer's contractual stick. If an aspect of the service does not meet the level stated in the service level table the contractor pays the relevant stated amount.

Option X20 is the contractual carrot, effectively an incentive scheme. This clause requires the contractor to report performance against KPIs. Failure to hit the target set would result in the contractor having to submit proposals for improving performance to the employer's service manager. The contractor is paid the amount stated in the Incentive Schedule if the target stated for a KPI is reached or exceeded.

It is not expressly stated that a deduction can be made based on the Incentive Schedule mechanism although clause X20.5 seems to imply this could be the case.

> *X20.5 The Employer may add a key performance indicator and associated payment to the Incentive Schedule but may not delete or reduce a payment stated in the Incentive Schedule.*

There could be confusion among some users on how the treatment of a potential reduction under the Incentive Schedule would tie in with a possible payment deduction under Option X17. The draftsmen of the contract clearly intended that they should remain separate. To avoid confusion, where use is made of both Options X17 and X20, it would be better practice to keep the service level table of Option X17 as the mechanism for agreed deductions and the Incentive Schedule X20 as the separate basis for incentive payments, although both would invariably share common service types.

5.2.3 Service credits and limitations on liability

A service credit or performance point system has clear benefits to the employer as it links with the services agreed but they must be carefully drafted to avoid being unenforceable. Under English contract law a penalty is not enforceable. A penalty is a contractual provision which allows one party to deduct amounts of money from the other which do not reflect a genuine pre-estimate of the loss or reduction in value to be suffered at the time it was set.

There are two very simple concerns to be balanced. First, the contractor's concern that service credits overly compensates the employer and, second, in certain circumstances the service credits may not be sufficient to compensate the employer particularly if a service level cap is insisted upon by the contractor where the only deductions can be made are those under the service credit system. Such a provision would act as a limitation on the contractor's liability. The employer will need to resolve this issue and also avoid his solution being deemed unenforceable.

A number of approaches may be used to resolve this problem. The following are some examples:

- The employer is only allowed to make deductions from sums due to the contractor under the service credit system for certain breaches by the contractor but may bring breach of contract claims in relation to areas of performance not covered by the service credits.

- The employer may choose whether to claim damages or the credit within a specified period of time.

- The service credit is treated as an adjustment to the price but where damages are claimed the credit is deducted from the damages.

- Up to a certain minimum threshold the service credit is treated as the sole remedy of the employer, but where performance dips below the threshold general damages may be claimed.

5.3. Contract term and exit strategy
5.3.1 Term

Where relevant the duration of an outsourced facilities management agreement is limited to the figure stated in the notice placed in the Official Journal of the European Union (OJEU) at the time the contract was tendered. In addition, the European Union (EU) regulations placed a cap of a period of four years on the term of such contracts where the employer is in the public sector and the contract is procured as a framework agreement.

The length of the term of facilities management contracts to be agreed by the parties and not subject to EU procurement regulations is dependant on a number of factors. In IT facilities management contracts, for example, the rapid evolutionary development of the technology and consequent changes in the employer's requirements and price recommends that the contract duration is no longer than two to three years.

In addition to likely technological change, other factors relevant to determining the duration of the contract include the likelihood of material change to the strategy of a company or a public sector body and the life expectancy of the asset to be managed or the equipment used to provide the services.

The financial consequences to both the employer and the contractor of the duration of the contract also have to be weighed up. The employer will generally wish to have the flexibility of a shorter contract as it may be unable to predict its market or strategy or level of funding. In addition, if this is the first time it has used a particular contractor, it will be understandably reluctant to commit to a lengthy contract term. Conversely, the contractor will wish to delay the administrative difficulties on termination and will look to have the comfort of a lengthy pipeline of work. It should be noted that the administrative difficulties of termination will also be a concern for the employer but it will have the desire to avoid dependency on the contractor to counteract this factor.

5.3.1.1 Triggers for termination

It is unlikely to be sufficient in facilities management contracts and particularly those with an agreed long term to agree only to use standard termination provisions such as those for material breach(s) which remain unremedied following notification of breach or termination due to the insolvency of either of the parties.

Attention should be given to drafting termination clauses where the employer is entitled to terminate for repeated failure of the contractor to attain agreed service levels and where specific recommendations made pursuant to a contractual benchmarking procedure have not been implemented.

The inclusion of a clause in the contract allowing the employer to terminate irrespective of any default on the part of the contractor would address many of the employer's concerns relating to the term of the contract. The contractor will not agree to such a termination notice becoming available until it has recovered its investment costs including start up costs (e.g. plant and equipment to undertake the services), redundancy payments and the costs in terminating its supply chain contracts.

5.3.2 Exit strategy

An 'exit' is the extraction of the employer from the contract either to bring the services in-house or to place such services with a replacement contractor. An effective exit strategy should be viewed as an intrinsic part of the outsourcing procurement for the employer. The danger of an ineffective or non existent exit strategy is that the employer will not have a strong bargaining position when the contract term is drawing to an end. The cooperation of the incumbent contractor is important for the contract to be retendered or for the services to be taken back in-house. Unless there are provisions in place dealing with how the transfer of people, assets and the knowledge developed during the contract term is to be effected, the employer is taking a risk and is increasing his dependency on the contractor for the future provision of such services.

Exit provisions should, in view of their importance, be dealt with at the time of the initial negotiation of the contract. If, as is often the case, it is not possible to deal with these provisions at the outset the employer would be advised to set a date during the contract transition phase by which an exit plan is agreed. If this latter route is adopted the risk of slippage in the agreement or delivery of the plan by the contractor is usually defended by the employer by requiring payments to be conditional on agreement of the exit provisions or payments being reduced due to delay in their agreement. Of the standard forms that are considered as having the better provisions in respect of the assignment of assets, contract, knowledge and information, one example is the NEC3 TSC.

The applicable procedures for termination or consequences of termination depend on the reason for termination.

- In all circumstances the employer may complete the services and may use the plant and material provided by the contractor. Plant and materials are defined in the NEC3 TSC as items intended to be included in the property.

- In circumstances other than termination due to release from further performance by law, or where the services are frustrated for a period of more than 13 weeks or if termination is given for a reason not specified in the contract following suspension for a period of 13 weeks the employer may instruct the contractor to remove any equipment (items provided by the contractor used in providing the services) plant and materials and assign the benefit of any subcontract or other contract related to the services.

- Where the employer has terminated for reason of frustration the employer may use any equipment to which the contractor has title to complete the service. The contractor is also to remove the equipment when notified that it is no longer required.

- For all termination reasons the contractor is required to provide information and other things specified in the document known as the 'Services Information'. It is for the parties to specify in the Services Information the information and items the contractor is to provide.

The GC/Works/10 2000 and CIOB Facilities Management Contract do not offer provisions covering the points above apart from one provision in the CIOB contract stating that on termination the employer may require the contractor to terminate its subcontracts and remove equipment not belonging to the employer. Such a provision is common to construction and engineering contracts in any event.

The need for an exit strategy highlights the need for an effective facilities management manual. Facilities management manuals are described in greater depth at section 5. The aspects of a facilities management manual relevant to an exit strategy primarily relate to assets management, equipment, subcontracts and supply agreements and the transfer and management of knowledge.

The employer would need to ensure that all details of assets owned by it are known in order to re-tender the services. In addition, the ownership and value of the equipment and plant is required in order to ascertain the equipment to be replaced in the event of a change of contractor. Details of material subcontracts and supply agreements should also be kept up to date and made available on request together with information on whether either party to such contracts are in breach or whether there is a current dispute. Such information is needed for the employer to assess whether contracts need to be assigned or novated.

The potential retention of some of the contractor's employees is one aspect of the transfer of knowledge from the contractor or

the retention of knowledge of the services by the employer. Issues on the transfer of personnel are dealt with at section 5.3.3.

By including information on the way in which the services are delivered by the contractor in the facilities management manual and including a provision requiring this reporting of process in the manual to be updated, the employer can help to manage the transfer of knowledge. The facilities maintenance manual is the information base and a service reference for the management of the facility. The contractor will, reasonably, seek to ensure however the processes or techniques unique to the contractor or which are confidential are not included.

5.3.3 Personnel transfer considerations

As a general rule of thumb, it should be assumed that the Transfer of Undertakings (Protection of Employment) Regulations 2006 (TUPE) will apply to the outsourcing of facilities management contracts in the UK. TUPE could apply:

- on the initial outsourcing of the activities;

- to the transfer of the activities to a subsequent contractor, or

- when the activities are taken back in-house following a period of outsourcing.

The legislation would apply irrespective of the provisions of the contract. TUPE has its origins in EC legislation, Directive 2001/23/EC known as the Acquired Rights Directive with the result that similar rules will apply to other EC Member States.

TUPE protects the rights of employees where a business or a part of a business is transferred in order to ensure that staff who transfer benefit from the same terms and conditions of employment together with continuity of employment. TUPE also protects staff against dismissal for reasons connected with the transfer in the absence of an economic, technical or organisations (ETO) reasons and imposes consultation requirements.

A fuller description of TUPE and what constitutes 'a relevant transfer of an undertaking' is dealt with in the chapter *Employment law*. This is a complex area of law and great care is required in forming obligations within a facilities management contract to address this issue.

The concerns of the employer and contractor in relation to TUPE to be addressed in a facilities management contract can be set out as follows:

- Cross party indemnities are often required in respect of claims which may arise due to the failure of the parties to consult with affected employees.

- The contractor will usually require an employer's warranty in respect of information provided on its employees transferring to the supplier.

- Indemnities will be sought by the contractor in respect of liabilities arising prior to the commencement of the facilities management agreement in relation to those employees being transferred.

- The employer will often wish to include obligations on the contractor to maintain the quality of the staff assigned to the contract and not to increase the number of staff engaged on the contract beyond the number agreed, particularly towards the end of the contract period or following the notice period for termination for convenience – what is sometimes known as a 'standstill period'. This is to offset the risk of 'social dumping' where the contractor cherry picks the employees it perceives as its best from the contract and replaces them with those it perceives as its worst.

- In addition, the contractor will be prohibited from manually varying the terms and conditions of the employment contracts of staff beyond those applicable at the commencement of the facilities management outsourcing. Clearly the terms applicable will need to apply for different categories of staff to allow for staff progression and promotion.

- Obligations are usually placed on the contractor to obtain and maintain relevant employment details, disciplinary details to keep such information confidential and where necessary to obtain confidentiality undertakings from potential in coming subcontractors or replacement contractors. The employer may also require the contractor to indemnify him in relation to losses incurred due to deficiencies in the information provided.

- The employer may also include obligations requiring assistance from the contractor as the end of the contract period to enable the employer to tender for the next contract period – a handover period.

The points made above reflect general TUPE considerations. In addition, the transfer of a business can involve complex pension issues arising from the Pensions Act 2004 and Regulation 10(2) of TUPE 2006 and the obligation of the transferee to provide prescribed pensions to transferring employees. Further consideration is given to this in the chapter *Employment law.*

Another employment law issue often relevant to facilities management arrangements is the consultation obligation under the Trade Union and Labour Relations (Consolidation) Act 1992 and the Information and Consultation of Employees Regulations 2004. These provide that where 20 or more employees face redundancy at a single establishment within a 90 day period, the employer is obliged to consult with representatives of the employees within specified time periods.

5.4 Other key FM issues: cost, change and comparables
5.4.1 Pricing options

The complexity of the charging or price provisions in a facilities management contract depends largely on the length of the term agreed and the often related difficulty of defining the nature and volume of the services required.

There are a number of differing approaches available, for example:

- lump sum
- cost-plus or reimbursement contract

- target contract or cost-plus with an element of risk and rewards
- part-variable basis with a fixed minimum commitment and a variable element in relation to the volume of services required.

5.4.1.1 Application of HGCR to payment provisions

It should be remembered that where the contract for facilities management services in the UK relates to services that arise within the definition of 'construction operations' under Part II of the Housing Grants, Construction and Regeneration Act 1996 (HGCR) the payment provisions of the HGCR apply. The HGCR will accordingly apply to many hard FM services. Where only part of the services can be classified as construction operations, only the part of the contract dealing with such services is subject to the provisions of the HGCR. In contracts where construction operations are significant, however, it makes sense for the reasons of clarity and simplicity for the provisions of the HGCR in relation to payment (and also dispute resolution) to have contractual affect and for those provisions to apply to the contract in its entirety.

5.4.1.2 Standard form approaches to price and payment
GC/Works/10 (2000)

A lump sum approach is taken in this form of contract. The contract price is an annual lump sum price which is stated to be inclusive of all costs and expenses incurred and risks assumed by the contractor. The contract price is broken down into prices and rates which are to be shown in a schedule to the contract.

The only options given in the pricing provisions of the GC/Works/10 Contract is the choice of allowing price indexation to the parties or not. It is suggested in the Model Forms and Commentary document accompanying the contract that where the services relate to building maintenance, the Royal Institution of Chartered Surveyors (RICS) BCIS Building Maintenance Index is used. If no index is specified, the Retail Price Index applies.

The amount to be paid under the contract on a monthly basis is simply one twelfth of the contract price allowing for adjustments due to variations or amounts to be withheld by the employer.

CIOB Facilities Management Contract

A lump sum or cost reimbursable options are available in this contract. Where the lump sum option is chosen expenses of overtime costs, travel costs and subsistence costs are not inclusive.

An annual fee is the basis of payments of both the lump sum and cost reimbursable options under the latter option the facilities costs payable to subcontractors and the administration fee on such costs are also payable. Indexation applies to both options. The parties have a choice of applying either the RICS Building Maintenance Index or the Retail Prices Index.

TPC 2005

The options available in this contract are to be outlined by the parties in a document entitled the 'Price Framework'. The approach taken is not as expressly structured as in the other standard forms but essentially allows the use of a schedule of rates, lump sum or an open book approach. The open book pricing system is encouraged by the TPC 2005. The level of profits, central office overheads, and site overheads would all need to be agreed separately between the employer and the contractor (in this contract referred to as the 'Client' and 'Service Provider' respectively).

The open book approach (where used) is assisted by the requirement on the contractor to submit a business case in respect of any subcontracting or subconsulting arrangement. To the extent that a business case is not accepted an open book tender in respect of any element of the price framework is to be undertaken.

Indexation is not covered in the TPC 2005.

NEC3 TSC

Three pricing options are available with the NEC3 TSC: a lump sum approach (Option A: Priced contract with contract list) target contract (Option C) and cost reimbursable (Option E). It should be noted that the letter order for the options does not follow sequentially but reflects the lettering of the options available in the main form of NEC3 contract, the ECC.

In addition, the TSC allows in its secondary option provisions for indexation (Option X1) and adjustment where multiple currencies are used (Option X3).

5.4.2 Controlling change

5.4.2.1 Variations

It is important in term contracts involving many services for variations to the contract or the services to be managed in a consistent fashion and for the affects of change to be evidenced efficiently whether in terms of cost, specification and targets.

At a basic level the procedure for a variation by the contractor should require the proposal for change to be expressed as a notice and for the provision of the timeframe within which a response can be expected together with a timeframe for further information to be provided by the contractor on request. The procedure should also outline the information to be set out in the notice and format of the notice itself. An example of the information to be specified would be:

- the service or provision to be changed
- the date of the change proposal
- the reason for the change
- specification or details of the change proposed
- the cost consequence of any of the change using any agreed pricing schedule
- a proposed programme for implementing the change

- details of the potential impact of the change and other aspects of the facilities management contract including the personnel to be assigned, the programme and working arrangements and changes in contract documents.

It should also be made clear that unless a note of the change signed by both parties or at least the employer is made no change is effected to the contract.

Changes can also be suggested by the employer. In such an instance, the employer would request a quotation from the contractor setting out its response to the instruction. The instruction would need to be in sufficient detail to allow the contractor to furnish a response with the detail set out above.

The provision would need also to deal with the default position if the parties could not agree on the cost of the change within a designated period of time. The contract should also deal with the basis upon which a contractor may justifiably refuse to implement an instruction.

5.4.2.2 Cost savings

Contracts often encourage a contractor at any point during the period of services provision to submit proposals outlining efficiency savings or other method of reduction this, after all, is the justification for outsourcing the contract – relying on the knowledge of the contractor to implement services more efficiently than could be achieved in house.

Such provisions for cost savings will normally be dealt with in accordance with the contract procedure for change or variation control generally.

5.4.2.3 Risk management

Of the standard form considered, the better approach to risk management is found in the NEC3 TSC and the TPC2005. Both promote the use of risk registers and risk management meetings in respect of potential hazards to the services.

Where certain risks need to be specified as being such that the contractor is entitled to additional payment in the event they occur then such events need to be controlled not only in terms of the way in which they are drafted but also in how they are implemented. In term contracts, the parties need to deal with such events in real time. The danger is that claims may appear many months after the event giving rise to the claim and put huge pressure on the employer to verify whether the claim is justified. The employer may also be severely inconvenienced in terms of cash flow where several such claims are aggregated together. Certain contracts such as the NEC3 TSC take the approach of prohibiting claims from the contractor where the claim is not brought within a specified period of time when the causal event should have been considered by the contractor.

5.4.3 Benchmarking and market testing

5.4.3.1 Introduction

Significant price fluctuations in the market are one of the uncertainties faced by the employer in setting the term and price of the contract. This uncertainty arises most frequently, for example, in IT facilities management contracts where rapid technological advances can result in vast price cuts by computer hardware suppliers where the provision of equipment is part of the contract. Simple cost saving provisions may not adequately reflect the loss of bargain for the employer. In such situations, the contract would need to include benchmarking provisions.

Benchmarking is the procedure which allows the employer to require the contractor to compare its costs or those of its subcontractors against the market price of the same or similar services. The cost to the employer would be revised where the actual costs of the services differs from the market prices.

Benchmarking is meant to be an objective analysis of equivalent and competing services. It was defined by Leibfried and McNair (1992) as:

> an external focus on internal activities, functions or operations in order to achieve continuous improvement

Organisations often engage in one-to-one discussions and reviews with another organisation, although this occurs less frequently in the construction and engineering sectors. The exchange of information by such means assists to highlight possible improvements in process and procurement and, therefore, better value and prices. As benchmarking is targeted at managerial or technical processes commercially sensitive information is not likely to be revealed.

Benchmarking is distinct from market or value testing. Market testing is usually only made against soft services which do not involve capital expenditure of significance or the value of capital assets. Market testing is the process by which the contractor is required to re-tender soft services to determine whether the contract represents value for money.

Due to the long-term nature of PFI and PPP contracts market testing provisions are included to address the risk of cost increases the PFI or PPP company or its subcontractors would otherwise factor into their price.

5.4.3.2 Benchmarking provisions in FM contracts

Benchmarking provisions are often contained in more complex bespoke facilities management contracts. Not one of the featured standard form contracts contains a benchmarking requirement and procedure. Special conditions would need to be drafted and incorporated into such contracts to allow benchmarking.

All benchmarking clauses refer to an external reference point for all or some of the services and will compare these to the contractor's internal costs. Some contracts go further and permit the employer to require the contractor to obtain quotes from third party organisations for certain services. The contractor would then either have to match the lowest quotation or give reasons for the difference between its price and the third party's quotation.

A sophisticated benchmarking clause will outline that an independent benchmark organisation ('Benchmarker') would be appointed. Most commonly the employer and the contractor jointly appoint the Benchmarker. The Benchmarker will set out a timetable for the review and the information required by the parties. The Benchmarker will also be given details of the methodology to be used and details of benchmarking organisations which offer equivalent services.

If it is determined in the report produced by the Benchmarker that the contractor does not provide the defined equivalent value the employer may, where the contractor's reason for the difference is not accepted, require the contractor to reduce its prices to reflect those outlined in the Benchmarker's report. Alternatively, the contractor can refer the matter to dispute resolution usually offered only on the narrow grounds of breach of process or manifest error.

One of the problems in obtaining a comparable quotation is that the incumbent contractor's prices will contain an element to reflect the risk allocation it has determined for the project and an element in respect of recovery of its set up costs and tender costs. This has to be factored into a comparison but a truly open book approach to pricing should assist in this. Another problem is that certain prices for services are easier to compare than others. Where, for example, a contractor has taken time with the employer to develop a service procedure that meets the exact requirements of the employer on a complex asset it will be difficult to benchmark. For this reason the contractor would be advised to ensure the benchmark provisions require the Benchmarker to consider the particular context of some or all or the services whilst undertaking its analysis. The key to ensuring the contractor is amenable to benchmarking and to avoid a referral to the contract's dispute resolution procedures is to ensure good comparables.

It is unlikely that a benchmarking exercise will be conducted on a more frequent basis than an annual review.

5.4.3.3 Market testing in FM Contracts

It is the Treasury's view that market testing is the preferred approach for reviewing the prices of soft FM services. This is due to the perception that market testing:

- allows soft FM service provision to be reassessed at the time the exercise takes place rather than allowing the mere comparison of prices and is, therefore, more flexible

- the soft services market is more mature and more competitive and is more likely to provide the best value for money

- market testing offers greater opportunity for transparency.

An example of a detailed market testing procedure is contained in Schedule 5 to the NHS LIFT SPA Version 5.

The project company takes responsibility for the marketing testing procedure. This procedure takes place far less frequently than benchmarking due to the administrative cost and notification time of retendering such services. Usually a market testing exercise is undertaken every five to seven years. Market testing in some prison contracts takes place at 10 to 14 year intervals as the entire operating subcontract is subject to review.

The initial aspect of a market testing exercise is the need for agreement between the employer and contractor as to which services are to be grouped together to be tested before the tendering commences.

5.5 Facilities management manuals
5.5.1 Introduction to facilities management manuals

A facilities management manual should provide the information database to meet the needs of the employer, contractor and, if different to the employer, the occupiers or building or facility owners. Systems and equipment manufacturers and equipment suppliers would also benefit from reviewing a facilities management manual.

Amongst the primary issues to be covered in a manual are:

■ details of the services to be provided and service procedures

■ the operational requirements of the facility

■ construction details, building history and records of maintenance

■ operating and maintenance instructions

■ applicable performance guarantees and warranties

■ information detailing applicable legislative requirements and compliance with such requirements.

Given the different levels of expertise of those using such manuals and the differing degrees of specificity, facilities management manuals are often written on a number of levels. The initial level may provide a general overview with summaries of information on the key services to be provided and the different subcontractors and suppliers providing such services together with emergency contact details.

The next level would offer detailed information on the services and service provider, details of applicable terms and conditions of the subcontractors and suppliers, and performance levels. Many manuals have further levels containing complex technical information and specification.

Even the first level described above containing high-level information should be a comprehensive document. The benefit of such a document can only be fully apparent if the manual is kept up to date during the lifespan of the asset.

5.5.2 Benefits of a facilities management manual

The usefulness of a facilities management manual in assisting the employers exit strategy and competitive tendering has already been discussed. Other benefits of a manual include:

■ an up to date reference point to assist with maintenance, operation and planning and to record changes in use, subcontractors, extension or refurbishment work

■ awareness of legislation including health and safety requirements for maintenance and servicing of the facility and associated compliance with legislation

■ a source in assessing the energy efficiency of the facility and other performance criteria

■ a training resource for new contractors, subcontractors and suppliers

■ efficiencies and forward planning in spares and replacement ordering

■ continuous improvement in understanding and defining the services provided and specification

■ ease of access of information and specification on components for the facility together with information on the constraints of the components use.

A well-structured and maintained facility management manual cannot help but provide cost savings.

5.5.3 The cost and commissioning of a manual

The facilities management manual should be instigated at the commencement of work on a facility. Clearly in PPP and PFI projects where the project team and maintenance subcontractor is known, it is in the interests of the project company to commission the manual as the building or facility is being built. The confirmation and commissioning information such as the health and safety plan, commissioning and testing results, as-built drawings and product guarantees will feed into the production of a manual naturally. The key component of manual documents in a PPP project is entitled 'Works and Facilities Information'.

In circumstances where the role of the facilities management contractor is not to be tendered until following completion of the facility, the employer would still be advised to commission the initial work on such a manual. It is recommended that authorship is placed in the hands of a single identifiable person to begin the work until the facility is handed over to a facilities management contractor. This initial draftsperson would need to coordinate the input of information into the manual with the design team and contractor for the construction phase of the facility. The provision of information at this point in the life cycle of the facility will not have a significant cost implication, although the cost of drafting the manual should be itemised separately.

The cost of compiling a manual following construction may be significant. It will, nevertheless, still be likely to produce a cost benefit in complex facilities.

A CIRIA publication entitled *Facilities Management Manuals: a best practice guide* (Armstrong, 2002) helpfully estimates that each page of a facilities management manual will equate to a minimum of an hour in preparation time cost. A page of text to be compared, edited and agreed by the parties is estimated to cost between five and ten hours.

This publication includes an excellent structure and template for a manual of a newly constructed building together with guidance on its key components. This document was based on an extensive series of research activities with participants in the sector.

5.5.4 FM manuals in the standard forms

Strangely, the standard forms of contract do not generally give guidance on the use of facility management manuals. They are not mentioned in the GC/Works/10 or CIOB Facilities Management Contract form. The standard form with the best approximation to a manual is the NEC3 TSC. The relevant document is the 'Service Information'.

The NEC3 TSC does not currently offer a template or structure of a Service Information but the references within the contract itself together with some brief information in the accompanying guidance notes to the contract give an indication of its content and the beginnings of a structure. A brief review of the contract would indicate the following elements of a Service Information:

- service description, this should be detailed enough to allow the parties to understand what would constitute a defect in service provision (clauses 11.2(4), 11.2(15) and 43.1)

- an acceptance and procurement procedure (clause 11.2(6))

- description of the equipment to be used by the contractor but not to be included in the facility (clause 11.2(7))

- a description of any constraints to the performance of the services (clauses 11.2(15) and 15.1)

- details of the access and other things to be supplied by the employer (clauses 15.2 and 25.2)

- the contractor's plan and the information and processes to be shown on the plan to which all subsequent programme iterations should be subject and to which all additions to the risk register should refer (clauses 21.2 and 21.3)

- the design criteria specified by the employer (clause 23.1)

- details of others with whom the contractor is required to co-operate (clause 25.1)

- the health and safety requirements relevant to the site or sites (clause 27.3)

- descriptions of the tests and inspections to be carried out (clause 40.1 and 41.1)

- requirements for records to be kept by the contractor to enable the cost to be checked (clause 52.2 in Option C (Target Contract with price list) and Option E (Cost Reimbursable Contract)).

References

Armstrong, J. (2002) *Facilities Management Manuals: a best practice guide* (C581). CIRIA, London, UK

Leibfried, K.H.J. and McNair, C.J. (1992) *Benchmarking: a tool for continuous improvement*. Harper Business Press, New York, USA

Moss, Q. Z., Abbott, C. and Alexander, K. (2006) *FM Market Analysis in the Public Sector of England*. Office of Government Commerce, London, UK

RCIS (2010) *Building Maintenance Price Book 2010*. BCIS, London, UK

Referenced legislation, regulations and standards

Directive 2001/23/EC of 12 March 2001 on the approximation of the laws of the Member States relating to the safeguarding of employees' rights in the event of transfers of undertakings, businesses or parts of undertakings or businesses. *OJ*, **L82**, 22/03/2001, pp.16–20 (Acquired Rights Directive)

Housing Grants, Construction and Regeneration Act 1996

Information and Consultation of Employees Regulations 2004

Pensions Act 2004

Trade Union and Labour Relations (Consolidation) Act 1992

Transfer of Undertakings (Protection of Employment) Regulations 2006 (TUPE)

Further reading and useful web addresses

HM Treasury (2006) *Operational Taskforce Note 1: Benchmarking and market testing guidance*. HM Treasury, London, UK. Available for download: www.hm-treasury.gov.uk/ppp_operational_taskforce.htm

Construct IT (1997) *Benchmarking Best Practice Report: Facilities Management*. Construct IT, Salford, UK

Construct IT (1996) *Benchmarking Best Practice Report: Briefing and Design*. Construct IT, Salford, UK

Keith Alexander (1996) *Facilities Management: Theory and Practice*. Taylor & Francis, Oxford, UK

Olomolaiye, A., Liyanage, C. l., Egbu, C. O. and Kashiwagi, D. (2004) *Knowledge Management for Improved Performance in Facilities Management*. (Paper delivered to the International Construction Research Conference of the RICS, 7–8 September 2004). RICS, London, UK. Available for download: www.rics.org/site/scripts/download_info.aspx?fileID=2545&categoryID=562

Carassus, J. (2005) *Public private partnership: A service innovation. The Treasury Building case*. (Paper given to the Conseil International du Bâtiment Helsinki Symposium 2005 June). Available online: http://desh.cstb.fr/file/rub49_doc47_1.pdf

DLA Piper and Practical Law Company. *Outsourcing overview*.

Websites

Association of Consultant Architects (ACA); www.acarchitects.co.uk

British Institute of Facilities Management (BIFM); www.bifm.org.uk

Chartered Institute of Building (CIOB); www.ciob.org.uk

Construct IT; www.construct-it.org.uk

European Committee for Standardization (CEN); www.cen.eu

Institution of Civil Engineers (ICE); www.ice.org.uk

NEC contracts; www.neccontract.com

Office of Government Commerce (OGC); www.ogc.gov.uk

Official Journal of the European Union (OJEU); http://eur-lex.europa.eu/en/index.htm

Royal Institution of Chartered Surveyors (RICS); www.rics.org

Chapter 6

Procurement route

Steven Carey Speechly Bircham LLP, London, UK
Melanie Tomlin Speechly Bircham LLP, London, UK

Procurement describes the merging of activities undertaken by the client to obtain a building or engineering structure. An overview of the main procurement methods is provided including traditional contracting, design and build, two-stage tendering, management contracting, construction management and partnering. For each procurement method, the overview includes a description of the general structure, how risks are allocated, the allocation of design responsibility, responsibility for the work of the various subcontractors or works contractors, relative speed, price certainty and cost control. The relative prevalence and popularity of various procurement methods are highlighted and examples of standard form contracts for each procurement method are provided. Key legal developments are highlighted, such as case law on the liability of management contractors and construction managers and no loss arguments in the context of novation. There is a summary of the perceived advantages and disadvantages of each procurement method.

doi: 10.1680/mocl.40878.0079

CONTENTS

6.1 Introduction

No construction project is risk free. Risks can be managed, minimised, shared, transferred or accepted. It cannot be ignored. The client who wishes to accept little or no risk should take different routes for procuring advice from the client who places importance on detailed hands on control. (Latham Report, 1994)

Contracts, in essence, are vehicles for allocating risks inherent with the construction process, setting out the parties respective responsibilities and outlining the rewards.

Factors such as speed, price certainty, quality, control or single-point responsibility and level of risks to be accepted are all critical to the procurement method chosen.

At the turn of the last century, the 'traditional' method was, not surprisingly, the only show in town. Not so now. Are we now spoilt for choice and is the number of options always a good thing?

6.2 Traditional contracting
6.2.1 Overview

The contractual structure generally accepted as the traditional method of procurement, developed in the 19th century, is detailed in **Figure 1** (also see the chapter *The construction contract*). For much of the period between then and now, this was used for the vast majority of construction and engineering projects.

As one can see from **Figure 1**, the key feature of the traditional method is that the design is separated from the construction phase and was driven by the supremacy of the earlier designers (such as Brunel) over the 'builders' who simply did what they were told.

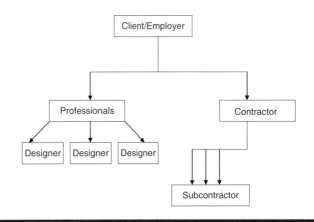

Figure 1 The traditional method of procurement

The employer enters into contracts of service appointing various consultants to design the project and perform certain ancillary services.

The types of consultant required will depend upon the nature of the project. For example, in building projects, a mechanical and electrical engineer, structural engineer, and quantity surveyor may be appointed together with specialist consultants such as an environmental consultant. Together they form the professional team who undertake to produce a complete (or almost complete) design and specification for the project. However, if the project is one for the construction of say a dam, one may require a site investigation specialist, geologist, hydrologist, geotechnical engineer, civil and structural engineers and so forth.

The theory is that the design is fully completed and contractors are simply asked to build what has already been designed although in practice, it is unusual for a project to be fully designed from the very beginning. Further, to work up a fully functioning design is time consuming and this creates tension with the employer's understandable desire to hasten a return on its investment, and provide that much needed infrastructure to the general public.

The design forms the basis on which tenders are invited from contractors. After considering the tenders, the employer will then enter into a separate contract with a contractor for the carrying out and completion of the relevant work to the consultant's design, normally, by an agreed date (which is subject to extension in specified circumstances).

Typically, the building contract will be administered by the engineer (in engineering projects) or architect (in building projects).

It is usual for the main contractor to then subcontract out various aspects of the project to subcontractors. However, unlike management contracting, the main contractor is legally responsible for the works carried out by its subcontractors.

6.2.2 Design responsibility

With the traditional method, the theory is that there is a complete separation of responsibility for the design and the construction of a project.

The engineers and/or architects appointed undertake a responsibility to the employer to exercise reasonable care and skill when producing their designs and specification for the project. The main contractor agrees to build the project according to the building contract and the design and specifications supplied.

The theoretical separation between the design and the construction of a project is becoming more artificial. The architect, for example, will not usually undertake all aspects of design in a traditional contract. This is because, as projects and processes are becoming more complex, it is increasingly common for specialist subcontractors to take on design responsibility for certain elements of the project such as piling, lifts, fire prevention systems and air conditioning. Standard form contracts may therefore provide for certain elements of the works to include design elements – for example, the Joint Contracts Tribunal (JCT) Standard Building Contract 2005 includes an option for a Contractor's Designed Portion. In a similar vein, the Institute of Civil Engineers (ICE) 7th Edition at clause 8(2) provides that a contractor can be responsible for the design of the Permanent Works but only to the extent that the contract so expressly provides. Similarly, at clause 21.1 of the New Engineering Contract 3 (NEC3) form of contract, the contractor is responsible for as much of the design as is specified in the Works Information.

To give the employer an additional layer of protection, the design work by a specialist subcontractor can be covered by a collateral warranty between the subcontractor and the employer so that the employer has direct recourse to the subcontractor if, for example, the contractor is no longer solvent and defective works manifest themselves.

By using specialist subcontractors in this way or by utilising more than one designer, one can instantly see the potential for

disputes as to who is at fault for design defects. This could be between any number of the professional team who have completed the main design and the main contractor (who is responsible for the work, including design, carried out by its specialist subcontractors) and the specialist subcontractors. Further, the distinction between a defect which has emanated from 'design' as opposed to defects arising from the construction process is often blurred with the designer blaming the contractor and *vice versa*.

Such interface issues are not uncommon within the construction process no matter what form of procurement method is chosen but the traditional form is certainly susceptible to the parties being able to point to others as being the culprit.

6.2.3 Timescale

There are supposed to be three distinct stages in traditional contracting: the design phase, the tender phase and the construction phase although again in practice there can be a blurring between the phases. The theory of traditional contracting is that each phase is completed in sequence.

As each stage follows the other in sequence, without overlap (or very little overlap), the project tends to take longer to complete than other procurement methods. The trade-off is that there is usually increased price certainty as more accurate bids for the construction work can be proffered once the design is complete and arguably there is less of an ability for the cost to increase with design being complete and the scope of works required of the contractor, being set in stone. However, this presupposes that (i) the design is in fact complete and (ii) the employer resists the temptation to make changes to the design/scope of works.

6.2.4 'Buildability'

As the contractor is only appointed once, the design is completed (or is almost complete) so that there is little or no input from the contractor during the design phase, one of the perceived drawbacks of traditional contracting is the lack of contractor input regarding what is termed 'buildability'. This means that there is limited input on more practical matters, for example, the availability of materials or sequencing the works.

It is not uncommon for contractors to suggest that if they had been engaged in the process earlier, the design which satisfies the employer's demands could have been made easier to build. This can potentially raise costs for the employer. Materials specified in the design could be uneconomic or unavailable.

The lack of early contractor involvement can also be said to limit the contractor's opportunity to advise on identifying, eliminating or managing 'construction risks'. These are risks associated with the construction process and can vary widely and include changing materials or the design to accommodate methods of construction to ensure that it is suitable to meet any time constraints imposed on the project or is more amenable to the site conditions.

6.2.5 Payment

Traditional contracting is probably the method of procurement which provides the greatest flexibility for the employer in terms of the basis upon which payment can sensibly be made to all construction team members.

Consultants can be paid on a flat fee basis, hourly rate or percentage of the projected construction costs and payment can be on monthly, quarterly or on the achievement of a milestone. Generally, traditional contracting is said to provide greater price certainty for the employer. However, the extent of price certainty depends upon the basis of payment adopted. The contractor might be paid on any of the bases discussed in the following sections.

6.2.5.1 Lump sum contracts

A lump sum method of payment is commonly used in traditional contracting and is one in which the contractor agrees for a pre-agreed price to execute certain defined works. The advantage of using a lump sum contract within the traditional method is that the employer has an early commitment to a maximum price for the project. If the employer is inexperienced then this is likely to be reassuring or if there is a specific budget it needs to work to.

Although the lump sum is the starting point, the lump sum will normally be adjusted in specified circumstances, for example, to allow for variations, fluctuations, provisional sums and in the event of the occurrence of certain 'risk' events that the contractor has not taken the financial responsibility for.

For example, a contractor is unlikely to be willing to accept the risk of pre-pricing any variation an employer may instruct. The treatment of 'independent' risks, such as adverse weather conditions or unforeseen ground conditions, are more controversial. For example, should the contractor be asked to price for these risks or should an adjustment to the contract sum be provided for in the event that these risks do affect the works? If the latter is chosen, then the contractor can put in a lower price but of course this means that the employer has less price certainty. If the former, then the employer is paying for events that may not happen.

The two main types of lump sum contract are the JCT Standard Building Contract 2005 and the JCT Design and Build 2005. As regards the former, there are two main types of lump sum contract.

6.2.5.2 'With quantities'

Bills of quantities are one way of specifying the works which involves describing the exact quantities of items necessary for the works. It is these quantities which the contractor will price. Generally, the contractor will be bound to carry out work in excess of that stated in the bills to complete the works but this will attract additional payment and therefore is not something an employer driven by the requirement for price certainty will find attractive. If extra works are instructed, the contractor will

normally be paid based upon his rates included in the bills. (Also discussed in *The construction contract*.)

It has been said that with this type of contract the risk rests more on the employer, as it is very difficult to know beforehand the exact quantities necessary to complete the work.

6.2.5.3 'Without quantities'

Alternatively, a contract may contain a description of the works in drawings and/or a specification or other written description such as activity schedules other than the bills. The contractor is required to price the works shown on the drawings and/or as described.

The contractor takes the risk in estimating the actual quantities required. The risk here rests more on the contractor, as in this type of contract the contractor can either gain or lose depending on the accuracy of his estimating.

6.2.5.4 'Measure and value' or 're-measurement' contracts

Re-measurement contracts to an extent combine lump sum and prime cost contracts. In such contracts, the parties do not agree a price for the works as a whole but they do agree the rates to which the contractor is entitled, such as by reference to the amount of work done (e.g. per m³ of excavation or per m³ of concrete laid). The rates are normally to be found in a bill of quantities (although there could be some other schedule of costs or other such formula). The lump sum contract which states that 'all works are subject to re-measurement on completion' is in fact a re-measurement contract.

The key difference between a re-measurement contract and a lump sum contract is, of course, that in the absence of variations the contractor in the latter case is paid the lump sum whilst in the former case, it all depends upon the re-measure. Further, if the contractor has correctly stated his price per unit of measurement but has incorrectly multiplied the number of units by that price, with a lump sum contract the contractor will be stuck with his error and no adjustment would be made to the price. On the other hand, with a re-measurement contract, the contractor would be entitled to be paid for the actual volume of the work, as measured, multiplied by the rate quoted. The sanctity of those rates was further emphasised by the Court of Appeal in the case of *Henry Boot Construction Ltd v. Alstom Combined Cycles Ltd [2000] BLR 247, CA*. In this case, which related to the applicability of bill rates to variations under an ICE 6th Edition, the court held that an error in the bills, which led to the contractor getting a windfall payment, did not prevent the use of those rates to value a subsequent variation. If the error had been the other way the contractor would, equally be bound by the rates.

However, re-measurement contracts are useful where the nature of work is uncertain. For example, in a tunnelling job where the precise geology of the ground is unknown or in a land reclamation scheme where the amount of remedial works is dependant upon the actual quantities of materials that are required to be excavated, cleaned or removed from site. Traditional civil engineering contracts, such as the ICE Conditions of Contract 7th edition, tend to use a re-measurement contract for computing the price (see the chapter *The construction contract*).

6.2.5.5 Cost plus

In the process industry, a common traditional form of contract uses cost plus reimbursement. In addition, cost reimbursement contracts have been in use for many years in civil engineering projects which involve unforeseeable amounts of kinds of work such as the repairs to a dam or collapsed tunnel, or repair of sea defences.

However, the building industry is traditionally less familiar with this form.

The basis of payment for the works is the actual cost (or prime cost) of the works as performed subject to an implied (if not express) term that the contractor will perform the works efficiently. The contractor is entitled to be paid whatever the work actually costs him and often an additional fee (by way of a fixed fee or a percentage of the actual cost) to cover overheads and profit.

As it is very difficult for the employer to predict or control the actual costs of the contractor, not surprisingly employers tend not to favour prime cost contracts suggesting that it can amount to a 'blank' cheque for the contractor. If an employer needed to get a quick start (at the expense of almost everything) then a cost plus is something it could consider but it would be impossible for the employer to be able to have any control of the outlay costs, and price certainty would be a non-starter. As discussed earlier, this method is also used where the scope of works is particularly difficult to identify before the works are actually undertaken.

6.2.5.6 Guaranteed Maximum Price (GMP) or Target Cost

Another payment method which is becoming a little more popular is the Guaranteed Maximum Price (GMP), or Target Cost.

In the case of the GMP, if the cost of the works exceeds the GMP, the contractor has to bear those costs itself. However, despite it being called a Guaranteed Maximum Price it will need to be adjustable in certain circumstances such as where the employer instructs a variation.

In effect, the GMP operates as a cap on the cost of the works, albeit that the cap is adjustable in fewer circumstances than the lump sum payment would be under a traditional contract. Given this, arguably the contractor is incentivised to set a GMP which is probably higher than the lump sum it would have quoted on a traditional lump sum contract.

The use of a Target Cost is often combined with a GMP and more clearly incentivises the contractor to control costs. Often this is achieved by sharing the costs in excess of the target between the parties in a pre-agreed proportion, and similarly sharing any savings achieved against the Target Cost (i.e. sharing pain/gain). This mechanism is often combined with a GMP behind which the contractor takes all the risks.

An example of this form is the NEC3 with Option C (Target Cost with Activity Schedule) or NEC3 with Option D (Target Contract will Bill of Quantities) and ICE Conditions of Contract Target Cost Version, 1st Edition.

6.2.6 Summary of perceived advantages of traditional contracting

The perceived advantages of traditional contracting may include as follows:

- *Control and quality of design* – By appointing and managing the design team, the employer can ensure the design is developed as he would like. Further, the design consultants are able to act with professional independence, having no direct financial interest in sacrificing quality to minimise construction cost, which is a criticism often levied at design and build.

- *Price certainty* – By only awarding the construction contract once the design is complete, contractors can put forward accurate bids. This means that fixed price contracts are less likely to be adjusted upwards. Arguably, completing the design before starting reduces the likelihood of construction phase variations.

- *Familiarity* – This is the method of procurement many employers and contractors are used to. Arguably, this increases the likelihood of a successful project, although over the last 10–20 years, design and build contracts are more prevalent in building projects if not in the civil engineering field.

- *Experienced contract administrators* – If the employer is inexperienced, having an independent professional monitoring the work and certifying payments can help protect the employer's rights.

6.2.7 Summary of perceived disadvantages with traditional contracting

The perceived disadvantages of traditional contracting may include as follows:

- *No single point of responsibility* – The division of responsibility between consultants and the contractor can make it difficult to ascertain responsibility for many problems. In the event of a dispute, it is common for the main contractor to blame the consultants and *vice versa*. This can leave the employer faced with multi-party actions which can be even more troublesome if the separate agreements between the employer and contractor/consultants contain arbitration clauses as the risk of inconsistent decisions between various tribunals is very real. Further the employer may end up paying the legal costs of the party absolved of any wrongdoing by the tribunal.

- *Increased potential for contractor claims* – Arguably, the division of responsibility between the consultants and the contractor increases the potential for contractor claims. For example, the contractor is heavily dependant on the architect/engineer sending information and instructions on time; insofar as delays are suffered due to the consultant's failure to do so, the contractor may bring a claim.

- *Lack of early contractor involvement* – There is no real opportunity for 'construction' input at the design stage on matters such as 'buildability' or on value engineering with the consequent loss of potential for cost and time savings.

■ *Slow and inflexible* – As the design stage has to be completed before a contractor is appointed, there is little opportunity to start works earlier, or to pre-order items with long lead in times whilst any significant elements of design remain to be undertaken. It has also been said that the inflexibility of this approach makes it difficult to take advantage of any market changes.

6.3 Design and build
6.3.1 Overview

It is now common for contractors to perform some or all of the design responsibilities traditionally performed by the professional team, adopting a design and build procurement method. Certainly for commercial developments over the last 10–15 years or so, the use of design and build in the UK construction industry has grown exponentially.

Originally, design and build contracts were intended for projects with purely low-level designs. However, increasingly design and build contracts are being used for more sophisticated projects. Very often today it is the contractor alone who possesses the specialist knowledge and skill to design and carry out specialist works.

Examples of standard form design and build contracts include the ICE Design and Construct Conditions 2nd Edition, JCT Design and Build Form 2005 Edition, FIDIC Conditions of Contract for Plant and Design-Build and NEC3 (to the extent that the contractor specifies it is to undertake the design in the Works Information). The Standard JCT Form 2005 Edition also provides for elements of the overall design to be undertaken by the contractor.

6.3.2 General structure

The contractor takes responsibility for completing the design of the project, which has not already been prepared by or on behalf of the employer, in addition to carrying out and completing the works. The extent of the design prepared by or on behalf of the employer can vary although it is clearly envisaged that this should be limited so as not to end up simply recreating the traditional approach. The employer normally employs a team of consultants to prepare the initial design or undertake the initial design himself. It is common for these consultants ultimately to end up under contract with the successful tendering contractor through a process referred to as novation (see the chapter *The consulting engineer's appointment*).

In the case of *Co-operative Insurance Society Ltd v. Henry Boot Scotland Ltd, TCC 1 July 2002,* the court determined the extent of the obligation imposed on a contractor who took on the responsibility to 'complete' a design. The court decided that in the act of completing the design, the contractor assumed responsibility for the underlying design (even though undertaken by others). Under the JCT Design and Build 2005 Edition, this is addressed by making it clear that the contractor does not assume this responsibility. In contrast, the ICE 2nd Edition at clause 8(2)(b) provides that where any part of the

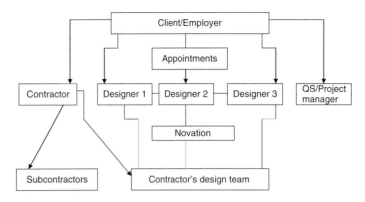

Figure 2   Design and build general structure

works has been designed by or on behalf of the employer and that design has been identified in the employer's requirements, then the Contractor is responsible for checking that design and accepting responsibility for it.

It is common for the standard form contracts to be amended (if necessary) so that the responsibility for the initial design (carried out by the employer's pre-construction consultant team) and the design undertaken by the contractor (in 'completing' the design) rests entirely with the contractor.

This has the advantage for the employer of only having one source of remedy for any problems that may arise with the project. It means the employer only has one person to blame for defects, as the person responsible for the design is also responsible for the construction of the project. This single point liability avoids the problems outlined above of the employer having to claim against a multitude of parties.

In the traditional method, the architect or engineer administers the contract, whereas with the design and build method, it is the employer's agent who usually administers the contract, with a costs consultant to assist in matters such as valuing variations and administering the payment regime.

The employer's agent should be chosen carefully. He could be a key member of the employer's organisation or a professional consultant or a project manager. Further it should be made clear to what extent the agent is authorised to act for the employer.

The contractor may employ an 'in house' design team but will usually need to appoint some independent consultants to complete the design of the works in conjunction with specialist subcontractors. As explained, these are often the same consultants used by the employer in drawing up the initial design which are transferred to the contractor by way of novation.

The typical structure is detailed in **Figure 2**.

6.3.3 Design responsibility

The employer has to draw up what are often called the 'employer's requirements' (as called in the JCT, ICE and FIDIC forms). This is an outline design and specification of the type of building he wants. The employer may employ a professional team to draw up the outline design. The extent of this outline design can vary from a brief description of the main aspects of the project with one or two drawings to a far more detailed design contained in several volumes of specifications and numerous drawings. It is important that the employer clearly identifies his requirements from the outset. If not careful, a lay client can be faced with a poorly designed building which is, nevertheless, in compliance with the employer's requirements.

In theory, in response to the employer's requirements, the contractor provides details of the majority of his proposed design (called the 'contractor's submission' in the ICE form or 'contractor's proposals' in the JCT form) at tender stage. However, the theory does not always reflect the practice.

For example, it is not unusual for the contractor's submissions/proposals to be produced in conjunction with the employer with limited or even no design having been previously prepared by the employer so that the contractor's proposals/submissions are in effect adopted as the employer's requirements.

The employer can appoint the contractor by negotiating with a single contractor (sometimes called 'Single Direct Design and Build'), or approach a number of contractors and choose between their proposals. This is called 'Competitive Design and Build' which can take longer, but can result in a more detailed design with greater cost and time certainty. The tender should make clear what criteria will be used when evaluating the different tenders and state whether price is a prime consideration.

A source of continual disputes relates to who bears the responsibility for inconsistencies within the employer's requirements and/or the contractor's submissions/proposals. Standard forms often try to address who carries this risk. It is not uncommon for amendments to place even errors in the employer's requirements at the door of the contractor.

6.3.3.1 Responsibility for employer's requirements

As is described earlier, in the standard form design and build contracts, the employer often retains responsibility for the design contained in the employer's requirements, whereas the contractor only takes responsibility for the design contained in the contractor's proposals. As this leaves scope for argument about whether a design error is attributable to the employer's requirements or the contractor's proposals, as stated earlier, it is common practice to amend the standard forms to make the contractor responsible for the design contained in the employer's requirements. This is to maximise the benefit of single-point responsibility afforded by design and build.

For example, Recital 3 of the JCT Design and Build 2005 Edition states that 'the Employer has examined the Contractor's Proposals and, subject to the conditions, is satisfied that they appear to meet the Employer's Requirements'. This is often amended so that it is the contractor who warrants that the contractor's proposals satisfy the employer's requirements.

6.3.3.2 Novation of design team

In order to avoid the contractor having to charge for the checking of the employer's requirements (the employer already having had to bear the cost of that design being prepared), this is usually accompanied by the novation of the design team appointments to the contractor. There will be a novation of the obligations under the original appointment that remain to be performed as well as a novation of liabilities arising out of the performance of obligations already performed. This is intended to give the contractor recourse against those consultants should there be errors in that design.

However, the contractor should bear in mind that these are liabilities that have accrued in favour of the employer, even though the contractor may now take the benefit of them. So if the consultant is negligent in a way which gives rise to a claim by the employer for loss (e.g. for the cost of repairing defective work resulting from a defect in the consultant's design), following novation, the employer can no longer pursue that claim (subject to exercising rights it may have under a warranty) because the right to do so has been transferred to the contractor.

However, the claim may be of little or no value to the contractor, because the loss claimable by the employer may be different to the sort of loss that has been suffered by the contractor. The consultant may not be liable at all for the loss suffered by the contractor because it was not under any duty to avoid that kind of loss with respect to the employer. This issue arose in the Scottish case of *Blyth & Blyth v. Carillion Construction Ltd [2001] 79 ConLR 142.*

The claim was based on alleged deficiencies in the employer's requirements, which had been prepared by the consultants. The contractor said that these deficiencies led to their tender being too low, and as they had now accepted responsibility for the design, they had to bear this loss. However, the court held that this was not the kind of loss which the consultants were under any duty to the employer to use reasonable skill and care to avoid (in fact, the employer had made a saving as the tender price was lower than it would otherwise would have been) and so no claim could be made against them. The loss in question was of a kind that could never, by its very nature, be suffered by the employer. This is sometimes referred to as the 'black hole'.

Following the *Blyth & Blyth* decision, employers and contractors often seek to include wording in the novation agreement aimed at allowing the contractor to recover the sort of losses the contractor in *Blyth & Blyth* could not. Any such wording needs to be carefully drafted so as to, in effect, alter the scope of the consultant's liability retrospectively by making the performance of the consultant prior to novation and his potential liability for work done prior to novation judged on the fictitious basis that during that time the consultant had in fact been engaged by the contractor – the *ab initio* approach. There are various ways that a novation agreement can be drafted to seek to avoid the problem identified in *Blyth & Blyth*.

The inclusion of wording along the lines set out above will often be resisted by consultants (and their insurers) on the basis that it would involve a retrospective variation in the scope of the consultant's duty.

Another consideration when drafting novation agreements is whether all the post-novation services remaining to be performed are appropriate given the consultant's duty is now owed to the contractor, where the contractor's interests and concerns are different from the those of the employer. Some of the services set out in the original appointment may not be appropriate for an engagement by a contractor. For example, a provision which provides that the consultant is to assist the employer in any dispute with the contractor. Clearly this provision would be inappropriate post-novation. There may also be services in the original appointment that should be differently worded in circumstances where they are being performed for the contractor rather than the employer and there may be additional services not mentioned in the original appointment that the contractor would like the consultant to perform. The situation has to be addressed at the time of novation and the parties can, if they wish, agree to a variation in the services remaining to be performed.

Finally, following a novation the potential for conflict of interest will be there as consultants will have to act in the interests of the contractor, although previously having done so for the employer. See also the chapter *The law of contract*.

6.3.4 Fitness for purpose

At common law, a design and build contractor must provide works which are fit for purpose (*Independent Broadcasting Authority v. EMI Electronics Limited & BICC Construction Limited (1980) 14 BLR 1*). This is an implied term.

This is a major advantage to the employer. The contractor is absolutely liable on his promise that the works will be fit for purpose unless excluded by the express terms of the contract.

In a traditional contract, an architect or engineer's obligation to the employer will usually be that the architect or engineer promises only to use reasonable skill and care in the design. The contractor will provide no fitness for purpose warranty – his obligation will simply be to use reasonable skill and care in carrying out the works as described in the architect's/engineer's plans including (which is beyond the remit of this chapter to discuss fully) any duty to warn the employer against a defective and dangerous design which may be imposed on the contractor. However, where the contractor is offering a 'package deal' of both design and construction, the employer may insist on an express term (and not just rely on an implied term) of fitness for purpose. This is an extremely valuable warranty. If the design turns out to be unsuitable, it is no defence to the contractor that he has exercised all reasonable skill and care in its preparation. The fact that the design is not fit for its particular purpose is enough to found liability.

However, not surprisingly, contractors are often unwilling to accept this level of liability. In fact many of the standard form contracts (such as the JCT Design and Build Contract 2005 Edition and the ICE Design and Construct 2nd Edition) reverse the common law position so that the contractor has an equivalent liability to the employer for the design as would an architect acting independently under a separate contract with the employer (i.e. to exercise reasonable care and skill).

Reversing the common law position also avoids any potential gap in liability where the contractor subcontracts some of the design elements to appointed design consultants or specialist subcontractors who themselves are unlikely to accept a fitness for purpose warranty. It is generally very difficult to obtain professional indemnity insurance for a fitness for purpose warranty.

6.3.5 'Buildability' of design

As explained earlier, with the traditional method, one of the perceived problems is the lack (or virtual lack) of input from the contractor during the design process with respect to 'buildability'. By contrast, with the design and build method, as the contractor is engaged much earlier in the process and it is its responsibility to complete or develop the design, this issue can be addressed. The contractor's input at this earlier stage may thus have the knock on effect of minimising delays and saving costs. In short, theoretically there is more potential for the contractor to add value for money for the employer. The ability of the contractor within this regard very much depends upon how detailed and prescriptive the employer's requirements are. The downside of this can be that sometimes the employer may get a poor quality design with lower-quality materials which whilst complying with the employer's requirements may ultimately mean that maintenance costs are higher – something that may not concern the contractor unduly.

6.3.6 Timescale

A major advantage of the design and build method is that it enables the construction to begin whilst the detailed design work is still ongoing. Put simply, there is an overlap of the design and construction processes which increases the potential for the contractor to finish the project works earlier than say, the traditional method where design and construction is sequential. The contractor and the employer therefore benefit from this flexibility.

In addition, with the design and build method the contractor is not reliant (or at least is much less reliant) on the employer in providing necessary information required to progress the works as the contractor is responsible for its own flow of information. Whereas there is a potential for delays arising in the traditional method as a result of stoppages in the flow of information between the employer and the contractor, this problem can be addressed in the design and build method. However, if the employer's requirements provide for information to be provided by the employer during the course of the contract, then this problem may persist. For example, clause 6 of the ICE Design and Construct 2nd Edition provides that the contractor may be entitled to additional time and money in the event that the employer's representative fails to provide to the contractor, within a reasonable period, any further information that is required for the design and/or construction of the works following a request from the contractor.

One advantage of having designers and estimators working closely together is that the contractor can use his knowledge of current market conditions and delivery time to ensure that the contract can progress smoothly.

6.3.7 Payment

As with the traditional method, payment is generally on a lump sum basis.

Although there is some price certainty by virtue of the fact that payment is usually on a lump sum basis, as design and build contracts generally place a higher level of risk on contractors, employers may expect to find this reflected in increased prices.

6.3.8 Costs control

Having a single point of responsibility reduces the possibility of claims and consequent price increases, as well as the need to take two or more parties to court to determine who is responsible.

Costs can also be controlled where there are multiple buildings with the same specification – this is because there is no need to appoint a designer every time one is built. For example, supermarkets are often constructed to the same design specification and there is little point in engaging a designer every time one is constructed.

The contractor may be able to obtain cost savings by choosing his own subcontractors and suppliers or by exerting his influence over the design and the materials to be used to make it more cost effective. This also relates to buildability by ensuring that the design and the materials compliment each other.

In addition, the employer can gain greater cost certainty if the contractor is made responsible for investigating site and subsoil conditions. However, it will be appreciated that a contractor will include this risk in his overall price. On large civil engineering projects the contractor may not be prepared to take the ground risk because the ramifications of extremely poor ground being found is too great or if it is prepared to take it, the price is increased to such an extent that the employer is unwilling to buy off this risk. More sophisticated clients are likely to be wary of any contractor that recklessly assumes the risk in its bid.

6.3.9 Quality of design

The level of control the employer has over the design will depend on the level of detail contained within the employer's requirements.

However, generally with design and build, the employer has little control over the detailed aspects of the design. It is said that one of the main drawbacks of the design and build method results from the fact that the employer leaves the completion of the design of the project to the contractor. For example, under the JCT Design and Build 2005 Edition, the contractor

has no obligation to seek the employer's consent for details of the design, as long as they are compliant with the employer's requirements.

As a result, this may compromise the quality of the design. This may be acceptable if the employer is satisfied about the outline of the scheme and the details are relatively unimportant. Nevertheless, there is potential for the contractor to minimise costs by reducing the quality of the detailed design, for example, in the quality of the finishes or by designing something in such a manner that it is less costly to build but more costly to maintain.

There is a large element of uncertainty and the employer's requirements are heavily relied upon properly to describe what is required. However, this is a balancing act because of the employer's requirements are too overly prescriptive, this can undermine the benefits of design and build.

To an extent, the ICE Design and Construct 2nd Edition addresses this issue. Where any part of the works has been designed by the employer and that design has been identified in the employer's requirements, although the contractor is responsible for checking that design and assumes responsibility for that design, the contractor is required to obtain the approval of the employer's representative for any modifications to that design which the contractor considers to be necessary. Further, to the extent required by the contract, the contractor is required to institute, and then submit, a quality assurance plan to the employer's representative for his consent before each design and construction stage is commenced.

In addition, the employer may seek to retain some control by identifying performance criteria within the employer's requirements on which to base tenders.

Without a professional team to advise the employer, inexperienced employers can find themselves in a difficult position when faced with a sub-standard design or construction. If the employer wants to take independent advice on design issues once the building contract has been entered into or the design team has been novated to the contractor, then he will have to pay for this himself.

6.3.10 Summary of perceived advantages to design and build

The perceived advantages of design and build may include as follows:

- *Single-point responsibility* – The employer has a single target to aim for if problems arise during the construction phase or after completion. This significantly reduces the difficulties in identifying who is responsible for problems as to progress and quality which can arise where responsibility is split.

- *Price certainty* – The imposition of single-point responsibility further reduces the possibility of claims and consequent price increases and as design and construction tends to be on a lump sum basis, the employer should know from the outset what it is paying for (subject of course to subsequent employer's variations and/or costs associated with risk events that still remain with the employer).

- *Buildability* – The involvement of the contractor in the design process does allow input on 'buildability' and value engineering with consequent cost and time savings.

- *Reflects practice* – Arguably, this method of procurement better allows for and reflects the extent of the design generally undertaken by specialist subcontractors.

- *Familiarity* – Employers and contractors are now used to this form of procurement which arguably increases the likelihood of a successful project.

- From an employer's perspective the loss of control during the construction phase to the contractor may be more than adequately compensated by the contractor assuming greater risk.

6.3.11 Perceived disadvantages of design and build

The perceived disadvantages of design and build may include as follows:

- *Lack of design control* – Unless adapted, the employer is leaving completion of the design of the project to the contractor. This places considerable emphasis on the employer's requirements to properly describe what is required without being over-prescriptive thereby undermining the benefits of design and build.

- *Inexperienced employer* – The absence of an employer's professional team can make it difficult for an inexperienced employer who may be faced with sub-standard design or sub-standard construction.

- *Inflexible* – It has been said that, given it is necessary to complete a significant aspect of the design to obtain cost certainty and ensure some satisfaction with the design, the inflexibility of this approach may make it difficult to take advantage of market changes.

6.4 Two-stage tendering
6.4.1 Overview

Two-stage tendering is typically used where the early appointment of a contractor is desirable allowing a quicker start on site date and early contractor input on the buildability of the scheme.

6.4.2 The first stage

Contractors enter competitive tenders on the basis of outline information. Contractors typically provide a construction programme, a price for preliminaries and a percentage for overheads and profit offered for the whole project. The employer decides between tenders on the basis of this information but also the skill levels, experience and resources that each tenderer can provide.

At the end of this stage, the successful tenderer (who is now known as the 'preferred contractor') is appointed to provide pre-construction services under a pre-construction services contract (or letter of intent) such as providing input on buildability, sequencing and subcontractor selection.

6.4.3 The second stage

This runs alongside the pre-construction phase. This typically develops as a negotiation between the employer and the preferred contractor in relation to the terms of the building contract and the price. The point at which agreement is reached will vary between projects, however, the more the design is completed the greater the cost certainty. The building contract is signed at the end of this stage and could be any form of contract procurement, that is, traditional, design and build and so forth. It is important to note that the employer is not always obliged to enter into the second stage contract with the preferred contractor although the preferred contractor is likely to have the 'inside' track.

6.4.4 Perceived advantages of two-stage tendering

- *Reduced cost of tendering for the contractor*. Two-stage tendering is less expensive and time-consuming than single stage tendering. For the contractor there is less money lost on unsuccessful tenders as his bid costs at risk only relate to him bidding on the limited basis of the first stage. Once appointed on the first stage, the contractor gets paid for the pre-construction services he provides.

- Earlier contractor involvement increases the opportunity for contractor input on buildability and value engineering. Having the contractor involved earlier may mean that anticipated problems in the construction phase can be considered earlier. This can shorten the construction programme.

- *Price certainty*. The common view is that the preferred contractor's second stage tender should reflect more accurately the final construction costs as the price is based on more information and the contractor has increased knowledge of the project.

6.4.5 Perceived disadvantages of two-stage tendering

- Once the preferred contractor is appointed at the first stage, the employer's main lever of peer to peer competition is lost. The risk is that the contractor has the chance to talk up prices. However, the employer can include provision in the pre-construction services contract (or letter of intent) for an option to withdraw from the second stage in the event that the preferred contractor does not submit a competitive second stage bid.

- Where the project is sufficiently well defined at first stage tender, a common approach is to include a 'not-to-exceed price' for the works in the pre-construction services agreement. If this price is exceeded, the employer has the option to go back to the market for a single competitive tender. The employer could go further and exclude the preferred contractor from making a fresh bid on the grounds that they already submitted their best price.

- However, practically speaking, going back to the market is likely to be an unattractive option for an employer because a new contractor will require time to learn about the project. This will negate the time saved by using the two-stage process and the previous cost of getting a contractor involved early on will, in general, be largely wasted.

See the chapter *Tender process* for further details on tendering.

6.5 Management procurement

There are two distinct methods of procurement which identify the management of a project as a separate contract responsibility. These two management-based procurement methods are management contracting and construction management and essentially came of age in the UK in the 1980s. With these procurement methods, the contractor does not undertake any of the works, but solely manages the process.

Management procurement developed mainly for use on 'fast track' projects where there was an urgency to complete – with management procurement, construction commences before the design is finished.

Management procurement tends to be used where:

- maximum price competition for individual work elements is required to try and keep costs down (but cost certainty at the start is less important)
- an early start on site is needed and getting the building finished quickly is a priority
- the employer does not mind taking all the construction risk

6.5.1 Management contracting

6.5.1.1 Overview

Management contracting was hyped in the 1980s as the solution to all problems inherent in construction projects created by adversarial lump sum forms of contract. It was also perceived as more accurately reflecting the structure of the industry with its dependence on the expertise of major specialist subcontractors and less work carried out by a multi-skilled main contractor. However, this form of procurement is now used very little today.

Examples of standard form management contracts are the JCT Management Building Contract 2005 Edition and the NEC3 Engineering and Construction Contract Option F: Management Contract (June 2005). (Also see *The construction contract*, this volume.)

6.5.1.2 Description and structure

A 'management contract' (i.e. the agreement between the employer and the management contractor) is a cost reimbursement contract.

The employer appoints a management contractor under a management contract to manage the construction phase of a project on his behalf and to manage a series of 'works contractors'.

Crucially it is the works contractors who carry out the work, not the management contractor whose only function is to manage and supervise the works contractors. The idea being that a contractor is best-placed to control the management process as they are, in essence, a poacher turned gamekeeper.

The management contractor enters into a series of works packages with the works contractors, who will look to him for payment. Typically, the works contractors will be selected by

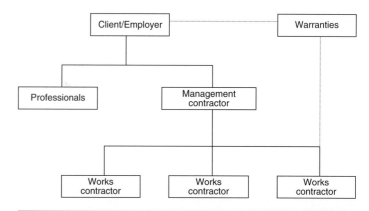

Figure 3 Typical management contracting structure

way of a competitive tender procedure described in the management contract and be employed on an agreed form of works package.

The management contractor is reimbursed any costs which it expends in employing the works contractors (prime cost) (save for those costs incurred through his own negligence) and is paid a management fee which will either be a lump sum or a percentage of the prime construction cost.

The employer therefore does not have any direct contractual relationship with the works contractors (unless he obtains collateral warranties from them) (**Figure 3**).

6.5.1.3 Responsibility for works contractors

At first glance, management contracting looks like traditional contracting but with the contractor subcontracting out 100% of the work. However, the NEC3 Option F provides a mechanism whereby the management contractors can undertake elements of the work. In effect, the contractor has become more of a consultant, getting rid of most of his labour force, plant and equipment and minimising his otherwise significant operating costs. Instead each works contractor will bring and be responsible for his own basic items, such as scaffolding. The management contractor may also provide a site management group and preliminaries such as offices, temporary power and a canteen.

Crucially, however, under the terms of certain management contracts the management contractor is not responsible for the default of the works contractors. The aim is to distribute the contractual risk for the construction of the building between the employer and the works contractors so that the management contractor is not legally responsible for the default of the works contractors. In short, although the management contractor agrees to ensure that the work is carried out without defects and on time, the management contractor is protected if the only reason for breach of this obligation is a breach by the works contractor. Provided that the management contractor complies with the terms of its contract, and administers the work contract properly, it is reimbursed for all sums payable to the works contractors. So the management contractor does not take the risk of their defective works or delay – but this is subject to the management contractor not having breached his contract itself. This potentially leaves the management contractor with very little risk.

However, the proviso above is important as was demonstrated in *Copthorne Hotel v. Arup Associates* (more particularly described below), where a management contractor ended up out of pocket after a works contractor went insolvent.

One of the main purposes of a management contract – namely to limit the exposure of the 'main contractor' to risk – is not quite as stark as it sounds. One of the fundamental principles underlying the apportionment of risk is that where a risk is transferred from one party to another, a financial adjustment should be made to balance that risk. The types of project that are usually seen as most suitable as management contracts involve a high degree of commercial risk. If a contractor under the traditional approach was asked to tender for such a project, then the tender would have to be inflated to accommodate the associated risk. Therefore, it is in both the contractor's and employer's interests for there to be low risk contracts.

The 'relief provision' in certain management contracts, such as clause 5.1 in the JCT Management Contract 2005 Edition, will typically contain a mechanism whereby the management contractor consults with the employer in the event of a default by the works contractor, taking the employer's instructions on how to proceed as to the replacement of any defaulting works contractor. The management contractor will usually be obliged to take all necessary steps to enforce the terms of the works contracts (which may include pursuing the works contractor in dispute proceedings if the employer so directs).

Further if another works contractor makes a claim against the management contractor in respect of losses they have incurred due to the breach or non-compliance by the defaulting works contractor, then the management contractor shall in consultation with the employer 'meet any such claim' made by such works contractor. The management contractor would then pursue recovery from the defaulting works contractor. If this is not possible (due to insolvency for example) then the employer has to make up the shortfall. Thus, the employer takes the insolvency-risk of the works contractors – in contrast, under a design and build contract or traditional procurement route, the main contractor would normally take the insolvency risk of a subcontractor.

Indeed, in general, if there is any shortfall between the amount recovered by the management contractor from the works contractor in default and all the costs the management contractor has incurred because of the default, then the management contractor will usually be entitled to recover the shortfall from the employer. The amount the employer can recover from the management contractor for any breach by a works contractor's default is capped by the amounts which the management contractor recovers from the defaulting works contractor. The general effect is that it is the employer who bears the risk of any default of a works contractor.

However, other management contracts may not contain this relief provision. For example, the risk of delays by works contractors may be imposed on the management contractor so that

the management contractor is liable for liquidated damages even though the delay was caused by works contractor default rather than any default of the management contractor in the performance of his management obligations. Some argue that contracting on this basis, however, would undermine the management contractor's incentive to act in the employer's best interests. For example, imposing this provision may mean it will be in the management contractor's interest to ensure the works contractors were entitled to extensions of time. However, it should be noted that under the JCT Management Contract 2005 Edition the management contractor cannot give extensions of time under a works contract without consulting with the architect/contract administrator about the proposed decision, so the employer retains an element of control.

With both the JCT Management Contract 2005 Edition and the NEC3 Option F, the management contractor pays the amounts due to the works contractors prior to receiving payment from the employer, that is, the management contractor must incur the cost prior to being reimbursed from the employer. There is therefore a risk that the employer may have insufficient funds to reimburse the management contractor, which may potentially leave him 'out of pocket'.

Nonetheless, even where the management contract does include the relief provisions such as limiting its liability for defaulting or insolvent works contractors to amounts it recovers from the works contractors, the management contractor will not be able to rely on the relief provision to recoup its losses from the employer to the extent that it has itself caused or contributed to such losses by failure in its own management responsibilities (*Copthorne Hotel (Newcastle) Ltd v. Arup Associates and Others (1998) 85 BLR 22*).

The issue before the Court of Appeal in *Copthorne Hotel* was whether Bovis, as management contractor, could be liable under the contract for any defects which occurred as a consequence of a breach by a works contractor. Bovis sought to rely upon the 'relief provision' in the JCT Management Contract 1987 Edition to exclude its liability. The 'relief provision' of the management contract protected the management contractor, so that he was only obliged to pass on amounts actually recovered from the works contractor. However, the court held that the extent of this protection was limited. It only applied to breaches by the management contractor of obligations to achieve a result or to 'ensure', or to 'secure', or the like, fulfilment by a works contractor of the latter's obligations.

The management contractor would, however, be liable without any such limitation for damages if he breached obligations which were not within the protection of the 'relief provision'. The court drew a sharp distinction between the liabilities which are, and those which are not, the 'result' of work contractors' breaches.

The 'relief provision' did not protect the management contractor where he was under a duty to 'supervise' the works contractors (the equivalent of clause 2.3.5 in the JCT Management Contract 2005 Edition). In practical terms, this means that if a works contractor is penniless, so that the management contractor cannot recover against him for breaches of workmanship obligations in the works, the question may then arise as to whether those workmanship defects have arisen, as a question of fact, from breaches by the management contractor of his separate obligations to provide 'supervision'. If the facts show that the management contractor is indeed in breach of his supervisory role, then he is responsible to the employer in his own right. He must then bear responsibility regardless of the fact that he, the management contractor, cannot recover against the works contractor because of the latter's impecuniosity.

In addition, a management contractor may have to account to the employer for liquidated damages insofar as delays have arisen as a result of the management contractor's failure to perform its management services.

6.5.1.4 'No loss' argument

Self-evidently, if a party incurs no loss resulting from a breach then it cannot recover damages. We have already noted that in certain relief provisions, the management contractor is only liable to the employer to the extent that he recovers from the works contractor. Thus, if he recovers nothing from a defaulting works contractor, he has nothing to account to the employer. Thus, if nothing is awarded to a management contractor from the defaulting works contractor he is in no worse or better position that he would have been if the management contractor had been awarded damages. This is called the 'no loss' argument. Various devices such as seeking to distinguish between a management contractor's 'liability' to the employer as opposed to the employer's ability to 'recover' from a management contractor, and provisions seeking to prevent a works contractor from running a 'no loss' argument and direct agreements between the employer and the works contractors are used in an attempt to get around this perceived problem.

6.5.1.5 Overlap between design and construction

In the fashion of traditional procurement, the employer engages independent design consultants to carry out the design. The contractor is also appointed during the design phase so that the contractor can work with the professional team and contribute his construction expertise to the design process. Because of this it is usual for a management contractor to be an experienced contractor, although this is not necessarily a pre-requisite.

The early appointment of the management contractor effectively enables the contractor to become part of the design team, thereby providing benefits such as value engineering and potentially giving advice on the buildability of design proposals without the client giving up control of the design (and hence what the employer ultimately gets) to the contractor which is more likely to happen in design and build procurement.

The contractor will also look at the proposed divisions of the building work into works packages (and the content there in) and at pricing, programming and procurement. Each works package is tendered and let as and when sufficient design information is available and which suits other information and actual progress on site. The design and construction phases are intended to overlap as this not only provides a longer period for completion of each activity in itself but also improves the speed of the project to completion.

One advantage of letting the building work in packages is that it permits flexibility as design decisions can be left until a later stage than in traditional contracts.

Put simply, management contracting should enable the project to finish more quickly than if the contract had been let on a traditional procurement basis where design and construction are sequential.

Because of the distinct role the management contractor can have during the design phase, some standard form contracts such as the JCT Management Building Contract 2005 Edition distinguish between the pre-construction phase and construction phase. This enables the employer to terminate the employment of the contractor after the design phase before construction work actually commences.

6.5.1.6 Perceived advantages of management contracting

In summary, the perceived advantages of management contracting may include as follows:

■ Individually tendered work packages may achieve cost savings because each package may be more competitively priced (in theory). In consultation with the management contractor, the works packages may be more suitably bundled to suit the construction process.

■ Independent design advice for the employer is maintained.

■ The employer may achieve cost savings. The commercial argument given for this is that on a risky project (i.e. a complex building in a city centre), the contractor on traditional contracting will price for the risk leading to an inflated construction cost. Thus, if the risk is removed from the contractor, the contractor should drop his price for the work, thereby achieving cost savings for the employer. Certainly, the management contractor can use its market position to negotiate keen prices and maximise any discounts (which will be passed on to the employer).

■ *Fast tracking*. The completion date can be achieved more quickly than with other procurement methods. Early packages can be let to works contractors and construction of the project can start before the design of the later packages is completed.

■ *Buildability* – The overlap between design and construction enables early input on 'buildability' and value engineering with consequent cost and time savings. In practice, this approach does carry risk, particularly the risk of variations to earlier packages as a result of the development of design of later packages.

■ Reduction in adversarial attitudes by employing the contractor as 'manager' and relieving him of risk for cost and time overruns caused by works contractors. Who is more ideally placed to manage and co-ordinate the works contractors than a contractor?

6.5.1.7 Perceived disadvantages of management contracting

In summary, the perceived disadvantages of management contracting may include as follows:

■ The final cost of the project is uncertain until the last works package is let and the downside of letting packages early may lead to increased number of variations as the design develops through the process.

■ Design and construction liability is very diffuse. It is split between the many works contractors and consultants and in the event of a major dispute is likely to either lead to a multitude of proceedings or multiparty proceedings. The diffuse nature of this procurement route means that interface defences are easily raised by potential defendants and may be difficult to rebut.

■ The only person taking overall responsibility for the default of all the works contractors is the employer. This responsibility falls on the contractor in traditional or design and build procurement routes.

■ There is no direct contractual link between the employer and the works contractors (unless collateral warranties are used).

■ Employer takes insolvency risk on works contractors (this is obviously an advantage to the contractor).

6.5.2 Construction management

6.5.2.1 Overview

Construction management is a relatively recent development in the construction industry reflecting the reluctance of major contractors to undertake all the risks inherent in the standard procurement routes.

6.5.2.2 Description and structure

Construction management is essentially the same as management contracting save for one major difference. It removes the problem of there being no contractual link between the employer and those actually doing the work that is inherent in management contracting. The employer (rather than the construction manager) enters into the works packages directly with the 'trade contractors' (called the 'works contractors' in management contracting).

Rather the construction manager occupies the managerial position in construction management. The construction manager acts as consultant and agent to the employer in engaging trade contractors to carry out the works packages.

As can be seen from **Figure 4**, the employer will need to engage its own professional team to undertake the design. As

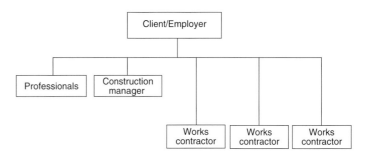

Figure 4 Construction management structure

with management contracting, the construction manager is ideally engaged at the outset of the project so that it can work as part of the professional team during the design stage.

The trade contracts may be negotiated or competitively bid and either lump sum or cost reimbursement.

6.5.2.3 Direct contractual link between employer and 'trade contractors'

The direct contractual links between the employer and the numerous trade contractors in construction management expose the employer to considerable risk due to insolvency and mismanagement. In view of the risk it is thought that the employer should be involved in the management of the risk. In addition, the employer is also likely to have to be involved in the day to day running of the project.

A further effect of the direct contractual relationship between the employer and the trade contractors is that trade contractors should be paid more quickly under this system than under the management contracting system. This may lead to substantial savings for the employer as the trade contractors do not have to budget for lengthy payment delays as cashflow for any contractor is extremely important.

6.5.2.4 Role of construction manager

In order for the construction manager to perform an effective role even though he is not a party to the trade contracts, the construction manager will usually need to be the contract administrator under the trade contracts. The construction manager will therefore perform services similar to the ancillary services traditionally provided by the professional team in other procurement methods.

Although the construction manager may be appointed as contract administrator, employers may wish to restrict his authority in certain respects. For example, in relation to the issue of instructions with particular consequences (such as costs or delays over specified levels), the acceptance of tenders or the termination of trade contracts. The employer may wish to be the party who ultimately makes these decisions.

6.5.2.5 Mismanagement by construction manager

Construction management has been described as a method of procurement whereby the construction manager manages the construction of the project without accepting the overall risks of time and cost, which remain with the employer. The extent of the obligations of construction managers was reviewed in *Great Eastern Hotel v. John Laing [2005] EWHC 181 (TCC)* which caused these basic principles to be viewed in a different light.

Great Eastern Hotel Ltd (GEH) was a consortium of hotel operators and owners who engaged Laing as construction managers for the redevelopment of the Great Eastern Hotel.

The construction management agreement contained fairly standard terms that the construction manager would carry out its services using the reasonable skill, care and diligence to be expected of a properly qualified and competent construction manager. The services to be carried out by the construction manager were set out in a schedule to the agreement and included, by way of example, that the construction manager would manage and minimise the effect of delays to keep the employer informed of anything that may affect the timing of the project.

GEH argued that those clauses amounted to an absolute obligation to achieve regular and diligent progress and completion by the due date. The court disagreed and held that the contract as a whole imposed upon the construction manager obligations of a professional man performing professional services as set out in the agreement.

The court, nevertheless, held that Laing had been in breach of various duties contained within the construction management agreement. Amongst other things, the court held that Laing had failed to place and manage certain package works effectively which consequently caused delay to the project. Further, it was held that Laing's attempts to re-programme and co-ordinate the works of the trade contractors, to seek to recover delays, was inadequate. In addition, Laing's misreporting of delays and failure to provide accurate information on programming matters deprived GEH of the ability to make arrangements to minimise additional costs associated with the delays.

The upshot of all this was that although the construction manager did not guarantee that the works would be completed for a lump sum or by a defined completion date, the schedule of the construction management agreement nevertheless imposed clear obligations upon Laing which were enforceable against them.

Laing were therefore held liable for the loss of profits from hotel operation as a consequence of the late completion, the abortive acceleration monies paid to trade contractors and the majority of the loss and expense claims paid to trade contractors who had been delayed and disrupted in the carrying out of their works as a consequence of Laing's failings.

Thus, depending on the precise terms of the construction management agreement, a construction manager could be held liable in circumstances where its mismanagement results in loss and damage.

6.6 Partnering

6.6.1 Overview

The concept of partnering has been developed out of the Latham (1994) and Egan (1998) reports and their emphasis on the need to reduce adversarial attitudes in the procurement of construction projects.

The definition of partnering has always been somewhat elusive. It is probably not a procurement method in itself, although aspects to the concept do have implications for the procurement methods referred to earlier.

The report *Partnering in the Team* published by the Construction Industry Board in 1997 defined partnering as follows:

> *Partnering is a structured management approach to facilitate team working against contractual boundaries. Its fundamental components are formalised mutual objectives, agreed problem resolution methods, and an active search for continuous measureable improvements.*

6.6.2 Description

Partnering arrangements vary but in essence, partnering requires a co-operative rather than confrontational approach to a project by all people involved so that parties will co-operate to achieve a 'successful' project acting fairly rather than serving their own particular interests.

An essential element of the process is an exchange of information by all those involved in the project as to how they can best contribute and what they wish to get out of the process.

6.6.3 Framework arrangement

Partnering often relies upon a continuous flow of work to encourage good behaviour by the contractor and his team, assisting the contractor to resource effectively as a consequence of the more reliable flow of work. The employer is encouraged to behave co-operatively and fairly by the prospect of lower costs and improved quality that arise out of the continuity of relationship and workflow. This often results in a 'framework agreement' providing for a commitment by the employer to ensure a continuous flow of work.

6.6.4 Pain/gain share arrangement

Partnering arrangements usually involve one or more of the following:

■ An estimated cost either being the capital cost of construction (sometimes called an Estimated Prime Cost or Target Cost) or possibly, where the contract involves construction and maintenance, a lifetime costing for the facility;

- A mechanism under which the contract parties can discuss ways of making savings to that estimated cost;
- A mechanism under which the contract parties are rewarded for any savings achieved (gain share) and under which the parties will share any cost overruns (pain share).

In theory, these payment arrangements can be achieved using a number of procurement methods, although many feel they are best suited to management-based methods of procurement. Partnering does not generally sit well with the traditional standard form contracts where the architect/engineer is given responsibility for design, project management, supervision of the contractor's work, payment certification and decision on claims.

6.6.5 Example standard forms of partnering agreements

6.6.5.1 Project Partnering Contract 2000 (PPC 2000)

Some promoting bodies such as the Association of Consultant Architects (ACA) have authored individual partnering agreements such as PPC 2000 – the first multi-party standard form partnering contract – and its sister contract SPC 2000, which was prepared to enable the partnering team in the PPC 2000 to enter into arrangements with their specialists. The PPC 2000 envisages that all persons involved with a project will enter into a single contract so they will be aware of each other's obligations. It also envisages that all members of the project team will be engaged before work starts on site to encourage contributions from the contractor and any subcontractors whilst design is being finalised. It also provides for the agreement of shared savings arrangements.

Those promoting this form of contract suggest that this is not cost plus, but is open book, where the team arrives at a fixed price at the end of the first appointment stage.

6.6.5.2 NEC3 Partnering Option X12

This agreement envisages that partnering arrangements will be included in each bi-party contract entered into by the employer in relation to a project rather than one multi-party contract for the whole project team. Amongst other things, it provides for an early warning of matters likely to result in increased price, delayed completion or impaired performance of the works in use.

6.6.5.3 JCT framework agreement and JCT framework agreement non-binding

The JCT have also published a form of partnering agreement. There is a binding and a non-binding version.

References

Construction Industry Board (1997) *Partnering in the Team*. Thomas Telford Ltd, London, UK

Egan, J. (1998) *Rethinking Construction: Report of the Construction Task Force*. HMSO, London, UK

Latham, M. (1994), *Constructing the Team*. HMSO, London, UK

Referenced cases

Blyth & Blyth v. Carillion Construction Ltd [2001] 79 ConLR 142

Co-operative Insurance Society Ltd v. Henry Boot Scotland Ltd, TCC 1 July 2002

Copthorne Hotel (Newcastle) Ltd v. Arup Associates and Others (1998) 85 BLR 22

Great Eastern Hotel v. John Laing [2005] EWHC 181 (TCC)

Henry Boot Construction Ltd v. Alstom Combined Cycles Ltd [2000] BLR 247, CA

Independent Broadcasting Authority v. EMI Electronics Limited & BICC Construction Limited (1980) 14 BLR 1

Websites

Institution of Civil Engineers (ICE); www.ice.org.uk

Joint Contracts Tribunal (JCT); www.jctltd.co.uk

New Engineering Contract (NEC); www.neccontracts.com

Project Partnering Contract (PPC) 2000; www.ppc2000.co.uk

Chapter 7

doi: 10.1680/mocl.40878.0095

The construction contract

Michael P. O'Reilly Adie O'Reilly LLP, Lincoln, UK

The construction contract is examined both within its wider context and on its own terms. In its wider context, its place relative to the multiplicity of other agreements and obligations will be examined. In examining a specific contract commonly used, the terms and structure of the New Engineering Contract 3 (NEC3) contract will be reviewed.

CONTENTS

7.1 Introduction

Construction projects generally comprise a number of phases: identification of need, consideration of alternatives, conceptual design, planning approval, detailed design, construction and ongoing maintenance. Contracts are important at all stages. During initial consideration of highway schemes for example, conceptual design highway engineers will be engaged in an extensive period of surveys, consideration of alternatives and so on, long before any construction takes place and these will be based on an agreement between the relevant highway authority or other promoter and the consultants.

In this chapter, however, we shall focus on the construction phase and shall examine the key contracts used.

7.2 The construction contract in context

A standard form construction contract does not alone properly define the parties' obligations. It requires various sections to be completed stating who the parties are, what work is to be done, the contract period, the price and so on.

In addition, on any project of complexity, the construction contract is surrounded by other obligations. It is important for the person putting the contract documentation together to have a proper overview of how all this documentation interlinks and how risk flows in the system. Lawyers or surveyors who set up complex construction contracts may spend only a small proportion of the time on the central construction contract; the difficult task is usually to coordinate all the obligations of the numerous parties involved.

Figure 1 shows a typical arrangement as might be seen in a traditional project. The numbers 1–9 refer to types of obligation which are necessary to consider. This diagram is simplified for the purposes of exposition, and a number of individual contracts are omitted to provide greater clarity. In practice, it is not unusual for there to be in excess of 100 contracts of various

types in play on a large project; coordinating these is a project in itself.

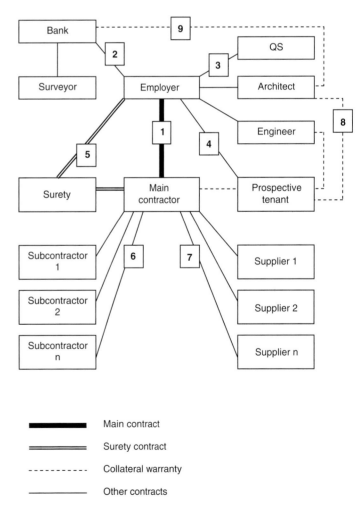

▬▬▬▬	Main contract
═══	Surety contract
-----------	Collateral warranty
───────	Other contracts

Figure 1   A typical arrangement as might be seen in a traditional project

The numbers refer to types of obligation which are necessary to consider.

Amongst the agreements in place are the following:

1. *Main contract.* This is the central contract which obliges the contractor to build the works and the employer to pay for them. This agreement will be examined in more details in a later section of this chapter.

2. *Finance agreement.* In the case of private sector projects, a bank or other lender will often finance the construction of the asset with the monies being repaid when the asset brings in revenue. The arrangement will be governed by a formal finance agreement and the bank will generally take a legal charge over the land and asset to secure its loan. The finance agreement will state what sums the employer is entitled to call for ('drawdowns'), when and upon what condition. The most common condition provides that drawdowns are permitted only if a surveyor – whose appointment is shown in **Figure 1** – appointed by the bank certifies that the work is done sufficiently to warrant payment requested so that the bank's security is maintained. The bank will often also take guarantees from, for example, the employer's parent company ('a parent company guarantee') or a guarantee from the employer's owners personally ('a personal guarantee') as additional security. Where – as is often the case – the employer is a 'special purpose vehicle', that is a company set up specifically to carry out the particular project, it will have little money of its own and hence the contractor will also be cautious and it is frequently the case that the contractor will insist that that the bank will agree to make direct payments to the contractor, rather than via the employer. (Also see the chapter *Bonds, parent company guarantees and other security.*)

3. *Professional appointments.* A typical project will entail the appointment of a number of professionals. Those shown in **Figure 1** are quantity surveyor, architect and engineer. Others will include the CDM (Construction (Design and Management)) Coordinator and may also include specialist engineers (such as mechanical and electrical services, acoustic engineers), planning consultants and so on. In the case of a consultant, the contract is often termed an appointment. In the case of consultants' appointments there can be some confusion in respect of the following factors:

   - co-ordinating the scope of individual appointments to ensure no overlap or gaps in coverage (and hence responsibility);

   - ensuring that there is a lead consultant whose function is to ensure a harmonious product.

The team putting the contract together should ensure that if a problem arises with the construction, the consultant responsible is readily identifiable. As well as dealing with payment, ownership in designs, insurance and so on, the appointment should also deal with the following factors:

   - *Standard of care.* Generally a consultant will owe a duty to act with reasonable care and skill. It is possible to produce a design which meets this standard but for a building constructed in accordance with the design to be defective nonetheless. An example would be where the architect specifies natural stone cladding in line with what appears to be common practice, but the cladding fails due to the specific geological characteristics of the particular stone selected for the project. It is possible to set a higher standard, namely that the building – if built in accordance with the design – will be fit for its purpose. Consultants naturally resist the imposition of such a standard and it leads to conservative design, insurance issues and so on.

   - *Novation.* Even where the main contract is to be let on a design and build basis, it is common for the employer to select and appoint the architect and structural engineer in the first instance. They will carry out an outline design showing layout and external appearance. They will also draw up the 'Employer's Requirements' which establish the main specification for the construction. But when the main contract is let, their appointment will be transferred to the contractor by a process known as novation. This involves dissolving the contractual link between the employer and consultant and re-establishing that link between the contractor and consultant. In this way the employer can reap the benefit of controlling the shape of the project whilst transferring all liability to the contractor.

   - *Liability period.* It is usually beneficial to require the appointment to be under seal to take advantage of the longer liability period of 12 years.

   - *Collateral warranties.* If it is intended that the consultants will give collateral warranties, this should be made an obligation of the appointment.

See the chapter *The consulting engineer's appointment* for further information.

4. *Agreement for lease.* In this case it is assumed that the building will be let to a tenant upon completion and that the tenant has been identified – indeed the tenant will often be instrumental in setting the specification. Such an arrangement is favoured by banks who like to be assured of an income stream upon completion. It is generally not appropriate to execute a lease for a building which does not yet exist; instead an agreement to execute a lease is entered into. In cases where the tenant will, for example, be a franchisee of a hotel chain, restaurant and so on, the franchisor will have standards of construction, appearance and accommodation and it is important that these are incorporated into the Employer's Requirements.

5. *Surety agreement.* A surety agreement – such as a guarantee – provides for the situation where there is a risk that a party may default. In this case the Employer may be concerned that the Contractor may default, for example, by becoming insolvent, leaving a partly completed building which is expensive to complete, causing loss. By taking a performance guarantee either from a parent company or a finance company, the default of the contractor triggers an entitlement to recover from the surety.

6. *Subcontractors.* Most projects involve subcontractors. Indeed, it is not uncommon for virtually the entire job to be

subcontracted. There are several factors to be considered by the employer when setting up the contract scheme:

- *Selection of subcontractors.* The employer will often reasonably require that subcontractors meet certain standards – for example, considerate construction, safety and environmental policies put into place and so on – and will wish to restrict access to the site to such subcontractors.

- *Flowdown of terms.* It is frequently appropriate for the employer to insist that any subcontract will be on a 'back to back' basis so that the subcontractor's obligations and entitlements in respect of an aspect of work are identical to that of the main contractor, except for the price.

- *Collateral warranties.* The employer will in some cases wish to take collateral warranties for some subcontractors. Where, for example, a bespoke glass structure is to be designed and built by a specialist firm, it may be appropriate to insist on a collateral warranty in favour of future tenants.

7. *Suppliers.* The same principles generally apply to suppliers as apply to subcontractors.

8. *Direct collateral warranties.* Collateral warranties are so-called because they involve a party (the warrantor) promising (warranting) to another person (the warrantee) that work it has done under a primary contract (e.g. in the case of an architect his appointment) meets the standards set in that other contract; the warranty is collateral to the primary contract. The function of the warranty is to establish a contractual link between parties which would otherwise not be in a contractual relationship; for instance a tenant would not normally be entitled to sue the architect for pure economic loss, but the collateral warranty establishes that entitlement. This is important to a tenant under, for example, a full repairing and insuring lease who is responsible for defects. Collateral warranties may be simple or under seal. In the latter case they enable the warrantee to take action for up to 12 years (for further information see the chapter *Collateral warranties*).

9. *Step-in warranties.* Only one is shown, but there may be an extensive network of these. These are generally executed in favour of a bank and as well as warranting that the work will be of a stated standard, provided that in the event the main contractor is removed from the project and the warrantee's nominee can step into the contractor's shoes and give instructions as if it were the contractor to enable the project to be completed under the warrantee's control. There are thus three parties to such a warranty.

7.3 The construction contract: principles

Construction contracts are, by and large, made, interpreted and enforced in the same way as any other commercial contract. Contracts for construction work in Britain, however, must comply with requirements of Part II of the Housing Grants, Construction and Regeneration Act 1996. This includes the

need for an adjudication clause, clauses dealing with stage payments and a prohibition on pay-when-paid clauses. Contracts in writing which do not comply with the Act become subject to the relevant provisions of the Scheme for Construction Contracts 1998. Note that in November 2009 an amendment to the Act was given Royal Assent; it is expected to come into force for contracts made after 2011. The new statute will, for example, extend the coverage of the statutory provisions to oral contracts.

7.3.1 The use and importance of contracts in construction

The vast majority of construction work is performed under contract. A contract is not a document, although it may be set out in a document. It is an agreement which obliges the parties to do specified things. Most importantly, in the case of a construction contract, it requires the contractor to build the works and requires the employer to pay for them.

Contracts have a number of functions including

- specifying the work to be done by the contractor (or subcontractor, etc.), including the required quality and time for completion of various parts of the work

- defining what amount is to be paid, how any additional or reduced payments are to be computed and when payments are to be made

- defining which party is responsible for events occurring outside the parties' direct control which affect the work; such events may include pre-commencement conditions in the planning permission, adverse weather, access difficulties, local authority restrictions, changes in the law, unexpectedly poor ground and so on

- defining who has responsibility for undertaking the various administrative or dispute resolution functions which may be required, including giving instructions, making decisions about claims, appointing adjudicators, arbitrators and so on

It may also provide a framework for computing any compensation due in the event that a party fails to do what it is obliged to do.

7.3.2 Types of contract

A number of types and features of construction contracts may be identified. These include 'traditional', 'design-and-construct' and 'concession' contracts. The selection of contracts will give rise to questions over control: it being imperative that the employer retains ultimate control in most cases.

Traditional. The description 'traditional' refers to the arrangement where the employer takes on consultants to provide advice on all aspects of the scheme, to design the works and to administer the construction through to completion. These contracts originated in the eighteenth century and are a direct product of the separation of design and construction activities. The contracts were drawn up with the advice engineers or architects and reflect the supreme position occupied by 'the Engineer/Architect' who was wholly responsible for the design, approval of complete work and certification for payment of that work. The same pattern was seen for both private and public schemes. To begin with, contracts were highly individual; Brunel, for instance, liked to ensure that he had absolute say over every aspect of the work. By the end of the nineteenth century, many local authorities (who had, by this time, taken over responsibility for the majority of civil engineering works), began to adopt 'standard forms'. Later, in the late 1930s, these were taken as the basis for an industry-wide standard contract, described as the ICE Conditions of Contract. This contract form is now in its seventh edition. The concept has been exported and the general shape of the ICE Conditions of Contract is seen in many contracts used overseas, not least the FIDIC Red Book Contract. In the case of building contracts, the RIBA Standard Form is now issued by the Joint Contracts Tribunal (JCT).

Design and construct. The major projects of the industrial revolution demanded unprecedented innovation, requiring the application of skills possessed by a mere handful of engineers or architects. There was only one viable pattern of contract for these works, namely contractors working to designs produced by an engineer/architect, constructed under his (very rarely *her*) direction. The situation today is very different. Contracting companies employ a range of skilled construction professionals and many have specialist design offices. There is, in short, far less need than hitherto to maintain the historical distinction between design and construction.

Contracts with contractor's design are variously described as 'design and build', 'package deal' or 'turnkey'. The true meaning of a contract is not determined from its description, but from its terms, read as a whole.

The benefits of contractor's design may include (a) single point liability; defects of every character are the contractor's responsibility, unless it can show some special defence; thus there will be less conflict on site and a reduction of defensive and uncooperative modes of behaviour, (b) enhanced design standard; under a design appointment, the designer is obliged to do no more than exercise reasonable care and skill whereas under design and construct arrangements the obligation may be (subject to any terms bearing on the point) that the works as designed will be suitable for their purpose and (c) opportunity for the contractor to enhance the constructability of the project and enhance both time and cost efficiency.

Concession (BOT) contracts. A concession (or Build-Operate-Transfer) contract is one where the concession-grantor (frequently, but not necessarily a government body) grants to the concessionaire a concession to develop a piece of infra-structure (often called an 'asset' or the 'facility') and to hold that facility for a defined period and in a defined way so as to recoup the initial cost of investment and also to make a profit. The facility is usually constructed using a turnkey contract and the concession-grantor usually takes the facility over at the end of the concession period. A concession contract is not primarily a construction contract. It is, in large part, a service contract in which the concessionaire provides to the concession-grantor (directly or indirectly) a service. In addition, it is a finance

mechanism – used in, for example, Private Finance Initiative (PFI) schemes – enabling the concession-grantor to have the service (and, ultimately, the facility) without having to find the initial capital (although it may have to underwrite it, directly or indirectly). Concession contracts often represent the ultimate risk assumption for a 'contractor' (concessionaire).

7.3.4 Contracts under hand and under seal

It is generally in the Employer's interests for the contract to be made under seal. This is a simple inexpensive formality which extends the limitation period from 6 years to 12 years.

7.3.5 Statutory controls and impact

English law is sometimes described as 'delivering what it says on the tin'. In other words one reads the contract to determine the obligations of the parties. There is little interference from statute. However, parties must always be aware of overriding statutory obligations or entitlements:

- Planning law requirements: generally the employer will retain the responsibility and risk for obtaining relevant planning permission, but in every case consider the contract terms.

- Under the Construction (Design and Management) Regulations 2007 (CDM Regulations), the designer must ensure that any design which it prepares pays proper regard to risks during and after construction and gives priority to measures which will protect people. Where the employer's requirements contain a provision that the design will accord with the Regulations and the works are not safe, for example, for cleaning, as required by the Regulations, this may amount to a 'defect' entitling the employer to undertake 'remedial works', the cost of which may be claimed from the contractor.

- For work carried out within the UK, the Housing Grants, Construction and Regeneration Act 1996 provides mandatory standards for payment and dispute resolution. The provisions of the Act deal with two principal matters: payment and disputes.

7.4 Tendering practice: general

Under a traditional contract, the employer (or its engineer/architect) will have completed (or virtually completed) the design at tender stage. The employer will be able to approve the final drawings and specifications prior to tender. The drawings and specifications are passed to the tenderers who price the works. Traditionally, a bill of quantities is provided, showing the quantities, or at least their approximate values.

Under a design and construct contract, the position can be very different. The tender process can be described in terms of the number and types of stages it involves. In many types of work, tenders are generally 'single stage', that is the contractor receives documents and submits its tender based on those documents. Although described as 'single stage', there is often a significant period of negotiation following the submission of tenders (although less common in public projects because of EU procurement rules). Tender documents for a single-stage design and construct project will include the 'employer's requirements'. In its submission, the contractor offers the 'contractor's proposals'. The former describes the criteria in which the employer requires the design to meet and the latter sets out the ways in which the contractor proposes to meet them. Many design and construct contracts have a defined order of precedence in which the employer's requirements take priority over the contractor's proposals.

Note that for projects in the public or quasi-public sector – utilities contracts for example – it is generally necessary by EU law to advertise the projects and to establish objective criteria for selection of contractors.

For further information see the chapter *Tender process.*

7.4.1 The applicable law of the contract

Two types of law can apply to a contract – procedural law and substantive law. Where a dispute arises, the dispute may be referred to the court or an arbitrator. The rules about procedure, evidence and enforcement of the decision are part of the 'procedural law' of the country where the case is being heard. But the law which the court or arbitrator will apply when interpreting the contract ('the substantive law') need not be the same as the procedural law. For example, where a Spanish contractor builds an office building in Moscow for a Hungarian bank and there is a provision in the contract (written in English) for arbitration in Stockholm or Paris, it is necessary for the parties to agree explicitly which substantive law is to apply.

There is no such thing – as yet, at any rate – as general European law applicable to contracts, and the parties must decide which country's law is to govern such matters as interpretation of the contract. This is normally done in a single clause, using the wording: 'The law applicable to this contract is the law of England' (or Spain, Russia, etc.). Note that the law chosen must be that of a 'legal country' rather than political state. If the parties chose the 'law of the UK' or the 'law of the USA' this would cause ambiguity because the UK contains three legal countries – England and Wales, Scotland and Northern Ireland and each state in the United States has its own law.

It is quite possible for parties to agree that a contract which concerns the nationals of one country only will be subject to the law of a different country. Most countries, however, have rules forbidding the use of this 'flag of convenience' device for avoiding safety and welfare obligations. In this regard, it is worth noting that the Housing Grants, Construction and Regeneration Act 1996 applies to construction within Britain, irrespective of the applicable law of the contract.

7.4.2 Selection of standard form conditions of contract

Construction professionals frequently talk about 'procurement systems'. By this, they mean the entire process of acquiring the finished construction. A major facet of this process is, of course, the choice of the principal construction contract.

In civil engineering situations, two contracts have been particularly influential in the UK. Historically, the ICE Conditions of Contract has been used extensively and its derivative FIDIC Red Book used in many overseas situations. Latterly the NEC has come to prominence. Given that the ICE has now decided to withdraw from the ICE Conditions of Contract, the focus in this chapter is primarily on the NEC.

In the building sector, JCT contracts have been the most commonly used, but the NEC is increasingly used for these projects also.

For further information see *Procurement route* in this volume.

7.5 Documents forming part of the construction contract

Conditions of contract. A construction contract generally contains a standard form set of conditions of contract (amended or unamended). In addition, there will be a variety of documents, some of which will be standard documents and some of which will be unique to the project, setting out the details of the scope of the work to be done, the standard which is to be achieved, ancillary (e.g. safety) requirements and mechanisms for computing the sums payable at any stage. Furthermore, method statements and programmes are frequently produced; these may either form part of the contract, or be produced as a management tool without direct contractual status.

While a construction contract is normally contained within and defined by a series of documents, it should be noted in passing that, in a number of situations, the parties are entitled to look beyond the written documents. This may be so where an agreed oral term has not been written down or where the law implies terms to supplement an incompletely defined agreement.

Drawings and specifications. The scope of construction work is usually defined using drawings and specifications. The former set out the positional interrelationships between the items of work, while the latter set out the quality required. There are a number of standard specifications depending on the sector. Where no specification is provided, it will be implied into the contract, for example, that work is to be done with proper skill and care, using good quality materials that are reasonably suitable for their purpose. The specification documents tend also to contain a variety of requirements and stipulations as to the manner of working. It should be noted that parties frequently use the preamble to the 'specification' to deal with all manner of sundry matters. In some cases, one finds some of the most important clauses in the specification. In contracts – such as the ICE Conditions of Contract 7th Edition – which do not specify an order of priority for documents, specification clauses can have important effects; where they are inconsistent with terms found in the main conditions of contract, the specification clauses may in some cases take precedence.

Bills of quantities, schedules of rates and so on. Bills of quantities are lists of items with associated quantities. The effect of the bill of quantities within the contract is a matter of interpreting the contract as a whole in each case. The effect of the bill of quantities in one contract may differ from its effect in another because of amendments to the Conditions of Contract or even clauses introduced into the specification. As a result, caution is required and the following comments should be taken as indicative only. In contracts for a lump sum price, items required to complete the works must generally be provided despite their being omitted from the bill; if there is no mechanism in the contract for recovering payment for these extra items, the contractor will have to pay for them. For measure and value contracts, estimated quantities are set out for each class of work. When tendering, the contractor quotes a rate for each class. The bill total is the sum of all the products of rates and estimated quantities; but the sum payable is the product of the actual quantities and rates. The process by which the quantity of each item is determined is called 'measurement', which may be physical measurement on site or the computation of quantities using survey data. If an item of work is to be done for which there is no agreed rate, nor agreed mechanism for calculating its value, the contractor is entitled to be paid a reasonable rate/sum. In the ICE Conditions of Contract 7th Edition, for example, the contract states that the bills are deemed to be prepared in accordance with the Civil Engineering Standard Method of Measurement, 3rd Edition. The quantities in the bill are expressed to be estimates; any errors or omissions are to be corrected by the Engineer and any items required to be added in will be paid for in accordance with the contract. Accordingly, where items have been accidentally omitted from the bill, the contractor is compensated. In addition to documents described as bills of quantities, similar documents described as schedules of rates, schedules of prices, and so on are frequently used. None of these terms are terms of art and their effect is determined by interpreting the agreement in each case.

Programmes and method statements. Management tools such as programmes and method statements are frequently used in connection with construction contracts. The status of any programme or method statement is determined by interpreting the contract. The status of a programme or method statement may be one of the following:

- Provided solely for information. The contractor may be required to submit a programme solely for the purpose of demonstrating competence at tender stage. Such programmes or method statements normally have no contractual significance or effect.

- Provided in accordance with the terms of the contract. Some contracts – for example the ICE 7th Edition Contract – require the successful contractor to indicate how it proposes to execute the work using a programme; but such a programme occupies a rather passive role in the management of the project. In the NEC3 Contract, the programme assumes a more active role and is updated to enable positive management control.

- Programmes and so on which rank as contractual (i.e. as terms of the contract). Here the programme or method statement is included within the contract at the time it is made. As a result, the contractor is required and entitled to perform the work in accordance with the programme and method statement; if it is prevented from so doing for reasons at the employer's risk, and thereby suffers a loss, it will be entitled to claim damages.

7.6 The Engineering and Construction Contract, 3rd Edition (NEC3)

The NEC was created and drawn up by an ICEs' working group who published a consultative version in 1991. The first edition was published in March 1993. The second edition was published as the NEC Engineering and Construction Contract (EEC) in November 1995. The new title reflected the aspirations of the NEC Panel that the contract should be used for construction work in all sectors, including traditional building. Many of the changes in the second edition were derived from recommendations in the Latham Report (Latham, 1994). The third edition was published in July 2005, with minor amendments issued in June 2006 and is certified by the UK Office of Government Commerce as achieving the principles of Achieving Excellence in Construction and endorsed for public construction procurers.

Objectives of ECC. The ECC is designed to be flexible, clear and to stimulate good management. Whilst traditional contracts have focused on responsibility as between the parties should the project not progress as expected, the ECC focuses on getting the project built efficiently with both parties having a duty to identify risks, to collaborate in overcoming those risks and to ensure that the time and financial consequences are dealt with fairly. It expressly provides that the parties shall act in a spirit of mutual trust and co-operation.

The suite. The contract is not a single contract but a suite contracts which share a core body of definitions and interrelationships; there are Core Clauses, Main Option Clauses and Secondary Option Clauses, together with Contract Data. The contract is published as a system in a series of documents. These documents include the (a) 'Black Book' which houses the full inventory of clauses, (b) merged versions which contain clauses relevant to each of the Main Options, (c) guidance notes and (d) flow charts. As well as the main contracts the NEC family contains:

- Engineering and Construction Subcontract

- Engineering and Construction Short Contract

- Engineering and Construction Short Subcontract

- Professional Services Contract

- Adjudicator's Contract

- Term service Contract

- Framework Contract.

Style of drafting. The terms are set out as a series of short, crisp statements in the present tense. For example, Clause 20.1 reads: 'The *Contractor* Provides the Works in accordance with the Works Information'. Words with initial capitals are defined in the contract. Italicised words (save for direct quotations, this convention is not preserved in the text of this chapter) are identified in the Contract Data. A numbering system is used which immediately identifies the location and objective of each clause (thus the 30 series clauses all relate to aspects of time). The drafting is condensed, conveying the maximum amount of meaning in the minimum number of words. There is no cross referencing and the import of terms is frequently mysterious until its full interrelationship with the rest of the contract is understood. Consequently, it is not possible to dip lazily into the contract to any great profit; a full understanding requires considerable investment of time. Judge Lloyd QC (2008) expressed this as follows:

> Selection of a competent adjudicator (and, if possible, any later tribunal) manages some of the risk inherent in dispute resolution. In my view this is especially important for the NEC which has been written on the assumption that those operating it will have been trained in and will understand its concepts and philosophies. Whoever decides disputes arising under any construction contract must have the ability to stand in the shoes, as it were, of those who were there at the time and see things as they were then perceived. Applied to the NEC, this means not only having a good knowledge of ordinary construction industry practice, but also good knowledge of how a project using the NEC will have been assembled. A person who might approach an NEC dispute as if it were just another dispute should not be appointed as an adjudicator or arbitrator.

Core clauses. The core clauses, with their individual and invariable numbering scheme apply across the range of contacts. Thus, the advantages accruing to any standard form, such as familiarity, even-handedness, thorough checking and consultation are retained.

Option clauses generally. The pro forma for Contract Data Part One (Data provided by the Employer) invites the parties – and more specifically the Employer – to identify the following:

- Main option
- Dispute resolution option
- Secondary options.

Main Option clauses. There are six main options, identified by letters A to F. These differ principally in the method of remuneration and its attendant mechanisms and risks. They are:

- Option A Priced contract with activity schedule
- Option B Priced contract with bill of quantities
- Option C Target contract with activity schedule
- Option D Target contract with bill of quantities

- Option E Cost reimbursable contract
- Option F Management contract.

Alternatives such as partial or full contractor's design are accommodated within these options by inserting the extent of the design obligation into the Contract Data. The main options can be divided into two main branches. The first branch, Options A and B, are priced contracts, that is contracts for a lump sum for specific work – in the case of A, the pricing is by reference to a schedule of activities and in the case of B by reference to a bill of quantities. The second branch, Options C to F, are based on cost reimbursement plus a fee; the basic cost reimbursement option is Option E; Options C and D include a target arrangement (C based on a target fixed by reference to a schedule of activities and D by reference to a bill of quantities) and a 'management contract' where the Contractor subcontracts and manages all the work (Option F).

Dispute resolution option Clauses W. In previous editions of ECC, the 90 series clauses were 'Disputes and termination'. In the third edition, they are restricted to termination, with the dispute clause W1 and W2 being provided as a separate option. W1 is a default provision applicable generally, and W2 is designed for use in the UK wherever the Housing Grants, Construction and Regeneration Act 1996 applies.

Secondary Option clauses X. These provide a wide range of additional possibilities and are to be used in conjunction with the core clauses and a Main Option from A to F.

- X1 Price adjustment for inflation (only used with Options A, B, C and D)
- X2 Changes in the law
- X3 Multiple currencies (used only with Options A and B)
- X4 Parent company guarantee
- X5 Sectional completion
- X6 Bonus for early completion
- X7 Delay damages
- X12 Partnering
- X13 Performance bond
- X14 Advance payment to the Contractor
- X15 Limitation on the Contractor's liability for his design to reasonable skill and care
- X16 Retention (not used with Option F)
- X17 Low performance damages
- X18 Limitation of Liability
- X20 Key performance indicators.

Statute clauses Y. There are two Y options, Y(UK)2 and Y(UK)3. The former relates to the application of the payment provisions of the Housing Grants Construction and

Regeneration Act 1996. The latter relates to the application of the Contracts (Rights of Third Parties) Act 1999.

Additional clauses Z. The Parties are permitted to add clauses which can range from those which clarify, amend or indeed re-write the existing provisions. In many cases the crucial clauses applicable in many situations will be in the section containing the Z clauses.

General comments about NEC3. NEC3 is not designed to be understood on first reading. It is a professionals' contract designed for practitioners with training and experience. It is inadvisable to specify this contract unless one fully versed in it terminology and how it will apply in practice. Any contract which seeks to incorporate the terms using words such as 'The conditions of contract will be those in the NEC3' is based on a misunderstanding of what the NEC3 is. It is not a single contract, but a building kit for a contract which contains a large number of variants. The same is true of contractors – and subcontractors – embarking upon a project governed by the NEC3; training is required.

7.6.1 Selection of the main option

As noted above, the main options are:

- Option A Priced contract with activity schedule
- Option B Priced contract with bill of quantities
- Option C Target contract with activity schedule
- Option D Target contract with bill of quantities
- Option E Cost reimbursable contract
- Option F Management contract.

The three most used options are A, C and E. In terms of structure, A and E represent distinct categories and Option C can be seen as a hybrid of them.

In the case of Option A, a schedule of activities is drawn up with prices. Thus, a bridge on a large highway project may be broken down into broadly defined items (**Table 1**).

Where Option E is selected the work is carried out at cost plus a fee. It is important for the employer to have proper systems in place to audit costs to ensure no overpayment; and for the contractor to have systems in place to record all proper costs.

Where Option C is used, the same principles as for Option E are used, except that there is a target and any excessive expenditure relative to the target will be shared between the parties. If the project comes in under target price, then both parties will share the benefit. The formula for sharing what is sometimes called the pain-gain formula and should incentivise both parties. Where there are variations, the target will be adjusted. Option A is equivalent to an Option C contract in

Item 134
Bridge 076, excluding approach roads

Ref	Activity	Price
134.1	West abutment, including earthworks	£128,000
134.2	East abutment, including earthworks	£141,800
134.3	Central support	£95,000
134.4	Steel for Deck 1, including bearings	£67,500
134.5	Steel for Deck 2, including bearings	£67,500
135.6	Concrete for decks	£69,200
135.7	Surfacing	£42,100
135.8	White-lining, rails and lighting	£35,650

Table 1 Example of NEC3 Option A: a schedule of activities is drawn up with prices
A bridge on a large highway project may be broken down into broadly defined items

which the contractor is responsible for 100% of the pain and 100% of the gain.

Clearly Option A is most appropriate where the scope of the work is known and can be priced. Option C is most appropriate where the scope is uncertain.

References

Latham, M. (1994) *Constructing the Team*. HMSO, London
Lloyd, H. (2008) Some thoughts on NEC3. *International Construction Law Review*. pp.468–483.

Referenced legislation, regulations and standards
Construction (Design and Management) Regulations 2007 (CDM Regulations)
Contracts (Rights of Third Parties) Act 1999
Housing Grants, Construction and Regeneration Act 1996
Scheme for Construction Contracts 1998

Further reading
Furst, S. and Ramsey, V. (2006) Keating on Construction Contracts, 8th Edition. Sweet & Maxwell
O'Reilly, M. P. (1999) Civil Engineering Construction Contracts, 2nd Edition. Thomas Telford Ltd, London, UK.

Websites
International Federation of Consulting Engineers (FIDIC); www.fidic.org
Joint Contracts Tribunal (JCT); www.jctltd.co.uk
Institution of Civil Engineers (ICE); www.ice.org.uk
New Engineering Contract (NEC); www.neccontract.com
Royal Institute of British Architects (RIBA); www.architecture.com
UK Office of Government Commerce; www.ogc.gov.uk

Chapter 8

Tender process

Ann Minogue Ashurst LLP, London, UK
Nico Beedle Ashurst LLP, London, UK

This chapter discusses the use of competitive tendering as a method for the selection of contractors, subcontractors and consultants for construction projects. Although the concept of tendering is appealing, providing an employer with a variety of options from which to choose, there are issues which must be considered throughout the tender process. These issues will differ depending on the procurement route to be taken, the nature of the contract in question, and whether or not the employer is a public body. A great deal of guidance has been published regarding how a tender process should be conducted, and on what basis tenders should be evaluated in order to ensure that the right tenderer is employed for the right reasons. This guidance makes clear that quality and value, in addition to price, should be important factors in the decision-making process. There have also been numerous disputes over whether or not a contract has been formed as a result of a tender process, and case law has clarified the rights of the respective parties in certain common scenarios.

doi: 10.1680/mocl.40878.0103

CONTENTS

8.1 Introduction

8.1.1 The reasons for tendering in construction

Construction projects have a number of features which separate them from most industrial processes:

- the design is very substantially separated from the production (even if in more recent times the design detailing is an integral part of the construction product);

- construction is subject to a high degree of regulation which is not only generic, such as Health and Safety and the Building Regulations, but is also specific to the individual project, such as planning and highways' permissions;

- a substantial part of any design is related to individual site location, conditions, and circumstances: ground conditions influencing foundation design; street pattern influencing elevational treatment; planning environment influencing quality of materials; exposure influencing envelope design and internal services; and so on.

There is inevitably a wide variety of prices for apparently similar projects and, indeed, a significant spread of potential cost outcomes for an identified project. There is an historic belief that the only way satisfactorily to determine the right price for a project is by using a competitive tender process to put it to the market place. To a client becoming involved in construction for the very first time, this may appear to be a straightforward way to proceed, but there are many pitfalls along the way. It is an unfortunate fact that the complexities and abuses that have developed alongside competitive tendering have meant that all too often the clients of the construction industry have been dissatisfied with the outcome.

Different procurement routes dictate different approaches to the tender process: historically, the client, advised by a master builder (the architect), would contract separately with contractors and specialists. These various contractors were co-ordinated on behalf of the client to create the completed construction project. Alternatively, the client accesses the industry via a single design and build contract, tendering all aspects of design and construction in a single price. Most commonly, however, clients let several contracts covering design and construction, and use competitive tendering to select some, or all, of the appointed organisations. For more detail on different procurement routes – see the chapter *Procurement route*.

8.1.2 The relationship between tendering and negotiation

The nature of competitive tendering, based upon a given set of parameters, is such that it is rarely possible to have absolute certainty on all issues. More commonly than not, tenders are not submitted as an inclusive single price, but are often accompanied by caveats qualifying that price. In such circumstances, the tendering process is followed by a negotiation. Such negotiations also follow situations where the tendered prices are higher than expected and there is then a need to reduce the price by changing the design and/or omitting certain elements. Post tender negotiations are problematic for public sector clients – see section 8.1.5. It is highly recommended that negotiations should be conducted before the letting of the contract, when the client's negotiating position is strongest.

8.1.3 The significance of parity of tendering

Tenders are meaningless unless put forward on the same basis. This is called parity of tendering. If contractors base their tenders on different information then the lowest tender may not have accurately priced the project. There is also the need to eliminate any small print which might qualify a tender so that what is being offered is different from that offered by another tenderer. It is vital to ensure that tenders are on the same basis, both to assist in selecting a contractor and also to ensure that the client accepts the best value offer.

8.1.4 The range of tendering elements

Traditionally, competitive tendering has been based substantially, if not exclusively, on price. When the design has been completed, and the works have been specified and even quantified, then (in theory at least) the only differentiating factor between the tenders is the price. The length of the contract period is usually determined by the client so that this is not a differentiating factor, although it is common to invite alternative tenders with the contractor selecting his optimum contract period. A slightly higher price may be offered for a shorter period but the saving for the client achieved by earlier completion may more than offset the higher price. The analysis of tenders in such circumstances is, however, still quite straightforward. But more recently there have been significant developments in procurement methodologies with price being only one of the selection criteria. Tenders are often invited on the basis of provision of alternative designs, reflecting different levels of quality, based upon different programmes, using different construction methodologies and other construction variables. In addition, more intangible factors may also be taken into account in selection including the contractors' understanding of the client's objective, the contractor's management team, his approach to health and safety and sustainability issues and the degree to which the client and his team feel the contractor is compatible with them. Yet a further element that is sometimes part of the offer is the ability to finance the construction works. Clearly when some, or all, of these variables are part of the tendering process, the analysis of the tender is far more complex and it is important to ensure that sufficient time is allowed properly to analyse the tenders. Very often it is necessary to hold meetings and to receive presentations to clarify exactly what is on offer before a final decision is made.

8.1.5 Tendering and partnering

Partnering is about the establishment of a long-term relationship with the award of repeat business in return for high levels of service and commitment. It is acknowledged that prices may be higher than might be received by competitive tendering but, in the overall analysis, the expectation is that the project (or, more likely, series of projects) will produce better value by earlier finishes, higher degrees of co-operation between contractor and client, fewer disputes and higher quality. Partnering pre-supposes a high level of trust being built up between the client and the contractor. Partnering does not sit completely comfortably with price competition. Nevertheless, partnering cannot achieve its objectives if the price paid for achieving higher levels of co-operation and the elimination of disputes is so high that the project becomes unviable. There is, therefore, a need to have some basis for fixing price. This

can be done by a tendering process where some prices are included in a competitive process, such as levels of overhead and profit, preliminary costs, labour constants and so forth recorded either formally or informally on a framework basis. Such prices would then be used as the basis for negotiating individual contracts. Alternatively, some form of benchmarking may be adopted where it is a condition of the partnering relationship and the award of repeat business that prices are benchmarked against other similar projects. Using expert and experienced advisors, it is possible to ensure that the contract prices are sufficiently close to competitive pricing levels to be confident that in overall terms the client is receiving good value for money.

8.1.6 The law and tenders in England

Except in relation to government contracts which are examined in the chapter *Public sector projects*, there is no statutory intervention into tender procedures. The law relating to tenders in England sits within the general framework of common-law rules relating to contracts. An invitation to tender made by or on behalf of a prospective client is not an offer to enter into a contract. It does not usually oblige the client to accept the lowest or any tender. It is merely an invitation to negotiate with those who respond. The contractor's tender to carry out the works is usually regarded as the 'offer'. The offer must be definitive, unqualified and unambiguous. Accordingly, it is usual practice to require conforming bids to be submitted even if tenderers also offer alternative bids as part of the tender process. If the offer is qualified in any way, then it cannot be accepted until the qualification has been removed by negotiation. So, for example, the practice adopted by many consultants and contractors of stating in tenderers that:

> …if our tender is of interest, there are one of two matters which we would wish to discuss with you on the terms and conditions of contract

prevents unequivocal acceptance of the tender without further negotiation.

8.1.7 Tendering cost

All tendering exercises carry with them a cost that has to be borne by the tenderers. Such tendering costs form a substantial part of a company's overheads and are passed back to clients in the overhead additions made on successful contracts. In other words, clients indirectly pay the tendering costs. It is important from the perspective of the costs incurred by the industry generally that tendering costs are kept to a sensible level. It should particularly be borne in mind that the cost of tendering is multiplied by the number of companies submitting tenders. There is a direct relationship between, on the one hand, the cost of tendering, the likelihood of success and the potential returns; and, on the other hand, the willingness of contractors to commit the necessary outlays required by any given tender in order to be competitive. Thus, if there are a very high number of tenderers, then it may well be that few or none are willing to commit the necessary resources to submit a competitive tender, so that a long tender list can have a counter-productive effect. If the cost of tendering is high, such as in a design and build contract where it is necessary to devote resources to producing designs as well as those necessary to price the project, then this inevitably means that there should be fewer tenderers. There is generally no obligation on the client to accept the lowest or any tender and the significant costs incurred by the contracting industry in submitting tenders are borne by it. In certain situations however, there may be an implied obligation on the client to consider a conforming tender in conjunction with other conforming tenders, and failure to do so will be a breach of contract. Though very much more developed in other Commonwealth jurisdictions, the English Court of Appeal has held in exceptional circumstances a tenderer is to be given some protection in law. (See comments in section 8.10.) Furthermore, if an invitation to tender is issued and it can be shown that the client has no intention of letting the contract to the person invited to tender or to one of a number so invited, the invitation is clearly fraudulent and an action will lie in the tort of deceit enabling recovery of expenses by way of damages. Examples here are few and far between because of the difficulties of proving fraud/deceit.

8.2 Tendering construction contracts

This section deals with the processes involved in tendering contracts to carry out construction works.

8.2.1 The process

The entire tendering process for main contract works starts with the identification of the need to approach the market place to obtain competitive prices to carry out the works and ends with the formal execution of the contract. The common steps in this process are as follows:

Pre-qualification

It is first necessary to determine which contractors are going to be able to submit bona fide tenders and are demonstrably likely to be able to complete the works satisfactorily. It is usually necessary to conduct a pre-qualification exercise in order to identify the tenderers. At one extreme the pre-qualification may be no more than a response to an advertisement such as those placed in the *Official Journal of the European Union* (OJEU) (Advertisements placed in the OJEU can be found online at http://ted.europa.eu). Where 'open tendering' is being used it may merely be necessary for prospective tenderers to put forward credentials demonstrating their ability to meet the criteria and applying for the tender documentation. Such a system is rarely followed since it results in a very high number of tenders of variable quality giving rise to high reproduction costs for the tender documentation, difficult evaluation and the receipt of

tenders from companies which, despite meeting the qualification criteria set out in the advertisement, are in fact unsuitable for the project for other reasons. In other words, this process tends to be very wasteful and is rarely, if ever nowadays, used. More commonplace is 'selective tendering', a system whereby firms are invited either through placing advertisements in the OJEU or by invitation to companies known to the client and/or his professional advisors, to submit pre-qualification information. **Table 1** sets out the sort of information that might be requested in a pre-qualification questionnaire. A significant problem in the industry is the wide diversity of formats in which pre-qualification information is requested, thereby imposing potential tenderers with increased overheads merely to responding to such pre-qualification questionnaires. General pre-qualification information can be obtained without the need to approach the individual contractor from Constructionline. Constructionline is a database, sponsored by the government, containing most contracting and consulting organisations that are active in the construction industry. Based on the information received, possibly in conjunction with interviews, a tender list is agreed. On many occasions, particularly in the private sector, the client and its advisors will agree a tender list based on their own experience and knowledge without the need to conduct a formal pre-qualification exercise.

Tender lists

It is important that the length of the tender list agreed by the client and his advisors is appropriate to the type of contract being tendered – see section 8.5 of this chapter for the recommendations on numbers of tenderers for the different types of contract. It is advisable that two reserves should be identified that can easily be slotted in should one of the chosen contractors withdraw. Once the list has been agreed, it is advisable to contact those on the list, preferably in writing, informing them of their selection and providing sufficient information about the contract to enable them to decide whether they are interested (such information might include anticipated value, size of project, type of project, location of project, professional team, client, type of contract, site information and any other relevant information) and to confirm that they are able and willing within the envisaged timescale to submit a bona fide tender. Any declining contractor at this stage can be replaced by the reserves.

Tender preparation

Tender documentation should be sent to the selected list of tenderers providing exactly the same information to each and should be sent out to each at the same time. A set time should be allocated for the return of tenders. The tender period allocated should be sufficient to reflect the size, nature and complexity of the project and the type contract envisaged. Tender periods usually range from three weeks where tenders involve the pricing of bills of quantities on a small project, up to three months on a design and build project where significant design

Category of information	Details required	Purpose
General business information	Name, company registration information, names of directors, membership of professional bodies	Establish unequivocal identification of organization and its bona fides
Financial information	Company accounts for (usually) past 3 years: parent company accounts; recent management accounts	Establish financial strength and capability of organization
Organization information	Company structure: staff and operative numbers and cost classifications; geographical areas of operation; sectors of operation	Establish organization type and operational capability
Project information	Information on recent projects undertaken similar (in size, type, complexity, location) to the one envisaged	Establish extents and depth of experience relevant to the project
Proposed personnel	Names of senior and intermediate personnel likely to be involved; CVs including qualifications and relevant experience	Establish relevant competence of personnel available for the project
References	Names and contact numbers of (usually) three clients	Establish a satisfactory track record
Project specific information	Comment on the specific project including, for example, method statement, programme, procurement	Establish project capability and approach
Health and Safety record, sustainability policies etc.	Details of past records, approach etc.	Satisfy CSR policies etc.

Table 1 Typical pre-qualification information

development is necessary in order to submit a tender. It may be appropriate to conduct meetings with the tenderers to ensure that they have adequately understood the requirements and where questions can be asked of the client to assist contractors in progressing their tender. Where clarification is given to one tenderer which is not commercially sensitive to that particular tenderer, then that clarification information should also be provided to the other tenderers to ensure parity of tendering. Tenders should be submitted in unmarked envelopes identifying that they contain a tender for the particular project, but not identifying which contractor is the tenderer. The tender envelopes should be opened as a formal process preferably by more than one person and the key elements (such as the price and construction period offered) noted on a proforma and signed as being the tenders submitted by those opening the envelopes. Late tenders should be excluded and the tender envelopes returned unopened.

Tender receipt and evaluation

Tenders should then be checked for completeness and accuracy and to evaluate the bids submitted. Evaluation will depend entirely on the type of contract envisaged and may be as simple as ensuring that the financial offer is complete and unqualified or as complex as evaluating a variety of different elements such as price, design, programme and methodology using evaluation criteria, usually predetermined, enabling the client to weight all the relevant factors and determine a preferred contractor.

In addition, a public authority must adhere to the following key principles of EU law when evaluating tenders:

- **Transparency**: The contracting authority must evaluate the tenders using objective criteria which are known to the tenderers in advance.

- **Fairness**: The requirements imposed upon tenderers by the contracting authority and the evaluation criteria must be related to the subject matter of the contract.

- **Equal treatment**: All tenderers and potential tenderers must be treated equally based on the same criteria and information, and the contracting authority must evaluate them in a non-discriminatory manner.

Please note that the principles set out above apply to all public contracts, even those which fall below the relevant threshold as set out in the Public Contracts Regulations 2006. In *JB Leadbitter & Co Ltd v. Devon CC*, Leadbitter submitted a tender after the expiry of the deadline set by the Council, and claimed that the Council's failure to consider its tender was a breach of its obligations under the Public Contract Regulations 2006, and furthermore claimed that the Council had breached its duty to treat tenderers equally and in a non-discriminatory way, as well as its duty to exercise proportionality. Although on the facts it was held that there was no evidence that the Council had acted disproportionately, the decision makes clear that a public body must exercise proportionality in its treatment of tenderers.

Clarification

Before it is possible to arrive at a preferred contractor is often necessary to seek clarification of certain issues raised as part of the tender and to negotiate the removal of qualifications attaching to the tender. It is also necessary to deal with any errors that have been found in the tenders and there are two established ways of dealing with any arithmetic errors:

(1) any arithmetic errors would be corrected and the tender adjusted with the tenderer asked whether he would like to stand by his original tender, or amend his tender to the adjusted figure; or

(2) any arithmetic errors should be notified to the tender who is then given the choice of standing by his original tender or withdrawing his tender.

It is usual that the method of dealing with arithmetic errors is notified to the tenderers prior to the submission of their tenders.

Selection

In all cases, the basis of selection should be the tender that, it is believed, represents the best value for money and not the tender that is merely the lowest price. The client should be wary that a low price is not merely the result of substantial errors which will create future difficulties for both the contractors and the client; or that it is due to poor tender documentation in which the contractor has spotted weaknesses which it intends to manipulate to its benefit at a later stage; or that it contains qualitative deficiencies which are not clearly apparent based upon the documentation submitted; or that the contractor is cynically buying the project with the intention of using every available avenue, fair or foul, to manipulate a higher-ultimate price or lower-quality product at the end of the project.

Appointment

It is then necessary to accept the successful tender, appoint a contractor and it is strongly preferable to do this in writing setting out the terms and conditions accepted. The appointment of a contractor can be made in one of several different ways – addressed in more detail in section 8.9.

8.2.2 Tendering different procurement routes and selection criteria

Very often it is the case that the final price paid by the client is very substantially different from the price tendered by the contractor. In truth, there are a number of variable elements inherent in a tender which are beyond the bottom line price submitted.

Different procurement strategies will affect the way the works are designed, the documentation used in tendering and a number of different tenders required within the development process. **Table 2** sets out the different tender process must be borne in mind. There are many bespoke and hybrid forms of procurement and it is always important to produce documentation that is appropriate to the particular circumstance rather than regurgitate standard or previously used documentation.

8.2.3 Two-stage tendering

Once a tender list has been formulated, selection can proceed on a single stage tendering basis, or a two-stage tendering basis. A single stage tender is one where prices and other information is submitted as a one off operation and a contractor is selected as a result of those tenders which represent a complete offer. Two-stage tendering is where less than complete information is used as a basis for tendering the first stage either to select a preferred contractor, or to eliminate all but, say, two contractors. The second stage would then be a negotiation of the complete contract, whether with one or both of the 'preferred' contractors. The complete contract is then signed following the second stage negotiation.

8.3 Tendering consultant contracts

8.3.1 Similarities/differences with construction tenders

A substantial amount of the last section also applies when tendering consultancy contracts. There is, however, one very real and important difference: construction tenders are geared to producing a product which has a clear definition whilst consultancy contracts are purely for the provision of a service where, more often than not, whilst the nature of the service may be known, the full extent and implications inherent in the provision of the service are not. The workload will depend upon a number of issues such as planning permission, building control, site conditions, the client's decision making process, client change of mind, performance of other consultants, the performance of the contractor, difficulties created by the contractor and so on. The time and, therefore, the cost of providing the service may differ very dramatically from one building to an apparently identical one. More significant than price, is the quality of the service provided. After all, it is highly detrimental to the client's ultimate needs if a designer is appointed because he offers the lowest price, when in fact the construction project is poorly designed and is inefficient to operate. Then, the saving in fees is dramatically outweighed by the detrimental effects of a poor service. It is imperative that the quality of the service being provided is given a high level of importance and, in this regard, reputation is probably the most significant factor in assessing that quality.

8.3.2 Price versus value

A major issue when tendering consultants' services is, therefore, the need to devise a means whereby all of the relevant considerations can be properly evaluated. The usual way of balancing price and service to arrive at 'best value' is by seeking a dual bid, with a financial offer and a qualitative proposal setting

A	B	C	D
Procurement Strategy	**Tender Options**	**Pricing Document**	**Comment**
1. Cost reimbursement	1.1 Percentage fee on prime cost (PC) 1.2 Lump sum fee (LSF)	1.1 Estimated price cost (EPC) 1.2 Estimated price cost (EPC) except in very unusual circumstances.	Contractor reimbursed all costs incurred (as defined) plus quoted fee. Not recommended
2. Management contact	2.1 Percentage or LSF fee on PC 2.2 Fee on PC; priced Preliminaries 2.3 Package tenders based on similar basis to 3, 4 and/or 6 below.	2.1 EPC 2.2 EPC and schedule of preliminaries 2.3 As 3, 4 and/or 6 below.	Management Contractor does not carry out works packages. All packages tendered on open-book basis. Major issue over whether management contractor is 'reimbursed' preliminaries or paid against quoted figures. Former can lead to uncontrolled expenditure; latter to abuses of costs passed down to package contractors (i.e. paid for twice by client).
3. Bills of approximate quantities (BAQ)	3.1 Priced, extended and totalled BAQ including preliminaries, measured work and subcontract work	3.1 BAQ	Rates inserted into BAQ should be extended and totalled to give 'approximate' contract value; care should be taken to avoid manipulative pricing designed to take advantage where quantities likely to change in final measure.
4. Single stage lump sum contract (not design)	4.1 Lump sum for work shown on drawings and described in specification 4.2 Bills of quantities (BQ)	4.1 Priced specification and/or schedule of works 4.2 BQ	4.1 should only be used for straightforward work where scope is clear and change unlikely 4.2 BQ gives advantage of clear basis for valuing works done and pricing change. Disadvantage that 'lump sum' really only relates to work described and measured in BQ and not necessarily work called for or implied from drawings/ specifications. Accuracy depends upon quality of documentation prior to tender. Open to abuse and thought by many to be unduly expensive.
5. Two-stage lump sum	*First Stage* 5.1.1 Overheads and profit (OH&P) 5.1.2 OH&P and priced preliminaries 5.1.3 OH&P, priced preliminaries and priced measured works (e.g. schedule of rates or BAQ) *Second Stage* 5.2.1 Tender by short-listed contractors with first stage tender information applied to and amplified on documents as 4.1 or 4.2 or hybrid documentation 5.2.2 Negotiation with preferred contractor based upon documents as 4.1 or 4.2 or hybrid Documentation	*First Stage* Documentation written to suit level of design and project development, usually in some form of schedule *Second Stage* Ultimate documentation should vary little from single stage documents	Two-stage process is usually used to identify a preferred contractor at an early stage to assist in design development/financing/construction advice etc, particularly in circumstances where the lead in period is short. Care should be taken not to create unwittingly a substantial contractual commitment without completing the second stage negotiations at least to a sufficiently advanced stage.

(continued)

A	B	C	D
Procurement Strategy	Tender Options	Pricing Document	Comment
6. Single stage D&B	6.1 Statement of requirements – simple document setting out spatial and qualitative information 6.2 Statement of requirements – more complex document using drawn as well as written information including, for example, site information, operational parameters and relationships, planning Constraints 6.3 Fixed brief for the building including detailed drawings as attached to and including planning permission 6.4 Substantially completed design contained in requirements document leaving only production design information to be provided by the contractor	6.1 Statement of price broader context than where the entire design is 6.2 Simple Price Schedule 6.3 Analysis of price in a variety of forms from elemental cost estimate to detail schedule of works to full or abbreviated bills of quantities 6.4 As for 6.3	Design and build procurement is used in a much provided by the contractor as part of a lump sum bid to meet a simply stated set of requirements. At the other extreme it can be successfully used where design is substantially complete but the issuance of final design details becomes a contractor responsibility, thereby avoiding the risk of such details being the centre piece of contractual claims.
7. Two-stage D&B	Two-stage D&B follows the principles of ordinary two-stage tendering but with design capability forming part of first stage and design proposals part of second	As 5 above	

Table 2 Tendering under different procurement strategies

out the service, approach, experience and the like. These two are then assessed independently, weighted and a decision made based on the resultant weighted score. A typical set of weighted qualitative assessments is shown in **Table 3**. Qualitative assessments, particularly in the public sector, need to be objective (see comments under 'Tender receipt and evaluation' under section 8.2.1), and as such they concentrate on the standard of the proposal documents submitted. In truth, this process does not really evaluate the quality of service but relies more on marking the firm's ability to submit a convincing proposal document. The true measure of quality of performance is best ascertained by assessing previous experience and the views of previous clients and others who have had direct working experience with the particular consultant. As the performance of the consultant is to a significant extent a subjective matter it is difficult to attempt to evaluate suitability without incorporating subjective views of performance into the evaluation with a high level of weighting. This is commonly the case when the private sector client chooses its consultants but appears to find little favour in the public sector because of the inability to provide a satisfactory audit trail on subjective issues.

8.3.3 Deliverability

It is important to establish the ability of a consultant to deliver the required service within the price quoted. It is totally counterproductive to base initial budgets on fee quotations if those quotations are inadequate. The range of prices received from consultant tenders usually vary much more dramatically than for construction works and often the range can be several hundred percent. This reflects both the difficulty in truly assessing the extent of work required in a fair and reasonable way. The reality with price tendering of consultant contracts is that it is actually far more difficult to achieve satisfactory outcomes than in tenders for construction contracts. Prices received should be judged with extreme caution. Assessment of anticipated resources with reasonable normal hourly rates should be made against the prices received to determine sufficiency and it is in the client's best interest that any bids which are significantly inadequate in this

PROJECT:			
SERVICE:			
COMPANY:			

QUALITY CRITERIA

Project organization	Weighting	Marks	Weighted marks
Details of proposed team	10		
Previous experience of team	15		
Previous experience of practice	10		
Proximity of office from site	10		
Proposed resources to be applied	15		
Ability to cope with peak demands	10		
Quality of team leader	20		
Experience of interface with IT	10		
Current workload 10			
Project execution			
Method of approach to design coordination	15		
Means of ensuring programme compliance	10		
Process of collating user requirements	10		
Means of ensuring compliance with EMG	25		
Means of establishing design freeze	15		
Method of establishing and controlling design changes	20		
Method of dealing with on site quality monitoring	15		
Method of dealing with snagging and project handover	20		
Quality			
Quality assurance methods	20		
Approach to CDM	10		
Attitude to environmental and security issues	10		
	Total mark		
	Tti quality		
		Mark/100	

Table 3 Consultant selection – example weighted assessments

respect should be rejected. Selection should be based largely upon the evaluation of the service and reputation, the price representing a very small element in the decision. However, please note that, in accordance with the Office of Government Commerce (OGC) guidance discussed below, experience may not be a basis for choosing a specific tenderer at the award stage.

8.4 Subcontract tendering
8.4.1 Traditional tendering

Very often, the subcontract tender process is carried out at least twice during a project duration. First, when a main contractor in preparing his tender, he needs to organise subcontract tenders for all trades and work which he is unable to supply

himself (nowadays, usually most). These tenders then form the basis of his own tender for the main contract. Some of these subcontract tenders are, however, for works considerably in the future and it is normal practice, therefore, to return to the market-place for updated tenders closer to the carrying out of the works. Very often subcontract tenders are less formal than the main contract tenders and they rely, to a considerable extent, on repeat business and a form of partnering. Generally speaking, however, the guidelines appropriate to main contract tenders are also appropriate to subcontract tenders.

8.4.2 Problems for the main contractors

Subcontract tenders are provided by organisations with a very wide variety of sophistication. It can sometimes be to the contractor's advantage that subcontractors are unsophisticated, but the reverse can be the case, particularly when the effect is that the enforceability of the subcontract is difficult due to the point blank refusal of a subcontractor to be bound by subcontract terms. In reality, the substance of the organisation is such that resort to law is futile so that the ongoing working relationship between main contractor and subcontractor is of very high importance. It is, nonetheless, important that subcontracts are on a back-to-back basis, as far as possible, with the main contract. For this reason, it is advisable to use a suite of contract forms which are compatible. This is obviously relevant in the area of contractual claims and it is contractor's objective to be able to pass all potential claims from subcontractors directly through to the client. Contractors should also be conscious of the higher likelihood of subcontractor liquidation and receivership which in inherent in organisations with very little financial substance.

8.4.3 Problems for the subcontractors

Subcontractors have very often been the whipping boys of the construction industry. Practices such as pay-when-paid clauses were commonplace, the contractor having no contractual obligation to pay the subcontractor until he received the money from the client. This practice has now been outlawed by the Housing Grants, Construction and Regeneration Act 1996. Design work is often carried out by specialist subcontractors but the cost of this design is recovered only once the works are underway and the subcontractor has, therefore, to fund these design works. There is obviously a significant risk where the design work is carried out without a firm subcontract order as the specialist subcontractor may not ultimately be awarded the subcontract. There is invariably a high degree of negotiation around subcontracts but very often the balance of power in the negotiations lies within the contractor as size and legal know-how are on the contractor's side as well as the gift of this and future work. It is advisable and in the best interest of the ultimate client that as much as reasonably possible is done to protect the subcontractor in these circumstances, including the insistence on standard forms and by selecting contractors who have a reputation for fair dealings with their subcontractors.

8.5 Tendering guidelines
8.5.1 Introduction

Against the backdrop of the boom years of the 1980s and the major recession of the early 1990s, a number of reports were commissioned by various sectors of the construction industry to see how the industry could operate more efficiently. Re-examination of selection/tendering procedures formed a significant part of most of these reports. This section looks at each of the reports in chronological order and then examines some of the Codes of Practice which ensued.

8.5.2 Construction procurement by government: an efficiency unit scrutiny: July 1995. Chaired by Sir Peter Levene

This excellent and far reaching report was designed to consider how government could ensure that it become a best practice client. It concluded that:

> As key clients of the industry, government bodies are far from blameless for the way in which it behaves ... to get the industry to change its way, government will have to change its own behaviour, practice and procedures.

Among a large number of very far reaching recommendations, the specific recommendations and actions points in relation to tendering are relatively limited.

Recommendation 17 required that:

> Departments, working with CUP [Central Unit On Procurement based in HM Treasury] should develop more effective arrangements to build up and share knowledge about the performance of particular firms and the construction market generally so that their decisions about tender lists and tender evaluations and about the appointment of consultants and contractors are better informed....

The rationale for this is that a better informed client will be more likely to get the invitation to tender right and be in a much stronger position when going through the process. It is also much more focused in judging tenders especially in evaluating criteria like experience and past performance.

Recommendation 20 requires that:

> Departments should examine the scope for partnering, provided that 'partners' are selected by a competitive process. Where for example they appoint consultants on term contracts, they should appoint at least two so that they have some basis for comparison and measuring performance on different jobs.

While the Levene Report concluded that fully developed partnering (with open books and very long-term commitments by the client) is not appropriate for Departments because they must be demonstrably open to new entrants and to market testing. Departments must realize that there is scope for wider application of partnering procedures and they are not inhibited by accountability rules or by EU constraints. This is in fact wrong: EU constraints do limit the scope for partnering in the public sector but do allow frameworks – see *Public sector projects* in this volume.

Generally, the Levene Report demanded that Departments give a client lead to the industry by avoiding the conflict arising from the linked issues of the government's supposed tender price policy and the alleged claims conscious culture of many in the industry especially main contractors. If price is the dominant or deciding factor on bids the scene is set for confrontation from day one. The Departments should tender with the aim of getting those who offer 'the best service'. They should also spurn wasteful tendering methods and reduce absurdly long tender lists. The Levene report required reduced lists: a maximum of three for design and build and six for others. It also urges better preparation of bids to cut-out re-tender costs. The Levene report too recognised the need to reimburse tenderers' cost particularly where Departments themselves increased the costs by making late changes.

8.5.3 Re-thinking construction: the report of the Construction Task Force to the Deputy Prime Minister, John Prescott, on the scope for improving the quality and efficiency of UK construction: July 1998. Chaired by Sir John Egan

The Construction Task Force was set up against the backdrop of deep concern that the construction industry was under-achieving both in terms of meeting its own needs and those of its clients. It identified five key drivers of change to set the agenda for the construction industry at large: committed leadership, focus on the customer, integrated processes and teams, a quality-driven agenda and commitment to people. In order to achieve integrated project processes, the four key elements were identified as product development, project implementation, partnering the supply chain and production of components. These, it concluded, were incompatible with competitive tendering. Accordingly, Egan insisted that the industry must replace competitive tendering with long-term relationships based on clear measurement of performance and sustained improvement in quality and efficiency. Specifically:

- An essential ingredient in the delivery of radical performance improvements in other industries has been the creation of long-term relationships or reliances through the supply chain of mutual interest. Alliances offer the co-operation and continuity needed to enable the team to learn and take a stake in improving the product.

- The industry must now go a stage beyond partnering and develop long-term alliances that include all those involved in the whole process.

- The criterion for the selection of partners is ultimately about best overall value for money not about lowest price. All players in the team share in success with proper incentive arrangements to enable cost savings.

- There must be an end to reliance on contracts.

- Discipline to relationships between clients and their suppliers must be based on the introduction of performance measurement and competition against clear targets in relation to quality, time-lines and cost. Such relationships are much more demanding and regarding than those based on competitive tendering.

- Alliancing saves tendering costs. The task force believes that value for money can be adequately demonstrated and properly audited through rigorous measurement of performance as outlined above. The Treasury with the Department for Environment, Transport and Regions (DETR) must consider the appropriate mechanisms further and give guidance to public bodies.

8.5.4 Code of Practice for the selection of main contractors: May 1997, Code of Practice for the selection of subcontractors: April 1997, produced under the auspices of the Construction Industry Board

As noted above, these Codes of Practice were commissioned by the Construction Industry Board. Both Codes specifically apply to competitive tendering processes: both single-stage and two-stage. The Code for the selection of subcontractors applies to the selection of subcontractors for work above £10 000 in value. Both Codes look at each step in the tender process in turn.

Tender list. The aim of the list should be to state a minimum number of comparable, competent suitable organisations willing and able to tender from whom compliant bids will be received. In-house tenderers may be included but other tenderers should know if they are. The criteria to be used in assessing tenders should be notified during the selection process and stated in the tender enquiry document.

The Codes note the criteria for qualification:

- Quality of work
- Performance record
- Overall competence
- Health and safety record
- Financial stability
- Appropriate insurance cover
- Size and resources
- Technical and organizational ability
- Ability to innovate
- For design and construct procurement, the capability to offer design (*only applicable to main contractors*).

Having devised the preliminary list, potential tenderers should be asked if they are willing to tender. This should establish anticipated available capacity and grasp an enthusiasm for the works. Details of the works, likely durations, number of tenderers to be invited to submit and details of the main contract client and relevant consultants should be given at this stage. The more information is given, the more likely compliant bids will be submitted. Briefing sessions may be appropriate. Again, the Codes prescribe maximum numbers of invitations to issue: maximum of six for traditional tenders (with two reserves) and a maximum of three for single design and build tenders (with one reserve) and five narrowing to two for two-stage design and build. If tender enquiry documents are not despatched within three months of the date of the confirmation of willingness to tender, those on the list should be asked to reconfirm.

Tender invitation and submission. The best available information should be prepared and issued under identical conditions to all tenders. The procedures for submission of tenders and the criteria for assessment should be clear and should apply equally. Multiple rounds of tendering should be eliminated. All parties should respect confidentiality. The Codes each set out at Annex One a list of the information which must be included in tender enquiry documents. The better the information, the better the tender. Standard forms of tender should be used where possible. The Codes stress the need for adequate time for tendering. The time required will vary from project to project and will be affected by size and complexity, the need for specialist design, the sourcing of unfamiliar or overseas products. For the recommended suitable periods for tendering, see **Table 4**.

If alternatives are acceptable in addition to compliant tenderers, this should be stated. If a tenderer raises a query, he should do so in writing and all responses should be circulated to all tenderers. If the contractor decides to amend the tender documents, all tenderers must be informed and if possible the time for submission of tenders extended where necessary. A deadline should be set after which queries will not be considered. Extensions to the tender period should not be necessary if adequate time has been allowed for preparation of tenders but again if one is granted all tenderers must be notified. Tenders should not be opened before the date and time stated for receipt. When opened, forms of tender should be signed and prices should be listed against the names of the tenderers. This list should be signed by the person opening the tenders. Late tenders should not be accepted.

Tender assessment. The principles of balance in quality and price must be applied and reference is made by the Codes to the CIB document *Selecting consultants for the team: balance in quality and price* (discussed in section 8.5.5 below). The tenders should be scored against the criteria stated in the invitations to tender. Tenderers cannot be assessed on an equal basis unless all submit compliant tenders. Any non-compliant tenders not accompanied by a compliant tender should be rejected. Further tenders may be necessary from the reserve list. If unsolicited tenders are received at any time during the process they should be rejected. It undermines the willingness of tenderers to put forward their best price in their initial tender. It may be necessary to interview tenderers in order to clarify or amplify their submissions but interviews must be carefully controlled to avoid the suggestion of supplementary rounds of tendering. Minutes should be taken. Changes to tender prices post-tender may be appropriate but only in very exceptional circumstances, for example, if programme or scope alter. Changes may also be appropriate in following up an alternative tender. Care should be taken to avoid practices such as second round tendering.

Tender acceptance. When selecting main contractors, the successful contractor should be formally notified as soon as negotiations and/or other post-tender procedures have been completed, the basis of the contract has been agreed and the client has decided to place the contract. If the main contract is in place, the subcontract tender should be accepted immediately. Otherwise, acceptance should occur after the main contract award. Following placing of the relevant contract, a list of compliant tender prices and tenderers should be available to tenderers on request. The names of the tenderers should not be matched to the prices. All unsuccessful tenderers should be informed and debriefed if appropriate. Throughout the Codes, great emphasis is placed on:

- the need to use unamended standard forms

- the need to avoid practices which encourage collusion

- the need to respect confidentiality.

8.5.5 *Selecting consultants for the team: balancing quality and price* (December 1996) produced under the auspices of the Construction Industry Board

The Code notes that the mechanism set out can be used where selection is based on quality alone with price simply negotiated and also where both quality and price form the selection criteria. The advice is compatible with the Public Services Contracts Regulations 1993, which have now been repealed and replaced by the Public Contract Regulations 2006. The Code identifies various steps in the selection and assessment processes:

Preparation of the brief. The role of the brief as the fundamental basis of the project is emphasised, but the fact that the client might need assistance in developing the brief is acknowledged. *Briefing the Team:* published by the CIB is referred to as the source of guidance on matters to be included in the client's brief. The Code acknowledges that feasibility studies may need to be carried out by either the client in-house or using outside professional advice before the level of professional team involvement can be properly judged. Any such appointment should be made only for the feasibility studies after which it may terminate or may be expanded. At this stage it may also be possible to establish the likely form of contract which itself impacts on the professional team involvement. From the brief, it should be possible to establish:

- preliminary contract strategy (procurement route)

- the make-up of the consultant's team

- the need for stage appointment of consultants

Contract type	Minimum tender time: weeks (for main contractors)	Minimum tender time: weeks (for subcontractors)
Design only	–	3
Construct only	8	6
Design and Construct	12	10

Table 4 Suitable periods for tendering

- the level of their individual involvement
- the sequence and programme of appointment (section 8.3)

The key steps in establishing the quality/price mechanism are:

- appointment of Tender Board to set and apply the mechanism
- the Tender Board should then establish the quality/price ratio appropriate to the project. Complexity, the degree of innovation and flexibility required in its execution are influencing factors. For examples see **Table 5**
- weighting of quality criteria: once the quality/price ratios are established, the Board must establish project-specific quality requirements to assess tenderers. The Code draws on the suggested weighing and key aspects provided by CIC's *Guidelines for the value assessment of competitive tenderers*. (See also **Table 3**.)
- marking and scoring: an objective rating system for assessment must be established using an absolute scoring system. The weighted mark is then calculated by multiplying the awarded mark by the project weighting for that criterion
- quality threshold: this is the absolute minimum quality score acceptable and must be determined by the client and established prior to the issue of tenders
- price scoring: the mechanism for evaluating the price is that the lowest price is given 100 points and 1 point is deducted from the other tenders for each one percentage point above the lowest.

Preparation of the tender list. Usually a long list should be drawn up which is then subjected to a pre-selection to reach the short list. The consultants register should be consulted. A pre-qualification questionnaire is then usually used to gather information from the long list in order to establish a short list. Two weeks should be sufficient to respond to it. Again, an objective scoring system should be used and excessively long or short lists should be avoided.

Preparation of the enquiry/tender invitation will usually comprise:

- letter of invitation which should list other tender documents and note how many tenderers are on the list
- instructions to tenderers including date and time of submission
- project brief
- consultant's brief setting out the services required of the consultant
- principles of assessment giving the order of priority and weighting
- questionnaire to draw out issues such as methodology, management, personnel, and so on

Type of project	Indicative quality/price ratio
Innovative projects	80/20
Straightforward projects	50/50
Repeat projects	20/80

Table 5   Example quality/price ratios appropriate to the project

- conditions of appointment
- basis of fee required
- insurance requirements for professional indemnity.

Tender assessment and award. Again, a series of steps is applied. These comprise:

- assessment of each tenderer's quality by the Tender Board without prior knowledge of the commercial terms in accordance with the marking system previously established: application of quality threshold if appropriate so that tenders below it can be discarded
- interviews arranged with preferred candidates with questions being asked on a common-structured basis so quality scoring can be reviewed afterwards
- price assessment on the basis outlined above. Extraordinarily low tenders should be reviewed and resource levels should be compared
- final quality/price assessment
- notification of award and debriefing.

The Code includes sample forms relating to each step of the process.

8.5.6 *Selecting the Team* (June 2005), produced by the Construction Industry Council

Selecting the Team (STT) sets out a systematic approach to selecting a team for a project based on a set of criteria that are collectively identified as critical to the success of the project, rather than simply selecting contractors, subcontractors and consultants on the basis of the lowest price. STT is a tool designed to assess the ability and merits of firms and organisations applying to work as an integrated team on a project, and sets out a two-stage process:

- Stage 1 consists of forming a selection panel, establishing and prioritising selection criteria and drawing up a shortlist of applicants.
- Stage 2 comprises evaluating the shortlisted applicants and choosing the best one for the relevant role.

Forming a selection panel. Membership of the panel which is to select members of the team to carry out the project should be as widely representative of the industry as possible to ensure that it contains a suitable range of views and opinions, and should include strong representation from:

- the client organisation
- the end user/s, who will ultimately be using the facility
- third parties with a vested interest in the project
- a partnering adviser (or independent client adviser).

The guidance recommends that the selection panel has no less than three and no more than 12 members, and once the selection panel has been assembled a co-ordinator should be nominated who should ensure that the selection process is fair for all parties throughout the STT process.

Selection Objectives. Selection objectives cannot be developed until the team has come to a conclusion about the project objectives and 'value criteria'. The guidance sets out various means by which the selection panel may explore selection factors, from simply brainstorming to the more structured format of a selection objectives workshop. Once the selection objectives have been determined, the selection panel must prioritise these objectives, following which a selection pack should be sent to all prospective applicants.

Selection Pack. The selection pack should contain all the information needed by any applicant so that it can provide the necessary responses from which the selection panel can make a reasonable assessment of its work. The guidance states that the selection pack should comprise all, or a considered selection from, the following: a strategic brief; a selection factor questionnaire ('Section A'); a request for a statement of quality ('Section B'); and a request for references ('Section C'). The strategic brief should include all project-specific requirements and constraints that may be pertinent, and should state any time or budgetary constraints. When the selection packs are returned the applicants' scores are to be compiled, with each of the three Sections A, B and C, earning a possible 100 marks towards a predetermined qualification benchmark. The ultimate goal of Stage 1 of the STT process is to narrow the field and create a shortlist of ideally three, but possibly more, applications. Each application should be evaluated against the set of pre-determined ranked selection factors drawn up by the selection panel.

Evaluating shortlist. Those firms that have made it to the shortlist should then be evaluated further. This will involve comparing in more detail the selection pack of each shortlisted organisation with the profiles of the selection panel. This will help to flag any particular concerns and areas of conflict. STT envisages that the applicants will be interviewed by the selection panel and that following interviews the panel should evaluate and ultimately select the most compatible and qualified organisation for the project. The co-ordinator of the selection panel should then compile the individual score sheets once all the short-listed firms have been evaluated.

8.5.7 Requirement to distinguish between 'selection' and 'award' stages of a public procurement, and to give suppliers complete information about the criteria used in both stages (29 April 2009), published by the Office of Government Commerce

This guidance sets out that a distinction must be maintained between the selection and award stages of a procurement process and the criteria which must be applied at each of these stages. At the selection stage contracting authorities may require suppliers to satisfy minimum levels of economic and financial standing and/or technical or professional ability, and this is often assessed by means of a pre-qualification questionnaire (PQ). The selection process should focus on the suppliers' characteristics and suitability in principle to provide the contracting authorities' requirements. At the award stage the employer should consider the merits of the eligible tenders to assess which tender is the most economically advantageous. When evaluating tenders at the award stage, contracting authorities may only use criteria linked to the subject matter of the contract. The guidance makes clear that contracting authorities must ensure that selection criteria are not used at the award stage, and that experience must not be a consideration at this stage, as such a consideration may perpetuate the advantage of an incumbent or previously used supplier to the detriment of other qualified candidates. Contracting authorities must also ensure that they disclose award criteria and weighting rules to tenderers, and should also disclose selection stage scoring and weighting rules and minimum requirements to suppliers.

8.5.8 Implementation of the remedies directive: OGC guidance on the 2009 amending regulations (December 2009), published by the Office of Government Commerce

On 17 December 2009, the OGC published guidance on the Public Contract (Amendments) Regulations 2009, which is covered in detail in the chapter *Public sector projects*. The OGC guidance on the 2009 Regulations is split into three parts:

- **Part 1: About the rule change, including transitional provisions** provides a summary of the background and scope of the rules introduced by the 2009 Regulations. It also provides an explanation of the obligation imposed upon a contracting authority to notify applicants when they are excluded from a procurement process prior to the decision awarding a contract.

- **Part 2: The new rules on the standstill period** explain the basis of the introduction of a standstill period, and the purpose of this mechanism as introduced by the new Regulations.

- **Part 3: The new remedies rules** offers guidance on the new rules, particularly on the remedy of ineffectiveness, explains the practical implications of ineffectiveness, and provides guidance on steps which may be taken to avoid breaching the Regulations. There are also appendices to the guidance which may be of practical use for both contracting authorities and prospective tenderers under a public procurement process in order to ensure that the process in question complies with the Regulations.

8.5.9 *Implementing e-tendering* (March 2010) published by the Office of Government Commerce

In November 2008, the Glover review recommended that the government should issue all tender documentation electronically by 2010, that such documentation should be kept as brief as possible, and that businesses should be permitted to tender electronically for all public sector contracts by 2010. This guidance is intended to ensure that government bodies and other public sector organisations which do not currently make full use of e-tendering should move to do so as soon as possible. It provides a brief description of e-tendering and its benefits, highlights the issues which need to be considered when using e-tendering, and gives pointers to further sources of information relating to this area.

8.5.10 Standard forms of tender

Various industry bodies produce standard forms of tender and/ or invitations to tender. The model forms with the GC/Works Contracts include an Invitation to Tender and a Schedule of Drawings, together with a Tender and Tender Price Form. The 1999 editions of the International Federation of Consulting Engineers (FIDIC) suite of contracts include letters of tender and the MF forms published for the Joint IMechE/IEE Committee by the Institution of Electrical Engineers include forms of tender. The Joint Contracts Tribunal (JCT) has published a Practice Note (Practice Note 6) on Main Contract Tendering as well as various Invitations to Tender and Tenders as part of its Works Contracts forms and the documentation for named or nominated subcontractors. The New Engineering Contract 3 (NEC3) suite of contracts also includes a sample form of tender.

8.6 Public sector tendering

Special considerations govern the award of public sector contracts, which are also subject to review under administrative law procedures. These issues are dealt with comprehensively in the chapter *Public sector projects* and are not referred to here.

8.7 The risk in tendering

The main risks that have to be identified and priced as part of all tender processes are set out in the following sections.

8.7.1 Ascertaining costs

The ease with which it is possible to determine the basic cost of any given contract depends entirely on the type of contract that is envisaged. On the one hand, a contract based upon bills of quantities is easy to assess as the amount of resource required is easily identified. The risk relates only to pricing levels, or purchasing ability, for the various items of resource. At the other extreme, PFI/PPP contracts need considerable work to determine how best to meet the client's outputs before levels of resources can be determined and then priced. However, the basic cost of providing the resources whether those resources be financial, personal or material based, will represent the substantial proportion of the total tender and it is vitally important that those skills exist to estimate both the levels of resources and the appropriate price.

8.7.2 Construction risk

Successful tendering relies on the ability to understand, assess and price all of the risks that are inherent in the construction works. These will of course vary very substantially, again depending on the type of contract, but all construction related contracts carry with them some level of risk. Too often in the past, risks have been ignored in the attempt to win business because of the high emphasis on pricing within the competition. In order to deliver the project on time and to the satisfaction of the client, it is essential that risk evaluation is a major factor in the preparation of tenders.

8.7.3 Overheads and profit recovery

This is an area that is relatively simple to determine. Over any reasonable period it is a matter of straightforward arithmetic to ascertain what the overhead and profit requirements are in relation to the value of contracts undertaken. It is, however, the area where, in the attempt to win a project, a project is deliberately under priced. The usual result of this is the inevitable attempt by the contractor to recover the short fall in overheads and profit by the manipulation of increases through disputes and by over-pricing of changes. The proper pricing of overheads and profit is, therefore, important for the wellbeing of the industry. Most contracting organisations have an overhead and profit requirement of at least 5% and up to 10% of contract value. No substantial contracting business is sustainable with overhead and profit recovery of 1% or 2% or even 3% of the contract value. Nonetheless, this is the level of return, added to contract costs, in many tenders. In evaluating companies' offers it is interesting to compare what is added for overheads and profit and what is achieved in the audited accounts. There is rarely very much correlation. What makes up the difference?

8.7.4 Inflation and market conditions

A major risk, particularly in the periods of low inflation that we have had for the last several years, is the actual level of inflation within the construction market. Few contracts nowadays have an inflation mechanism built into them over the construction period. The risk of anticipating inflation during the construction project is entirely the risk of the contractor. Of course, the main contractor tries to limit this risk by passing it down to his subcontractors. However, this strategy tends only to be successful for the earlier packages as sometimes, particularly with large projects, the subcontractor does not start work for several months or years after the tender is submitted and an unconditional fixed quote is not achievable. There is a considerable degree of exposure that rests with the main contractor.

8.7.5 The effect of change

Change can be derived from a number of sources; the client, force majeure, legislation, site conditions, planning conditions and so on. The degree to which the contractor is at risk for these changes depends upon the contract conditions. Where change is at the contractor's risk, the likelihood of change must be properly evaluated. Most changes, however, are derived for reasons for which the contractor is not responsible – in the main, the client's or designer's change of mind.

8.8 PFI/PPP/DBFO contracts

Public–Private Sector Partnerships have been dealt with in detail in *Public–private sector partnerships* in this volume and this section deals briefly with issues surrounding the tendering of such contracts.

8.8.1 Generic format

The generic format of PPP/PFI contracts, as described in *Public–private sector partnerships* assumes that the contractor accepts the risk of (as a minimum):

- the design of the asset
- the financing of the asset, both short and long term
- the construction of the asset
- some part of the operation of the asset, usually at least the building and engineering maintenance and life-cycle replacements.

Clearly, this is more than a construction contract. The tendering and the selection process is, therefore, more complex and more drawn out than any construction or consultancy contract.

8.8.2 Tendering process

There are a number of potential formats for a tender for the PFI/PPP contract but the most common is in the form of an annual charge for a given concession period (commonly in the order of at least 25 years). This single price is subject to some inflationary mechanism and to other price adjustments periodically following market testing or benchmarking exercises. The difficulty in analysing tenders is that the single annual price, described as an annual unitary charge or an annual rental, is made up of a large number of different prices which, in more traditional circumstances, would be tendered quite independently including:

- lead design fees (architect or engineer)
- support design fees (e.g. structural engineers, services engineers, town planning, acoustic design etc.)
- quantity surveying fees
- land purchase costs (not always)
- property advisor's and agent's fees
- construction cost
- specialist equipment
- fittings and furniture

- short-term funding based on the cost of funds, margin and MLAs
- long-term funding based on the cost of funds, margin and MLAs
- lender's legal fees
- lender's due diligence costs
- loan arrangement fees
- supplier's set-up costs
- facilities management fees
- facilities management set-up costs
- supplier's financial advisor costs
- supplier's financial modelling costs
- supplier's legal fees
- rolled-up development interest
- development returns
- income from sale of land or other assets
- maintenance costs
- annualised costs of replacements over concession period (i.e. annual sinking fund for replacements)
- cleaning costs
- security costs
- facilities management costs
- supplier's management costs
- costs for senior debt
- costs for subordinated debt
- returns on equity.

In addition, there are other costs which are common to all construction projects and which are also reflected in the annual charge such as:

- planning fees
- building regulation fees
- corporation tax
- non-recoverable VAT
- insurance
- specified reimbursements to the client body
- planning Section 106 contributions
- other taxes and levies that are relevant.

Tendering evaluation and selection is consequently complex. The normal tendering process employed is as follows:

- Ascertain the level of interest in the market-place through informal contact with perspective bidders.

■ Ascertain formal expressions of interest through advertisements. In the case of public sector contracts over a contract value of £ must be tendered in the *Official Journal of the European Community (OJEU)*.

■ Send out pre-qualification questionnaire to be completed by those expressing interest.

■ Select long list of six to twelve bidders (numbers depending on the size, nature and complexity of the project and the number of respondents to the advertisement).

■ Seek further information from respondents to reduce to short list of no more than four and usually three.

■ Sometimes an additional stage can be inserted between long list and short list referred to as an invitation to supply outline proposals (ISOP).

■ Send out documents to be used as basis for preparing a priced proposal usually refers to as Invitation to Negotiation (ITN) documents.

■ Based on ITN proposals, select short list of two (or sometimes three) as final short list.

■ Send out refined documents for final short list to submit best and final offer (BAFO).

■ Following receipt of BAFO submissions, carry out negotiations to identify best value proposal and to ensure that affordability and value for money criteria are capable of being met.

■ Select a preferred contractor, usually referred to as preferred bidder or preferred partner.

■ Negotiate detailed contract conditions and work up all details of the scheme including design, management and facilities proposals.

■ Based on final proposals, submit full business case (FBC) for approval.

■ Once FBC approval is given and negotiations are complete, enter into contractual commitment (contractual close) and the financial commitment (financial close).

8.8.3 Evaluation of tenders

Evaluation is generally carried out by a team drawn both from the client organisation and from outside advisors and consultants. The client's team would normally include legal advisors, financial advisors, technical advisors, construction and facilities advisors, a project sponsor and a project manager. An evaluation of tenders is normally made against pre-set criteria which are published to the tenderers in advance of the tenders being submitted. An example of typical PFI tender evaluation criteria is given in **Table 6**.

8.9 Turning tenders into contracts
8.9.1 Introduction

This section looks at what happens after a tender has been submitted and evaluated. It examines when and how a contract arises and the effect of various commonly used terms and practices.

A Tender requirements	B Main evaluation criteria	C Sub-criteria	D Weighting
Technical content	Service delivery	Satisfy output specification	
		Flexibility	
		Specialist provision	
		Maximize income	
	Project management	Project structure	
		Programme	
		Control procedures	
	Design	Aesthetics	
		Adjacencies	
		Environmental	
		Planning impact	
	Facilities management	Hard services	
		Soft services	
		Replacement reserve	
		Risk transfer	
Deliverability	Funding	Cost of funds and margins	
		Debt:equity ratios	
		Cover ratios	
		Senior debt support	
		Subordinated debt support	
		Equity support	
	Construction	Programme	
		Methodology	
		Phasing	
		Commissioning	
		Decanting strategy	
	Removals	Temporary arrangements	
		Organisation	
Quality	Overall	Comprehensiveness	
		Co-ordination	
		Compatibility	
		Added value	
	Quality assurance	Design	
		Construction	
		Operation	
	Management	SPV structure and management	
		Client liaison and co-ordination	

(continued)

A	B	C	D
Tender requirements	Main evaluation criteria	Sub-criteria	Weighting
		Construction variation management	
		Change management	
		Dispute resolution	
Price	Annual charge	Comparative cost	
		Public sector comparator	
		Affordability	
		Value for money	
		Risk transfer	
		Land subsidy	
		Third party income generation	
	Price mechanism	Availability	
		Performance adjustments	
		Benchmarking/ market testing	
	Inflation mechanism	Index	
		Risk	

Table 6   Example PFI tender evaluation criteria

8.9.2 Letters of intent: different types

The term is used to embrace a number of different contractual arrangements. Enormous care is needed in the formulation of a letter of intent to ensure that the correct relationship is created. The different forms of letters of intent are summarised below and in each case reference is made to a particular reported case to give an example of the wording used. A letter of intent ordinarily expresses an intention to enter into a contract in the future but creates no liability in regard to that future contract. In other words, it may have no binding effect. That is not however always the case and the following types of letter of intent arise in practice:

> The letter of intent constitutes an interim contract so that the contractor is entitled to interim costs for the work undertaken by the contractor after the date of the letter of intent. If the intended future contract is not made, it may also be construed as containing other obligations, e.g. in relation to the quality of work done. A good example of this type of letter of intent arose in the case of *Turriff Construction Limited v. Regalia Knitting Mills Limited.*

Facts. Turriff submitted a tender to Regalia for a design and build project. Negotiations took place. The work was urgent. It was impossible to sign a formal contract because several matters and terms remained to be agreed. Regalia sent Turriff a letter which stated:

> As agreed at our meeting on 2nd June 1969…it is the intention of Regalia to award a contract to Turriff to build a factory…phase 1 to be on a fixed price basis…the commencing date to be 1st August and the terms of payment to be negotiated…All this to be subject to obtaining agreement on the land and leases…The whole to be subject to agreement on an acceptable contract.

Work could not start on the planned date but Turriff prepared a detailed design and negotiated with Regalia's architect over terms of contract. They discussed the issue of an 'indemnity' in respect of work to be done by Turriff before the contract could be signed. Turriff applied for an interim payment of £3500 for design work. The project was then cancelled and Regalia denied liability.

Judgement. There was an ancillary contract for the preliminary costs claimed, albeit no contract for the project since this was still being negotiated. Regalia was obliged to pay Turriff for all of the services provided after the meeting of 2 June 1969. The Judge noted that normally letters merely expressed in writing a party's present intention to enter into a contract at a future date and that, save in exceptional circumstances, they would not have binding effect. However, what happened on the facts of this case was more than this: he looked at the background to the issue of the letter quoted and noted that minutes of meetings suggested that the letter was to provide, in Regalia's own words, *'indemnity'* in respect of work done between 2 June and the execution of the contract. Clearly no design and build contract for the whole job had come into existence but Turriff had offered to proceed with urgency provided it had an *'indemnity'* from Regalia. The letter issued amounted to acceptance of that offer.

The letter of intent creates an entitlement to be paid on a quasi-contractual basis but without creating a formal contract for the project. Here, the case of *British Steel Corporation v. Cleveland Bridge Engineering Company Limited* provides a good example.

Facts. CBE sent to BSC a letter of intent against the backdrop of incomplete negotiations and no formal contract stating:

> We are pleased to advise you that it is the intention of [CBE] to enter into a subcontract with your company…the price will be as quoted in your telex…the form of sub-contract to be entered into will be our standard form of sub-contract…a copy of which is enclosed for your consideration…We understand that you are already in possession of a complete set of our detailed drawings and we request that you proceed immediately with the works pending the preparation and issuing to you of the official form of sub-contract.

BSE were not in possession of a full set of drawings and did not reply expecting a formal offer shortly. They did not agree the conditions of subcontract or the price as noted. But they began preparation for manufacture so as not to delay deliveries. There were further discussions about specification and programme issues. Despite outstanding matters, it was agreed that BSE should proceed with the first casting. Further, technical problems arose and there were further discussions about price and delivery, deliveries of steel nodes, however, continued despite the failure to agree contract terms. A steelworkers' strike caused further delays. CBE made no payment but submitted to BSE a claim for damages for late delivery. BSE in turn claimed payment for goods sold and delivered in quasi contract as a quantum meruit (i.e. reasonable costs plus profit).

Judgement. The letter of intent was no more than a statement of intention: it created no contractual obligations. BSC was not contractually bound but was entitled to a quantum meruit as compensation for CBE's unjust enrichment. With no contract, CBE had no claim for damages against BSC. This case was different from the Turriff case because the request to proceed was qualified by the reference to the fact that it was *'pending the preparation and issuing…of the official form of sub-contract'*. The parties were quite clearly still in negotiations and had not agreed primary obligations in relation to quality and time for performance. The parties had made no contract at all.

However, please note that the case of *Diamond Build Ltd v. Clapham Park Homes Ltd* made clear that where a letter of intent is deemed to be legally binding and there is a cap on the liability of the employer under the terms of the letter, the contractor's right to payment will be limited to that cap, even if the contractor carries out work exceeding the value of the cap set out in that letter.

Where the letter of intent sets out the basis of contract and provides for reimbursement of reasonable costs. This is perhaps a more common version of the letter of intent. It is illustrated by the case of *Sims (CJ) Ltd v. Shaftesbury plc.*

Facts. The builder submitted a tender. The owner responded with a letter of intent which advised that the builder would be awarded the contract on the terms of JCT 1980 but that works should start at once. The letter further stated that if the contract did not proceed the builder would be reimbursed reasonable costs *'such cost to include loss of profit and contributions to overheads, all to be substantiated by our quantity surveyor'.* The dispute related to whether the builder had to substantiate all costs or merely the profit and overheads element.

Judgement. The builder had to establish all costs. The letter of intent established a contract on a cost plus basis for work done under it.

The letter of intent may be construed as creating an 'if' contract so that if the contractor carries out certain work he is entitled to be paid for it. Here a good example appears in the case of *Monk Construction Limited v. Norwich Union Life Assurance Society.*

Facts. The project manager issued to the builder a 'letter of intent' which stated that 'our client instructs us to authorise you to proceed with preliminary work to a maximum expenditure of £100 000. In the event that no contract is concluded with you, your entitlement is limited to proven costs incurred

by you in accordance with the authority granted by this letter'. Two months later the builder was asked to start main contract works. He wrote to the project manager confirming commencement 'for the client's benefit under the terms of the letter of intent without prejudice to the contract terms on which we are not yet agreed'. No formal contract was executed. The question was whether the letter of intent created an 'if' contract and, if it did, did that cover the main contract work?

Judgement. The letter of intent authorized the builder to expend only up to £100 000 on preliminary works but did not mention main contract work. The 'proven costs' stipulation applied only to the situation where no contract was concluded and no main contract work was carried out: the term was not intended to apply to any work done under the main contract. Accordingly, the cap did not apply to further work carried out at the project manager's request, which work was to be paid for on a quasi-contractual basis (as in *British Steel v. Cleveland Bridge* above). There was no 'if' contract here in respect of the main work. An 'if' contract arises where a standing offer is held out that if the builder performs, the client will pay and the contract becomes binding when the builder, by its performance, accepts the offer.

The letter of intent as pure 'letter of acceptance': here the letter of intent unequivocally accepts the tender offer. This type of letter of intent is looked at in more detail later.

8.9.3 Letters of Intent: expiry

There are obvious dangers for a client who allows a project to proceed (and in some cases to be completed) on the basis of a letter of intent which does not incorporate all the terms envisaged by the formal contractual documentation. A good example of this is provided by the case of *Tesco Stores Ltd v. Costain Construction Ltd.*

Facts. Tesco issued a letter of intent to Costain stating that it was its intention to enter into a formal contract on Tesco's standard documentation under which Costain would be engaged to design and build a new supermarket. Costain signed and returned a copy. In the course of later alteration works at the store, a fire broke out causing substantial damage. Tesco argued the spread of the fire was due to the absence of proper fire stopping measures. It brought claims against Costain. Under Tesco's standard documentation, Costain would have assumed liability for design as well as construction, notwithstanding that Tesco had separately engaged architects. Costain relied upon the fact that there was no formal contract to argue that it had not accepted contractual responsibility for the design. Tesco alleged that the terms of the standard documentation had been incorporated because the parties had conducted themselves in a manner that would have been appropriate if the contract had been completed and come into effect; it was Tesco's position that 'offer' and 'acceptance' were not relevant.

Judgement. Tesco's argument was rejected. While there was a contract between the parties, it was a 'simple contract' in the terms of the letter of intent. The express term of that contract was that Costain would commence construction in advance of making a formal contract and in return Tesco would pay Costain. While Costain accepted responsibility for its own works, it had not accepted responsibility for the work of the architects or other professionals retained by Tesco. There were implied terms in the contract that Costain would perform any construction work under the contract in a good and workmanlike manner and that any design element would be reasonably fit for its intended purpose. However, it had not accepted responsibility for the whole design of the project. It was also not a term of the contract that the limitation period in respect of breaches would be 12 years.

There are also dangers for a contractor who carries on working after the expiry of the letter of intent. This is highlighted by the decision in *Mowlem plc (T/A Mowlem Marine) v. Stena Line Ports Ltd* a case where the parties accepted that the letters of intent entered into between them operated as 'if' contracts but differed as to their interpretation of those contracts.

Facts. Mowlem carried out works for Stena in relation to the construction of a new ferry terminal. The works were carried out under a series of letters of intent issued by Stena. The last letter of intent confirmed Stena's commitment to expenditure up to a maximum of £10 million. This was stated to enable Mowlem to proceed with the works until 18 July 2003. Mowlem continued to carry out works after 18 July which it alleged were over a value of £10 million and claimed that it was entitled to be paid a reasonable sum for those works on the basis of an implied term in the letter of intent.

Judgement. There was no such implied term and it would be contrary to commercial common sense if the financial limit could be avoided by Mowlem simply exceeding the limit and continuing work after 18 July. There was no evidence to suggest that Stena had conducted itself in such a way as to lead Mowlem to believe that it would not seek to rely upon the terms of the last letter of intent; there was no request or instruction to Mowlem to complete the works; and there was no evidence of any waiver by Stena as to its rights to rely on the terms of the letter.

Where work proceeds after the expiry of the letter of intent with the consent of the client but without a contract in place, the question arises as to how the work is to be valued. This is illustrated by the case of *ERDC Group Ltd v. Brunel University*.

Facts. ERDC submitted a tender for the construction of a new sports facility at Brunel's Uxbridge campus. The university did not want to enter into final contractual documentation until full planning permission had been granted. Instead, it issued a number of 'letters of appointment' instructing ERDC to carry out certain work. The letters stated that the work would be paid for in accordance with *'the normal evaluation and certification rules of the JCT standard form of building contract with contractor's design'*. The last letter expired on 1 September 2002 but ERDC continued work on site until March 2003. In November 2002, the University issued contract documents for signature by ERDC. The latter refused to sign them and argued that it was entitled to be paid for all the work it had

carried out on a quantum meruit basis. The basis for the quantum meruit valuation, argued ERDC, was its costs in carrying out the work, together with a reasonable amount for profit.

Judgement. The letters of appointment were binding contracts. Under those letters, the work carried out was to be valued according to the JCT valuation rules. Once the letters of appointment expired, there was no contract between the parties. While the basis of recovery for work completed during the period when there was no contract was therefore quantum meruit, the same rates (i.e. the JCT rates referred to under the letters of appointment) were to be used: it was not appropriate to move from a rates-based assessment to one based upon ERDC's costs.

RTS Flexible Systems Ltd v. Molkerei Alois Muller GmbH & Co KG established that in certain circumstances, following the expiry of a letter of intent, where parties have negotiated terms 'subject to contract' and all the terms of the contract have been agreed, a binding contract will be deemed to have been formed.

Facts. RTS and Muller had entered into negotiations regarding RTS supplying and installing machinery for Muller. Although the parties had intended that a written contract would set out the terms on which the work was to be carried out, work had begun before the terms were finalised. The parties entered into a letter of intent, which provided for the agreed contract price and contemplated that the contract terms would be based on 'MF/1' terms. By July 2005, a draft final contract was produced, which stated that it would not become effective until each party had exchanged signed contracts. This was never done, but with all terms having been agreed substantial works were carried out, and the agreement was later varied. The issue was whether, after the expiry of the letter of intent, the parties had entered into a contract and, if so, on what terms.

Judgement. By 5 July 2005, the parties had reached an agreement designed to operate as a composite whole, and none of the issues outstanding were regarded as crucial matters requiring agreement before the contract could be binding, and on the facts in this case it was held that a contract had been formed. The judges made clear that the assessment of whether or not a contract has been formed in any given circumstances depends on the facts of the specific case in question.

8.9.4 Acceptance

An unequivocal tender may be accepted at any time after it has been made unless, before it is accepted, it is expressly withdrawn or it is rejected (after which it cannot be revived except with the tenderer's agreement) or if it is revoked by a counter-offer.

It is common practice in the construction industry to stipulate that tenders remain open for acceptance for a certain period. Clearly, upon the expiry of this period the offer lapses and can no longer be accepted but, even within the period, the offer can be withdrawn at any time by the tenderer even though the period stipulated in the invitation has not expired. The use of bid deposits which are forfeited if tenders are withdrawn or bid bonds which can be called in the same circumstances are devices designed to protect clients from abortive costs which they may incur in these circumstances.

There is an acceptance of the offer bringing a binding contract into existence when the client unequivocally accepts the offer and communicates to the contractor that acceptance. If the acceptance contains new terms which were not contained in the original tender, then it amounts to a counter-offer which revokes the tender offer. The steps of offer and counter-offer are very frequent aspects of negotiations on construction contracts and the analysis required to ascertain the moment when agreement has been reached and the parties have genuinely concluded a contract is not always easy. It is for this reason that it is undeniably good practice to issue a formal letter of acceptance once final agreement has been reached in a long-running negotiation and, ideally, to execute a formal written agreement (see also section 8.9.7).

Once unequivocal acceptance has occurred and a contract has arisen, a party seeking to introduce a new term after that critical point will of course be seeking to renegotiate the terms of an existing contract and this can only be done with the express agreement of the other party. It is inevitably difficult to determine sometimes whether this sort of renegotiation is being contemplated or whether in fact this is an aspect of continuing negotiations about the original terms of the contract.

8.9.5 Effect of the phrase 'subject to contract' or 'subject to board approval'

The phrase 'subject to contract' means subject to and dependent upon a formal contract being prepared. It will usually be construed as meaning that no contract can arise until the formal contract is executed. It is important in commercial negotiations and plays a part in risk allocation. By use of the term, the parties guard against contractual force without more detailed discussion and agreement. Use of the term demonstrates lack of willingness to be bound. A good example appeared in the case of *Regalian Properties plc v. London Docklands Development Corporation (LDDC)*.

Facts. LDDC accepted Regalian's offer *'subject to contract, valuation, quality of design and the obtaining of detailed planning consent'*. Delays ensued while design and budget schemes were prepared at LDDC's request. Design costs increased. Further negotiations took place but no contract followed. Regalian sought a quantum meruit payment for expenses incurred. It argued that both parties had intended to bring about a contract and consequent to that understanding they had incurred expense to the benefit of LDDC.

Judgement. LDDC was not liable. By the deliberate use of the words *'subject to contract'* both parties accepted that if no contract was entered into any resultant loss would lie where it fell. Either party could have withdrawn without legal consequence from the negotiations at any time. Although LDDC encouraged Regalian to incur costs, it was in an attempt to

satisfy LDDC's requirements before a contract could be entered into. It was not directly requested by LDDC so as to create any liability on their part to reimburse those costs. There was no ascertainable benefit accruing to LDDC and they obtained no copyright in the designs. The parties were in negotiation, subject to contract.

Apart from *'subject to contract'*, other conditions sometimes appear in invitations to tender/acceptances, for example, *'subject to board approval'*, *'subject to loan sanction'* or *'subject to satisfactory planning permission'*. It is a question of construction whether the condition is a condition precedent to the contract coming into being or a condition of the contract itself: in other words, whether the parties are bound at all or whether they are bound but subject to the contract being cancelled if the condition does not occur. If work is carried out in anticipation of an approval not subsequently obtained then, of course, there may be an argument that the contractor is entitled to remuneration on a quasi-contractual basis.

Alternatively, while the main contract may be *'subject to contract'* and not binding, a more limited, interim contractual arrangement may have been created. A example of this situation is provided by the case of *Skanska Rasleigh Weatherfoil v. Somerfield Stores Limited*.

Facts. An invitation to tender was sent to Skanska on behalf of Somerfield. Skanska sent in its tender with a list of 'salient points'. Following consideration of this, further tender documentation was sent to Skanska and further exchanges of correspondence followed. Somerfield then sent Skanska a letter headed 'subject to contract'. The letter expressed Somerfield's desire to appoint Skanska to provide maintenance services to Somerfield on the terms of a draft facilities management agreement (FMA). The letter made it clear that the appointment was *'strictly subject to contract, and to the approval of… [Somerfield's] board'*. The letter went on to say that, while the parties were negotiating the terms of the FMA, Skanska should provide the services 'under the terms of' the draft of the FMA enclosed with the tender until 27 October 2000. Skanska carried out services and the 27 October date was extended twice expressly, first to 26 November 2000 and then to 21 January 2001. There was no further express extension but Skanska continued to carry out services. Meanwhile, the parties continued to negotiate the terms of the FMA, including 'timing-out' provisions to the effect that, if Skanska did not submit an invoice within a certain period, Somerfield would not be liable to pay it. Somerfield expressed dissatisfaction with Skanska's performance and a dispute arose between the parties as to the terms of the contractual relationship between them, particularly after 21 January 2001. Somerfield started to implement the timing-out provisions even though the FMA had not been signed by Skanska. The court had to consider whether the statement in the letter of that services were to be provided 'under the terms' of the draft FMA meant all of the terms of the draft FMA were incorporated or only some of them; whether the contract created by the letter continued in force after 21 January 2001; and whether or not Skanska was bound by the 'timing-out' provisions.

Judgement. Only those terms of the draft FMA that were necessary to define 'the Services' to be carried out by Skanska were incorporated. After 21 January 2001, the parties continued to conduct themselves on the basis that an agreement between them was subsisting. On that basis, the contract continued until and unless they agreed on some other contractual basis. There was, however, no binding agreement between about the 'timing-out' provisions. The fact that this was an interim arrangement only, pending the negotiation of an acceptable FMA, was demonstrated by Somerfield's use of the phrase 'subject to contract' and its distinction between 'the Contract' (used to refer to the FMA) and 'the Agreement' (used to refer to the letter of intent).

Other difficulties can arise when, despite apparent acceptance, the employer lacks the necessary powers to contract, for example, where a statutory corporation purports to enter into a contract which goes beyond its powers as set out in the act of parliament which created it, that purported contract is ultra vires and therefore void. Local authorities must make standing orders with regard to the making of contracts by them or on their behalf for the execution of works but usually a person entering into a contract with a local authority is not bound to enquire whether the standing orders have been complied with and non compliance does not usually invalidate any contract entered into on its behalf. However, questions do arise as to the authority of persons purportedly acting on behalf of the local authority.

Where parties actually perform obligations under a document which is stated to be 'subject to contract', the agreement can no longer be considered conditional. This is illustrated by the case of *Rugby Group Ltd v. Proforce Recruit Ltd.*

Facts. Proforce and Rugby signed a document which contained 'proposals' for a service cleaning contract and which stated that Proforce would supply workers to Rugby and would also purchase from Rugby items of cleaning equipment. The document, which incorporated Proforce's standard terms and conditions, stated that it was 'subject to contract'. Proforce purchased the equipment and supplied the workers. Additional labour was then sought by Rugby from third parties and Proforce claimed that Rugby had breached part of the agreement which stated that Proforce was to hold 'preferred supplier status' during the term of the agreement. One of the arguments put forward by Rugby was that the document was not enforceable as a contract because it contained the words 'subject to contract'.

Judgement. The agreement could not be considered as being conditional because after it was signed the parties carried out their obligations under it. While generally, except in very strong and exceptional cases, the effect of the words 'subject to contract' prevented a contract from coming into existence, the parties to this agreement were taken to have entered into a binding contract on the terms of the agreement.

8.9.6 Acceptance by conduct

Although it has limited application in the case of construction contracts, it is possible for acceptance of a tender to be evinced by conduct which shows an intention to accept the terms of the tender. It is a question in each case whether conduct shows such an intention. So, a client who, without any express acceptance, or counter-offer, permits a contractor to carry out work pursuant to a tender submitted by the contractor can be bound by the terms of the tender.

8.9.7 The execution of documents

As noted above, no formal requirements are necessary to give rise to a contract. It may be written, oral or partly oral and partly in writing. It is this fact which causes the difficulties in relation to negotiation of construction contracts which are outlined above. As a result, it is good practice to sign a binding contract. It clarifies the question of when a contract has arisen and avoids the offer/counter-offer debate. It clarifies precisely the terms of the contract and which documents are to form part of the contract. In the case of the client, it may have the additional advantage, if the contract is executed as a deed, of creating a twelve-year limitation period for claims for breach of contract rather than the period of six years which exists in the case of a simple contract (for discussion of limitation periods: see the chapter *Law of tort*). There are also requirements for the contract to be in writing for the provisions of the Housing Grants, Construction and Regeneration Act 1996 to apply. Most standard forms of contract publish as part of the suite a formal contract agreement. So Institution of Civil Engineers (ICE) Conditions of Contract contain a form of agreement comprising simple reciprocal obligations on the parties to carry out works and to pay for them respectively together with a list of documents incorporated into the agreement. Under clause 9 of the ICE Conditions the contractors are required to enter into the formal agreement even though the acceptance of contract may have been carried informally. In the case of the JCT, it is assumed that the Articles of Agreement are executed when the contract is made. Where a formal contract is subsequently concluded, not only will it usually be interpreted as superseding any previous agreement, but in the absence of indication to the contrary, it will be treated as applying retrospectively so as to validate actions or claims under the contract in respect of the period prior to execution of it.

8.10 Tender abuses
8.10.1 Recovery of tender costs

As noted in above, there is generally no obligation on the client to accept the lowest or any tender and the costs of tendering are borne by the tenderer. In certain situations, however, where there has been abuse of the process, the courts will impose implied duties on the client to consider a conforming tender in conjunction with other conforming tenders, and failure to do so will be a breach of contract. Though very much more developed in other Commonwealth jurisdictions, the English Court of Appeal has held in exceptional circumstances a tenderer is to be given some protection in law.

By way of example, in *Blackpool and Fylde Aero Club Limited v. Blackpool Borough Council.*

> The Council do not bind themselves to accept all or any part of the tender. No tender which is received after the last date and time specified shall be admitted for consideration.

The club's tender was duly delivered well before the deadline but the Council staff did not empty the letter box on the deadline. The box was emptied the next day and consequently the club's tender was date stamped and endorsed 'late' and not considered by the Council who accepted another tender. The events were reported to the club who complained and, having established the true facts, the Council then re-tendered. But the successful tenderer from the first round argued that its tender had been accepted and a contract created. Accordingly, the Council then abandoned the second tender round. The club argued that the Council had warranted that, if a tender was submitted by the tender deadline, it would be considered along with other tenders duly submitted and that the Council was in breach of this warranty by failing to consider the club's tender. The club claimed damages against the Council for breach of contract. The Council argued that no contract came into existence until the Council chose to accept any tender and there was no scope for implied warranties.

Judgement. There had been a clear intention to create a contractual obligation on the Council to consider the club's tender in conjunction with other conforming tenders and that the Council were, in principle, contractually liable to the club. The Court clearly took into account the fact that tenderers are put to significant expense in preparing a tender usually without direct recompense and that that expense is borne by tenderers without any commitment from the client that the project will necessarily go ahead. But:

> The invitee is…protected at least to this extent: if he submits the conforming tender before the deadline he is entitled, not as a matter of mere expectation but of contractual right, to be sure that his tender will, after the deadline, be opened and considered in conjunction with all other conforming tenders or at least that his tender will be considered if others are.

Just how widely can this decision be applied? The judgement is obviously limited to the circumstances of the case. The Court emphasised, in particular, the facts showed that the formal requirements imposed by the tender invitation were precise and the need for tenders to be returned in an official endorsed envelope was important. All of these factors indicated that the case was a 'rare exception' to the general rule that an invitation to tender is no more than an invitation to negotiate.

But in reality, just how special are the circumstances listed? In a decision of the Privy Council in a New Zealand case, *Pratt*

Contractors Limited v. Transit New Zealand. Lord Hoffmann acknowledged that this area of law concerns an important question for both tenderers and those who invite tenders about the extent to which the procedure for competitive tendering should be judicialised.

Facts. Transit's request for tenders (RFT) for a major road contract made it clear that tenderers would be evaluated according to a 'weighted attributes method' whereby marks were to be given for certain qualitative attributes as well as for price. It was accepted that the contract included an implied duty to act fairly and in good faith. Where the parties differed was over exactly what those procedural obligations were and what counted as acting fairly and in good faith.

Judgement. The Privy Council, agreeing with the Court of Appeal of New Zealand, held that the RFT said only that tenders would be evaluated in accordance with the weighted attributes method. While the detailed procedures prescribed by the internal manuals were intended to guide Transit, they were not something on which an outsider could rely. Although the question of a duty to act fairly and in good faith was a somewhat controversial question, the parties had accepted that a duty existed. What this required, however, was quite limited:

'In their Lordships' opinion, the duty of good faith and fair dealing…required that the evaluation ought to express the views honestly held by the members of the panel evaluating tenders. The duty to act fairly meant that all the tenderers had to be treated equally. One tenderer could not be given a higher mark than another if their attributes were the same. But Transit was not obliged to give tenderers the same mark if it honestly thought that their attributes were different. Nor did the duty of fairness mean that Transit were obliged to appoint people who came to the task without any views about the tenderers, whether favourable or adverse. The obligation of good faith and fair dealing also did not mean that Transit had to act judicially.

While there is no general implied duty of good faith under English law contract, public sector clients tendering for contracts are subject to the provisions of the EC procurement rules. In certain circumstances, this may lead to an implied contract imposing various obligations on the client such as, that tenderers who respond to an invitation must be treated equally or fairly: *Harmon CFEM Facades (UK) Ltd v. The Corporate Officer of the House of Commons.* The implications of the EC procurement rules for public sector clients and projects is discussed in *Public sector projects* in this volume.

8.10.2 Remedies for breaches of PFI tenders

The Public Contract (Amendments) Regulations 2009 came into force on 20 December 2009 and provide a greater range of remedies for companies which suffer as a result of breaches of the rules on public procurement contained in the Public Contract Regulations 2006. For a discussion of the Regulations please see the chapter *Public sector projects.*

8.10.3 Bribery and secret commissions

If a contractor obtains acceptance of his tender by offering of commission to the client or any of his employees or agents, the client can either repudiate the contract or treat it as subsisting. He can also recover the bribe and, in addition, damages both from the agent and the contractor.

The Bribery Act 2010 was passed in April 2010 and is due to come into force later in 2010. The Act provides a modern and comprehensive scheme of bribery offences to equip prosecutors and courts to deal effectively with bribery in the UK and abroad. The Act sets out that in prescribed circumstances bribing another person, or being bribed, is an offence where the person being bribed performs any of the following functions improperly:

- all functions of a public nature

- all activities connected with a business (which includes a trade or profession)

- any activity performed in the course of a person's employment

- any activity performed by or on behalf of a body of persons (whether corporate or unincorporated.

The Act also creates a separate offence of bribing a foreign public official. Furthermore, the Act provides that a commercial organisation is guilty of an offence if a person associated with it bribes another person for the advantage of that organisation, unless the organisation can show it had in place adequate procedures designed to prevent bribery.

8.10.4 Collusive tendering

The courts have over the years had to look at the enforceability of agreements between tenderers to the effect that they would not tender in competition with each other or that they put forward prices which are not genuine in the sense that, rather than refuse to tender altogether, they tender a price higher than that 'taken' from another contractor. In broad terms, the courts have enforced these agreements provided that their dominant purpose was to protect and extend the business of the parties rather than inflicting damage on the client. So, in the case of *Jones v. North* quarry owners agreed to sell stone to one of their group because that member was about to tender to Birmingham Corporation to supply its need for stone. By this agreement North agreed to sell stones to Jones and North agreed not to supply stones to the Corporation during the year in question. The Court enforced the agreement against North, and Jones' claims for breach of contract were allowed to proceed. Similarly, in *Harrop v. Thompson and Others* Harrop agreed to buy Thompson's farms at a public auction. Prior to the auction, Harrop entered into an agreement with another potential bidder to the effect that that person should stay away from the action and as a consequence Harrop acquired the farms at a cheap price. Thompson discovered the existence of the knock-out agreement and refused to complete the sale.

Thompson argued that the agreement between Harrop and the other potential bidder was against public policy as being in restraint of trade and that Harrop should not succeed in an action for specific performance of the contract of sale in relation to the farm. 'No' said the court: an agreement not to bid is not contrary to public policy.

However, it is clear that on other facts an English court could find that a conspiracy amongst tenderers not to bid or to bid a price which was not arrived at independently when invited to tender by a client is a fraud against that client. The damages for such fraud seem likely to cover the client's costs of re-tendering and interest and other losses caused by the consequent delay. Increased construction costs and/or a drop in property values might also be consequences of the fraud.

There are several forms which collusive tendering might take. A group of potential tenderers might make an agreement that only one or a limited number should submit a tender in response to a particular invitation. They might agree as to what price is to be submitted by each tenderer, or might even agree to submit the same price. Collusive tendering might arise as a result of premature disclosure of bids and the fault may lie with both the client and the tenderers. Collusive tendering can involve activities popularly referred to as 'cover pricing' and 'ring forming'. Cover pricing is described above and ring forming is where a group of tenderers arrange prices between them so that the 'chosen' firm wins. An even work load is achieved by each tenderer taking its turn to succeed. Collusive tendering is now subject to the statutory regimes created by the Competition Act 1998 and the Enterprise Act 2002. Chapter 1 of the Competition Act prohibits agreements or practices which may affect trade within the United Kingdom and have as their object or effect the prevention, restriction or distortion of competition within the UK. Price-fixing is expressly prohibited by Chapter 1.

Under the Enterprise Act, it is a criminal offence for an individual to dishonestly agree with at least one other person that two or more undertakings will engage in prohibited cartel activities in the UK. These cover direct or indirect price-fixing, limitation of supply or production, market or customer sharing and bid rigging, that is, an agreement as to which party will bid or an agreement as to the terms of any bid submitted.

There has been considerable activity in this area recently. On 22 September 2009, the OFT announced that it had fined 103 construction companies a total of £129.2 million for their involvement in bid-rigging of construction contracts, contrary to the Chapter 1 prohibition of the Competition Act 1998.

The decision, published by the OFT on 20 November 2009, stated that between 2000 and 2006 the companies in question had engaged in the following bid rigging activities:

- **Cover pricing**: 'Cover pricing' occurs where a potential bidder colludes with a competitor in the tender process with the result that the competitor submits an inflated tender which is not designed to win the contract but gives the appearance of a competing bid. Such collusion gives the impression that there are more companies competing for the contract than is actually the case. Furthermore, by ensuring that competitors submit inflated tenders, those companies interested in winning the work may be able to submit higher bids than would otherwise have been the case.

■ **Compensation payments**: As well as cover pricing, the OFT found instances of compensation payments. In some cases the OFT found that payments were made in exchange for the submission of a cover price. In other cases the companies involved agreed that the successful tenderer would pay the losing tenderer an agreed sum of money, and such payment was compensation for the costs of preparing the tender.

The OFT concluded that collusive tendering, whether by way of cover pricing, cover pricing where compensation is paid, or compensation payments made to losing tenderers where no cover pricing is evident, constitutes a clear restriction of competition, and its object is to prevent, restrict and distort competition. The OFT found that compensation payments had an impact on the final tender bids submitted by the party making the payment. In such cases, customers may face loss as tender bids may be inflated to cover the compensation costs payable by the successful tenderer.

Twenty-five appeals were lodged by addressees of the decision with the CAT. Most of these appeals only challenge the level of the penalty imposed by the OFT (the penalty appeals). However, six of the appeals (by GMI Construction, Quarmby Construction, Durkan, AH Willis, North Midland Construction and ISG Pearce) also challenge certain of the OFT's findings of infringement as well as the level of penalty (the liability appeals). At the time of going to press these appeals are still being heard.

8.11 Freedom of Information Act 2000

Both public sector clients and contractors submitting tenders to public authorities need to be aware of the provisions of the Freedom of Information Act 2000 (FOIA) which places new legal duties of disclosure on 'public authorities' in the UK and grants the public a right of access to information held by public authorities subject to various exemptions. Depending on how it is used, the FOIA potentially enables private entities to gain information about public authorities' business relationships, as well as the chance to find out information concerning competitors. Therefore any private entity who submits sensitive information to a public authority will want to try and prevent such information being disclosed to competitors, the press and others. There is no guaranteed way of achieving this. The public sector client will need to be aware of its statutory duties and not restrict its ability to comply with those. However, under Section 41 of the FOIA, if information is being provided in confidence and disclosure would amount to a breach of that confidence, the public authority does not have to disclose the information and, in some circumstances, does not even have to comply with the duty to confirm or deny the existence of that information.

The decision in *Express Medicals Ltd v. Network Rail Infrastructure Ltd* while relating to disclosure under the Civil Procedure Rules, may be of relevance to the question as to what will amount to confidential information in tenders.

Facts. Express Medicals was an unsuccessful tenderer to Network Rail (formerly, Railtrack) for occupational corporate healthcare services. It brought a claim for damages against Network Rail alleging that the latter had failed to comply with the principles of transparency and equality of tenderers under the Utilities Contracts Regulations 1996. The invitation to tender stated:

> The tenderer shall treat the contents of the documents enclosed with this invitation as private and confidential. Railtrack will treat your tender likewise.

Judgement. The court found that all the obliterated information was confidential. The continued confidentiality of the information was very important to the successful tenderer as it operated in a small, competitive industry where price, client lists, referees and business plans were closely guarded.

References

Construction Industry Board (1996) *Selecting consultants for the team: balancing quality and price.* Thomas Telford Ltd, London, UK

Construction Industry Board (1997) *Briefing the Team.* Thomas Telford Ltd, London, UK

Construction Industry Board (1997) *Code of Practice for the selection of main contractors.* Thomas Telford Ltd, London, UK

Construction Industry Board (1997) *Code of Practice for the selection of subcontractors.* Thomas Telford Ltd, London, UK

Construction Industry Council (1994) *The procurement of professional services – guidelines for the value assessment of competitive tenders.* Construction Industry Council, London, UK

Construction Industry Council (2005) *Selecting the Team.* Construction Industry Council, London, UK; www.cic.org.uk/services/SelectingtheTeam.pdf

Egan, J. (1998) *Re-thinking construction: the report of the Construction Task Force to the Deputy Prime Minister, John Prescott, on the scope for improving the quality and efficiency of UK construction.* Department of Trade and Industry, London, UK

Levene, P. and Cabinet Office (1995) *Construction procurement by government: an efficiency unit scrutiny.* HMSO, London, UK

Office of Government Commerce (2009) *Requirement to distinguish between 'selection' and 'award' stages of a public procurement, and to give suppliers complete information about the criteria used in both stages.* (Action Note 04/09, 29 April 09). OGC, London, UK

Office of Government Commerce (2009) *Guidance on the UK Regulations – Part 1: About the rule change, including transitional provisions; Part 2: The new rules on the Standstill Period; Part 3: The new remedies rule.* OGC, London, UK; www.ogc.gov.uk/procurement_policy_and_application_of_eu_rules_guidance_on_the_UK_regulations.asp

Office of Government Commerce (2010) *Implementing e-tendering.* OGC, London, UK; www.ogc.gov.uk/documents/e-tendering_Guidance.pdf

Referenced legislation, regulations and standards

Bribery Act 2010
Competition Act 1998
Enterprise Act 2002
Freedom of Information Act 2000
Housing Grants, Construction and Regeneration Act 1996
Public Contract (Amendments) Regulations 2009
Public Contracts Regulations 2006
Public Services Contracts Regulations 1993

Referenced cases

Blackpool and Fylde Aero Club Limited v. Blackpool Borough Council [1990] 3 All E.R. 25
British Steel Corporation v. Cleveland Bridge Engineering Company Limited [1984] 1 All E.R. 504
Diamond Build Ltd v. Clapham Park Homes Ltd [2008] EWHC 1439 (TCC)
ERDC Group Ltd v. Brunel University [2006] EWHC 687 (TCC)
Express Medicals Ltd v. Network Rail Infrastructure Ltd [2004] EWHC 1185 (TCC)
Harmon CFEM Facades (UK) Ltd v. The Corporate Officer of the House of Commons [1999] All E.R. (D) 1178
Harrop v. Thompson and Others [1975] 2 All E.R. 94
JB Leadbitter & Co Ltd v. Devon CC [2009] EWHC 930 (Ch)
Jones v. North (1874–75) L.R. 19 Eq 426
Monk Construction Limited v. Norwich Union Life Assurance Society (1994) 62 B.L.R. 107
Mowlem plc (T/A Mowlem Marine) v. Stena Line Ports Ltd [2004] EWHC 2206 (TCC)
Pratt Contractors Limited v. Transit New Zealand [2003] UKPC 83
Regalian Properties plc v. London Docklands Development Corporation [1995] All E.R. 1005
RTS Flexible Systems Ltd v. Molkerei Alois Muller GmbH & Co KG [2010] UKSC 14
Rugby Group Ltd v. Proforce Recruit Ltd [2006] EWCA Civ 69
Sims (CJ) Ltd v. Shaftesbury plc (1991) 60 B.L.R. 94
Skanska Rasleigh Weatherfoil v. Somerfield Stores Limited [2006] EWCA Civ 1732
Tesco Stores Ltd v. Costain Construction Ltd [2003] EWHC 1487 (TCC)
Turriff Construction Limited v. Regalia Knitting Mills Limited (1971) 9 B.L.R. 20

Further reading

Griffith, A., King, A. and Knight, A. (2003) *Best Practice Tendering for design and build projects.*
Lewis, H. (2009) *Bids Tenders and Proposals: Winning Business Through Best Practice, 3rd Edition.*
Carey, S. (2007) *Costs of Tendering.*

Websites

Constructiononline; www.constructionline.co.uk/static/
Construction Industry Council; www.cic.org.uk
International Federation of Consulting Engineers (FIDIC); www.fidic.org
Institute of Mechanical Engineers (IMechE); www.imeche.org
Institution of Civil Engineers (ICE); www.ice.org.uk
Institution of Electrical Engineers (IEE)/Institution of Engineering and Technology (IET); www.theiet.org
Join Contracts Tribunal (JCT); www.jctltd.co.uk
New Engineering Contract (NEC); www.neccontracts.com
Practical Law Company; http://uk.practicallaw.com

Chapter 9

Construction insurance

David Hayhow Lockton Companies LLP, London, UK
Update of previous text authored by Marshall Levine, Marshall F. Levine & Associates, London, UK

This chapter provides an introduction to insurance and, in particular, how it applies in its various forms to construction and civil engineering contracts. It first looks at the overriding intentions of an insurance contract and the fundamental protection that different sorts of insurance contracts are intended to provide. It explains how insurance contracts are formed, how and where the ability to insure assets, financial exposures and liabilities arise and the process that needs to be undertaken before a contract of insurance may be formed. It then focuses on the various types of insurance that are most relevant to the construction industry. It looks at the insurances that are purchased by employers, contractors and consultants and provides information on these different insurance products.

doi: 10.1680/mocl.40878.0129

CONTENTS

9.1 General insurance
9.1.1 Insurance and risk management

It is to be hoped that properly arranged insurance programmes do not lead to disputes but rather to the speedy settlement of valid claims. Unfortunately, there is always considerable speculation about the attitude of insurers and therefore, before examining the main elements of construction insurance, it is worthwhile considering the background to this viewpoint.

Insurance does have a very important role to play in business life in general. If matters go smoothly it is rarely apparent. Unfortunately, things do go wrong and that is when it is needed. The cover provides the financial resources required for legal obligations to be met, damaged property to be replaced and a business to be maintained. This protection is especially important when undertaking a project in unfamiliar territory, one where business practices taken for granted in Western Europe may not always be encountered.

Insurance is the traditional way of transferring risk. As such it forms only a part of the risk management process. This consists of a three-part process:

- risk analysis and quantification
- elimination or reduction of risk
- transfer or retention strategies.

It is not appropriate to undertake a detailed examination of the whole risk management process. This can be dealt with very simply but effectively by your professional insurance advisors. The minimisation and reduction process should be an ongoing one. Insurers can quite rightly, and legally, expect that an insured will be taking all reasonable steps to avoid a claim. Insurance is there to protect against the unexpected and fortuitous. Insurance should never be considered as a licence

for poor performance, although occasionally it is regarded as such. A valid method of risk reduction is by careful contract drafting.

Many organisations, after adequate thought, are well able to absorb a certain amount of risk. This is often more cost effective than insurance which theoretically involves profit for a number of other parties. For many larger organisations, this absorption is achieved by means of their own captive insurance company. For others the answer may lie in a mutual insurer, as many firms of major UK architects discovered when they set up the WREN to insure their professional indemnity risks. Yet another option is merely to expose the profit and loss account. However, when a particular risk exposure threatens the stability of the balance sheet, some other form of risk transfer may be considered. Insurance may, of course, be imposed contractually; leases, funding agreements and building contracts are typical examples. Another possibility is the statutory imposition of an insurance requirement, as found under the The Road Traffic Act or The Employers Liability Compulsory Insurance Act 1969.

Finally, the importance of regular monitoring cannot be overemphasised. There is little value in carrying out an extensive analysis exercise only to let it gather dust on the shelf.

Whether imposed or chosen, the insurance route is well trodden. The UK is fortunate in having London as the world centre of the insurance market. Western Europe also has one of the most mature markets in the world. In common with most things, however, insurance requires careful preparation. Unfortunately, all too often this does not happen and the inevitable shortcomings are detected once a claim arises. Extreme diligence and caution should be exercised both professionally and personally in the handling of insurance affairs. There is a need, as never before, for specialist and expert advice – insurance today is not for amateurs. It demands careful consideration by the client, consultants and contractors to ensure that each one is adequately protected against their own risk exposures.

With this background in mind, we can now move on to examine some key principals of insurance law.

9.1.2 Insurance definition

Insurance in the construction context is generally a contract to indemnify; the insured will recover compensation for its actual loss and in order to recover will have to prove that loss. For claims relating to damage, the basis of settlement will usually relate to repair or replacement costs. For liability claims, this may occur where judgement has been given, or an award made against the insured, or where, with the insurer's consent, the insured has reached a settlement with the third party. The principle of indemnity will be implied in the contract. This type of contract should be distinguished from insurance contracts that promise to pay a specified sum upon the happening of an insured event (e.g. life insurance and contracts of guarantee, performance bonds, etc.).

An excellent general description of the nature of insurance was given by Channell J in *Prudential Insurance Co. v. IRC* [1904] 2 KB 658 where he stated:

> It must be a contract whereby for some consideration, usually but not necessarily in periodical payments called premiums, you secure to yourself some benefit, usually but not necessarily the payment of a sum of money, upon the happening of some event … the event should be one that involves some amount of uncertainty. There must be either uncertainty whether the event will happen or not, or if the event is one which must happen at some time there must be uncertainty as to the time at which it will happen. The remaining essential is … that the insurance must be against something.

Most insurance lawyers will break down this definition into five main requirements.

Contract

There must be a valid binding contract to indemnify the insured in certain circumstances (so the usual contractual principles of offer and acceptance, capacity, legality, etc., apply), that is, it should not be within the insurer's discretion as to whether or not it will pay out any claim. The insured is contracting for certainty that its claim will be properly considered, not that a discretion may be exercised in its favour. For a detailed discussion of these contractual principles see, for example, *Chitty on Contracts* (Beale, 2009) The contract may be in any form, although a policy document is usually issued after the insurance is entered into (i.e. when the insured's proposal has been accepted by the insurer initialling a document known in the London market as a 'slip'). The slip sets out the main terms of the insurance. However, the slip is not the contract of insurance but merely evidence of its terms, and in fact the policy can be rectified if it does not accurately reflect the terms of the slip.

The Insurance Industry is regulated by the Financial Services Authority. Resulting from this regulation are two important

principles to which all insurance companies and brokers must adhere. These are Contract Certainty and Evidence of Cover:

Contract Certainty. This demands that the principal and/or material terms, conditions and exclusions of an insurance policy or contract must be agreed and understood by both parties to that contract prior to its inception.

Evidence of Cover. This demands that a document accurately evidencing that the insurance cover is in place must be provided to the policyholder within a reasonable time period following the inception of policy cover. Whilst this statement is capable of being interpreted in different ways a reasonable interpretation would be that the policy wording or contract itself should be issued within one month of the insurance policy incepting.

Consideration

Consideration is usually represented by a premium. Although Channell J refers to a payment of a premium, there is little authority on the significance of payment of premium. However, in *Hampton v. Toxteth Co-operative Provident Society Ltd* [1915] 1 Ch 721 a majority of the Court of Appeal held that the absence of a premium was not fatal to the existence of insurance. In addition, periodical payments for premium may be inappropriate; for example, with contracts of indemnity insurance where only one payment of premium is made under each contract. In practice, many insurance contracts state that payment of the premium is a condition precedent to the insurer's liability under the contract.

Benefit on the happening of some event

Although Channell J assumes that the benefit provided by an insurer will normally be money, benefits may be conferred which are 'money's worth'. Megarry V-C in *Medical Defence Union v. Department of Trade* [1979] 2 All ER 421 doubted that a fully satisfactory definition of insurance could ever be given and indicated that not every benefit can be the subject matter of a contract of insurance, but he was not prepared to go as far as holding that only a benefit in money or money's worth would suffice.

Megarry V-C stated that in most cases there were three elements to insurance and that in the absence of any of them, a contract was unlikely to be one of insurance. However, he stressed that the list was not necessarily definitive.

The three elements according to Megarry V-C are:

(a) the contract must give the insured an entitlement to a specified benefit on the occurrence of some event;
(b) the event must involve some element of uncertainty; and
(c) the insured must have an insurable interest in the subject matter of the contract.

Section 1 of the Life Assurance Act 1774 states that no insurance shall be made if there is no insurable interest and contracts contrary to the section shall be null and void. The Act, despite its title, applies to insurances on lives or 'any other event or events whatsoever' and therefore seems wide enough to include indemnity insurance, apart from those risks expressly excluded in section 4 (insurance on 'ships, goods and merchandises'). The Act also requires the policy to name all persons interested in the policy or on whose account the insurance is underwritten (section 2) and restricts the insured's recovery to an amount not exceeding its interest (section 3).

Megarry V-C also drew a distinction between indemnity contracts and contingency contracts. He described the former as giving an indemnity against some loss such as in a fire or marine policy. The latter is a payment contingent on an event such as death. However, he did not mention that indemnity policies can also be 'valued' (whereby the insured states in the proposal the specific value of the insured item for the purpose of any claim) so that a payment is made even if it does not reflect the true loss.

Uncertainty

The uncertainty to which Channell J refers relates to the occurrence of the event, for example, in relation to loss due to a latent defect (i.e. physical damage resulting from defects in the design or construction of a building which is not discovered until after completion), theft or the possibility of an archaeological find that would delay the project and incur expense. The uncertainty is whether the event will occur at all, as contrasted with life assurance where the uncertainty relates to timing of death.

Against something

The insurance must be against something, which generally means that the insured must have an insurable interest in the subject matter of the insurance.

9.1.3 Insurable interest

Construction insurance contracts are examples of contracts of indemnity, whereby the insurer undertakes to indemnify the insured against pecuniary loss caused by or arising from particular risks. Therefore, an interest is required by reason of the nature of the contract itself. Unless the insured has such an interest at the time when the insured event occurs, he cannot claim under the contract because he has suffered no loss against which he can be indemnified. Furthermore, if the insured's interest is less than the full value of the subject matter, he can suffer no loss greater than the total value of his actual interest at the time of the loss.

It is common practice in the construction industry for the head contractor on a site to insure, in its name and on behalf of the subcontractors, the entire contract works against all risks. This is known as contractor's all risks insurance. The validity of such an insurance was challenged in *Petrofina (UK) Ltd v. Magnaload Ltd* [1983] 2 Lloyd's Rep 91 where the main issue was whether the insurers could subrogate in the lead contractor's name against an allegedly negligent subcontractor, who had caused the loss on which the claim was based. The court

held that the insurer could not recover on two grounds. First, on a true construction of the policy the defendants were technically subsubcontractors for the purposes of the policy (therefore joint assureds) and rights of subrogation would be unavailable. Second, each insured was covered in respect of the whole contract works.

9.1.4 Utmost good faith

In addition, contracts of insurance are one of the few forms of contract subject to the principle of *uberrimae fidei*, or utmost good faith, which requires each party to make full disclosure of all material facts which may influence the other party in deciding to enter into the contract. To a limited extent, contracts for the sale of land, family settlements, the allotment of shares in companies and contracts of suretyship and partnership are also subject to this principle but in insurance utmost good faith remains fundamental to the contract.

The principle is generally understood to apply to the insured prior to entering into the insurance contract as the insured is in possession of all the facts concerning the risk so the insurer is entitled to trust the insured's representation. (See *Carter v. Boehm* (1766) 3 Burr 1905.)

9.1.5 Non-disclosure

The principle of utmost good faith applies to both parties to the insurance contract (see *Banque Financie`re de la Cite´ S.A. v. Westgate Insurance Co. Ltd* ('Westgate') [1988] 2 Lloyd's Rep 513. Where utmost good faith has not been shown by one party, the other party can avoid the contract. In such a case, the contract would be at an end and the insured would have no insurance cover. The House of Lords' decision in Westgate confirmed that the principle applies equally to the insurer. This may be relevant, if, for example, that insurer becomes aware of facts about a third party contractor involved in a joint venture with an employer which it does not pass on to the insured employer, who may be arranging a joint names policy, where knowledge of such facts would affect its decision to take out the insurance. The most important aspects of the principle relating to the duty imposed on the insured are:

(a) to disclose all facts known to the insured that are material; and

(b) not to make a statement that amounts to a misrepresentation of a material fact.

Such non-disclosure or misrepresentation would enable the insurer to avoid the contract. Claims already settled will therefore need to be repaid and a refund of the premium will be required. However, the insurer will not be entitled to damages.

The insured must disclose all material facts which lie within his knowledge, including those material facts which the insured ought in the ordinary course of its business to know or have known. The test as to whether a fact is material is whether it might (but not would) influence the judgement of a prudent insurer in deciding whether to accept the risk and at what level to fix the premium. Many facts are obviously material to the risk, for example, where the subject matter is exposed to a higher than normal degree of risk, as with the construction of the Channel Tunnel and/or Channel Tunnel Rail Link, where construction techniques were pushing engineering practices to their limits and where the nature of the project involved new hazards for the construction teams. Claims experience is also regarded as material.

9.1.6 Duration of the duty of disclosure

As a general rule, the proposer is not only under a duty to disclose material facts during the negotiations leading up to the formation of the insurance contract but also upon the renewal of such insurance, since the renewal is a new contract. The contract is concluded when offer and acceptance coincide, which depends on the formation procedure adopted. The relevant date for a Lloyd's policy is when the slip is initialled by the underwriter. A contract initiated by a proposal or other application will be concluded when the insurer accepts the proposal, although the parties may postpone commencement of the contract, for example, until the first premium is paid.

In the context of construction contracts, however, the common law position is often modified by an express provision for the insured to notify the insurers of any material change in the risk or any other material factors affecting the risk during the term of the contract. This is due to the enormous practical significance where any changes to the building risks are involved. A failure on the part of the insured to comply with this condition renders the contract voidable from the date of the breach at the insurer's option, so the insured will need to ensure that it has adequate systems in place, and exercises necessary supervision throughout the construction project, to enable compliance with the rule.

In this context, any material change in the risk would include, for example, an extension of activities or any other material factors affecting the risk during the currency of the contract, for example, any defects or change in working conditions on a construction project which arise to render the risk more than usually hazardous. Accordingly, this is a very onerous duty on those involved with the construction at least for the duration of the project, and in relation to a latent defects policy which may be taken out after completion, for up to 12 years.

9.1.7 Misrepresentation

As part of their duty of good faith, the parties must not only make accurate statements, but must also ensure that accurate answers are provided to questions. The common law duty is enacted in s. 20(1) of the Marine Insurance Act 1906:

> Every material representation made by the assured or his agent to the insurer during negotiations for the contract, and before the contract is concluded, must be true. If it be untrue the insurer may avoid the contract.

Misrepresentation includes making statements which are true, but which by reason of their being incomplete are misleading

(*Aaron's Reefs v. Twiss* [1896] AC 273). If a statement is untrue the insurer is still entitled to avoid the contract; it does not matter that the insured thought that the statement was true when it was made. However, where the insured qualifies the statement, adding that it is true to the best of the insured's knowledge and belief, then some protection may be afforded provided that the insured believed the statement to be true and the belief was reasonable (*Wheelton v. Hardisty* [1857] 8 ExB 232 (Exch Ch)).

If the contract provides that the truth of the statements is a condition precedent to the insurer's liability, then 'reasonable belief' will not assist and the insurer will not be liable under the contract. The truth of statements made by the insured in the proposal, and any other placing information, will often be made a condition precedent to liability under the insurance contract and incorporated as part of the contract. This means that the accuracy of such statements is effectively guaranteed so that even breach of a minor term will enable the insurer to avoid the contract.

9.1.8 Indemnity

It is a fundamental principle that the insured can only recover what it has lost, so it is an implied term of the insurance contract that it will provide no more than indemnity. There are three exceptions to this: first, relating to life policies (not discussed here); second, in relation to valued policies whereby the parties agree at the outset the value of the insured subject matter; and third, where a surplus is available following a subrogated claim.

9.1.9 Proximate cause

The principle of proximate cause implied in a contract of insurance requires an insured to show that the loss was caused by an insured peril. The proximate cause means the effective, dominant or real cause (*Symington & Co. v. Union Insurance of Canton Limited* [1928] 45 TLR 181) and will be a question of fact in each case. Application of the principle depends whether the question is any one of the following;

(a) Was the loss caused by an insured peril?
(b) Was loss caused by an excepted cause?

The principle may be modified or excluded by the contract.

9.1.10 Subrogation rights

Another fundamental principle of insurance is that under a contract of indemnity, and following payment of a claim to the insured, the insurers have the right to be placed in the position of the insured to pursue rights and remedies against third parties. This obviously puts them in an advantageous position compared with others who may suffer a consequential or economic loss as a result of a situation in which they had no direct contractual relationship. However, insurers have no subrogation rights against the insured, who is not a third party – one of the reasons why standard forms of contract require construction insurance to include all contracting parties as joint insured.

However, it may not be possible to obtain joint insured status. For instance, this frequently happens when a contractor is undertaking fit-out works in an existing building, insured by a party other than the client. It is possible that the insured, likely to be the landlord, may be prepared to request the insurers to waive subrogation rights but would certainly not be willing to allow a contractor to have joint insured status. This is an issue which is frequently causing problems as both insurers and insured become reluctant to waive subrogation rights, leaving the client in breach of contract unless the issue has been addressed at an early stage. Although a tenant reimbursing the landlord with the premium is likely to have some protection, either under the lease or as a result of the decision in *Mark Rowlands Ltd v. Berni Inns Ltd* [1986] 1 QB 211 (CA), the tenant's contractors will have no such protection. In those circumstances, it may be necessary to extend the public liability cover to include damage to the existing building, something that would not normally be required if the standard terms of the contract were complied with.

9.1.11 Insurer solvency

In the past number of substantial construction risk insurers have suffered financial problems. Many well-known names, including The Builders Accident, Reliance and the Independent Insurance Company have entered into some form of insolvency proceedings. Internationally there have been many more examples, both of direct insurers and of reinsurers. Although the insured will not have any relationship with reinsurers, failure of your insurers reinsurance arrangements will have a substantial effect on the ability of the direct insurer to meet claims.

It is important to monitor the ongoing solvency of insurers. Public liability claims often emerge some years after the project has been completed and the subsequent failure of an insurer covering the risk during the contract period can expose the insured to an uninsured loss or, at best, considerable uncertainty as to whether any funds will be available from the insolvency to meet the claim. In the case of professional indemnity insurance, which has to be kept in force for the whole period of liability under the contract or collateral warranty – being on a claims made basis, the situation is equally vulnerable. Only careful monitoring of the cover for the whole potential period of liability will allow the beneficiaries, who may well not be the direct insured, to attempt to make alternative arrangements prior to a claim situation arising.

9.1.12 Due diligence

The importance of thorough due diligence cannot be overstated. This is sometimes undertaken to satisfy a bank when a transaction is undertaken but is rarely followed up to check that any policy subject to renewal has indeed been maintained on at least the same terms as the original. Most parties involved in the construction process will have obligations to maintain insurance in a fairly detailed format, failure to do so will not

only lead to a potential breach of contractual duties but, more importantly, may leave an uninsured exposure which could be disastrous to the long-term financial viability of the project. The failure of an insurance company is only one area of concern. Others will be the reduction in the extent of cover or the increase in the underlying excess which could be imposed by insurers or chosen by the insured party in order to save costs. Not knowing what the cover is until a serious claim occurs could prove very expensive to the party at risk – often not the party arranging the actual cover.

9.2 Types of insurance

Construction insurance cover will be provided by either a single-project policy, an annual policy or a combination of both. A single-project policy provides cover for the whole or part of a specific construction project. An annual policy covers all relevant turnovers during the period of insurance. There are various classes of policy that construction contracts normally require, including liability policies (employers' liability and public liability), material damage policies, and consequential loss policies.

Care should be taken when analysing indemnity and insurance clauses under contracts to make sure they dovetail (see *Scottish Special Housing Association v. Wimpey Construction UK Limited* followed by *Scottish & Newcastle plc v. GD Construction (St Albans) Limited* [2003] EWCA Civ 16) which related to an IFC 84 Contract (JCT), and contractor's indemnity limited by insurance provisions.

Another recent case is *Tesco v. Constable & Others* which highlighted that indemnity clauses need to be agreed with insurers if the liability they impose extends beyond the normal scope of Public Liability insurance. In this case, Tesco were undertaking the construction of a supermarket with part of the works being the construction of a tunnel for the railway passing through their site with subsequent building above. Part of the tunnel collapsed and the railway had to be closed for over seven weeks. Two indemnities were involved – one to Network Rail the owners of the network and one to Chiltern Railways who were the train operator. The Public Liability insurers met the claim in respect of the indemnity to Network Rail but did not provide indemnity in respect of the contractual liability to Chiltern Railways as no damage had been incurred to their property; their losses were purely of a consequential or economic nature, not just for the period of closure but for the subsequent reduction in passenger revenue. This distinction between losses flowing from property damage and pure economic losses is one that affects the need for specific insurance in respect of latent defects (see section 9.5).

9.2.1 Liability policies

The principal types of liability policy are employers' liability, public liability and professional liability. These policies are designed to cover the insured's legal liability to third parties (i.e. liability to persons who are not a party to the insurance contract) subject to certain exceptions. The employer's liability policy covers the liability of an employer to its employees (i.e. those persons under a contract of service or apprenticeship to the employer) for personal injury or disease arising out of or in the course of their employment. The public liability policy provides an indemnity against personal injury claims by the public (other than employees) and property damage claims by any third party, including employees. Professional liability insurance (PI) covers those professionals such as architects, engineers, surveyors and other design-related consultants involved with the construction project, against claims of professional negligence. Large contractors, particularly those engaged in design and build works, carry one annual policy which covers activities on several sites and works of varying types undertaken within their business.

Strictly an insurer is not liable to pay under a liability policy until the loss has been incurred and ascertained although insurers take an interest earlier than this in establishing liability under the policy. The loss may be established as a result of a bona fide settlement with a third party or a result of an arbitrators award/judgement of the court (see *Pilkington UK Limited v. CGU Insurance plc* [2004] EWHC Civ 23).

In addition, it should be noted that a global settlement between a contractor and an employer, which brought into account issues that were not definitively evidenced was not sufficient for an insurer on its own to conclude that those issues led to a reasonable settlement, as specific evidence would need to be deduced to prove liability of insurers under the policy. (See *Lumbermans Mutual Casualty Co. v. Bovis Lend Lease Ltd* [2004] AER 36).

Environmental impairment insurance

Following the introduction of further legislation regarding environmental impairment, property owners, contractors, tenants and funders may all find themselves liable for remediation costs in a variety of circumstances.

The standard public liability policy will cover liability for personal injury or damage to property resulting from pollution or contamination provided it is caused by a sudden unintended and unexplained happening. In addition, the cost of removing or cleaning up such contamination will only be covered in the same circumstances.

The insurance market is willing to provide cover for gradual pollution in a variety of ways. However, all the options are likely to require detailed site investigation and, possibly, monitoring of the construction process. The cover is usually transferable to future owners and funders and will therefore give comfort to those involved on a long-term basis.

Product liability insurance

The standard public liability cover is likely to exclude liability arising out of the failure of work undertaken or products and services provided by the insured party to perform as intended.

Legal indemnity insurances

These are a group of policies with similar intent which may not be required for every development. However, when they are, they are vital to ensure that the insured event does not affect the financial outcome of the project. The two of particular interest are Defective Title and Rights of Light policies.

Defective title insurance has been in existence for many years. It is called into play when there is some concern about the title of the site to be developed – often the case when this comprises of a number of separate parcels of land which often have either gaps or question marks over ownership. The insurers will provide indemnity in respect of any claim by a party alleging rights over land in question which can lead to the payment of damages, the increase in costs associated with change of plans needed to accommodate the challenge and the consequential losses that may flow from that or even the termination of the project entirely. The cover may also be purchased if there is a restrictive covenant on the site; for instance an old property, previously owned by a religious institution, may forbid the sale of alcohol but the planned new supermarket will certainly be doing that. The beneficiaries may be untraceable or no longer in existence, but the prudent developer will arrange cover to insure that at least the legal costs of defending the claim are met even if no damages can be justified.

Rights of light had a resurgence of interest with two recent cases – *Regan v. Paul Properties DPF No. 1 Limited* [2006] and *Tamares (Vincent Square) Limited v. Fairpoint Properties (Vincent Square) Limited* [2006]. In the former, the developer was instructed by the court to demolish part of the new project in order to restore the light to an acceptable level to his neighbour. In the second the building was allowed to remain but the developer had to pay a substantial part of his anticipated profit to the affected landowner. The rights of light policy would meet all the costs associated with these outcomes together with the legal costs incurred in reaching a settlement.

In both these types of insurance, the underwriters play a very active role in analysing the legal documentation and often appointing their own professional consultants to advise on the risk exposure. They may demand that certain action is taken to either protect their position or to flush out potential beneficiaries. Only after they are satisfied that these steps have been taken will they be willing to issue a policy.

9.2.2 Non-negligent damage – JCT Clause 6.5.1 (previously known as Clause 21.2.1)

The cover required under this clause reflects the liability of the employer in tort for damage to third party property, when this does not flow as a result of the negligence of the contractor. This legal principle was established in 1958 following the case of *Gold v. Patman and Fotheringham*. The insurance required under the contract follows damage by certain specified risks: collapse, subsidence, heave, vibration, weakening or removal of support, or lowering of groundwater. Once again, the appendix to the contract states the limit of indemnity which is required. This must be considered separately to the public liability risk and indeed the cover may not be necessary at all, if working in a greenfield site.

Wherever possible, the cover should be arranged with the same insurers who cover the contractor's public liability risk. This will avoid any delay in settlement of a claim while different insurers dispute which has the effective policy.

9.2.3 Material damage policies

This type of policy covers loss or damage to property in which the insured has an insurable interest, either during the ownership or possession or contract to acquire that property. The material damage policy only covers loss or damage to the property specified. A contractor's all risks (CAR) policy is a material damage policy.

Damage to the contract works (i.e. the building, factory, road, bridge, etc.) may also include machinery and electrical plant while being installed.

Cover may be provided for:

(a) contract works including temporary works
(b) construction plant – for example, cranes, scaffolding, while in the course of construction or while in storage on site
(c) plant erection – loss/damage to construction plant while being erected or dismantled on site
(d) goods in transit – loss or damage to contract works materials during transit and incidental storage off site
(e) damage to employees' property (other than contract works)

Cover is generally available for the period when the contractor is on site and stops at completion of works, that is, extends to defects during the defects liability period. It does not embrace cover for completed works or structures.

9.2.4 Composite and combined policies

Contractors frequently have a combined policy, covering both the liability and material damage risks referred earlier. The policy is divided into sections covering the usual types of liability, that is, employers' liability, public liability and loss or damage to the contract works, construction, plant and equipment, machinery, and so on, usually known as contractor's all risk or CAR.

Composite policies may include extra cover for consequential loss. Composite policies have the following advantages over separate policies:

(a) they can be significantly less expensive in terms of premiums and discounts;
(b) only one proposal form is required;
(c) as only one policy is issued, a single renewal notice and renewal premium is required; and
(d) only one declaration of turnover for the purposes of adjusting the premium is required.

9.2.5 Difference in conditions method (DIC)

The DIC method is normally only effected by contractors in certain circumstances where the employer has arranged project insurance (see below) and involves extending one or more of the four main policies – CAR, PI, employers' liability and public liability by closing any gaps in cover. A shortfall in cover may exist where the policy arranged by the employer is limited in scope, a deductible or excess applies to any claim made under the policy, levels of indemnity are inadequate, and so on, and where such limitations on cover are not acceptable to the contractor, perhaps because its usual cover is more extensive or the contract insurance requirements have not been met. A risk assessment will be required to determine what additional cover is needed.

The DIC method involves treatment of the conventional policies as an additional layer with the limits of indemnity they provide being used to supplement or replace the cover provided under the project specific arrangements. This situation generally results in a variety of insurance arrangements, for example:

(a) public liability cover in excess of the contractual requirement
(b) additional cost of working; this would cover, for example, following a loss, additional plant, machinery, and so on, required by the contractor to complete the project on time to meet contractual requirements
(c) marine and transport insurance
(d) non-negligent liability and damage insurance
(e) differences in excess limits

DIC cover is not required where the employer has already arranged adequate insurance. The arrangement of comprehensive insurance cover is quite often the most cost-effective option as it should prevent unnecessary insurance costs from being included by the various contractors within their tender returns.

9.2.6 Project insurance

Comprehensive project insurance provides an all-embracing insurance policy, as an alternative to requiring every participant in the project to arrange its own separate insurance policy for its part of the project and its own plant and equipment. Project insurance is a combined insurance policy arranged by the employer (although the contractor retains its contractual responsibilities and liabilities) frequently in the joint names of the employer and all contractors. Project insurance is usually limited to conventional risks covering CAR and public liability and does not generally include professional indemnity for the professional design teams, as this is a class of insurance written in a smaller, specialised insurance market, or employees' liability cover.

However, some insurance companies do provide a wider CAR project policy to include cover for damage resulting from a defect in design, plan specification workmanship or materials. The policy only covers damage to the works caused by negligence (not defects without such damage) which arises during the construction period (not for any period thereafter). Although the cover is convenient, many underwriters load the premium rates and levels of excess of CAR insurance arranged by the employer because the employer's insurers do not know the identity of all the contractors from the inception of the project and therefore have no basis to rate that aspect of the risk.

However, significant advantages for such project insurance include

(a) inclusion of defective design risk in the same policy, which overcomes settlement delay problems (due to the necessity of establishing the cause of loss or damage) and prevents the design team from being isolated from the employer
(b) in large contracts with many contractors, avoidance of consideration of various policies and consequential delay and possibly dispute between insurers, which would otherwise result in very complex settlement arrangements
(c) premium saving due to reduced administrative and other overheads of brokers, insurers and reinsurers. Premium is also saved due to the elimination of double insurance which necessarily involves payment of more than one premium. The cost can be assessed before the insurance is taken out
(d) the gap created by some insurers by separating the employer's and contractors' risks which they insure, can be eliminated without issuing a second CAR and public liability policy
(e) inconvenience caused by any dispute between the parties involved in a loss, damage or liability claim is avoided
(f) uninsured risks in large projects, where there are or could be many separate insurance policies are avoided
(g) special covers can be incorporated into the programme, for example:
    (i) the cost of completing outstanding works
    (ii) loss of anticipated profit/income by employer, and
    (iii) end of term covers
(h) convenience

9.2.7 Annual policies

Annual policies enable the insured to maintain cover on an annual basis to provide cover for all projects undertaken during the term of the insurance. The insured is required to declare its annual turnover (together with details of any claims experience) at renewal.

Cover is provided for the contractor and usually also the employer and subcontractors, for losses in connection with the work described in the policy.

Cover is provided for all risks and within stated limits not usually more than £50 million per contract. The insurer effectively waives its right to specific information for each contract. Furthermore, the insurer has given up any right to decline a particular risk and has accordingly waived disclosure because

the insurer has no decision to make regarding acceptance of the risk providing that it falls within the categories of work agreed at inception. The policy will usually exclude or limit cover for construction of dams, bridges, tunnels, and so on, that is, the more hazardous risks.

Reliance by either the client or the bank on a contractor's annual policy brings additional risks. Generally, those policies do not specifically include the interest of any client or their bank and very often the insurers are not even aware of the identity of those parties. It therefore follows that, in the event of insolvency or termination of the cover – including just non-renewal – insurers would not know who to advise even if there were some contractual obligation that they should do so. The ultimate beneficiary could therefore find themselves uninsured and it is unlikely that the insurers would have any duty to attempt to trace them in order to appraise them of the situation.

9.2.8 Consequential loss policies insurance for liquidated damages

The opportunity to purchase insurance protection in this area has existed in the past and the opportunity to insure against this was defined in Clause 22D of the JCT 98 suite of contracts. However, the insurance market is no longer able to offer this cover and so in the drafting of the JCT 2005 suite of contracts reference to a 22D equivalent is no longer made.

Anticipated loss of income or profits

There is a fundamental proviso under consequential loss insurances that a successful claim for material damage must precede one for consequential loss. This is to ensure that the funds are available to repair the physical damage that gives rise to the consequential loss, thereby minimising the period of that loss. It is therefore important to ensure that the material damage and consequential loss covers are on the same basis – if they are not provided under the same policy. This is unlikely to be the case if the contractor insures the construction risk because the employer's consequential losses will not be of interest to the contractor, and in any event he would have no insurable interest in them.

The range of exposures really needs to be carefully analysed for each project. For a developer, there is loss of rental and other income which may be exceeded by the continuing burden of interest on development finance. Terrorism damage could cause loss of attraction, especially to residential or retail property. Denial of access may cause considerable delays without any real damage to the works. For the owner occupier there is an additional range of possible losses linked to the delayed occupation of the property. These all need detailed consideration before cover can be placed to provide realistic protection.

9.2.9 Terrorism insurance

Almost all UK insurers included an exclusion clause relating to damage caused by terrorist activities in all commercial insurances covering material damage and any subsequent consequential losses.

The insurance industry and the government established a mutual insurance company – Pool Reinsurance Company Limited, generally known as 'Pool Re'.

It is not within the remit of this manual to go into detail about terrorism insurance. Basic policy wordings now exclude terrorism cover and if it is required the cover has to be purchased as an extension to the policy. Some insurers deal with this by amending the policy whilst others issue a separate certificate. Either way, the loss is settled by insurers in the same way as other claims. Insurers then protect themselves against large individual claims or a series of claims in any one year by purchasing reinsurance protection from the Pool Re. This involves payment by them of substantial reinsurance premiums to Pool Re and they recover these by charging their own rates to insured. This has introduced an element of price competition between insurers. It is also the intention that insurers should bear a larger part of the terrorism risk themselves as time goes on so the level at which they buy reinsurance protection from Pool Re decreases year by year.

9.2.10 Insurance premium tax (IPT)

On 4 November 1993 the then Chancellor of the Exchequer announced that he was imposing a tax on most insurance premiums effective from 1 October 1994.

This has resulted in a taxation on gross premiums (i.e. premiums inclusive of commission) and applies to all those insurances normally associated with shopping centres. Originally, the tax stood at 2.5% but this was increased to 4% from 1 April 1997 and now (2010) stands at 5%. Further increases can be expected in the future as the UK rate is considerably lower than that in many other EU countries.

The tax is under the care of HM Revenue and Customs, and the tax point is the date on which the 'premium is written'. In insurance terms, this is the renewal date or any other date that the risk attaches to the insurance company rather than the date that the premium is debited.

It should be noted that the inspection fees for plant and machinery no longer incur IPT but now attract VAT.

9.2.11 Good management

Insurance is no substitute for vigilance and good management; these should go hand in hand. Indeed, as we have seen, to rely too heavily on an insurance policy may excuse the insurer from honouring a claim or generate an increase in the premium.

Insurance is not for amateurs, and the passing of uneventful years without claims should not lull the insured into forwarding a routine cheque in response to a renewal notice. The policy needs an overhaul every twelve months in order to make sure that it functions properly and efficiently.

At each overhaul the questions to be asked are as follows:

- What are the insurance requirements of the contract?

- What additional cover would be prudent?

- What risks are to be insured and in what sums?

This should be followed by an examination of the policy documents to check that the intended cover has been secured and that the premium is competitive.

The responsibility for arranging the insurance may not lay directly with the party most at risk. This is no excuse for not taking an active interest in the cover and any claims.

9.2.12 Loss prevention

In response to the continued high level of claims being incurred by construction insurers, the Association of British Insurers combined with a number of other parties to publish a *Joint Code of Practice on the protection from fire on construction sites and buildings undergoing renovation*. This joint code has been through a series of revisions, which have seen it become industry standard practice.

It is therefore unlikely that any construction policy, either project based or annually based, will not have a condition requiring compliance with the joint code. This condition will give the insurers the right to suspend or cancel all cover after a specified date, which must be a minimum of 60 days after issuing an appropriate notice, if the required remedial action has not been completed.

In order to ensure compliance, the insurers have the right to inspect the contract site at all reasonable times. In the event that they decide to issue a notice of breach they must do so to the employer and the contractor. In the case of a project policy they will obviously have the identities of the parties concerned readily available, but if the cover is under a contractor's annual policy the service of notices may not be so easily achieved. It should be noted that if the construction risk cover is suspended it is almost certain that the terrorism insurance will also be affected.

9.3 Construction insurance provisions under traditional building contracts and civil engineering contracts

9.3.1 Traditional building contracts

Under a traditional building contract such as the JCT 2005 family of contracts there are usually two important sections (apart from the definitions) that are relevant to insurance. The first relates to the indemnity provisions, and the second to the insurance provisions that follow it. In broad terms, the contractor is responsible for, and will usually indemnify, the client against liabilities (whether under the contract, statute or common law) in relation to personal injury or death caused by the works. In addition, the contractor will usually be similarly liable and responsible for loss or damage to property arising from the carrying out of the works.

There usually follows in the building contract an obligation in relation to insurance of the works either for the contractor to take out construction all risks insurance for the works itself in the joint names of the employer and the contractor, or for the client to take out such insurances in the joint names of the contractor and the client. How each option is decided will be based on the requirements of client or contractor, the cost of premiums offered to each, or the type of building that is being insured and the practicalities of allowing several insurances to apply to a single building. For example, if the employer carries buildings insurance in relation to the shell and core, and the works which relate to the fitting the building out, it would be more practical for the employer to insure rather than the contractor, to avoid the danger of having too many policies in relation to one building.

The provisions would then go on to describe the basis of all risks insurance, the type of risks and the definition of loss or damage.

It is also common for the construction all risks insurance arrangements to lie alongside professional indemnity insurance carried by the Contractor and professional consultants at the request of the client. Alternatively, a projects insurance policy can be procured (see section 9.2.6) which wraps all the risks up together, excluding the risks associated with professional indemnity insurance.

Design and build contractors will be expected to carry professional indemnity insurance (see *Professional indemnity insurance*) alongside CAR insurance in any event because of their designer's liability.

The JCT published the Major Project Construction Contract in 2005. This takes a radically different view about insurance and requires that the actual policy wordings are appended to the contract rather than some abbreviated description of what cover is required. This approach echoes the requirements of the Financial Services Authority in demanding 'contract certainty at inception' for insurance.

9.3.2 Civil engineering contracts

The standard civil engineering contract is now the ICE 7th Edition being a measurement version issued in September 1999 by the Institution of Civil Engineers (ICE), Association of Consulting Engineers and the Civil Engineering Contractors Association.

The broad principles enunciated in relation to traditional building contracts are applicable under the ICE Terms and Conditions except that because the nature of the works are civil engineering biased, the choice of the employer or the contractor insuring does not exist.

The contractor is expected to take full responsibility for the care of the works and the materials, plant and equipment from the commencement of works until the works are completed. The contractor is obliged to rectify loss or damage to the works over which it has care.

The contractor is usually obliged to insure in the joint names of itself and the employer all the works other than in relation

to the accepted risks as defined (this is similar to the accepted risks referred to in traditional contracts).

There is a similar provision in relation to indemnification by the contractor for death or injury to persons or loss or damage to property which is the contractor's responsibility under the ICE 7th with some suitable exceptions carved out.

9.4 Professional indemnity insurance (PI)

This section is intended to provide a broad overview of Professional Indemnity insurance (PI). Please refer to the chapter *Professional indemnity insurance* for detailed guidance in this area.

PI cover is usually taken out individually by the members of the project's design team to indemnify them against claims brought by the employer or by third parties for loss suffered as a result of professional negligence. PI cover includes a wide range of liabilities; therefore, the negotiated insurance terms are central to the effective insurance of any construction project. Consequently, the insurance arrangements often represent a significant factor in the choice of consultants engaged and in the subsequent negotiations of their contracts of appointment.

It should be noted that this cover, unlike public and employers liability, is on a claims made basis. The policy in force when the claim is made against the consultant is the one which will respond, rather than the one in force when the negligent act is committed.

In the case of design and build contracts and ICE Design and Construct, the contractor will also require PI to cover those aspects of the project normally undertaken by independent consultants (e.g. the architect or engineer).

9.4.1 The cover

Cover provides indemnity against the consultant's legal liability for damages and costs in respect of claims for breach of professional duty by reason of any negligence, error or omission.

The usual policy wording will not provide indemnity in respect of breach of a 'fitness for purpose' obligation since its terms provide cover solely for 'negligent act, error or omission'. Thus, where the consultant has given an express or implied warranty that its design will be fit for the purpose required, there may be no cover for breach of that warranty.

9.4.2 Products liability insurance

Contractors and subcontractors required to deliver PI insurance often counter that they cannot obtain it but offer Products Liability as an alternative. It is often stated that these provide the same protection but this is absolutely not correct. Products Liability is indeed another legal liability policy but it only covers death or injury to third parties or damage to third party property that arises from a defective product supplied by the insured party, the contractor or subcontractor. Products Liability cover is precisely the same as Public Liability Insurance.

Both Public and Products Liability are more accurately dealt with under the general heading of Third Party Liability or General Liability Insurance.

Product Liability cover specifically excludes the costs of making good any defect and almost certainly will also exclude any inconsequential losses that arise from the defect so far as the client is concerned. As such it is therefore of no benefit to the client and one should disregard it when considering what risk exposure there is arising from the design failure of any contractor or subcontractor who is insured in this way.

By way of an example, some lift manufacture and installation contractors have historically declined to offer Professional Indemnity cover offering Products Liability cover in its place. They cite the reason that the lift is their product and so product liability is more relevant. However, as we have stated earlier whilst Product Liability would protect the manufacturer if someone were to be injured whilst travelling in the lift, it would not indemnify the manufacturer in the event that the purchaser of the lift were to sue the manufacturer for the lift's non-performance.

9.5 Latent defects insurance
9.5.1 Type of policy

Latent defects insurance, sometimes referred to as building defects or inherent defects insurance has become increasingly popular since 1989 when several major UK insurers entered the market. More and more purchasers see it as a much better alternative to reliance on collateral warranties or the Contracts (Rights of Third Parties) Act 1999 and this is hardly surprising as it is a first party policy requiring insurers to pay valid claims without the need to prove negligence against a third party. The demand for the cover to be in place is often driven by lenders or tenants. For lenders it has the benefit of reducing risk because if the policy is in force there is much less likelihood of the borrower having to pay for expensive repairs and for tenants it reduces their potential liabilities under full repairing leases.

The basic cover indemnifies an insured against damage to the whole of a building caused by a latent defect in the structural parts (as defined) of the building. However, it is most unusual and certainly unwise to buy just this basic cover. In practice most policies also automatically include indemnity against physical damage caused by water entering the building due to a defect in the weatherproofing envelope of the building at or above ground level or the waterproofing seal below the ground floor.

A more detailed explanation of the insurance protection is given in the following paragraphs but the basic cover available from the limited number of insurers prepared to issue policies does not vary much from one insurer to another. However, there are a number of pitfalls that could result in the extent of

cover being misunderstood or too much premium being paid so advice from an expert familiar with the class is advisable. The reluctance of many insurers to underwrite the cover is because of its long tail nature. The policy commences at practical completion of a new building and continues in force for up to 12 years. It cannot be cancelled and is assignable to new owners or lessees or anybody else acquiring an insurable interest.

Although latent defects cover may be taken out after the project is completed, this is inadvisable as it will cost a lot more, a higher deductible will usually apply and the market is limited. More importantly perhaps the benefits of the technical auditors referred to below will not be secured. It is far better if the decision to procure this insurance is taken before construction work commences. The insurer will appoint a firm of independent consulting surveyors or engineers to monitor the progress of construction and to liaise with the professional team. This independent firm are commonly referred to as the technical auditors. The insurance will be conditional on the technical auditor appointed being supplied with all necessary technical information. The technical auditors will ensure that not only is the structure designed to a reasonable standard but that it is constructed in accordance with the plans and good building practice. If the consultants refuse to pass any aspect of the work, damage arising from those aspects will be excluded from the policy. However, it is very rare for a policy to be issued with restrictions. Indeed, most consultants would see it as their role to try and make certain this does not happen.

9.5.2 The cost

The cost of latent defects insurance, with a standard excess, usually ranges from 0.65% to 1% of the total contract value, inclusive of the inspection service fee. However, cheaper terms, particularly when a high deductible is selected, have been known. If waivers of subrogation rights in favour of contractors and professional team are required the premium element of the total cost will rise.

9.5.3 Contents of the policy

The insured

The policy is often affected by the developer but is freely assignable to new owners, lessees or financiers and can be in one name or several names.

Policy cover

As mentioned earlier, the basic policy covers physical damage to the property caused by a latent defect in the structural parts. The policy will also cover any remedial work essential to prevent actual collapse during the period of insurance, for example, even if there is no physical damage to the premises but there is a latent defect in the structure which threatens its stability and strength.

A 'latent defect' is any defect in the structural works notified to the insurers during the period of insurance which is attributable to defective design or workmanship or materials and which was undiscovered at the date of issue of the certificate of practical completion.

The policy also provides cover against the cost of demolition and removal of debris, reasonable legal, professional or consultants' fees incurred in connection with such physical damage or threat of imminent instability (excluding fees solely incurred in preparing claims) and additional costs of repair or reinstatement following damage arising out of alterations in design, use or application of improved materials or improved or altered methods of working incurred solely in compliance with any building or other regulations.

It is important to appreciate that a latent defect alone will not constitute a claim. It has to cause actual physical damage, or there has to be the threat of imminent physical damage, before any claim can be made but the damage itself can be anywhere in the building. However, under the basic policy cover the damage to the building must arise from a latent defect in the structural works as defined in the policy. A typical definition reads as follows but they do vary and the variations are a factor to consider when comparing quotations:

(i) all internal and external load-bearing structures essential to the stability or strength of the Premises including but not limited to foundations, columns, walls, floors, beams; and

(ii) all other works forming part of external walls and roofing but excluding moveable elements of external windows, doors, skylights and the like.

The property insured includes all works forming part of the completed contract for which the certificate of practical completion and technical agent's certificate are issued. This includes, in addition to the above, all landlord's fixtures and fittings, permanent mechanical, electrical and other services necessary for the functioning of the building and external works immediately adjacent, for example, drainage, road and car park surfaces, walls and landscaping.

Whilst the basic cover protects the whole building against damage caused by a latent defect in the structural works as defined, it is possible to extend the policy to include other causes of damage.

Damage caused by a defect in the weatherproofing and waterproofing cover is usually but not always included as standard within the basic cover. As wall cladding and roofing is a major source of damage it is always best to include it. There is an exclusion of cover for the first twelve months after practical completion. Insurers take the view that the contractors should rectify defects in weatherproofing and waterproofing during that period.

The weatherproofing envelope will usually comprise roof coverings, skylights, external walls and cladding, external windows and doors (but excluding moveable elements) and the ground floor slab. The waterproofing envelope comprises those elements of the building below ground level that keep the damp out.

Some insurers now offer cover against damage to the building insured caused by a defect in the non-structural parts of the building. Non-structural parts are generally regarded as being all other parts of the building not included under the headings of structural, weatherproofing and waterproofing but excluding protective coatings, decorative finishes and floor coverings (but not permanent floor finishes).

Some insurers will also offer cover against damage caused by a defect in the mechanical and electrical services. This cover can either be added to the main Structural Latent Defect insurance policy or arranged via a separate Mechanical and Electrical or Building Services Latent Defects policy.

Mechanical and electrical services will usually comprise heating, ventilating and air conditioning systems and fresh and waste water systems, lifts and escalators, window cleaning equipment, electrical distribution systems (including fixed lighting), building management systems and building security equipment (including car park ticket machines and barriers and all types of electrical security doors). However, external services are excluded.

Period of cover

Cover used to be for ten years' duration but with more insurers prepared to offer twelve years this has become more common.

It may be possible for an interested party to buy an option for cover thereby allowing a long-term investor or tenant to take protection if required. This is done prior to the start of works, enabling the technical control to take place and avoiding the penal provisions which are charged for cover taken out after practical completion.

Obtaining cover

If an employer requires latent defects insurance it will contact its broker during the planning stage and provide details of site location, ground conditions, nature and design of the building and the contractors and professionals who will be engaged on the project. The insurer will require the employer to complete a proposal form.

At the date of practical completion, insurers ask for the estimated cost of reinstatement of the property at that date inclusive of the cost of complying with European Union and Public Authorities Stipulations, site clearance, debris removal, professional fees and landscaping. This should be the same figure (i.e. the Declared Value) as is supplied for the annual material damage/buildings insurance The actual premium payable for the basic latent defects cover is then calculated using this figure.

When comparing initial quotations for building defects insurance it is important to take account of how different insurers build into their policies adequate allowance for inflation during the ten or twelve year period of insurance.

Some insurers rely on index linking and/or regular reviews of sums insured and these may entail extra premium payments during the period of insurance.

Rent

The actual sum insured at practical completion should represent the annual rent receivable multiplied by the indemnity period selected. The premium will be based on this and the cover will be for the duration of the policy, usually 10 or 12 years.

Again, care is needed because different insurers allow for rent inflation in different ways.

Other consequential losses

Most insurers now offer a separate annual policy covering occupiers' business interruption and the sums insured would need to be assessed for each individual risk in the same way as they are for the tenants' usual all risks business covers.

Exceptions

The latent defects policy contains a number of reasonable exclusions, none of which appears unfair to the insured although the insured may require deletion or amendment in particular cases. Common examples include:

(a) structural alterations, repairs, modification materially affecting the stability of the property (unless insurers have been informed, the policy endorsed and any additional premium paid);

(b) inadequate maintenance of structural works or abnormal use of the property;

(c) inadequate maintenance or abnormal use of the weatherproofing materials or any structural alterations, repairs, and so on, which materially affect the weatherproofing;

(d) wilful acts, omissions or negligence of the insured;

(e) changing colour, texture, and so on, or other ageing processes;

(f) nuclear exclusions;

(g) war, invasion, act of foreign enemy, hostilities, and so on;

(h) failure to carry out finishing operations after issue of the certificate of practical completion;

(i) substandard, unsatisfactory, and so on, workmanship, design and materials notified to the insurers by the technical control referred to in the certificate of approval or the certificate of practical completion and not subsequently rectified and approved by the insurers;

(j) subsidence, heave or landslip from any cause unrelated to a latent defect (these risks will usually be covered under the building insurance);

(k) defects for which the insured's architect or engineers or building contractor are responsible and which are notified to the insured before the issue of the certificate of practical completion, unless subsequently rectified and accepted by the insurers;

(l) the insured's failure to repair damage or reinstate for which an indemnity is recoverable under the insurance unless the delay is due to reasons beyond the insured's control; and

(m) consequential or economic loss of any kind (although loss of rent and other consequential loss cover is available).

9.5.4 NHBC Guarantee

The National House-Building Council (NHBC) Buildmark Warranty is a form of Latent Defect Insurance. This product protects residential homeowners for the 10 year period that follows the completion of the construction of a new home. The product is paid for by the house-builder and the Buildmark Warranty or Certificate is provided to the homeowner at the time of purchase. The Buildmark Warranty is intended provide assurance to the homeowner and their mortgagee that the house-builder will ensure that any defects within the new home are rectified in the first 10 years. In most situations , when a defect occurs the Warranty is not called upon as either the homeowner or the NHBC are able to bring the house-builder back to the property to rectify the defect.

Up until recently Zurich insurance offered a product which was very similar to the NHBC warranties. However, Zurich have now withdrawn this product and it is no longer available. Other similar products that offer an alternative to the NHBC are The Premier Guarantee and Building Life Plans.

References

Beale, H. (ed) (2009) *Chitty on Contracts, 30th Edition.* Sweet & Maxwell, UK

Association of British Insurers, Chief Fire Officers Association and London Fire Brigade (2009) *Fire Prevention on Construction Sites: Joint Code of Practice on the Protection from Fire on Construction Sites and Buildings Undergoing Renovation, 7th edition.* Construction Federation, UK

Referenced legislation, regulations and standards

Contracts (Rights of Third Parties) Act 1999. TSO, London, UK

The Employers Liability Compulsory Insurance Act 1969. HMSO, London, UK

Life Assurance Act 1774

Marine Insurance Act 1906

The Road Traffic Act

Referenced cases

Aaron's Reefs v. Twiss [1896] AC 273

Banque Financie`re de la Cite´ S.A. v. Westgate Insurance Co. Ltd ('Westgate') [1988] 2 Lloyd's Rep 513

Carter v. Boehm (1766) 3 Burr 1905

Gold v. Patman and Fotheringham

Hampton v. Toxteth Co-operative Provident Society Ltd [1915] 1 Ch 721

Lumbermans Mutual Casualty Co. v. Bovis Lend Lease Ltd [2004] AER 36

Mark Rowlands Ltd v. Berni Inns Ltd [1986] 1 QB 211 (CA)

Medical Defence Union v. Department of Trade [1979] 2 All ER 421

Petrofina (UK) Ltd v. Magnaload Ltd [1983] 2 Lloyd's Rep 91

Pilkington UK Limited v. CGU Insurance plc [2004] EWHC Civ 23

Prudential Insurance Co. v. IRC [1904] 2 KB 658

Regan v. Paul Properties DPF No. 1 Limited [2006]

Scottish & Newcastle plc v. GD Construction (St Albans) Limited [2003] EWCA Civ 16

Scottish Special Housing Association v. Wimpey Construction UK Limited

Symington & Co. v. Union Insurance of Canton Limited [1928] 45 TLR 181

Tamares (Vincent Square) Limited v. Fairpoint Properties (Vincent Square) Limited [2006]

Tesco v. Constable & Others

Wheelton v. Hardisty [1857] 8 ExB 232 (Exch Ch)

Websites

Association of British Insurers; www.abi.org.uk

Association for Consultancy and Engineering (ACE); www.acenet.co.uk

Civil Engineering Contractors Association (CECA); www.ceca.co.uk

Financial Services Authority; www.fsa.gov.uk

Institution of Civil Engineers (ICE); www.ice.org.uk

Joint Contracts Tribunal (JCT); www.jctltd.co.uk

Lloyd's; www.lloyds.com

NHBC Buildmark Warranty; www.nhbc.co.uk/Homeowners/Homewarranties/ResidentialHousing/Buildmarkwarranty/

Pool Reinsurance Company Limited (Pool Re.); www.poolre.co.uk

WREN – The Wren Insurance Association Ltd; www.wrenmutual.co.uk/en/Wren_Mutual/index.cfm

Chapter 10

doi: 10.1680/mocl.40878.0143

Bonds, parent company guarantees and other security

Finola O'Farrell QC Keating Chambers, London, UK

CONTENTS

This chapter explains the nature and purpose of bonds and guarantees for use on construction projects. Security is often given in the form of a bond (a promise by deed whereby the issuer of the bond undertakes to pay to the beneficiary a sum of money) or a guarantee (an undertaking by the guarantor to the beneficiary to accept liability for any failure on the part of a third party to perform existing and future legal obligations). The protection afforded by such security can be of use to employers, contractors and consultants, in particular to avoid the consequences of the default or insolvency of one of the other parties. Such securities range from documentary credit, where an on-demand bond requires the bank to pay without questioning any underlying liability, to guarantee, where default must be established before any demand can be made from the bank or other surety. This chapter discusses the differences between various types of bonds and guarantees and the mechanisms available to enforce and challenge such instruments. This chapter considers the appropriate form of security available for the protection required together with the advantages and disadvantages associated with each.

10.1 Introduction

The aim of bonds and guarantees is to offer an assurance of performance, payment or compensation from one party in the event of default by another party in the construction process. Whilst a recognised mechanism in international trade, they have become very much part of the standard toolkit in construction contracts. A contractor or consultant requires security to ensure that payment is made in respect of the work carried out in the event of default or insolvency on the part of the employer. An employer requires security to ensure that the work is completed and any advance payment is returned or compensation paid in the event of default or insolvency on the part of the contractor.

Particular care and skill is needed in drafting the documents to make sure that the wording fulfils the purpose for which the security is needed and is consistent with the underlying contract. Poor drafting or timing can jeopardise the security of the bond or guarantee, risking loss of substantial sums in respect of liability that may be unarguably owed to the innocent party but which becomes unenforceable.

Securities are used in construction projects to provide insurance against the risk allocation agreed between the parties under the contract. There are many types of bond and guarantee available: bid bonds, advance payment bonds, retention bonds, defects liability bonds, performance bonds and performance guarantees. This chapter discusses the differences between various bonds and guarantees together with the mechanisms available to enforce and challenge such instruments.

10.2 Suretyship

Bonds and guarantees are governed by the law of contract. A contract of suretyship is a contract under which one person ('the Surety') agrees to answer for the existing or future liability of another person ('the Principal') in favour of a third party ('the Beneficiary').

The nature and extent of the liability of the Principal is governed by the terms and conditions of the underlying construction contract, for example, the responsibility undertaken by a contractor or consultant for performance of engineering works and the responsibility undertaken by an employer for payment.

The nature and extent of the liability of the Surety is governed by the terms and conditions of the guarantee or bond as a free-standing agreement. The guarantee or bond identifies the circumstances in which the Surety is required to meet the liability of the Principal to the Beneficiary, usually where the Principal has failed to perform its obligations under the construction contract.

A Surety who has satisfied the liability of the Principal to the Beneficiary is entitled to be indemnified by the Principal. **Figure 1** shows the operation of such sureties.

10.3 Guarantees

A contract of guarantee is an undertaking by the Surety ('the Guarantor') to the Beneficiary to accept liability for any failure on the part of the Principal to perform existing and/or future legal obligations.

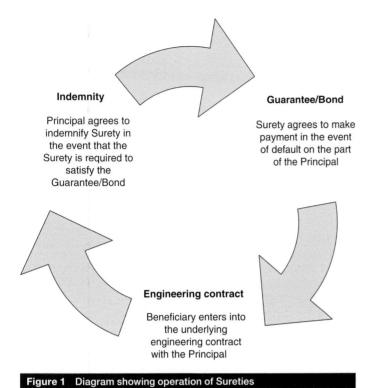

Indemnity

Principal agrees to indemnify Surety in the event that the Surety is required to satisfy the Guarantee/Bond

Guarantee/Bond

Surety agrees to make payment in the event of default on the part of the Principal

Engineering contract

Beneficiary enters into the underlying engineering contract with the Principal

Figure 1   Diagram showing operation of Sureties

The essential characteristics of a contract of guarantee were set out by Lord Diplock in *Moschi v. Lep Air Services Ltd.*

■ The contractual promise of a Guarantor to guarantee the performance by the Principal of his obligations to the Beneficiary arising out of the underlying engineering contract gives rise to an obligation on the part of the Guarantor to see to it that the Principal performs his own obligations to the Beneficiary.

■ The liability of the Guarantor is always ancillary, or secondary to that of the Principal who remains primarily liable under the engineering contract to the Beneficiary.

■ The Guarantor has a right in equity to compel the Principal to perform his obligations under the engineering contract. The Guarantor has a right to seek an injunction in appropriate cases to compel compliance with the engineering contract, although it should be noted that the courts rarely grant injunctions that require a contractor or consultant to carry out work or that require an employer to engage someone as an employee.

■ The Guarantor is not entitled to notice from the Beneficiary of the Principal's failure to perform an obligation which is the subject of the guarantee, although it should be noted that most standard form guarantees contain an express provision requiring such notice to be given.

■ If the Principal fails to perform an obligation under the engineering contract which is the subject of the guarantee, the Beneficiary can recover from the Guarantor as damages for breach of the contract of guarantee the sum that the Beneficiary could have recovered from the Principal as damages for breach of the engineering contract.

■ The Beneficiary's cause of action against the Guarantor arises at the moment of the Principal's default and the limitation period then starts to run.

■ The Guarantor is liable under the guarantee to the same extent as the Principal is liable to the Beneficiary under the engineering contract (the principle of co-extensiveness).

In practice this means that the liability of the Guarantor is no greater or less than that of the Principal under the engineering contract, whether in terms of amount, time for payment or the conditions under which the Principal is liable.

■ The Beneficiary has to establish its entitlement to damages and the measure of such damages: *Trafalgar House Construction (Regions) Ltd v. General Surety & Guarantee Co Ltd.*

■ The measure of such damages is the same as the measure of damages that could have been recovered by the Beneficiary from the Principal.

■ Any defences available to the Principal are also available to the Guarantor under the guarantee, including defences of set-off and defences of invalidity, such as illegality, fraud or misrepresentation, rendering the underlying construction contract void or voidable.

■ The Principal's liability to the Beneficiary must exist at the date on which the Guarantor's liability for damages arises although any later release by the Beneficiary, for example, by termination or rescission does not affect the Guarantor's liability.

A guarantee is required by Section 4 of the Statute of Frauds Act 1677 to be in writing or evidenced by a written memorandum or note signed by the Guarantor or his authorised agent in order to be enforceable: *Actionstrength Limited v. International Glass Engineering IN.GL.EN Spa*; *Elpis Maritime v. Marti Chartering*; *J Pereira Fernandes SA v. Mehta.*

The secondary liability of the Guarantor and the principle of co-extensiveness distinguish a contract of guarantee from a contract of indemnity. Unlike a contract of guarantee, under a contract of indemnity the Surety assumes primary liability to the Beneficiary, either alone or jointly with the Principal. Such liability is independent of the nature and extent of the liability which may arise between the Principal and the Beneficiary. An indemnity is simply an obligation to make good a loss suffered by another. The fact that the obligation to indemnify is primary and independent has the effect that the principle of co-extensiveness is not applicable, so that for example the risk that the underlying transaction between the Principal and the Beneficiary might be void or otherwise unenforceable remains with the Surety.

This distinction was explained in *Alfred McAlpine Construction Ltd v. Unex Corporation* by Evans LJ:

> A guarantee in the strict sense is a contract whereby the surety undertakes to be responsible, in addition to the principal, for the due performance by the principal of his obligations to the creditor, if he fails to perform them. The liability essentially is secondary to that of the principal and, in general, it can be said to be co-extensive with it. A contract of indemnity, on the other hand, is an independent undertaking to make good a loss suffered by

another … These differences make it essential to give effect to the wording of the contract in the particular case, rather than to categorise the contract as one of guarantee or indemnity and then seek to impose certain characteristics upon it…

It should be noted that the distinction between a guarantee and an indemnity depends on the construction of the words used in the document and not on the description of the document in the title. In *Moschi v. Lep Air Services Ltd* Lord Diplock stated:

> Whether any particular contractual promise is to be classified as a guarantee so as to attract all or any of the legal consequences … depends upon the words in which the parties have expressed the promise. Even the use of the word 'guarantee' is not itself conclusive. It is often used loosely in commercial dealings to mean an ordinary warranty. It is sometimes used to mis-describe what is in law a contract of indemnity and not of guarantee. Where the contractual promise can be correctly classified as a guarantee it is open to the parties expressly to exclude or vary any of their mutual rights or obligations which would otherwise result from its being classifiable as a guarantee. Every case must depend upon the true construction of the actual words in which the promise is expressed.

However, in practice, the use of the word 'guarantee' to describe the document will be of evidentiary value as to the intention of the parties. In *Clement v. Clement* Gibson LJ stated that the use of the word 'guarantee' in the agreement was not conclusive but that it could, in cases of doubt and if used repeatedly, provide some guidance to the court. A further guide to construction would be whether the Beneficiary's rights against the Principal and against the Guarantor were co-existent. If the person liable under the contract might be liable for a greater amount than the Principal, the contract was probably one of indemnity and not of guarantee.

Box 1 sets out examples of wording typically used in guarantees for construction contracts.

However, it is emphasised that many 'guarantees' are hybrids that do not fall into the strict categorisation of a true guarantee as a result of the express provisions incorporated into the document. It should not be forgotten that a guarantee must be construed like any other contract to give effect to its terms. The parties are free to choose their contractual terms. The wording for each guarantee should be selected to reflect the allocation of risk agreed between the parties and the purpose for which the guarantee is required.

10.3.1 Enforcing the guarantee

The Beneficiary's remedy for any failure on the part of the Guarantor to satisfy liability under the guarantee is to claim the sum due as a debt and/or damages for breach of contract.

If, on a true construction of the words used in the guarantee, the Guarantor does not undertake to ensure performance of the engineering contract by the Principal and the guarantee is limited to an undertaking to satisfy any loss and damage suffered by the Beneficiary as a result of the Principal's breach, liability

Box 1 Typical wording used for performance guarantee

Example 1

We unconditionally guarantee the proper and punctual performance by the Contractor of all its obligations, undertakings and responsibilities in relation to the Engineering Contract and we shall forthwith make good any default there under on the part of the Contractor and we shall pay or be responsible for the payment by the Contractor of all sums, liabilities, awards, losses, damages, costs, charges and expenses that may be or become due and payable under or arising out of the Engineering Contract in accordance with its terms or otherwise by reason or in consequence of any such default on the part of the Contractor.

Example 2

Now the Condition of the above-written Guarantee is such that if the Contractor shall duly perform and observe all the terms provisions conditions and stipulations of the said Contract and the Contractor's part to be performed and observed according to the true purport intent and meaning thereof or if on default by the Contractor the Guarantor shall satisfy and discharge the damages sustained by the Employer thereby up to the amount of the above-written Guarantee then this obligation shall be null and void but otherwise shall be and remain in full force and effect.

Example 3

The Guarantor guarantees to the Employer that in the event of a breach of the Contract by the Contractor the Guarantor shall subject to the provisions of this Guarantee Bond satisfy and discharge the damages sustained by the Employer as established and ascertained pursuant to and in accordance with the provisions of or by reference to the Contract and taking into account all sums due or to become due to the Contractor.

does not arise until default has been established and the debt or damages have been quantified:

Workington Harbour Dock Board v. Trade Indemnity Co Ltd (No.2) – see Lord Atkin:

> proof of damage and not mere assertion thereof is required before liability under such a bond arises.

Trafalgar House v. General Surety – see Lord Jauncey:

> It is well established that in such an action the plaintiff has to establish damages occasioned by the breach or breaches of the conditions, and, if he succeeds, he recovers judgment on the whole amount of the bond, but can only issue execution for the amount of the damages proved.

The default that has to be established is a breach of the Principal's obligations under the underlying engineering contract, for example, failure of the contractor or consultant to perform the work or services or failure of the employer to make payment.

Insolvency is one of the most common reasons for a Beneficiary seeking to claim under a guarantee. However, guarantees do not always make adequate provision for such an event, as exemplified in *Rainy Sky v. Kookmin Bank*. In many standard form contracts there is a contractual mechanism for determination of the primary obligations of the parties in the event of any insolvency. In such contracts there is provision for an accounting exercise to determine liability but insolvency does not constitute breach of contract and therefore does not give rise to default for the purpose of the guarantee: *Perar BV v. General Surety & Guarantee Co Ltd*; *Laing and Morrison-Knudson v. Aegon*. Default would not arise unless and until the accounting exercise established a debt on the part of the insolvent Principal that remained unsatisfied.

The debt or damages must be established and ascertained in accordance with the terms of the underlying construction contract, taking into account any sums due or to become due to the Principal by way of accounting, set-off or counterclaim: *Paddington Churches Housing Association v. Technical and General Guarantee Company Limited* – see HHJ Bowsher QC:

> The defendants are liable as surety only, and it seems to me to be plain on the face of the bond that the defendants are liable to pay the amount (if any) shown to be due to the plaintiffs on a statement made by the employer in accordance with the terms of the contract…Both in case of default and in case of determination on insolvency…the damages are calculated by reference to the code of the contract, which are in any event unlikely to be different from the damages at general common law. The accuracy of the employer's statement might be challenged in the courts, but the employer's statement is required before the damages can be said to be ascertained and there is no liability on the defendant until those damages are ascertained.

The guarantor is not automatically bound by an arbitration award unless the wording of the guarantee so provides as explained by the Court of Appeal in *Re Kitchin*:

> … If a surety chooses to make himself liable to pay what any person may say is the loss which the creditor has sustained, of course he can do so, and if he has entered into such a contract he must abide by it. But it would be a strong thing to say that he had done so, unless you find that he has said so in so many words. The arbitration is a proceeding to which he is no party; it is a proceeding between the creditor and the person who is alleged to have broken his contract, and if the surety is bound by it, any letter which the principal debtor had written, any expression he had used, or any step he had taken in the arbitration would be binding upon the surety. The principal debtor might entirely neglect to defend the surety properly in the arbitration; he might make admissions of various things which would be binding as against him, but which would not, in the absence of agreement, be binding as against the surety. It would be monstrous that a man, who is not bound by any admission of the principal debtor, should be bound by an agreement between the creditor and the principal debtor as to the mode in which the liability should be ascertained.

In *Sabah Shipyard (Pakistan) Limited v. Pakistan* the Guarantor agreed to guarantee the obligations of the Principal under a power purchase agreement in the following terms:

> … the Guarantor hereby irrevocably and unconditionally guarantees and promises to pay [the Beneficiary] any and every sum of money [the Principal is] obligated to pay to [the Beneficiary] under or pursuant to [the Agreements] that [the Principal] has failed to pay when due in accordance with the terms of those agreements, which obligation of [the Guarantor] shall include monetary

damages arising out of any failure by [the Principal] to perform its obligations under [the Agreements] to the extent that any failure to perform such obligations gives rise to monetary damages.

A dispute arose between the Principal and the Beneficiary in respect of their respective obligations under one of the agreements. The dispute was referred to arbitration (to which the Guarantor was not a party) and an award was made in favour of the Beneficiary. The Principal failed to pay the sum awarded by the tribunal and the Beneficiary demanded that amount from the Guarantor under the guarantee. The Guarantor refused to pay, arguing that it was necessary for the Beneficiary to establish its case against it independently from the award made in the arbitration proceedings. The court held that the Guarantor was not liable to meet the demand. The Beneficiary could not rely upon the award made in the arbitration proceedings in order to establish that a sum was due from the Guarantor under the guarantee.

It is likely that this would apply equally to adjudication awards. The Guarantor would have a strong argument that the 'rough justice' approach and temporarily binding nature of adjudication awards should not require it to pay out to a Beneficiary who might become insolvent and unable to repay the award if overturned in subsequent proceedings. Of course, this concern could be addressed by affording the Guarantor an opportunity to participate in any adjudication. The Beneficiary has a clear interest in having an effective guarantee against which to enforce any adjudication award. Therefore, the guarantee should make express provision for resolution of disputes and state whether it is intended that the guarantor should be bound by any findings against the Principal in other proceedings: *Alfred McAlpine Construction Ltd v. Unex Corporation Ltd*. **Box 2** sets out typical wording for binding a Guarantor to decisions in adjudication, arbitration or litigation.

> **Box 2** Typical wording providing for guarantor to be bound by findings of other tribunals in respect of the Engineering Contract
>
> Any money judgement of the court or arbitrator's award or decision of an adjudicator against the Employer in favour of the Contractor under the Construction Contract shall be conclusive evidence for the purposes of this Guarantee as to any liability of the Employer to which such judgement or award or decision relates (unless and until the same is set aside by any competent tribunal).

10.3.2 Challenging enforcement of the guarantee

Unless there is express provision to the contrary, any material change to the terms of the underlying contract which prejudices the position of the Guarantor relieves the Guarantor of liability under the guarantee: *Holme v. Brunskill*.

Examples of cases in which the courts have considered whether the Guarantor's obligation has been discharged as a result of variation to the underlying contract include the following:

- In *National Bank of Nigeria Ltd v. Awolesi*, it was held that where a guarantee had been provided in respect of a bank account as it existed at the date of the guarantee, by permitting the opening of a second account the Beneficiary had permitted a substantial variation of the terms of the contract without the Guarantor's knowledge and to his detriment, with the result that the Guarantor was discharged.

- In *Moschi v. Lep Air Services Ltd,* the House of Lords held that as the Beneficiary would have the right under the common law rules of contract to accept the Principal's wrongful repudiation of the underlying contract, the exercise of that right would not constitute a material variation of the contract such as to discharge the Guarantor's liability.

- In *National Westminster Bank v. Riley,* the court held that a non-repudiatory breach of the underlying contract did not discharge the Guarantor from its obligations under the guarantee. May LJ stated:

  I do not think that a non-repudiatory breach of the principal contract will, with nothing more, discharge a surety who has guaranteed that contract. A repudiatory breach, if accepted, will certainly do so, but a non-repudiatory breach will not unless it can be shown in fact to amount to a 'departure' from a term of the principal contract which has been 'embodied' in the contract of guarantee…

- In *Mercers v. New Hampshire,* the court held that a short delay in giving possession of the site (for which there was no ability to extend time under the building contract) was not regarded as a substantial breach so as to give rise to a discharge of the building contract and, as the breach did not alter the extent or nature of the risk undertaken by the Surety, was not sufficient to relieve the Surety by discharge of the bond.

- In *Marubeni Hong Kong and South China Limited v. Government of Mongolia* [2005] 2 Lloyds Law Reports 231, the court (at first instance) held that alterations to a principal contract comprising a series of debt rescheduling exercises were substantial and prejudicial to the Guarantor such that it discharged the Guarantor from liability under the guarantee.

The Guarantor may not remain liable under the guarantee in the event of any invalidity of the underlying contract (e.g. contract void or voidable, contract terminated). In *Silverburn Finance (UK) Limited v. Salt,* the Court held that in the absence of any specific provisions requiring form or notice of termination, the guarantors were entitled to revoke unilaterally a continuing guarantee in respect of future liabilities when the underlying agreement was terminated.

In order to avoid the risk that the guarantor will be relieved of liability under the guarantee by reason of a change to the engineering contract, it is prudent to incorporate express provisions into the guarantee to state that the guarantee will be unaffected or discharged by, and will remain in full force and effect in the following circumstances:

- insolvency on the part of the Principal

- termination of the engineering contract

- repudiation of the engineering contract

- waiver or forbearance on the part of the Beneficiary in respect of any obligation or breach on the part of the Principal

- any alteration or variation to the terms of the engineering contract

10.4 Bonds

A bond is a promise by deed whereby the issuer of the bond (usually the Bank) undertakes to pay to the Beneficiary a specified sum at some future date or upon the happening of some particular event.

Such bonds are contracts of indemnity rather than contracts of guarantee because they do not depend on the validity of the underlying engineering contract and there is no co-extensiveness, that is, liability of the Bank may be greater or less than liability of the Principal. The underlying commercial purpose of these securities is to provide a cash payment which is readily, promptly and assuredly made when the particular event occurs.

The wording of such bonds has been criticised by the courts – see *Trade Indemnity v. Workington Harbour and Dock Board* – see Lord Atkin:

…it is difficult to understand why businessmen persist in entering upon considerable obligations in old-fashioned forms of contract which do not adequately express the true transaction.

However, these forms continue to be preferred by Banks and other Sureties as less risky (and therefore less expensive) than new drafts because they provide a degree of certainty, having withstood the scrutiny of the courts over many years.

A simple bond is a promise to pay the bearer of the bond on the due day with no conditions attached (e.g. an irrevocable documentary credit).

In the construction industry, two principal types of bond are used: (i) the conditional bond, where payment is subject to conditions such as proof of default ('performance bond') and (ii) the demand bond, with or without supporting documents ('on-demand bond'). **Box 3** contains typical wording used in on-demand donds.

Box 3   Typical wording used in on-demand bond

Example 1

We ['the Issuing Bank'] hereby undertake irrevocably to pay to the Employer without any notice, reference or recourse to the Contractor, any sum or sums up to a maximum of [£ sum] within [x days] of the Employer's first written demand during the validity of this Guarantee

Example 2

We ['the Issuing Bank'] hereby undertake irrevocably to pay to the Employer without any notice, reference or recourse to the Contractor, any sum or sums up to a maximum of [£ sum] within [x days] of the Employer's first written demand during the validity of this Guarantee

    PROVIDED that each demand shall specify [notice to Contractor, grounds of default, quantum of claim etc.]

    AND PROVIDED that each demand shall be supported by [certificate of defaulter or other form of proof]

10.4.1 Conditional/performance bond

Where the condition is the due performance of the underlying agreement by the Principal, it is the failure to meet the condition that results in the bond becoming forfeited, or absolute. In the construction industry, the condition for a performance bond is usually the contractor's due performance of his contract, with the liability of the Bank up to a stated amount in the event of failure. In order to avoid the obligation of payment under the bond, the condition must be strictly performed so as to carry out the intention of the parties. In the absence of such express provision, it is not necessary for there to be any demand for performance, although such a provision is usually stipulated by an express term in the bond.

It is critical to have certainty as to the nature of the condition since it is the event which triggers the obligation of the bondsman to pay, which in turn will activate the counter-guarantee given by the Principal to the Bank. A successful call on a bond could have severe implications for the cash flow and credit-rating of the Principal.

A proven default bond requires the Surety to pay only when default occurs in the performance of the underlying contract. Usually it is specified that payment will be made only on admission or proof of default in court or arbitration (or adjudication) proceedings. In the absence of a judgement, award or agreement, the Beneficiary must prove default and loss in order to establish liability under the bond: *Trafalgar House v. General Surety & Guarantee Co.*

The Beneficiary is entitled to be paid only the amount of loss proved up to the limit set out in the bond.

The conditional bond has been thought the more desirable for the Principal as the Bank's obligation to pay will be conditional upon proof by the Beneficiary of the requisite default. This reduces the risk to the Principal that an unwarranted call will be made by the Beneficiary and met by the Bank.

There are disadvantages to the Beneficiary by having in place a proven default bond:

- delay and the costs of proving the underlying contractual claims before receiving the money
- difficulty in proving the underlying contractual claims in the event of the contractor's insolvency: *A.Straume (UK) Ltd v. Bradlor Developments Ltd*
- unless stipulated as a ground for payment in the bond, insolvency of the contractor does not constitute default: *Perar BV v. General Surety & Guarantee Co Ltd.*

Such an instrument is also less attractive to the banking community because of the lack of certainty. It may draw the Bank into complex contractual disputes as between the Principal and the Beneficiary and requires the Bank to make difficult assessments of the merits of a dispute in which it has no interest or control.

However, it does offer valuable long-term protection against loss suffered as a result of breach of the underlying contract, for, upon proof of default, the Beneficiary is assured of a solvent paymaster for the sums by way of compensation found to be payable.

10.4.2 On-demand bonds

In the construction industry, security for protection against non-performance by a contractor has developed in the form of a performance bond issued by a bank or other surety organisation requiring proof of default and of damage suffered. However, this level of protection has become extended by the requirement for the provision of types of bond where actual default or loss is irrelevant to the enforcement of the security (sometimes referred to as an unconditional performance guarantee or on-demand bond).

Under an on-demand bond an issuer, namely, a bank, financial institution or other independent party, agrees irrevocably to make a payment to a beneficiary against the presentation of documents without any consideration of the underlying transaction or the merits of the demand for payment by the beneficiary. The bank's sole overriding obligation before making payment is to ensure that the documents that are presented conform strictly and in all respects with the requirements set out in the bond.

On-demand bonds vary from those where a simple demand may be made at any time to those where conditions are attached to the form, timing and supporting evidence required.

The bank is obliged to pay provided that the written demand is presented in accordance with the terms of the bond. The courts have held that such a bond must be satisfied if the demand has been made in accordance with the terms of the bond regardless of any underlying dispute as to the Beneficiary's entitlement to the proceeds.

In *Edward Owen Ltd v. Barclays Bank International Ltd* it, was stated by Lord Denning MR that:

> …these performance guarantees are virtually promissory notes payable on demand… So long as [the Beneficiaries] make an honest demand, the banks are bound to pay: and the banks will rarely, if ever, be in a position to know whether the demand is honest or not. At any rate they will not be able to prove it to be dishonest. So they will have to pay…

> …the performance guarantee stands on a similar footing to a letter of credit. A bank which gives a performance guarantee must honour that guarantee according to its terms. It is not concerned in the least with the relations between the supplier and the customer; nor with the question whether the supplier has performed his contracted obligation or not; nor with the question whether the supplier is in default or not. The bank must pay according to its guarantee, on demand, if so stipulated, without proof or conditions. The only exception is where there is a clear fraud of which the bank has notice.

In *Howe Richardson v. Polimex,* Roskill LJ stated:

> Whether the obligation arises under a letter of credit or under a guarantee, the obligation of the bank is to perform that which it is required to perform by the particular contract…the bank here is simply concerned to see whether the event has happened upon which its obligation to pay has arisen.

In *R.D.Harbottle (Mercantile) Ltd v. National Westminster Bank Ltd,* Kerr J famously stated:

> It is only in exceptional cases that the courts will interfere with the machinery of irrevocable obligations assumed by banks.

They are the life-blood of international commerce. Such obligations are regarded as collateral to the underlying rights and obligations between the merchants at either end of the banking chain. Except possibly in clear cases of fraud of which the banks have notice, the courts will leave the merchants to settle their disputes under the contracts by litigation or arbitration as available to them or stipulated in the contracts. The courts are not concerned with their difficulties to enforce such claims; these are risks which the merchants take... The machinery and commitments of banks are on a different level. They must be allowed to be honoured, free from interference by the courts. Otherwise, trust in international commerce could be irreparably damaged.

Therefore, save for the exceptional circumstances, discussed next, a contractor would not be able to restrain the bank from meeting a demand on the basis of disputed claims under the engineering contract. By way of example:

■ In *Caja de Ahorros del Mediterraneo v. Gold Coast Ltd*, the court upheld a finding that refund guarantees were on-demand guarantees that could and should be honoured by the banks regardless of disputes in arbitration in respect of the underlying contract.

■ In *Standard Bank London Ltd v. Canara Bank*, the court held that the defendant bank was obliged to satisfy a call made in respect of an on-demand bond even where there was an argument that the underlying contract was a sham.

10.4.3 Making the demand

In making a demand on a bond, it is important to consider (a) whether or not the undertaking to pay is related to a failure to perform under some other agreement; (b) what triggers the obligation to pay and (c) whether there are any preconditions to making a valid demand, such as notice to the Principal.

It is common for on-demand bonds to provide for certain preconditions or formalities. The bank's obligation remains an obligation to pay on demand, but the demand must include or be accompanied by a specified document or documents, or the obligation to pay may be subject to their production. This mechanism is a means of providing in advance proper evidence that there are grounds for calling the bond. Such documents might include:

■ notice of default given by the Beneficiary to the Principal

■ sum claimed and/or breakdown of the sum due

■ grounds on which it is said that the Principal is in default under the underlying contract

■ certificate from the engineer (in respect of the contractor's default) or quantity surveyor (in respect of the employer's failure to pay sums due);

■ certified report of an independent expert

■ award or judgment in adjudication, arbitration or litigation.

The requirement for production of such documents gives some protection to the Principal against unfair demands without detracting from the security for the Beneficiary that the bank

will meet the demand. In theory, this strikes a fair balance between the parties but it is always a question of construction whether the documents produced comply with that required. The general rule is that where the Beneficiary is required to produce certification of default or the occurrence of some other event, the bank is not usually required to investigate beyond the face of the documents.

The courts take a firm but pragmatic approach to the question of construction. In *IE Contractors Ltd v. Lloyds Bank plc and Rafidain Bank* the bonds were in terms of undertakings to pay '*...unconditionally, the said amount on demand, being your claim for damages brought about by ... [the contractor]...*'. The court held that this required more than a mere demand; in addition, the Beneficiary had to state that it was a claim for damages brought about by the contractors. The demands made had requested withdrawal of the guarantees '*In view of the non-discharge by [the Principal] of its contractual obligations in making good the deficiencies...*'. The demand made was regarded as sufficient in substance even if it did not expressly state that the claim advanced was damages for breach of contract.

The counter-guarantees between the banks were for: (i) '*any sum or sums which you may be obliged to pay under the terms of your guarantee*' and (ii) '*...any amount you state you are obliged to pay under the terms of your guarantee*'. The demand simply stated '*At beneficiaries' demand please credit full guarantees amount ... due to shortages not finished yet*'. The court held that this was sufficient in the case of the first counter-guarantee because liability to indemnify arose automatically by reason of the bank's obligation to pay under the bond. In contrast, the demand in respect of the second counter-guarantee was not sufficient because it did not amount to a statement of an obligation to pay.

In *Kvaerner v. Midland Bank and Polyprima*, Cresswell J granted an injunction to prevent the Beneficiary maintaining its demand where it was clear that a false statement was made in the demand:

In the wholly exceptional case where a demand under a performance bond or Standby Credit purports to certify that a written notice has been given as required by the underlying agreement; when it plainly has not been given, the court will, in the exercise of its discretion, grant an injunction to restrain the beneficiary from maintaining the demand accompanied by what is in fact a false certificate. To grant an injunction in such a case is not inconsistent with the general principles set out above, It is, in my view, clearly arguably in the present case that the only realistic inference is that the demand was made fraudulently and it is, in my view, further arguable that it is , in the circumstances, dishonest to maintain the demand.

However, in *Montrod Ltd v. Grundkotter Fleischvertriebs GmbH,* the Court of Appeal declined to accept the proposition that the nullity of documents that on their face complied with the bank's requirements would disentitle the Beneficiary to payment. This decision emphasises that the court will not investigate any underlying dispute between the Principal and the Beneficiary in order to evaluate the documentary evidence produced to the bank. Provided that the documents comply with the express requirements of the bond, the bank will be obliged to meet the demand.

In all bonds and guarantees the period of time for which the Surety remains liable is critical. At common law completion or release of the promise guaranteed discharges the surety from further obligations: *Lewis v. Hoare* (1881) 44 L.T. 66 (H.L.). Defective work from a failure to perform and observe all the terms of the engineering contract might come to light long after completion. The issue seldom addressed in performance bonds or guarantees is the potential liability for undetected defects that appear subsequent to defects liability periods and within the permitted limitation periods. The protection of the employer could end just when he might need it most. Likewise, many bonds fail to provide for any alteration to the expiry date to take account of variations to the completion date under the engineering contract, such as the changed mechanism on insolvency that prevents completion from being achieved.

The importance of this issue is demonstrated by *OTV Birwelco Ltd v. Technical & General Guarantee Co Ltd*. In that case, the court was concerned with a bond that became null and void *'if a Final Certificate shall be issued pursuant to the provisions of the Main Contract.'* The court determined that the issue of the Final Certificate meant that the bond ceased to have effect for the future but continued to be enforceable in relation to obligations which had already crystallised. The court further determined that the date of crystallisation will usually, but not invariably, be when a call or demand is first made on the bond. On the facts the call on the bond had preceded the issue of the Final Certificate and the Surety was therefore obliged to make payment.

That case can be contrasted with *Lorne Stewart v. Hermes Kreditversicherungs AG. In Lorne Stewart*, the terms of an on-demand bond stipulated that the bond would remain in full force and effect up to and including the termination date but also that the bank had no obligation to make payment if the demand was not presented before the termination date. The demand was presented on the termination date. The Court held that the demand was made too late and granted an injunction preventing the bank from paying out on the bond and preventing the beneficiary from receiving or dealing with the proceeds.

The call on the bond is as between the Beneficiary and the bank. It is a separate contract. The Principal is not party to it. The bank will have its interest secured by a counter-indemnity. The sum finds its way into the hands of the Beneficiary. The underlying engineering contract between the Beneficiary and the Principal will usually have provisions for dispute resolution but typically such provisions will not extend to any dispute in respect of the bond.

The parties involved should consider incorporating into the bond or the underlying engineering contract an express term that the proceeds of the bond should be brought into account as

between employer and contractor following any call together with provisions dealing with interest and costs.

In the absence of such provision, probably there would be an implied obligation on the part of the Beneficiary to account for any amount paid under the bond that exceeded the true amount of the Beneficiary's entitlement to damages (governed by the engineering contract): *Cargill International SA v. Bangladesh Sugar & Food Industries Corp*; *Comdel Commodities Ltd v. Siporex Trade SA*. The Principal would be entitled to immediate repayment of any excess (together with interest) if found, following an accounting exercise: *Tradigrain v. State Trading Corporation of India.*

10.4.4 Challenging on-demand bonds

If the Principal becomes aware that a call on the bond has been made, or is about to be made, it can apply to the court as a matter of urgency to seek an order (a) preventing the Beneficiary from making a demand or (b) preventing the bank from paying out against a call.

It is very difficult indeed to obtain an injunction to restrain the Bank from meeting any demand. The starting point is that it is established by authority that a performance bond must be satisfied if the demand has been made in accordance with the terms of the bond regardless of any underlying dispute as to the Beneficiary's entitlement to the proceeds.

The English courts have developed a clear non-interventionist approach to such bonds and will not grant an injunction to prevent a demand being made unless there is strong evidence of fraud, dishonesty or bad faith. In *Cargill International SA v. Bangladesh Sugar and Food Industries Corp* (Comm.Ct.), approved by the Court of Appeal, Morison J stated:

> I start with the commercial purpose of a performance bond. There is a wealth of authority concerned with the question whether and in what circumstances an interlocutory injunction may be granted (1) against the bank which issued the bond to restrain it from paying in accordance with its terms, and (2) against the beneficiary of the bond to prevent it from calling the bond.
>
> The court will not grant an injunction in either case unless there has been a lack of good faith. The justification for this lies in the commercial purpose of the bond. Such a bond is, effectively, as valuable as a promissory note and is intended to effect the 'tempo' of parties' obligations, in the sense that when an allegation of breach of contract is made (in good faith), the beneficiary can call the bond and receive its value pending resolution of the contractual disputes. He does not have to await the final determination of his rights before he receives some moneys. On an application for an injunction, it is, therefore, not pertinent that the beneficiary may be wrong to have called the bond because, after a trial or arbitration, the breach of contract may not be established; otherwise the Court would be frustrating the commercial purpose of the bond. The concept that money must be paid without question, and the rights and wrongs argued about later, is a familiar one in international trade, and substantial building contracts...

There are grounds that can be relied on to prevent the Beneficiary from making a demand or to prevent the bank from making payment against a demand but they are difficult to establish:

- Invalidity of the Guarantees or the demands
- Fraud
- Bad faith

10.4.4.1 Invalidity

Where the underlying validity of the bond is challenged, the courts may refuse to enforce the Beneficiary's claim to payment against the bank: *Solo Industries UK Ltd v. Canara Bank*. In that case, the Court of Appeal refused to grant summary judgement to the Beneficiary on the ground that the bank had a real prospect of establishing that the issue of the bond had been obtained by fraud.

However, the Courts will construe the bonds objectively as commercial instruments and they are reluctant to give effect to technical arguments of construction that must not have been intended. The courts adopt a commercial approach to the interpretation of contracts and, in particular, the courts will look at the intention of the parties at the time of the bond although the starting point is still the express words used by the parties: *ICS v. West Bromwich Building Society*; *BCCI v. Ali*; *Static Control Components (Europe) Ltd v. Egan*.

In each case, the question to be asked is what would a reasonable person, in the circumstances in which the parties were placed at the time, have understood the parties to have meant by the use of specific language: *Sirius International Insurance Co v. FAI; Rainy Sky SA v. Kookmin Bank*.

The courts will intervene to prevent the bank meeting the demand if the bond is invalid or has expired, if any preconditions have not been satisfied or if presentation of the demand (with any required documents) on its face is not in accordance with the terms of the bond.

However, the courts are unlikely to intervene and grant an injunction against the bank solely on the ground that a demand under the bond was for a sum that exceeded the damages due under the engineering contract. In *Enka Insaat ve Sanayi AS v. Banca Popolare Dell'Alto Adige SPA*, the court held that as a matter of interpretation the words which obliged the employer to state *'accordingly [the Employer] is entitled to receive payment'* did not impose on him an obligation either to state, expressly or by implication, or to have reason to believe that he had suffered damage in the amount claimed. The meaning which the word 'accordingly' would convey to the reasonable commercial man familiar with the nature of performance guarantees and bonds was that the entitlement to the sum demanded from the banks arose under the guarantees in circumstances where, and because, a demand had been made under the guarantees stating that the contractor had failed to fulfil its obligations under the contract.

10.4.4.2 Fraud

There is an established exception to the rule that a performance bond must be satisfied in the case of fraud but the test is very difficult to satisfy. In *Edward Owen* Lord Denning MR stated:

> To this general principle there is an exception in the case of what is called established or obvious fraud to the knowledge of the bank…the bank ought not to pay under the credit if it knows that the documents are forged or that the request for payment is made fraudulently in circumstances when there is no right to payment…
>
> In cases of obvious fraud to the knowledge of the banks, the courts may prevent banks from fulfilling their obligation to third parties.

The requirement for clear evidence of fraud and the Bank's knowledge was also stated by Ackner LJ in *United Trading v. Allied Arab Bank*:

> The evidence of fraud must be clear, both as to the fact of fraud and as to the bank's knowledge. The mere assertion or allegation of fraud would not be sufficient…We would expect the Court to require strong corroborative evidence of the allegation, usually in the form of contemporary documents, particularly those emanating from the buyer. In general, for the evidence of fraud to be clear, we would also expect the buyer to have been given an opportunity to answer the allegation and to have failed to provide any, or any adequate answer in circumstances where one could properly be expected, If the Court considers that on the material before it the only realistic inference to draw is that of fraud, then the seller would have made out a sufficient case of fraud.

In *GKN Contractors Ltd v. Lloyds Bank plc*, Parker LJ considered what was necessary in order to establish fraud on the part of a Surety, referring to cases such as *Edward Owen*:

> In those cases the fraud considered was a fraud on the part of the beneficiary, and in my view plainly refers to what may be called common law fraud, that is to say, a case where the named beneficiary presents a claim which he knows at the time to be an invalid claim, representing to the bank that he believes it to be a valid claim. That, however, does not appear to me to be enough, and on the cases is not enough. It must be shown, before the principal who gave the original instructions can rely on it, that the bank was clearly aware of the fraud at the time that it paid and passed on the demand, or that the circumstances were such that the only reasonable inference was that the original demand was fraudulent. There can, however, clearly be cases where, albeit the ultimate beneficiary was not fraudulent, the bank itself may have been fraudulent. The claim presented by the ultimate beneficiary may have been presented in good faith and honesty albeit owing to some mistake was an invalid claim. In such a case, if the invalidity of the claim was known to the bank which received it, it appears to me that, if that bank were to pass on the claim as a valid claim and demand payment, it would be guilty of fraud which would justify non-payment of the demand, notwithstanding that the demand on its face appeared to be valid.

In *Themehelp Ltd v. West,* the Court granted an injunction preventing the Beneficiary from giving notice under a performance guarantee where the only reasonable inference that could be drawn from the circumstances was that the Beneficiary's conduct had been fraudulent. However, this case should be treated with caution as authority for the proposition that, in cases of underlying fraud that do not affect the validity of the contract, the courts will grant such relief.

In practice, it is often very difficult to establish fraud and the requisite degree of knowledge on the part of the bank so as to persuade a court to prevent the Beneficiary making a demand, the bank making payment under the bond or the bank recovering through its counter-indemnity. In *Banque Saudi Fransi v. Lear Siegler Services,* the Principal was unable to demonstrate that it had a real prospect of establishing the fraud exception so as to resist summary injunction by the bank on a counter-indemnity.

10.4.4.3 Bad faith

Lack of good faith was identified as a possible ground on which to challenge a call or potential call on an on-demand bond by Morison J in *Cargill.*

In *Team Telecom International Limited v. Hutchison 3G UK Limited,* His Honour Judge Thornton QC set out the circumstances in which the court could restrain the Beneficiary from making a demand under a bond for bad faith:

- total failure of consideration in the underlying contract or failure by the Beneficiary to provide an essential element of the underlying contract on which the bond depends, for example, a demand against an advance payment bond by the employer where the employer has failed to make the advance payment: *Potton Homes Ltd v. Coleman Contractors Ltd;*

- misuse by the beneficiary of the guarantee by failing to act in accordance with the purpose for which it was given, for example, shipowner imposing a second lien over goods as soon as it had persuaded the cargo owners to provide a guarantee to lift the first lien and making a demand under the guarantee: *Elian and Rabbath v. Matsas;*

- lack of an honest or bona fide belief by the beneficiary that the circumstances, such as poor performance, against which a performance bond has been provided, actually exist, for example, where there is clear evidence that the employer has prevented the contractor from performing the contract see: *Samwoh Asphalt Premix PTE Ltd v. Sum Cheong Piling PTE Ltd.*

On the facts of that case, the court refused to grant an injunction to prevent the beneficiary making a demand under the bond. However, the principles set out above indicate that it would be possible to persuade a court to grant such an injunction if there was evidence of bad faith.

An example of a case where an argument of bad faith succeeded is *HLC Engenharia v. ABN Amro* [2005] EWHC 2074 (QB), in which a company under a PFI contract with a local authority entered into a 'turnkey' contract as employer and obtained an on-demand bond from the contractor's bank ('the Bondsman'). The bond was then assigned by way of security to the bank providing finance to the employer. The employer went into administration and the bank made a call on the bond. The contractor obtained an interim injunction restraining the bank from making payment. The bond was an on-demand bond which did not, on its face, allow the Bondsman to delay or avoid payment for any reason. However, on the evidence served by the contractor, the employer admitted that the contractor was entitled to a full extension of time and the bank's expert evidence showed that there were no defects in the works, that is, there was no default justifying a call on the bond. The court held that the only inference to be drawn from the evidence was fraud by the bank in seeking to enforce the bond solely to reduce its financial exposure on the project. HHJ Coulson QC stated:

> it is plainly arguable that [the Principals] were right when they said that this was not a bona fide demand on the bond, but an attempt by [the bank], as [the Principal's] financiers, to reduce their current financial exposure on the energy centre project. I am, of course, quite unable to say whether or not these arguments will ultimately be successful, but I can say that they have a real prospect of success. There is therefore a serious issue to be tried as to the alleged fraud in the making of the demand on the bond.

10.5 Types of guarantees/bonds in construction projects

The **bid bond**, or tender guarantee will accompany the contractor's tender and is an alternative to a deposit. It gives assurance to the potential employer of the contractor's intent to enter into the construction contract if his tender is acceptable, and provides a mechanism for the payment of compensation if the contract has to be re-awarded to someone else because the contractor refuses to contract after it is proposed that his tender be accepted.

Bid bonds will exist without the underlying construction contract between the employer/beneficiary and the contractor. The potential disputes that might arise as to the scope and nature of any contract between the employer/beneficiary and the contractor are part of the risk that requires to be secured by the tender bond.

Advance payment bonds/repayment guarantees safeguard the employer in regard to repayment of sums advanced before or early in the construction process. Depending on its terms it may have a purpose of redress to a client upon contractual default by the contractor or be restricted to the unapplied balance of the advance.

Retention money bonds are used as a substitute for the withholding of retention monies by the employer. The employer gives up his right to retention of the sums and relies instead on the independent obligation of the guaranteeing bank under the retention money bond. The object of the retention money bond is to enable payment of the retention sums to be made to the contractor without waiting for the expiry of the defects period, and in the hands of the issuing bank it represents those sums that would otherwise fall due for deduction from the retention.

Maintenance or defects liability bonds are issued to guarantee that a contractor will fulfil his obligations during the defect liability or the commissioning and testing periods. This provides protection for the employer once the project completion has been achieved.

The **performance bond/guarantee** will not ordinarily be tied to any particular default within the range of the contractor's obligations. Rather it may be required simply to cover a given percentage of the tender total without regard to the increasing value of performance received by the client throughout the period of construction. It is an incentive to performance without regard to the nature and extent of any particular default.

10.5.1 Selecting and drafting bonds/guarantees

The form of bond or guarantee used will depend on the purpose for which it is required, commercial negotiations between the parties and the price payable:

- An on-demand bond should be used where it is a substitute for cash, for example, a bid bond, an advance payment bond or a retention bond.

- A certificate of default bond should be used where ready access to cash is required in the event of default but the intention of the parties is that a call should be made only in respect of certain types of default. In such cases, the bank should be obliged to require some evidence that the event triggering the bond has occurred, for example, service of a notice of default, certificate that a contractor has refused to proceed to contract, and so on.

- A performance bond requiring proof of default should be used where the purpose of the bond is to give long-term security in respect of contractual disputes arising out of the underlying contract.

In each case, regardless of the label that can be attached to the form of the bond or guarantee, the parties should ensure that the wording used serves the purpose of the security:

- Type of protection required – this should reflect the allocation of risk assumed in the underlying contract and the contract matrix as a whole

- Nature and extent of the liability covered by the bond or guarantee

- Amount of the bond or guarantee

- Period of validity of the bond or guarantee.

The parties should ensure that they have considered and dealt with the formalities required in order to ensure that the bond or guarantee is valid and enforceable:

- Consideration is necessary – usually the bond or guarantee will be executed as a deed.

- The signatories to the bond or guarantee must have authority to bind the parties.

- A 'see to it' guarantee must be in writing or evidenced by a written memorandum or note signed by the guarantor or his agent.

- The governing system of law should be specified

- The method of dispute resolution should be specified

- The jurisdiction should be selected. The practicalities of enforcing the security should be considered before the transaction and not after the Principal has defaulted.

Finally, and of greatest importance, the parties should check that any bond or guarantee is given by someone who is good for the money. A parent company guarantee by a shell company with no realisable assets is of no use if the contractor has become insolvent.

References
Referenced cases

A.Straume (UK) Ltd v. Bradlor Developments Ltd (2000) 2 TCLR 409 (CH.D.)
Actionstrength Limited v. International Glass Engineering IN.GL. EN Spa [2003] 2AC 541 (HL)
Alfred McAlpine Construction Ltd v. Unex Corporation (1994) 70 BLR 26
Banque Saudi Fransi v. Lear Siegler Services [2006] EWCA Civ 1130 (CA)
BCCI v Ali [2002] 1 AC 251 (HL)
Caja de Ahorros del Mediterraneo v. Gold Coast Ltd 6.12.2001 (CA)
Cargill International SA v. Bangladesh Sugar and Food Industries Corp [1996] 2 Ll.Rep. 524 (Comm.Ct.)
Cargill International SA v. Bangladesh Sugar & Food Industries Corp [1998] 1 WLR 461 (Comm)
Clement v. Clement (1996) 71 P&CR D19 (CA)
Comdel Commodities Ltd v. Siporex Trade SA [1997] 1 Ll.Rep. 424
Edward Owen Ltd v. Barclays Bank International Ltd [1978] 1 QB 159 (CA)
Elian and Rabbath v. Matsas [1966] 2 Ll.Rep.495 (CA)
Elpis Maritime v. Marti Chartering [1992] 1 AC 21 (HL)
Enka Insaat ve Sanayi AS v. Banca Popolare Dell'Alto Adige SPA [2009] EWHC 2410 (Comm)
GKN Contractors Ltd v. Lloyds Bank plc (1985) 30 BLR 48 (CA)
HLC Engenharia v. ABN Amro [2005] EWHC 2074 (QB)
Holme v. Brunskill (1878) 3 QBD 495
Howe Richardson v. Polimex [1978] 1 Ll.Rep.161 (CA)
ICS v. West Bromwich Building Society [1998] 1 WLR 896 (HL)
IE Contractors Ltd v. Lloyds Bank plc and Rafidain Bank (1990) 2 Lloyds Ll.Rep. 496
J Pereira Fernandes SA v. Mehta [2006] 1 WLR 1543 (Ch.D.)
Kvaerner v. Midland Bank and Polyprima (1998) *(QB Transcript)*
Laing and Morrison-Knudson v. Aegon (1997) 86 BLR 70 (TCC)
Lewis v. Hoare (1881) 44 L.T. 66 (H.L.)
Lorne Stewart v. Hermes Kreditversicherungs AG (22.10.2001) (QBD)
Marubeni Hong Kong and South China Limited v. Government of Mongolia [2005] 2 Ll. Rep. 231(CA)
Mercers v. New Hampshire [1992] 1 WLR 792; 60 BLR 26 (CA)
Montrod Ltd v. Grundkotter Fleischvertriebs GmbH (CA: 20.12. 2001)
Moschi v. Lep Air Services Ltd [1973] AC 331 (HL)
National Bank of Nigeria Ltd v. Awolesi [1964] 1 WLR 1311 (PC)
National Westminster Bank v. Riley (1986) BCLC 268 (C.A.)
OTV Birwelco Ltd v. Technical & Genera Guarantee Co Ltd [2002] 4 All E.R. 668 (TCC)

Paddington Churches Housing Association v. Technical and General Guarantee Company Limited [1999] BLR 244 (TCC)

Perar BV v. General Surety & Guarantee Co Ltd. (1994) 66 BLR 72 (CA)

Potton Homes Ltd v. Coleman Contractors Ltd (1984) 28 BLR 19 (CA)

Rainy Sky SA v. Kookmin Bank [2010] EWCA Civ 582 (CA)

R.D.Harbottle (Mercantile) Ltd v. National Westminster Bank Ltd [1978] 1QB 146 (QBD)

Re: Kitchin (1881) 17 Ch D 668 (CA)

Sabah Shipyard (Pakistan) Limited v. Pakistan [2008] 1 Ll.Rep. 210

Samwoh Asphalt Premix PTE Ltd v. Sum Cheong Piling PTE Ltd [2002] BLR 459 (Singapore CA)

Silverburn Finance (UK) Limited v. Salt [2001] 1 All ER Comm. 438 (CA)

Sirius International Insurance Co v. FAI [2004] 1 WLR 3251 (HL)

Solo Industries UK Ltd v. Canara Bank [2001] 1 WLR 1800 (CA)

Standard Bank London Ltd v. Canara Bank 22.5.2002 (QBD)

Static Control Components (Europe) Ltd v. Egan [2004] 2 Ll. Rep.429 (CA)

Themehelp Ltd v. West [1996] QB 84 (CA)

Trade Indemnity v. Workington Harbour and Dock Board (1937) A.C. 1 (H.L)

Tradigrain v. State Trading Corporation of India [2006] 1 Ll.Rep.126 (Comm)

Trafalgar House Construction (Regions) Ltd v. General Surety & Guarantee Co Ltd [1996] 1 AC 199 (HL)

TTI Team Telecom International Limited v. Hutchison 3G UK Limited 2003 [EWHC] 762 (TCC)

United Trading v. Allied Arab Bank [1985] 2 Ll.Rep.554 (CA)

Workington Harbour Dock Board v. Trade Indemnity Co Ltd (No.2) [1938] 2 All ER 101 (HL)

Further reading

Beale, H. (ed) (2009) *Chitty on Contracts, 30th Edition.* Sweet & Maxwell, UK

Andrews, G. and Millett, R. (2007) *Law of Guarantees, 5th Edition.* Sweet & Maxwell, UK

Wood, P. R. (2007) *International Loans, Bonds, Guarantees, Legal Opinions, 2nd Edition.* Sweet & Maxwell

Section 2: Operational issues in an engineering practice
Section editor: Jenny Baster

Chapter 11

Ways of operating

William Wastie Addleshaw Goddard LLP, London, UK
Louis Baker Crowe Clark Whitehill LLP, London, UK
Aster Crawshaw Addleshaw Goddard LLP, London, UK
Nigel Glover Crowe Clark Whitehill LLP, London, UK

doi: 10.1680/mocl.40878.0157

CONTENTS

When starting a new business, a decision that needs to be made and reviewed on a regular basis is whether or not the trade is, or should be, carried on through an incorporated entity such as a company or limited liability partnership. The main alternatives to incorporation are to carry out the business as a sole trader or possibly in partnership with others. The decision on whether to incorporate will ultimately centre on the trade-off between the limited liability of the owner(s) for the liabilities of the business and the significant regulatory burden that comes with it.

The equally important question which follows a decision to incorporate is which form of incorporated entity is appropriate? The choice is no longer limited to different forms of company (i.e. public, private, limited by guarantee or limited by shares) but has, since 2001, been broadened to include limited liability partnerships which are now popular both inside and outside the professional practices sector. Further, European vehicles such as the European Economic Interest Grouping offer a more targeted option for cooperative ventures within the European Union.

Both decisions demand consideration of numerous tax, accounting and commercial factors.

11.1 Sole practices

11.1.1 Nature

Where an individual carries on a business other than through a limited company and on their own, they are called sole traders or sole principals. Given the absence of any other participator, there are few formalities that need to be observed in setting up such a business. However, it must comply with certain requirements set out in the Companies Act 2006 (the '2006 Act') when operating under a business name and it must register with the appropriate taxation authorities (i.e. personal tax, national insurance contributions (NIC) and value added tax (VAT)). A sole principal is liable for all the obligations of a business without limit of liability. While such firms are usually small, in some construction industry practices sole practitioners have sizeable businesses created by employing many professional staff. A problem often encountered with sole practices is succession. Selling such practices is not easy unless the principal is willing to commit to ensuring that the goodwill, which is usually very personal, is secured through the principal's continuing commitment to the successor practice.

11.1.2 Taxation

A sole practitioner may make two types of profit: income and capital. Both of these are taxable. Where the profits are recurrent on a periodical basis (e.g. trading, rent, interest), the sole practitioner will face a possible charge to income tax. Where profit derives from the disposal of an asset owned by the sole practitioner (e.g. the premises), a possible charge to capital gains tax may arise.

The profits of a business usually derive from the carrying on of a trade and will therefore be assessed to income tax under the Income Tax (Trading and Other Income) Act 2005 (ITTOIA). The net profit or net loss (the chargeable receipts of the trade less its deductible expenditure) is used by HM Revenue & Customs as a starting point for ascertaining the figure which is taxable. If these profits have not been calculated in accordance with generally accepted accounting policies (GAAP), then the profits have to be recomputed onto a GAAP basis as a first step.

Receipts of the trade derive from the trading activity rather than from circumstances not directly connected with the trade. Receipts of the trade are only chargeable to income tax if they are of an income as opposed to capital nature. If something is purchased for the purpose of resale at a profit then the proceeds of sale will be of an income nature. Receipts of a capital nature will generally derive from the sale of an asset, which was purchased for the benefit, or use of the business on a more or less permanent basis rather than for resale.

In calculating taxable profit, there must be deducted from income receipts of the trade any expenditure, which is of an income nature, which has been incurred wholly and exclusively for the purposes of the trade, and deduction of which is not prohibited by statute (e.g. ITTOIA 2005, s.34). Capital expenditure is not deductible. For expenditure to qualify as income expenditure, it must also have a quality of recurrence (e.g. electricity, rents, staff salaries, interest on borrowings, etc.) rather than being once and for all (e.g. the purchase of assets such as premises, vehicles or furniture). To be deductible, the expenditure must also have been incurred wholly and exclusively for the purposes of the trade, thus the expenditure cannot have a dual purpose, although some expenses are allowed to be apportioned between business and private usage for the purposes of income tax deduction.

Expenditure which is not deductible in calculating profits because it is of a capital nature, may, nevertheless, qualify for income tax relief under a separate system. Under the Capital Allowances Act 2001 where expenditure is incurred on certain assets, notably the purchase of machinery and plant, an annual percentage of the capital expenditure will be allowed as a deduction from trading profits (see the corporation tax section within 11.3.3 for more detail). The allowances for industrial buildings are being phased out over the period 2008–2011.

For an established and ongoing business, income tax is assessed on the profits of the 12-month accounting period, which ends in the tax year. There are, however, special rules for determining the assessable profits in the opening or closing years of a trade.

11.1.3 Opening years

When a business commences, the assessable profits in the first three years of trade will depend not only on the chosen accounting date, but also on the length of the opening years' accounting periods. Largely, profits will be assessable as shown in **Table 1**.

The only way to ensure a true matching of taxable profits with years of assessment is to employ a fiscal year accounting period, that is, either a 5 April or 31 March year end. (Note that the HM Revenue & Customs will usually treat a 31 March year end as coterminous with the tax year.) Such a year end is also likely to simplify calculations, for example for loss claims in the opening years.

If a fiscal year accounting period is not used, some profits earned in the early years will be assessed to tax in more than one tax year. Therefore, in order to ensure that over the whole life of the business the profits earned equal the profits taxed, it is necessary to identify the 'overlap profits', that is, the profits that are taxed twice. This overlap profit is then carried forward, and only relieved either when the business ceases to trade, on incorporation or the accounting period end is changed to a later date in the same fiscal year.

11.1.4 Closing years

Unless the final period of assessment is only the second year of assessment (in which case all profits are assessed on an actual pro rata basis), the basis period for the final year of assessment will be the profits arising in the period commencing with the day immediately following the end of the last assessed basis period and ending with the day of cessation. Should the final accounting period exceed 12 months straddling a complete tax year, the last two years of assessment are as follows:

- *penultimate year*: 12 months beginning immediately after the end of the basis period for the previous year

- *final year*: period beginning immediately after the basis period for the penultimate year, and ending with the date of cessation.

11.1.5 Payment of income tax

Under self-assessment, tax on income is payable in three instalments, being

(a) a payment on account due on 31 January in the year of assessment (based on 50% of the prior year total income tax liability)

(b) a second payment on account due on 31 July following the year of assessment (again based on 50% of the prior year total income tax liability)

(c) a balancing payment/repayment due 31 January following the year of assessment.

Interest will be charged on any amounts not paid by the normal due dates.

If the total income tax liability for a year is expected to be less than the total income tax liability of the previous year, an appropriate claim may be made to reduce the payments on account accordingly.

Once the income tax liability is established on the submission of the tax return, the reduced payments on account are recomputed to 50% of the tax liability (unless the liability now proves to exceed that of the previous fiscal year). To the extent that the reduced payments on account subsequently prove inadequate interest is charged on the underpayments.

Year of assessment	Accounting period ending in year of assessment	Basis of assessment
1st year	Irrelevant	Actual profits arising from date of commencement to 5 April following
2nd year	Less than 12 months	Pro rata profits for the first 12 months of trading
	12 months or more	Pro rata profits of the 12-month period ending with the accounting date
	No relevant period	Actual profits of the tax year (pro rata)
3rd year	12 months or more	Pro rata profits of the 12-month period ending with the accounting date

Table 1 Assessment of profits for new businesses

11.1.6 Trading loss relief

The calculation of receipts of the trade less expenditure (including capital allowances) may produce a loss. Various provisions in Income Tax Act 2007 (ITA) allow the taxpayer to deduct a trading loss from other income in order to provide relief from tax on that other income. There are restrictions if the trade has not been carried out on a commercial basis. Where the circumstances are such that relief could be claimed under more than one provision, the taxpayer may choose under which to claim. It may be that the taxpayer's loss is greater than can be relieved under just one of these provisions; if so, the taxpayer may claim as much relief as is available under one provision and then claim relief for the balance of the loss under any other available provision.

Start-up loss relief (section 72 ITA 2007)

If the taxpayer suffers a loss in any of the first four tax years of a new business, the loss can be carried back and deducted from any other income of the taxpayer in the three tax years prior to the tax year of the loss. This provision might be particularly useful to a person who starts a new business after being made redundant. While the new business becomes established, it may make losses, but the practitioner may be cushioned by claiming back from the HM Revenue & Customs some income tax paid during the previous years' employment.

Carry-across relief for trading losses generally (section 64 ITA 2007)

A trading loss which arises in an accounting period, which does not match a tax year, is treated as a loss of the tax year in which the accounting period ends. The loss can be carried across to be deducted from any income or chargeable capital gains of that tax year and/or of the preceding tax year. If the taxpayer claims to set the loss against income or chargeable capital gains of that tax year and they are not sufficient to fully absorb the loss, the balance of the loss can be set against income or chargeable capital gains of the preceding tax year.

If the taxpayer claims this relief, the loss must be set against all available income, which may result in the taxpayer having no income left against which to set the taxpayer's personal relief(s); this would mean that the taxpayer's personal relief(s) for that year were wasted, since there is no provision for personal reliefs to be carried to another tax year.

The 2009 Finance Act extended the period for which trading losses can be carried back against previous profits from one year to three years, up to a maximum of £50 000 of losses. This extension will apply to trading losses made in tax years 2008/09 and 2009/10. Losses must be carried back against later years first.

Carry-forward relief for trading losses generally (section 83 ITA 2007)

If a taxpayer suffers a trading loss in any year of a trade, the loss can be carried forward indefinitely to be deducted from subsequent profits of the same trade, taking earlier years first. This has the disadvantage for the taxpayer, compared with relief under section 64, that he or she must wait until future profits of the trade would become taxable before the taxpayer benefits from the loss relief. Also, this section is more restrictive than section 64 in that it only provides for the loss to be set against profits, which the trade produces – it does not provide for relief against other sources of income or against capital gains.

Carry-back of terminal trading loss (section 89 ITA 2007)

If a taxpayer suffers a trading loss in the final 12 months in which he or she carries on the trade, this loss can be carried back to be deducted from trading profit in the three tax years prior to the final tax year. The taxpayer may thus reclaim from the HM Revenue & Customs tax, which he or she has paid. Note that section 89 does not allow relief against non-trading income or against capital gains.

Carry-forward relief on incorporation of business (section 86 ITA 2007)

If the taxpayer has suffered trading losses which have not been relieved, and transfers the business to a company wholly or mainly in return for the issue to himself or herself of shares in the company, the losses can be carried forward and deducted from income received from the company, such as a salary as a director or dividends as a shareholder. In order to be 'wholly or mainly in return for the issue of shares', at least 80% of the consideration for the transfer must consist of shares in the company.

11.1.7 National insurance contributions

A sole practitioner will pay two types of NICs, that is, Class 2 and Class 4. Class 2 NIC is a weekly contribution (£2.40 for 2010/11), and Class 4 NIC is calculated as a percentage of profits between certain levels (8% on annual profits between £5 715 and £43 875 for 2010/11 and 1% on profits in excess of £43 875). For 2011/12 it has been announced that the percentage will increase from 8% to 9% and the additional rate from 1% to 2%.

On becoming a sole practitioner, a professional should contact their local HM Revenue & Customs office to make arrangements for payment of the Class 2 NIC. The Class 4 NIC, on the other hand, will form part of the total income tax liability for the year, and will be collected under the normal payment arrangements detailed above.

11.1.8 Summary of sole practice

A sole practice is a very simple means of operation. Accounts are very straightforward and are not subject to audit or other statutory requirements. Administration and administration costs should, therefore, be minimal and the business results are not available for public inspection. Subject to tax adjustments to profits, the professional will be taxed on the profits the business earns whether amounts are drawn and used personally by the professional or not. National insurance costs are relatively low and the proprietor can withdraw funds from the business without accounting for PAYE or becoming involved in any other employee administration (assuming that no one else is employed in the business). This means of operating is also fairly flexible, in as much as when the business grows the proprietor can take on partners to work as a partnership or incorporate into a company or limited liability partnership at a later date.

However, a sole practitioner may encounter difficulty in raising finance, if he finds that professional indemnity insurance is more expensive than may otherwise be the case or, indeed, finds that some businesses are unwilling to contract with him or her simply because the business appears to the outside world to be small scale and therefore possibly without the finances to deliver on its promises. The biggest disadvantage of all though is, of course, unlimited liability. If the business fails the professional will be liable for the business debts to the full extent of his or her personal wealth.

11.2 Partnership
11.2.1 Nature

There are three types of business structure referred to as partnerships:

(a) General partnerships in which the partners have unlimited liability and are jointly and severally liable for the debts of the firm. These are governed by the Partnership Act 1890 but it is advisable to have a partnership agreement, which overrides much of this Act and regulates fully the relationship between the partners.
(b) Limited partnerships in which limited partners have limited liability up to the amount of their capital contribution but which must have at least one general partner carrying on the business who cannot have limited liability. Limited partnerships are governed by the Limited Partnerships Act 1907.
(c) Limited liability partnerships (LLPs), where all the members enjoy limited liability. Created by the Limited Liability Partnerships Act 2000 LLPs are now an established business vehicle. LLPs are regulated by that Act together with the Limited Liability Partnerships Regulations 2001 and the Limited Liability Partnerships (Application of the Companies Act 2006) Regulations 2009. Although retaining some of the characteristics of a partnership, an LLP is a body corporate, having its own separate legal personality. Its members are technically identified as 'members' rather than 'partners' and it is only for taxation purposes that an LLP is treated as a partnership.

11.2.2 General partnerships

Section 1 of the Partnership Act 1890 defines a partnership simply as 'the relation, which subsists between persons carrying on a business in common with a view of profit'.

There is no set procedure for the formation of a partnership. A partnership may be established orally or in writing. If two people come together and carry on a business with a view to making profits they will create a partnership governed by the Partnership Act 1890. Because that Act is structured to govern smaller partnerships based on equality which have to be dissolved when any member leaves, it is most unwise for a professional practice not to draw up a formal partnership agreement and there are many modern cases on the difficulties which arise on the final distribution of the assets of a business which operates as a 'partnership at will' (i.e. without a partnership agreement).

Sharing facilities is not normally seen as evidence of partnership; sharing profits is. It is therefore strongly advisable to put the terms of any partnership into writing.

Every partner is an agent of their firm and their other partners for the purpose of the business of the partnership. Any act by a partner within the scope of the usual business is within the implied authority of the partners (although partners do not usually have implied authority to execute Deeds), so long as that act is the usual way that it would be done in businesses of that kind. These acts will bind the other partners and the firm.

Every partner in a firm is liable jointly with the other partners for all debts and obligations of the firm incurred while they are partners. Partners are jointly and severally liable for the wrongful acts or omissions of any of them which cause loss or damage to third persons if such acts are either done by a partner in the ordinary course of the business or with the authority of the co-partners. They are also jointly and severally liable where a partner receives and misapplies the money or property of a third person while acting within the scope of his or her apparent authority and where the firm receives, in the ordinary course of its business, money or property which is misapplied by one or more of the partners while in the firm's custody.

Consent of all existing partners is required to change the nature of the partnership business. A majority of partners cannot expel any partner unless the power to do so has been conferred by express agreement between the partners.

Larger partnerships are often managed by a single partner (known as the managing partner) or a group of partners (who are selected by the managing partner or elected by their peers).

A managing partner, like any other partner, is not entitled to remuneration for acting on partnership business unless there is an express or implied agreement to that effect.

General partnerships often consist of different categories of partner. These may be known as, for example, equity, fixed equity, salaried and associate partners.

The difference between an equity partner and a fixed equity partner is that the latter usually has a first charge over the profits of the firm, whereas an equity partner participates only in any remaining profits.

The terms 'salaried' and 'associate' partners are misleading as the persons concerned are not usually, in truth, partners at all but employees of the practice (and are often given an indemnity by the equity and fixed equity partners against any claims). However, if it is shown that a salaried partner has been held out as a partner in the firm, that person is jointly and severally liable to the party to whom they are held out. Putting a partner's name on letterhead is not definitively holding out, because each case has been shown to depend on its facts, but no one should let their name go forward without being aware of this risk. There is a pattern of cases, usually involving smaller firms, which show the danger of being held out when the firm or its insurance cover fails or is exhausted.

The rule that partnerships may not consist of more than 20 partners unless they were given a specific exemption under company law or were exempt by virtue of their profession was repealed with effect from December 2002.

11.2.3 Limited partnerships

A limited partnership is governed by the Limited Partnerships Act 1907. Such partnerships are rare in the professional practices world but they are commonly encountered in property, investment funds and other areas of finance. It is a partnership where some of the members have liability limited to the amount of capital or property they have advanced to the firm. The purpose of such partnerships is to encourage investment in firms by sleeping partners who take no part in day-to-day management. However, because limited partnerships are not usually an appropriate vehicle for commercial operations this section is deliberately brief.

11.2.4 Limited liability partnerships (LLPs)

Origins of the LLP

Limited liability partnerships (LLPs) first emerged in the United States and, since the State of Delaware passed its law in August 1993, have become commonplace. The Limited Liability Partnerships Act 2000 (LLP Act) and the Limited Liability Partnerships Regulations 2001 (LLP Regulations) provide the foundation of LLP law and came into force on the 6 April 2001. The law relating to LLPs was again significantly amended by the Limited Liability Partnership (Applications of the Companies Act 2006) Regulations which came into force in 1 October 2009 and brought the majority of LLP regulation into line with that applicable to companies. The law now applies to Great Britain and Northern Ireland and by the summer of 2010 over 52 000 LLPs, mostly in England and Wales,

had been registered showing how popular these business vehicles are becoming, and not just for professional firms. Most major practices that were general partnerships in 2001 were LLPs by 2010.

Characteristics of the LLP

The fundamental characteristics of a UK LLP are that:

- it is a body corporate with limited liability incorporated under statute
- its registration details have to be filed at Companies House
- the LLP has the capacity to contract in its own name with the members and staff acting as its agents when making contracts
- internally, it may be governed by a members' agreement, which will be a private document, and not articles of association
- members have limited liability except where, under common law principles, a litigant can prove them personally liable for tort (such as negligence) or breach of contract
- it is 'tax transparent' meaning that the profits of the LLP are taxed in the hands of its members as if they were partners in a general partnership.

Liability profile

Given the absence of joint and several liability, the flexibility of organization and the tax transparency, LLPs are proving particularly attractive to construction industry professionals who are exposed to ever-increasing risk in a market where professional indemnity insurance is often not available to underwrite the larger projects. Although there is an obligation to file audited accounts, this is unlikely to be an issue in the construction industry because many rival firms will already be incorporated and therefore under the same duties of financial disclosure. Because of the rise of the LLP, there are few major general partnerships left in the construction industry.

A non-negligent member will not be directly liable to third parties dealing with the LLP even where the LLP's assets have been exhausted. Nevertheless, LLPs are not a reason to reduce PI cover because the business will still be liable to the full extent of its assets. Further, clients dealing with the practice may require disclosure of the PI cover before commissioning work. Still, for new members there will be the added comfort of knowing they are not potentially 'liable to the grave' for the actions of their fellow partners whilst they were in partnership.

There is some uncertainty regarding the position of a member's (as opposed to the LLP's) liability for his or her own wrongful acts or defaults. It is hoped that the courts will apply the same rules applicable to company directors and only find a member personally liable where the member has accepted a close and personal responsibility which has been relied upon by the claimant. Inevitably much will turn on the facts of each case. The Courts approach to the liability of professionals is a notoriously difficult area, with a mixture of public policy and causation interfering with the chain of legal precedent.

On an insolvent liquidation of an LLP, liability can arise for members in much the same way as it can for directors of a limited company, for example for fraudulent or wrongful trading or for clawback of profit distributions improperly made.

Body corporate status

There are important consequences of the LLP being a body corporate. The most significant of these are that much of UK company and insolvency law is applicable to the LLP, conferring upon it statutory power to grant fixed and floating charges in favour of its bankers, requiring it to appoint auditors (upon reaching a certain size) and providing that the corporate insolvency regime governs its failure or dissolution.

The members' agreement will need to cover those issues dealt with in a general law partnership agreement such as profit share and retirement rights but, because of the substantial statutory law applicable to the LLP, there will need to be a careful review of each company and insolvency law provision to decide how, if at all, it should be dealt with internally in the private arrangements between the members. The LLP Act specifically states that partnership law does not apply to LLPs and, as a result, established concepts such as duties of good faith need to be set out in the agreement if the members wish them to apply. The regime set out in the LLP Regulations as the default in the absence of a members' agreement is unlikely to be suitable in practice and, just as with a general partnership, those issues should be addressed in the agreement.

Designated members and accounts

Every LLP has to have at least two designated members who are primarily responsible for many of the statutory duties imposed on the LLP. If two members are not nominated for this purpose, all the members will be liable as designated members. Their responsibilities are akin to those of a company secretary, although rather more onerous in that they share some of the responsibilities borne by company directors.

Because the LLP is incorporated, it must file statutory accounts drawn up essentially in the same form as a private limited company. Those accounts will need to be audited by a registered auditor, except where the LLP qualifies as small or dormant under the Companies Act.

Partnerships seeking to convert to LLP status must seek advice from their accountants as to the effect that statutory accounts may have on partnership accounting policies and practices. A statement of recommended accounting practice (SORP) (last revised with effect from 1 January 2010) seeks to assist LLPs in complying with the 2006 Act accounting requirements while allowing the accounts to show third parties what they want to know without creating some of the distortions that will otherwise arise. One issue, which has arisen, is when some or all of a member's profit share and capital contribution must be shown as a debt owed by the LLP to the member. The application of corporate accounting standards to LLPs is not always harmonious. Under the SORP, what members perceive to be permanent capital of the LLP may not be reported as such. This may require explanation to institutions lending to LLP, or could even restrict some LLPs' capacity to borrow without personal guarantees from members. However, most informed readers of LLP accounts will understand the distinction which is drawn between 'debt' and 'equity' of the LLP.

In any winding-up of the LLP a member's interests in the LLP might rank alongside other ordinary creditors, particularly if that member has advanced a loan to the LLP. Those lending to an LLP may well wish to enter into agreements with members subordinating members' interests to those of other creditors. There is also a requirement that a provision should be recognised for annuities with the contingent cost being accrued and reported subject to actuarial calculations in each set of accounts.

LLP conversions

To become an LLP it is necessary not only to incorporate a new business entity but also to transfer to the LLP all the business that is currently being carried on. This business transfer may be a time consuming project. Although transferring a business from a partnership to an LLP should be tax neutral it will involve looking at contracts, leases, insurances, employment terms and, provided the transfer is of an existing partnership business (there being severe but manageable risks in transferring a limited company to an LLP), a host of other issues (including entering into new banking arrangements). Carefully planning this process to effect the transfer is vital. The process will be similar to that involved in the incorporation of a general partnership. The forms necessary for registration of LLPs are very similar to those used for incorporating companies.

With its stricter legal and accounting regime and full financial disclosure, it must not be assumed that all general partnerships will become LLPs. But the LLP format has proved to be particularly attractive to larger and multi-disciplinary partnerships where it is very difficult for each partner to be aware of the skills and risks his or her fellow partners are exhibiting or assuming.

11.2.5 Taxation

Because a partnership does not have a separate legal identity it is the partners themselves who have a taxation liability rather than the partnership as an entity. The partnership income, however, is taxable, but each partner has sole responsibility for the tax owed in respect of their share of partnership profits. The profits (or losses) of a trade or profession are computed taking the partnership as a whole as if it were a single entity. Once these are determined the question is how the taxable profits are allocated to the individual partners. Each individual partner is assessable on their share of the taxable profits of the partnership as a whole.

Although an LLP is a body corporate, the income of the LLP is taxed in the hands of the members as if it were partnership income. Borrowings for subscribing partnership capital to the LLP will also attract tax relief in the same way as borrowings into a partnership. There is a stamp duty and stamp duty land tax exemption on the transfer of assets from the old partnership to the LLP. This is subject to certain conditions, the most important of which is that on transfer there must be no change in the constitution of the partnership and the LLP in terms of membership. NIC due from the members of the LLP are the same as for partners (who are assessed as being self employed – see the earlier section on sole practitioners), which will represent significant savings for those who would otherwise have incorporated. The LLP is the taxable entity for VAT registration.

For the purposes of assessing the taxable profits of a general partnership, or a LLP, each partner is treated as setting up business when they become a partner; they are then assessed on the current year basis of assessment (see under section 11.1.2 of this chapter) while they continue to be partners. A partner is treated as discontinuing business either when he or she ceases to be a partner or when the firm itself ceases to be in business.

The partnership is required to submit a partnership return, to facilitate the taxation of the individual partner, not to tax the partnership as a whole. This return should contain a partnership statement which should show all the information necessary for the calculation of the trading profits of the partnership, including any capital allowances claims. It should show the total income, losses, tax credits and charges of the partnership for each period of account included in the return. It should also show the shares in which those sums are allocated to the particular partners.

The individual partners must replicate this information in their individual tax return, and both the partnership and partners' individual returns must be submitted to the Inspector of Taxes by 31 January following the year of assessment, if penalties are not to be charged.

Under self-assessment, all the partners are required to keep such records as may be required to enable correct and complete returns to be made. All the records required for the individual or corporate partners' tax returns and the records required for the partnership statement must be kept until five years after the 31 January following the end of the relevant year of assessment.

The records required to be kept include records of all amounts received and expended in the course of the business and what each receipt or item of expenditure is for. If the business deals with goods, records of all sales and purchases of goods must also be kept.

A partner is able to obtain tax relief on the interest on a loan to subscribe capital to the partnership (section 398 ITA 2007) provided the partnership employs the funds in pursuing its trade.

A partner making a loss in a LLP conducting a trade is only able to obtain tax relief on his loss up to the level of his capital in the LLP (section 107 ITA 2007). This restriction to loss relief does not apply to a loss in a LLP conducting a profession.

The section 64 ITA 2007 loss relief is restricted for 2007/08 losses onwards of non-active partners, or limited partners, to £25 000.

Non-active partners are those who spend less than 10 hours a week involved in partnership activity.

Corporation tax rules apply to the share of profits attributable to a partner who is a company rather than an individual.

Otherwise, the loss reliefs, payment of tax and NIC liabilities are as for sole practices as mentioned above.

11.2.6 Name of practice

The provisions of Part 41 of the 2006 Act regulate those general partnerships where the business name differs from that of the partners. Chapter 2 of that Part requires a general partnership to display prominently in the business premises the names and appropriate service addresses of the partners (such addresses may be that of the business premises). Non-compliance with this provision is a criminal offence and the firm may be prevented from enforcing any rights it has under contracts entered to whilst the business was not in compliance.

The 2006 Act provides that the business documentation of the general partnership must set out the names of each of the partners. However, if there are more than 20 partners, the names of the partners need not be set out if the documentation in question

■ does not set out an individual partner's name otherwise than in the body or as a signatory to the document;

■ discloses the name and address of the principal place of business; and

■ states that a full list of partners' names and relevant addresses may be inspected there.

The rules applying to LLPs are broadly the same as those applicable to companies and require that, whether a trading name is being used or not, the LLP's legal name and further statutory details appear on business premises and business documentation. See section 11.3.2 of this chapter (Correspondence and business documents) for further detail.

11.2.7 Service companies

Service companies are formed to provide services to a general partnership or LLP. They may employ staff and own premises and provide professional services and equipment to the practice. Service companies were initially established because of the inability of general partnerships and LLPs to retain untaxed profits and the differing marginal rates of tax between a company and a partnership.

11.2.8 Outline of partnership agreement

A partnership agreement should at the least cover

■ the commencement date

■ the firm name including its protection

- place and nature of business

- the capital required, whether it is provided in terms of assets or cash, how much each partner is contributing and whether interest is payable on each contribution (and possibly the question of future increases in contributions if such increases are anticipated)

- the division of income profit and losses if such are not to be shared between all of the partners equally. Profits may be split in a variety of ways. For example, many partnerships have fixed percentage shares that have to be renegotiated from time to time; other practices may operate a strict 'lockstep' system, whereby a partner obtains an escalating number of shares in the firm over, for example, a 5–10 year period. Alternatively, the parties may pay themselves a notional salary, with the balance being split in a way which reflects merit and/or seniority

- details of the firm's banking account and the drawing of cheques, particularly the amount that each partner can withdraw from the business from time to time in respect of their shares of the profits. An agreement may state a monthly limit and stipulate the consequences of exceeding the stated limit

- the procedures for drawing up and adopting accounts including whether all partners must sign them

- particulars of ownership of assets and increases or decreases in asset values and the shares each of the partner has in these with particular attention to goodwill and any freehold premises that may be used in the business

- work input of each partner and their role in the business

- the provision of insurance and in particular purchasing any minimum professional indemnity cover required by a regulator and the provision of cover to retired partners – this being of particular concern to construction professionals

- the decision-making processes of the firm, which for larger firms may be along corporate lines but with regular partners' meetings

- loans by a partner to the firm

- provisions for holidays and illness

- provisions for admitting new partners

- provisions for the expulsion and retirement of a partner and the financial entitlements of departing partners

- the circumstances which would lead to the dissolution of the partnership (either by effluxion of time or the death, bankruptcy or retirement of a partner). The continuing partners may be required, or given an option, to purchase the share of a deceased or retiring partner, in which case the partnership agreement may provide for an indemnity against partnership liabilities

- provisions restricting competition after a partner has left the practice. These may include 'non-competition' or 'non-solicitation' clauses and will be enforceable only if they are reasonable and designed to protect the on-going business. They are governed by a different body of law than restraints in employment contracts and depend substantially on their being freely arrived at between the partners as a fair bargain

- means of resolving disputes between partners. Often partnership agreements contain arbitration clauses as arbitration is seen as being a more private means of resolving disputes than litigation. But

with the strong growth in mediation, many professional firms are committing themselves to mediate disputes before incurring the costs of arbitration proceedings

- whether any provision will be made in the accounts for the partners' tax on the profits of the business, and if so, how this will be dealt with. (Although partners' tax liabilities on partnership profits are their own responsibility, many partnerships provide for tax in the accounts, and withhold tax liabilities from drawings, to ensure that the individual partners are able to meet their responsibilities.)

In the absence of any express agreement to the contrary, partners of a general partnership have the following rights and obligations under the Partnership Act 1890:

- to take full part in its management

- to have an equal share in profits and capital

- to contribute equally to any losses sustained by the firm

- to object to the admission of a new partner

- to object to a change in the nature of partnership business

- to an indemnity from a fellow partner(s) in respect of liabilities incurred by that partner in carrying out necessary acts in the ordinary and proper course of partnership business

- to inspect the partnership books

- not to be expelled

- to dissolve the practice on immediate notice to the other partners.

The LLP Regulations 2001 provide for a similar set of default rules, which, like those for general partnerships, will normally be unsuitable in practice. Such issues should always be addressed in the LLP members' agreement or partnership agreement.

11.2.9 The reform of partnership law

The Law Commission's proposals to reform partnership law in 2000 gathered some very positive and other negative comments, particularly around the proposal that partnerships should have continuity (to avoid the damage caused by dissolution) and separate legal personality. Given the controversy it would appear that the 1890 Act still has much life in it. It remains, however, the authors' concern that there are still partnership cases, involving usually small firms, but no written agreement, that have unfavourable outcomes, especially at first trial in local courts, and which have to be 'remedied' at considerable cost and inconvenience by the Court of Appeal. In some instances, the reforms would have prevented costly litigation. The government has, despite 'shelving' the reform of partnership law, committed itself to reform of the law relating to Limited Partnerships to be implemented in stages over the next few years.

11.2.10 Summary of partnerships

The advantages and disadvantages of general partnerships are much the same as for a sole trader, except on a larger scale, whereas LLPs are much more similar to companies although with greater flexibility. With more than one professional, the business will seem much more substantial to the outside world, and so finding finance and cheaper indemnity insurance may be easier. The following are other particular advantages of partnership or LLP as a means of operating over a limited company:

- They are ideal for professional firms where personal energies can be channelled into the goal of achieving partnership with its apparent equality of status.

- Each partner has a personal stake in the business, providing a further strong motivational force for its success.

- The affairs of the business are private, not public; for example, there is no obligation on partnerships, other than LLPs, to publish accounts.

- Partnerships are characterized by flexibility, by the freedom of contract and by the absence of registered shares.

There are, however, the following disadvantages:

- Each of the partners, other than in a LLP, has unlimited liability for the debts of the business.

- There are fewer sources of finance for a general partnership (there being no shareholders from whom to raise more funds) and lending is often guaranteed by all partners.

- Partnerships are potentially less easy to manage if each partner considers that they have a say in the business. This requires different leadership skills from those which a corporate chief executive might display.

11.3 Companies

A company is owned by its members (the shareholders) and managed by its directors under the supervision of its shareholders. However, it is an entity which is a distinct and separate legal entity to its members and directors.

A company may be limited by shares or by its shareholders' promise to pay up to a fixed sum on insolvency (known as limited by guarantee) or unlimited. If it is unlimited the shareholders are liable to pay the liquidator whatever is needed to pay all of its debts and obligations in the event of it being wound up. To that extent, an unlimited company differs little practically from a partnership and now that partnerships of more than 20 persons are widely permitted, unlimited companies are very rare.

The 2006 Act is a substantial consolidation and revision of UK company law and has replaced almost the entirety of the Companies Act 1985 and related legislation. The government introduced the 2006 Act in stages, with the final provisions coming into force on 1 October 2009.

11.3.1 Private company limited by shares

Limited companies may be private or public. Public companies can apply to be listed on the London Stock Exchange or other public markets and offer their shares or debt securities to the public and may thereby raise capital in the public arena.

Private companies cannot be listed or offer their shares to the public. It is however possible to convert a private company into a public company and vice versa.

11.3.2 Procedure for incorporation

Incorporation of a new company

A company is incorporated by sending to the Registrar of Companies the necessary fee, certain constitutional documents signed by the initial shareholders (see later) and Form IN01 which details the registered office (the formal address, which need not be the principal place of business), the first director(s) and secretary, a statement of capital and initial shareholdings and a declaration of compliance with the 2006 Act. The company may also need to appoint auditors, once it is operational, who must be members of a 'recognized supervisory body'.

The actual incorporation of a company takes place when the Registrar issues the certificate of incorporation and this normally takes approximately two weeks from the papers being filed. For a small increase in fee, incorporation can be done on a same-day basis.

Small private companies may benefit from an exemption from the requirement to audit their annual accounts. In order to qualify for audit exemption as a small company in its first financial year, the company must qualify as a small company for accounts and reports in that year. To qualify as a small company in subsequent years, it will be necessary to fulfil the conditions in that year as well as the preceding year. For accounts and reports for financial years beginning on or after 6 April 2008, two of the following three criteria must be met to benefit from the small company exemption:

- The company's annual turnover is not more than £6.5 million.

- The company's balance sheet total does not exceed £3.26 million.

- The company's average number of employees is no greater than 50.

Shelf company

An alternative to incorporating from scratch is to purchase a 'shelf company', that is, one which has already been incorporated but has never commenced business. The shelf company will usually have nominees as its directors, secretary and subscribers. New directors can then be appointed, the subscriber (i.e. the initial) shares transferred, the name of the shelf company changed and, if necessary, the articles of association altered to meet any special requirements. Clients usually opt for purchasing a shelf company because it is a quicker method.

Names

The name of the company must include the word 'Limited' if a private company, or 'public limited company' or 'plc' if a public company. However, a private company limited by guarantee may be exempt from the need to include the word limited in its name if it satisfies certain criteria. The choice of name is restricted such that a name cannot be used if there is already a company with that name on the index of names at Companies Registry. The Registrar may refuse the use of a proposed name in certain circumstances; where, for instance, the name may suggest a connection with the royal family or the government. Certain other words can only be used if certain conditions are met. The most common of these are 'Group', 'Holding' and 'International'. A company may carry on business under a name other than its corporate name but must nevertheless always comply with various requirements relating to disclosure of the corporate name and address.

Correspondence and business documents

The company letterhead and email or other electronic communications, its business letters, its websites and all order forms must set out the company's name, registered office, the registered number and the country of registration. If it is exempt from having 'limited' as part of its name or, in the case of an LLP, its name does not end in 'limited liability partnership', it must disclose that it is a limited company or a limited liability partnership. If it is a private community interest company, an investment company or a charitable company whose name does not include the word 'charity' or 'charitable', a company must disclose this fact. Also, any disclosures of the company's share capital in such documents must be references to paid up share capital. Further, the registered name of both companies and LLPs must appear, amongst other things, on invoices, cheques, notices, demands for payment and other forms of business correspondence and documentation (which could include compliment slips and business cards). A company or LLP must also display its name so that it may be easily seen by visitors at its registered office, any location where company/LLP records are kept for inspection and every place where it carries on business. Where a company displays the name of a director on its business letters apart from in the body of the letter or as a signatory, it must display all the names of the directors. Similarly, where an LLP displays the name of a member on its business letter apart from in the body or as a signatory, it must list the names of all the members on the letter unless the LLP has more than 20 members and states in the letter that a list of members' names is available for inspection at its principal place of business.

If a company or LLP is being wound up, is in administration, receivership or a moratorium is in force in respect of its debts then every invoice, order for goods, business letter or order form (including when these documents are in electronic form such as email) must contain a statement that the company or LLP is being wound up.

Registered office

Every UK company must have a registered office, which must be located in the country of registration (England, Scotland etc.).

Constitutional documents

Every limited liability company must have a constitution consisting of a Memorandum of Association and Articles of Association. The Memorandum of Association has diminished in importance greatly since the implementation of the 2006 Act but remains an essential requirement in any application for registration (and therefore incorporation) of a company. The Articles of Association and any members' resolutions which amend them (discussed later) have now assumed the role previously undertaken by the two documents.

Memorandum of association

The memorandum of association sets out the intention of the signatories (the subscribers) to form a company, to become members and, in the case of a company that is to have share capital, to take at least one share each.

For companies incorporated under the Companies Act 1985, the memorandum of association contained the objects clauses which set out the businesses a company proposed to carry on and any incidental or ancillary powers required to allow it to conduct its business. A company so formed should not act outside the objects which are set out expressly or by implication in the memorandum. If it does so, the action may be invalid depending on the circumstances and the directors may face a personal liability.

Articles of association

The primary role of this document is to set out a company's regulations for its internal management although it will also contain any restrictions on the business activities of the company which were previously contained in its memorandum of association. For companies incorporated on 1 October 2009 onwards, there is no restriction on the business it may carry out unless one is expressly inserted into the articles of association.

The articles of association will cover such matters as the rights of shareholders, procedure on an issue or transfer of shares, rights attaching to shares, the appointment, removal and powers of directors and the conduct of Board and general meetings. Many of the rules for meetings and so on, are set out in the 2006 Act but companies have a wide scope to adapt this to suit their particular requirements. The 2006 Act provides for Model Articles of Association ('Model Articles'). A company may adopt all or any of the Model Articles as its articles of association but is also generally free to amend the manner in which the Model Articles apply and to choose whatever form of articles of association they wish.

11.3.3 Structure, management and administration

Funding and profit distribution

Companies limited by shares must have an 'initial' share capital on registration as previously discussed earlier. For private companies there is no minimum share capital value and share capital may be in a currency other than pounds sterling. However, a public company must have at least £50 000 sterling of issued share capital or the Euro equivalent as specified by the Secretary of State from time to time. At least 25% of this share capital must be paid up. Once these requirements have been met, the public company must obtain the necessary trading certificate under section 762 of the 2006 Act before it can trade or borrow money.

A company may distribute its profits by means of payments to employees, including its directors provided they are not at uncommercial and excessive rates, or by distribution of dividends. Dividends must not exceed the company's 'distributable profits'. The method for determining a company's 'distributable profits' is set out in the 2006 Act and varies between a more generous test for private companies and a stricter test for public companies and investment companies. Public companies must meet net asset thresholds before profits can be distributed in order to ensure that a public company's net worth is at least equal to its capital.

Shareholders and directors

A private company must have at least one registered shareholder but this may be a nominee for a third party whose name need not appear on official documents. A private limited company must also have a board of directors (consisting of at least one director) in whose hands the management of the business is usually placed. A public company must have a minimum of two directors. In both instances, at least one director must be a natural person. There are no restrictions on the nationality or residence of shareholders or directors and meetings may be held in or outside the UK. However, care must be taken to not unwittingly make a company liable under more than one tax regime by holding meetings outside of the UK and therefore effectively conducting company business abroad. There are also no requirements for a director to be a shareholder in the company. However, a public company (but not a private company unless it is so required under its articles) is required to have a company secretary who is responsible for the maintenance of certain registers in the UK.

Board meetings

Proceedings at board meetings are governed by the company's articles. The Model Articles for private limited companies are silent on how often directors should meet but good corporate governance requires a company to hold sufficient board meetings to ensure the company's business is properly conducted. Many companies have a board meeting each month to review the previous month's financial and general performance.

The frequency of meetings will depend on the nature of the company's business and the composition of its board. Where there are both executive and non-executive directors, board meetings will normally be held at monthly intervals with intervening committee meetings of the executive directors usually on fixed days. Notice of board meetings should be given to all the directors (as provided for in the Model Articles) unless the company's articles provide otherwise. Proceedings at board meetings are usually informal but if there is no unanimity on any item of business the chairperson should put the matter formally to a vote.

Modern communication techniques now enable directors to hold meetings without being physically present in the same room (e.g. by video conferencing) though care should be taken to make sure the articles allow this (Article 10 of the Model Articles does). If urgent business arises and it is inconvenient to summon a board meeting at short notice, it is useful to take advantage of the provisions of Article 8 of the Model Articles by sending one or more copies of the resolution by post or email and so on, to each director for written indication of their agreement. Such resolutions are equivalent to a resolution passed at a board meeting and should be inserted in the minute book.

General meetings

Shareholder general meetings may be either general, annual or class (the last only being held in the case of business when shareholders hold different classes of shares). A general meeting ('GM') may, subject to the articles and fulfilment of statutory notice periods, be convened at any time.

The only business which may validly be transacted at a GM is the business specified in the notice convening the meeting. Business that would be undertaken at GM by means of resolutions (voting) would include the following:

(a) *Ordinary resolutions*: (these require over 50% of the votes cast to be in favour)

■ the giving of authority for the allotment of securities

■ removal of directors.

(b) *Special resolutions*: (these require a 75% of the votes cast to be in favour)

■ alterations to the articles of association

■ change of name

■ reduction of capital (which for public companies also requires a court order and for private companies requires either a court order or solvency statement from the directors)

■ disapplication of allotment pre-emption rights

■ various alterations to the company's status by re-registration

■ purchase of own shares (although public companies may only require an ordinary resolution if they are purchasing their own shares through a 'recognised investment exchange').

Shareholder written resolutions

Anything which may be effected by a resolution of a private company in general meeting (other than removing a director or auditor) may, instead of a meeting being held, be done by a written resolution. It is important to note that written resolutions are not available to public companies. The 2006 Act lays down the procedure for written resolutions. Generally, these must be circulated by the board to all eligible members and to be valid must be signed and returned to the company by the requisite majority within 28 days (or, if different, the period provided in the articles). Who needs to sign them depends on the class or resolution. An ordinary resolution being passed by written resolution needs to be signed by (at least) those members who in a general meeting would have been able to cast over half the total votes on the resolution. A special resolution being passed as a written resolution must be specified as such on the face of the written resolution and needs to be signed by (at least) those members who in a general meeting would have been able to cast 75% of the total votes on the resolution.

Annual general meetings (public companies only)

Every public company must hold a general meeting in each calendar year as its annual general meeting (AGM). These must be held within six months of the company's accounting reference date.

The usual business at AGMs includes consideration of the reports and accounts laid before the meeting, the declaration of a dividend (if any), the election of directors, the reappointment of the auditors and fixing of their remuneration, renewal of directors' authority to allot shares and disapplication of pre-emption rights.

A private company is not required by the 2006 Act to have an AGM though it may be inserted as a requirement in its articles of association if that is desired.

Powers of directors and officers of a company

A director of a UK company owes certain duties to the company (which in most cases, means to its members as a whole, but can, in some cases, extend to its creditors as well) including a duty to act in a manner he believes is most likely to promote the success of the company and a duty to carry out his or her responsibilities with reasonable care and skill. Breach of some of these duties can result in the director incurring personal or criminal liability. It has become increasingly common to take out insurance at the expense of the company to protect directors against civil claims for breach of duty and other director's risks.

Statutory books

A company is obliged to maintain certain statutory books: the register of members (listing details of shareholders), the register of directors, the register of secretaries (for public companies and those private companies who opt to have a secretary), the register of charges, the register of directors' interests in shares and minute books of the shareholders' and board meetings. The statutory books are in certain cases open to public inspection and copies must be provided on request. Each year, the company is obliged to file an annual return with the Registrar of Companies, giving details of share capital, shareholders, directors, its activities and the location of its registered office and statutory books.

Accounting requirements

A company must maintain accounting records showing cash flow and the assets and liabilities of the company. The directors are required to produce a profit and loss account and balance sheet in respect of each financial year of the company which (in the case of a public company) may be laid before a general meeting. In practice this general meeting will be the AGM. They must also produce a directors' report ('Annual Report') on the development of the company's business. If subject to an audit, the company's auditors must produce a report on the accounts ('Auditors' Report') confirming that the accounts give a 'true and fair view' of the company's affairs. The exact content of the accounts and annual report is determined by the 2006 Act. Small and medium-sized companies (defined by reference to turnover, balance sheet and number of employees) are exempted from certain accounting requirements and dormant companies are exempt from the requirement to appoint an auditor (but may appoint one if they wish).

Taxation

There are two taxes which will potentially affect a company registered in the UK, whether or not it is a subsidiary of a non-UK based company. These are corporation tax and VAT.

Corporation tax

A UK-incorporated business will pay corporation tax on both income profits and chargeable gains. The main corporation tax rate has been 28% since 1 April 2008. This applies if the combined income profits and chargeable gains of a single company, unconnected with any other, are £1.5m or more. The rate at which small single companies unconnected with each other, with profits and gains of up to £300 000, pay corporation tax is 21% from 1 April 2008. Between the two thresholds of £300 000 and £1.5 m, a marginal rate applies. Where a number of companies are connected with each other, or 'associated', these limits, for each company, are divided by the number of companies that are associated with each other.

The main rate is due to reduce to 27% from 1 April 2011 and then down to 24% in 2014/15 in annual 1% reductions. The small companies rate is due to reduce to 20% on 1 April 2011.

Companies that pay tax at the small companies rate or at marginal rates, are generally required to pay corporation tax nine months after the end of the financial year. However, companies that pay tax at the full rate are generally required to make quarterly payments on account of the estimated tax due for a year in the middle of the 7th, 10th, 13th and 16th months following the beginning of the financial year. Interest will be charged and paid on any payments on account that do not equal those which should have been paid, once the final tax liability has been determined.

Capital allowances are generally available in respect of capital expenditure on plant, machinery and industrial buildings. Such allowances can then be set off against taxable profits in the relevant period.

In relation to plant and machinery, the annual allowance is 20% (to reduce to 18% in April 2012) of the original cost less any allowances already given. Certain expenditure on integral features however is placed into a special rate pool with a reduced annual allowance of 10% (to reduce to 8% in April 2012). From 1 April 2008, first year allowances have generally been replaced by an Annual Investment Allowance. The first £50 000 of qualifying capital expenditure can be deducted in full in the year of acquisition. However, from 31 March 2010 the allowance increased to £100 000, but from 1 April 2012 it will decrease to £25 000. In addition, for the year 1 April 2009 to 31 March 2010 the first year allowance was reintroduced allowing small and medium sized entities a further allowance at 40% on qualifying expenditure above the £50 000 allowance. Industrial buildings have an allowance of 4% of the original cost per year however; these will be abolished by April 2011 and are currently undergoing a phased withdrawal, beginning from April 2008.

Losses

A trading company can only utilise trading losses in a limited number of ways. They can be set off against other income and capital gains of the current financial year or the previous year, or carried forward indefinitely against future trading profits from the same trade. (Note that the losses may not be carried forward and set off against other income or capital gains arising in the future.) An additional measure was introduced for companies with accounting periods ending between 24 November 2008 and 23 November 2010. This allows for a maximum of £50 000 to be carried back for a further two years after a carry back to the preceding year. This applies for each 12 month accounting period that ends between 24 November 2008 and 23 November 2010.

Alternatively, where a trade ceases, terminal losses of the last 12 months' trade may be carried back up to three years against other income and capital gains.

VAT

VAT law is harmonized across Europe and UK VAT law is mainly contained in the Value Added Tax Act 1994 (VATA 1994). VAT is chargeable on each stage of the supply of goods and/or services process. There is a credit mechanism for VAT registered businesses which provides that the amount of VAT payable to Customs and Excise (C&E) is calculated by deducting the amount of VAT a taxable person charges his or her customers (i.e. the output tax), from the VAT charged to the taxpayer on business purchases (i.e. the input tax). The resulting balance is the amount of VAT due to C&E. Normally, VAT cannot be reclaimed if it relates to non-business activities or 'exempt' supplies. In principle, VAT is neutral for businesses, as taxpayers are collecting tax from their customers on behalf of the government and reclaiming from the government tax which they have had to pay out to their suppliers.

VATA 1994, Schedule 9 details specific businesses that can make 'exempt supplies' (in which case no VAT is chargeable), these include the granting of an interest in land and buildings – although there are exceptions, and it is also possible to waive the exemption by 'opting to tax' thereby creating a supply subject to VAT.

The supply of services by construction industry professionals is likely to be a taxable supply, provided the taxable limits have been reached.

The UK standard rate of VAT is currently 17.5% but will rise to 20% from 04 January 2011.

All new businesses will need to register with Customs and Excise for VAT purposes if taxable supplies of goods and services are in excess of the set threshold. The registration limit is reviewed annually in the UK budget (see HM Revenue & Customs VAT website for details of current thresholds).

National insurance contributions

A company is not required to pay NICs in respect of its own profits. However, it must pay employer's NIC, at variable rates up to a maximum of 12.8% (for 2010/11) and 13.8% (from 2011/12) of any amounts paid to its employees. As 'employees' includes any shareholders/directors, this constitutes an additional charge on amounts drawn by way of salary by the owners of the business. This charge is in addition to the NIC payable by the employees themselves, at rates of up to 11% (for 2010/11) increasing to 12% (for 2011/12).

The employer's NIC charges mentioned earlier may be avoided if income is taken by shareholders/directors by way of dividend, rather than salary. However, taking a reduced salary in preference for dividends can have other repercussions, for example in terms of the maximum amount of pension contributions that may be made. The amount of income taken by way of salary versus dividend must, therefore, be weighed carefully in each individual case.

11.3.4 Public limited company

Nature

A public limited company is a company limited by shares or limited by guarantee and having a share capital and whose certificate of incorporation states that it is a public company and has been registered as such. Public companies limited by guarantee can no longer be formed. Any other company is a private company.

A public company must include the words 'public limited company' (or the abbreviation 'plc') at the end of the company's name and before commencing trading it must satisfy requirements as to the minimum amount of issued share capital.

A public company may (but need not) apply to have its shares listed on the London Stock Exchange or on the Alternative Investment Market or another public market. In each case, this means that a price will be quoted at which dealings in the company's shares will take place.

The listed market

Other than in exceptional cases, only a large public company, which has traded for at least three years, can apply for its shares to be listed on the Official List maintained by the UK Listing Authority (UKLA) (a branch of the Financial Services Authority) and admitted to trading on the main market of the

London Stock Exchange. The main market is the London Stock Exchange's 'regulated market' with the onerous obligations which that entails. To list on the main market, a company must comply with the initial and ongoing requirements of the UKLA and the London Stock Exchange as to publication of information about the company's affairs. Listing on the Official List/main market means that the company's shares are among the most marketable of all shares; only around 2 700 of the UK's companies are listed on the London Stock Exchange, compared with a total of over 1 000 000 companies registered in the UK.

The Alternative Investment Market (AIM)

AIM, which was set up in June 1995, is less stringently regulated than the main market of the London Stock Exchange. AIM deals in the shares of smaller and growing companies and provides a market place with lower costs and less regulation than the main market and, therefore, conversely a higher degree of investment risk. There is no minimum market capitalisation requirement, no minimum number of shares required to be in public hands and no requirement for an established trading record (although related parties and employee shareholders will be prohibited from selling their shares for the first year after admission where the company has not been independent and earning revenue for at least two years).

Differences between public and private companies

The 2006 Act applies to both public and private companies but there are many differences of detail that (in the case of a public company) apply to all public companies, not just listed companies.

- A public company must have at least two directors while a private company can have just one director who may also be the only shareholder.

- A private company is no longer required to have a company secretary (subject to express requirements in its articles) but if it does have a secretary, the secretary need not be specially qualified or experienced. The company secretary of a public company must have certain professional qualifications and the requisite knowledge and experience for the position.

- Only a private company can buy back the shares of a member who wishes to leave the company where the company's accumulated profits are not sufficient and it is necessary to use capital for the purchase.

- A private company is prohibited from offering its shares to the public.

- There are more onerous provisions regulating directors' dealings with their company if the company is a public company.

- Private companies up to a certain size may be permitted to file abbreviated accounts with the registrar of companies.

- Only a private company is eligible for an exemption from the requirement to have its year-end accounts audited.

- Private companies have no statutory obligation to hold an annual general meeting.

- Only private companies can dispense with the formality of holding general meetings by having shareholders sign resolutions in writing.

Differences in practice

- In a private company, the directors and shareholders are often substantially the same people. In a public company (especially if it is listed) there will usually be significant differences in the identity of the shareholders (who are likely to include institutional investors) and the directors (whose position is more like that of employees who are paid to manage the business).

- In a private company, the shareholders cannot easily sell their shares because the articles of association usually contain restrictions on transfer (often in the form of directors' power of veto on the registration of the transfer) and because of difficulties of valuation, given that there is no ready 'market' for the shares. In a public company, there is less likely to be any restriction on transfer and, if the shares are listed on a public market, such as the main market of the London Stock Exchange or AIM, there can generally be no restriction.

- A private company may, or may not, choose to pay dividends to its shareholders; many private companies pay no dividend at all. In practice, a public company, which is listed, must have a record of paying dividends every year in order to encourage investment in that company.

- In the case of a company with only one class of shares, the directors of a private company have authority to allot an unlimited number of shares for an indefinite period absent any restriction in the articles of association.

11.3.5 Procedure for incorporation

A company can either be incorporated as a public company or an existing private company can be re-registered as public.

The process of incorporating as a public company is similar to the incorporation of a private company in that certain documents must be lodged with the Registrar of Companies, namely the memorandum and articles of association, Form IN01 (Application to register a company) and a fee. A public company, incorporated as such, cannot trade until the aggregate nominal value of its allotted share capital satisfies the minimum of £50 000 and it has applied for and obtained a trading certificate (using Form SH50). Alternatively, it can be registered as private so that a trading certificate is not required.

The articles of association must be in a form suitable for a public company. The name must end with the words 'public limited company' or 'plc' (the Registrar will accept 'plc') or the Welsh equivalent for companies registered in Wales (if the promoters wish).

A private company may be re-registered as a public company by passing a special resolution to that effect. The 2006 Act provides that as well as approving the re-registration, the special resolution must also make such alterations to the memorandum and articles of association as are necessary to conform with the requirements of the 2006 Act relating to the constitution of a public company. An auditor's report and balance sheet are also required.

At the time when the special resolution is passed, the nominal value of the company's allotted share capital must not be less than the authorized minimum. This reflects the requirement applicable to companies first incorporated as public companies on applying for a trading certificate. Further, each of the allotted shares must be paid up at least as to one-quarter of the nominal value of that share and the whole of any premium on it. Certain shares, such as shares allotted under an employees' share scheme, are disregarded both when considering whether the allotted shares are adequately paid up and when determining whether sufficient capital has been allotted.

After the passing of the special resolution, the company then applies for re-registration using form RR01. The form must be signed by a director or secretary and be accompanied by the following documents:

- a printed copy of the revised articles of association
- a copy of the relevant balance sheet (prepared not more than seven months before the application) and of the auditors' unqualified report on it
- the auditor's written statement that, in his opinion, at the balance sheet date the amount of the company's net assets was not less than the aggregate of its called-up share capital and undistributable reserves
- a 'valuation report', subject to certain exceptions, where shares have been allotted by the company otherwise than for cash between the date of the relevant balance sheet and the date on which the special resolution was passed
- if there is no existing company secretary, a statement of the proposed secretary of his/her/its consent to act as secretary
- a statutory declaration in the prescribed form made by a director or the secretary.

When a private company re-registers as a public company there is no separate need to apply for or have a trading certificate.

Once a company is incorporated as a public company, the company name must appear in a conspicuous position at every place in which it carries on business and on business letters, invoices, cheques and other items of stationery (further details on the required trading disclosures are set out under section 11.3.2 *Correspondence and business documents*). The company and any officer in default are liable to a fine and an officer in default may also be personally liable. If the company has a common seal it should also be changed.

Memorandum of association

The memorandum is the same as that for private companies.

Articles of association

These are as for private companies. If the public company is listed, the rules applicable to listed companies also specify certain additional provisions be included in the articles.

11.3.6 Structure, management and administration

Board of directors

English companies do not (as is the case in many European jurisdictions) have separate supervisory and executive boards. Rather, the articles typically vest management in a single board of directors. There is no company law reason why there should be more than two directors for a public company. Commonly, however, particularly in the case of substantial companies, the board often contains a number of directors, both executive and non-executive. Whereas the executive directors perform executive functions over and above their duties as directors (for which they are separately paid), the non-executive directors play a less active role, which may extend simply to regular attendance at board meetings and meetings of committees.

The Combined Code on Corporate Governance (FSA, 2003) (a set of rules applicable to Officially Listed companies admitted to the main market of the London Stock Exchange) suggests that all directors, whether executive or non-executive, should be subject to election by shareholders at the first opportunity after their appointment and thereafter every three years.

The board of directors includes a balance of executive and non-executive directors so that no one individual or small group of individuals can dominate board decisions.

In addition, the UK Listing Authority (UKLA), when deciding whether a company is suitable for the admission of its securities to the Official List, places great emphasis on whether the composition of the board displays the range of skills and experience appropriate for a quoted company.

In order for a company to be efficiently run, the Institute of Directors states that the members of the board

> must possess sufficient breadth of experience and knowledge in the wide range of subjects, situations and disciplines which may impinge upon the company's affairs and its business environment … the executive directors must provide specialist knowledge and a close understanding of the workings of the company and the practical implications of executing policies and strategies … complementary skills [of] worldly wisdom, objectivity, independent judgement and broad experience of the non-executive directors provide the necessary additional ingredient to ensure that the board can adequately address all the complex issues which are required of it.

The board is overseen by the chairperson who may or may not also be the chief executive (managing director). The chairperson is primarily responsible for the working of the board and its balance of membership subject to board and shareholders' approval. He or she should retain sufficient distance from the day-to-day running of the business to ensure that the boards are in full control of the company's affairs. The chief executive is, however, in day-to-day operative control of the company. Generally, it is recommended that the two roles are not combined and listed companies will be required to explain any decision to do so in contravention of the recommendations of the *Combined Code*.

Executive directors

The executive directors provide the top level of day-to-day management and often within particular spheres of specialism which may be reflected in their titles such as finance director, marketing director, and so on. Usually the executive directors have service contracts with notice or contract periods generally of one year and, frequently, their remuneration includes not only a basic salary but other benefits over and above, such as performance-related earnings and/or share options designed to align their interests closely with the interests of the company's shareholders.

Non-executive directors

The non-executive director's role varies depending on the circumstances. In some cases, the director may be a nominee of a major shareholder appointed for the purpose of monitoring that shareholder's investment but it is recommended that the majority of non-executive directors should be independent of the company, its management and any business or other relationship which could interfere with their independence.

A non-executive director has equal status and legal responsibility like the executive directors. They are equal board members and participate fully in board decisions. Their role is:

- to provide a balancing influence between those who have an interest in the company and the public

- to give the board independent advice and provide a greater depth of skill and experience

- to monitor the activities of top management and the board itself and report any deficiencies to the shareholders

- to help ensure that adequate financial information about the company is disseminated to shareholders and the public.

Non-executive directors are usually appointed for an initial period of three years.

Audit committee

The audit committee is primarily concerned with the copious amount of financial information which statutory and London Stock Exchange regulations require to be disseminated to the shareholders and the public. Usually it will select accounting policies, review draft accounts and discuss various matters with the auditors, such as the nature and extent of the audit and any problems arising from it. It is recommended that such a committee comprises at least three members (two in the case of smaller companies) all of whom should be independent non-executive directors.

Duties of directors

Prior to October 2007, directors' general duties were to be found in the common law and therefore in the judgements of a large number of cases. In an attempt to make them more accessible, the 2006 Act has taken the government's perception of the most important of them and put them into statute for the first time. Among other duties, the 2006 Act requires directors to act within their powers, not to accept benefits from third parties, to avoid conflicts of interest and to exercise reasonable skill, care and diligence. Above all, the 2006 Act requires directors to promote the success of the company for the benefit of the members taken as a whole while taking into consideration a non-exhaustive list of factors (including employees and the wider community) and the likely consequences of a decision in the long term and its impact on the environment.

Directors still have a number of general duties remaining at the common law, such as the duty to consider the interests of creditors in circumstances of potential insolvency. In addition, they have numerous specific statutory and regulatory duties including the duty to have certain transactions between them personally (or their family etc.) and their companies first approved by shareholders.

Directors owe their duties to the company and not to individual shareholders. Until October 2007, if directors breached their duties (subject to certain exceptions), only the company, acting through its board, could bring a claim. The exceptions broadly require an element of personal benefit and wrongdoing by the directors, generally tainted by fraud. The 2006 Act gave individual shareholders the right to bring an action in the name of the company against directors for negligence, breach of duty or breach of trust.

Where a public company obtains a listing, the directors must steer the company through the flotation process and are also responsible for the accuracy of the prospectus (effectively the document which 'sells' the company to investors and forms the basis of the contract between the two). Errors or omissions in the prospectus may give rise to personal liability on the part of the directors. Following the flotation, the directors must ensure that the company complies with the requirements of the 'continuing obligations' imposed by the Listing Rules and other FSA Handbooks. Some of these obligations directly impinge upon the director's personal freedom of action.

One of the key advantages of a public company is that it can offer its shares or debentures to the public. Although there are considerable advantages in being able to raise finance from the public, a company is subject to a much more exacting statutory regime upon becoming public.

Share capital

- The authorised minimum capital of a public company must be in issue and allotted shares must be paid up as to at least one-quarter of their nominal amount plus the whole of any premium.

- A public company is obliged to obtain a valuer's report on the allotment of shares for a non-cash consideration (with certain exceptions).

- The statutory rights of pre-emption on an issue of securities may only be disapplied in respect of shares which the directors already have authority to allot and must be done by means of a special resolution or a provision in the articles. Private companies have the additional flexibility of being able to exclude pre-emption indefinitely if enabled to do so through a provision in their articles.

- Where the net assets of a public company have fallen to half or less of its called-up share capital, the directors must convene a General Meeting to decide what to do.

- A public company may not purchase or redeem its own shares out of capital without first re-registering as a private company which, as discussed earlier, has such powers.

Directors

- Public companies need at least two directors.

Shareholders

- The shareholders of a public company must notify the company of certain interests in the company's shares upon request.

Administration

- A resolution of the company in general meeting or a resolution of a meeting of a class of members will usually be required in order to perform certain actions, especially if the public company is listed.

Financial assistance

- A public company is generally prohibited from giving financial assistance to a third party where the principal purpose is to facilitate acquisition of its own shares. Limited exceptions apply such as, for example, for employee share schemes.

Accounts

- The period for laying and delivering accounts is generally six months after the end of the relevant accounting period.

Listed companies

- Once a company seeks a listing, it becomes subject to more regulation, especially as a result of the Listing Rules and the Disclosure and Transparency Rules, the application of which is overseen by the UKLA. The rules (in addition to other, more procedural, requirements contained in the London Stock Exchange's Admission and Disclosure Standards) lay down the procedures for obtaining a listing of securities and the obligations to which a company and its directors will be subject once the securities are listed.

- A company whose shares or debentures are listed on 'prescribed markets' (these include the main market, AIM and PLUS markets – formerly OFEX) must notify the Exchange of information about its listed securities disclosed to it by a director complying with his or her obligations (i.e. duty to disclose the shareholdings of the director and those of persons connected to him).

Marketing

The marketing of a public company's securities is strictly regulated in order to afford as much protection as practicable to potential investors. On the issue of securities to the public, a company must generally issue a formal document known as a 'prospectus' containing detailed information about the company and its business. The purpose of this document is to ensure that potential investors have sufficient information to be able to make an informed decision as to whether or not to invest.

The Alternative Investment Market (AIM)

As discussed in section 11.3.4 earlier, the AIM is a distinctly separate market from the Official List. Companies may choose never to move to the Official List, although they may do so if they wish (assuming that they meet the procedural and suitability criteria).

Features of the AIM in comparison with the Official List are that:

- there are no minimum limits on capitalisation (with the exception of investment companies) or on the amount of shares in public hands. It is a basic condition of listing on the Official List that the expected market value of the shares for which listing is sought be at least £700 000 and that at least 25% of the shares be in the hands of the public at the time of admission to listing (and on an ongoing basis)

- there is no minimum trading record requirement (generally an Official Listing requires a three-year trading record)

- there are considerably less continuing obligations imposed on the company and its directors following admission to AIM.

Certain basic conditions must still be satisfied, however, before a company will be admitted to the AIM:

- the issuer must be a public company;

- its securities must be freely transferable;

- all issued shares of the same class must be admitted to trading;

- all shares must be capable of electronic settlement;

- the company must have published accounts which conform with International Accounting Standards; and

- a nominated adviser must be appointed and retained at all times.

Taxation, VAT and NIC

All these are as for private companies.

Summary of companies (public or private)

In summary, the advantages of limited companies are:

- the limited liability of the members – shareholders are not liable for the torts and obligations of a limited company other than to the amount (if any) unpaid on their shares

- the ability to raise capital from outside the existing membership

- the ability to borrow money in the company's name

- a company is taxed in its own right as distinct from its members

- the continuing existence of the business notwithstanding the debt or bankruptcy of all or any of its existing members.

The disadvantages of limited companies are:

- the application of disclosure requirements under the 2006 Act

- greater formality and procedure in setting up, running and winding up a company

- a potentially greater tax burden

- the need to formally audit accounts each year (upon reaching a certain size).

11.4 European Economic Interest Groupings (EEIGs)

11.4.1 Nature

An European Economic Interest Grouping (EEIGs) is a special form of business organization set up by the European Community in 1989 with a view of making the single market more accessible. The purpose of an EEIG is to enable cooperation between individuals and organizations in different member states. It may operate in any part of the EU and enter into arrangements with organizations outside the EU.

11.4.2 Advantages

- An EEIG is a flexible structure and no fixed capital contribution is required.
- It is a legal structure recognized in all member states.
- It enables cooperation without loss of independence.
- It has legal capacity and tax transparency.

11.4.3 Disadvantages

- There is no public investment.
- It cannot buy shares in its members or other EEIGs or employ more than 500 people.

- Its members have unlimited joint and several liability.
- It must carry on the same or similar business to its members, with the aim of enabling its members to improve their own results, but cannot be formed with the object of making a profit (although it may do so as a consequence of its normal operations).

11.4.4 Procedure for setting up an EEIG

An EEIG is formed by virtue of the drawing up of a contract which is registered either in the member state where it has its centre of administration or where one of its members has its central administration. In the UK, EEIGs are registered at Companies House. There must be at least two members based in different member states. The contract must include at least the name, address, objects and duration (may be indefinite) of the EEIG and details of its members.

The establishment of an EEIG must be announced in the *Official Journal of the European Communities (OJEC)* and the *London Gazette*.

The name of the EEIG must include either 'European Economic Interest Grouping' or the abbreviation 'EEIG' – otherwise substantially the same restrictions apply as do to UK companies.

11.4.5 Constitutional documents

The EEIG is formed by a contract between the members, which in the UK is registered with the Registrar of Companies.

Limited company	LLP, partnership or sole trader
Profits subject to corporation tax at max. 28% for the financial year 2010 where profits exceed £1 500 000 (reducing to 27% on 1 April 2011). Profits taxed at 21% for the financial year 2010 if below £300 000 (reducing to 20% on 1 April 2011)	Profits subject to income tax at max. 40% where individual's taxable income exceeds £37 400 (for 2010/11) and at 50% on taxable income above £150 000
Owner/manager subject to income tax on amounts withdrawn as dividend or remuneration	Owner/manager subject to income tax on net profits irrespective of amounts withdrawn. No tax on drawings themselves
Owner/manager and family member employees must be paid the national minimum wage (NMW). Dividends do not count as pay for NMW purposes	The NMW does not apply to the genuinely self-employed. Furthermore, guidance on NMW indicates that it does not need to be paid to family members who live at home and participate in the family business
Owner/manager's salary an allowable deduction from company's profits	Owner's salary not allowable
Income tax charge on company car and other benefits provided to owner/manager	Private mileage and expenses disallowed in business accounts
Start-up losses can only be set against company profits	Start-up losses in first four years can be carried back three years against other income prior to start of trading
National Insurance Contributions payable by both employer (max. 12.8%) and employee (max. 11%) on remuneration paid to employees and directors. Contributions are levied at a reduced rate of 1% on earnings above £43 888 p.a. (for 2009/10) for employees. These increase from 12.8% to 13.8%, 11% to 12% and 1% to 2% for 2011/12.	Two types of National Insurance Contributions payable by self-employed: flat rate of £2.40 (for 2009/10) per week (£124.80 p.a.); plus 8% on annual profits between £5 715 and £43 875 (for 2009/10) and 1% on profits above £43 875. These increase from 8% to 9% and 1% to 2% for 2011/12.
National Insurance also payable by company in respect of company cars and private fuel	No National Insurance on proprietor's car

Table 2 Tax and NI obligations

11.4.6 Structure, management and administration

The members decide (usually in the contract of formation) how the EEIG will be run. There is no requirement for regular meetings or for decisions of the members to be taken only at meetings. Each member has one vote, but this can be overridden by the contract of formation. Unanimous decisions are required on issues concerning the existence and certain operational aspects of the EEIG (see Article 17 of the EC Regulation).

The members appoint managers (individuals or companies represented by individuals) who run the EEIG and make routine decisions, according to the powers conferred on them by the members. The EEIG will be bound by the actions of each manager. The members may seek to prevent the EEIG from being bound by unauthorised actions of the managers by inserting a provision in the contract of formation to the effect that the EEIG will only be bound by the joint action of two or more managers. This is called the 'double signature' and notice of such a provision must be published in the appropriate Gazette (London, Edinburgh or Belfast) to be effective.

The EEIG has legal personality as a 'body corporate' in the UK from the moment of registration and is subject to EC and UK competition rules.

An EEIG can be financed by capital invested by the members or by loans or donations from outside. Members may make contributions in terms of skills and services but are not obliged to subscribe any capital. No public investment is allowed.

Taxation

For tax purposes, an EEIG is regarded as acting as the agent of its members, rather than as a taxable entity in its own right. The members are treated as owning shares of the EEIG and its property in the proportions specified in the contract of formation, or if nothing is said, then in equal shares. Hence, the EEIG is tax transparent, as each member is taxable on its own share of the results. The EEIG is VAT registrable.

11.5 Summary

When starting a new business, a decision that needs to be made and reviewed on a regular basis is whether or not the trade is, or should be, carried on via an incorporated entity such as a limited company or a limited liability partnership. The main alternatives to a company or LLP structure are to carry out the business as a sole trader or in partnership with others.

There are numerous tax, accounting and commercial factors that need to be considered before the decision is made. The tax and NI table (**Table 2**) summarizes some of the more important factors. From a tax point of view, the decision will depend primarily on the level of profits and the amount that the proprietors wish to withdraw from the business.

References

Financial Services Authority (2003) *The Combined Code on Corporate Governance* www.fsa.gov.uk/pubs/ukla/lr_comcode2003.pdf

London Stock Exchange. *Admission and Disclosure Rules* www.londonstockexchange.com/companies-and-advisors/main-market/rules/regulations.htm

UK Listing Authority. *Listing Rules*. FSA http://fsahandbook.info/FSA/html/handbook/LR

UK Listing Authority. *Listing Disclosure Rules*. FSA http://fsahandbook.info/FSA/html/handbook/DTR

Referenced legislation, regulations and standards

Capital Allowances Act 2001. TSO, London, UK

Companies Act 1985. HMSO, London, UK

Companies Act 2006. TSO, London, UK

Finance Act 2009. TSO, London, UK

Income Tax Act 2007. TSO, London, UK

Income Tax (Trading and Other Income) Act 2005. TSO, London, UK

Limited Liability Partnerships Act 2000. TSO, London, UK

Limited Liability Partnerships Regulations 2001. TSO, London, UK

Limited Liability Partnerships (Application of the Companies Act 2006) Regulations 2009. TSO, London, UK

Limited Partnerships Act 1907. HMSO, London, UK

Partnership Act 1890

Value Added Tax Act 1994. HMSO, London, UK

Websites

Companies House; www.companieshouse.gov.uk/about/guidance

Financial Services Authority (FSA); www.fsa.gov.uk

Form IN01 (Application to register a company); www.companieshouse.gov.uk/forms/generalForms/IN01_application_to_register_a_company.pdf

Form RR01 (Application by a private company for re-registration as a public company); www.companieshouse.gov.uk/forms/generalForms/RR01_application_by_a_private_company_for_reregisration_as_public_company.pdf

Form SN50 (Application for trading certificate for a public company); www.companieshouse.gov.uk/forms/generalForms/SH50_application_for_trading_certificate_for_a_public_company.pdf

HM Revenue & Customs; www.hmrc.gov.uk

HM Revenue & Customs, VAT; www.hmrc.gov.uk/vat/index.htm?_nfpb=true&_pageLabel=pageVAT_Home

Belfast Gazette; www.belfast-gazette.co.uk

Edinburgh Gazette; www.edinburgh-gazette.co.uk

London Gazette; www.london-gazette.co.uk

London Stock Exchange; www.londonstockexchange.com

Official Journal of the European Communities; http://eur-lex.europa.eu/JOIndex.do

Chapter 12

doi: 10.1680/mocl.40878.0177

Joint ventures

Paul Henty Speechly Bircham LLP, London, UK

Joint venturing is a business model which has become enormously popular. It is a generic term for businesses working together on a common project. The nature of consultants' work makes joint venturing more relevant today than ever before. Complex projects require the collaboration of parties with complementary and diversified skill-sets. The increase in overseas opportunities, particularly in emerging markets, has made venturing a popular means of accessing new markets. The model is not straightforward and an overview of some of the challenges to be overcome is provided with specific examples of successful and unsuccessful ventures. The business model is however a flexible one, with parties having a choice of structures through which to operate, each offering its own advantages and disadvantages. There are also specific regulatory issues which affect the venture, arising from company, competition and criminal law. Recent legal developments are highlighted, such as the findings on negligence and vicarious liability connected with the UK Buncefield oil refinery joint venture. In closing, the author gives his thoughts on the lessons learned and what parties should be doing at each step of the journey to ensure they realise the enormous potential that is offered by this increasingly prevalent business structure.

CONTENTS

12.1 Introduction

The subject of joint ventures has always been of relevance to the construction and engineering industries, owing to the multidisciplinary nature of the work in this field. Projects will frequently bring together design engineers, building contractors, funders and/or providers of facilities management services.

The term 'joint venture' is a loose one. Joint ventures, while having no precise legal definition, generally involve two or more businesses being engaged together in a business activity, with a view to mutual profit. The parties to the venture may decide to collaborate through a corporate vehicle, such as a company limited by shares. Alternatively, they may elect to work together in an unincorporated consortium. Consultants usually opt to work with others under an unincorporated structure, although there have been exceptions.

Across all industries, recent times have seen a dramatic increase in the number of different businesses working together in 'joint venture'. It is common for participants to pool resources into the venture, whether in the form of management expertise, employees (often under secondment arrangements), intellectual property and know-how.

More specifically, within the construction and engineering industries, reasons for the growth of joint ventures have included the following:

- A dramatic increase in overseas projects (a large number being in emerging markets such as India and China), leading to a need for businesses to team up with a local partner with contacts or experience of the particular jurisdiction.

- An increasing number of complex or large-scale projects which require businesses to join forces, sometimes because they do not individually possess all of the required skills and on other occasions because of the need for enhanced financial standing.

- An increased need for companies to access and develop technologies. Joint ventures, which entail pooling of resources and sharing of costs, can present a less expensive means of access than acquisition of the technologies or researching or developing alone.

- The increase in popularity of public private partnerships has also seen a rise in the number of ventures engaged in public projects, especially those of a long-term nature, aimed at delivering and maintaining infrastructure through a special purpose vehicle, jointly owned by the public and private sectors (see the chapter *Public-private sector partnerships*).

Examples of recent and ongoing ventures in the industry include the following:

- The Connect Plus joint venture, which is engaged in a Design Build Finance and Operate (DBFO) project for the widening of the M25 orbital road around London. The project is being carried out as a Public Private Partnership. The Joint Venture is being run through a corporate vehicle, owned by members of the corporate groups of Atkins, Skanska Infrastructure Development, Balfour Beatty and Egis.

- Arup's joint venture with Worsley Parsons to provide engineering, procurement and construction management services for a 24-inch diameter, US$2 billion New Multi-Products Pipeline (NMPP) from Durban to Johannesburg in South Africa for Transnet. The development of the NMPP is part of South Africa's energy security strategy and is expected to be operational by 2011.

- Impact Partnership, an innovative joint venture between Mouchel, Agilisys and Rochdale Metropolitan Borough Council. The Partnership delivers Highways, Property and ICT services to support the regeneration of the borough over a 15 year period from April 2006. Impact was presented with the 'Public Private Partnership achievement of the year' award at the Municipal Journal annual awards ceremony on 24 June 2010.

- A joint venture led by engineering design consultancy Atkins, working with Ali Khadir-Harbi, Ahmed Omar Radi engineering consultancy (RGC), which has been appointed by the Royal Commission for Jubail and Yanbu to deliver engineering design services for the long-term development of the city of Ras Al-Zawr. The contract value is reportedly around US$16 million. Ras Al-Zawr is a development of strategic importance for industry in Saudi Arabia, on the coast of the Arabian Gulf approximately 80 km north of Jubail Industrial City.

Whilst joint ventures open up possibilities for parties wishing to work together, they also bring complications and risks, which are touched upon in this chapter. Corporate joint ventures must observe the requirements and procedures of company law (see sections 12.6.2 and 12.6.6). When working abroad, parties must be aware of the local laws applicable to their activities. They should have in place effective supervision mechanisms, particularly given risks arising from fraudulent and corrupt practices.

When the parties which collaborate are in competition, thought must be given to the possible application of competition law, particularly given the serious penalties which may be imposed for contravention of these laws. This is discussed in section 12.8.

Within construction and engineering, much has been said in recent years about partnering and alliancing (see *Procurement route* in this volume). This chapter therefore contains a section on that issue and tries to explain the interface between joint ventures and partnering and alliancing structures.

12.2 Reasons for establishing a joint venture

This section outlines some of the more common drivers for setting up joint ventures. The reasons for creating a joint venture will vary from one situation to another.

12.2.1 Spreading project costs and risk

As one industry professional has commented: 'due to the increased costs of many construction and property developments, companies are considering alternative ways to raise the finance required, and a joint venture with a partner is becoming an increasing popular choice' (Reid, 2007).

To illustrate, in order to construct a hospital, a large bank loan will be needed by the building contractor (inevitably, to be secured against the project assets). Aside from the cost of the loan itself (which may include the funders' advisers' fees, arrangement fees and interest costs), the parties will also need to provide subordinated debt and equity (which typically accounts for around 10% of any construction project). Such costs can be shared amongst joint venture participants.

Other shared outlays can include procurement of insurance policies, research and development costs, employment or equipment costs or capital investment programmes.

12.2.2 Limitation of liability

The sharing of risk between participants is a particular consideration where the parties are engaged in large-scale or capital-intensive projects, which can entail an elevated financial risk. For example, sizeable projects, such as for the design and build of power stations or natural resource or infrastructure projects are rarely undertaken by a single contractor alone.

A joint venture structure permits the spreading of responsibilities and liabilities between the parties, thereby reducing the potential exposure of each. On the other hand, it is important to bear in mind that the client or a third party such as a funder may look to each of the parties to assume joint and several liability in respect of the joint venture's obligations.

Even where participants are jointly and severally liable, they will still be able to apportion liability between themselves. Most parties will agree that specific risks should be allocated to the party best able to manage that risk. Alternatively, the liability for a specific risk related to a service carried out by a particular party may be allocated to that party in a proportionate or disproportionate share. It is quite common for joint venture agreements to allocate to each participant specific risks and opportunities which are considered to relate to that party's specific role within the arrangement.

In contrast to this approach, in purer forms of 'alliancing' (discussed later), the economic effects of a particular risk will generally be shared through a payment mechanism, although the liability to third parties for performance fault will ultimately be borne by the party responsible. That is the ideal. In practice, it can be difficult to establish where pain and gain share ends and performance fault begins.

Frequently, parties are also attracted to setting up joint venture companies (JVCs) as a means of risk management. They will assign to the joint venture company (JVC) responsibility for the running of the operations of the joint venture, in the expectation that should things go wrong, it is that vehicle (and not the parents of the JVC) which will be legally responsible. As a matter of company law, the limited liability status of the JVC should 'ringfence' liability to the JVC itself.

On this theory, a cautionary note must be sounded. Under most joint venture structures, it is the parents themselves, not the JVC, which will be responsible for providing the personnel to carry out the JV's operations. The parents may be legally responsible for monitoring the activities of those employees and therefore, vicariously liable for their acts and omissions.

For example, in 2005, a large explosion occurred at a large oil storage depot at Buncefield in the UK. Formally, that installation was under the general management of a JVC, Hertfordshire Oil Storage Limited (HOSL), owned by two oil companies, Total and Chevron. One of the key questions was whether the pipeline supervisor, who had been careless on the night of the explosion, should be regarded as the employee of HOSL, making HOSL vicariously liable for his negligence.

Legal action followed to establish which party had responsibility for the losses and damages connected with the explosion. Although the contractual arrangements for the joint venture showed that the operator of the site was HOSL, Chevron argued that in practice the site was operated and managed by Total. The court looked at the management structure regarding operations at the site, and considered which company had the right to control the site supervisor's method of work.

The Court observed that, on the facts, Total and not the JVC was the employer of the workers (including the site supervisor) and was able to direct their activities. The High Court rejected Total's claims that the JVC, and not Total, was responsible for the negligent acts of Total employees, when acting on behalf of the JVC. The JVC itself was owned 60% by Total and 40% by Chevron. The decision confirmed that claims for damages, estimated at up to £750 million, would be met by Total rather than the JVC and liability would not be distributed in line with the shareholding of the two companies (*Colour Quest Limited and Others v. Total Downstream UK PLC, Total UK Limited and Hertfordshire Oil Storage Limited* [2009] EWHC 540 (Comm)).

12.2.3 Pooling of resources

A complex project is likely to require a myriad of different skills, capabilities and fields of expertise, which may not all sit under the same roof.

To give examples, a public authority may wish to procure the construction, financing and operation of a toll road. A building contractor may have impressive construction credentials, but lack of experience in maintaining or managing transport facilities. In those circumstances, it makes sense for the contractor to find a partner to fill the missing expertise 'gaps'. Likewise, the construction of a nuclear power plant may require the knowledge and collaboration of both a consultant, working in tandem with a civil and mechanical contractor.

As stated at the beginning of this chapter, a concern to access technology has been a driver in the increased popularity of joint ventures. For certain projects, it may be possible for participants in a joint venture to obtain from each other licences to processes or technologies protected by intellectual property rights, which will again benefit the grouping as a whole.

In a tender process, the combining of specialist expertise in this way will benefit the joint venture as a whole, thereby maximising its prospects for appointment as the preferred bidder.

12.2.4 Exploitation of opportunities overseas

Globalisation has brought about a rise in collaborations between businesses located in different jurisdictions. Businesses can now contest project opportunities overseas more easily. However, in order for them to do so, they must often find a local partner in the jurisdiction where the project will be realised. Sometimes, the involvement of a local partner may even be one of the client's requirements. On other occasions, it will simply make sense, as the local partner will have direct experience of working in the jurisdiction and will know its way around the commercial and regulatory environment.

Furthermore, a joint venture may be the only *practical* way of accessing certain markets, particularly in developing countries. For a consultant, the involvement of a partner 'on the ground' not only provides the venture with a permanent representative able to represent the venture's interests to the client, but may also be invaluable for the purposes of translation, accessing data, obtaining licences and consents. For a contractor, this may provide the opportunity to source building materials and manpower than would otherwise be the case.

A company may wish to form a collaboration arrangement with a company based in another jurisdiction which goes beyond a single project, however. It may be, for example, that a local partner can be identified which is able to bring to its attention opportunities in that country. The local partner may have political or other valuable relationships in the target jurisdiction.

12.2.5 A harmonised approach

When well done, a client dealing with a joint venture may enjoy liaising with a single management team responsible for all aspects of the project. The alternative will be liaising with a myriad of different contractors, which may duplicate time and cost.

Whether or not this potential benefit of a joint venture is delivered will depend upon the parties' ability to put in place an effective and coherent management team, a visible and responsive single point of contact acting on behalf of the venture, as well as an effective system of internal (and external) communication.

12.3 Challenges of a joint venture

The reasons and advantages for establishing a joint venture having been explored, it is important to map out some of the problems which the participants must overcome.

12.3.1 Corporate governance

Occasionally, confusion can surround who is really running the joint venture: the management of the parent companies themselves or the dedicated management team of the venture itself?

Bringing together managers from two or more different organisations, who may not have worked together before, can lead to a more considered and negotiated approach to decision making than would otherwise be the case. It may also be difficult for members of the management team, who are employed by the parents of the joint venture, to devote adequate amounts of their time to the joint venture's affairs.

The differing interests and backgrounds of the different members of the management team will also diverge. For example, a party with a pure design responsibility for a piece of equipment may not be attuned to the operational issues affecting a civil engineering contractor's requirement to import plant to a remote location.

12.3.2 Cultural differences

A study carried out in 2004 (PriceWaterhouseCoopers and CFO research Services, 2004) found that when joint ventures fail, 30% of the time they do so because of differences in culture between the venturers. Cultural differences will be most accentuated when the parties are based in different jurisdictions. However, even where the participants are of the same nationality, differences in corporate style, approach, values and priorities can present a significant hurdle to the success of a joint venture.

In the construction and engineering context, public–private partnerships are perhaps a good example of arrangements where the outlooks of participants, being from the private and public sectors, can be markedly different.

12.3.3 Different or changing commercial objectives

This is another frequent cause of venture failure (a change in objectives was at the heart of 40% of all Joint Venture failures, according to the PriceWaterhouseCoopers study). The commercial goals of a venture will not always be or remain the same. Occasionally, it will emerge only after the joint venture has been established that the parties failed to recognise that they were actually pursuing different aims from the joint venture (possibly due to inadequate discussions at an early stage).

One joint venture, between French and Japanese corporations, foundered for exactly this reason. In the face of early losses, the Japanese partner was content to provide further capital, provided the venture maintained its market share. The French corporation, on the other hand, had envisaged an early return on its investment and was not prepared to make further capital injections. Ultimately, this divergence of aspirations (which was only discovered years *after* the joint venture had been formed) forced the French corporation to buy out its Japanese partner and end the collaboration between them (p.15, Simmons and Simmons, 2009).

12.3.4 Liability issues

As set out earlier, one of the perceived advantages of a joint venture is the ability of the parties to apportion and limit risk between themselves. In reality, however, risk and liability are issues which present difficult questions for the venturers, some of which are highlighted in the following paragraphs.

Many clients will seek joint and several liability from each of the joint venture participants, meaning they are each liable up to the full amount of the relevant obligation. This will be seen as a risk mitigation exercise from the client's perspective. If one of the parties cannot be sued or prosecuted (e.g. in the case of its insolvency), the remaining participant would still bear its share of responsibility to the client. Similarly, joint and several liability is perceived by clients as an excellent way of managing the adverse effects to the project of one party's insolvency.

Even where a joint venture agreement faithfully reflects the genuine intentions of the parties regarding liability apportionment, this may still be fraught with complications. Applying the principles of the clause during the course of the project is also very likely to be difficult and contentious.

Apportioning liabilities between participants can lead to difficulties in obtaining insurance. Insurers prefer joint venture arrangements to be clear and unambiguous. Their reluctance towards apportionment will be increased where one participant is providing a fundamental expertise which is not shared by the other party.

It was also noted earlier in this chapter that attempts to limit liability by way of forming a JVC may sometimes be misconceived. The Buncefield example showed how a joint venture shareholder may have vicarious liability for the acts and omissions of employees who have been seconded to the JVC.

It is also possible for one joint venture partner to have liability for the acts and omissions of fellow participants. This is well illustrated in the international context. Frequently, a joint venture will include a participant which has been selected for its contacts in the local jurisdiction. That participant will be expected to source and realise opportunities, perhaps acting as a pure intermediary. Where this is the case, the parties should aim to put in place effective monitoring of the intermediary's activities on their behalf. As is discussed in Section 12.9, participants can be liable for foreign or corrupt practices of local intermediaries that have been known to engage in fraudulent or corrupt practices. Even where the foreign participants are not aware of such conduct, they may still have liability for those acts, not only under the laws of the host jurisdiction, but also under their domestic laws.

12.4 Principal considerations in establishing a joint venture to tender

The different considerations to be examined when setting up a joint venture are numerous, but the main practical and legal issues are as outlined in the following sections (written primarily from a UK point of view, references to statutes relate to those in force in the UK).

12.4.1 Choice of partner

This is the primary question for any business contemplating the entry into a joint venture. The key to the success of any joint venture is the ability of two or more organisations to work together in realising common aims and objectives. Finding a partner which is a good 'fit' for one's own organisation is therefore of paramount importance.

In the context of a construction or engineering project, the choice may not always be a free and open one. For example, in the context of a procurement for a public–private partnership, a private contractor may be required to 'team up' with the contracting authority or associated governmental organisations. Under the UK government's NHS LIFT initiative, for example, this will involve the setting up of a special purpose 'LIFT Co', whose shareholders will comprise of an NHS Primary Care Trust, Community Health Partnerships Limited (a unit of HM Government entrusted with overseeing NHS LIFT projects), together with the preferred bidder (also see *Public-private sector partnerships*).

In other procurements (whether private or public), the client may decide from the outset that a joint venture is the most suitable vehicle to carry out the project. Therefore, groups of companies may be invited to tender for the contract. Alternatively, a number of companies may decide to tender together as a joint venture and put themselves forward to the client for a particular project. This latter situation is more common as it allows the joint venturers to choose their partners. In addition, the local law of the country where the work is to be carried out may impose on the participants an obligation to involve a local partner as a party to the joint venture.

In addition to finding a partner which is culturally compatible, it is also important to ensure that the partner has complementary resources, skills and assets. Where the partner has claimed to have specific know-how or intellectual property rights which are important for the project on which the parties will collaborate, it will obviously be essential to verify these. It may be possible to carry out searches of ownership registrable intellectual property rights with agencies such as the UK Patent Office (see *Intellectual property*).

Before entering into a binding agreement with the partner, a certain amount of 'due diligence' should be undertaken on the potential partner. Broadly, the following questions should be asked:

- How well has the partner performed, generally, and on projects on which the joint venture will be working?
- What is the partner's attitude to collaboration and will there be a shared level of commitment?
- Does the partner share the same business objectives?
- Can the partner be trusted?
- Are the brand, environmental and corporate social responsibility values of the partner complementary or in conflict with the other partner or partners?
- What kind of reputation does the partner have?
- Is the partner financially secure?
- Does the partner have any credit problems?

- Does the partner already have joint venture partnerships with other businesses?
- What kind of management team does the partner have in place?
- How is the partner performing in terms of production, marketing and workforce?
- What do their customers and suppliers say about the partner's trustworthiness and reputation?
- Does the candidate partner has sufficient insurance for the needs of the project?

In conducting this research, it may be possible to obtain references from the partner's customers or other contracting parties. Where the partner is an incorporated entity, there may be publicly available filings which can be accessed (e.g. from Companies House).

It is of particular importance that the financial resources, creditworthiness, expertise and reputation of each of the participants are carefully examined before forming the joint venture. The principal reasons for exercising caution being

- the potential liability that each of the participants may incur as a result of, for example, the insolvency of another participant
- the scope for potential conflicts of interest, management, clashes of personalities and cultures
- the possible liability which one joint venture partner may bear as a result of the actions of its joint venture partner
- the potentially detrimental effect on business reputation which the actions of a business associate may have.

Often, the ideal partner is one with whom a business has worked before, meaning that the parties already have realistic expectation of how the collaboration will work in practice.

12.4.2 Management and supervision of the joint venture

As stated earlier in this chapter, a frequent cause of failure of joint ventures is the inability for partners to put in place a management structure which works for them. Early discussions are needed on how the venture will function on a day-to-day basis. Who will take decisions, at what level and when?

The parties also need to consider who will represent the joint venture externally to third parties such as the client or other customers or suppliers. How will these individuals be accountable? What forms of reporting will they make and when?

Other questions relate to meetings: how often will representatives from the partners meet to discuss progress and, if necessary, to take decisions. Will this be on a weekly, monthly or quarterly basis? How will meetings be convened? Where the parties are in different jurisdictions, it is likely to make sense for the parties to convene meetings by telephone or video conferencing, a possibility that can be stated explicitly in the Joint Venture Agreement itself.

12.4.3 Status of the client

In order to ensure that the client is fit to comply with the obligations under its contract with the joint venture, the joint venturers should satisfy themselves of the identity, resources and strength of the client and also that the project is well defined.

This due diligence, insofar as it examines the client, could involve some of the types of questions listed in section 12.4.1.

12.4.4 Split of work and costs

Once the decision has been taken, the parties should agree on the terms of the joint venture before the tendering process starts, including the roles and responsibilities of each party and the way in which the joint venture is to proceed. It is good practice to put in place confidentiality agreements at the outset so that parties to the joint venture can be more open in their discussions.

The distribution of the work should also be established. This can be a difficult area where the work is not specialised but influential in relation to the management and control of the joint venture. The price and the ratio of sharing the expenses incurred in the preparation of the tender can also be a sensitive subject which needs to be dealt with clearly at the outset; as does the split of fees. How the risks are to be shared and the insurances that each party to the joint venture may put in place should also be addressed.

12.4.5 Taxation

Tax considerations are an important consideration in determining the structure which the parties choose for their joint venture. For example, where the parties choose to incorporate a UK resident venture as a JVC, they are likely to take profits from the vehicle through dividends issued to them as shareholders. In contrast, where an unincorporated venture is used, profits will flow to members directly.

In any event, the tax positions of the individual members of the joint venture must be considered. They should each consider the most tax efficient way for them to be taxed upon the profits they receive from the joint venture. For example, where the venture is set up through a JVC, this might involve transferring the shares held in the company to an offshore vehicle.

Where a JVC is formed, as an independent entity, it will be taxed in its own right. Tax issues will arise, for example, where the parties transfer assets to the JVC. The contribution by the joint venture parties of assets or entire businesses to the JVC (often in exchange for shares in the JVC) will normally constitute, for tax purposes, disposals by them of those assets or businesses.

This may give rise to the following:

- tax on chargeable gains (if the assets have increased in value since their acquisition by the joint venture parties)
- balancing charges (if the consideration, or in certain circumstances, market value, is greater than the tax written down value of the asset)
- tax on income profits (if the transfer of trading stock is deemed to take place at market value, the transfer pricing rules apply or the assets transferred comprise intangible property).

The acquisition of assets may have further tax consequences which typically fall on the JVC. These may include the following:

- stamp duty (if shares/marketable securities are transferred)
- stamp duty land tax (SDLT) (if land or interests in land are transferred)
- VAT (the transfer of an entire business or part of a business may be outside the scope of VAT if it qualifies as a transfer of a going concern. The transfer of individual assets may give rise to VAT unless the parties are members of the same VAT group although it is now less common for joint venture parties and JVCs to be within the same VAT group).

Given that these tax charges can be an expensive aspect of setting up a JVC, the way in which they will be borne by the parties and/or the JVC deserves consideration at the outset.

If these issues cannot be resolved, the parties may wish to consider an alternative structure to the formation of a JVC.

The parties should also consider the availability of tax reliefs which may be available, either for themselves or the JVC. Another important question is whether the JVC forms part of a 'relevant tax group' with any of the parties, which can have significant tax implications.

Where a project is carried out in a foreign jurisdiction, the parties should consider whether their profits will be taxed in that jurisdiction, as well as or instead of on repatriation of profits. The question will often turn on whether or not the joint venture partners have created a 'permanent establishment' in the host jurisdiction, effectively an entity formed on a lasting basis which is capable of being taxed. This is a question of fact which must be resolved with specialist advice from the host jurisdiction. Even unincorporated ventures can constitute permanent establishments. In India, for example, tax authorities have been aggressive in construing contractual joint ventures between foreign and Indian businesses as an 'association of persons' for the purposes of the tax rules (Section 2(7) of the Indian Income Tax, 1961 (ITA) defines the term 'assessee' as a person by whom tax or any other sum of money is payable under the ITA. Section 2(31) of the ITA defines 'person' to *inter alia* include an association of persons (AOP). An AOP is subject to tax as a separate entity). This finding can lead to the foreign participant being subject to taxes in India.

Where the host taxation regime will apply, the parties should consider the applicable rates of taxation, as well as whether any withholding tax will apply to royalties or dividends received from the joint venture.

Where a foreign regime applies, the parties also need to consider whether there will be double taxation (e.g. will the joint venture's profits be taxed in the host and the home jurisdictions). If so, it will be worth considering whether there is any double taxation treaty which applies between a party's home state and the host jurisdiction, in order to relieve the participants from the same tax burden twice.

If the joint venture purchases goods or services from one of its parents, issues may arise in relation to transfer pricing. In the context of a construction project, for example, this may arise if one of the parents of the joint venture, a consultant, provides services to the JVC for less than its normal arm's length charges.

Finally, where the joint venture relates to a project carried out in the EU, the host state may be obliged, pursuant to the EU Treaty, to grant equivalent tax reliefs to parties from other member states as it grants to businesses in the home state. A recent UK case (*Philips Electronics v. HMRC* [2009]), illustrated that the UK could not deny consortium relief to a parent company owning more than 50% of the JVC, on the basis of its residence in the Netherlands. Consortium relief in the UK allows a corporate investor in an incorporated joint venture to set off the trading losses of the venture against profits of other members of the group (see HM Revenue & Customs (HMRC) website). Previously, the applicable law (section 403D(1)(c) ICTA) allowed such losses to be surrendered only to companies which were UK resident.

Also see *Ways of operating*.

12.4.6 International joint ventures: repatriation of profits

Where a joint venture is established with a cross-border dimension, the parties must consider whether it is possible for them to take home profits made by the joint venture in that jurisdiction. It is common, particularly in developing countries, to encounter restrictions on exchange control and repatriation, which can have the effect of requiring foreign venturers to re-invest their profits in the host jurisdiction. Given that this may well be unacceptable to foreign venturers, this must be considered at the beginning of the project.

A related issue is currency convertibility. Parties should consider not only whether the profits from their transaction can be converted into their home currency, but also how long the process will take (In Uzbekistan, for example, this can reportedly take up to six months. This has been a major factor behind the withdrawal of US investment in that country). Often whether profits can be converted into home currency comes down to whether the transaction is defined as a 'current account transaction' or a 'capital account transaction', the former being more easily converted. An overview of the system in India and the Foreign and Exchange Management Act 2000 can be found online, see *Currency Convertibility and its impact on BOP* and *Current Account Transactions*). For a comparison with the Chinese system, see Guijun and Schramm.

12.4.7 Concerns relating to intellectual property and confidentiality

Trade secrets and intellectual property are potentially an extremely valuable asset to every company (for an overview, see Chapter 17 of Hewitt, 2008). The collaboration with other parties creates an obvious risk that know-how will cease to be proprietary to the company from which it has originated. In the construction and engineering projects, competitors will often 'team up', leading to an accented risk that know-how will be lost. Even where a party enters into a venture with a business which is not a direct competitor, that company may enter into other ventures with competitors, creating an equivalent risk.

This risk can be mitigated, to some extent, by the entry into a robust confidentiality agreement at the outset of negotiations, although the provisions of such an agreement are occasionally difficult to enforce. Where the fellow venture is not a competitor, confidentiality provisions may be backed up by restricting that venturer's participation with the venturer's competitors, but that provision will need to be limited to a reasonable scope and period, in order to ensure its enforceability (see section 12.8.3 on the possible application of competition laws to such provisions).

Where the joint venture operates in another country, the parties should consider whether the jurisdiction has in place a proper legal system of intellectual property, in order to avoid, for example, the risk that enterprises in that jurisdiction might start to exploit a patentable technology without regard to the rights of the patent owner (for an introduction and overview of certain current issues in China, see China-Britain Business Council, 2004). Trade mark protection is also an important consideration. There have been previous examples of large consultancy firms operating in foreign jurisdictions through joint ventures, finding that their name has been used in an unauthorised way in connection with purposes unconnected to the joint venture.

12.5 Documenting the joint venture
12.5.1 The memorandum of understanding (MoU)

It is good practice for the parties to a joint venture to agree a memorandum of understanding (MoU) between them as a first step in putting together the joint venture. This is a simple document which sets out the headline issues for the joint venture agreement. It should be commercial rather than legal in its tone and, for that reason, should be drafted by the venturers rather than their lawyers (although it may be wise for lawyers to review the draft to check for ambiguity or 'loopholes').

MoUs, usually, are not legally binding. They are valuable though as they enable senior negotiators to focus on establishing the basic principles of the venture and help to keep the transaction moving, at what is often a sensitive stage. The final MoU should address the following issues:

- Purpose of the joint venture – why is it being formed?
- Spirit of the venture – what is the commitment to the venture which both parties are seeking?
- Key objectives and responsibilities – who is responsible for what?

- Method for decision making – who is responsible for taking which types of decisions and who reports to whom?

- Resource commitments – what specific financial and non-financial resources are needed for the success of the venture? Who will be responsible for providing these?

- Assumption of risks and rewards – what are the expected rewards – how will profits be divided?

- What is the intended structure of the venture? – will this be in the form of an incorporated venture or unincorporated consortium?

- Transformation – how will the joint venture evolve and unwind? Will there be any obligations after the project ends? Who will be responsible for these and how will the parties deal with post-termination requirements generally?

12.5.2 The Joint venture agreement – main provisions

Each joint venture agreement will differ, but there are some fundamental provisions that should be considered whatever contractual arrangement is adopted, including the following.

12.5.2.1 Identity of the parties

Who should be the parties (consider the most appropriate members of the group of each)? Will parent company guarantees be required?

12.5.2.2 Allocation of work

Will work be carried out by the joint venture on a pooled basis or will work be subcontracted in separate agreements to the joint venture participants (or to third parties)?

12.5.2.3 Management

The parties need to give serious thought to how the venture will be managed on a day-to-day basis.

It is usually necessary to have a board or management forum through which decisions are taken. If the parties decide upon such a board or committee, they must then consider who should sit on this board or committee. Will it be composed of representatives of each of the parties? Alternatively, there may be a two-tier structure with delegation to a project committee responsible for the day-to-day co-ordination and execution of the work.

This forum will need rules as to quorum and decision making, and also access to information on which decisions can be based. A critical area is deadlock, therefore the possibility of having a chairperson with a casting vote, or having to refer the deadlock to senior management, for example, the chief executives of the respective parties, a professional body in the industry or mediation or even arbitration. However, to be truly effective there does need to be a mechanism for resolving everyday differences at site level without escalation.

If the parties are not equal, it may be appropriate to specify that, on certain issues, there is weighted voting. However,

agreement of all the parties is normally required for key issues such as:

- setting a budget

- appointment and removal of key personnel and approval of their remuneration

- incurring of debt and the provision of security over assets

- third party guarantees

- profit distribution

- material changes in the joint venture's objectives.

- management of the project, particularly in its form, procedure for its appointment, and powers and liabilities *vis-à-vis* the joint venturers

- scope of services to be provided by each participant, particular arrangements for the use of equipment or personnel

- financial arrangements, including split of fee, maintaining accounts, procedures in submitting and payment of invoices.

When the parties are jointly and severally liable, the procedure to be followed in the event of default by one of the parties should be set up, including prior risk allocation and indemnity.

Cross-indemnification is likely to be necessary so that each party is held responsible for the work it performs for the joint venture or for that portion of the project that is commensurate with the profit/loss sharing arrangements in the joint venture agreement.

12.5.2.4 Duration and termination

Terminating a joint venture can be a difficult and divisive issue. It is important to have in place a well-drafted termination provision to ensure that matters are not unnecessarily complicated further.

This may be linked to the scope of services provision or to the date of the success or otherwise of the tender. Reasons for early termination should be stipulated: for example, on default of a party or insolvency. Provision could be made (if desired) for the joint venture to continue following default or insolvency of a participant, which may be appropriate if there are more than two venturers. The termination clause could also provide for the preparation of a final account, if necessary.

12.5.2.5 Dispute resolution and applicable law

Dispute resolution and applicable law are two discrete questions. The dispute resolution clause will set out a procedure for the settlement of disputes, this may include a procedure for the continued operation of the joint venture in spite of the dispute and a provision to arbitrate, and for termination in the event of the parties falling out without prospects of reconciliation. Frequently, an escalation process to handle disputes between the parties is included in the joint venture agreement. More sophisticated ways of dealing with disputes include reference to determination by an independent third party expert or by the inclusion of deadlock provisions, so that where there is an inability to agree on operational matters, a call option or sealed bids clause could enable one of the parties to buy out the others' interests or be bought out by the other parties.

Further information on dispute resolution can be found in Section 4: *Construction disputes*.

The relevant law which is to govern the joint venture agreement should be established from the outset, together with the procedure and forum for the settlement of disputes. The choice of law will depend on whether the project has a national or international dimension, where the work is to be carried out, who are the main parties, and the presence of any requirements on the part of any financiers/lenders involved. Local law may impose certain legal constraints on the joint venture, such as part-ownership by a local company or use of local materials and labour. The client may, of course, also seek to influence the choice of law applicable to the joint venture.

12.5.2.6 Intellectual property

Each party will normally grant a non-exclusive licence to the other parties in respect of its relevant existing IPR in order to ensure that all the parties have all IPR needed for the successful realisation of the project. It is normal (and wise) to license such IPR *only* for the purpose of the project.

Where the project will result in the emergence of new IPR the agreement will need to set out which party will own this and who may use it.

Further information on IPR can be found in *Intellectual property*.

12.5.2.7 Liability

The agreement should detail what responsibility each party will have to the others for performance of its work and the work of the joint venture. As noted earlier, drafting clauses to cover issues of liability can be a difficult process. In addition to those matters noted at section 12.3.4 above, the parties should ensure any liability limit or exclusions they wish to rely on are legally enforceable.

It is common to see clauses included in joint venture agreements, under which each party undertakes to cross-indemnify the other for any loss or damage suffered as a result of any errors or omissions on its part. These clauses, in practice, will give rise to difficulties as the party responsible will need to be identified.

One way of re-distributing risk and minimising loss is by way of insurance. Which parties are covered will depend on the type of joint venture arrangement and will be of far greater relevance if the tender is successful. However, consideration should be given to such issues as minimum umbrella coverage, termination of liability and extent, type and duration of cover. Insurers will have views in relation to subrogation rights which have to be reflected in the way in which the joint venture operates. In essence, insurers will need to understand where risk lies and how it is to be controlled and managed. See *Professional indemnity insurance*.

Letters of credit or bonds may be required as security for any indemnities. On larger projects, consultants are frequently asked to provide parent company guarantees for the subsidiary involved in the project. See *Bonds, parent company guarantees and other security*.

Alternatively, participants may be asked to provide bid bonds and (if the tender is successful) performance bonds. These can be in the name of the joint venturers, with provision for the costs of procurement to be divided on the same basis as each party's interest in the joint venture or they may be supplied to the client by each joint venturer on a *pro rata* basis.

12.5.2.8 Relationship with client

The joint venturers should consider carefully the terms of the main contract with the client and its potential interrelationship with the joint venture agreement.

Full consideration of the client's perspective should always take place whether there is an express requirement for a joint venture or not. Inevitably, the business drivers for the joint venture partners should take priority while complying with the client's requirements.

For more information on project joint venture agreements see Hermitt (2008) at 4.17–4.21.

12.5.3 Ancillary agreements

Certain issues affecting the joint venture may be best set out in agreements that are ancillary to the main agreement. These include, for example, agreements for the secondment of employees and intellectual property licence agreements.

12.6 Types of legal structure

The choice of legal vehicle with which to tender will depend on the particular characteristics of the project for which the participants are tendering. If the project requires a variety of different skills, a corporate structure may be appropriate. If, on the other hand, the project is carried out by two or three partners in the same field, a consortium agreement may be more suitable.

As a general comment, it is far more common for consultants to be involved in ventures through an unincorporated structure.

The joint venture entity can be structured either vertically or horizontally. Where two or more undertakings are engaged in similar or the same type of business and possess similar capabilities and expertise they may integrate horizontally to pool these resources. Horizontal integration is far more common in the construction and engineering sectors, for example, involving the teaming together of consultants with contractors and financiers.

Vertical integration involves joining two or more parties who are upstream and downstream of each other, possessing different capabilities and resources. This structure may be used by a main contractor and equipment supplier, or by the main contractor and a design professional. This may occur when the project to be constructed is large, complex and carries great risk and two or more similar businesses join forces to produce a body of expertise and experience whose value is far in excess of that of each of the individual firms. In construction and engineering, it is rarer to see vertically integrated ventures. It is far more usual for vertical relationships to be set up through a subcontract. This allows the main contractor to maintain a greater degree of control.

Where the work is performed by the joint venture parties as if by a single entity, the relationship can be said to be integrated – profits and losses are shared in accordance with an agreed ratio. A non-integrated arrangement may be preferred where one or more of the parties has specialized areas of expertise and for the most part will undertake its respective portion of the work separately. In this arrangement, profits and losses will not be split up, but each party will deal separately with its own financial arrangements. Equally, a hybrid of the two may be appropriate.

Consideration should also be given to the way in which personnel will be employed if the tender is successful. They may be employed directly by the joint venture, furnished by the participants pursuant to a subcontract or other seconding type arrangements. While a straightforward arrangement such as personnel being employed by the individual participants of the joint venture has its benefits, it has to be decided on merit. In particular, consideration should be given to the impact on an individual's personal motivation if this course is followed.

While liability for the other parties to the joint venture can be apportioned accordingly, if any gaps appear, the residual liability will have to be shared by all the parties. Some smaller organizations may not wish to see this happen. For example, design consultants or other professionals are unlikely to be prepared to assume the risks of construction by entering a joint venture arrangement with a contractor. Indeed, they are unlikely to have available capital to share in the funding. Therefore, in these circumstances separate terms of engagement may be more appropriate. A principal contractor may also prefer to enter the necessary subcontracts to procure certain specialist work or equipment in order to enjoy the advantages of retaining total (or certainly greater) control of a project and of reaping the rewards.

The main structures which joint ventures usually adopt are as follows:

- consortium agreement
- limited liability company
- societas europaea (european company)
- partnership
- limited liability partnership.

12.6.1 Consortium agreement

This is a structure widely used in construction single-project joint ventures, and which provides the joint venturers with a more flexible way of catering for their particular needs than a partnership, but without having to create a new legal entity.

It differs from a partnership mainly in that there is no distribution of profits on a joint basis and the principle of agency does

not apply. In addition, the parties' contributions are regulated by the agreement, to which contract law primarily applies.

Joint venturers should be careful in respect of the extent of their cooperation, otherwise they may in effect establish a partnership. The partnership rules for partnership matters including liability for each partner's acts and omissions, termination and ownership of the property will apply if the partners' behaviour fulfils the definition contained in the Partnership Act 1890.

Consortium agreements are quite common, particularly in a start up situation (new service offered to the market-place) or an initiative to develop business in a new geographical region. These are frequently loose arrangements and it is only when an individual opportunity is identified that the arrangement is formalized on a project specific basis.

Joint and several liability is generally an essential feature of a consortium agreement and one of the reasons why such a structure is used in joint venture tendering. The client will normally insist that the consortium agreement caters for this type of liability before the project is awarded to the tenderers and this arrangement can act as a deterrent for some companies who would otherwise enter joint venture arrangements.

Under a joint and several arrangement, each of the participants is responsible for the completion of the project, notwithstanding that one or more participants have abandoned the project or otherwise breached the contract. Under the principle of agency, each participant can also bind the others when acting on their behalf. This, undoubtedly, represents a clear benefit to the client and participants entering into this type of joint venture should be aware of the full implications of such an arrangement.

As regards the consortium's management, the day-to-day decisions are taken by one of the participants who will, in addition, be in charge of harmonizing the operation of the whole project. The important decisions are taken by the management committee, which is formed by representatives of the joint venture participants.

12.6.2 Establishing a limited company as a joint venture

This involves the creation of a new legal entity for the purposes of tendering. Its main features include the following:

(a) A separate legal existence from that of its shareholders – thus, the company can sue and be sued and own property in its own right. The liability of the shareholders is, however, in principle, limited to the amount contributed by way of their shares. However, this limited liability is normally qualified by the requirement for guarantees. The parties, for instance, may decide to set up a subsidiary with very small capital for a specific project. The subsidiary's liability will be limited in principle to its capital. However, the employer or the financier will often insist on the parent company giving direct guarantees. The provision of a parent company guarantee gives rise to some drafting issues, particularly in relation to ensuring that there is no greater liability passed on to the parent company than there is in the main contract.

(b) The incorporation of a limited company as a joint venture follows the same pattern as any other limited corporate structure. Therefore, articles of association are necessary and a shareholders' agreement may well be desirable.

(c) A management team will normally be appointed for the day-to-day running of the company's operations and negotiations with the client. Due to the high costs involved in recruiting new staff, the normal practice is for the joint venturers to provide the management team from their own employees, thus cutting expenses, which may not be recoverable if the tender fails.

(d) Directors of the company will be appointed. They are responsible to the company as a whole and have ostensible authority to bind the company. They could also be personally liable in the event of an insolvent liquidation if they are found guilty of fraudulent or wrongful trading. In addition, the Companies Act 2006 codified duties of directors. The main new statutory duty is that of 'enlightened shareholder value'. This duty requires the Directors to act in such a way in which they consider is most likely to promote the success of the company for the benefit of its members while having regard to matters which a responsible business should such as the long-term consequences of their decision and the effect of their actions on the company's employees, the community and the environment. The duties on directors set out in the new Act are not exhaustive and duties in other statutes will continue to apply such as duties on directors pursuant to environmental law, health and safety law and competition law. Directors can be pursued legally by the shareholders in the event of a breach of their duties. The Companies Act 2006 makes it easier for minority shareholders to bring a claim in the company's name against directors.

This legal structure has proved valuable where some of the participants contribute more work and resources to the project than others. This will be reflected in an unequal allocation of shares and voting rights, which will give some shareholders more benefits and control than others.

Other circumstances when a limited company may be a suitable legal structure include where the participants are large companies, a mixture of partnerships and companies, or when the participants wish to create a long-standing relationship.

The incorporation of a limited company must comply with certain statutory requirements set out in the relevant Companies Acts. These Acts contain restrictions as to shareholders consent being required for certain transactions with directors, the decrease and withdrawal of capital and the winding-up procedure that must be followed.

Some disadvantages can be perceived with this particular structure, which include the following:

■ The parties have to go to considerable expense (drafting articles of association and possibly a shareholders' agreement) at an early stage in the preparation of the tender.

■ If the client requires the parties to be jointly and severally liable in respect of their obligations to the client and third parties, this legal structure becomes a less favourable vehicle than other options, where liability can be dealt with more easily.

■ The majority shareholders must respect the rights of the minority. These rights can be contained in the shareholders' agreement or, in its absence, there are certain statutory minority rights, such as the right to block certain decisions and to call meetings which will apply. These rights cannot, however, be ignored by the majority shareholders. Pursuant to the Companies Act 2006, minority shareholders will also have 'derivative rights' which are enforceable through the courts.

■ If the parties have equal shares in the company, or where unanimity is required by the shareholders' agreement to take certain decisions, a deadlock can take place. The shareholders' agreement should cater for these and other disputes. Possible solutions are arbitration, sale of one party's shares to the others, or termination when the parties cannot find a solution.

12.6.3 European Company

On 8 October 2001 the European Union's Council of Ministers adopted a regulation to establish a European Company Statute (ECS) (Council Regulation (EC) No 2157/2001) and the related Directive concerning worker involvement in European Companies (Council Directive 2001/86/EC). The ECS came into force in October 2004.

Basically, a European Company will operate on a European-wide basis meaning that companies operating in more than one member state will have the option to establish as a single company under EU law. This will mean that the company will be able to operate throughout the EU using one set of rules and a unified reporting and management system, rather than all the different laws of each member state.

The main benefits include the following:

■ By using a single set of rules and unified management and reporting system, companies will be able to avoid setting up a network of subsidiaries in various member states, which can be time consuming, administration-heavy and therefore expensive in terms of legal and administration costs.

■ If costs are cheaper, companies may attract more business overall, in particular European Companies may find it easier to attract venture capital than if they are operating in several member states.

■ European Companies will be able to avoid the burden of winding up and reregistering in a new EU state every time they want to move into another country to do business.

■ A business will be able to restructure easily and quickly enabling it to take advantage of the opportunities in the market place and move across borders according to the needs of the business.

A European Company may be set up in one of four ways:

■ By the merger of two or more existing public limited companies from at least two EU member states;

■ By the formation of a holding company promoted by public or private limited companies from at least two EU member states;

- By the formation of a subsidiary of companies from at least two different EU member states; or

- By the transformation of a public limited company which has, for at least two years, had a subsidiary in another EU member state.

The European Company is a new entity and therefore may change as it develops.

The administration of the European Company is currently as follows:

- Registration – Each European Company will be registered in the member state where it has its administrative head office on the same register as companies established under the national law of that state.

- Taxation – The European Company will be taxed at national levels according to national fiscal legislation within each member state. It will pay tax in each member state where it has a permanent establishment.

12.6.4 Partnership

Whether a partnership is in existence or not is a matter of fact.

The Partnership Act 1890 stipulates that a partnership exists between persons who carry out a business or occupation in common with the view to profit. The preparation and negotiations carried out for the purpose of tendering for a specific project will normally fit this definition. If the arrangement falls within the Act, stricter rules will apply to its termination and the issue of joint and several liability of all the parties to the partnership will arise.

This legal structure is suitable for small- and medium-sized participants or where the parties are sharing benefits and contributing to the project on an equal basis, and where the parties are unlikely to subcontract the work. However, the partners can establish in a partnership agreement an unequal ratio of contributions and benefits among the partners.

Many of the matters considered in relation to a consortium agreement apply equally to a partnership.

Many venturers will avoid an unincorporated partnership due to the existence of unlimited joint and several liability of all the partners to it.

12.6.5 Limited liability partnerships

As from 6 April 2001, limited liability partnerships (LLPs) became available in the UK as the newest form of business medium. LLPs are incorporated at Companies House and are required to file at Companies House annual accounts and an annual return. Therefore, there is more transparency and information available to the general public than with an unincorporated partnership.

As with limited companies, LLPs have a separate legal existence and accordingly will enter into contracts in their own name. Members of an LLP will enjoy the benefit of limited liability subject to similar instances when that limited liability could be eroded.

Despite LLPs having the structure of a company, the LLP is taxed on the whole as a partnership.

It should be noted that the government has now taken steps to extend certain provisions of the Companies Act 2006 to LLPs. The first set of regulations, which will extend the rules on audit and accounting to LLPs came into force on 1 October 2008. The remaining regulations came into force on 1 October 2009.

LLPs are not required to have a memorandum or articles of association and accordingly the LLP will enjoy a great deal of flexibility to organise its own internal affairs. Matters usually contained in the articles of association of a company or in a shareholders' agreement should be drawn up in a 'members agreement'.

The LLP Agreement does not have to be filed at Companies House.

It is essential to carefully consider with the venturers' legal and financial advisers whether a LLP is the most suitable structure to form the basis of a joint venture.

12.6.6 Directors and Officers of UK JVCs

Before moving on, thought should be spared for the position of directors of JVCs. These are frequently full-time employees or directors of one company, effectively 'lent' to the JVC, either permanently or on an 'as needed' basis.

Aside from their duty to the JVC to do what they consider to be in its best interests, they are frequently employed by, or even directors of, one of the shareholders of the JVC. As such, they also owe duties to the party which has nominated them onto the board of the JVC. In a recent case, *Hawkes* v. *Cuddy*, the Court of Appeal has confirmed that, legally, duties owed to a nominator can never override those owed to the JVC. That, however, does not change the fact that the JVC directors will be answerable to their full-time employers. It may be worth inserting into the joint venture agreement that directors' duties to the JVC are secondary to their duties to nominators. It should be noted that the effectiveness of such provisions has not yet been fully tested in the Courts.

Section 175 of the Companies Act 2006 codifies a legal duty for directors to avoid any actual or potential situation where they may have a conflict of interest. JVC directors have such a *potential* conflict on the basis that the interests of the nominator and the joint venture will not always coincide. To illustrate how a conflict may arise, a director may learn through the JVC of a commercial opportunity which would also be of interest to its employer. The employer may very much like to exploit that opportunity alone and possibly expect the matter to be reported back to it in full with a view to exploiting it.

Where the JVC was incorporated after 1 October 2008, the directors have a statutory power to authorise the conflict situation. If it was incorporated before that date, the JVC's articles will require amendment in order to allow the directors to sanction the conflict.

Because the principles of the Companies Act 2006 have now been extended to LLPs, many of the same issues also apply to the officers of LLPs.

12.7 Employment law issues

The parties will need to put at the disposal of the venture the human resources necessary for the implementation of the project. As mentioned in section 12.6, there are essentially two choices, each of which is briefly examined. The parties may either:

■ second employees of the parties to the venture to a JVC or other vehicle; or

■ transfer the employees permanently to the venture.

Where employees are seconded, the employer should conclude an agreement with the venture identifying the employees and stating the responsibility of each exactly. One issue to be determined will be which party is responsible for the supervision of employees. As stated earlier, in the Buncefield case, the employer in practice continued to supervise the secondees, which meant it was also vicariously liable for their negligent actions while on-site.

Employers are likely to require the consent of employees to a secondment, whether or not their employment contracts contain a 'mobility clause', requiring them to work wherever (reasonably) directed by their employer. Employees are likely to have concerns over the duration of their secondment and that their agreement to it will not result in a loss of promotion prospects or a reduction in their overall take-home pay.

A consent is not required where a business unit is permanently transferred to the joint venture. If employees are associated with that unit, their employment, under their existing terms and conditions (and pay and benefit entitlements), will automatically transfer to the venture by virtue of the Transfer of Undertakings (Protection of Employees Regulations) 2006. The employer, however will need to observe certain consultation obligations prior to the transfer.

Other issues to be addressed include the employees' pension rights, a sensitive and complex issue. Where non-EEA employees are involved, the parties must also ensure all necessary work permits are in place.

For further detail see *Employment law*.

12.8 Competition aspects
12.8.1 Competition Law – overview

The possible application of Competition Law is an important consideration when setting up a joint venture. There are (at least) two separate sets of laws which may apply to a UK-based venture, EU and UK Competition Law.

Each of these systems throws up a number of discrete issues for consideration, each of which are set out below. As a general comment, joint ventures can create problems for competition policy where they:

■ create or strengthen market positions in the areas where they operate; or

■ enable the parents to the venture to co-ordinate their competitive activities in a way which is detrimental to their competitors, clients or suppliers.

12.8.2 Merger control questions

A joint venture can, in certain circumstances, constitute a merger for the purposes of competition law. It may be necessary for the parties to seek merger clearance from a competition authority of competent jurisdiction before implementing the proposed arrangement.

Under EU Law, a clearance need be sought only where a joint venture has a 'community dimension', which is established by turnover tests set out in the EU Merger Regulation (Council Regulation (EC) No 139/2004) (**Box 1**). The Regulation applies only to those ventures which 'are full-function joint ventures'. This applies to a venture which is self-standing, has its own resources and employees and operates on a market, adding value to services or goods being provided (see Commission Notice on the concept of full-function joint ventures under Council Regulation (EEC) No 4064/89).

Box 1 EU Merger Regulation (Council Regulation (EC) No 139/2004)
A merger or creation of a joint venture has a community dimension where the combined aggregate worldwide turnover of all the undertakings concerned is more than EUR 5 billion and the aggregate EC-wide turnover of each of at least two of the undertakings concerned is more than EUR 250 million. A concentration that does not meet the thresholds laid down above has a community dimension of the combined aggregate worldwide turnover of all the undertakings concerned is more than EUR 2.5 billion; in each of at least three member states, the combined aggregate turnover of all undertakings concerned is more than EUR 100 million; in each of at least three EC member states included for the purpose of point; (b) the aggregate turnover of each of at least two of the undertakings concerned is more than EUR 25 million; and the aggregate EC-wide turnover of each of at least two of the undertakings concerned is more than EUR 100 million unless each of the undertakings concerned achieves more than two thirds of its aggregate EC-wide turnover within one and the same EC member state.

In practice, although most single-project joint ventures fall outside the rules, there have been some exceptions. For example, as part of the arrangements for the refurbishment of the London Underground, four existing management companies were brought under the common control of Metronet SSL and Metronet BCV, two JVCs established for the purpose of the project. In these circumstances, the JVCs had sufficient resources to operate on a lasting basis and needed merger clearance from the EU Commission (Case No COMP/M.2694 – *METRONET / INFRACO*).

Once notified, the Commission must reach a decision on whether to clear the venture unconditionally, clear it with conditions or prohibit it. In reaching this decision, the Commission will consider whether the venture:

■ significantly impedes effective competition in the markets on which it operates, as a result of the creation or strengthening of a dominant market position; or

■ co-ordinates the competitive behaviour of two or more parents of the venture, contrary to Article 101 of the Treaty on the Functioning of the European Union (TFEU).

The Commission will carry out an investigation and reach a 'Phase I' decision within 25 working days. This must generally be concluded within 25 days of notification. If the Phase I decision finds potential competition problems, the Commission must then proceed to an in-depth 'Phase II' investigation. A final decision must generally be reached within a further 90 working days.

Where a joint venture is caught by the EU Merger Regulation, penalties apply for failing to notify. Each party to the venture may face a fine of up to 10% of its worldwide turnover in the preceding financial year.

Where the EU Merger Regulation does not apply, there is a possibility that UK merger control might. The relevant rules are set out in the Enterprise Act 2002 (**Box 2**).

Box 2 UK Merger Control-Enterprise Act 2002 'rules'

Under this legislation, any transaction is notifiable where it involves 'two or more enterprises' ceasing to be distinct and:

■ the merger will create a common 25% share of supply of a particular type of product or service in the United Kingdom (or a substantial part of it); or

■ the turnover in the UK of the enterprise being taken over exceeds £70 million, determined by aggregating the total value in the United Kingdom of the enterprises that cease to be distinct and deducting:

■ the turnover in the UK of any enterprise that continues to be carried on under the same ownership or control (e.g. the acquiring enterprise); or

■ if no enterprise continues to be carried on under the same ownership and control (e.g. the formation of a new joint venture), the turnover in the UK which, of all turnovers concerned, has the highest value.

The UK merger control system is administered by two bodies, the Office of Fair Trading (OFT) and Competition Commission (CC) (in October 2010 the UK government announced its intention to combine the two bodies into a single entity). Notifications are, in the first instance made to the OFT, which has responsibility for carrying out a 'first screening' for the possibility that the deal may result in a 'substantial reduction in competition' in the markets concerned. This phase must usually be carried out within 20–40 days. If the OFT concludes there may be a substantial lessening of competition (SLC), it will refer the matter to the CC for a more in-depth investigation. Generally, this must be carried out within 24 weeks (extendable by 8 weeks for special reasons).

Unlike the EU system, notification of a venture is not mandatory under the Enterprise Act, even where the share of supply thresholds are reached. However, it may be advisable. The OFT may refer a completed joint venture for scrutiny by the CC. If that body concludes the venture substantially reduces competition, it is empowered to order that it be unscrambled or that the parents sell off parts of their assets or business to remedy the perceived problem. A voluntary notification allows the party to put their side of the story to the regulators and avoids the suspicion as to why they did not notify in the first place.

12.8.3 Restrictive covenants and other contractual issues

Article 101(1) Treaty on the Functioning of the European Union prohibits agreements or concerted practices between undertakings whose object or effect is to prevent or restrict competition. This prohibition applies to agreements or concerted practices with an EU cross-border dimension. The Competition Act 1998 ('CA') contains an identical prohibition applicable to agreements or concerted practices with an impact on trade in the UK. In either case, an agreement or concerted practice which falls foul of the rules, can still be exempted from the prohibition, under Article 101(3) Treaty on the Functioning of the European Union or Section 9 Competition Act respectively. Exemptions are generally available where the arrangements proposed are, on balance, pro-competitive.

Penalties for non-compliance are serious. The parties to such arrangements can be fined up to 10% of their annual worldwide turnover in the previous financial year. The arrangements in question will also be legally void, either in whole or in part.

It is normal practice for joint venture agreements to contain covenants restricting competition. For example, the parties may agree that they will not compete with the venture. Any restrictions must be proportionate and not unduly restrictive of competition. Problems become more likely to arise where participants in the arrangements have a high market share or the restrictions go beyond what is reasonably necessary for the venture to succeed.

Where the joint venture has an effect on UK trade, such covenants must be drafted in the context of UK competition law and avoid breaching the Chapter I prohibition of the Competition Act 1998. Article 101 of the Treaty on the Functioning of the European Union applies to arrangements for working together which may affect trade to an appreciable extent between member states of the European Union. The parties to such an agreement should follow the Commission's notices on permissible forms of co-operation in order to avoid infringing Article 101(1) (at the time of writing, these are set out in the EU Commission's *Guidelines on the applicability of Article 101 of the Treaty on the Functioning of the European Union to horizontal co-operation agreements*. These are due for replacement in the coming months.). Much of the Commission's advice will also assist parties in avoiding an infringement of Chapter I of the Competition Act 1998.

Currently, the EU Commission's Guidelines are under review and a consultation exercise is underway. The draft guidelines give greater consideration to the interplay between competition law and joint ventures. The Commission has said that agreements between joint ventures and their parents should fall outside of Article 101(1):

- where the parties to the joint venture are engaged on a project that neither of them could undertake alone, possibly for reasons of size or a need for a combination of skills (in those circumstances, the parties' collaboration *adds* competition, rather than reduces it)

- where the parents exercise 'decisive control' over the venture. In that situation, the agreement should be seen as an internal allocation of tasks within a corporate group rather than as an agreement between independent businesses. However, the Commission has also said that any agreement that governs matters between the parents could still be caught by Article 101(1).

The draft Guidelines are generally helpful. However, they leave a number of questions unanswered and parties are well advised to seek competition law advice when drafting and implementing a joint venture agreement.

12.8.4 Public procurement rules

The public procurement rules require any contract opportunity above a certain value to be subject to a compulsory EU wide advert in the Official Journal of the European Union. These are potentially applicable to Public Private Partnerships (see *Public-private sector partnerships*; *Procurement route;* and *Tender process*).

In most cases where a public authority wishes to involve private parties in a joint venture, there will need to be a competition amongst potential private sector participants. This could involve the full application of the Public Contracts Regulations 2006 (as amended by the Public Contracts (Amendment) Regulations 2009). Even where the full scope of the Regulations does not apply, it is likely that the private sector participants will need to be selected in accordance with the EU Law general principles of transparency, equal treatment and non-discrimination. Specific guidelines are set out in the Commission's Interpretative Communication on Institutionalised Public Private Partnerships (EU Commission's *Interpretative Communication on the application of Community law on Public Procurement and Concessions to institutionalised PPP (IPPP)*).

12.9 Issues related to bribery and corruption

Whilst frequently overlooked, anti-bribery and corruption rules are becoming ever stricter. They have a particular relevance for joint venture partners, as is now explained.

12.9.1 The international context

Frequently, when a venture includes a 'local' participant which has a good knowledge of the conditions in the local jurisdiction, the other participants will allow the local partner to do what needs to be done there, without adequately questioning what is actually being done. That may arise from a belief that a party cannot have responsibility for activities of which it is unaware.

This is an extremely high risk strategy. In the United States, for example, the Foreign Corrupt Practices Act 1977 ('FCPA') provides that a party can have liability where it is aware of a 'high degree of probability of the existence' of circumstances that might involve bribery. Article 1 of the *OECD Convention against Bribery of Foreign Officials in International Business Transactions* (OECD, 2010) prohibits bribes to officials 'either directly, or through intermediaries'. Articles 15 and 21 of the United Nations Convention on Corruption (United Nations, 2004) similarly forbids 'direct or indirect' payments of bribes. These multinational agreements have had a great deal of influence on the laws of a significant number of states.

The practical effect has been to impose a positive legal duty on foreign participants to ask questions of their local counterpart. This is illustrated by the case of the Lesotho Highlands Water Project, a large-scale infrastructure project sponsored by the World Bank and the European Investment Bank. Twelve foreign companies were prosecuted in Lesotho after it emerged they had paid large bribes to the former chief executive of the Project. The defence of one of those companies was that it had not made the payments in question, but simply made payments to its local agent, whom it claimed to have responsibility. The Court rejected that defence. The local agent was not providing any actual services to the foreign company and, much of the time the relationship subsisted, had been living outside Lesotho. Further suspicions arose from the existence of a document called the 'Representative Agreement', under which the agent's payments were made, but which the parties had mysteriously kept secret. In the circumstances, it was held that the foreign company either knew or ought to have known that the local agent's involvement in corruption. Consequently, it received a fine of US$2 million.

12.9.2 The UK context

On 8 April 2010, the Bribery Act 2010 received royal assert. Its provisions, which take effect from mid-April 2011 considerably tighten up the prohibitions on the payment and receipt of bribes generally and go further by creating an offence for bribing a foreign public official. A person will be guilty of that offence if he or she 'offers, promises or gives' an 'advantage' to a foreign public official. An offence is committed where that advantage is intended (1) to influence that person in his or her capacity as a foreign public official and (2) to obtain or retain business or some other advantage in the conduct of this business.

Of even greater concern for joint venture partners is the creation of a strict liability for the failure of commercial organisations to prevent bribery on their behalf. This offence is committed where (1) a person who is performing services on behalf of a company or partnership, (2) bribes another person intending to obtain or retain business or an advantage in the conduct of business of that business/partnership and (3) the company/partnership did not have adequate resources in place to prevent people performing services on its behalf from engaging in bribery. The offence applies to all companies or businesses which have all or part of their activities in the UK Liability is strict, meaning that in order to establish the offence, prosecutors do not need to show that the defendant had been negligent in failing to prevent the act arising.

A company will have a defence if it can show that, before the corrupt act occurred, it had put in place procedures to prevent bribery. There is uncertainty over the lengths to which the company must have gone before it can invoke this defence successfully.

The penalties for any breach of the new law are as follows:

■ ten years' imprisonment for an individual guilty of an offence

■ an unlimited fine for a company found guilty.

The severity of these potential organisations means that the parties would be well advised to put in place an anti-fraud policy and to ensure this is effectively monitored.

12.10 Partnering and alliancing: is this the same as a joint venture?

A frequently asked question is what is the difference between partnering and joint venturing? This section plots an answer.

Partnering and alliancing are two forms of co-operative working which have become popular in the construction and engineering industry, particularly since the 1990s when a need was perceived to move away from methods of working which contributed to poor relations and distrust in the industry, as well as excessive capital and operating costs.

12.10.1 Partnering

Partnering has been defined as

> a generic term embracing a range of arrangements each aimed at establishing joint working and co-operation at varying degrees of formality....advocated as a means of achieving reduced costs and improved performance [in the delivery of projects]. (Roe and Jenkins, 2003)

Usually, parties to a partnering arrangement will set out their guiding principles in an overarching document. That can be a non-binding document such as a charter or a binding agreement which has the effect of modifying existing contractual relationships and working methods. Partnering can be project specific or long term. Long-term partnering often has the advantage of setting off high start-up costs with long-term benefits, such as repeat work for contractors or consultants. Forms of partnering will sometimes, but not always, involve joint ventures. For example, one form of partnering involves

multi-party framework agreements, in which contractors will compete against each other to be awarded work.

12.10.2 Alliancing

Alliancing is a specific form of collaborative arrangement in which the participants share profit and risk sharing (see generally, *AOF Commercial Toolkit: Alliancing*). Arguably, it lends itself better to joint ventures than partnering, as participants in an 'alliance' will share the same fortune. In fact, its key difference from many other forms of joint venture is that it aims to align members to a set of shared objectives. Usually, the rewards of all alliance members will be connected to the overall result of the project in which they are involved, rather than each participant's individual performance.

To achieve this, alliancing arrangements will usually involve a financial incentive scheme which encourages cost reductions while also usually promoting quality, safety and performance. This has the effect also of encouraging co-operation between different participants.

The co-operative environment which emerges from an alliance reduces the scope for conflict and disputes between the parties. On the other hand, when conflicts do arise, these can be more costly and complex. That is partly because parties do not believe that disputes can arise in an alliancing environment and, accordingly, do not maintain the same level of vigilance in maintaining project documents and supervising each other's activities.

An early example of a successful alliance was BP's Project Andrew, which involved the construction of an oil platform in a marginal oil field in the North Sea (Roe and Jenkins, 2003, p.6.). Initial studies concluded that the construction would need to use a vastly different type of construction procurement method in order to achieve the cost savings required to make the project viable. Eight design consultants were invited to tender and the selection of Brown & Root as preferred bidder owed as much to that company's commitment to the alliancing principles as to their technical expertise. Santa Fe was selected as contractor. At the end of the project, the participants had incurred £160 million less cost than had originally been projected and oil was produced six months ahead of schedule.

Alliancing has also been employed in the nuclear industry (Norton Rose LLP, 2009). British Energy has used forms of partnering and alliancing in the construction of its stations. The form used in these alliances usually involves the adoption of a set of partnering principles, which sits alongside a binding agreement based on the nuclear industry's standard terms and conditions. A challenge in the nuclear industry arises from the fact that under statute the operator is responsible for any fault which arises from a functioning power station and the extent of liability can be catastrophic. This problem can be mitigated, to some extent, with indemnities from the contractor and consultant to the operator for their portion of the operator's liability.

When adopting a partnering or alliancing scheme, a JVC may or may not be created. For example, it may make sense, particularly in the context of an alliance, for participants to be shareholders in an incorporated joint venture. If they are rewarded by means of a dividend, the amount of distributable profits available to each of them will depend on how the venture has fared, which in turn, to a degree, will hinge on how well they have worked together. The Wandoo alliance, for example, involved the creation of a new entity which was involved in the exploitation of an oil field off the coast of Western Australia.

On the other hand, parties may often prefer an unincorporated venture, for instance, to facilitate the cross licensing of expertise or sharing of facilities or expertise without the creation of an identifiable business.

12.11 Conclusions

This chapter has provided an overview of opportunities and pitfalls which venturing offers. This section concludes by bringing strands together and summarising some of the issues of which parties must be aware and points of action, at each step of the conceptualisation and implementation of their venture (for another view on steps to be taken at each step of the process see Applegate, 2001).

12.11.1 Pre-contract

At this stage the parties should engage in a thorough discussion of the commercial drivers for the joint venture. Any possible points of divergence between them must be identified and 'bottomed out'. We saw in section 12.3.3, that the differing expectations of what the parties would get from the venture can either cause its downfall or lead to it failing to deliver the benefits which any or all of the parties desired.

We saw at section 12.5.1 that a MoU can be an extremely helpful document when it comes to drafting the joint venture agreement. This document acts as a 'guiding post' during contractual negotiations and focuses the parties' discussions upon the important commercial parameters of the deal.

The next step is for the parties to agree the most desirable structure for the joint venture. Should their collaboration take the form of an incorporated or unincorporated venture? The final decision will be shaped by considerations related to tax, the parties' attitude to liability, as well (possibly) as the requirements of the project itself and the employer. At this stage, the parties may also wish to consider whether or not an alliancing structure is desirable, involving a painshare/gainshare mechanism.

Considerations of 'structure' do not end at whether or not the venture is to be incorporated or unincorporated. The parties must also decide how the venture will be managed, how often the management team will convene, as well as who will be responsible for what and who will represent the venture to third parties such as the employer.

Once those commercial aspects and structure have been adequately discussed and agreed, they must be faithfully reflected in the joint venture agreements themselves. The drafting of the documents may be led by lawyers but should not be their sole responsibility.

The parties should review the proposed agreements attentively, actively considering the implications of the drafted provisions for their every day operations and whether, in practice, these solutions are workable on a day-to-day level. It is tempting, for example, to gloss over provisions such as termination clauses. In practice though, how and why the venture is ended is a matter of considerable importance to the parties. Even something as apparently trivial as how a notice is to be served by one party on another in reality can cause the parties significant difficulties if this cannot be implemented in practice.

12.11.2 Contract phase

There is little point in going to the considerable effort and expense of drawing up joint venture agreements and policies if these are ultimately ignored. Once the realisation of the project begins, the parties must adequately monitor progress and ensure that their proposals are kept to. For example, if the parties have agreed that the management team will meet on a monthly basis, the temptation should be avoided to allow the frequency of meetings to occur less frequently.

That is not to say that the parties' initial arrangements should be set in stone. These should be reviewed as the project progresses to ensure that they continue to meet the parties' needs. For example, it may become apparent that monthly management meetings are simply not workable. In that case, the parties may wish to consider an alternative means of ensuring that the venture's proper functioning, such as the provision of a monthly report to team members and the ability to convene meetings in light of the monthly report, with regular meetings on a quarterly basis.

During the contract phase, it is also vital that the parties ensure that meetings of the joint venture adequately supervise and report on all aspects of the venture's activities and the carrying out of its legal obligations. For example, the agenda of meetings should include a regular point on health and safety matters.

Aside from corporate governance, the venture parties may also wish to have in place policies on legal matters which affect its functioning. This could include, for example, policies to combat fraud or policies to ensure compliance with competition law. These policies too may need updating, for example, to reflect changes in the law itself.

12.11.3 Post-contract

Matters are not always concluded once the project has been completed. For example, the contract documents should contain provisions dealing with site clean-up or plant removal matters. The parties should also consider how any matters will be dealt with that relate to latent or other 'tail-end' liabilities, which may not crystallise until long after the joint venture has ceased to exist.

In conclusion, when parties to a joint venture work together effectively, there are great rewards to be enjoyed. Together they can be more than the sum of their parts, expanding their horizons, in terms of the location, scope and scale of the projects they tackle. However, as the age old business adage goes, risk and reward go hand in hand. This chapter has mapped out and highlighted some of the issues which venturers must tackle and the hazards of which they must be aware. The good news though is that with sound planning and advice, these matters are manageable and the huge potential of joint venturing, the reason for the phenomenal growth of this business model, can be fully realised.

Acknowledgement

The author wishes to thank Jenny Baster for her comments on an earlier version of this chapter. The author also wishes to thank Caroline Skinner and Caroline Cree, whose original chapter in the ICE Construction Law Handbook served as a basis for sections 12.4 and 12.5 of this chapter.

References

Applegate, D. B. (2001) Controlling Joint Venture Risk. *Internal Auditor*. Available at: http://findarticles.com/p/articles/mi_m4153/is_3_58/ai_77151368/

AOF Commercial Toolkit: Alliancing. www.aof.mod.uk/aofcontent/tactical/toolkit/content/topics/allig.htm

China-Britain Business Council (2004), *Intellectual Property Rights in China: Risk Assessment, Avoidance Strategy and Problem Solving (The China IPR Guidelines)*. Available at www.chinabusinesssolutions.com/dbimg/china_ipr_guidelines1.01.pdf

Current Account Transactions. Available at: http://business.gov.in/doing_business/current_account_transaction.php.

Currency Convertibility and its impact on BOP. Available at: www.scribd.com/doc/21814664/Currency-Convertibility-and-its-impact-on-BOP

EU Commission. *Commission Interpretative Communication on the application of Community law on Public Procurement and Concessions to institutionalised PPP (IPPP)*, Brussels, 05/02/2008 C(2007)6661. Available at: http://ec.europa.eu/internal_market/publicprocurement/docs/ppp/comm_2007_6661_en.pdf

EU Commission. *Guidelines on the Applicability of Article 101 of the Treaty on the Functioning of the European Union to Horizontal Co-Operation Agreements*. (Shortly to be replaced [2010]). Available at: http://ec.europa.eu/competition/consultations/2010_horizontals/guidelines_en.pdf

Guijun, L. and Schramm, R. M. *China's Progression Toward Currency Convertibility: A Review and Assessment*. Available at: http://mesharpe.metapress.com/link.asp?id=xt8egvv7dhpwdr90

Reid, G. (2007) *Considering a Joint venture?* Johnston Carmichael (online). www.jcca.co.uk/Default.asp?DocumentID=84e613ff-367e-41cb-b4fa-d6c89d385e43&ShowMenu=&MenuID=

Norton Rose LLP (2009) *Alliancing in the nuclear industry in the UK*. www.nortonrose.com/knowledge/publications/2009/pub21336.aspx?lang=en-gb&page=all

OECD (2010) *Convention against Bribery of Foreign Officials in International Business Transactions (OECD Anti Bribery Convention)*. Available at: www.oecd.org/dataoecd/4/18/38028044.pdf

PriceWaterhouseCoopers and CFO research Services (2004) *The CFO's Perspective on Alliances*. CFO Publishing Corp, Boston, MA.

Roe, S. and Jenkins, J. (2003) *Partnering and Alliancing in Construction Projects*. Thomson Publishing

Simmons and Simmons (2009) Joint Venturers & Shareholders Agreements, Third Edition. Bloomsbury Professional, London

United Nations (2004) *United Nations Convention against Corruption*. United Nations, Vienna. Available at: www.unodc.org/documents/treaties/UNCAC/Publications/Convention/08-50026_E.pdf

Referenced legislation, regulations and standards

Bribery Act 2010

Commission Notice on the concept of full-function joint ventures under Council Regulation (EEC) No 4064/89 on the control of concentrations between undertaking. OJ **C 66**, 02/03/1998.

Companies Act 2006

Consolidated versions of the Treaty on European Union and the Treaty on the Functioning of the European Union. OJ, **C83**, 30/3/2010

Council Directive 2001/86/EC of 8 October 2001 supplementing the Statute for a European company with regard to the involvement of employees. OJ **L294**, 10/11/2001, pp.22–32

Council Regulation (EC) No 139/2004 of 20 January 2004 on the control of concentrations between undertakings (the EC Merger Regulation). OJ, **L24**, 29/01/2004, pp.1–22

Council Regulation (EC) No 2157/2001 of 8 October 2001 on the Statute for a European company (SE). OJ **L294**, 10/11/2001, pp.1–21

Enterprise Act 2002

Foreign Corrupt Practices Act 1977 (USA)

Foreign and Exchange Management Act 2000 (India)

Partnership Act 1890

Public Contracts (Amendment) Regulations 2009

Public Contracts Regulations 2006

Referenced cases

Colour Quest Limited and others v. Total Downstream UK PLC, Total UK Limited and Hertfordshire Oil Storage Limited [2009] EWHC 540 (Comm) – available at: www.bailii.org

Hawkes v. Cuddy [2009] EWCA Civ. 291

METRONET / INFRACO – Case No COMP/M.2694. Decision available at: http://ec.europa.eu/competition/mergers/cases/decisions/m2694_en.pdf

Philips Electronics v. HMRC [2009] – summary available at: www.grantthornton.co.uk/tax/tax_stories/the_philips_v_hmrc_case_has_no.aspx

Further reading

Cree, C. and Henty, P. (2009) *Working with Others*, Chapter 2.2 in Ramsey, V., Minogue, A. Baster, J. and O'Reilly, M. (eds), Construction Law Handbook, 2009 edition. Thomas Telford Ltd, London

Hewitt, I. (2008) *International Joint Ventures*. Sweet and Maxwell, London

Sayer, S. (2005) *Negotiating International Joint Venture Agreements*. Sweet and Maxwell, London

Websites

Arup and Worsley Parsons joint venture, New Multi-Products Pipeline; www.arup.com/Projects/Multi-products_Pipeline.aspx

Atkins-led joint venture, Ras Al-Zawr; www.utilities-me.com/article-629-ws-atkins-consortium-awarded-ras-al-zour-contract/

Bribery Act; www.justice.gov.uk/publications/bribery-bill.htm.

Bribery Act, useful article; www.control-risks.com/default.aspx?page=1663

Companies House; www.companieshouse.gov.uk

Competition Commission (CC); www.competition-commission.org.uk

Consortium tax relief (HMRC); www.hmrc.gov.uk/manuals/ctmanual/ctm80530.htm

Joint ventures and partnering, practice advice from Business Link; www.businesslink.gov.uk/bdotg/action/layer?topicId=1073864682

Mouchel, Agilisys and Rochdale Metropolitan Borough Council, award winning joint venture; www.mouchel.com/media/latest_press_releases/release.aspx?id=76335

NHS Lift; www.dh.gov.uk/en/Aboutus/Procurementandproposals/Publicprivatepartnership/NHSLIFT/DH_091676

Organisation for Economic Co-operation and Development (OECD); ww.oecd.org

Office of Fair Trading (OFT); www.oft.gov.uk

The Impact Partnership; www.impactpartnership.com

US withdrawal of investment from Uzbekistan; http://www.state.gov/outofdate/bgn/u/81746.htm

Wandoo Alliance, offshore oil platform; www.engineeringicons.org.au/engineering-icons/australian/wandoo-offshore-oil-platform/

ice | manuals

Chapter 13

International offices

Richard Abigail Arup Group Limited, London, UK
Update of previous text authored by Steve Priddy, Arup Group Limited

This article provides an overview of the key risks and considerations that a consultant engineer should bear in mind when working internationally. It considers the strategic aspects of international expansion in the context of the global economic downturn. The article then focuses on the establishment of a local presence before concluding with a detailed analysis of the tax implications of doing so.

doi: 10.1680/mocl.40878.0197

CONTENTS

13.1 Introduction

The march of globalisation continues in most industries and consultant engineers have been as active as many in establishing a local presence in foreign countries. Even before the recent financial troubles, there was a drive to diversify the engineer's geographic source of income. Moreover, the rapid growth in certain regions, such as the Middle East, has attracted many more engineers to consider working abroad.

The credit crunch has increased risk to consultants both in their home markets and abroad. In the home market, large public and private debt will weaken future demand for consultancy services. Therefore, to drive growth, engineers are looking internationally. However, those international markets have also suffered in the credit crunch and from a slow-down in activity, none more so than Dubai. Moreover, international working brings with it a host of cultural, legal, financial and operational risks. These need to be managed and controlled.

This article initially focuses on the considerations that should be taken when approaching international work. It then considers the practical implications of establishing a presence abroad and addresses key business risk. The final section considers corporate and personnel tax issues.

13.2 Strategic considerations

13.2.1 Choosing to work internationally

The engineer must, at the outset, be clear why he or she wants to work internationally. This should be embedded in the overall strategy for the organisation. Clear direction needs to be given from the corporate Board as working internationally is a long-term investment for any organisation. Significant resources need to be allocated to developing overseas markets and the role of the Board will be to ensure the organisation's scarce resources are allocated to the projects which most closely meet its strategy.

Strategic reasons may include expansion in a certain geographic market to diversify the source of income; having the right person to lead the venture; diversifying the business by penetrating economies in different phases of the construction cycle or; obvious engineering opportunities.

However, most international markets have a number of highly competent local firms operating. Moreover, other international engineers may have a presence. Therefore, the overriding reason to work internationally is the competitive edge that can be brought to the market-place. This competitive edge will need to be refined and guarded. It is likely to be either at the forefront of existing technology, that is, the engineer is doing something that no one else can currently do; or an innovation that produces a leap in the quantity of what can be produced; or, perhaps more likely, it has come about via multidisciplinary working, that is, the solution was arrived at by solving a problem in another field.

It may be the case that the organisation's competitive edge is in a niche area where a local presence is not required. The nature of engineering consultancy and the service bias of its product mean that it will be possible to deliver on these projects in non-UK locations on a fly-in/fly-out basis. This can be done without attracting any of the regulatory restrictions outlined later in this chapter.

However, whatever the competitive edge is, and no matter how well it is protected, it is likely to be common property in the profession within 18 months unless backed by economies of scale to deliver a broad range of skills such as Building, Engineering, Infrastructure, Acoustics, IT, Fire, Facades, Sustainability and so on from the same organisation.

This presents a key strategic question for all consultants – will the international work be home based in niche areas or will it be 'on-shore' competing with other local providers. In practice many consultants adopt a hybrid approach with general skills being delivered locally and niche skills acquired from other parts of the organisation.

In many cases, engineering consultants start working in a particular geography from their home base. It is only after their understanding of the environment has developed that they decide to establish a more permanent presence in the foreign country.

13.2.2 Market research

The first key question, regardless of intended entry approach, is which market to enter?

This may be simply answered because an existing client wishes to carry out a project in a new territory and therefore the engineer follows. Once working in that country, research can be carried out on the market.

However, it may be more likely that the engineer is reacting to other news about a market. Maybe it is in response to general economic growth (such as India or China) or a particular event (Brazil hosting the football World Cup and Olympics in 2014 and 2016 respectively).

Data on these markets is widely available and therefore the first stage of analysis can be desk based in the UK. It is important to understand the basic macroeconomic and social background to the particular country.

A good starting place is the Foreign & Commonwealth website or its US equivalent, The World Factbook on the CIA website. These websites provide basic information on most countries in the world such as economic data, political structure, security and travel advice and key points of contact (e.g. embassies).

For more business orientated information the *Doing Business Report* ranks 183 economies on their ease of doing business. It assesses whether the regulatory environment is conducive to the operation of business.

A further excellent source of information is UK Trade & Investment (UKTI) (www.ukti.gov.uk), which has a local presence in a significant number of countries. They organise frequent trade events and can provide support and guidance on the ground.

13.2.3 Cultural awareness

With respect to cultural awareness, there is no substitute for field work. No matter how well the engineer understands the official version of the territory in which they intend to work, the reality will be different. They will need to understand the power brokers and the patrons of the built environment as well as the local professional cliques. They will have to learn to navigate the bureaucracy. In many countries they will have to recognise and handle corruption risks which may be prevalent in both the public and private spheres of business.

A key area of cultural awareness is the use of language and in particular assuming English as a global business language. Even though English may be suitable in some situations as the written and spoken medium, there are many situations when the local language must be used and even English words may carry different meanings in different countries, for example, 'schedule' or 'programme'; 'program' or 'brief'.

While the language of many engineering contracts may be specified as English, design development, design arguments, defending the client's budget against change from architects or others in the design team, handing over a design at a pre-agreed stage to a local engineer, all these instances may be conducted vigorously in the local language. The importance of this cannot be overestimated.

Many organisations provide cultural awareness training and these courses should be considered for engineers travelling to a new region for the first time.

13.2.4 Competitor analysis

Another feature of working internationally that cannot be over-estimated is understanding thoroughly the cost structure of the local consultancy profession, their profitability and productivity, how that relates to the service they provide and how the international engineer differentiates himself.

The engineer will bring to the local situation a higher-cost base – they are likely to have a leader on an attractive remuneration package (because he or she will be in great demand). Overheads are likely to be higher as they will be carrying a central overhead cost. Productivity is likely to be lower, particularly in the opening years of the venture and this will also push up overheads. Incidental job expenses such as travel, translations, hotel bills and subsistence in particular, are likely to be higher than local competitors.

Because of these factors, the engineer must be clear about the limiting factors on their venture's financial performance and where competitive edge resides.

The engineer should conduct serious analysis of the financial position of competitors. As noted earlier, local competition may be from local engineering firms as well as other international firms. Find out specifically:

- What is the optimal size of consulting organisation in the territory?
- What is the optimal mix of staff by age and grade and salary level?
- How do local organisations account for salary and overhead costs?
- What is the typical profit margin?
- What is an accepted level of credit (both officially and in practice as these can differ widely)?
- What is the typical cash flow profile of a local consultancy?

Obtaining this kind of information may not be easy but will repay dividends in understanding, and beating, local competition.

13.2.5 Business risks

The engineer must totally understand the regime of fee calculation and duties and scope of service. They must understand the extent to which different countries value design, reward design and integrate cost into design. The variations between even two very similar Western cultures – the UK and the United States – are astonishing. They may become even more significant with other countries.

More detailed analysis of key business risks is provided later in this chapter.

13.2.6 The business plan

A business plan is an essential step. While the plan may not really yield the answers required, it will provide a good focus and also a source of motivation for those who will lead the business. Moreover, it provides the Board with a document which can be considered, commented upon and, hopefully, ultimately approved.

The plan must have clear short-, medium- and long-term measurables which will indicate success or failure of the investment in the new country. It must also detail the rationale for the investment and the competitive edge the engineer can bring to the market.

In many cases, business plans are presented to the Board a number of times as each stage of research is completed with the resultant information incorporated into the plan.

13.3 The local presence
13.3.1 The type of presence

Once the decision has been taken by the Board to work in the foreign country, the question of how the engineers will organise themselves in the new territory will need to be answered. Will they aim to continue with a reconnaissance office? Will the project office become independent and look for further work locally and in its own right? Will it be necessary to establish a locally registered branch or company? Or is it intended to work in joint venture? Or even to acquire a local well-established practice?

In many countries, the type of legal entity available to foreign engineers may be restricted or may require a significant element of local ownership. In addition, local sponsorship or 'agency' relationships (either by an individual or company) may be required. Significant care should be given to selecting the right sponsor/agent. Due diligence should be carried out on the sponsor/agent to ensure no risk of exposure to corruption.

A sponsor/agent may develop influence over the operations of the engineer and this may not always align with its strategy. Therefore, clearly defined written legal agreements should be drawn up between the consultant engineer and the sponsor/agent. This should define the scope and more importantly, the limitation of powers of the sponsor/agent. It should also include an 'exit' if the relationship needs to be ended, which, under local legislation may require a significant payment to be made to sponsor/agent.

Each option for the type of presence will have its benefits and drawbacks and therefore expert local advice should be considered from accountants and lawyers.

13.3.2 Identifying the leader and staff

For most countries the position of leader cannot be filled by a young enthusiast who is technically excellent. Increasingly, clients are looking for 'grey-hairs' who bring many years of experience and reassurance. It is necessary to have the technical and design flair behind the wisdom, but this alone is not sufficient. The leader, by definition, will be wholly exceptional. Nationality, linguistic skill and cultural awareness and a good commercial head may be more important than technical skill.

Expertise in business development will need to be combined with controlling cash flow, all aspects of facilities management, staff recruitment, human resources (HR), legal/contractual matters as well as project delivery. Nationality is an important marker. In most of the sophisticated mainland European economies, there can be no substitute for the native speaker as leader. In some of the most regionalised European economies, the right accent or dialect can be critical. In many of the emerging markets expatriate leadership is accepted, but a rapid transfer of know-how and power will be expected.

With the right leader must come the right human resources (HR) strategy. Because the centre of any technical consultancy is its people, the HR policy is critical to financial success. The policy has to be firm, fair and realistic, while dovetailing with the legal and customary framework of the specific territory. The remuneration and benefits package has to be a balance between motivating staff while not becoming prohibitively expensive in the market-place. Also critical here will be skill sets and achieving the right mix between technical- and business-orientated people.

Competitor practice needs to be considered. For example, expatriates in many countries expect to be provided with free accommodation and a car whilst in a foreign country. If a competitor is offering these benefits then it is likely that they will have to be matched.

In a number of countries there is wish to transfer international skills to local employees and a ratio of local employees to expatriate is set. How these rules are enforced in practice differs from country to country and therefore local advice should be sought.

13.3.3 International project management

Bringing the international aspect to project management will be a key ingredient in the commercial success of any venture outside home territory. Collaborators will be keen to have an international engineer on the team, and will go to great efforts in those early days to help with the administrative set-up. Much of the early technical work will be at the level of a concept and scheme design as understood in the UK.

This may itself lead to failure – the delivery should be to the client's needs, not necessarily UK standards. There may be comparatively few drawings. Reports may be written and accepted at a fairly abstract level. This early warmth and the attractiveness of the abstracted level of service, coupled with an apparent low-risk atmosphere can easily lead to a sense of false security.

Effective international project management will depend on crystal clear lines of communication and responsibility, agreed inter-office trading protocols and scopes of service, and a programme and critical path which all parts of the consulting firm have agreed to. For the international client, it is also necessary to demonstrate constantly that the entire resources of the international engineer's network are available and able to deliver the product.

Face-to-face contact, the experience of working with someone in the past, knowing and respecting each others' strengths and weaknesses will all be vital ingredients for success.

13.3.4 Sub-consultancy

External sub-consultancy can be an effective method of delivering the international project. To work well, the sub-consultant must be well known to the engineer and they must mutually respect each other in the delivery of their respective tasks. In some countries, sub-consulting can be viewed adversely by clients as an abdication of responsibility. Conversely this may be required in other places. The use of high-skill/low-cost locations may also be an option to consider in sub-consulting arrangements.

All sub-consulting relationships require careful management. However, it is particularly important with local sub-consultants. Ultimately, the risk will be carried by the lead engineer.

13.3.5 External consultants and Banks

Building relationships with local professional advisers will be critical. Increasingly, the old professional barriers between law, accounting, tax, HR and company secretarial functions are breaking down. Business consultancy is able to provide a 'one stop' shop to setting up a sustainable presence in new territory. In addition, there are State bodies, investment agencies, commercial attachés and the like, who will be keen to encourage UK investment in their country.

Building the relationships is a process of asking the same question from as many perspectives as possible to as many listeners as possible and testing independently wherever possible.

Establishing a strong relationship with a reputable bank at the outset of the international venture is also very important. The bank must understand international business and have its own strong links to the home country bank. Building up trust quickly means that the bank will act swiftly on your instruction. Banks may also be able to provide advice or key contacts.

13.3.6 Information technology and communications

Information technology (IT) is the backbone of any modern office, and implementation can be expensive and time consuming. The IT plan for a new office cannot be developed in isolation, it needs to support the business plan, but also inform the plan. For example, despite the benefits of using the organisation's existing accounting package, the need to invest in a local accounting package may be dictated by the cost and availability of bandwidth.

It will be necessary to establish the constraints on software, communications and IT generally. The effectiveness of the system's architecture will be a function of PC capability, application requirements, area networks and communication links. And it is vital to be able to communicate effectively and seamlessly with local clients and collaborators.

13.3.7 Business, financial and administrative systems

A robust system of working on internationally resourced projects will need to be in place. The business systems of the local venture must be carefully selected both to be appropriate and adequate for local requirements but also provide sufficient information to the centre to meet the organisation's statutory and management accounting requirements.

Therefore early involvement of the organisation's accounting function is fundamental.

Procedures will be needed in relation to internal sub-consultancy arrangements. How are internal scopes of service to be defined? What are the profit and loss sharing arrangements? Do the management accounting arrangements have the blessing of the UK and local taxation authorities?

An additional overhead attaches to the engineer working internationally because of the double reporting requirement, both to local regulatory frameworks, but also back to the centre. As the business develops, the systems required become more complex.

At the start of operations the financial and administrative staff will very often be recruited locally. The recruitment should probably be done earlier rather than later in the process. However, it is common for a senior executive going abroad to bring with him or her key administrative personnel from their home office.

A decision will need to be made as to the level of independence the local office will have with its back-office systems. Will it adopt its own, say, accounting and payroll packages or will it utilise the existing systems in place at the home office.

A key consideration in determining the independence of systems will be the level of local information to be provided in differing formats. For example, local payroll tax requirements mean it is cheaper and more efficient to use a local package (or outsource the task locally) rather than re-configure a global system. In some countries, audit of overhead costs for government contracts is commonplace. In many countries, these books will have to be maintained in the language and currency of the territory.

Other systems will often have to be developed from scratch. For example, the database of business contacts, new leads, probable and possible projects, target clients and corporations will only be relatively poorly developed in the centre. Similarly, technical software may need to be purchased locally to meet local requirements. In order to transmit and translate drawings over borders and time zones, high-level decisions will have to be taken about software purchase and system development.

13.3.8 Accommodation and location

An important factor is the location of the office in the new country both in terms of which city to establish the office and within which area of a chosen city. It may be common practice for consultant engineers to gather together in one city and one particular district.

In other territories, to get above a certain critical size it may be essential to be established as a network of offices spread throughout the country. This relates to the business objectives in the first place, for example, a focused boutique or an all-encompassing engineering practice delivering major infrastructure projects.

Moreover, location can be an important means of communicating an intention. For example, setting up shop in the financial sector might endear you to large banking and other financial institutions, but it might alienate one-off building clients, industrialists, heavy civils work or local architects. Great sensitivity is needed and clear thinking about the message which the engineer wants to convey about their presence in the territory.

Once a location has been determined, the size and rental method should be considered. Should the consultant establish an office immediately or will a serviced office suffice? Careful consideration of the headcount growth plan needs to be made. In addition, a watchful eye needs to be kept on the cost of exiting a lease if the operation is deemed to have failed.

The type of office that the client walks into provides a critical first impression and needs careful design consideration. Finding an office can be time consuming and a distraction from delivering projects in the early days of entry when administrative teams are small. Consideration should be given to the organisations overall corporate branding and image. Moreover, staff being seconded from their home offices will have an expectation of the type of office space they expect.

13.3.9 Infrastructure

A good understanding of the physical infrastructure is essential. Physical infrastructure will involve considerations such as getting from A to B and the relative merits of road, rail and air transport. The mode of travel feeds through to relative costs and, ultimately, how such costs are built into local fee proposals to clients. The client looking for an international perspective will expect a clear and non-parochial approach to incidentals such as travel, translations, hotel and subsistence costs.

Equally, for travel and communications not directly related to the job, establishment in the wrong location with a poor understanding of the local, national and international infrastructure can lead to unacceptably high overhead costs.

A further key issue is security for staff and the company's assets. Many new markets for engineers are in volatile, violent and corrupt locations. A new office should minimise risk to staff and assets. Moreover, consideration needs to be given as to where the staff will live and how they will commute to and from the office and clients. In some territories staff security may be the key determining factor in whether the engineer decides to work there or not.

13.4 Business risk and mitigation

In operating the local presence, the consultant engineering will be exposed to a number of key risks to his business. A summary is given in the following section.

13.4.1 Legal

The legal environment of a particular country will shape the overall risk mitigation approach. In developed countries, a significant level of reliance can be placed on the adherence to well-established and understood local laws and regulations.

In less developed countries, local laws and regulations may be much more difficult to identify with certainty and institutions generally may be very much less established or transparent. Both here and in those countries where an entirely different foundation for legal principles exist, (e.g. Sharia law in the Middle East) the consultant will face considerable challenges in navigating a way through. Wherever possible in these cases, the consultant should seek to agree internationally accepted contracting terms such as Fédération Internationale des Ingénieurs-Conseils (FIDIC, see below), a recognised set of arbitration rules in preference to local courts, and a well-established law such as English law in preference to local law. In practice, however, it may very well be difficult to contract on this basis and local laws and contract terms will apply. This means that there may be great uncertainty about how issues such as dispute resolution or enforcement of recovery are handled.

Decennial liability is a particular concern to professionals working in France or a number of other countries, including many countries in the Middle East, whose legal system is based on the French Civil Code. Decennial liability is a form of strict liability which applies as a matter of law in the case of latent defects to construction projects where the defects are of a significant nature. Liability runs, as the name suggests, for 10 years and applies irrespective of negligence. There are practical insurance implications arising from decennial liability, which are discussed in the following section.

13.4.2 Insurances

Different territories with their varied legal systems can have their own insurance regimes with specific requirements. For example, there is a requirement in France and certain other countries for decennial insurance to be effected to cover any risk of decennial liability. Most UK professional indemnity policies do not cover decennial liability and will not meet this requirement. It will be necessary to purchase separate decennial liability insurance to meet this requirement and certainly in France this is a difficult process and premiums can be significant.

The engineer's professional indemnity (PI) insurer will be able to give advice on the cover provided in specific territories of operation. It is unwise to assume that PI automatically gives global cover and in particular US activities are often excluded. Moreover, many territories now require insurance policies to be issued locally. To accommodate this requirement, 'fronting policies' are often used whereby a local insurer provides local cover but on the basis that it is backed up by the engineer's normal policy so that any liability is simply passed back to the engineers principal insurers. (See *Professional indemnity insurance*).

It may be necessary to consider other insurances such as public liability insurance and employer's liability or workmen's' compensation insurance which generally have to be arranged locally. The engineer may wish to consider whether to arrange insurance for credit risk and advice on this can be obtained from the Export Credit Guarantee Department of the UK Government.

Further information on insurance can be found in the chapter *Construction insurance*.

13.4.3 Client credit risk

One of the simplest and most common commercial risks an engineer can face is that a client is unable or unwilling to pay the fees which are due. This may be because of the client's insolvency or indeed for any number of reasons, which may or may not relate to the engineer's performance. Establishing the client's commitment to the project, in a situation where the engineer has never worked with that client before, and the project is in a territory which is also unfamiliar, involves shrewd commercial judgement. The reality is that problems of payment are more likely to arise when working internationally and the prospect of trying to enforce payment by taking legal proceedings in local courts is unlikely to be an attractive or productive option. Credit rating agencies can provide limited information about the financial strength or otherwise of the potential client, but agencies rely on limited sources of hard financial information (e.g. the filing of financial statements) as well as unofficial sources. In certain territories, the latter becomes the predominant source of information.

Where the engineer is not familiar with the client or has concerns about payment, the following practical guidance is offered, although what is customary in different territories may vary.

(a) Make the agreement conditional on a mobilisation payment before commencement of work.
(b) Try to match a monthly invoicing schedule to the s-curve of cost associated with the performance of the project.
(c) If possible, build in a 'right to stop work' should fees not be paid within the payment terms of the agreement. Include interest payments on outstanding invoices.
(d) Try to ensure that payment of fees is not linked to 'approval' of deliverables; ensure that any link between technical progress and fee invoicing is via neutral terms such as 'receipt' or 'delivery' of drawings, reports or calculations, not via their 'final approval'.
(e) Recognise that relatively long payment terms can be the cultural norm in many countries.
(f) Understand credit control procedures. In many countries, credit control must be done face to face by the project team rather than the UK model of a central specialist credit control team making telephone calls.
(g) Don't invoice fees and incidental expenses together – why hold up hundreds of thousands for a missing taxi receipt?

Many clients will only accept invoices after a deliverable and therefore will neither accept a mobilisation payment nor a monthly billing schedule. Therefore, it is helpful to build into the project plan frequent and easily met deliverables. So for example, a project kick-off meeting can be used as a deliverable and hence invoiced in lieu of a mobilisation payment.

13.4.4 Rights and responsibilities for design

The engineer needs to understand what rights they have over their design. This will vary across territories. Moreover, in some poorer countries, plagiarism of design may still be an issue. Further details on rights can be found in *Intellectual property*.

13.4.5 Professional or technical registrations

The key question here is: is the engineer legally competent to conduct engineering consultancy in the territory? Two separate issues are commonly encountered. The first is whether the engineer's locally registered branch or company is properly structured to work legally. In many territories there is a requirement that local nationals must make up a significant part of the either the leadership or the ownership structure of the entity. The second issue is a local prohibition against 'foreigners' being on site or directing site operations; or drawings being issued unless they have first been approved by a local qualified engineer. This latter point is not uncommon in the Middle East.

Being ignorant of such registrations and procedures can at worst lead to court actions against the engineer and at best to significant delays, reworking and consequent eroding of profit margins. This can apply individually and corporately.

13.4.6 Contracts for services, fee scales, stages and deliverables

Some territories have standard contract forms and fee scales which may vary considerably from UK standards. Each territory may have its own more or less well developed fee scale book. Reading what the book says is one thing; understanding what it means in terms of resourcing and delivering a project is altogether a much harder task.

FIDIC Client/Consultant Model Service Agreement is a standard form of agreement that has been developed for international use by consulting engineers. It represents the highest level of consensus between various national engineering institutions and provides a useful basis on which a proposal or contract can be made.

In the United States, the defined project stages are fairly commonplace. Programming (DPP), Schematic Design, Design Development, Construction Documents, Bid and Construction Administration. Some organisations have very defined deliverables for each stage, others less so. The key thing is to understand fully the local requirements at the outset and get documents from other projects to see what is the standard.

A particular concern when working internationally can be obtaining consents or approvals from local building control authorities. It is important to understand the responsibility the consultant engineer will take for approvals from the outset. Very often the approvals procedure is outside the engineer's control and it can become very protracted, especially when the building control authorities may not always be familiar with the design approach. Moreover, it is sensible not to link payments with approvals as this would introduce a significant uncontrollable element to the consultant's cash flow.

13.4.7 Guarantees, bonds, powers of attorney

Bonds and guarantees are a common requirement in some parts of the international construction industry. The following are the most typical.

- *Tender (Bid in the USA)*: to guarantee that the tenderer will not renege on his or her commitment – normally valid for the period between the submission of tender and the date of announcement of tender award.
- *Advance payment*: to guarantee that the consultant will not disappear having received a payment in advance of work being performed.
- *Performance*: to guarantee that the consultant will perform his or her duties properly.
- *Retention*: to allow early release of retained portions of fees.

Most guarantees are issued 'without recourse', that is, no conditions are attached to the guarantee being called. Some guarantees also contain no expiry date. Their effective expiry is therefore only when they are returned by the client and can be cancelled and destroyed. Some advance payment guarantees include an implicit performance guarantee in that the client can recover the monies if the consultant has not performed his duties. Moreover, in certain territories, performance guarantees can be extremely difficult to get released by the client. Guarantee fees continue to be levied by the bank until the bond is cancelled.

A guarantee represents a cost, both in the annual banking charges but also because guarantee commitments are set against any engineer's bank borrowing facility. In many cases, the client requires the guarantee to be issued by a local bank. This can increase the cost considerably as the local bank receives a counter indemnity from the engineers UK bankers. Or cash will be required to be deposited with the bank, mitigating the benefits of say an advance payment guarantee.

Where available, a parent company guarantee will generally be a cheaper option for the engineer, while still providing security to the client.

There is also the option of taking out insurance for the unfair calling of performance bonds. There are a number of commercial providers that offer this service. Moreover, the

Export Credit Guarantee Department of the UK Government also offer this service.

Powers of attorney will be required in almost all new locations since legal proof will be required to demonstrate that the named individual can act on behalf of the engineer. Powers will normally need to be written in the language of the territory and will often require notarisation and legalisation.

13.4.8 Notarisation

Working internationally, the engineer will often be required to provide notarised documents many of which will also need to have a formal stamp from the relevant territory's Embassy. Notarisation can be required, for example:

- in providing bank signatories on a local bank account
- in the setting up of a branch or subsidiary
- in connection with major public sector bids.

In addition, *Official Journal of the European Communities* (OJEC) bids are increasingly requesting references from the bidders' home country and/or certificates from the tax authorities and self declarations showing the good financial health and probity of the bidder. If these are not provided on time or in the right format the bid can be delayed or disqualified.

13.4.9 Professional bodies

In some territories, there may be certain local professional rules which preclude engineers from being able to be considered in competitive tender for certain kinds of work. For example, in Spain there exists a process of 'clasificacion' which entails presenting a portfolio of work and references together with background material on the engineer's staff and organisation to the local college of engineers. Only after approval is the engineer able to bid in his or her own right for public sector contracts in clearly defined building types. Without the qualification they must always link up with others to prepare a consortium bid.

Such networks are becoming rarer on mainland Europe although they are still very important in the newly emerging central and eastern European states.

In California (and other States), registration is required by the State Department of Consumer Affairs or similar for company and individuals. For Federal work there are complex security requirements that have, of course, become stricter. Professional bodies have less impact in the United States, at least for engineers. However, drawings have to be stamped and signed by the Professional Engineer (PE) in each major discipline.

13.4.10 Understanding bureaucracy

An inevitable, but often new, experience for the internationally based engineer will be recognition of, and navigating through, bureaucratic regimes. On our home territory we already do this, albeit unconsciously. The cost of bureaucracy should not be underestimated, both in terms of fees and management time. In many countries it is common (if not a necessity) to employ a local with good contacts to help with bureaucracy increasing the cost of doing business.

We become frustrated with procedures and regulations which we take for granted at home. Bureaucracy is often identified with the public sector but it is rarely confined to that sector.

The engineer needs to be able to recognise that in certain countries a realistic maxim to observe is that a written, signed fee agreement is a good basis for negotiation.

In certain countries there is a fine distinction between bureaucracy and corruption. This is obviously a very sensitive area. What constitutes corruption must be carefully considered. Reference to both the local and home country legal frameworks should be made. Particular care needs to be given to the UK Bribery Act 2010 which defines 'bribery' in wide terms and covers bribery within and outside the UK.

Under this new legislation, individuals will face up to 10 years in jail and companies could be hit with an unlimited fine and face disqualification for failing to take adequate measures to stop employees paying and receiving bribes.

13.4.11 Exchange rate risk

This non-technical risk category is perhaps the most volatile and the hardest to predict. In the main, hedging instruments are difficult to utilise for the international engineer.

The engineer should therefore seek to maximise currency of income to currency of expenditure. This can be particularly important when employing local sub-consultants who wish to receive funds in the local currency. In this case it may be beneficial for the client to pay the sub-consultant directly.

Moreover, contractual terms should be utilised to ensure that movements in exchange rates do not impact cash flows significantly. For example, a formula can be included in the contract which adjusts the contract price, up or down, when the foreign exchange rate moves.

13.4.12 Exchange control risk

Foreign exchange controls are various forms of controls imposed by a government on the purchase/sale of foreign and/ or domestic currencies.

Common foreign exchange controls include:

- banning the use of foreign currency within the country
- banning locals from possessing foreign currency
- restricting currency exchange to government-approved exchangers
- fixed exchange rates
- restrictions on the amount of currency that may be imported or exported.

Some countries which claim no such controls can often impose significant bureaucratic hurdles which then may lead to months of delays in repatriating funds deposited in a local bank. Cash dividends may only be declared and paid once a year and be the sole means of transferring funds between affiliated companies and across national boundaries. Without sufficient understanding of the foreign exchange controls, the engineer's cash flow could be seriously adversely affected.

13.5 Tax considerations
13.5.1 Introduction

As noted earlier, an engineering firm may be involved in international projects in various ways, it may:

- undertake one-off projects in various non-UK territories;
- 'set up shop' in a non-UK jurisdiction where it will undertake several projects;
- provide designs from its UK base and only send personnel abroad on a very temporary basis – say for a site visit; or
- second an employee to a company overseas to assist it with its own business without undertaking any specific project.

Although commercial considerations should be the most important factor, each excursion to an overseas jurisdiction has its own tax consequences and these needs to be considered well in advance of undertaking the project. Tax is often the last thing on the engineer's mind, but it is an operating cost and, like any other overhead, needs to be factored into the investment plan. Advice should be sought from the engineer's tax department and in many cases external tax advisors.

From a practical point of view, dealing with non-UK tax authorities, many of whom do not speak English, can be frustrating for even the most diligent taxpayer. With careful tax planning in advance, it should be possible to mitigate the effect that overseas taxes will have on the project. A thorough analysis of the legal and tax systems of the country where the engineering firm proposes to do business will prevent bitter and often expensive problems.

The starting point of the analysis is to ascertain whether or not domestic law imposes tax on the profits or payments made in connection with the project. It is then necessary to check if there is a double taxation treaty between the UK and the overseas country which either reduces or eliminates the tax payable.

13.5.2 What taxes may be payable in the non-UK territory?

(a) *Corporation tax or corporate income tax* (federal and state, where applicable): this is a tax on profits. With tax planning it may be possible to keep income to a minimum and maximise deductions, keeping taxable profits low. Remember that fees and charges from related entities must be determined at arm's length to comply with transfer pricing requirements.

(b) *Withholding tax*: this is a tax which is deducted at source from various payments – for example, interest or royalties. It may be reduced or eliminated under a tax treaty between the country of residence of the paying and recipient entities. Withholding taxes create a cash flow cost. In the UK, it is possible to credit foreign tax withheld against UK tax on the same income but it will be an absolute cost to the extent it cannot be relieved in the UK. The withholding applies to the gross payment, so that if the profit margin on, say, fees or royalties is low, the withholding may actually exceed the profit.

(c) *Local and municipal taxes*: many local authorities have taxing rights and may levy charges by reference to different criteria, such as the amount of corporation tax paid, turnover, profits, number of employees, location, type of industry.

(d) *Value added tax/sales tax (VAT)*: branches and companies may need to register for VAT. To the extent that the VAT is recoverable, it should only be a cash flow issue. Where fees are received from overseas, the branch or subsidiary may have to reverse charge itself. Early registration and fulfilment of all legal requirements are important to ensure full recovery. Some countries require a minimum turnover to be able to register for VAT. In other countries, registration may be required irrespective of turnover and before the entity is entitled to carry on economic activities.

(e) *Payroll and income taxes*: resident employees will have to pay local income tax on their wages. When seconding employees abroad it is also important to understand if and at what point they become liable to pay local income tax. Often the company or branch is liable for deducting income tax from wages but it may also be necessary for individuals to file their own tax returns.

(f) *National Insurance Contributions/social security charges*: these are normally payable by reference to the employee's salary, but in many countries it is difficult to know in advance what the charges will amount to. Different criteria may apply, such as the amount of the salary, risk of the employment, category (skilled/unskilled), age, number of employees working for the entity. In countries where unemployment is high, tax breaks (such as reduced contributions) may be available, but this will be more likely to apply to the unskilled local workforce rather than highly qualified architects or engineers who have arrived from the UK or other countries.

(g) *Other taxes*: There are varying other taxes in overseas territories which may apply. These need to be investigated on a case by case basis but may include *stamp duty* on contract values, *religious taxes* calculated on various basses and *asset taxes* calculated on the value of assets in a territory.

13.5.3 Is there a double taxation treaty between the UK and the overseas country?

The existence of a double taxation agreement between the UK and the non-UK territory will help to determine (and, generally, narrow down) the circumstances in which the UK entity has a taxable presence in the non-UK territory and the tax on

any income it derives. Fortunately, the UK has a very large treaty network (with over one hundred countries). Depending on what specific corporate vehicle the UK firm has adopted (see section 13.5.5 of this chapter), the most relevant articles of the treaty are likely to be those relating to permanent establishments, business profits, royalties, avoidance of double taxation and non-discrimination. Many, but not all of the treaties signed by the UK, are based on the *Organisation for Economic Co-operation and Development (OECD) Model Convention and Commentary* is a useful aide.

Some countries have made reservations on how they interpret specific treaty provisions and this may be especially relevant in determining if a particular payment is subject to withholding tax. These are noted in the Commentary, which should always be checked.

13.5.4 Foreign taxes and the existence of a taxable presence overseas?

It is not necessary to carry on business in the non-UK territory to be subject to tax there, and the local tax legislation of the non-UK territory will, in the first instance, determine when a non-resident entity will be subject to tax. Depending on the commercial requirements and the local law, the UK entity may establish (have to establish) a local company, have a taxable presence (referred to as permanent establishment – see below) or simply be subject to local withholding taxes on the fees it receives.

Local company

The most obvious form of taxable presence overseas is a subsidiary. The basic position is that where an overseas subsidiary is set up to carry out a project, it will be considered 'resident' for tax purposes in that country and all its profits will be taxed locally. If a subsidiary is not set up, the business profits arising from the project will normally only be taxed in the non-UK territory if the UK parent has a permanent establishment (see below) in that country.

Permanent establishments

A permanent establishment is defined as a fixed place of business. It exists where a foreign enterprise carries out business in another country through a fixed place which is of more than a temporary nature. It amounts to a projection of the foreign enterprise of one country into the soil of another country.

Most treaties have an illustrative list of what type of presence does or does not constitute a permanent establishment in the signatory countries. A place of management, a branch, an office, a factory and a workshop will normally constitute a permanent establishment. However, the maintenance of a fixed place of business solely for the purpose of carrying on, for the enterprise (i.e. head office) any activity which is of a preparatory or auxiliary character is unlikely to constitute a permanent establishment. Carrying out initial site visits may fall within the preparatory category. Short-term non-recurring visits to an overseas location – for example, for the purposes for information gathering – should not generally be enough to constitute a permanent establishment, though the position for the country concerned should be checked before any such visits are undertaken. Whether or not a presence abroad is sufficient to constitute a permanent establishment can be affected by the length of time the employees concerned stay in the country as well as type of activity they carry on. Again the rules applicable in the particular case should be investigated.

Care needs to be taken when employing local sub-consultants as these can be considered as an extension of the activity of the engineer in the local country and therefore 'count' towards the creation of a permanent establishment.

A permanent establishment will also be deemed to exist where a person has authority to, and habitually does, enter into contracts on behalf of the foreign entity. In order to avoid unnecessarily establishing a permanent establishment in case of travelling employees, employees visiting the overseas country should not enter into legally binding obligations on behalf of their employing company or substantially conclude their negotiations.

Many treaties provide that 'a building site or construction or installation project' constitutes a permanent establishment where it lasts for a period exceeding 12 months (six months in some treaties, such as with Greece and Turkey), whereas other treaties are silent. Some countries have made reservations as to the length of the project and the type of activities included within the definition of 'a building site or construction or installation project'. The Commentary to the Model Convention should be checked to confirm whether the country in which the firm intends to operate has made any such reservations. In the absence of a treaty between the UK and the non-UK territory, what amounts to a taxable presence in a non-UK territory is determined solely by that country's domestic law. In the case of construction work, the taxable presence is most likely to result from having a physical presence in the non-UK territory. The implications of trading through a company or a permanent establishment are considered below.

Where a permanent establishment exists the non-UK jurisdiction will subject the profits to local corporation or other business profits tax. The treatment of business profits under any double taxation treaty will then be relevant as it will determine how the taxable profits should be calculated. Most treaties state that the taxable profits of a permanent establishment are only those profits which it might be expected to make if it were a distinct and separate enterprise engaged in the same or similar activities under the same or similar conditions.

It is not unusual for some of the preparatory work for a specific project to be done in the UK before even touching base in the non-UK territory and later to send one or more engineers on site to supervise the construction. In some cases, it is possible to claim that fees for such work are not part of the business profits of the permanent establishment and so not subject to tax in the non-UK jurisdiction. However, although the work may have been carried out in the UK, some non-UK jurisdictions will seek to tax the profits attributable to it on the basis that such fees are connected with the permanent establishment in their territory even if paid directly by the client to the head office. This is known as the 'force of attraction' rule. It may be possible to mitigate the force of attraction rule by ensuring that preparatory work in the UK is carried out by a company in the group different from that which will carry out the construction work overseas through a permanent establishment.

The force of attraction rule may also result in having attributed to the permanent establishment other income arising in the overseas jurisdiction which is not related to the construction project, such as interest on loans or fees from unrelated assignments in that jurisdiction carried out in the UK by the head office.

Withholding taxes on royalties and other payments

Most countries charge withholding tax on payments of royalties outside their jurisdiction. Usually, the definition of royalties in double taxation treaties includes fees for information concerning industrial, commercial or scientific know-how. It is important to check with the overseas tax adviser whether, under the relevant treaty, fees charged for designs produced by engineers will be treated as royalties. Some countries also apply a withholding tax to any service fees paid abroad.

A tax treaty will often reduce or even eliminate a withholding tax. It may be necessary to make sure that the wording in the contract is properly drafted to support the argument that the fees are not subject to a withholding – or that only part of the fees are so taxed.

Such withholding taxes can arise – where applicable – irrespective of whether or not the UK entity has a taxable presence in the local jurisdiction. It is necessary to consider the impact of such withholding tax:

- if the payment is made directly by the client to the UK head office
- by a local permanent establishment to the head office or another group company
- by a local subsidiary to another group company.

In some cases, the UK company may be able to choose – either under local law or in the way it structures the operation – to have a local taxable presence (permanent establishment or company) to be paid fees in the UK subject to a withholding tax.

Because withholding taxes are charged on gross fees not profits, if the withholding tax is high in comparison with the commercial profits generated by the activity (it could even be higher in some cases), it may be worth while choosing to establish a local taxable presence so as to be able to offset the costs and only bear foreign tax on the actual profit. This will also depend upon the extent to which the UK entity can use the credit for foreign taxes against UK tax on its other profits.

13.5.5 Choosing the form of investment: branch or subsidiary? joint venture, consortium, alliance?

Some countries impose restrictions on ownership by non-nationals or non-residents either by limiting the value or size of their shareholding in a local company or simply forbidding it altogether. Although not imposing such restrictions, other countries require that directors be either nationals or residents in the country. These conditions by themselves are likely to have a significant impact on the choice of corporate vehicle. Where no limitations apply, or these are not insurmountable, tax considerations come next.

Where a significant amount of work will be carried out in a non-UK jurisdiction, it is important to determine in advance whether to trade through a branch of the UK company (no separate legal identity) or through a subsidiary incorporated in the non-UK territory (a separate legal entity).

In the case of one-off projects, a branch may be simpler, as the legal requirements are usually simpler than those involved in incorporating a company. However, some countries tax branches at a higher rate than companies and, in addition, some apply withholding taxes on remittances back to the head office, increasing the tax burden. For one-off projects, a branch may nevertheless be advisable where the complications of liquidating a company are too cumbersome and leaving a dormant company in place is expensive (e.g. because dormant companies need to file certain documents on an annual basis) or, very simply, because setting up a company for each and every project is likely to result in a very complicated group structure.

Where the UK consulting engineering company has longer-term projects outside the UK, it may also be advantageous to start trading with a branch if it is expected that losses will be incurred in the first years of trading. These losses will normally be deductible from other profits arising in the UK. Once the non-UK operation becomes profitable, the branch can be incorporated without incurring UK tax. It is crucial to know how the non-UK territory will tax the incorporation. Some jurisdictions may tax the transfer of goodwill from the branch to the company or claw back deductions granted for losses where the parent company (UK head office) has used them to reduce its profits at home (the United Kingdom).

It may still be possible to use non-UK tax losses in the UK where a subsidiary is incorporated in the non-UK territory. Subject to treaty provisions, a company incorporated outside the UK but managed and controlled in this country is tax resident in the UK. The place of central management and control broadly means the ultimate place where control is exercised. This is a matter of fact and the UK HMRC considers several factors, such as the place where the Board meets, place of residence of the directors, powers given to local managers. Thus, the losses of the overseas company could be set against the profits of its UK parent company (or other UK company in the group) under the 'group relief' provisions. When it is anticipated that the non-UK operation will start making profits, the company may be able to leave the UK tax net by migrating, although this may not be necessary if the local rate of tax is higher than the UK rate. The tax implications of migrating need to be considered.

It is possible that the company may be tax resident in two jurisdictions at the same time for example because the other country treats a locally incorporated subsidiary as being tax resident. Some countries (e.g. the USA) limit the use of losses against their local tax charge where a dual resident company can use losses in another jurisdiction.

Another consideration in determining whether to operate through a branch or subsidiary is the taxable base. Even if the rate of corporation tax is the same and there is a treaty according to which a permanent establishment will be taxed as if it were an independent company, it will not necessarily be so. Different items may be taken into account when computing income and deductions (for instance, many countries refuse the permanent establishment's deductions for payments to the head office on the basis that the company is paying itself). Also, double taxation treaties apply to persons (including companies) resident in the territory of one of the signatory parties. Permanent establishments are part of the same entity as the head office and are treated as resident for tax purposes where the head office is located. This results in certain treaty benefits being denied to permanent establishments which would normally be available to resident companies.

Frequently, the UK engineer will work on international projects jointly with other firms (UK and non-UK) of technical engineers. The use of the joint venture, consortium or other forms of alliance may be an attractive organisational option. The format of this joint venture work is very important for tax purposes and needs to be considered in advance of teaming up. The format could include setting up a jointly owned local subsidiary, operating through a local partnership, or simply a contractually arrangement which does not have any presence in the overseas country. However, often the best result is to ensure that the affairs of the joint venture will be tax transparent so that each joint venture partner is treated independently and according to its own particular circumstances for tax purposes.

However informal the arrangement, there should always be a written agreement reflecting the rights and responsibilities of each participant towards the common client and towards each other, as this will impact on the tax treatment. It is also necessary to consider the legal and accounting issues arising from a joint venture. The rules may differ depending upon the type of arrangement and the location of the venture.

13.5.6 Mitigating the non-UK tax burden

To minimise the taxable profits of a non-UK entity, it is important both to reduce the items of income arising to it and to maximise deductions. The following should be considered.

(a) Can part of the work be done outside the non-UK jurisdiction, and so outside its tax net?

(b) Can the non-UK entity claim a deduction for fees paid? Some jurisdictions will not allow branches to claim a deduction for fees or interest paid to the head office (on the basis that the entity cannot do business with itself). In such cases, it should be considered whether an entity other than the head office (e.g. another group company) could provide the service and charge the fee. In all cases, when fees are paid between connected entities, fees should be at arm's length to comply with transfer pricing regulations.

13.5.7 Repatriation of funds: withholding tax

Withholding tax is an absolute cost of the overseas operation if the UK parent cannot get full relief for the withholding tax suffered. Double taxation treaties generally reduce or even abolish withholding taxes. Where no treaty is in place, the domestic rate of withholding tax will apply. Whether withholding applies needs to be considered by reference to payments of fees, interest, royalties and dividends

- from a non-UK branch or subsidiary to the UK parent company;

- from a third party in the non-UK territory to a branch of the UK company in that non-UK territory;

- from a third party in the non-UK territory to the subsidiary of the UK company in that non-UK territory; and

- from a third party in the non-UK territory directly to the UK company.

Where a fee for, say, design services is subject to withholding tax, it is important to bear in mind that the withholding will be calculated by reference to the gross fee, not just the profit element. It is important to calculate the impact of the withholding in the UK as all or part of it will be wasted if the tax payable in the UK on that fee and so on, is lower than the tax withheld overseas.

As a practical point, and where trading through a branch, some non-UK tax authorities agree to limit the level of withholding tax to the actual amount of tax payable in their country. This possibility should be explored, as it may do away with the need to prepare tax returns and claim a refund for overpaid tax which, in many countries may take years or simply not happen.

13.5.8 Employee issues

A UK company which has decided to engage in projects overseas, whether on a long- or short-term basis, would normally employ one or more local employees for administrative tasks. Engineers and other skilled personnel are likely to be seconded from the UK.

Many countries impose restrictions on non-residents and may refuse to recognise the qualifications of technical staff qualified outside their jurisdiction. This normally results in having to employ local architects and/or engineers. In some countries there has to be a certain ratio of local to expatriate employees.

Income tax for employees

The tax treatment of those posted to a non-UK jurisdiction (host country) will usually depend on whether the employee is or is not tax resident in the host country and the UK.

Generally speaking, a person is treated as resident for tax purposes if he is physically present in a country for a period of at least 183 days in the relevant fiscal year. Residence can be also determined by a person's intentions. The rules vary from country to country so advice should be sought.

Where an employee is seconded abroad from the UK, but remains resident in the UK, the employee may be taxed in both the UK and the host location. He should usually receive a credit in the UK for overseas tax paid; ensuring that double taxation does not arise.

In some countries non-residents are subject to a lower flat rate of tax, but may be disadvantaged by not being able to claim deductions. Tax residents are normally subject to the local rates of income tax on their worldwide income (few countries have the UK concept of 'domicile', according to which for those who are not 'domiciled' in the UK but are tax resident here, non-UK income may not be taxable unless remitted to the UK). This can lead to seconded employees being subject to tax on all their income – even if it is not related to their employment in that country.

Income tax is normally chargeable on all emoluments, including benefits in kind. In some countries benefits in kind allow scope for tax planning, especially if these are akin to travel and subsistence costs such as accommodation, utilities and in certain cases, per diem allowances.

Tax breaks

Some jurisdictions offer special tax breaks for individuals who bring particular skills to their economy. Some territories will specify a maximum period for which the allowance can last and if the maximum period is exceeded the tax benefits already granted may be clawed back. Employers should ensure that any conditions for obtaining these allowances are, or will be met, before agreeing terms with employees.

Delivery of salary and multiple employment arrangements

It is not unusual for an employee posted overseas for two or three years to want to receive part of his or her income in the UK. This could be due to financial commitments (family, mortgage) or simply because the overseas currency is unstable, payment in foreign currency may not be possible, or exchange control regulations make it impossible or very expensive to take money out of the host country.

As a result employers may wish to consider splitting the delivery of the salary between the home and host country where this is practicable. This can result in tax savings, as some locations will provide relief for amounts paid and retained offshore. Structuring of this kind is common but such arrangements must be checked on case by case basis, and must, obviously, involve full transparency for the local tax authority. Advice should be sought.

Alternatively, a few countries will permit multiple employment arrangements, that is, dual contracts. In this case, the employee has two contracts. One contract will be for services rendered in the host country with the remuneration under that contract being subject to tax in that country. Under a second contract of employment, the employee is paid outside the host country for services rendered outside that country. Even where dual contracts are accepted, there must be commercial substance and it is usually necessary to prove that the employee does indeed render services in other jurisdictions. Having two roles which are kept completely separate with no cross over of where the duties are performed can also be a requirement in certain jurisdictions.

Where split contracts are not possible there may be alternatives which ensure that the employee can receive amounts which are outside the local tax net. Such arrangements must be checked on a case by case basis and must, obviously, involve full transparency for the local tax authority.

Exchange control

Usually an employee will need to bring back funds to the UK, either during the overseas posting or at the end of it (bank charges could be incurred and the employee may suffer as a result of an adverse movement in exchange rates, etc.). In a limited number of countries exchange control restrictions exist; however, it is not given that the secondee will fall within these rules. The employer will need to address these issues at the very beginning to determine how the secondee will be paid and the employee should be made aware of these issues also so that he may plan his affairs and to ensure no case for claiming compensation for loss from the employer will arise (unless this is part of the intended policy).

Pensions

Most UK employers contribute to the employee's UK pension fund. The following questions arise: first, is it possible to continue to contribute to that fund in the UK especially where the person sent overseas may cease to be an employee of the UK company? Second, if a contribution is made, what are the tax implications in the UK and non-UK jurisdiction? Is it a taxable benefit of the employee? Third, if the pension contribution is recharged to the non-UK branch or subsidiary, is it a deductible expense for the latter and does it become taxable locally?

Local tax rules need to be checked in each case to ensure that local laws have been complied with.

In addition, many countries require employers and/or employees to contribute towards a pension in that country. In some cases, this will be money lost as entitlement to draw the pension may never arise. But some jurisdictions will refund contributions made where the employee remains in the country for a short period. It is always worth inquiring.

It should be also borne in mind that there are implications where a worker is seconded to a country within the European Union for a period of five years or more and remains in the UK plan. This could trigger cross-border status for the UK plan and may lead to funding implications.

Tax equalisation

Employees sent overseas will expect not to pay more tax as a result of working in the host location than they are paying in the UK, unless this is already compensated for in the salary being offered. Employers often institute 'tax equalisation' or 'tax protection' policies to deal with this. Under a tax equalisation policy the employer will reduce the salary by an amount equivalent to the tax which the employee would have paid if he had remained in the UK. In return for this, the employer agrees to pay any UK or host country tax arising on employment income. Under tax protection, the employee initially bears all taxes but has the right to ask the employer to reimburse any amount in excess of the UK tax which would have been due.

Often employees will be provided with benefits abroad to which they would not have been entitled had they remained in the UK, such as accommodation. These benefits might attract a tax liability. It will be appreciated that most or all of the tax so arising is in excess of the tax which the employees would have suffered in the UK.

Both tax equalisation and tax protection policies can prove expensive. Not only is there a potentially high cost in terms of tax if an employee works in a high-tax country, but also the administration involved can prove costly. Furthermore, the employee will usually be taxed on the tax equalisation element meaning that it has to be grossed up. However, these policies will aid the mobility of workers especially if the employer needs to move its workforce to a high-tax country and can also encourage consistency. The employer will need to consider the location of the secondment and the number of workers involved.

Often social security contributions will be regarded in the same way as tax and incorporated into a tax policy.

Social security

To determine where social security should be paid the world is split into 3 groups which are the European Economic Area (EEA), Reciprocal Agreement Countries and the 'rest of the world'.

Most employees seconded overseas who remain employed by the UK company will continue to pay UK Class 1 contributions for a given number of years if they are seconded to a country within the EEA or a Reciprocal Agreement Country.

For 'rest of the world' countries, the UK contributions will cease after the first 52 weeks of the assignment and the employer will need to consider whether a liability arises in the host location. The individual could elect to pay voluntary Class 2 or 3 contributions to maintain their UK social security record and may wish to obtain a Pension Forecast to establish any shortfall in their record. They may also be subject to host country social security contributions.

If the employment contract moves to a non-UK entity then Class 1 contributions will cease.

References

Referenced legislation, regulations and standards

Bribery Act 2010. TSO, London, UK

Websites

Deloitte International Tax and Business Guides; www.deloitte.com

Export Credit Guarantee Department (UK); www.ecgd.gov.uk

Foreign & Commonwealth Office (FCO); www.fco.gov.uk

International Federation of Consulting Engineers (FIDIC); www.fidic.org

Official Journal of the European Communities; http://eur-lex.europa.eu/JOIndex.do

Organisation for Economic Co-operation and Development (OECD); www.oecd.org

OECD Model Tax Convention and Commentary; www.hmrc.gov.uk/manuals/intmanual/intm159000.htm

PKF Country Taxation and Business Guides; www.pkf.com

The Doing Business Report; www.doingbusiness.org

The World Factbook (on the CIA website); www.cia.gov

UK Trade & Investment (UKTI); www.ukti.gov.uk

Chapter 14

The consulting engineer's appointment

doi: 10.1680/mocl.40878.0211

Clive Marsden Alan Baxter & Associates LLP, London, UK
Rachel Barnes Beale & Company, London, UK

CONTENTS

This chapter discusses principles of contract law where these apply to consulting engineers' professional services contracts. Bespoke and standard forms are compared and different levels of duty of care reviewed. Obligations that cause difficulties are emphasised and measures to mitigate such obligations are suggested. Attention is paid to the consequences of accepting warranties for fitness for purpose, strict obligations and the issuing of certificates. Commencement of work and suspension and termination are examined. Indemnities, limitations and exclusions of liability are discussed and the dangers explained. The importance of describing services unambiguously is highlighted. The meaning of liquidated damages, set-off and retention is explained. Health and safety obligations through the Construction (Design and Management) Regulations are introduced and discussed. The desirability of engaging sub-consultants on a 'back-to-back' basis is stressed and the consequences of not doing so are pointed out. The problems of working for a design-and-build contractor are reviewed and the meaning of 'supervision' explained. Methods of calculating fees are compared in detail and the pros and cons of each method discussed. Dispute resolution is introduced. Observations are made on the effect of the Construction Act on consulting engineers' forms of appointments. Finally, the 2009 ACE Agreements are compared with other standard forms of appointment.

14.1 Form of appointment

The general principles relating to the formation of a contract with a contractor have been set out in the chapter *The construction contract*. Exactly the same principles apply to the contract between a client (including a contractor client) and a consulting engineer. This chapter deals with some aspects of the formation of the contract that affect consulting engineers.

14.1.1 Exchange of letters

Again, as with a contractor's contract, the appointment of the consulting engineer can be contained in an exchange of letters. At its simplest, this could be a letter from the consulting engineer to carry out certain services for a specified fee that is then accepted by the client. However, there is nothing to prevent such letters being much more complex, and going through offers and counter-offers until agreement is reached and the contract concluded. Whether there is indeed a concluded contract will depend on the general principles of contract law – see *The law of contract*.

14.1.2 Incorporating standard terms

Consulting engineers' appointments can incorporate standard terms such as the Association for Consultancy and Engineering (ACE) Agreements or the firm's own standard terms. If accepted by the client, those terms then become incorporated into and form a part of the contract. Care needs to be taken to match the conditions of appointment to the project in question. There should also be no inconsistency between the letter or agreement incorporating the conditions of appointment and the conditions themselves. Further, an ACE Agreement, for example, has a memorandum and other sections that need to be completed. If they are not completed, or the requisite information is not in an accompanying letter or document, there is a danger that some important terms of the appointment are considered as not having been completed and agreed and that therefore no contract has been concluded. It is always prudent to attach a copy of the standard terms referred to so that there is no doubt as to the identity of the document or, indeed, the edition being used.

14.1.3 Bespoke forms

Many clients have their own forms of appointment. Negotiations on these can be lengthy and if the appointment document is not fully agreed, the general principles of contract law will determine whether there is a concluded contract. If the draft appointment document is incomplete or refers to documents which have not been provided, the consulting engineer should insist on having all the missing information before agreeing to the appointment. Something may be contained in this information that could significantly affect the fee or the services or substantially alter the risks that the consulting engineer is being asked to undertake.

14.1.4 Standard forms

There are at present only four institutions that produce standard forms of appointment for consulting engineers – the Association for Consultancy and Engineering (ACE), the Institution of Civil Engineers (ICE), the Construction Industry Council (CIC) and the International Federation of Consulting Engineers (FIDIC). Some large client bodies, such as Network Rail, and government bodies, such as the MoD and NHS Trusts, have their own standard forms, but these should be treated as 'bespoke forms'.

The ACE has produced a series of standard conditions for the appointment of consulting engineers. The latest editions are the 2009 Agreements, which supersede the earlier 2002 (revised 2004) versions, though much of the content remains the same. The references in this chapter to an ACE Agreement are to Agreement 1 of the 2009 edition incorporating June 2009 amendments and the quotations from the ACE Agreement in this chapter are quotations from the same Agreement 1. ICE has produced the Professional Services Contract as part of the NEC contract documents. The third edition of this contract (PSC3) was issued in June 2005. More recently, in 2007, the CIC has published The CIC Consultants' Contract Conditions together with a comprehensive CIC Scope of Services. FIDIC has produced a Client-Consultant Model Services Agreement known as 'The White Book' that is now in its fourth edition (2006). A brief description of each of these standard forms is contained in section 14.5 of this chapter.

14.1.5 Signing under hand or as a deed

The effect of signing an appointment under hand or as a deed has been set out in *The law of contract*. If an agreement or a collateral warranty is being signed as a deed after the services have been started, or even after their completion, consideration should be given to incorporating a term that reduces the number of years for bringing any claims under that agreement or collateral warranty. If this is not done, the client may have a longer time for bringing claims than would otherwise have been permitted by law.

It is also important that all the agreements relating to a particular project are signed in the same manner. For example, where the consulting engineer employs sub-consultants, each of the sub-consultants' appointments must be signed as a deed if the consulting engineer's appointment is so signed. If not signed in this way and if the consulting engineer were sued in respect of something that a sub-consultant had done, then the consulting engineer could find that it is unable to sue the sub-consultant under the sub-consultant's appointment because the claim was time barred.

14.2 Key issues that arise in appointment documents

This section looks at some of the key issues that arise in appointment documents and their implications for the consulting engineer and compares clauses that can be found in bespoke appointments with the equivalent clauses in the ACE Agreement.

14.2.1 Duty of care

As has been stated elsewhere, the standard of care imposed on consulting engineers at common law is to carry out their services with 'reasonable skill and care'. The test is that of the ordinary skilled and competent practitioner in the relevant profession. The ACE Agreement incorporates this duty expressly:

> The Consultant shall exercise reasonable skill, care and diligence in the performance of the Services

Bespoke appointments can, however, impose a higher duty of care, for example:

> The consulting engineer shall exercise the skill, care and diligence to be expected of a properly qualified consulting structural engineer experienced in carrying out work of a similar size, scope and complexity to the project.

Such a higher duty may be acceptable if the consulting engineer has the requisite experience, but other factors may also be relevant, such as the nature of the project, any professional indemnity restrictions and whether all other professionals, any sub-consultants and any contractors or subcontractors (or others with design or other responsibilities that may affect the services) have undertaken an equivalent duty of care in respect of their services.

14.2.2 Warranties for fitness for purpose

'Fitness for purpose' requirements sometimes arise in bespoke appointments and in collateral warranties. A detailed description of warranties for fitness for purpose is contained in *Collateral warranties*. The important distinction in law is that a consulting engineer provides professional services and is obliged by law to exercise reasonable skill and care, whereas a contractor carries out construction and is obliged by law to warrant that the completed works will be fit for their intended purpose. In practice, too, the consulting engineer designs the works but does not physically construct them, nor does the consulting engineer have the same control over workmanship or choice of materials as the contractor.

A contractor under a design and construct contract may take on a 'fitness for purpose' obligation in relation to design and seek to pass this on to the consulting engineer it engages. Neither ICE nor Joint Contracts Tribunal (JCT) standard forms of design and construct contracts, however, imposes fitness for purpose obligations in relation to design. Warranties for fitness for purpose as to design should be strongly resisted, because the attainment of the objective is likely to be outside the consulting engineer's control.

If a consulting engineer gives a warranty for fitness for purpose, for example that the completed works will be fit for their purpose, and they are not, the consulting engineer will be liable even if it has used reasonable skill and care and therefore has not been negligent. The damages flowing from a breach of warranty (which, very briefly, represent the cost of making the works fit for their purpose) are different from and can be higher than those for negligence (which, again briefly, are the reasonably foreseeable losses caused by the negligence). Further, a 'state-of-the-art' defence would not be available. A consulting engineer could not therefore argue that a particular piece of knowledge was not available at the time the design was prepared.

The professional indemnity insurance arrangements of consulting engineers reflect the obligation imposed on them by law – that is, to exercise reasonable skill and care. Thus, a professional indemnity insurance policy that is on a negligence-only basis would not cover warranties for fitness for purpose and nor do most policies on a civil or legal liability basis. Some will cover them but exclude that element of the damages which are greater than those which would have been payable if the warranty for fitness for purpose had not been given.

The ACE, NEC, CIC and FIDIC Agreements do not contain warranties for fitness for purpose.

14.2.3 Absolute or strict obligations

Bespoke appointments often contain absolute or strict obligations, for example 'The consulting engineer shall ensure the most efficient and cost effective solution' or 'The consulting engineer shall comply with the Employer's Requirements' or 'The consulting engineer shall procure that the construction is in accordance with the consulting engineer's design'.

The effect of undertaking an absolute or strict obligation is exactly the same in law as if the consulting engineer had given a warranty for fitness for purpose – see earlier. The performance of such obligations is also often dependent on factors outside the consulting engineer's direct control or is dependent on other parties, such as the contractor, doing certain things. It would therefore not be possible for the consulting engineer alone to fulfil such an obligation.

'Ensure' means to guarantee and is an absolute performance obligation. 'Comply' and 'procure' are also absolute performance obligations. If the obligation is 'to comply' with the employer's requirements, it could also amount to the consulting engineer undertaking a warranty for fitness for purpose because the employer's requirements often contain such warranties.

None of this means that the consulting engineer can disregard the client's brief or requirements or budget. A consulting engineer must have regard to them as part of its professional duties. The ACE Agreement does not include such duties expressly, but some bespoke appointments do include obligations to have 'due regard' to the client's objectives.

14.2.4 Time-scale for professional services

If nothing is said in a consulting engineer's appointment about the time for performing services, the law implies a term that they will be carried out within a reasonable time. In the ACE Agreement, apart from acting diligently, the obligation is expressed as

All requests to the Client by the Consultant for information, assistance, or decisions shall be made in a timely fashion. Subject always to conditions beyond the Consultant's reasonable control (including acts or omissions of the Client, any Lead Consultant if the Consultant is not so appointed, any Other Consultants or third parties), the Consultant shall use reasonable endeavours to perform the Services in accordance with the programme set out in Part D: *The Programme for the Services* or with any programme agreed with the Consultant from time to time.

The qualifications 'subject always to conditions beyond the Consultant's reasonable control…' and to use 'reasonable endeavours' are necessary because there are many factors that can cause delay or non-compliance with a programme over which the consulting engineer has no control, for example, late information from the client or other consultants or late approvals from statutory undertakers or other third parties.

Bespoke appointments may include a specific requirement, with no qualification at all, that the services are to be completed within a certain time-scale. (The difficulties inherent in undertaking strict or absolute obligations have been considered earlier.) 'Time is of the essence' is an example. This should only be agreed to where the programme is absolutely achievable. A failure to comply can lead to a client (who may be a contractor) incurring losses that are claimable from the consulting engineer.

A client's late delivery of information (whether this is to be supplied by the client or its other professionals or contractors), instructions or approvals to a consulting engineer can result in delays to the consulting engineer's timetable. Generally, if nothing is said expressly, it will be implied into a contract an obligation that such matters will be provided by the client in a reasonable time so as not to delay the consulting engineer. The ACE Agreement includes such an obligation expressly and it is better that it is so included, particularly where the programme is very tight and/or where it is helpful to the client to spell out what has to be provided to the consulting engineer and when.

14.2.5 Certificates and statements

This section is not concerned with the certificates that have to be given by consulting engineers under construction contracts, for example, as to the value of the work carried out by the contractor – these are outside the scope of this section. This section deals with certificates or statements required by clients, often to be given to third parties, for example, as to what the consulting engineer's services may or may not have achieved or in respect of matters concerning the construction works. Government departments often require such certificates.

Any claims arising out of such certificates (and this does not include any other claims that the client might be able to bring in contract or a third party might be able to bring in tort) would arise under the Hedley Byrne principle (see the chapter *Law of tort*).

The problem for the consulting engineer arises if the statement made, for example, about what the works will achieve, turns out to be untrue. The consulting engineer will be liable, despite having used reasonable skill and care in relation to its own services.

The consulting engineer should seek to ensure that:

(a) the appointment does not compel the consulting engineer to give a certificate in a certain form to a certain person, regardless of the actual circumstances at the time. The consulting engineer will then not be in breach of contract if it then refuses to give or qualifies the certificate
(b) the certificate is in such a form that it accurately records only what the consulting engineer has or has not done and does not amount to a statement as to what others have done or what they or the works will or ought to achieve.

These principles apply equally to any other statement that the consulting engineer may be required to give to a third party, for example, to a funder in a letter concerning the works or in a collateral warranty to a third party, for example, using a standard CIC form of warranty, or in a report to a prospective purchaser. If the statement made is not true, the consulting engineer can become liable under the Hedley Byrne principle to that third party as if a contract had been made with that third party, regardless of whether or not any fee was paid for the production of the statement.

The standard schedules of services published by ACE contain no duty to give certificates to the client or third parties, nor to make any statements.

14.2.6 Terms 'for the benefit of third parties' and the Contracts (Rights of Third Parties) Act 1999

Clients may have complex arrangements with funders and other third parties, such as future purchasers or tenants, none of whom will have a contract with the consulting engineer as they are not parties to the appointment. In these circumstances, clients may seek a guarantee that interested third parties can recover the more extensive damages from the consulting engineer that would have been available had those third parties been a party to the original contract and there had been a breach of contract. This can only be achieved by including provisions in the appointment that would bring the third parties within the circumstances required by law. For example, there could be a clause requiring the consulting engineer to acknowledge that if it is in breach of contract identified third parties will suffer loss and damage and that this is foreseeable as a result of the breach. Alternatively, the contract could state that the contract has been entered into on behalf of, or for the benefit of, identified third parties as well as the client.

The Contracts (Rights of Third Parties) Act 1999 confers rights on third parties to enforce any term of a contract that is

for their benefit. Detailed consideration of the effect of this Act is contained in *Collateral warranties*.

In the writers' view, it is better to deal expressly in the appointment with the rights of any third parties – for example, by agreeing to the provision of collateral warranties in an agreed form – so that the extent of the obligations and liabilities to any third parties that the consulting engineer is prepared to assume is clear. At the same time, the Contracts (Rights of Third Parties) Act should be excluded. Excluding the Act would also remove any uncertainties as to whether any obligations in the appointment, such as an obligation to give information to the contractor for passing to the subcontractor, gave that subcontractor, as a third party, a right to enforce the term directly. The ACE Agreement excludes the Act by providing that '…nothing in this Agreement confers or purports to confer on any third party any benefit or any right to enforce any term of this Agreement pursuant to the Contracts (Rights of Third Parties) Act 1999' but it does allow the parties to agree whether collateral warranties are to be given and to whom.

14.2.7 Deleterious materials

Deleterious material clauses are sometimes included in bespoke appointments and often in collateral warranties. The consulting engineer is usually required to state that it has not and will not specify certain listed deleterious materials.

A consulting engineer already has a duty 'to exercise reasonable skill and care', and this extends to the specifying of materials, so such a clause is not necessary. It is not included in the ACE Agreement. The consulting engineer may be prepared to agree to such an obligation expressly, provided the list is acceptable and not too widely drawn.

The obligation should also be limited to the time that materials are specified, and not to the time of their use, unless the consulting engineer has agreed to check the specifications again at the time of use.

The obligation is also often extended so that it extends to 'ensuring' or 'seeing that' such materials are not used in the construction of the project, that is, offering a guarantee that such materials will not be used. Even if such an obligation is limited to those parts of the project where the consulting engineer is carrying out site inspections, it is not acceptable because a consulting engineer will not and cannot know all the materials that the contractor and subcontractors have used. It may be acceptable, in these circumstances, for the consulting engineer to agree to notify the client if the consulting engineer becomes aware that any deleterious materials are being used.

14.2.8 Commencement, termination and suspension of appointment

Commencement

The time at which the terms of any appointment are agreed will depend on the circumstances of each case. Sometimes the formal appointment is not agreed and signed until well into a project, or even after it has been completed. In such circumstances, it is usual to include in the appointment document that the effective date of the commencement of the appointment is the earlier of the date of signature or the commencement of the services. The ACE Agreement has such a provision. It is important to check, however, that the terms and the services described in the appointment correctly reflect what has actually been done – there could have been variations since the consulting engineer first started to perform the services or the project could have taken much longer to complete

Termination

Historically, the right of a client to terminate a consulting engineer's appointment was usually limited to breaches of contract or insolvency. Clients were prepared to employ their consulting engineers on the basis of a 'whole appointment' – that is for the whole project. The consulting engineer, as a result, could plan both work and fee accordingly. The ACE Conditions prior to the 1995 edition were written on the basis of a whole appointment with limited rights to terminate. This meant that if a client terminated the appointment for any reason not stipulated in the appointment, the consulting engineer would be entitled to the losses that flowed from that 'repudiatory breach'. Such losses could include unavoidable expenses such as redundancy costs and loss of profit.

Present-day appointment documents (including the ACE Agreement) almost invariably contain an express right for the client to terminate at any time. The entitlement to payment is also often restricted to the amount due up to the date of termination and any claim for any damages against the client for loss of profit or other losses arising out of termination is excluded altogether.

There is also usually an express right for the client to terminate if the consulting engineer is in breach of its obligations or is insolvent. The consulting engineer should also have such an express right, particularly where the breach is non-payment, otherwise the consulting engineer can only bring the appointment to an end if the non-payment amounts to a repudiatory breach, which can be difficult to establish, and in the meanwhile the consulting engineer has to continue to perform the services.

Some bespoke appointments seek to deal with the consequences of a breach of contract (e.g. by saying that any breach will be deemed to be a repudiatory breach) or by stipulating what the client may or may not be entitled to claim as damages in those circumstances. The common law has sophisticated rules for assessing the damages payable and any such express provisions will usually be intended to improve the client's position.

Suspension

The client's right to suspend is usually tied in with the right to terminate and generally the client reserves the right to suspend at any time. This may be essential because of the nature of the project. However, the consulting engineer needs to consider how many times the client can do this and how long

the periods of suspension should be before the fee and/or the services fall to be reassessed. Bespoke appointments often do not recognize the disruption that many or lengthy suspensions can cause to a consulting engineer's work, and the costs that ensue. The ACE Agreement gives a right to the client to suspend at any time for periods of up to nine months in aggregate, following which the consulting engineer has the option to give notice of termination. The ACE Agreement also gives a right to the consulting engineer to suspend for up to 26 weeks if it is being prevented or impeded from carrying out the services as a result of circumstances outside the consulting engineer's control.

There is a right under some standard appointments to stop work if a payee has not been paid, but in these circumstances the payee takes the risk that it may eventually be held by the courts or in arbitration that the payer was justified in not paying. In those circumstances the payee would be liable for the costs incurred by the payer as a result of the suspension of its work.

The Housing Grants, Construction and Regeneration Act 1996 ('the Construction Act') also gives a statutory right to suspend performance if there is non-payment of any sum due under a 'construction contract' and an effective notice of withholding has not been given within the proper time limits.

14.2.9 Client obligations

Bespoke appointments usually place no obligations on the client except the obligation to pay. Although common law will generally imply a term into such appointments that the client will provide the information and decisions that the consulting engineer will need, it is better that the appointment sets out the client's obligations in relation to information, decisions, approvals and assistance so that it is clear to the client what it has to provide or do. A timetable for the release of crucial information or decisions should also be included in a bespoke appointment.

The ACE Agreement places an obligation on the client that it will supply the information needed, including that in the possession of other consultants or contractors. The client also undertakes that it will give, and procure that other consultants and contractors give, such assistance as the consulting engineer needs and that all the client's decisions, instructions, consents or approvals will be given in such reasonable time so as not to delay or disrupt the performance of the consulting engineer's services.

14.2.10 Indemnities

Indemnity clauses are often included in bespoke appointments. Indemnities have particular characteristics of which consulting engineers should be aware.

A contract of indemnity can be defined in several ways. In this section 'indemnity' is being used in its narrow sense, that is, to cover only the specific forms of indemnity that consulting engineers can be required to give to clients under their appointments.

The amount that the consulting engineer will have to pay under an indemnity in respect of some default on the consulting engineer's part will not normally reflect and could be greater than the damages that would have been due if the claim had been decided in the absence of an indemnity. The indemnity often extends not only to the amount the client has suffered but also to the amounts that the client has to pay to third parties because of the consulting engineer's default.

An indemnity could allow the client to recover the following types of damages:

(a) those that would not normally be recoverable because they are too remote
(b) those that would otherwise be reduced by the client's duty to mitigate its loss or by reason of the client's contributory negligence
(c) those that would not be recoverable because they may not have been properly or reasonably incurred

They could also include the liquidated damages that a contractor client has to pay to its employer.

It is also possible that an indemnity will allow legal costs and expenses to be recovered that would otherwise be disallowed on an assessment of costs conducted by the court.

A consulting engineer may not necessarily have been negligent before becoming liable to pay under an indemnity if it is not based on negligence. If a client has suffered a loss for which the consulting engineer is providing an indemnity, the consulting engineer has to pay regardless of whether or not the loss can be recovered from the consulting engineer's professional indemnity insurer. In many instances such a loss is not covered by professional indemnity insurance (also see *Professional indemnity insurance*).

Settlements of claims can also give rise to difficulties. A client may decide for commercial reasons to settle a claim with a third party for, say, half a million pounds when the damages properly payable by the consulting engineer if decided by the court would be £350000. If the indemnity is drafted in a certain way, the consulting engineer will have to pay the £500000.

The client has from 6 to 12 years from the time the indemnified loss is suffered to make a claim under the indemnity, depending on whether the indemnity is contained in a contract under hand or in a deed unless the indemnity is against 'liability' in which case time will start to run from the time of the breach, that is, from the time/date that the consulting engineer failed or omitted to do something that it had said that it would do under its contract. It is therefore possible that a claim can be made under an indemnity after the limitation period in respect of the original appointment has expired (limitation periods are covered in more detail in *Law of tort*).

Indemnities are not needed. If a consulting engineer is in breach of the terms of appointment, a client will be entitled to the damages prescribed by law, and it may also be able to sue the consulting engineer in negligence. If third parties sue the client because of something the consulting engineer has done, the consulting engineer can be joined in those proceedings or damages can be claimed from the consulting engineer afterwards in contribution proceedings. An indemnity therefore only makes it easier for a client to collect money from a consulting engineer and can increase the damages it can recover.

14.2.11 Limitation and exclusion of liability

Many standard forms of appointment for construction professionals now include clauses limiting liability. An increasing number of bespoke appointments also do so. This can be vital where the project carries unusual risk or where the risk is out of all proportion to the fee, as can happen, for example, in environmental impact assessments or urban masterplanning.

The law relating to clauses limiting or excluding liability and the details about the Unfair Contract Terms Act 1977 are set out in the chapter *The law of contract*. Where the appointment is with a consumer, as defined by the Unfair Terms in Consumer Contracts Regulations 1994, those Regulations may also apply to limitation and exclusion clauses. The same principles apply to professional appointments.

Parties to an appointment can never agree to limit or exclude liability for damages for personal injury or death because this is expressly prohibited by law. They are, however, able to agree to limit or exclude any other liability they may incur to each other. It is not possible to exclude or restrict liability in relation to third party claims because there is no contract with that third party. For example, if a claim is made against a consulting engineer by a tenant of a building designed by the consulting engineer under a contract with the building owner, the consulting engineer will not be able to rely on any limitation agreed with the building owner because that limitation was not contained in a contract with the tenant and agreed with the tenant. The only way in which a consulting engineer can be protected against such third party claims is if the client will agree to give the consulting engineer an indemnity against them.

However, if the consulting engineer were to enter into an agreement directly with the third party, for example, in a collateral warranty, a clause limiting or excluding the liability of the consulting engineer could be included and could be effective.

A party in breach of contract cannot rely on a clause excluding or limiting liability for any breach unless that clause is 'reasonable'. What is reasonable is determined by having regard to the circumstances known to the parties at the time the contract was made. It is therefore important that these clauses are considered at the time the appointment is being negotiated.

Such clauses have to be clear, because they are construed strictly against the party relying on them. The clause is more likely to be considered reasonable if it restricts liability rather than excludes it (although exclusion may be reasonable in some circumstances).

In deciding the maximum liability that it is prepared to accept, the consulting engineer should assess the nature of the risks for the particular project and also the damages that could be payable if the consulting engineer is in breach of contract or is negligent. These will include not only the costs of putting things right but could also include other losses that could be caused to the client, because, for example, it is unable to use or rent its building. An assessment would also need to be made of the damages that could flow from any particular matters, such as contamination if the consulting engineer has advised on this.

If the limitation is by reference to a monetary amount, the court is required by the Unfair Contract Terms Act to have regard to

(i) the resources the consulting engineer could be expected to have available to meet the liability, for example, the assets of the company or partnership; and
(ii) how far it is open to the consulting engineer to cover itself by insurance.

This does not mean that if the consulting engineer has £5 million insurance cover, the limit of liability for every appointment should be £5 million. The monetary amount included in the limitation clause should be appropriate for the type of commission being undertaken.

An obligation in an appointment to maintain professional indemnity insurance does not limit a consulting engineer's liability to the amount of cover provided by that insurance. A separate, express clause is needed, agreeing that liability should be limited.

In *Moores v. Yakeley Associates* (Court of Appeal 1999) the Court of Appeal considered the effect of a monetary limitation in RIBA's standard form of appointment SFA/92. The Court of Appeal upheld the judgement of the judge at first instance. The judge had held that a limit of £250 000 was reasonable because it was not an arbitrary figure but was based on the architect's assessment of the likely cost of the works; the fees were in the order of £20 000 and the ceiling was ten times that amount; the client was in a stronger bargaining position than the architect – he could have instructed any architect; the client and its solicitor had both been aware of the clause and had had an opportunity to object, and a comparison of their respective resources showed that the architect had none and the client was very wealthy. The fact that the architect had insurance cover of twice the amount of the ceiling did not make the amount unreasonable.

Liability can also be limited by reference to other matters. For example, liability could be limited to the costs of repair or of cleaning up a site, or to the amount recoverable under a consulting engineer's professional indemnity insurance. Certain types of damages can be excluded or limited, such as relocation costs, loss of profits or consequential losses.

If liability is to be limited by reference to the sort of damages payable, this needs to be approached very carefully with appropriate advice. A discussion of all the damages that may flow from any breach of a consulting engineer's appointment is outside the scope of this section.

There is no reason why a clause limiting liability cannot use the amount of the consulting engineer's 'net contribution' as a means of establishing a maximum that should be paid in relation to a claim. Such a clause may be necessary where the consulting engineer has to review, check or supervise the work of others as described in section 14.2.16 of this chapter and thus becomes jointly liable with others. The objective of the clause is to limit the consulting engineer's liability to its part of the overall damages where the other parties with whom it is jointly liable have no or insufficient assets to pay their part. In a case involving monitoring a contractor's work, for example, where both the consulting engineer and the contractor have been negligent, such a clause could limit the consulting engineer's liability to 20% or 30% of the total damages suffered by the client. It needs to be remembered, however, that such clauses can only apply where the claim is such that two or more parties are 'liable for the same damage'. If the consulting engineer is found to be solely responsible for the damage arising out of that claim, such a clause will not be effective in limiting liability at all.

As has been said, in exceptional cases it can be 'reasonable' to exclude liability in respect of some particular claims or matters. For example, if a consulting engineer has not been asked to consider pollution or contamination in relation to a particular project because the client is taking separate specialist advice about this, it could be reasonable to state in the appointment that the client is doing this and any liability of the consulting engineer for any claim arising out of or in connection with pollution and contamination is excluded.

Limiting the time within which claims can be brought must also satisfy the requirement of 'reasonableness'. This may prove difficult because there are different time periods for bringing claims in contract and in negligence.

Time limits that relate only to claims in contract will more readily satisfy the test of reasonableness – 6 to 10 years might be reasonable, depending on whether the contract is under hand or signed as a deed (see section 14.1.5 of this chapter) because such claims can only be brought within 6 or 12 years from the date of the cause of action. Claims in negligence, however, can be brought long after any claim in contract would be time barred. A limitation that excluded claims in negligence after, say, six years from completion of the services might not be considered 'reasonable' as it could be a sizeable reduction in the position under the law at present.

Examples of tailored limitation of liability clauses are to be found in the ACE Agreement.

14.2.12 The obligation to maintain professional indemnity insurance

A discussion of professional indemnity insurance is contained in *Professional indemnity insurance*.

Most professional appointments contain specific obligations to maintain professional indemnity insurance. (This is positively desirable where there is a limitation or exclusion of liability, so as to help with the test of 'reasonableness' under the Unfair Contract Terms Act 1977 – see section 14.2.11 of this chapter.)

The consulting engineer should check that the obligation matches its present professional indemnity insurance arrangements, including any particular restrictions or exclusions such as those that can attach to pollution and contamination claims, asbestos or terrorism claims. The consulting engineer also needs to bear in mind that the nature of professional indemnity insurance can change and that professional indemnity insurance could become prohibitively expensive or even be unavailable for some or all claims. It is the policy in existence at the time the claim is made that is the relevant policy.

As a result, any obligation to maintain professional indemnity insurance should be qualified. First, the consulting engineer should be relieved of the obligation to insure if insurance is not available at commercially reasonable rates. Second, the length of time for which the consulting engineer undertakes to maintain insurance should be reasonable. For example, if the appointment has been signed under hand, the obligation should only last six years.

The amount of the insurance cover also needs to be considered. The amount should be appropriate for the risks associated with the particular project, not the amount of the cover presently maintained by the consulting engineer. Agreeing to maintain professional indemnity insurance in a certain amount is not the same as limiting liability to that amount: a common misunderstanding – see section 14.2.11 of this chapter.

Some clauses concerning the maintenance of professional indemnity insurance in bespoke appointments seek to stipulate the terms of that insurance, for example, that it is in joint names of the consulting engineer and the client, or the amount of the excess, or that the insurer should be a UK insurer. These sorts of provision could severely restrict the consulting engineer's ability to obtain professional indemnity insurance and should be considered carefully before being accepted. An obligation not to settle or compromise any claim that the consulting engineer may have against its insurer in respect of the client's claim without the client's consent may be expressly prohibited in the consulting engineer's professional indemnity insurance policy.

The ACE Agreement includes an obligation to maintain professional indemnity insurance in an amount and for a period of time to cover its liabilities under the appointment. There is also a proviso that such insurance has to be available at commercially reasonable rates and subject to all exceptions, exclusions and limitations to the scope of cover that are commonly included in such insurance at the time it is taken out. This is to reflect the fact that in recent years, further limitations and exclusions to the scope of cover have been introduced by insurance companies.

14.2.13 The Construction (Design and Management) Regulations 2007 (CDM)

CDM Regulations are dealt with in *Construction health and safety I* and *II*. As far as the consulting engineer is concerned, it

is only necessary in this section to reiterate that any obligations as 'designer' are imposed by statute and last only while acting as designer and while the construction work is under way, even though such matters as demolition and maintenance and the future use of the building as a workplace have to be taken into consideration during the design process.

Because the designer's obligations under CDM Regulations are imposed by statute, there is no need for an appointment to set out the designer's obligations under the Regulations. The Regulations have specific provisions concerning civil liability but do not impose civil liability generally in respect of breach of the Regulations. Some bespoke appointments include such words as: 'The Designer shall comply with all its obligations under the Construction (Design and Management) Regulations 2007'. This is a strict obligation – see section 14.2.3 of this chapter – but the obligations in the Regulations concerning designs are qualified, for example, by 'so far as is reasonably practical to do so'.

If the obligations are set out in full, the wording should be identical to that in the Regulations. If other wording is used, the consulting engineer will have to comply both with the Regulations and with the specific obligations set out in the appointment. Paraphrases or extensions of the consulting engineer's duties can be dangerous because they can be misleading and/or they can increase the consulting engineer's risk by extending the duties beyond those in the Regulations.

ACE's Schedule of Services contains no specific CDM services, except a reminder to discuss with the client the role of the consultant and its relationship with (and in the case of the lead consultant the need for) other consultants and contractors, subcontractors and CDM co-ordinators in accordance with the Regulations.

14.2.14 Sub-consultancies

A consulting engineer may sometimes subcontract (sublet) to another consulting engineer part of a project or may be asked by the client to employ all the other professionals, regardless of their disciplines.

The important thing to remember is that in both cases the original consulting engineer is the person who is responsible to the client for fulfilling all the obligations under the appointment. Therefore, that consulting engineer will remain responsible for all the services that it has undertaken, notwithstanding that some were carried out by a sub-consultant, and if that sub-consultant is negligent the consulting engineer will be liable to the client for all the resulting losses. Because the consulting engineer will in turn have (or should have) a 'back to back' contract with the sub-consultant (making the sub-consultant's obligations identical to those of the consulting engineer), the consulting engineer should be able to pass those losses on to the sub-consultant and recover them from the sub-consultant. If, however, the sub-consultant has gone into liquidation, or has insufficient professional indemnity insurance cover, the consulting engineer will still have to pay the client in full. The consulting engineer should therefore make a careful selection of sub-consultants and make sure that its insurance arrangements cover the acts or omissions of sub-consultants. The consulting engineer also needs to check that its appointment does not prohibit any subcontracting of any of its obligations.

The consulting engineer will also have independent obligations to the sub-consultant, for example, in relation to payment, information and decisions, and these too should be in the sub-contract. Historically, payment to sub-consultants has been on a 'pay when paid' basis, but this is no longer permitted where the contract is a 'construction contract' under the Construction Act. The exception is where the consulting engineer's client becomes 'insolvent'.

The ACE Agreement provides that the consulting engineer may recommend to the client that some of the services are sub-let to a specialist sub-consultant and that the client may not unreasonably withhold consent to such a recommendation.

14.2.15 Remuneration

Experienced clients will tailor a consulting engineer's fee to the concept of certainty. A fully defined series of tasks may well allow a fixed fee to be negotiated to the benefit of both parties. In instances where the client has not yet made up its mind, or where several options are to be investigated by the consulting engineer, a more flexible approach to fees has to be more appropriate.

Lump sum fees These include both a fixed lump sum and adjustable lump sums. One important aspect is the need to provide fully for circumstances in which a fixed lump sum may vary, for example, by the lapse of time, by performance of additional work beyond that contracted for or by accelerated or delayed completion of parts of the contracted services before or after stated dates. Adjustable lump sums generally require a 'shopping list' of tasks from which the client chooses what it wants doing and in what order. Since many construction projects take place over an extended period, it is important that even lump sums include a mechanism for variation, for example, linking them to a price or cost index.

Ad valorem fees The fees are calculated as a percentage of the capital cost or construction out-turn cost. However, payment on this basis can be seen as arbitrary. The method relies on the consulting engineer's professionalism in producing a design that results in a minimum construction cost. However, *ad valorem* fees invariably include a full client service – a client can expect to be able to call on its consulting engineer frequently without receiving additional invoices. A percentage figure based on experience and adequate definitions of capital cost or construction out-turn cost are essential to the proper assessment of an *ad valorem* fee.

Time-based fees Typically, these cover salary multiplier rates and all-inclusive rates. Generally, each is given as a range of rates according to seniority, experience and speciality of the person concerned. Such rates are charged on an hourly, weekly or monthly basis. Salary multiplier rates have a built-in

protection against inflation and promotion and should include benefits in kind and annualised costs of pension, life insurance and national insurance, as well as overheads, amongst others. All-inclusive rates are generally regarded as including all elements of salary multiplier rates plus, possibly, printing costs, travel costs and any other costs necessary to bring the consulting engineer's commission to a conclusion. All-inclusive rates are usually effective for a predetermined period but should have an escalating factor should the period be exceeded. Non-productive time must be dealt with – for example, does time spent travelling, sickness, public holidays or overtime come within or without chargeable time? To the extent that they do not, they must be covered within the rate.

Expenses Sums necessarily expended in the course of providing the services, other than the time of the staff involved, for example, printing of documents and travelling, have to be covered in one way or another. They may simply be costed into the fee, charged separately, for example, on an at-cost reimbursable basis or, perhaps, subject to a percentage handling-charge.

Additional work/site inspection work The agreed fee (including treatment of expenses) will generally only apply to the services described in the contract between client and consulting engineer. Additional work (or work that has to be repeated) occurs if requested by the client or rendered necessary for reasons beyond the consulting engineer's control. For example, additional work on a lump-sum contract could be paid for by reference to similar work already in the contract or by reference to a schedule of time-charges especially designed to cater for such an eventuality. Whatever method is chosen, it would be wise for the consulting engineer to give its client an approximate estimate of the additional fee in advance so as to allow the client the opportunity of arranging any additional funding. Repeated work generally occurs when a new instruction or a reason beyond the consulting engineer's control renders earlier work abortive. Care should be taken to make sure that the cost of the abortive work is included in any estimate given to the client. 'Change control' ought to be an intrinsic element of the consulting engineer creating a design efficiently.

Site inspection and monitoring work is probably best paid for on a time basis to accommodate construction period over-runs.

Terms of payment

The remainder of this section deals with the provisions in the Construction Act concerning payment. It will be recalled that the Construction Act (the Housing Grants, Construction and Regeneration Act 1996) only applies to 'construction contracts' – see the chapter *The construction contract*.

Intervals for payment of fees and amounts payable

Except where the work lasts less than 45 days (or where the parties agree that it is to last less than 45 days) the payee is entitled to payment by instalments. If the construction contract fails to provide the instalment intervals, the Scheme for Construction Contracts (England and Wales) Regulations 1998 ('the Scheme') will stipulate that this is 28 days. However, the Construction Act itself does not prescribe any minimum or maximum periods for the intervals – the parties are free to agree what these should be.

The parties are also free to agree the amounts of the payments due at each interval or the method of calculating the amount. If they do not do so, again the relevant parts of the Scheme will apply. It is not advisable, however, to adopt this part of the Scheme or indeed to have it incorporated in a consulting engineer's appointment. This is because the Scheme was drawn up with contractors', not consulting engineers', contracts in mind.

Where *ad valorem* fees are due the final out-turn capital cost or construction cost will not be known at the time of payment of any instalment, save the last. This can be dealt with by payments on account, by reference to the latest estimate of capital cost, adjusted as necessary when the final capital cost is known.

The ACE Agreement provides an opportunity to agree payment in instalments at pre-determined intervals. The amounts due at each interval will depend on the method of payment, and, for example, whether this is to be on an hourly basis, a lump sum basis or a percentage fee basis with instalments at the completion of various stages.

When payment becomes due and the final date for payment

Each construction contract has to contain an adequate mechanism for determining when payments become due and a final date for payment of any sum that becomes due.

Again, under the Construction Act the parties are free to stipulate the 'due' date and to agree the period between the date on which a sum is due and the final date for payment.

It is a moot point as to whether stating intervals for payment, such as the first of each month, also means that the payment is 'due' on that first day of the month. It is more usual, and probably better practice, for the appointment to state when an amount is due. The ACE Agreement states that 'payments … shall become due for payment on submission of the Consultant's invoices…'. It also provides that the final date for payment is 28 days thereafter.

If nothing is said, the Scheme provides that the 'due date' is the later of 'the expiry of seven days following the relevant period or the making of a claim by the payee'. The 'relevant period' is the 28-day period prescribed by the Scheme for instalment periods (if the 'construction contract' fails to provide for this) or the instalment period is fixed by the appointment itself. 'Making a claim' is 'a written notice given by the party carrying out the work under a construction contract to the other party specifying the amount of any payment or payments that he considers to be due and the basis on which it is, or they are, calculated'.

An invoice or an application for payment would qualify as 'making a claim', provided that it contains the information prescribed by the Scheme.

The 'final date for payment' under the Scheme is 17 days after the due date. This makes a total time of 24 days in which

payment should be made following receipt of the invoice. It was the intention of the Construction Act to encourage regular and fair payments. However, as the parties are allowed to agree the due date and the final date, payment periods in appointments can be very much longer than the 24 days under the Scheme. It is important, therefore, to check the due date and the final date for payment.

If the contract is so short that there are no instalments, or where the payment is the last payment, the Scheme provides that payment becomes due on the expiry of 30 days following completion of the work or the making of a claim by the payee, whichever is the later, and the final date for payment is again 17 days thereafter.

Notice of payment and of withholding payment

The Construction Act requires formal notices to be given both in relation to payment and the withholding of payment. The payer has to give notice

> not later than five days after the date on which payment becomes due from him under the contract, or would have become due if:
>
> (a) the other party has carried out his obligations under the contract and
> (b) no set off or abatement was permitted by reference to any sum claimed to be due under one or more other contracts
>
> specifying the amount (if any) of the payment made or proposed to be made and the basis on which that amount was calculated.

If the construction contract does not contain anything about the giving of notices, the relevant provisions of the Scheme apply. The Scheme simply repeats the provisions set out earlier.

The notice of payment must be given, even if payment is to be made in full or if no payment will be made.

Failure to give the notice of paying is a breach of contract (although it is difficult to see what loss a payee suffers in the absence of such a notice if it receives the amount asked for by the final date for payment).

The five-day notice period for the notice of paying is the only mandatory period in the payment provisions of the Construction Act. The parties cannot alter it, but they can agree the due date (by reference to which the notice is fixed) so that it minimizes administrative inconvenience.

It is not necessary to set out in an appointment document the payer's obligation to give a notice of paying in respect of each payment, because this will be implied into every 'construction contract'. The ACE Agreement sets out the requirement expressly, however, as a reminder to payers and this requirement will apply even where the appointment is not a 'construction contract'.

As to notice of withholding, the Construction Act provides:

(1) A party to a construction contract may not withhold payment after the final date for payment of a sum due under the contract unless he has given an effective notice of intention to withhold payment.

(2) To be effective such a notice must specify:

(a) the amount proposed to be withheld and the ground for withholding payment, or

(b) if there is more than one ground, each ground and the amount attributable to it, and must be given not later than the prescribed period before the final date for payment.

(3) The parties are free to agree what that prescribed period is to be.

As usual, if the appointment does not set out what the prescribed period is to be, the Scheme will apply. The Scheme stipulates that the prescribed period is not later than

> seven days before the final date for payment determined either in accordance with the construction contract or, if there is no such provision, in accordance with the provisions of the Scheme.

The notice of payment can be used as the notice of withholding (although it would have to be given earlier) provided that it contains the information prescribed by this section.

Many bespoke appointments provide that the notice of withholding has to be given not later than one day before the final date for payment to give the client the maximum time to decide whether it is going to withhold any monies and to calculate the amount. The ACE Agreement again expressly incorporates the notice of withholding provisions with the notice to be given not later than seven days before the final date for payment – as in the Scheme.

The Construction Act also includes a right to suspend performance if there is non-payment if no effective notice of withholding has been given in the correct time before the final date for payment. This is considered in section 14.2.8 of this chapter.

Conditional payment/pay when paid

The Construction Act severely restricts the rights of parties to 'construction contracts' to make any payment conditional on the receipt of monies from a third party. For non-construction contracts, of course, such provisions are not outlawed.

The only time when a pay-when-paid condition is allowed is when the third person on whom the payee relies in order to make its payments is 'insolvent'. Insolvency in such an instance is defined in the Construction Act and was subsequently amended because some commentators suggested that the definition was incomplete. The definition should be checked by anyone seeking to take advantage of such an eventuality.

Other factors affecting remuneration

The Late Payment of Commercial Debts (Interest) Act 1998 now applies to all contracts for professional services. The Act stipulates that there is a statutory right of interest on late payment. The late payment interest rate is the 'reference rate' plus the statutory rate of interest (currently 8%). Alternatively, the parties are free to agree an interest rate that will apply provided

it is 'substantial'. The ACE Agreement now applies the Late Payment Act provisions to late payment.

It is vital that a VAT clause is added to the effect that VAT is payable in addition. Otherwise, the recipient will have to account to Customs and Excise for the relevant percentage from its receipts.

Adjustment of fees to account for inflation is best done by reference to standard indices, but these are only necessary for fees that do not have inherent inflation protection, for example, a fixed lump sum.

A right of the client to audit some of the consulting engineer's records could be inserted where appropriate, so as to verify for example the number of chargeable hours worked. This would not be appropriate in the case of lump sum fees.

Situations where the consulting engineer's invoices are disputed by the client should be catered for in any contract for professional services, so that interest charges on late payments do not apply in the case of legitimately challenged parts of an invoice, save to the extent subsequently shown to be valid.

14.2.16 The services

A clear description of the tasks involved in a professional appointment is essential in order to clarify the respective responsibilities of all parties to the project. If a consulting engineer has agreed to carry out something specifically, but has in fact done something else, that will be a breach of the consulting engineer's obligations under the appointment.

It cannot be emphasised strongly enough that the more attention is paid to the sections in a contract dealing with what will be done and delivered, and what and when the consulting engineer is to be paid, the less effective will be any clauses that are disadvantageous to the consulting engineer. Of equal importance are the services that the consulting engineer will not provide – if only to concentrate the minds of the parties at the outset. The trouble is that too much time in pre-contract negotiations between a client and a consulting engineer is spent on contingent risk distribution and not enough on what the client is to get for what the client is prepared to pay.

Initially, the person draughting the contract should describe in outline a chronological set of duties or tasks required of the consulting engineer by the client, tailored to the eventual outcome, namely the achievement of a design brief, which brief should be obtained from the client in the client's own words. It is possible that the brief will have been provided in the bidding documents, if any, for the job in question.

Next, each duty should be considered to see whether or not its performance requires any contribution from others. This could involve any one or more of the following:

(a) consent to move to the next stage from the client and/or the client's client and/or an external party, for example, the local planning authority;

(b) design or information supplied by the client and/or others working on the project, for example, contractors, subcontractors, other consultants and/or statutory undertakers;

(c) the results of work by others on the project, for example, geotechnical investigations;

(d) assistance by the client, for example, licences, permits, customs clearances, access to sites;

(e) facilities provided by the client, for example, site offices; and so on.

The draughtsperson should then describe, in as much detail as possible, using advice from those who will carry out the work, the series of tasks, but this time qualifying such tasks by reference to the contribution from others over which the consulting engineer has, or will have, no control.

Finally, consideration might be given to events that are not only beyond the control of the consulting engineer but also of anyone else, including the client: strikes, civil insurrection, Acts of God, are examples – a *force majeure* clause will deal with such eventualities. *Force majeure* clauses are more common in overseas forms of appointment than they are in forms of appointment generally used in the UK.

Clearly, all words should be used in their ordinary meaning. If technical terms have to be used they should be defined with the lay person in mind.

Many purchasers of consulting engineering services, even on major projects, have limited technical background but are, as it were, general buyers where detailed knowledge of what is being bought is not considered essential provided that the buyer can construct an adequate brief. It is not only important to describe the services in the detail suggested earlier, in a sequence and subject to qualifications and explanations, but, so as to avoid any doubt in the mind of the lay person, also to state

(i) what is not being provided by the consulting engineer within the fee, and

(ii) further, if a service is not being provided (presumably because it was not asked for within the client's brief and has been identified by the consulting engineer as an essential missing service), what it would cost if the consulting engineer were able to provide that missing service.

Having produced a full description of the services to be provided, in sequence, subject to various consents, provision of assistance, information, data and facilities, together with a section on what is not included, it is recommended that the whole sequence is subdivided so that each section requires the consent and/or approval of the client before it is begun.

It can be most helpful to set up a contractual organization with regular meetings and a reporting system. This should include named representatives on both sides, fixed meetings at regular intervals, with decisions recorded (and signed off) by both sides.

It is important to realise that if a consulting engineer undertakes to approve, review, comment on, examine or otherwise check someone else's work it will incur some responsibility for that work jointly with others. However, the law provides that each person who is jointly liable with another is 100% liable to

the person to whom they owe the duty – usually the employer. The employer can choose whom to sue and from whom to collect the damages he has suffered. A contribution can then be sought from the other parties who are jointly liable with the payer. If that person has insufficient or no assets, insufficient or no contribution may be recovered.

The extent of the responsibility to approve, review, comment, examine or check will depend on what was required to be undertaken as well as what was actually undertaken. It is always prudent to state the exact nature and extent of the review and its purpose and the purpose of any approval.

In November 2007 the CIC produced, in conjunction with its new Consultant's Contract, a comprehensive schedule of services covering the roles of a range of consultants employed for major building projects. However, the Construction Industry Council's schedule of services may be used with other forms of agreement provided any appropriate adjustments in text are made. Likewise, the schedule of services published with the ACE Agreement may be used in a similar independent manner.

'Supervision' of construction The contractor is responsible for actually supervising the work being constructed. Whatever the level of 'supervision by the consulting engineer', that is, inspection, witnessing or monitoring of construction, the contractor remains responsible for the standard of the materials and workmanship. 'Inspection, witnessing or monitoring' of construction by the consulting engineer can be nothing more than selective monitoring by means of random inspection, witnessing and testing.

'Supervising' or monitoring a contractor's work has peculiar difficulties and this is described in section 14.3 of this chapter. In order to avoid the misunderstanding that the word 'supervision' can cause, the words 'supervise' and 'supervision' have been excluded from the ACE Agreement, the more correct description of 'monitor' or 'monitoring' being used instead, combined with a statement as to the purpose of such monitoring. It is vital that the actual job of the monitoring team is specified in detail or covered by adequate generic wording. For example

> to monitor that the Works are being executed generally in accordance with the contract documents

is used in the ACE Agreement.

The question of site staff is, of course, linked to 'supervision' or 'monitoring'. The ACE Agreement includes a provision whereby the consulting engineer recommends the appointment of site staff if appropriate and agrees details, scope, payment, the number of site visits and so forth, with the client. The consulting engineer may well be advised to make sure that the construction contract makes it clear to the contractor that the provision of site staff or periodic visits to the site by the consulting engineer shall not in any way relieve the contractor or any subcontractor of the obligation to construct the Works in compliance with the contract documents.

A client will sometimes attempt to alter a consulting engineer's site staffing establishment. However, it is the consulting engineer's duty to recommend to a client the resources necessary to administer the contract. If the client insists on employing an insufficient number of site staff, it is most important to specify what will be monitored and what will not.

As implied earlier, particular attention needs to be paid where the consulting engineer is specifically asked by the client to 'supervise' or inspect a contractor's work without the frequency of such 'supervision' or inspection being agreed. Since a contractor's own supervisory activities are assumed to be those necessary to enable the contractor to meet its 'fitness for purpose' obligation, the purpose of the consulting engineer's 'supervision', therefore, needs to be made clear. Failing clarity, an agreement to 'supervise' or inspect could cause the consulting engineer to become involved in any claim that is made relating to the contractor's work on the basis that the consulting engineer failed to pick up defective work by the contractor. If the consulting engineer is found to be jointly liable with the contractor, and the contractor has gone out of business, the consulting engineer could be liable for 100% of the damages (see above in this section and section 14.2.11 of this chapter concerning net contribution clauses).

A particular case in point is where the consulting engineer is employed by a contractor on a design-and-construct contract. The contractor is thus the consulting engineer's client. It often happens that the consulting engineer is asked by the employer to inspect, 'supervise' or comment upon the contractor's workmanship. The consulting engineer should avoid being placed in this position and should decline if asked. It is the consulting engineer's duty to design the works and it is the contractor's to construct them. To repeat what is stated earlier: the former is prepared with reasonable skill and care and the latter to achieve fitness for purpose. If the consulting engineer is not careful, it may find itself saddled with an uninsurable obligation. The converse also presents problems; if the contractor attempts during the design process to impose on the consulting engineer measures that the consulting engineer considers unwise, or, especially, a risk to health and safety, then the consulting engineer has an obligation to the contractor and, perhaps, to the public at large, to resist such measures. Thus, many design-and-construct contracts produce tensions between designer and contractor that can only be overcome by understanding and experience on both sides.

'As-built' or 'as-constructed' drawings Bespoke appointments sometimes require the preparation and issue of 'as-built' drawings and documents. However, 'as-built' drawings and documents may not fully represent the as-built condition, as a consulting engineer's site staff cannot be expected to measure and record the actual detail of everything that the contractor constructed or supplied. It is arguable that on a large project not even the contractor will be able to complete such a task accurately but, almost certainly, will be better placed than the consulting engineer. There is a risk that, if the consulting engineer undertakes production of 'as-built' drawings, the client could find itself relying on substantially incomplete or inaccurate information and will incur unexpected costs, which the client then attempts to recover from the consulting engineer. 'As-built' drawings are therefore best left to the contractor to prepare, though the consulting engineer may well undertake the task of vetting the completeness, relevance, clarity and subsequent delivery to the client of the drawing and document sets, but not the accuracy of individual drawings and documents.

14.2.17 Bonds, parent company guarantees, liquidated damages, set-off and retention

Bonds, parent company guarantees, liquidated damages, set-off and retention are all measures introduced by clients into bespoke consulting engineering appointments in an attempt to secure performance by financial control. It is arguable whether any of them are necessary. If something has gone seriously wrong with a design that by due legal process has been shown to be down to the consulting engineer's negligence, insurance is there to cover that contingency. For less serious matters, withholding of fees, like any commercial deal, has proved an adequate means of putting matters right. With the possible exception of parent company guarantees, all the remaining measures are simply punitive and often do not lead to solution of the difficulty that caused them to be applied in the first place (discussed at greater length in *Bonds, parent company guarantees and other security*).

Liquidated damages

Such provisions have been common in construction contracts for many years in order to provide an automatic mechanism for claiming for the effects of culpable delay in the completion of such contracts. Providing that the figure inserted in the contract, usually an amount per week, is a genuine pre-estimate of the expected loss due to delay, it stands, and there is no need, upon culpable delay occurring, to assess the actual losses incurred.

However, unlike a contractor, the consulting engineer is often in the hands of others with regard to the timing of its design work and it may find itself unable to control events as it endeavours to complete on time and thus avoid the application of liquidated damages. A consulting engineer that finds itself with a bespoke contract that includes an obligation to pay liquidated damages should ensure there is a mechanism whereby the completion date is extended should the client's requirements change or unexpected events occur that are not within the consulting engineer's control.

One major problem with liquidated damages clauses for the consulting engineer is that they are uninsurable. First, delay may not be due to negligence and second, even if delay is due to negligence, liquidated damages are, by definition, not equivalent to the losses payable as a result of negligent delay, which are the type of losses which are covered by professional indemnity insurance. Therefore, consulting engineers should resist such clauses. If accepted, they should be viewed as commercial risk and treated as such. For a fuller explanation of the ramifications of entering into a commitment to pay liquidated damages see *Administration of claims*.

Set-off

In order to isolate commercial risk a consulting engineer might have very good reasons for resisting set-off where these rights extend to allowing amounts which arise under one contract to be put against (or set off against) amounts due under an entirely separate contract and may well wish to negotiate on the matter before signing the design appointment with the client. Until the relevant part of the Construction Act came into force on 1 May 1998, all a client had to do was to withhold payment of fees and fight the matter out in court, if the consulting engineer was so minded, where the competing claims would be decided and a balancing award made. The Construction Act does not ban this practice; it merely interposes certain procedural requirements to the right of set-off. These procedural requirements amount to a period within which a notice must be given specifying the amount being withheld and the reasons for withholding. Thus, set-off remains the traditional mode of financially controlling the relationship between the consulting engineer and client.

Retentions

Retentions are commonly used in construction contracts and sometimes appear in clients' bespoke appointments. In recent years, the use of retentions in construction contracts has received a great deal of adverse comment. Retentions do not add anything to the quality of construction, do not result in shorter construction periods and simply add to the price. The use of retentions in both construction and consulting engineers' contracts is contrary to the principles of partnering and the sharing of risk as set out in Sir John Egan's Rethinking Construction. Many central government departments and local authorities have abandoned retentions as a means of achieving their required standards of quality.

The argument in favour of retention under a construction contract goes thus: a construction contract has been handed over to the client, most of the work is satisfactory and the client has released half of the sum of 5% that it had hitherto retained in an attempt to secure the contractor's performance during the construction period. The remaining 2.5% is retained so as to make sure that the contractor deals with a number of minor problems during the maintenance period. It is generally assumed that the release of the final element of retention is wholly within the contractor's hands and that the contract is finalised on time to the satisfaction of both client and contractor. In effect, the retained sum is acting as a form of performance bond (see *Financing the project*).

In the case of a designer, the argument does not hold. Errors are generally not known at the end of the design, nor, often, at the end of the construction period. Any errors in design appear much later – long after the contractor has left the site and long after the client has been using the constructed works for the

purposes, and sometimes not for such purposes, for which they were designed. A retention provides nothing of benefit to the client and merely retards the consulting engineer's cash flow, the cost of which the consulting engineer may well include in its fee.

14.2.18 Dispute resolution

This section deals only with adjudication under the Housing Grants, Construction and Regeneration Act 1996, 'the Construction Act', and not with other methods of dispute resolution, such as mediation, which might be included in consulting engineers' appointments. The Construction Act provides a right to either party to a 'construction contract' at any time to refer a dispute arising under that contract to adjudication under a procedure that complies with the Construction Act, regardless of whether such a right is expressly incorporated in the contract.

If there is no adjudication provision, or if the adjudication procedure in the contract does not comply with the Construction Act, the Scheme for Construction Contracts (England and Wales) Regulations 1998, 'the Scheme', will apply. The Scheme governs both the appointment of the adjudicator and the conduct of the adjudication.

The Scheme is suitable for consulting engineers' appointments. The Scheme does not, however, deal with the right to challenge the adjudicator appointed by a third party/nominating body. It may be best, therefore, to agree the identity of the adjudicator beforehand (or the body to nominate the adjudicator). Because a consulting engineer will not know the nature of the dispute until it arises, it will usually be best for a large organisation to be appointed, such as CIC or ICE, which can then select an adjudicator of the right discipline for the dispute in question. If the Scheme is incorporated expressly, consulting engineers should check to see that no amendments have been made to it. Such amendments in bespoke appointments sometimes favour the client or are not entirely even-handed.

Under the Construction Act and under the Scheme, there is no express power to award either of the parties' costs, so each must bear their own. However, sometimes there are clauses within a bespoke contract that introduce other 'schemes' that may alter this. Examples of such private schemes are ICE, Technology and Construction Solicitors Association (TeCSA) and CIC schemes. Some major clients have also produced their own. Each scheme should be considered individually and checked with the consulting engineer's insurer who will sometimes impose conditions or limitations, for example, that the adjudicator's decision should not be final and binding, or that the adjudicator can only base his or her decision on legal grounds, not commercial grounds or fair and reasonable grounds. Many insurers also prefer that adjudicators should give the reasons for their decisions.

It would also be prudent if the appointment stated that a specific person in the consulting engineer's firm has to be served with any notice of adjudication and that service is not effective until the notice has been received by that person. This is because of the very short timetable for dealing with the dispute and within which the adjudicator has to give a decision. It could prejudice a consulting engineer's ability to deal properly with any referral if a notice was sent by post, for example, and the recipient failed to realize its importance or was on holiday and did not return until most of the 28 days had expired.

14.2.19 Copyright

Broadly speaking, the purpose of intellectual property rights is to confer on their owner the exclusive right to use the particular intellectual property concerned. These rights can then be commercially exploited by the owner, by licensing them on appropriate terms to others.

Copyright protects literary and artistic works (among others) and also the output of consulting engineers, architects and other professional disciplines involved in the built environment. Copyright is dealt with at greater length in *Intellectual property*.

14.3 Working for a design and construct contractor

Consulting engineers are often engaged by contractors for design and construct projects. The main difficulties here relate to the obligations taken on by the contractor, which it will seek to pass on to the consulting engineer, and the question of inspection or 'supervision' during construction.

Design obligations

In the absence of an express provision in the construction contract, the contractor will have undertaken an obligation to ensure that the construction will be fit for its intended purpose. This is a different and more onerous obligation from that imposed on designers under common law, which is to use reasonable skill and care in carrying out their designs. However, commonly used standard conditions of contract, such as the ICE Design and Construct Conditions of Contract, for use on design and construct projects do provide that a contractor's design liability shall be the same as that of a consulting engineer, that is, one of reasonable skill and care (or a close variation of those words). Thus, difficulties are avoided as long as the level of duty of care in the consulting engineer's appointment is no more onerous than that in the contractor's contract with the employer.

Serious risks, though, are run by consulting engineers that sign up to contractors' bespoke forms of engagement that simply seek to pass on the contractor's obligations to its employer in their entirety. It is a fact of life that many such bespoke forms treat the supplier of a design as if it were the supplier of materials or a constructor of the works, that is, the obligations in the contractor's contract with the employer are simply passed down to the consulting engineer with no amendment, or, perhaps even worse, confusing, ambiguous and onerous amendments. Such bespoke contracts pass a level of risk down

to the consulting engineer, which is invariably the party least able to accommodate such risks. Bespoke forms of contract that do not reflect the inability of the consulting engineer to influence events once construction has commenced often lead to tension between contractor and consulting engineer. Such tension can be avoided by separating the contractor's obligations to its employer from the consulting engineer's obligations to the contractor – the ACE has produced 2009 Agreement 3 for just this situation.

'Supervision'

As to 'supervision', a consulting engineer may sometimes be asked by a design-and-construct contractor to undertake 'supervision' of the works that the consulting engineer has designed and that the contractor is in the process of building. With the sole exception described in the following paragraph, the consulting engineer would be well advised to avoid any such 'supervision' of the contractor's work. Quality of workmanship and supervision of that workmanship are the contractor's responsibility, and there is no good reason why the consulting engineer should share that responsibility.

A consulting engineer engaged by a contractor undertaking a design-and-construct project should normally visit the site at the contractor's invitation and then only to obtain confirmation or information (e.g. ground conditions) related directly to the consulting engineer's design services.

However, it is recognised that a contractor may well expect its consulting engineer to attend regular meetings on site, especially if those meetings involve the contractor's employer. In such instances the consulting engineer should exercise discretion when invited to inspect a particular part of the construction or to accompany both contractor and employer for a general tour of the site. Consulting engineers often find themselves in difficult situations when asked to comment on the contractor's workmanship, for example, approval of concrete with low cube-test results or sanctioning the next stage of construction (with an implication that all work undertaken during the previous stage is acceptable). There is, admittedly, a fine line between commenting on quality of work and solving a problem of detail that has not adequately been addressed in the consulting engineer's drawings. Possibly the best thing to do is make it clear at the outset that the contractor is solely responsible for quality. Corrective design work undertaken to overcome the contractor's poor quality control will inevitably mean increased risk for the consulting engineer. It is for this reason that ACE Agreement 3 – Design and Construct – and its associated set of Services do not provide an option for the consulting engineer to visit site. If such services are required then both contractor and consulting engineer will have to 'opt in' by coming to a separate arrangement.

14.3.1 Assignment and novation

The general legal principles concerning assignment and novation have been set out in *Insolvency in construction*. This section deals with the particular implications for a consulting engineer where its appointment by the client is assigned or novated to a design-and-construct contractor.

Some bespoke appointments expressly prohibit the assignment of any rights of action in respect of accrued breaches (i.e. 'benefits') without consent. More usually, a client will not want any restrictions on its freedom to assign the benefits of its contract to third parties, such as funders or tenants.

Except under certain conditions the ACE Agreement does not permit assignment of the benefits by either party without consent in writing.

Where both the contractual benefits and obligations are to be assigned to a third party, this is achieved by both the parties to the original contract and the third party, entering into a new agreement (a novation agreement) whereby it is agreed that the obligations of one of the first two parties will now be undertaken by the third party.

Such a novation agreement replaces the original contract, so the usual requirements for the validity of contracts will apply to the making of the novation agreement.

Unless already stipulated in its appointment, a consulting engineer does not have to agree to a third party taking over the client's obligations under the appointment. For example, the consulting engineer may not wish to work for that particular third party, who might be close to insolvency or there may be a conflict of interest. Some bespoke appointments, however, may provide for the assignment of the burdens and benefits of the contract without consent, or may oblige the consulting engineer to agree in advance to a novation in a certain form to a third party. This arises most often where there is to be a design-and-construct contractor and the client wishes to novate its consulting engineer (and others) to that contractor.

Where the novation is to be from one client to another client (not a contractor), the following matters should be considered:

(i) The novation agreement should be checked for any unusual or onerous terms in the same way that any other contract would be checked. A novation agreement should not be used as an opportunity to change the terms of the original contract.
(ii) The novation agreement should also be drafted so that the retiring party is discharged from any further liability and thus steps out of the contract completely, and the new party assumes responsibility for all the contractual obligations, including past obligations.
(iii) Some clients want to split responsibility between the old and new client, and, for example, make it a term that the original client is responsible for any past defaults, including non-payment of fees. This is not satisfactory. The new client is going to want to sue the consulting engineer for any breaches that may have occurred before it took over and this should work both ways.
(iv) There should also be no variation to the time within which claims can be brought. The time limits to apply should be those that would have applied if the original client had

remained the consulting engineer's client throughout. Also, if the original appointment was under hand, the novation agreement should not be signed as a deed.

However, some important additional considerations apply where a consulting engineer is to be novated to a design-and-construct contractor. The consulting engineer will, in these circumstances, have performed some services for the original client and after novation will perform different services for the design-and-construct contractor. The consulting engineer does not re-perform for the contractor the services it has already carried out for its original client and this distinction ought to be preserved in any 'novation' agreement.

In *Blyth & Blyth v. Carillion*, the contractor sought to recover from the consulting engineer the losses associated with an underestimate of steel reinforcement made by the consulting engineer whilst working for the original client before being novated to the contractor. The court held that these were not losses that the original client would have suffered and were therefore not recoverable by the contractor under the novation agreement signed by the consulting engineer. Particular care therefore needs to be taken in considering the effect of any clauses in novation agreements designed to address this point. These are mainly included in 'ab initio' novation agreements that seek to impose liability on the consulting engineer on the fictitious basis that it has been employed by the contractor (as well as by the original client) from the beginning of the project. Thus, the clauses in such agreements seek to recast the consulting engineer's duties retrospectively. Other agreements seek to state the sort of losses for which the consulting engineer is to be responsible. All such clauses need to be considered very carefully if the consulting engineer is not to be made liable for matters for which it was not responsible and in respect of which it did not provide advice to the contractor. In the writers' view, the correct basis for the novation in this context is that set out in the CIC Novation Agreement published in 2004. The CIC Novation Agreement was written on the basis that the contractor 'steps in' as the client under the appointment only from the date of novation, which is usually when the construction contract is let and the consulting engineer performs its services for the contractor only from that date.

There is no difficulty, in the context of a CIC-type novation only, in a consulting engineer giving a warranty to the contractor in respect of the services provided to the original client up to the date of novation, but this should be on the basis that the consulting engineer has exercised reasonable skill and care in the performance of those services for the original client.

Further, in some bespoke agreements the original client may try to ensure that some of the obligations of the consulting engineer continue to be owed to the client, even though the consulting engineer has been novated. For example, the client could either, through the novation agreement or by a direct contract, ask the consulting engineer to supervise the works or report to it on various matters during construction. There is a self-evident conflict of interest here, which could have serious repercussions for the consulting engineer.

14.4 Framework agreements

Framework agreements have become commonplace in recent years. The concept is relatively simple: an employer organisation has a pre-selected list from which to choose a contracting party to undertake a piece of work. The contracting party knows that it is on the employing party's list and knows who else is on the list. The employing party may have different lists for different uses: consulting engineers, contractors, project managers, facilities managers and so on. The list is usually valid for a set period of time and every so often the list is reconstituted by various means. The whole structure and process of creating such lists are known generically as 'frameworks' and the contracts that underpin such frameworks are known as 'framework agreements' or 'framework contracts'. Frameworks generally exist in the public sector, though large companies in the private sector operate not dissimilar arrangements by the creation of 'approved' suppliers of goods and services.

The benefit to an employer organisation, is that the capabilities and resources of the consulting engineers, for example, on its framework list from whom it is intended to purchase consultancy services, are well known even at the stage of the first decision to procure such services. The procedure for choosing any one consulting engineer from the framework list is a matter of procedure known to everyone on the list. Such procedures are regulated in the public sector by, for example, The Public Contracts Regulations 2006, whilst the private sector has its own arrangements based more on the laws of contract rather than statute. Depending on the circumstance, any one consulting engineer may be invited to undertake work either by selective invitation or by competitive 'mini-tender'. Consulting engineers on a framework list also benefit by knowing that the client will only seek to employ from a select pool and that there may well be a steady stream of work throughout the lifetime of the framework. Detractors of such frameworks say that conditions become too cosy and that innovation and true competition are stifled. There have also been suggestions that frameworks are not as favourable to consulting engineers as they ought to be, in that clients sometimes seek to procure outside the framework if they believe that more competitive prices may be obtained.

One further benefit to both client and consulting engineer is that the costs of pre-qualifying for a place on a tender list are dramatically reduced once a framework is in place. The procedure is that consulting engineers compete for a place on the client's list every so often (typically, every three or four years) and that the list is refreshed as new firms come on and other firms drop off. To achieve a place on a framework list it is usually necessary to demonstrate that a consulting engineer has the necessary skills and resources to undertake the type of work for which a framework is being created. This procedure is often time-consuming and expensive, but once having 'pre-qualified' the consulting engineer will know that every so often it should be contacted with a view to providing services to its client, either without further ado or by 'mini competition' against others in the framework.

14.5 Standard forms
14.5.1 The ACE conditions

In 2009 ACE published new forms of agreement 1 to 4 to replace earlier editions, together with four new agreements (5 to 8) for specialist use. These are all described in general terms as follows:

- Agreement 1, where the consulting engineer's client intends to appoint a contractor to construct works designed by the consulting engineer;

- Agreement 2, where a client does not intend to appoint a contractor to construct any works designed by the consulting engineer;

- Agreement 3, where a consulting engineer is engaged to provide design services for a design and construct contractor;

- Agreement 4, where a consulting engineer intends to employ a sub-consultant;

- Agreement 5 is a homeowner's agreement;

- Agreement 6 is an expert witness agreement for use by an individual;

- Agreement 7 is an expert witness agreement for use by a firm; and

- Agreement 8 is for use by an adjudicator.

Unlike the previous editions of the ACE Agreements, the services have now been separated from the forms of contract in order that consulting engineers may 'mix-n-match' or even write their own suite of services.

The sets of services that are currently available and are compatible with the ACE 2009 Agreements are as follows:

- Part G(a) – Civil and structural engineering. Non-lead duties;

- Part G(b) – Mechanical and electrical engineering (detailed design). Non-lead duties;

- Part G(c) – Mechanical and electrical engineering (performance design). Non-lead duties;

- Part G(d) – Civil and structural engineering. Lead duties;

- Part G(e) – Mechanical and electrical engineering, Lead duties;

- Part G(f) – Civil and structural engineering. Design and construct;

- Part G(g) – Mechanical and electrical engineering (detailed design). Design and construct; and

- Part G(h) – Mechanical and electrical engineering (performance design). Design and construct.

Some amendment sheets to the English versions of the Agreements and Services Schedules were published in June 2009 but a new edition was printed in May 2010 incorporating these amendments. These are called the '2009 Edition incorporating June 2009 amendments'.

All 2009 Agreements and sets of Services were produced in November 2009 in separate editions designed specifically for use under the laws of Scotland and electronic versions of all the Agreement and the Services Schedules were made available in May 2010. All these incorporate the June 2009 amendments.

Adjudication is provided for in accordance with the CIC's Model Adjudication Procedure but only if the agreement is a construction contract.

14.5.2 The professional services contract

The series of standard form contracts produced by the New Engineering Contract (NEC) Panel have been described in *The construction contract*.

The NEC Professional Services Contract (PSC) was first published in 1994. The 2nd edition was published in June 1998 and a 3rd edition (PSC3) was published in June 2005.

As with the other contracts in this family, the contract contains core clauses dealing with the parties' main responsibilities, time, quality payment, compensation events, rights to material, indemnity insurance and liability and disputes and termination.

There are then four main option clauses: for priced contracts with activity schedule, target contracts, time-based contracts and term contracts.

Finally, there are secondary option clauses dealing with such things as price adjustment for inflation, changes in the law, parent company guarantees, sectional completion, delay damages, collateral warranty agreements and the Housing Grants, Construction and Regeneration Act 1996 and the Contracts (Rights of Third Parties) Act 1999.

PSC3 is substantially different from the ACE Agreement, the main differences being as follows:

Duty of care

Under Clause 21.2 of PSC3, the Consultant's obligation is 'to use the skill and care normally used by professionals providing services similar to the services [as defined]'. This is different from 'reasonable skill and care', which is the duty of care in the ACE Agreement and under the common law.

Defects

Under Clause 41.2 of PSC3, the Consultant is obliged to 'correct Defects within a time that minimises the adverse effect on the Employer or Others'. If the Consultant does not correct 'Defects' within the time required by the contract, the Employer assesses the cost of having Defects corrected by other people and the Consultant pays this amount.

A Defect is defined (in Clause 11) as a part of the services (as defined) that is not in accordance with the Scope or the applicable law. The Scope is defined as 'information which specifies and describes the services or states any constraints on how the Consultant provides the services'. This information is set out in a document identified in the Contract Data, provided by the employer or in an instruction given in accordance with the contract.

There is no indication that a Defect can only result from a failure to exercise reasonable skill and care. Thus, the Consultant could be liable to pay for the costs of rectifying a Defect even if the Defect is not the result of a failure to exercise reasonable skill and care, or in cases where the Employer may have suffered no loss, where nominal damages only might be payable. This is fundamentally objectionable and insurers may refuse to indemnify consulting engineers.

The Consultant also has to notify the Employer of Defects at completion and until the Defects Date. This may go beyond the duty imposed on a consulting engineer under common law in certain circumstances.

The ACE Agreement contains no similar provisions, leaving the matter of damages arising from any defect and the question of notification to be dealt with under the common law.

Limitation on liability

In PSC 2nd edition the 'Consultant's liability' to the employer 'resulting from a failure to Provide the Services' was limited to the amount stated in the Contract Data. This has been replaced by a new Clause 82.1 in PSC3 giving a total liability in an amount to be agreed for all matters other than excluded matters and this is to apply 'in contract, tort or delict and otherwise to the extent allowed under the law of the contract'.

The excluded matters include delay damages, loss or damage to third party property and death of or bodily injury to a person other than an employee of the Consultant.

A new Option X18 has been added that allows the parties to agree other limitations, for example, for indirect or consequential losses and for defects not found until after the defects date. It is not clear how this fits in with Clause 82.1. The parties can also fix a time limit for claims.

The ACE Agreement's limitation of liability is far broader, being simply limited to an aggregate or total sum other than claims for death or serious injury where, like PSC3 no limit applies.

Clause 82.2 is meant to be a net contribution clause. This is clear from the guidance. However, what Clause 82.2 says is that 'the Consultant's liability to the Employer is limited to that proportion of the Employer's losses for which the Consultant is responsible under this contract'. Since the proportion for which the Consultant 'is responsible' would be 100% in such circumstances, this clause could be ineffective.

Time obligations

PSC3 has strict obligations on the Consultant to comply with Key Dates and the Consultant is relieved of that obligation only if the event preventing the achievement of the Key Date is a compensation event.

This is again a very different basis to that in the ACE Agreement – see section 14.2.4 – where a test of' reasonable endeavours' applies.

14.5.3 FIDIC Client/Consultant Model Services Agreement

The Client/Consultant Model Services Agreement entered its fourth edition in 2006. It is familiarly known as 'The White Book' and is published by FIDIC (Fédération Internationale Des Ingénieurs-Conseils). Its primary use is for international consultancy contracts where the parties are free to choose a number of aspects that would normally be taken 'as read' in any other standard form of contract used in the UK. Examples of the choices available are those of language, governing law and currency of payment.

The fourth edition of the FIDIC Client/Consultant Model Services Agreement, much like the ACE Agreement, imposes, through Clause 3.3.1, a duty on the consulting engineer 'to exercise reasonable skill, care and diligence in the performance of his obligations'. The contract also allows the consulting engineer to agree a total limit of liability, rather than a recurring 'each and every' limit of liability, a principle that has been adopted in the ACE 2009 Agreements. In addition, and unlike the other standard forms discussed in this chapter, Clause 6.4.1 introduces an indemnity clause, which should be treated with a great deal of caution as highlighted in section 14.2.10 earlier.

Generally speaking, the FIDIC White Book is a form of agreement that transmits itself across frontiers without too much difficulty. In the writers' view any attempts to amend the wording so as to make it overly sophisticated or more suited to a particular legal jurisdiction may be wasted effort. Consulting engineers run significant commercial risks in working internationally and one of those risks is the interpretation of the wording of the contract by clients and legislators whose first language may not be English. Relying on elaborate legal argument in some cases might not prove effective.

14.5.4 The CIC Consultants' Contract Conditions

The CIC published the first edition of its Consultants' Contract Conditions in November 2007 together with a comprehensive scope of services, which is now available on-line using DefinIT software. This standard form is specifically tailored for use by experienced clients and consultants of all disciplines undertaking large commercial building developments.

One of the primary intentions of the CIC Consultants' Contract is that it is used to engage all members of the professional team. The attitude of the client is, therefore, of paramount importance in achieving this objective. The result will be that the project manager, architect, civil and structural consulting engineers, building services consulting engineer, landscape architect, cost consultant, CDM co-ordinator, quantity surveyor and any other consultants are all on an equal contractual footing and all working within a scope of services, the elements of which have been clearly allocated to individual members of the design team.

The layout of the CIC Consultants' Contract is not dissimilar to that of the ACE Agreement, in that the first part of the contract (the Form of Agreement and Schedule) identifies the parties, and sets out what is intended to be achieved and the amount to be paid.

The CIC Consultants' Contract imposes a higher duty of care on the Consultant than does an ACE Agreement. Such duty of care is one of 'reasonable skill, care and diligence to be expected of a competent consultant of the relevant discipline undertaking the relevant role who is experienced in providing similar services in connection with projects of similar size, scope and complexity to the Project'. As stated earlier in this section, a consulting engineer entering into an ACE Agreement is simply committing itself to acting with 'reasonable skill care and diligence in the performance of the Services'. The Consultant's limit of liability under the CIC form of contract is one of total liability, just like the FIDIC Model Services Contract described earlier, which approach the ACE 2009 Agreements have followed.

Attempts to settle disputes are via a mediation and adjudication route, with a final decision resting on legal proceedings through the courts.

References

Egan, J. (1998) *Rethinking Construction: Report of the Construction Task Force.* HMSO, London, UK.

Referenced legislation, regulations and standards

Construction (Design and Management) Regulations 2007 (CDM)
Contracts (Rights of Third Parties) Act 1999
Housing Grants, Construction and Regeneration Act 1996
Late Payment of Commercial Debts (Interest) Act 1998
Public Contracts Regulations 2006
Scheme for Construction Contracts (England and Wales) Regulations 1998
Unfair Contract Terms Act 1977
Unfair Terms in Consumer Contracts Regulations 1994

Referenced cases

Blyth & Blyth v. Carillion
Moores v. Yakeley Associates (Court of Appeal 1999)

Further reading

Edwards, L. and Barnes, R. (2000) *Professional Services Agreements.* Thomas Telford Ltd, London, UK
The Merchant of Venice by William Shakespeare

Websites

Association for Consultancy and Engineering (ACE); www.acenet.co.uk

CDM Regulations (SI no. 320); www.opsi.gov.uk/si/si-2007-index

Construction Industry Council (CIC); www.cic.org.uk

Housing Grants, Construction and Regeneration Act (1996) (The 'Construction Act'); www.opsi.gov.uk/acts

Institution of Civil Engineers(ICE); www.ice.org.uk

International Federation of Consulting Engineers (FIDIC); www.fidic.org

Joint Contracts Tribunal (JCT); www.jctltd.co.uk

New Engineering Contracts (NEC); www.neccontract.com

Scheme for Construction Contracts (1998); www.opsi.gov.uk/si/si1998/19980649.htm

Royal Institute of British Architects (RIBA); www.architecture.com

Technology and Construction Solicitors Association (TeCSA); www.tecsa.org.uk

Chapter 15

Collateral warranties

Hamish Lal Jones Day, London, UK

doi: 10.1680/mocl.40878.0231

The so-called rule of 'privity of contract' prevents third parties relying on contracts to which they are not a party. Whilst, the Contracts (Rights of Third Parties) Act, 1999, has sought to circumvent this rule, many agreements expressly exclude the Act and collateral warranties continue to be commonly used. A collateral warranty is entered into between two parties which would not normally have a direct primary contractual relationship. The benefit of a collateral warranty is freely assignable without the consent of the other party, but it is typical that the person giving the warranty will seek to limit the number of assignments or insist on prior written consent. A question is often asked whether a dispute under or in connection with a collateral warranty can give rise to statutory adjudication under the Housing Grants, Construction and Regeneration Act, 1996 – it appears that adjudicators and many in the industry consider that this Act does not apply to a typical collateral warranty because it is not a contract 'for' the carrying out of construction operations.

CONTENTS

15.1 What is a collateral warranty?

A collateral warranty is entered into between two parties which would not normally have a direct primary contractual relationship. Before, during and after the completion of the project there will be many parties who are interested in a successful project outcome: essentially there are many stakeholders in the project – stakeholders who do not all have direct contractual relationships. The so-called 'privity of contract' doctrine holds that, generally, a contract cannot confer rights or impose obligations on any person save those who are party to the contract. The point was established in 1861 in *Tweddle v. Atkinson* and in 1915 the then Lord Chancellor, Viscount Haldane, delivering his judgement in *Dunlop Pneumatic Tyre Company Limited v. Selfridge & Co. Limited [1915]* said that:

> ... in the law of England certain principles are fundamental. One is that only a person who is a party to a contract can sue on it.

In practical terms this means that although a Funder will have issued funds its involvement will not stop there because it will want safeguards to ensure that its investment is suitably protected. Another example would be a purchaser/tenant of a new property – as the property has not stood for very long it is not tried and tested (there may be snagging problems) and they will want assurances that the building will not collapse! More realistically, they will want assurance that if a roof is leaking or a window is not closing properly then it will be fixed. Indeed, it is often the case that developers are making use of contaminated land. Before this can be sold the developer will want it cleaned up and will also want assurances that this has been done properly and to the appropriate environmental standards.

In all these examples the Funder and the purchaser/tenant could try to rely on the tort of negligence but establishing the duty of care is both time consuming, costly and not guaranteed. Indeed, in recent years the courts have condensed the use of negligence. English law has developed so that it is usually difficult or impossible for a buyer, tenant or funder to recover that loss using a tort claim. The House of Lord's decision in *Murphy v. Brentwood District Council* [1991] AC 398 precludes recovery in tort where the loss suffered is pure economic loss (which can include the cost of carrying out repairs). However, it should be noted that a claim in tort for personal injury or for damage to a neighbouring/third party property may still succeed. Therefore, a direct agreement, the collateral warranty is a tangible way of formalising this duty of care in a binding contractual document and avoids the time and costs in establishing a duty of care under negligence. With a collateral warranty in place if a problem arises (for example, after the sale, the land is discovered to still be contaminated) then the purchaser has a range of options. It may still choose to take action against the seller – however, if that seller is fiscally weak then there will be little point in taking action against them. This is where the collateral warranty becomes vital because the purchaser can instead choose to take action against one or all of those who actually carried out the work and/or professional services.

A recent case which explains the commercial intent of collateral warranties is *Scottish Widows Services Limited v. Harmon/CRM Facades Limited* [2010] ScotsCS CSOH 42, where the learned Judge stated that:

> ... the problem of the legal 'black hole', whereby loss is sustained by a party who has no right of action and the party with the right of action suffers no loss, is avoided [by collateral

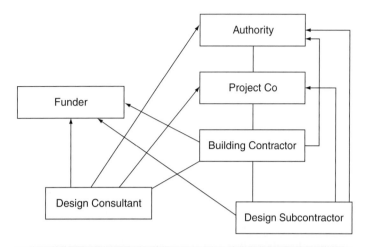

Figure 1   Collateral warranties in a PFI structure

warranties]. Such warranties are an important feature of modern practice in the construction industry. In my opinion they must be construed in such a way as to further their essential purpose, namely to ensure that the party who suffers loss has a right of action against any contractor or member of the professional team who has provided defective work.

Collateral warranties usually run for a period of 12 years from the date of practical completion of the works or the completion of services. Collateral warranties issued under English Law are normally given by way of a deed and therefore have a limitation period of 12 years.

There are many parties involved in giving and receiving collateral warranties. As shown in **Figure 1** these include

- between Building Contractor and Funder;

- between Building Contractor and Authority (especially in PFI arrangements);

- between Design Consultant and Funder;

- between Sub-Contractor and Funder and

- between Sub-Contractor and Project Co.

15.2 Commonly used warranties

There are two main types of building agreement, the Joint Contract Tribunal (JCT) Building Contract (Private with Quantities) and the JCT Building Contract (with Contractor's Design).

In the first the Contractor agrees to follow the design, drawings and plans prepared by the Developer's architect, mechanical and electrical engineers, structural engineer and other consultants. The Contractor will enter into the JCT Building Contract directly with the Developer who will appoint the architect, mechanical and electrical engineers, structural engineer and other consultants. The Developer will, therefore, be able to raise an action against any or all of these people for

breach of contract(s) on the basis that there is a direct contract relationship. As discussed earlier, the problems occur for Tenants and Funders and indeed anyone who has interest in the end product but who does not have a direct contract with the Contractor, the architect, mechanical and electrical engineers, structural engineer and other consultants. The problem can be remedied by collateral warranties.

In the JCT Building Contract (with Contractor's Design), the Contractor is effectively given an outline or employer's requirement and agrees to undertake the design using his own professional team or by appointing external architect, mechanical and electrical engineers, structural engineer and other consultants. It is important to understand that the only direct agreement in respect of the development is between the Contractor and the Developer. Neither the Developer, the Tenants and Funder have any form of contract with any member of the professional team. The Tenants and Funder will have direct form of contract with the Contractor. Again, collateral warranties, therefore, provide for the Tenant and/or Funder to be able to claim against either the Contractor and/or any of the professional team or, in the case of the JCT with contractor's design, for the Developer to have a claim against the professional team used by the Contractor.

It is commonly a requirement of the JCT contracts that the professional consultants agree to enter into collateral warranties with the Developer and Tenants and Funder of the new building. Clearly, this then allows the Developer, Tenants and Funder to bring an action against the Contractor and any member of the professional team for any breaches and defects which may occur in the property caused through the fault or negligence of that particular person. Collateral warranties are in addition to the defects liability period set out in the JCT Contracts. It is now common practise for Contractors to provide a 12-month defects liability period from the date of issue of the certificate of practical completion.

Members of the professional team will often seek to restrict their liability under a collateral warranty. It is common for members of the professional team to try to limit any liability for consequential and economic loss and, preferably, to exclude it from the warranty. A Tenant may not be able to use the premises because of defects arising through the negligence or breach of contract of one of the professional team. If the Tenant has agreed to limit liability for consequential and economic loss then that professional is only liable for the costs involved in remedying the physical defect. Loss of income of the Tenant is usually excluded under this type of collateral warranty. Naturally, there will be a requirement in the collateral warranty that the professional maintain indemnity insurance.

The collateral warranty will usually specify that there can only be a specified number of assignments of the warranty to another third party. It is important that the Developer and Tenant and Funder be able to assign the benefit of the warranty to any purchaser of the property. An assignee of the lease in that period would be advised to have the benefit of the warranty legally assigned to him so that he in turn could have recourse against the original Contractor and professional team.

The Construction Industry Council (CIC) published a liability briefing for use in the industry. It compares the following collateral warranties:

(i) CIC/ConsWa/F for use where a warranty is to be given by a Consultant to a Funder (first edition 2003) and
(ii) CIC/ConsWa/P&T to be given to a purchaser/tenant of the whole or part of a commercial or industrial development (first edition 2003)

and the equivalent British Property Federation (BPF) forms are:

(i) CoWa/F for use where a warranty is to be given to a company providing finance for a proposed development (fourth edition 2005) and
(ii) CoWa/P&T for use where a warranty is to be given to a purchaser or tenant of a proposed development (third edition 2005).

It makes the following recommendations:

15.2.1 The CIC warranties

The balance of risk between consultants and funders or purchasers/tenants is, in general terms, the same as under the old BPF forms. Points to note are as follows:

Cost of repairs – The damages recoverable by a purchaser/tenant are limited to the reasonable cost of repairs.

Net contribution – The others whom it is assumed have also provided contractual undertakings (warranties) are described generically and the list is very wide, being 'all other consultants and advisers, contractors and subcontractors involved in the [project]'. The wording of the clause has also been amended to take into account the decision in the *Co-operative Retail Services* case.

No greater liability – The consultant is entitled to rely on any exclusion of liability in the appointment, in addition to any limitation of liability. This takes account of the fact that, for example, the consultant's appointment may exclude liability for claims arising out of terrorism or asbestos, due to limitations on insurance cover available.

The consultant is also expressly entitled to raise the equivalent rights in defence of liability as it would have against the client under the appointment.

Deleterious materials – The clause refers to the publication *Good Practice in Selection of Construction Materials* (Ove Arup & Partners, 2006). The obligation is confined to the specification of materials and is subject to other instructions that may have been received from the client under the appointment.

Licence – The licence is subject to the fees being paid (or tendered), save that the licence in respect of the documents needed for the health and safety file is not subject to the payment of fees.

Insurance – The obligation to maintain professional indemnity insurance refers to aggregate cover available for pollution and contamination, asbestos and date recognition.

Assignment – Assignment of the purchaser/tenant warranty is limited to twice only and the funder's warranty to one other funder only.

Limitation – The time for bringing claims is not to be greater than a specific number of years (which is to be inserted) from practical completion or, if that is not achieved, from the date the consultant finishes its services. The warranties can be signed under hand as well as executed as a deed.

Third party rights – The rights given to third parties by the Contracts (Rights of Third Parties) Act are excluded, as is usual in collateral warranties.

15.2.2 The BPF warranties

These are similar in many ways, but differ in a number of important respects:

Cost of repairs – The purchaser/tenant warranty provides that the damages recoverable are limited to the cost of repairs, as did the old BPF warranties, but also provides for an additional sum to be stipulated for other losses. Liability for such further losses is not made expressly subject to the net contribution and equivalent three rights clauses; it could therefore be argued that it is not intended to be, resulting in a serious qualification to those clauses.

Net contribution – The net contribution clause has been revised from that in the old BPF warranties. Those whom it is assumed have provided warranties are described as the *Project Team*. What this term means will depend upon the definition (if any) in the underlying appointment (Clause 1). It is used in the BPF Consultants' Appointment, but the definition covers consultants only (in contrast with that in the CIC warranties). It may not therefore be wide enough to cover all those who are liable with the consultant. Moreover, if any other form of appointment is used, there is a danger that the term will not be used at all. The net contribution clause is not stated to be without prejudice to other limitations (e.g., limitations in the appointment incorporated into the warranty by Clause 2(c)).

No greater liability – The equivalent rights clause is very similar to that in the CIC warranty, save that it refers to limitation only, which might not include outright exclusion.

Deleterious materials – The clause also refers to the Ove Arup publication in the context of specification. There is a further provision which requires the consultant to use skill and care to see that materials as used in the construction are in accordance with the Ove Arup guidelines.

Licence – The licence is also subject to the fees being paid (or tendered), though there is no exception for documents for the health and safety file. There are references to *Intellectual Property* and *Design Documents*, terms which are used in the BPF Consultancy Appointment, but might not be used in any other form of underlying appointment.

Insurance – The consultant is not free to agree in relation to each warranty the amount of insurance and the length of time he maintains it, but is bound to the funder or purchaser/tenant in the same terms as in the appointment. There is a reference to Clause 8 of the appointment which will only apply if the BPF Consultancy Agreement is used. The test is *reasonable premium rates* rather than the more usual *commercially reasonable rates.*

Assignment – Assignment is limited (as in the CIC warranties) to twice only without consent (in earlier editions the parties could agree the number of assignments).

Limitation – The time for bringing claims is a fixed 12 years from practical completion or completion, or abandonment of the services if earlier.

Third party rights – The Contracts (Rights of Third Parties) Act is excluded.

15.3 Collateral agreements/contracts?

The Courts may find a collateral contract or agreement where they seek to construe the parties' relationship. An example of a collateral contract is found in *Shanklin Pier Ltd v. Detel Products Ltd* 1 [1951] 2 KB 854.

In *Shanklin Pier Ltd*, Shanklin, who were owners of a pier, entered into a contract with C.M. Carter (Erectors) Ltd for the repair and repainting of the pier, the repainting to be carried out with two coats of bitumastic or bituminous paint. Under the terms of their contract with Carter, Shanklin reserved the right to vary the specification; Detel were paint manufacturers who produced a product known as DMU which they represented to Shanklin as being suitable for the repainting of the pier in that its surface was impervious to dampness and could prevent corrosion and creeping of rust with a life of 7–10 years. In consideration of this representation Shanklin specified to Carter that Carter should only use Detel's paint. The paint failed and Shanklin sought to recover its loss. Shanklin claimed, not against Carter as main contractor, but against Detel as supplier of the paint.

Detel sought to argue that they had not given any warranty to Shanklin and even if they had it did not give rise to a cause of action because they were not parties to the contract for repainting the pier. The Court rejected Detel's argument and held that on the facts there was a warranty and that the consideration for the collateral warranty was that Shanklin required C.M. Carter (Erectors) Ltd to enter into a contract with Detel for the supply of their paint for repainting the pier. Further that the representations given by Detel to Shanklin were contractually binding in the form of a collateral contract. In *Greater London Council v. Ryarsh Brick Co Ltd* 1 [1985] 4 Con LR 85, in similar circumstances to *Shanklin*, Judge Newey QC accepted that even without express representations there may be a collateral contract containing implied terms as to fitness or suitability of the goods.

In *Shanklin*, Detel was aware that their product was to have a specific use by a third party. This was not the situation in *Wells (Merstham) Ltd v.* Buckland *Sand and Silica Co Ltd* [1965] 2 QB 170. Buckland Sand were sand merchants who warranted to Wells (who were chrysanthemum growers) that their sand conformed to a certain analysis that would be suitable for the propagation of chrysanthemum cuttings. Wells ordered sand direct from Buckland and a further two loads via a third party who were builders merchants and not horticultural suppliers. The third party purchased two loads of sand from Buckland for onward sale and delivery to Wells and gave no indication to Buckland that the sand was required for Wells or for horticultural purposes. The sand did not conform with the analysis and as a result Wells suffered a loss in the propagation of chrysanthemums. The court held that Buckland was liable on the basis of a collateral contract and that it was irrelevant that the purchase of the sand had been made through a third party; as between a potential seller and a potential buyer only two ingredients were required to bring about a collateral contract:

(1) A promise or assertion by the seller as to the nature, quality or quantity of the goods which the buyer might regard as being made with a contractual intention; and

(2) The acquisition by the buyer of the goods in reliance on that promise or assertion.

In *Ing Lease (UK) Ltd v. Harwood* [2007] ALL ER (0) 131 the Court considered the scope of statements alleged to constitute collateral agreements. It concluded that the relevant principles regarding pre-contract promises or assurances as collateral warranties may be stated as follows:

(1) A pre-contractual statement will only be treated as having contractual effect if the evidence shows that parties intended this to be the case. Intention is a question of fact to be decided by looking at the totality of the evidence.

(2) The test is the ordinary objective test for the formation of a contract; what is relevant is not the subjective thought of one party but what a reasonable outside observer would infer from all the circumstances.

(3) In deciding the question of intention, one important consideration will be whether the statement is followed by further negotiations and a written contract not containing any term corresponding to the statement. In such a case it will be harder to infer that the statement was intended to have contractual effect because the *prima facie* assumption will be that the written contract includes all the terms the parties wanted to be binding between them.

(4) A further important factor will be the lapse of time between the statement and the making of the formal contract. The longer the interval, the greater the presumption must be that the parties did not intend the statement to have contractual effect in relation to a subsequent deal.

(5) A representation of fact is much more likely intended to have contractual effect than a statement of future fact or a future forecast.

15.4 The Contracts (Rights of Third Parties) Act 1999

The Contracts (Rights of Third Parties) Act came into force on 11 November 1999 and applies to contracts entered into on or after 11 May 2000, unless the contract excludes the operation of the Act. The Act gives a person who is not a party to a contract (a third party) a right to enforce a term of the contract if the contract expressly provides that he may, or the term purports to confer a benefit on him. Section 1(1) of the Act provides that

> Subject to the provisions of this Act, a person who is not a party to a contract (a 'third party') may in his own right enforce a term of the contract if – (a) the contract expressly provides that he may, or (b) subject to subsection (2), the term purports to confer a benefit on him.

The first point to note is that the right created is to enforce a *term* of a contract, not the *whole contract* itself. For example, if a building contract contains a term that the contractor is required to use materials of good quality, then that term might be the subject of a third party enforcement right. For example, the Contract Data section of the New Engineering Contract (NEC)3 standard form of contract requires the Parties to expressly state which terms are to be the subject the Act. Option Y(UK)3 is the option dealing with the Act.

The Act does not apply if on proper construction of the contract it appears that the parties did not intend the term to be enforceable by the third party. The Act therefore facilitates third party rights, but these rights may be specifically excluded or excluded by implication on construction of the contract. Section 1(2) of the Act provides that

> Subsection 1(b) does not apply if on a proper construction of the contract it appears that the parties did not intend the term to be enforceable by the third party.

In *Nisshin Shipping Co Ltd v. Cleaves & Co. Ltd* [2003] EWHC 2602 (Comm) Section 1(2) of the Act came under particular consideration. The Court concluded that Section 1(2) of the 1999 Act does not provide that Subsection 1(b) is disapplied unless on a proper construction of the contract it appears that the parties intended that the benefit term should be enforceable by the third party. 'Rather it provides that Subsection 1(b) is disapplied if, on a proper construction, it appears that the parties did not intend third party enforcement. In other words, if the contract is neutral on this question, Subsection (2) does not disapply Subsection 1(b). Whether the contract does express a mutual intention that the third party should not be entitled to enforce the benefit conferred on him or is merely neutral is a matter of construction having regard to all relevant circumstances.'

The statute does not confer any right on a party to the contract to recover loss suffered by a non-party, an issue which remains a matter for the common law. For example, the beneficiary of a warranty cannot enforce a term of the Building Contract as

he has his own warranty to rely on. The Act removed the need for warranties, although the construction industry has been slow to embrace the idea. The industry's immediate reaction was to maintain the *status quo* and the effect of the Act was expressly excluded in all standard forms. The JCT 2005 and NEC3 standard forms are two notable exceptions.

A third party will only be able to enforce a contractual term if: the contract expressly provides for this to happen; or the term confers a benefit on the third party, unless it is clear that this was not intended. The provisions of the Act can be used to give rights to third parties without having to procure the execution of individual collateral warranties.

In practical terms, Sections 1 and 2 of the Act provide that:

- a person who is not a party to a contract (i.e., a 'third party') may, in his own right, enforce a term of that contract if either the contract expressly provides that he may do so or the relevant term purports to confer a benefit on that party

- the third party must be expressly identified either by name, as a member of a class or by a particular description

- the party need not be in existence when the contract is entered into

- the Act only confers a right to enforce contractual terms in accordance with the other relevant terms of contract

- the third party has available to it any remedies that would have been available to it in an action for breach of contract as if it had been party to the contract (including all equitable remedies such as injunctions for specific performance)

- finally, the parties to the contract cannot vary the contract or alter the rights of third party once a third party has communicated acceptance of rights or the party offering the rights is aware that the third party has not relied on them or it could have been foreseen that the third party would rely and had relied on such rights.

In order to give effect to this arrangement and remove the need for time consuming and costly individual collateral warranties in favour of third parties, some small amendments are required to be made to a building contract and the consultants' appointments, and there needs to be a memorandum or schedule setting out the rights enforceable by each third party. It should be noted that different third parties will require different terms of the underlying contract to be enforceable.

15.4.1 Advantages to consultants and contractors of the Act

Clearly drafted enforceable third party rights have the same effect and application as the rights contained in a collateral warranty. The advantage to the contractor/consultant of using the Act is that it reduces the administrative burden and the commercial tension which can arise when obtaining collateral warranties. In addition, the fact that these rights are crystallised once the Appointment/Building Contract is entered into protects the consultant/contractor from further amendments that can arise during the Developer's negotiations with beneficiaries.

Although the clause and the rights to be given to third parties would still require negotiation, there would be a cost and time saving in the avoidance of needing separate documents executed in favour of future tenants, purchasers, funders and other third parties when identified.

The third parties gaining rights need to be clearly identifiable in the same way that beneficiaries under collateral warranties are. For example, if the third party was identifiable at the outset then the identity of that third party would be set out in the clause bestowing the third party rights in the appointment/building contract. If the identity of the third party was not yet identified, such as a first tenant that had yet to sign up to its agreement for lease, then the clause would, for example, describe this interest 'a first tenant of the development'.

In practical terms the clearest and safest means of drafting third party rights is to create a schedule in the appointment/building contract which sets out the full extent of third party rights granted. This schedule would look almost exactly like a collateral warranty but without the parties and the recitals provisions at the beginning and without the formal execution provisions at the end.

The application of the Act would be restricted to the provisions contained within this schedule. The application of the Act would then be excluded throughout the rest of the appointment/building contract. This protects the consultant/contractor from entering into any obligations that are greater than they would have entered had they been obliged to provide collateral warranties.

15.4.2 Advantages to funder/purchaser/tenant of the Act

The rights granted in favour of these beneficiaries are the same whether granted by express collateral warranties or by a declaration that they are enforceable third party rights pursuant to the Act.

By setting out the full extent of the third party rights in a separate schedule, in a format similar to a collateral warranty, the relevant party is to have a clearly identifiable set of rights which are easily accessed in a separate section. A further benefit is that collateral warranties are often required after practical completion, when the parties providing them might either no longer be in existence or may be, in practical terms, reluctant to execute the documents. Reliance on the Act removes such problems.

Furthermore, rights contained in a collateral warranty are generally stated to be subject to the terms of the appointment/building contract. In practical terms, attempting to enforce the terms of a collateral warranty without reference to the express terms of an appointment or building contract is difficult. Therefore, with each beneficiary having a copy of the appointment/building contract containing their respective rights, enforcement would, in theory, be a relatively straightforward process.

By using the Act, the need for a power of attorney in the appointment or building contract, allowing the employer to grant a warranty in the name of the consultant or contractor (where they have failed to do so of their own accord), is also removed. Ultimately, the process of 'chasing' consultants and contractors for collateral warranties long after the underlying agreements have been concluded (both a costly and time-consuming exercise) is thereby avoided.

15.4.3 Disadvantages of the Act to be considered by all parties

15.4.3.1 Limitations of loss and net contribution clauses

Arguments over limitations are commonplace when collateral warranties are negotiated. The removal of collateral warranties (and use of the Act) will not make these issues go away. They will remain as important to the parties and, therefore, as contentious as they are now.

15.4.3.2 Step-in rights

It is very important to realise that the provisions of the Act can only provide the beneficiary with rights and not obligations. One of the provisions required to exercise in a right of step-in is an obligation upon the party seeking to exercise the right to commit to pay all sums due under the building contract and/or appointment as a condition of stepping into it.

This is commonly seen as a disadvantage but it can be dealt with by the Act. For example, the schedule containing third party rights would confer the right of step-in. Then, in common with all the step-in provisions, the exercise of the right to step-in requires the beneficiary to issue a notice to the contractor/consultant, stating that it is stepping in. The third party rights schedule would therefore state if, and only if, the third party beneficiary exercised its rights to step-in, then it would be a requirement upon stepping-in that the notice it served contain a commitment to pay the sums due. This is not inconsistent with the Act as the schedule grants the rights and then it is the exercise of the right and the serving of the notice that establishes the obligation on the beneficiary.

15.4.3.3 Assignment

The Act does not specifically cover the issue of whether a third party is able to assign its rights under the Act to another third party. The Law Commission has said that this was because the ordinary contractual rules of assignment would apply, but the issue has not yet been resolved by the courts. In practical terms, rights given under the Act can be assigned in the same way as any other right under an appointment/contract and it is therefore up to the parties to place any commercial limitation on assignment.

15.4.3.4 Variation to Contracts

Another argument sometimes used against the use of third party rights is that any variation to a contract can only be made with the consent of all of the recipients of the third party rights.

It has been suggested that this would apply to a variation under the building contract.

Although this is seen as a disadvantage it can easily be overcome. When conferring third party rights, the extent to which the parties to the contract (the employer and the consultant/contractor) can amend or vary the contract needs to be expressly set out. The legitimate interest to protect is that the contract parties cannot vary a third party right once vested, without the consent of the third party. Otherwise, agreed third party rights could be eroded. The drafting would also make it clear that the contract parties were able to vary the remaining contract terms. This puts the parties and third party beneficiaries in the same position that they would have been in if a collateral warranty had been in place.

15.4.4 The growing acceptance of the Act

Given the points outlined earlier, there is no reason why a well-drafted third party rights schedule cannot replace the need for collateral warranties. The disadvantages simply place the parties in a similar position to that which would be experienced when using collateral warranties. Given this, a beneficiary seeking to rely upon the Act for its rights against the contractor and professional team should experience no difference in enforcing those rights than it would have done relying upon a collateral warranty, provided the memorandum and appointment/contract are properly drafted.

The new JCT Major Projects Form of Contract relies exclusively on third party rights as opposed to collateral warranties, and this should give all parties comfort that third party rights are a safe and sensible method of protecting the rights of groups that have to date relied upon collateral warranties.

15.5 Standard terms of collateral warranties

The main provisions one would expect to see in a collateral warranty are the following:

- A clause confirming that the contractor or consultant (the warrantor) owes a duty of care to the beneficiary in carrying out the works or performing design services. The standard of care will usually be 'bench-marked' with reference to the standards expected of a competent and experienced professional person of the relevant discipline to carry out and complete the works using all reasonable skill and care or to ensure that the works will be fit for their intended purpose.

- The warrantor confirming that he has not used, specified nor permitted the use of materials that are known in the industry to be harmful or 'deleterious'. This provision normally only applies to building projects.

- A clause granting the beneficiary an irrevocable, royalty-free licence to use drawings and other documents prepared in connection with the contract, copyright in which is owned by the warrantor.

- The warrantor confirming that he will hold professional indemnity insurance covering risks arising from their work. Given that a warrantor's potential liability may far exceed the level of his assets, it is important that warrantors are required to hold and maintain such sufficient insurance cover or the warranty may be of little practical value.

- A clause allowing the beneficiary to assign the benefit of the warranty to a person taking an interest in the development. Any assignment by the warrantor of the warranty is usually prohibited. Assignment by the beneficiary of the rights and obligations under the warranty is usually permitted, without the warrantor's consent, to any person taking an assignment of the beneficiary's interest (subject to a maximum number of assignments).

- The warranty should be executed as a deed because this means that the warrantor remains liable for a longer period than if it is executed underhand (12 years rather than 6 years).

- In funder warranties, the warrantor should undertake that before exercising any right to terminate its employment or suspend its performance, it will give the funder notice of its intention to do so.

- Again, a funder-specific provision is that the warrantor undertakes, on the insolvency of the employer, to novate the contract to the funder on request or allow the funder to 'step in' and assume the employer's rights for a certain period.

15.5.1 Limitations

There are three main limitations which may have a significant impact on the enforceability of the warranty and/or recovery of loss under the warranty:

- The net contribution clause under which if there is more than one party at fault the warrantor will only be liable for any damage that he has caused and therefore a percentage of the total damage. In practical terms, therefore, it is necessary to consider carefully who else is providing warranties.

- The original contract limitation clause under which the original contract limitation clause, the warrantor owes the same liability to the beneficiary as he does to the party instructing him (making it important for the beneficiary to check the terms of the original appointment or contract to find out how the warrantor's liability is limited).

- The direct loss limitation clause the warrantor will only be liable for the costs of repair, renewal and/or reinstatement of the building, especially excluding consequential losses such as the loss of trading profits. Beneficiaries do not always agree to these limitations.

15.6 Fitness for purpose

A fundamental issue is the duty of care imposed on contractors which carry out design. Is it the same as the professional man, that is to say reasonable skill and care? Should their work be fit for purpose? A useful starting point is *Greaves & Co (Contractors) Limited v. Baynham Meikle & Partners* [1974] 1 WLR 1261 where Lord Denning stated that

> ... now, as between the building owners and the contractors, it is plain that the owners made known to the contractors the purpose for which the building was required, so as to show

that they relied on the contractors' skill and judgment. It was, therefore, the duty of the contractors to see that the finished work was reasonably fit for the purpose for which they knew it was required. It was not merely an obligation to use reasonable care. The contractors were obliged to ensure that the finished work was reasonably fit for the purpose.

In *Viking Grain Storage Limited v. T. H. White Installations Limited* (1985) 33 BLR 103, White Installations were contractors for the design and construction of a grain drying and storage installation. The installation was not fit for its purpose and the employer argued that there were implied terms of the contract that White Installations would use materials of good quality and reasonably fit for their purpose and that the completed works would be reasonably fit for their purpose, namely that of a grain drying and storage installation. The court held that there were no terms of the contract or any other relevant circumstances which were inconsistent with the implied terms of quality and fitness for purpose and further that there was no reason to differentiate between White's obligation in relation to the quality of materials and their obligation as to design. The employer had relied upon White in all aspects, including design, and on the skill and judgment of White, and in the circumstances, the terms contended for should be implied.

The position is not so clear cut for employers if an employer is deemed not to have relied on the contractor. For example, in *Norta Wallpapers (Ireland) v. Sisk & Sons (Dublin)* (1978) IR 114 where a roof structure, which had been supplied and erected by a specialist sub-contractor, subsequently leaked and was unsuitable for its purpose, the fact that the main contractor was given no choice but to use the specialist sub-contractor, his design and price constituted circumstances which meant that there was no reliance by the employer on the main contractor and, accordingly, there was no fitness for purpose obligation on the main contractor in respect of the specialist sub-contractor's failure.

In the (unreported) case of *Trolex Products Limited v. Merrol Fire Protection Engineers Limited* there was a question as to whether a design obligation was created by the bringing together of what otherwise would have been standard components. Trolex were the sub-contractors for the supply of an electronic control system which was incorporated into Merrol's own works comprising the installation of a fire protection system. In response to the submission by Trolex that there was minimal design obligation in the sub-contract, Potter J stated that

> I should perhaps add that at one stage I had evidence from Trolex which minimised the work of design carried out, suggesting that it was no more than, in effect, a matching of pieces of standard equipment to make up a package to do the job; or as Mr B put it 'logic design work created from standard equipment'. Even if that was so in fact, I am satisfied from the answers of Mr B that there was a conscious realisation that design work was involved and that Trolex were consulted as experts in their field. Further, it is clear that substantial time was spent on this work. Again, whether or not that was so, it is not suggested

that anything was said by Trolex to delimit or belittle the design work involved and the construction of the written contract is clear in my view, namely as one for work of design as well as the supply of goods.

Similarly, in *Gloucestershire County Council v. Richardson* [1969] 1 AC 480 the House of Lords found that the particular circumstances of the case excluded both the implied warranty of suitability and the implied warranty of merchantable quality. In that case Richardson entered into a contract with the employer for the construction of an extension to a technical college. The contract included bills of quantities provided for a PC sum for concrete columns to be supplied by a nominated supplier. Richardson contracted to erect the columns. Clause 22 of the conditions of contract dealing with nominated suppliers did not entitle Richardson either to make reasonable objection to a proposed supplier or to object on the ground that the supplier would not indemnify him in respect of his main contractor's obligation. The employer's architect instructed Richardson to accept a quotation given by the third party supplier for the supply of the concrete columns. The supplier's standard conditions of trade restricted their liability in respect of good supply by them. The columns supplied had latent defects because of faulty manufacture and after erection cracks appeared in them; the columns were unsuitable for use as structural members of the extension.

The House of Lords considered that the facts set out earlier indicated an intention on the part of the employer and Richardson to exclude from the main contract any implied terms that the concrete columns should be of good quality and fit for their required purpose.

15.7 Assignment

The first point to note is that if there is no provision for assignment, then the benefit of a warranty is freely assignable without the consent of the other party. Such an assignment can be legal or equitable. Where there is in a contract an express prohibition on assignment, then such prohibition is likely to be effective in law.

In practise, problems arise where a contractual provision seeks to impose a limit on the number of assignments that can be made. If that provision is simply incorporated into the warranty, then every time there is an assignment the assignee steps into the shoes of the assignor and he has the right to make two assignments – in simple terms the counting may never start. A practical legal solution to this difficulty is to include an express provision in the warranty that assignment is prohibited, save where the express consent in writing of the original giver of the warranty has been obtained – the provision could continue to recite that the giver of the warranty shall not withhold his consent where the assignment is a first or second assignment. The approach used in the JCT warranty, MCWa/F, is that there can be two assignments by way of a legal assignment, provided written notice is given to the contractor.

If a contract is a personal contract then the benefits of that contract cannot be assigned either by a legal assignment or by an equitable assignment. In any event it may be preferable, therefore, to prohibit assignment by an express term rather than seeking to do it by this indirect method.

15.8 Net contribution clauses

Contractors and consultants of all tiers and specialists and perhaps more importantly their insurers are concerned that if they provide collateral warranties and the other members of the professional teams do not, then they will be (solely) liable to the third party for the full amount of the loss. The problem for the sole provider is exasperated because he would be unable to claim contribution from those other parties who did not give collateral warranties and since those other parties cannot be liable in respect of the same damage, there will be no relevant remedy available under the Civil Liability (Contribution) Act 1978. The sole provider therefore seeks to ensure that they are not liable for the full amount of the loss in circumstances where other parties ought properly to be liable at the same time – this is the so-called 'net contribution' clause.

This provides that the liability under the collateral warranty be limited to such losses as is just and equitable having regard to the extent of the warrantor's responsibility and on the further basis that certain named parties (other contractors and consultants) are deemed to have given a warranty in similar form. This is the approach in the BPF warranties (CoWa/F and CoWa/P&T). A similar approach is adopted in the 2001 Editions of the JCT Collateral Warranties (MCWa/F, MCWa/P&T, SCWa/F and SCWa/P&T).

The Institution of Civil Engineers (ICE) has produced guidance to its members on how best to resist giving of collateral warranties:

- Everyone else is signing them: This may be true, but should not override the engineers' judgment as to whether in the particular circumstances the risk of providing a warranty outweighs the benefit of the fee being offered by the client. The client may pursue alternative solutions, such as commissioning a review of the design or a survey of the building, or by procuring latent defects insurance cover.

- If you are confident in your work, you should not hesitate to provide such a warranty: The loss which may be claimed by a third party may be far greater than loss which could be suffered by the original client. This constitutes an increase in risk which the warrantor would need to factor into the fee.

- This warranty is in the same terms as the normal obligations: The wording of the warranty can be misinterpreted. Legal opinion should be sought and obtained. However, there is no guarantee that a judge or arbitrator would agree with those opinions.

- This warranty only reflects the current state of the law: The warranty only reflects current market practices. It is, however, fixed in form once signed, so would preclude any possible benefit accruing to the warrantor from favourable changes in the law which may occur in the future.

- You are insured in any case: The insurer must be informed and must give its approval of the warranty. It is to be borne in mind that the insurers may not accept the terms of the warranty and that generally insurers do not cover liability assumed under an agreement which would not have existed in the absence of that agreement. In any case, the availability and the cost of insurance may change and may be totally different in the future.

Glasgow Airport Ltd v. Kirkman and Bradford [2007] CSIH 47 provides excellent warning on how net contribution clauses needed to be drafted more restrictively if they are to exclude certain types of damage.

In this case the airport engaged a building contractor, Kensteel Structures Limited, to build a cargo handling building. The contractor appointed the defendant to design the works. The airport argued that the floor slab was defective and sought to recover damages in the sum of £2 million directly from the defendant designer by using the collateral warranty. The contractor had entered insolvency and therefore was not a viable defendant. The defendant's liability was limited to £2 million under the appointment. The defendant also sought to rely on the wording of the net contribution to exclude liability for costs claimed by the airport in respect of losses sustained by tenants of the cargo handling building caused by the remedial works. In fact the tenants had sought to recover £2.15 million from the airport – this was expenses in relation to the replacement of the floor slab (£775 000) and losses in respect of disruption to their business and loss of profits.

The net contribution clause stated that

(a) the Sub-Consultant's liability for costs under this Agreement shall be limited to that proportion of such costs which it would be just and equitable to require the Sub-Consultant to pay having regard to the extent of the Sub-Consultant's responsibility for the same and on the basis that the Contractor and its subconsultants and sub-contractors shall be deemed to have provided contractual undertakings on terms no less onerous than this Clause 1 to the Employer in respect of the performance of their obligations in connection with the Works (other than those obligations which relate to the Services) and shall be deemed to have paid to the Employer such proportion which it would be just and equitable for them to pay having regard to the extent of their responsibility.

The defendant argued that 'costs' were limited to the costs of repair, renewal and/or reinstatement of any part of the works. The court ruled that the defendant, by giving a collateral warranty, undertook liability only for losses which would comply with the first rule of *Hadley v. Baxendale* [1854] (such as may fairly and reasonably be considered … arising naturally) but not for losses which could only, in ordinary course, be claimed if they complied with the second rule ('such as may reasonably be supported to have been in the contemplation of both parties, at the time they made the contract, as the probable result of the breach of it'). The court held that the reference to 'costs' was not restricted to the cost of reinstating the defective work but allowed recovery of all losses directly caused by the breach.

It is very clear that warrantors seeking to limit liability in respect of certain costs/losses/damages should do so very clearly in the body of the collateral warranty. The net contribution clause in this case was a common version and re-drafting/negotiation is contemplated.

15.9 No greater liability

Safeway Stores Ltd v. Interserve Project Services Ltd [2005] EWHC 3085 (TCC) (01 December 2005) provides a fundamental reminder of the problems, for beneficiaries, of so-called 'no greater liability' clauses.

Safeway was the employer for the construction of a new supermarket and two-storey car park. Safeway employed Chelverton Properties as the developer who in turn employed a contractor, Tilbury Douglas, (later known as Interserve) who in turn employed a specialist sub-contractor to install the waterproof surface to the car park. Problems occurred with and between the waterproof membrane and the concrete surface. The facts are further complicated because the developer was in liquidation.

Safeway raised an action against the contractor relying on a collateral warranty. Clause 3.3 of the collateral warranty stated that

> The Contractor shall owe no duty or have any liability under this deed which are greater or of longer duration than that which it owes to the Developer under the Building Contract.

Safeway had carried out remedial works in the sum of £413 048.82 and sought to recover this sum from the contractor. However, the contractor relied upon Clause 3.3 and argued that it could rely upon the defence of equitable set-off. This was because the developer owed the contractor £1 million when it entered liquidation. The contractor argued that had the developer raised the claim for £413 048.82 then it could have relied on its larger claim of £1 million by way of set-off. The court agreed and held that the contractor had a complete defence to Safeway's claim.

Following this case, employers have sought to resist the inclusion of such clauses as Clause 3.3. Ultimately, the success of such an approach will depend on the commercial framework.

15.10 Is a collateral warranty a construction contract under the Construction Act 1996?

A question is often asked whether a dispute under or in connection with a collateral warranty can give rise to statutory adjudication under the Housing Grants, Construction and Regeneration Act 1996 (Construction Act, 1996)?

Often, collateral warranties do not include a clause that deals with disputes and/or make express reference to adjudication. In such circumstances the question then becomes whether or not the collateral warranty is a 'construction contract' for the purposes of the Construction Act 1996. If yes, then there would be recourse to adjudication and if not then adjudication is not possible. There is no case law on this direct point. However, it appears that adjudicators and many in the industry consider that the Construction Act 1996 does not apply to a typical collateral warranty because it is not a contract 'for' the carrying out of construction operations. In such circumstances it is quite often the case that the adjudicator will resign unless both parties agree to give the adjudicator jurisdiction to decide the dispute (and so treat the collateral warranty as if it were a construction contract in writing).

It is submitted that the confusion whether the Construction Act 1996 applies to a collateral warranty arises because, neither the Construction Act 1996 nor the The Construction Contracts (England and Wales) Exclusion Order 1998 (SI 1998 No 648) (Exclusion Order, 1998) expressly exclude collateral warranties, even though the Exclusion Order 1998 does exclude bonds and guarantees.

Given the rising importance of the Contracts (Rights of Third Parties) Act 1999 it is important to also note that if a third party has a claim under a third party rights clause in a construction contract, there is no authority on whether the Contracts (Rights of Third Parties) Act 1999 allows the third party to adjudicate against one of the parties. Some commentators argue that the third party does not have an automatic right to use statutory adjudication because it is not a party to a construction contract. Clause 8 of the Act is restricted to the procedure dealing with allowing the third party to use the arbitration procedure.

References

Ove Arup & Partners. *Good Practice in Selection of Construction Materials*. Ove Arup & Partners, 1997, reprinted in 2002 by the British Property Federation (BPF).

Referenced legislation, regulations and standards
Civil Liability (Contribution) Act 1978
Contracts (Rights of Third Parties) Act 1999
Construction Contracts (England and Wales) Exclusion Order 1998
Housing Grants, Construction and Regeneration Act 1996 (Construction Act)

Referenced cases
Co-operative Retail Services
Dunlop Pneumatic Tyre Company Limited v. *Selfridge & Co. Limited* [1915]
Glasgow Airport Ltd v. Kirkman and Bradford [2007] CSIH 47
Gloucestershire County Council v. Richardson [1969] 1 AC 480
Greater London Council v. Ryarsh Brick Co Ltd 1 [1985] 4 Con LR 85
Greaves & Co (Contractors) Limited v. Baynham Meikle & Partners [1974] 1 WLR 1261
Hadley v. Baxendale [1854]

Ing Lease (UK) Ltd v. Harwood [2007] ALL ER (0) 131

Murphy v. Brentwood District Council [1991] AC 398

Nisshin Shipping Co Ltd v. Cleaves & Co. Ltd [2003] EWHC 2602 (Comm)

Norta Wallpapers (Ireland) v. Sisk & Sons (Dublin) [1978] IR 114

Safeway Stores Ltd v. Interserve Project Services Ltd [2005] EWHC 3085 (TCC) (01 December 2005)

Scottish Widows Services Limited v. Harmon/CRM Facades Limited [2010] ScotsCS CSOH 42

Shanklin Pier Ltd v. Detel Products Ltd 1 [1951] 2 KB 854

Trolex Products Limited v. Merrol Fire Protection Engineers Limited

Tweddle v. Atkinson [1861]

Viking Grain Storage Limited v. T. H. White Installations Limited (1985) 33 BLR 103

Wells (Merstham) Ltd v. Buckland *Sand and Silica Co Ltd* [1965] 2 QB 170

Websites

British Property Federation (BPF); www.bpf.org.uk

Construction Industry Council; www.cic.org.uk

Institution of Civil Engineers; www.ice.org.uk

Joint Contracts Tribunal; www.jctltd.co.uk

New Engineering Contracts; www.neccontract.com

Chapter 16

Professional indemnity insurance

Stephen Bamforth Griffiths & Armour, Liverpool, UK
John Moore Wren Managers Limited, London, UK

This chapter covers the key elements of professional indemnity insurance. Starting with an overview of insurance policies in general, specific details in relation to professional indemnity insurance are then provided including the operative clause and limit of indemnity and the key terms, conditions and exceptions. The importance of the 'claims-made' nature of the cover is explained. Brief sections on policy extensions, captive insurance arrangements, project insurance, disclosure requirements and working overseas are also included.

doi: 10.1680/mocl.40878.0243

CONTENTS

16.1 Introduction

Professional indemnity (PI) insurance has, in common with other categories of insurance, developed from three main sources: statute, principally the Marine Insurance Act 1906, the common law, and practice in the insurance industry. However, the general principles of contract law apply in respect of the creation of PI insurance policies as elsewhere. Insurance law is, of course, an additional strand of legal development which is touched upon where relevant. Any such references made are intended to be of general assistance only and are not in any sense a review of the relevant principles.

Frequently, differences arise between the insurer and insured as to the interpretation of certain clauses, terms and conditions of the PI policy. Where any dispute or ambiguity arises, the court may be asked to interpret the meaning of the policy. In most cases the policy should be read as a whole, the principle being that effect should be given to the intention of the parties where such appears from the words used.

The courts have developed a set of criteria or standards against which the terms in issue are considered. These include: the ordinary meaning of the words used; the business interpretation of them; the commercial objective of the policy; the technical meaning where terms of art are employed; the express definition of any term used (if such is set out in the policy) and the previous interpretation adopted by the courts where the words or phrases used have been held in earlier cases to have a particular meaning.

This application of precedent may, of course, be displaced if the words used are not precisely similar, or if the context or situation can be distinguished. The general principles referred to earlier are of equal application to PI insurance. However, this particular form of cover does have its own individual character.

PI is a third party cover. Its intention is to protect the professional against liabilities owed to third parties, including his client. The policy will only respond to the extent that a liability attaches to the insured consultant.

There is a common misconception within the construction industry that PI policies are in force primarily to protect the

client. This simply is not true. In order to access the policy proceeds, the client will need to establish liability against the consultant. Recourse to legal action is lengthy, uncertain and costly. Clients would be better advised to retain, manage and insure more risk rather than to seek to pass that risk out to others by way of contract.

16.2 Professional indemnity insurance

The prime intention and purpose of PI insurance is to provide protection to the insured against liability to pay damages for breach of professional duty. However, it is now common for these policies to extend into other areas, as referred to below.

16.2.1 The policy form

PI insurance policy wordings vary according to the nature of the work or profession to whom cover is being provided and the identity of the insurers underwriting the policy. Certain professional bodies, such as The Royal Institution of Chartered Surveyors (RICS) and The Royal Institute of British Architects (RIBA), require members to carry cover in accordance with certain requirements which underwriters have to meet in order to be included within an 'Approved List of Insurers'.

16.2.2 Requirements of professional bodies

The Architects Registration Board (ARB), set up under the terms of The Housing Grants, Construction and Regeneration Act 1996 has issued the *Architects Code: Standards of Conduct and Practice* which makes PI insurance for architects mandatory as from 1 April 1998.

The ARB also issues *Guidelines for Professional Indemnity Insurance* which contain provisions that the policy should be written on a civil liability wording, and 'any one claim' limit of indemnity; should cover 'standard' collateral warranty documents with extensions for loss of documents and criminal prosecution defence costs.

The minimum limits of indemnity should be £250 000 when the fee income is less than £100 000 per annum, and £500 000 when the fee income is between £100 000 and £200 000 per annum and £1 000 000 where fees exceed £200 000, all figures excluding legal costs.

The ARB review and amend their Code of Practice and Guidelines, so it is important for all architects to ensure that they are aware of the current requirements. Figures produced by other bodies show that the Institution of Structural Engineers (IStructE) have no requirement to insure, but a Council recommendation to consider taking cover has been issued. The Chartered Institution of Building Services Engineers (CIBSE) has no specific requirements as to PPI insurance. The Association for Consultancy and Engineering (ACE) has a Code of Conduct requiring members to maintain appropriate PI insurance arrangements. The Institution of Civil Engineers (ICE) has no requirement, but a strong recommendation to insure with a minimum cover of £100 000. The Chartered Institute of Architectural Technologists (CIAT) makes PI insurance mandatory for its members, but does not recommend a minimum level of indemnity, and the RICS requires that its private practice members have PI insurance, the minimum levels being based on fee turnover – practices earning up to £50 000 needing a minimum of £100 000 cover.

Since the insurance market-place and the liabilities of professionals practicing in the construction industry are dynamic in nature, each of the representative bodies referred to should be contacted to ensure that the appropriate code or guidelines as to PI insurance are adhered to.

16.2.3 Common features

There are a number of features which are common to almost all PI insurance policies within the construction industry and these are discussed later. Most commonly, the policy can be divided into five principal areas:

- the recital clause
- the operative clause
- exclusions
- exceptions
- conditions.

16.2.4 The recital clause

The recital clause is usually found in policies issued by Lloyd's Underwriters, and is now always a component of company policies. The recital clause may be used to establish a description of the insured, record the significance of the payment of the premium and it may also expressly incorporate the proposal form as the basis of the contract, thereby making every fact within it material.

If any material fact is later found to be inaccurate, the underwriter may be entitled to avoid the policy for non-disclosure or misrepresentation, without the requirement to prove that such would have been a significant element in a reasonably prudent underwriter forming a judgement as to the risk.

16.2.5 The operative clause

The operative clause sets out the basic cover that is provided by the policy. It is restricted and further defined by way of policy exclusions and conditions.

Not all operative clauses work in the same way. One common form seeks to limit the scope of the cover to liabilities which arise directly from the negligent performance by the insured of his or her professional services. A variation on this theme is to base cover on liability for breach of professional duty. Examples of policy wording commonly in use for these two variations are quoted below.

(a) 'The Insurers will indemnify the Insured in respect of any claim which may be made upon the Insured and which is notified to the Insurer during the Period of Insurance in respect of liability arising from any neglect, error or omission by the Insured in the provision of Professional Services'.
(b) 'The Insurers will indemnify the Insured in respect of any claim which may be made upon the Insured and which is notified to the Insurer during the Period of Insurance in respect of liability arising from any negligent breach of professional duty by the Insured'.

Policies with operative clauses limited to negligence or breach of professional duty are, in fact, quite restrictive. With the increasing proliferation of non-standard conditions of appointment and collateral warranties within the construction industry, it is not uncommon for consultants to accept contractual liabilities over and above simple negligence.

A wider basis of cover may be necessary in certain circumstances and most PI insurers are prepared to provide what is known as a 'civil liability' or 'full legal liability' cover. Reference to 'civil liability' is perhaps a misnomer in that the UK is not a civil code country. However, that is a matter of semantics as the 'civil liability' and 'full legal liability' bases of cover are essentially the same.

The operative clause of a full legal liability policy wording might read as follows:

> The Insurer will indemnify the Insured in respect of loss arising from any claim which may be made against the Insured and which is notified to the Insurer during the Period of Insurance in respect of any legal liability or alleged legal liability arising in connection with the conduct of the Business carried on by or on behalf of the Insured.

The distinction between the negligence and liability based covers is an important one. Subject to the policy exclusions, a full legal liability policy will respond to all liabilities that the insured may incur, including extended contractual liabilities. By contrast, the narrower form will only respond to the extent that the insured has been negligent.

More frequently these days, the insured may be a group of architects or engineers practicing as a limited liability company or a limited liability partnership. Historically, the insured would be a group of individuals practicing as a firm, in either case it is important to ensure that the practice is properly and fully described within the term 'insured'. Changes in the partnership, especially when new partners join the practice, should be immediately and fully disclosed to the underwriter or insurer.

16.2.6 Legal liability

This expression embraces all forms of legal liability that may result in an award of damages. It may include all potential liabilities for negligence, therefore it is usual for the legal liability to be qualified or restricted by words in the operative clause, exclusions or the recital clause itself.

Certainly, cover will be restricted to liability for breach of professional duty arising out of the work of an architect or engineer, there will be specific exclusions relating to public or general liabilities, for example road traffic accidents.

Insurers will almost invariably require to take over and manage the handling and settlement of any claim. Therefore, the original intention of the policy – that the insured must be found 'legally liable' to pay a claim before being entitled to an indemnity by insurers – is in practice rarely followed.

16.2.7 'Negligence only' wording

These policies do not usually provide protection in relation to claims arising out of additional voluntary liabilities, such as may arise out of collateral warranties.

Architects and engineers should ensure that their PI insurance policy gives them cover for as wide a class of claims or potential claimants as they require. The 'negligence only' wording may not provide such cover in all circumstances. If the architect or engineer has given, or is likely to be asked to give, collateral warranties, or may take on duties which may be considered to be outside the standard within his or her profession, it is advisable to consider the policy wording carefully, as even the legal liability based policy may exclude the more onerous terms.

16.2.8 'Claims made' policy

All PI insurance policies operate on what is known as a 'claims made' basis, and the relevant section from a typical operative clause is quoted below:

> ... any claim which may be made upon the Insured and which is notified to the Insurer during the Period of Insurance.

This distinction is important. It is the policy in force when a potential claim is first notified that dictates the extent of cover available and not the policy in force when the work in question was carried out or when the alleged act of negligence took place.

If a consultant cancels his or her PI insurance cover or allows it to lapse, the consultant is effectively uninsured for any work previously undertaken. It is for this reason that almost all professional appointments include requirements for consultants to maintain cover into the future provided, of course, that it continues to be available at reasonably economic rates.

The 'claims made' nature of cover can give rise to difficulties on retirement for sole traders. Most PI policies provide automatic indemnity to former partners, directors and employees. With sole traders, the problem is that there is no ongoing entity to maintain cover and yet the liabilities continue to exist. One potential solution is for sole traders to effect 6- or 12-year run-off policies, the premium for which can be off-set against tax during the final year of trading.

Although PI policies are written on a 'claims made' basis, they should more properly be described as 'claims made and circumstances likely to give rise to a claim' basis, or similar wording.

Almost all policies permit, and some even require, the notification of matters, situations or events which are likely to, or potentially may, give rise to a claim. If, subsequently, a claim is made, the effective date of notification is that on which the circumstance or event was reported, not when the claim itself was formulated.

Wordings or terms of PI policies vary between policies or insurers – some permit the notification of circumstances likely to give rise to a claim, others permit circumstances which may reasonably be expected to give rise to a claim.

Difficulties can arise when the insured changes insurer and the notification requirements of the old policy and proposal form requirements of the new are not compatible. In such a situation the insured can suffer the problem of not being in a position to notify a claim to the outgoing insurer (as none exists before the expiry of the policy) allied to a non-disclosure of a circumstance likely to give rise to a claim as required in the proposal form of the new insurer. If a potential claim or circumstance is identified in the proposal form to the new insurer it may well be specifically excluded. If there is no entitlement to notify a circumstance to the old insurer (before the expiry of the outgoing policy) the two policies create for the insured a potential black hole into which the claim falls without cover.

16.2.9 Limit of indemnity

The limit of indemnity is the maximum liability of insurers under the policy. It is a monetary amount selected by the insured based on a combination of

(a) the requirements of its clients; and
(b) an assessment of the maximum liability that might be incurred.

The limit of indemnity can operate on either an 'each and every' or an 'aggregate' basis.

Where cover operates on an 'each and every' basis, the limit of indemnity applies separately to each claim notified during the period of insurance. For example, if a consultant carries £5 m of cover on an each and every claim basis, that £5 m limit will apply in full to each separate claim that is notified during the policy period.

By contrast, where cover operates on an 'aggregate' basis, the limit of indemnity applies to all claims notified during the period of insurance. While most PI policies operate on an each and every claim basis, it is common practice for certain types of claim to be subject to an aggregate limit, most notably claims which involve pollution/contamination, date recognition issues or which arise out of the activities of design and construct contractors.

Selecting an adequate limit of indemnity is an important consideration for consultants. The limit should be set at a level which reflects the maximum likely damages which could flow as a consequence of any negligent act – both in relation to past and current work. The limit should be set so as to include awards made in relation to the claimant's legal costs in addition to damages.

It is also important to bear in mind that an agreement to maintain PI at a certain level is not a limitation of liability – a common misconception within the construction industry. Any contractual limitation of liability must be expressly stated as such and comply with the requirements of the Unfair Contract Terms Act 1977.

Other costs and expenses

Insurers will usually also pay for other costs and expenses incurred in defending claims. Such defence costs can either form part of the limit of indemnity (a 'cost inclusive' limit) or in addition thereto ('costs in addition').

16.2.10 Exceptions

A number of exceptions are common to most construction PI insurance policies, as follows:

(a) claims involving bodily injury to or death of employees (these claims should be covered under an employer's liability policy)
(b) claims for third party property damage or third party personal injury (such claims are covered by a public liability or motor insurance policies)
(c) claims arising from circumstances already notified under previous policies (to avoid duplication of cover) or which were known prior to the inception of the new policy
(d) claims arising from any agreement to pay fines, penalties or liquidated damages
(e) any loss, destruction, damage, and so forth caused by ionising radiations or contamination by radioactivity
(f) supersonic bangs
(g) war, invasion, and so forth.
(h) most construction PI policies now routinely exclude claims involving asbestos related liabilities; where cover for such claims is provided it is on an 'aggregate', 'cost inclusive' basis and does not apply to claims for personal injury or economic loss.

A number of the exclusions referred to above are worthy of further comment. Employer's liability insurance is a compulsory requirement in the UK. With some limited exceptions this form of cover is mandatory and is best dealt with by way of a separate, more appropriate policy. To avoid any duplication of cover, PI policies routinely exclude liabilities arising out of employment including, more recently, employment malpractice issues such as unfair dismissal and discrimination.

There is still much confusion between public liability claims and claims which fall to be dealt with by PI policies. The distinction is perhaps best seen by describing public liability claims as being those which arise from 'physical mistakes' whereas PI claims relate to 'intellectual mistakes'. If an engineer on site were to negligently injure a third party by way of a physical act that would give rise to a public liability claim. If the same injury were caused by spalling concrete, which arose as a consequence of defective structural design, that would be a matter for PI insurers. While the effect might be the same, the cause differs and it is the cause which dictates which policy will respond.

In addition to the generic exceptions listed earlier, which are common to most construction PI policies, there are also a number of exceptions peculiar to particular professions. Examples of these are set out below.

Consulting engineers/architects

It is usual, if not standard, for PI insurance policies issued to consulting engineers to exclude liability arising out of fitness for purpose and any other express guarantees. An example of the exclusory language often used in this regard is shown below.

The Insurers will not be liable in respect of any claim arising from

(a) an agreement by the Insured warranting or guaranteeing that any installations, structures or other works constructed in accordance with his advice or design or proposals will be suitable for any specified purpose;
(b) any other express guarantee insofar as his liability under such an agreement or express guarantee exceeds the amount of his liability in the absence of such agreement or express guarantee.

The exclusion of fitness for purpose guarantees is an important consideration. Fitness for purpose obligations represent strict liabilities – it is no defence for a party to claim that it had not been negligent or had acted in accordance with best industry practice at the time. PI insurers are not in the business of guaranteeing the work of their insureds. Despite the wide policy wordings that are currently available, PI insurers still operate against an expectation that their insureds contract on no wider a basis than the exercise of reasonable skill and care.

Liquidated damages present a similar problem. PI insurers provide cover in relation to proven losses which flow as a consequence of negligence on the behalf of their insured.

Liquidated damages only serve to cloud the issue – they may not be linked to negligence and may be set at a level in excess of any level of damages that might have been awarded. It is for this reason that an exclusion of liquidated or ascertained damages is incorporated into policies.

Surveyors

Due to the exposure of insurers in respect of survey, inspection and valuation reports, as evidenced by large numbers of significant claims in the late 1980s and early 1990s and more recently, insurers are keen that only suitable individuals undertake such work.

It is standard for policies to restrict cover to claims where the survey, inspection or valuation report was undertaken by a Fellow or Associate of a recognised professional body such as the RICS, or where the individual has at least 5 years' experience of this specific type of work.

16.2.11 Conditions

Conditions may be divided into three types. It is the consequence of each which makes them important.

(a) conditions precedent to the policy, the breach of which will void the policy from inception
(b) conditions subsequent to the policy, a failure to observe these by the insured rendering the policy voidable from the date of the breach
(c) conditions precedent to liability, breach of which relieves the insurer from liability to make a payment under the policy.

16.3 Claims

Accepting that PI insurance policies are written on a 'claims made' basis, two points should immediately be clarified. First, what is a claim? Second, when, and perhaps how, is it made?

The *Oxford English Dictionary* defines a claim as an assertion of a right to something. In the case of an architect or engineer, the claim is likely to be a demand for money.

Occasionally, the claim may be for the performance of a duty, but that is quite a rare situation.

The claim is likely to be against the professional individual for money, the demand being based on an alleged breach of duty or an act of negligence, whether by deed or omission.

The claim need not be made in writing to require notification to insurers, neither does it require to be justified. The unfounded or unattractive claim must be notified with the same promptness as one which clearly has merit.

16.3.1 Notification of claim

This is a very important policy condition which deals with the insured's obligations in relation to claims notification and the provision of information and assistance in relation to the defence of any claim. The condition usually also includes a

deeming provision dealing with the question as to when a 'potential circumstance' becomes a 'claim'.

An example of a wording in common use is shown below:

> The Insured shall give written notice to the Insurer as soon as reasonably practicable of any claim or intimation to the Insured of possible claim made against the Insured or upon the Insured becoming aware of circumstances which might give rise to a claim under this Policy regardless of any excess and the Insured shall upon request give to the Insurer all such information and assistance as the Insurer may reasonably require and as may be in the Insured's power to provide and will in all such matters do and concur in doing all such things as the Insurer may require. Any claim arising from such intimation to the Insured of possible claim or such circumstances which might give rise to a claim shall be deemed to have been made during the Period of Insurance in which such notice has been given.

An alternative wording requires the insured to give notice 'immediately' rather than 'as soon as reasonably practicable' which can give rise to practical difficulties. The looser wording is potentially of significant benefit to the insured. It is important that the insurers are informed of any potential claim circumstances as soon as practicable in order that legal opinion can be obtained and experts appointed, where this is necessary. Equally, however, the claims notification condition should be couched in terms that allow the insured to comply in practice.

If the condition requiring notification of the claim is expressed to be a condition precedent to the insurers' liability, any breach may permit the insurer to decline to indemnify in respect of any particular claim. It is unnecessary for the insurer to show prejudice.

If the clause is not expressed to be a condition precedent, then the insurers' remedy will be in damages, if any loss can be shown. If any delay in notification can be shown to have had no effect on the insurers' position, then a claim for damages is unlikely to be successful.

16.3.2 Late notification

In connection with late notifications, it has been held in relation to commercial cases at least that it is difficult to conceive of circumstances where it would be reasonable for an insured to delay notification of an occurrence by as long as a month.

16.3.3 Admission of liability

The insured is prohibited from admitting liability for or settling any claims without the written consent of insurers.

16.3.4 Circumstances likely or event

Almost all PI insurance policies require immediate, or at the very least prompt, notification of certain events. These may include

(a) claims made against the insured
(b) circumstances or occurrences that are likely to, or may, give rise to a claim under the policy

(c) any indication given verbally or in writing that a claim may be made against the insured

(d) the realisation, fear or concern that any party or person covered by the PI insurance policy may have, by act or omission, committed a breach which may give rise to a claim.

Notice of a claim may be required to be 'immediate', 'as soon as possible' or 'as soon as practicable'. In some policies a period is specified, for example within 14 days. If no period for notification is expressly set out in the policy it will be implied that notification must be given within a reasonable period of time.

Clearly, the insurer is concerned that there should be no unreasonable or prejudicial delay in notification of the claim in order that such steps or measures as are appropriate to investigate, defend or settle the claim may be taken within good time.

16.3.5 Blanket notifications

Whether 'blanket' or 'laundry list' notifications of circumstances may be acceptable or valid depends on the wording of the particular provision of the PI insurance policy and the facts of each case.

Generally, the architect or engineer must identify the relevant circumstance and there must be reasonable grounds for anticipating that a claim may arise out of the circumstance, as it appears at the date of notification.

It is likely that the court will be inclined towards the view and opinion of the architect or engineer in the matter, not least because the subject matter of any dispute between them and their insurer will be (what has become) a claim against them.

Blanket notifications cannot be rejected, however, as a matter of course. It is necessary to look at the whole position and particularly the wording of the PI policy.

16.3.6 The QC clause

The QC clause states that the insured shall not be required to contest legal proceedings unless a Queen's Counsel advises that the action has a reasonable prospect of success. The intent behind the clause is to deal with situations where there is a dispute or disagreement between insurer and insured as to whether or not to defend a particular claim. The insured may, for example, have a strong commercial relationship with a client which it would prefer not to prejudice. At the same time, and quite understandably, the insurer would be equally reluctant to pay out in relation to a claim against which a reasonable defence existed. In such circumstances an independent QC would be called upon to decide whether or not a defence had a reasonable prospect of being successful.

16.3.7 Fraudulent claims

If an insured deliberately submits a claim which he or she knows to be false or fraudulent, then the PI policy becomes void. All claims notified under that policy are negated as a consequence. What is the position under policies with multiple insureds where only one insured has been negligent? Court cases on this point have indicated that it is only the position of the fraudulent insured that is prejudiced and not that of the innocent insureds.

16.3.8 Innocent non-disclosure

Innocent non-disclosure provisions are becoming increasingly common. The intention behind such a provision is to prevent insurers from declining claims on the basis of, for example, late notification. Provided that the late notification is not deliberate or fraudulent then insurers will accept the claims notification. Where late notification occurs, although the claim is accepted it will be on the basis of the cover in force when the claim should have been notified. This prevents selection against insurers in circumstances where an insured delays notification until after renewal, by which time either the limit of indemnity has been increased or the excess decreased.

In the absence of an innocent non-disclosure provision, the only options available to insurers are to pay the claim regardless or seek to avoid the entire policy on the basis of material non-disclosure or misrepresentation. In order to do this, insurers need to satisfy two tests:

(a) that disclosure would have caused a prudent insurer to reject the risk or at least to have imposed more onerous terms; and

(b) that the non-disclosure or misrepresentation induced the insurer to enter into the policy.

16.3.9 Discharge of liability

This condition enables the insurer to discharge its liability under the policy by making a payment to the insured equal to the amount for which a claim could be settled.

The intention behind this condition is clear – it enables insurers to discharge their liability to the insured in circumstances where the insured is being either difficult or obstructive in reaching settlement with the plaintiff. The condition is rarely invoked but provides a useful protection to insurers. The condition can be invoked in circumstances where the limit of indemnity is clearly insufficient given the quantum and merits of the claim that is being brought by the claimant. Insurers have the option of paying to the insured the full indemnity limit, leaving the insured then to negotiate the best possible settlement with the claimant. The ability of insurers to discharge their liability under the policy in this way is a useful reminder of the importance of an adequate limit of indemnity.

16.3.10 Prejudiced claims

In circumstances where the actions of the insured result in prejudice to the handling or settlement of any claim, insurers are entitled to reduce the extent of indemnity in relation to that particular claim in proportion to the prejudice that has been caused.

16.3.11 Differences

Any differences which arise out of the policy are to be referred to arbitration. In the first instance, insurer and insured should seek to reach agreement as to the identity of the arbitrator. If they cannot, then either side appoints their own arbitrator who will endeavour to reach agreement on the points at issue. An umpire is then appointed by the two arbitrators to decide the issue(s) in the event that they cannot agree. See the chapter *Arbitration*.

16.4 Extensions

Almost all construction PI insurance policies include extensions to cover by way of 'bolt-on' extras. A number of these such extensions do provide important elements of additional cover and these are discussed subsequently.

Extensions to cover vary from profession to profession and between policies. Extensions for architects and engineers include damage resulting from the loss of documents and the cost of replacing, recreating or restoring such documents.

16.4.1 Libel and slander

This is a very common policy extension and provides indemnity against the consequences of libel or slander, provided that such libel or slander was committed in good faith.

16.4.2 Joint ventures

Where consultants participate in joint ventures they may attract joint and several liability, that is to say they can be held liable for the consequences of any neglect, error or omission by the co-venturers with whom they are working.

Whether a particular PI insurance policy would respond to such a liability will depend very much on the policy wording under consideration.

If the operative clause provides cover in relation to 'any legal liability', then it is sufficient for the policy to remain silent on the issue of joint ventures in order for cover to be provided. Assuming that a liability attaches to the insured and is not the subject of an exclusion, the policy will respond accordingly.

However, a number of insurers who issue 'legal liability' wordings feel that joint ventures are of sufficient sensitivity to warrant closer scrutiny and require that details of any proposed joint venture be provided in advance prior to cover being granted. This is normally achieved by way of a limitation to the effect that any claim arising from a joint venture is not covered unless the existence of the joint venture has been disclosed to insurers. It is always prudent for consultants to check with either their broker or insurer the operation of cover in relation to joint ventures. It is also an important risk management tool to check that any co-venturers carry adequate insurance.

16.4.3 Indemnity to employees

A majority of PI policies extend to include an indemnity to any employee who might be held personally liable. The extension either applies automatically or at the request of the principal insured – normally the employer.

Indemnity to employee extensions have become increasingly topical given the decision in *Merrett v. Babb*.

16.4.4 Loss of or damage to documents

Again, this is a standard extension applying to most PI insurance policies, it is intended to respond by paying the costs incurred by the insured in replacing or restoring lost or damaged documents.

However, this element of cover is, in itself, subject to conditions and limitations, mainly that

(a) any loss or damage is sustained while the documents are either in transit or in the custody of the insured

(b) the amount of any claim for costs and expenses is supported by proper documentary evidence.

16.4.5 Infringement of copyright

There is often a policy extension which covers legal costs incurred by the insured in seeking damages or an injunction following an alleged infringement of the insured's copyright. Usually this policy extension is subject to a rather modest inner limit of indemnity – a figure of £25000 in the aggregate is not unusual.

For further detail on copyright issues see *Intellectual property*.

16.4.6 Health and safety at work (prosecution defence costs)

Construction consultants are faced with increasing obligations in relation to health and safety issues, particularly following the implementation of the Construction (Design and Management) Regulations 2007. A failure to comply with those regulations could give rise to either a criminal prosecution or a civil action for damages, or both. In either event, as a matter of law it is the criminal prosecution that is heard first. It is important that the criminal prosecution be properly defended, if it is not, then the defence of any subsequent claim for damages could be prejudiced.

In order to ensure proper representation at any health and safety prosecutions it is now normal practice for construction PI insurers to include criminal defence costs within cover. However, the extent of cover is carefully controlled – insurers are particularly keen to ensure that any claims notified do relate to health and safety issues arising from professional services and not employment-related risks. Furthermore, no cover is provided in relation to any fines or penalties.

While some insurers seek to impose an inner aggregate limit of indemnity for prosecution defence costs cover, say

£300000, others prefer to allow the full limit of indemnity to apply to such claims, albeit on an aggregate basis.

For further information on the Construction (Design and Management) Regulations 2007 see the chapters *Construction health and safety I* and *II*.

16.5 Captives

Captive insurance arrangements are becoming increasingly common, particularly for larger insureds who carry substantial deductibles or excesses. A captive is, in its simplest form, an insurance company which is a wholly owned subsidiary of the insured. Its purpose is to provide funds, in whole or in part, to cover the cost of the excess/deductible should it fall to be paid. The captive is funded by premiums paid to it by the insured holding company – just as they are paid to conventional insurers – and can be adjusted from year to year to reflect the claims experience and the captive's appetite for risk.

Most captives are registered off-shore to avoid on-shore insurance company regulations to which they would otherwise be subject.

The perceived advantages of captive arrangements include smoothing of excess payments, guaranteed availability of ring-fenced funds when excess payments are required and the opportunity to benefit directly in the profits of the captive if claims are avoided by the effective application of risk management techniques.

16.6 Project insurance

Traditionally, project-specific insurance arrangements have been focussed on material damage to the contract works during the construction and maintenance periods caused by perils such as storm, flood, fire etc. Whilst it is common for such arrangements to include third party liability claims arising from the physical construction activities, it was unusual for the cover to include claims caused by the negligence of the design team – indeed such claims were normally specifically excluded. However, an increasing number of PI policies are now being written on a project-specific basis, particularly in relation to contracts undertaken overseas.

Historically, project PI insurance operated on a very limited basis. Premiums were high, the policy wordings were limited and although long-term periods of insurance were available, 'break clauses' allowed insurers to cancel or amend cover every three years or so. However, more recently the market for project PI has expanded and it is now possible to obtain policies with limits of up to £10m for periods of six years and with no break clauses.

It is usual for project policies of this nature to apply to all members of the design team.

With premiums reducing to more realistic levels, project insurance is now seen as a workable alternative in certain circumstances to reliance on annually renewable covers.

16.7 Disclosure requirements

Most, if not all, appointments in the UK require consultants to carry PI at a set level for an agreed number of years, provided that cover continues to be available at reasonable economic rates. It is also a common requirement for the consultant to produce on request documentary evidence that cover has been renewed and continues in force.

The format of documentary evidence varies. A number of clients insist on formal certification signed by either the broker or insurer, confirming details such as the period of insurance, policy number, identity of insurer and the applicable limit of indemnity and excess. By contrast, others are happy to rely on a broker's letter which simply confirms that cover is in place.

16.8 Working overseas

PI insurance can be arranged on a world-wide basis, although special conditions (or even exclusions) are likely to apply to claims arising out of work undertaken in North America.

However, overseas insurance requirements vary from country to country. When working in the so-called 'Civil Code' countries such as France, Belgium and Egypt, consultants are required by law to effect 10 year, non-cancellable insurances to match their statutory professional liability – traditional annually renewable PI arrangements are insufficient. A number of overseas countries also require consultants to carry cover provided by a locally domiciled insurer. Examples include the Gulf States, Malaysia and South Africa. To meet these requirements, consultants can either effect a fully fledged local policy whose premium would be based on the local fee income or put in place a 'fronting policy'. A fronting policy is a policy issued by a local insurer but which carries no risk – the risk is, in practice, re-insured to the consultant's global annual covers in the UK. As the name suggests, the local policy is merely a front – but it can be a cost-effective mechanism by which consultants can comply with local insurance arrangements.

Working overseas can raise complex issues and consultants contemplating working internationally are recommended to seek advice before they do so (also see the chapter *International offices*).

References

Architects Registration Board (2010) *Architects Code: Standards of Conduct and Practice*. ARB, London, UK. www.arb.org.uk/professional_standards/regulating_architects/architects_code_2010/default.php

Architects Registration Board Guidelines for Professional Indemnity Insurance. ARB, London, UK. www.arb.org.uk/publications/guidance/pii_guidance.php

Referenced legislation, regulations and standards

Construction (Design and Management) Regulations 2007
Housing Grants, Construction and Regeneration Act 1996
Marine Insurance Act 1906
Unfair Contract Terms Act 1977

Cases referenced

Merrett v. Babb

Websites

Architects Registration Board (ARB); www.arb.org.uk
Association for Consultancy and Engineering (ACE); www.acenet.co.uk
Chartered Institute of Architectural Technologists (CIAT); www.ciat.org.uk
Chartered Institution of Building Services Engineers (CIBSE); www.cibse.org
Institution of Civil Engineers (ICE); www.ice.org.uk
Institution of Structural Engineers (IStructE); www.istructe.org
Lloyd's Underwriters; www.llyods.com
Royal Institute of British Architects (RIBA); www.architecture.com
Royal Institution of Chartered Surveyors (RICS); www.rics.org

Chapter 17

Employment law

Jonathan Exten-Wright DLA Piper UK LLP, London, UK

doi: 10.1680/mocl.40878.0253

The construction industry relies on the engagement of millions of employees, workers and other individuals. Employment law is of daily importance in order for such engagements to succeed. Compliance with employment laws and regulations is crucial in avoiding the risk of actions by individuals, unions and other employee representatives, as well as regulatory sanctions from public bodies, including the Health and Safety Executive and HM Revenue and Customs, and even criminal liability. Furthermore, employee relations and how they are perceived play a major part in ensuring the effectiveness and competitiveness of a business.

Employment law is one of the most heavily regulated areas of UK law: recent years have seen a large amount of new legislation originating both in the UK and the European Union. The focus of employment law is the definition and regulation of the employment relationship and the protection of the rights of the employee, particularly in relation to working practices, pay, time off, dismissal, discrimination, benefits and collective representation.

CONTENTS

17.1 Contract of employment or contract for services?

17.1.1 Who is an employee?

When interpreting employment legislation, it is critical to distinguish an employee from a self-employed person. Legal rights enjoyed by each differ, although in areas such as anti-discrimination law, working time legislation and the national minimum wage, the trend has been towards extending rights to those with a wider working relationship with an employer.

Section 230(1) of the Employment Rights Act 1996 (ERA) defines an employee as 'an individual who has entered into or works under … a contract of employment'. Section 230(2) ERA states that 'contract of employment' means 'a contract of service or apprenticeship … whether express or implied'. The contract between the parties determines the status of the worker: is it a contract of service (employment) or a contract for services (self-employment)? Labels will not necessarily decide the issue. A Court will look at the exact nature of the relationship between the parties and all the facts in determining employment status.

17.1.1.1 Apprenticeships

The status of apprenticeships, along with the overall legal structure for apprenticeships, has been overhauled by the Apprenticeships, Skills, Childcare and Learning Act. The changes implemented under this Act will come into force in 2013. Under the current common law 'contract of apprenticeship' an apprentice is bound to his or her employer in order to learn a trade and the employer agrees to provide training in that trade. The new Act creates a new statutory structure for the Apprenticeship Contract, which will be regulated by a public body overseen by the Secretary of State. Under the current

system, an apprenticeship will be for a fixed term or until a set qualification is achieved, terminable only if gross misconduct occurs, a business shuts completely or if the apprentice refuses to perform his or her duties.

17.1.1.2 Secondment

On occasion an employee may be seconded from its employer (the Seconder) to a different organisation, perhaps a client, customer or subsidiary of the employer. The employee remains under the employ of the Seconder, although generally their day-to-day work will be for the host organisation and away from the Seconder's premises. Whilst the employee's contract of employment will remain with the Seconder it is clear that there is a risk that a court, or Employment Tribunal, could find that the employee is in fact employed by the host organisation or that a transfer under Transfer of Undertakings (Protection of Employment) Regulations 2006 (TUPE 2006) (see section 17.5) has taken place. Confusion should be avoided by ensuring that procedures which are generally associated with employers, such as direct salary payment and salary reviews, remain in the control of the Seconder. It is also advisable that the conditions of the secondment are captured in an agreement between the Seconder, host organisation and employee to avoid any future confusion.

17.1.2 Distinguishing between an employee and a self-employed person

The distinction between employed and self-employed status decides liability for income tax and national insurance contributions (NICs), entitlement to statutory sick pay and entitlement to employment protection. An employer is responsible for operating PAYE and Class 1 NICs where the worker is an employee. Where the worker is self-employed, however, the payer does not have such obligations. HM Revenue and

Customs (HMRC) has always sought to apply employment tax rules to individuals who are, in reality, employees, even where they are described as self-employed. On 6 April 2000, Intermediaries Legislation known as 'IR35' was introduced to enable HMRC to deal with situations where individuals supply services through personal service companies (PSCs) in circumstances where they would otherwise have been employees in order to avoid liability for income tax and NICs. The effect of IR35 is that most of the fees received by the PSC are deemed to be paid to the worker as salary. Income tax and NICs are collected from the PSC accordingly.

Deciding whether an individual is self-employed or whether they are an employee involves a three-stage inquiry:

- Did the parties enter a legally binding contract?

- If so, what were its terms?

- Was it a contract of employment?

The courts will imply terms to reflect the parties' true intention when making the contract, to give it 'business efficacy', that is, to make it work. The courts will investigate whether the apparent contractual status is a device to deprive employees of their employment protection rights or avoid any tax.

17.1.2.1 Employment indicators

The presence of the following non-exhaustive factors indicates that an individual is an employee. The first factor is critical as a bare minimum:

- Is there mutuality of obligation, that is, must the employer provide regular work and must the employee make him or herself available to do the work?

- Does the individual work under the company's direction and control?

- Must the work be done regularly, within a certain time?

- Does the employee have to provide personal service or can they nominate someone as a substitute?

- Are tools, equipment and/or clothing for doing the work provided by the company?

- Does the individual attend the company premises to work, or at places decided by the company?

- If, and when, the individual is at work, does he or she have similar terms and conditions to other staff?

- Is the individual paid by the hour, week or month? Is overtime payable?

- Are payments wholly or partially attributable to a regular basic wage, paid at regular intervals?

- Does the company deduct PAYE and social security contributions from payments?

- Is the individual required to work set hours or a given number of hours a week or month? Is attendance required at certain times on certain days? Are there any regular or assured working hours?

- Is permission required for time off?

- Is holiday pay, commission, bonus or similar payments made by the company?

- Is the 'engagement' subject to termination by notice from either side?

17.1.2.2 Self-employment indicators

The following factors indicate self-employment:

- Is the employer a professional client of the individual?

- Does the individual work for more than one client company or organisation?

- Is payment on a fee basis?

- Are services invoiced?

- Does the individual provide the main items of equipment needed to do the job?

- Is the individual free to hire other people on his or her own terms to do work which has been commissioned? Does he or she pay such additional workers directly?

- Has the individual invested his or her own capital in the business, gaining or losing from its commercial success?

- Is the individual recognisably in business on his or her own account, as a person, a partnership or a limited company?

- Has HMRC accepted that the individual is self-employed?

- Is the individual registered for value added tax (VAT)?

17.1.3 The legal consequences of the distinction

The legal consequences of distinguishing between the employed and the self-employed are outlined below. For certain purposes, self-employment is divided between those doing work personally and those doing business on their own account, as a provider to a customer or client.

17.1.3.1 Employment Rights Act 1996

Employees have rights under the ERA, including the right not to be unfairly dismissed provided (in general) that they have at least 1 year's continuous service. Generally speaking, workers do not have rights under the ERA. One exception is the right for workers (other than those in business on their own account), like employees, not to have unauthorised deductions made from wages.

17.1.3.2 Discrimination legislation

For the purposes of the protection of discrimination legislation relating to being married or in a civil partnership, being pregnant or on maternity leave, equal pay, sex, sexual orientation, gender reassignment, race (including ethnic or national origin, nationality and colour), age, religion or belief and disability, 'employment' means employment under a contract of service or apprenticeship, or a contract personally to perform any work, that is, self-employed persons who carry out the work themselves.

17.1.3.3 The Health and Safety at Work etc. Act 1974

This is not limited to the health and safety of employees: in addition, it covers the public who visit the employer's premises or who may be affected by the work carried out for the employer, or self-employed persons, or another employer's employees working alongside. The Health and Safety at Work Act 1974 covers work activities at a place of work and the risks created by the people working there, both for themselves and for those affected by them.

17.1.3.4 The Transfer of Undertakings (Protection of Employment) Regulations 2006 (TUPE 2006)

For business transfers covered by TUPE 2006 (see section 17.5), only employees' rights are protected (not those of the self-employed), with employment being transferred automatically to the new employer.

17.1.3.5 The Working Time Regulations 1998 (WTR)

The WTR (see section 17.6) apply to workers over the minimum school leaving age and protect 'workers', meaning all those individuals employed under a contract of employment or any other contract to provide personal work or services to the other party to the contract, where the other party is not a client or customer of any profession or business undertaking carried on by the individual. The definition of 'workers' includes employees, agency workers, temporary workers, freelancers and the self-employed but not those self-employed individuals who are genuinely pursuing a business activity on their own account. The term 'worker' also includes non-employed trainees, that is, those undertaking work experience or training on a course run by an educational institution or establishment whose main business is to provide training.

17.1.3.6 National Minimum Wage Act 1998 and National Minimum Wage Regulations 1999

The National Minimum Wage Act 1998 applies to workers who are over the school leaving age and who are working in the UK. The term 'worker' means an individual who either works under a contract of employment or a contract for services to provide work or services personally. The latter type of contract includes self-employed freelancers, who are not in business on their own account, and who work exclusively for an employer. Agency workers must be paid the national minimum wage by the entity which is responsible for paying them.

The national minimum wage increase came into effect on 1 October 2010, and the age limits for the standard and development rate changed on the same date: standard (adult) rate (workers aged 21 or over) £5.93 (up from £5.80); development

rate (workers aged between 18 and 20) £4.92 (up from £4.83), young workers rate (workers under 18 but above the compulsory school age, who are not apprentices) £3.64 (up from £3.57). A minimum wage of £2.50 per hour for apprentices was also introduced and applies to apprentices under 19 years of age or those aged 19 and more but in the first year of their apprenticeship.

17.1.3.7 The Public Interest Disclosure Act 1998 (PIDA)

PIDA, through its implementation in the ERA, protects 'workers' against dismissal or detriment for making a 'protected disclosure' about an employer's malpractice, so-called 'whistle-blowing'. The definition of 'worker' includes not just employees, but also those who are genuinely self-employed, such as freelancers and third party contractors whose work is controlled by the employer. The definition also includes homeworkers, trainees and agency workers. Workers who make 'protected disclosures' are protected from dismissal, selection for redundancy or from being subject to a detriment, such as the refusal of a pay increase or promotion. A worker may bring a claim in the employment tribunal if they are subjected to any detriment by any act, or any deliberate failure to act, by their employer on the ground that they have made a protected disclosure. There is no limit on the compensation which may be awarded in a claim for unfair dismissal which is related to whistle-blowing.

17.1.3.8 Part-time Workers (Prevention of Less Favourable Treatment) Regulations 2000 (Part-Time Workers Regulations)

The Part-Time Workers Regulations came into force on 1 July 2000 and entitle part-time workers to terms and conditions which are *pro rata* to comparable full-time workers. Employers are required to ensure that their terms and conditions do not discriminate against part-time workers.

17.1.3.9 Fixed-term Employees (Prevention of Less Favourable Treatment) Regulations 2002 (Fixed-Term Regulations)

The Fixed-Term Regulations came into force on 1 October 2002 and apply to employees (and not workers). The following individuals are specifically excluded from this legislation: apprentices, certain agency workers, employees undertaking work experience or temporary work schemes, students on work experience as part of a higher education course and members of the armed forces. Under the Fixed-Term Regulations, employees on fixed-term contracts have the right not to be treated less favourably than comparable permanent employees. If a fixed-term employee believes that his or her rights under the Fixed-Term Regulations have been infringed, he or she will be entitled to request a written statement giving particulars of the reasons for the treatment. Fixed-term employees are entitled to be informed by their employer of any suitable available vacancy which arises during their employment. In addition, an employee is entitled to claim automatic unfair dismissal where he or she is dismissed because he or she sought to enforce his or her rights under the Fixed-Term Regulations.

17.1.3.10 PAYE and NIC – Income Tax (Earnings and Pensions) Act 2003 (ITEPA) and Social Security Contributions and Benefits Act 1992 and regulations made thereunder

The main statutory provisions governing the taxation of employment income are to be found in ITEPA, which came into force on 6 April 2003. The main national insurance legislation can be found in the Social Security Contributions and Benefits Act 1992.

The PAYE regulations require all employers with employees in the UK to deduct tax and NICs from their earnings under PAYE and to report details of their non-cash benefits and expenses to HMRC. If an individual is deemed to be self-employed, there is no obligation to deduct tax or NICs at source unless the Construction Industry Scheme (CIS) applies (see section 17.1.6). As previously mentioned, special rules also apply if a person provides his services through a PSC and IR35 applies. The recipient of those services will not be under an obligation to withhold any income tax or NICs or pay NICs in that instance. VAT may, however, be payable.

17.1.4 Summary of differences

An employee enjoys (subject, in certain circumstances, to qualifying conditions) the following key rights:

- unfair dismissal protection;
- redundancy payment entitlement;
- written particulars of terms of employment;
- statutory minimum notice period;
- guarantee payments (when work is not provided in certain circumstances);
- medical suspension payment;
- protection from discrimination on grounds of marriage or civil partnership, race, sex, sexual orientation, gender reassignment, disability, religion, belief or age;
- equal pay;
- maternity rights;
- time off for trade union activities/public duties and so on;
- not to be refused employment because of trade union membership or non-membership;
- to be employed for the agreed period or to be given the agreed length of notice;
- to work in a healthy and safe working environment;
- to be paid statutory sick pay;
- to be paid wages without unauthorised deductions;

- for shop workers or betting workers, the right not to work on Sundays;
- automatic transfer of contract and protection of terms and conditions in business transfers;
- to benefit from the limits on working time under WTR;
- to receive the national minimum wage;
- protection against dismissal or detriment for making a protected disclosure under ERA; and
- not to be discriminated against because they work part time.

A worker enjoys the following key rights:

- to benefit from all entitlements under his or her contract for service;
- not to be discriminated against on grounds of marriage or civil partnership, race, sex, sexual orientation, gender reassignment, disability, religion, belief or age and to receive equal pay (if they must do the work personally);
- to be paid wages without unauthorised deductions;
- to benefit from the limit on the maximum working week/night shift working, rest periods, rest breaks and the right to paid annual holidays, under WTR;
- to receive the national minimum wage;
- not to suffer a detriment under WTR, the National Minimum Wage Act 1998/National Minimum Wage Regulations 1999; or for making a protected disclosure;
- to work in a healthy and safe working environment; and
- not to be discriminated against because they work part time.

17.1.4.1 Case study 1 – Self-employed consultant

Mr Adams has taken early retirement in order to set up his own business which offers specialist services in the design of steel structures. His former employer wishes to engage him on a regular part-time basis (two days per week) to use his expertise on various projects. A contract is drawn up, with payment based on an hourly fee plus reimbursement of all travel and other out-of-pocket expenses. Mr Adams wishes to be paid gross without deduction of income tax or NICs. However, Mr Adams has no other clients and has not established himself with HMRC as self-employed. The employer, therefore, has to treat Mr Adams as an employee, subject to PAYE and NIC. If Mr Adams later finds similar work with other clients and HMRC confirms that he is self-employed for tax purposes, he may then be paid gross.

17.1.5 The IR35 rules for PSCs

17.1.5.1 What is IR35?

Provisions relating to PSCs are now within ITEPA 2003. Under the typical PSC structure, an individual forms a company, with himself or herself as the sole director, shareholder and main employee and the PSC contracts with other organisations (the 'client') to provide services. The individual carries out the work and the PSC invoices the client and receives payment. Monies may be retained inside the company, used to defer expenses, or paid as salary or dividend to the employee/shareholder. This arrangement carries significant fiscal advantages compared with the taxation of employment income through PAYE: dividends do not attract NICs; companies enjoy more generous rules for expenses and borrowings; family members may be paid a salary; and pension provisions are advantageous. There are also commercial benefits such as status, limitation of liability and enhanced flexibility.

17.1.5.2 When does IR35 apply?

The main conditions for IR35 to apply are, *inter alia*:

- an individual has an obligation to provide services in person;

- the services are provided through an 'intermediary' (such as a PSC); and

- if instead the services had been provided directly between the individual and the client, the individual would have been regarded as employed by the clients 'in employed earner's employment' for NIC purposes.

17.1.5.3 How does IR35 work?

If the conditions set out earlier are satisfied, the PSC (and not the ultimate client) is responsible for applying the legislation. It is required to account to HMRC for an amount equivalent to PAYE and NICs on the excess of deemed employment income over actual employment income. Payments for the previous tax year are due by 19 April.

The relevant income constitutes, broadly, the amounts received by the intermediary plus any benefits received directly by the individual, less any actual salary paid by the PSC. The allowable deductions include a statutory 5% deduction from income received by the intermediary (to cover the company's overheads), plus expenses equivalent to those which would have been allowable if the individual had been an employee. The remainder is deemed to be the notional salary of the individual and the PSC is responsible for paying the tax that would have been payable under the PAYE and NIC regulations. If a PSC fails to pay over the correct amount of tax it may be subject to interest and/or penalties.

17.1.5.4 Interaction between IR35 and the Construction Industry Scheme

A PSC falling within IR35 may also be a subcontractor for the purposes of the CIS (further details of which are explained in section 17.1.6). In this situation, the PSC suffers a tax deduction on income received and is itself required to operate deemed PAYE and NICs under IR35. The IR35 payment is due on 19 April, so in many cases the company will have overpaid tax until its corporation tax return has been agreed. This problem has been addressed by the legislation introduced

by the Finance Act 2004. This allows a PSC to defer paying the tax due under the IR35 rules, so it will be able to set off the amounts deducted under the CIS scheme against the PAYE and NIC it owes.

17.1.6 Construction Industry Scheme

17.1.6.1 Overview of the CIS

The CIS sets out the rules regarding the handling by contractors of payments to subcontractors for their construction work. Under the CIS, a contractor may be required to make a deduction from payments made to subcontractors, and pay this to HMRC. This deduction would only be in respect of that part of the payment which does not represent the cost of materials incurred by the subcontractor.

On 6 April 2007, a new CIS was introduced with the aims of:

- reducing the regulatory burden on construction business;

- improving the level of compliance by construction businesses with their tax obligations; and

- helping construction businesses to correctly interpret the employment status of their workers.

Under the new CIS, contractors who make payments to subcontractors registered with HMRC are required to make deductions, where appropriate, at the rate of 20%, whereas if the payments are made to subcontractors who are not registered with HMRC, contractors are required to make deductions at the rate of 30%.

17.1.6.2 Interaction between the CIS and employment status

The CIS applies only to self-employed workers operating as 'contractors' or 'subcontractors' in the construction industry. It does not apply to employees subject to PAYE. The test for employment status must be considered for each engagement. A subcontractor may be registered with HMRC as a subcontractor but if he or she is deemed to be an 'employee' in relation to a particular job, the employer must operate PAYE for that work. This is because construction industry employers continue to be responsible for the deduction of PAYE and NIC for all employees under normal HMRC procedures. As with other industries, the hirer/employer is responsible for determining whether an individual is an employee. If an organisation incorrectly fails to operate PAYE, it will generally be liable to account to HMRC for the tax which should have been deducted (plus interest and possibly penalties). This is the case notwithstanding that the organisation acted in good faith. Conversely, if the organisation contracts with a PSC, it is the responsibility of the PSC to determine whether IR35 applies.

The terms 'contractor' and 'subcontractor' are broadly defined by HMRC. 'Contractor' means a business or other concern that pays subcontractors for construction work. Contractors may be construction companies and building firms but may also be government departments and local authorities. Non-construction businesses which spend on average £1 million per year on construction work (averaged over the previous 3 years) are counted as contractors. Consequently, any business authorising substantial amounts of building works will be caught by the CIS, irrespective of its industry sector. Businesses which spend less than an average of £1 million per annum on construction work and private householders are not contractors and will not be covered by the CIS.

A 'subcontractor' is a business engaged by the contractor to carry out construction work. 'Construction work' is restricted to work carried out in the UK and its territorial waters. Where a contract includes both construction and non-construction work, the labour element of the entire contract will fall within the CIS.

'Construction work' includes:

- construction, alteration, repair, extension or demolition of buildings/structures (including temporary structures);

- installation of heating, lighting, air conditioning/ventilation, water or power supply;

- installation of fire protection; and

- preparatory works, such as earth moving, site clearance or excavation.

It does not include:

- extraction of oil, natural gas or minerals;

- manufacture or building or delivery of engineering components, equipment, plant or machinery;

- manufacture or delivery of components for heating, lighting, air conditioning/ventilation, sanitation/water supply, draining or fire protection;

- artistic works;

- professional fees; and

- installation of security systems.

Note that some businesses may act both as contractor and subcontractor and will need to apply the appropriate set of rules for each transaction.

17.1.6.3 Mechanics of the CIS

All contractors must register for the CIS with HMRC. Subcontractors who do not wish to have deductions made from their payments at the higher rate (i.e. 30%) should also register with HMRC. Subcontractors who satisfy certain tests relating to business, finance and tax compliance can register for gross payment.

Before making a payment to a subcontractor for construction work, a contractor should verify with HMRC that the subcontractor is registered. HMRC will then check whether the subcontractor is registered and will inform the contractor of the rate of deduction to be applied to the payment, or whether the payment may be made without deductions.

If a deduction is required, the contractor must calculate the value of the deduction; deduct it from payment; record details of the payment, materials and deduction; make the net payment to the subcontractor; and complete and give a statement of deduction to the subcontractor.

Each month, contractors should send HMRC a complete return of all payments made under the CIS or report that they have made no payments. The return must reach HMRC by the 19th day of each month. Contractors who miss this deadline will be charged an automatic penalty of at least £100. The penalty will be charged for each month that a return is late. Contractors must also make a 'statutory declaration' on the return that none of their workers listed are employees.

17.1.6.4 Proposed changes to how employment status is determined in the construction industry

As part of its continuing efforts to address the perceived problem of subcontractors being wrongly classified as employed (and therefore not subject to PAYE or NICs), in July 2009 HMRC and HM Treasury published a joint consultation paper outlining proposals for changing the way in which payments made to workers within the construction industry are taxed. The main proposal made in that paper was that any payment made by a person whose main business is the carrying out or commissioning of 'construction operations' to a worker engaged to carry out those operations will be deemed to be employment income (for tax purposes only) unless one of the three criteria is met. These are as follows:

- the person *provides the plant and equipment* required for the job they have been engaged to carry out. This *excludes* the tools that it is normal for those in the industry to have themselves;

- the person *provides all the materials* to complete the job; or

- the person *provides other workers* to carry out operations under the contract and is responsible for paying them.

If enacted, this legislation would effectively override any other common law tests which might normally apply for the purposes of determining employment status.

The consultation closed in October 2009 and HM Treasury published its responses in March 2010. The response document reports that the overwhelming view of the respondents to the consultation was that the proposals would not achieve the desired aim of ensuring that those workers whose engagement in reality amount to employment are subject to PAYE and NICs.

A major concern that was expressed was that determining whether an employment relationship exists cannot be made purely on the basis of the three criteria suggested, as there are many situations where a worker who is genuinely self-employed would not be able to satisfy the tests. The government's response was that it remains convinced that its three originally suggested criteria provide the best starting point for new legislation. However, in the light of the comments received, it will develop the tests further to ensure that they operate effectively and do not exclude those who are genuinely running a business. In terms of timing, the original consultation paper recognised the potential effect of the proposals on the construction industry and the response document re-iterates that the measures developed will only take effect 'when the industry is in a stronger position'.

17.2 Defining a contract of employment

There is no legal requirement for a written contract of employment, but the ERA requires employees with at least one month's service to be given a written statement of their main terms and conditions of employment, for example, pay, hours, holidays and so on (see section 17.2.4). Such a statement is not, however, a contract of employment. Many other terms can be part of the contractual relationship, for example, a staff handbook, works' rules, disciplinary rules and procedures, terms in collective agreements and verbal agreements. Contracts may incorporate various types of terms which establish the rights and obligations of the parties, including the following:

- express terms – clearly agreed, whether written or verbal

- implied terms – necessary to give the contract effect or where deemed included, for example, by custom and practice

- incorporated terms – included from another source, for example, staff handbooks, collective agreements

- statutory terms – required by law, for example, minimum notice periods.

17.2.1 Employees' implied obligations

Some employees' obligations are implied. Breaching these terms could, if sufficiently serious, provide grounds for summary dismissal. Examples of such implied obligations include the following:

Duty of fidelity and good faith. The employer/employee relationship is based on mutual trust and confidence. It is implied that an employee will serve an employer with fidelity and in good faith. An employee must not compete with or act against his or her employer's business interests during employment. Employees must deal with their employer honestly, account for all property entrusted to them and disclose all information relevant to the employer obtained during employment.

Duty of confidentiality. While in employment, an employee must not disclose to third parties confidential information or trade secrets about an employer or an employer's clients which was gained during employment. This restriction continues after employment ends.

Duty to exercise reasonable care and skill. An employee implicitly undertakes that he or she has and will exercise reasonable skill and care in performing his or her duties.

Duty to obey lawful and reasonable orders. An employee implicitly consents to obey the lawful and reasonable orders of his or her employer under the contract. This duty provides a legal basis for compliance with company policies, for example, those contained in an employer's staff handbook.

17.2.2 Employer's implied obligations

Employers are subject to a number of implied terms. If breached, an employee may claim breach of contract and, in some circumstances, may resign and claim constructive dismissal. Such terms include those listed here.

Duty to pay wages. A duty to provide work (and thus wages to follow) will be implied for piecework; where wages consist entirely or in part of commission; and where the nature of the work means that the employee must work to maintain or develop skills.

Duty to ensure employee's safety. Employers must take reasonable care and reasonable steps to ensure employees' safety at work. Statute and various European directives implemented in the UK by health and safety regulations impose detailed obligations. Non-compliance constitutes a breach of this implied term and risks civil claims and statutory or regulatory penalties. This duty cannot be delegated and exists even when an employee works abroad on a site owned and controlled by another company.

Duty to monitor the environment. Employers must provide and monitor, to the extent that it is reasonably practicable, a working environment which is reasonably suitable for its employees to perform their contractual duties.

Duty to allow redress of grievances. Employers must reasonably and promptly give employees a reasonable opportunity to redress grievances.

In certain circumstances, employers may be under a duty to inform employees of a contractual benefit. While generally not under a duty to give a reference, employers are under a duty to exercise reasonable skill and care in giving a reference, which must be fair. A third party may sue an employer if it relied on a misleading reference and suffered loss as a result.

17.2.3 Obligations on the employer and the employee

The employer-employee relationship is based on mutual trust and confidence. There will be a breach of this implied term where one party behaves in a manner calculated or likely to destroy that trust and confidence, for example:

- unjustly operating a disciplinary procedure;

- abusing an express contractual right;

- making unwarranted suggestions that the employee is incapable; and

- not supporting an employee over harassment or bullying by fellow employees or the public.

17.2.4 Written particulars of employment

As previously mentioned, employees must be given a written statement of the main particulars of their employment.

Written details must be supplied to all new employees within 2 months of the start of their employment. It is prudent, however, to give this information to employees at the outset of employment. Existing employees not supplied with written details may request them and must receive them within 2 months of making such a request.

The details that must be included are:

- names of the employer and the employee;
- date on which employment began;
- date on which continuous employment began;
- the scale or rate of pay or the method of pay calculation;
- the intervals at which remuneration is paid;
- terms and conditions relating to working hours, including any overtime provisions;
- job title or, if this inadequately describes the duties involved, a description of the work;
- the place of work;
- for temporary employment, either the period for which it is expected to continue, or for a fixed term employment, the date it ends;
- terms and conditions for holidays, including public holidays, and holiday pay, enabling calculation of entitlement, including accrued holiday when leaving employment;
- any collective agreements affecting terms and conditions;
- any requirement to work outside the UK and, if so, the terms applicable;
- terms relating to sickness or injury, including any sick pay provision,
- terms relating to pensions and pension schemes;
- whether a contracting-out certificate is in force, that is, contracting out of the State Earnings Related Pension Scheme (SERPS);
- any disciplinary rules;
- the person (specified by description) to whom to appeal in the first instance if dissatisfied with any disciplinary decision, together with the appeal's method;
- any further steps available after the first stage of an appeal;
- the person (specified by description or otherwise) with whom to raise a grievance in the first instance and the method;
- any further steps available after the first stage of a grievance; and
- the length of notice to be given and received.

If there are no relevant details in respect of the above, that fact must be stated.

The employer must inform the employee in writing of changes to the aforementioned particulars as soon as possible and no later than 1 month after the change.

The key difference between a contract and a written statement is that a contract requires an agreement to be reached between two parties. A written statement does not as it simply constitutes information which must be given to employees.

To ensure that a written statement or notification of change is part of a contract, employers should:

- ensure that a letter offering employment to a prospective employee is accompanied by a statement of written particulars, stating that these form part of the contract;
- ensure that the written statement expressly states that it is part of the contract; and
- ensure that the employee signs off words such as *'I have read the above [terms and conditions of employment] [change/s to my terms and conditions of employment]. I fully understand the terms as detailed and accept that they form part of my contract of employment'*.

Employers wishing to change an employee's terms of employment should seek agreement from that individual. Non-consensual change could go beyond mere variation and could constitute a breach of contract. This could in turn form the basis of a constructive dismissal claim.

17.2.5 Types of employment contract

There are two types of employment contract:

(a) Permanent: the most common form for an indefinite, open-ended period which ends either when terminated by the employer, when the employee resigns or when he or she retires.
(b) Temporary: for either a fixed term or for the duration of a specific task or project, for example, where the contract is for a defined period and ends at a pre-determined fixed date or ends when a project or task is completed, or a specific event occurs. Expiry of a temporary contract will be treated as a dismissal at law.

17.2.5.1 Forming a contract

Forming a valid contract requires

- an offer: the employer offers to be bound by a clear and enforceable contract;
- consideration: value being exchanged between the parties such as wages for work;
- acceptance: the offer must be accepted completely and unconditionally; and
- intention to create legal relations: the parties must intend the agreement and its terms to be legally binding.

17.2.5.2 Conditions in an offer

Offers of employment can be subject to conditions, such as satisfactory references, evidence of qualifications, or a valid driving licence (where driving is essential). Such a contract is not complete unless or until the condition is satisfied and this should be made clear before the parties sign.

17.2.5.3 Illegal contracts

In general, no Court will enforce a contract which is forbidden by legislation or by common law, for example, one designed to defraud HMRC of tax. However, if a contract is illegal, an employee can still bring a sex, sexual orientation, gender reassignment, race, disability, age or religion or belief claim which is not based on that contract, for example, as to an act of discrimination in the workplace, but not discrimination in a contract term.

An employer and an employee cannot contract out of the rights conferred by any of the following legislation and attempts to do so render the contractual provision void:

- Sex Discrimination Act 1975, Race Relations Act 1976 or the Disability Discrimination Act 1995;
- Equal Pay Act 1970;
- Trade Union and Labour Relations (Consolidation) Act 1992 ('TULRCA');
- ERA;
- TUPE Regulations 1981;
- WTR;
- The National Minimum Wage Act 1998;
- The Public Interest Disclosure Act 1998;
- The Part-time Workers (Prevention of Less Favourable Treatment) Regulations 2000;
- The Fixed-Term Employees (Prevention of Less Favourable Treatment) Regulations 2002;
- The Employment Equality (Sexual Orientation) Regulations 2003;
- The Employment Equality (Religion or Belief) Regulations 2003; and
- The Employment Equality (Age) Regulations 2006 ('Age Regulations').

Much of the aforementioned anti-discrimination legislation has been subsumed under the Equality Act 2010, the majority of which came into force on 1 October 2010, and is discussed below.

17.2.5.4 Restrictive covenants

Contracts may also specify certain post-termination restraints, that is, restrictive covenants, limiting the ex-employee's activities after employment. The overriding rule is that such terms are unenforceable unless they protect a legitimate interest, are clear, specific and precise; and are otherwise reasonable. Only a well drafted covenant will, therefore, be enforceable. Typical restraints include:

- non-disclosure of trade secrets and confidential information;
- non-competition against the employer;
- non-solicitation (poaching) of customers;
- non-dealing with customers; and
- non-solicitation (poaching) of staff.

At common law, the remedy for breach of a restrictive covenant is an award of damages. However, in most cases, an employer would prefer to have the breach stopped by an injunction, that is, a court order preventing further breaches by the employee, as set out in the order. An employer cannot rely on a restrictive covenant in a contract of employment where it has itself breached the contract.

17.2.6 International agreements

17.2.6.1 General principles governing jurisdiction

Any international service agreement will need to address the following:

- the law applicable to the agreement;
- the country of jurisdiction for resolving disputes;
- the mandatory local laws which will prevail over any agreed terms in the agreement;
- if appropriate whether the agreement complies with the Posted Workers' Directive ('POWD').

There are three broad categories of employment contracts to be considered when working outside the UK:

- staff (of any nationality) who are already permanently employed in the UK or in another country and who are being assigned to work in another country as expatriates, on a short or long-term basis;
- staff (of any nationality) who are employed as expatriates just for the specific project and have no ongoing employment expectations after the expiry of their contract; and
- nationals of the country where the project is being undertaken.

Some considerations concerning the first category are given here.

17.2.6.2 Lawson v. Serco

Under Section 94(1) ERA, employees have a right not to be unfairly dismissed by their employer. Until 25 October 1999, when it was repealed, Section 196(2) ERA set out the territorial scope of the right to claim unfair dismissal and this excluded an employee 'who ordinarily works outside Great Britain'. When it was repealed, nothing was put in its place to offer guidance on the application of the ERA and the right to claim unfair dismissal, and, several conflicting decisions emerged before the issue of territorial scope was finally resolved to an extent by the House of Lords in the case of *Lawson v. Serco* in 2005.

The House of Lords identified three categories of employees who would be able to bring a claim under Section 94(1) ERA:

- employees who are working in Great Britain at the time they are dismissed, rather than what was contemplated at the time his or her employment contract was made;

- peripatetic employees, whose base should be treated as their place of employment; and

- expatriate employees. Section 94(1) ERA only applies to expatriates in exceptional circumstances; however, such as where an employee works abroad as the representative of a British employer for the purposes of a business carried on in Great Britain.

The decision in *Lawson v. Serco* has been followed by the Employment Appeal Tribunal (EAT) in the conjoined cases of *Burke v. The British Council*, *ADT Fire & Security plc v. Speyer* and *Camerson v. NAAFI*.

In 2007, the EAT found that the decision in *Lawson v. Serco* was limited to domestic legislation. In the case of *Bleuse v. MBT Transport Limited and Tiefenbacker* it said that regardless of whether the UK courts had exclusive jurisdiction to hear a claim different principles applied to directly effective rights conferred by European Union (EU) law. Applying this principle, the EAT accepted that the WTR give domestic effect to an EU right. Therefore where English law was the proper law of the contract, or where it provided the mandatory rules applicable to the employment relationship by virtue of the Rome convention, an English court properly exercising jurisdiction had to construe the English statute in a way which was compatible with the EU right. Mr Bleuse who was a German national, living in Germany but employed by a company registered in the UK (although never working in the UK) was therefore able to bring a claim under the WTR in the English courts.

The approach in *Bleuse* was followed in *Duncombe & Others v. The Secretary of State for Children, Schools and Families (formerly the Department for Education and Skills)* where a number of teachers working abroad in European schools on full time fixed term contracts argued in the EAT that the English Employment tribunal had jurisdiction to hear their claim under the Fixed-term Employees Regulations 2002. The EAT reluctantly decided to follow *Bleuse* (because the Regulations derived from a European Directive) and allow the appeal, however, it questioned the reasoning and resulting confusion created by the *Bleuse* decision and welcomed an appeal that would clarify these issues.

17.2.6.3 The Posted Workers Directive (POWD)

The POWD requires that, where a Member State has certain minimum terms and conditions of employment, these must also apply to workers posted temporarily by their employer to work in that State. A 'posted worker' is someone who, for a limited period, carries out his work in the territory of a European Community Member State other than the State in which he or she normally works. The POWD only applies to specified terms and conditions, such as minimum rates of pay, holiday entitlement, non-discrimination and so on. Existing UK legislation was amended as from the end of 1999 to guarantee minimum employment rights to workers posted temporarily to the UK. Employers posting workers throughout Europe will need to check that their contracts include local minimum provisions.

17.2.6.4 Existing employees transferred to another country

Staff employed in their home country, whether in the UK or elsewhere, may be asked to make short visits or to take up a longer-term assignment in another country. For short visits (e.g. up to 3 months, although this varies between companies), it is usual for an employer to pay all of an employee's travel expenses, subject to company guidelines regarding mode and class of travel. Other considerations for short visits include:

- daily allowances to cover accommodation, food, laundry and other personal expenses;

- alternatively reimbursement of actual out-of-pocket expenses;

- daily allowances or salary mark-up to compensate for additional and unsocial hours, hardship and separation from family and normal social life; and

- additional insurance cover for medical expenses and emergency repatriation.

For longer visits, it is usual for an expatriate to be offered an international service agreement, which provides for matters such as:

- start and end dates of the international employment (and provisions for any extension);

- role, terms of reference or job description;

- status with respect to dependants, for example, accompanied by spouse and children, accompanied by spouse without children, unaccompanied, single;

- salary based either on home country salary plus a mark-up to reflect extra and unsocial hours, relative hardship, relative cost of living and so on (a build-up system) or on local market salaries for similar staff (a host country package);

- working hours (normally in accordance with local custom and practice);

- leave – amount and timing;

- passages – beginning and end of tour, leave passages for self and family;

- accommodation standards and rent and utility allowances (and who finds and provides);

- assistance with school fees for any children in the home or host country;

- taxation – employees must remain responsible for home and host country income tax liabilities, but the employer should build in appropriate provision;

- the salary – sometimes salaries are quoted 'after host country tax', with the employer negotiating the amount due with the host country tax authorities. The employer may also agree to meet the cost of local professional advice taken by the employee in respect of this;

- medical costs – usually reimbursed under an international private medical insurance scheme. It is normal to require staff and accompanying family to undertake a medical examination before travelling. The agreement should clarify whether the costs of routine dental treatment, spectacles and cosmetic treatment are included and who bears the costs associated with any pregnancy;

- insurances – accident and property;

- pension scheme arrangements;

- termination and preparation provisions;

- rules requiring respect for local customs and other specific requirements; and

- rules for deduction of local tax and/or social security contributions.

17.2.6.5 Case study 2 – Deriving the international salary

Paula Bates is permanently employed in the UK and is going to Hong Kong on a 36-month assignment. The company use a build-up system based on the home country salary. She will not be liable to pay UK income tax on her salary from the date of departure, as the assignment extends over a complete tax year. She will, however, be liable to pay Hong Kong income tax at the applicable rate on that income. Elements of mark-up for cost of living, hardship and tax equalisation are added to the standard salary and paid gross.

17.2.6.6 Expatriates recruited for the project

A service agreement similar to that for existing employees is often used, but with changes to exclude certain benefits available to established employees, such as pension. Alternatively, in countries with developed economies and freely convertible currencies, it is often simpler to employ expatriates on the same terms as local staff, paying them the market salary.

17.2.6.7 Local staff

Local staff are often nationals of the country where the project is being undertaken and will be employed in accordance with local employment laws and standards. It may be necessary to work through an established, locally registered company, for example, a subsidiary, joint venture partner, or similar entity.

17.3 Taxation of subsistence and travel allowances in the UK

Generally, employees are taxed on all income they receive from their employment, including pay, benefits in kind (such as company cars) and any expenses payments (including

payments relating to business travel). However, employees are entitled to tax relief on expenses incurred wholly exclusively and necessarily in the course of their duties of the employment. Where tax relief is available for travel expenses, relief will also be available for 'reasonable' subsistence costs and for certain travel expenses.

17.3.1 Cost of travel to work

Tax relief is now available for 'ordinary commuting' costs: that is, travel from home or another non-workplace to a permanent workplace. Most travel from home to a temporary workplace will be allowable, for example travel to a temporary site. In addition, travel between workplace locations, for example different offices of the employing organisation, will also be similarly allowable. For most employees who have one normal workplace, the rules are fairly straightforward. Provision of free workplace parking is not currently a taxable benefit.

17.3.2 Private travel

Tax relief is now available for the cost of travel undertaken for private reasons: that is, a journey between:

- an employee's home and any other place they do not have to be for work purposes, or

- any two places where an employee does not have to be for work purposes.

17.3.3 Site-based employees and Working Rule Agreements (WRA)

Employees who are site-based may receive travel and subsistence allowances at a flat rate set out in a WRA negotiated between the relevant trade union and employers organisations. HMRC is not a party to such agreements, but will often have agreed the tax treatment of payments within the WRA. For many agreements, payments for travelling time will be taxable, but agreed travel and/or subsistence allowances after an initial threshold distance will often be non-taxable. This provides a measure of clarity for both employer and employee. This treatment only applies to travel and subsistence; if the individual receives other benefits (e.g. use of a van) normal taxation rules will apply.

17.3.4 General rules for site-based employees

Some individuals may have more than one 'normal' workplace; for example, someone who works in branch A on Mondays and Tuesdays, and branch B on Wednesdays to Fridays. As a general rule, HMRC applies a '40% test' so that where an employee attends a workplace for 40% or more of their time, that workplace will be considered 'permanent'. Below this threshold, HMRC will consider other factors, including frequency or pattern of attendance or the presence of 'permanent' office or support facilities. Where an individual has more than one permanent workplace, travel from home to either workplace will be considered as 'normal commuting' and any expenses reimbursed will be taxable. Travel between the workplaces will be allowable.

Conversely, where an employment is defined by a geographical area, (e.g. a sales area), and there is no permanent office or base, travel to the boundary of the area will be treated as 'commuting' but all travel within the defined area will be eligible for tax relief.

Site-based workers may spend short periods at each site before being relocated. In these circumstances, provided the assignment is not expected to (and does not in fact) exceed 24 months, the travel costs will qualify for relief.

17.3.5 Case study 3 – Travelling expenses and time

Fred Campbell is an engineer who is normally based in offices in London. He is assigned to a site for a period of 12 months and is reimbursed for the costs of local accommodation and travelling from home to site. This is paid tax free. However, the assignment is extended after 9 months so that the total assignment will be more than 24 months. From the time of the extension, both income tax and NICs are payable on any travel and subsistence costs paid.

17.3.6 The amount of relief

Tax relief can be claimed on the full costs incurred, provided these are reasonable. As a general rule, where travel costs are eligible for relief, reasonable subsistence can also be claimed. What is 'reasonable' will depend on the timing and duration of the journey and the seniority of the worker. In most instances there are no standard allowances. HMRC may require receipts or other evidence that expenses have been incurred. If the costs are borne or reimbursed in full by the employer, no further relief can be claimed. However, to the extent that costs are not reimbursed, the employee can claim tax relief on the outstanding amount through the self-assessment tax return.

Where travel involves an overnight stay, costs of personal incidental expenses (such as private telephone calls or newspapers) which would not otherwise be allowable, they can be reimbursed by the employer without incurring a tax charge. This relief avoids a charge to income tax, but cannot be used to claim tax relief on such expenses borne by the employee. The employer can claim the exemption treatment by obtaining a dispensation from the local office of HMRC as set out earlier.

If an employer pays 'round sum allowances' to cover expenses, the allowance will generally be taxable, but the employee will be able to claim relief for expenses incurred. Exceptionally, it may be possible to agree an acceptable level of expense allowance with HMRC, but this is generally only available for overseas travel in locations where it may not be practical to obtain full receipts.

17.3.7 Small allowances for clothing and tools

HMRC does allow standard levels of expenses for specific industries. These are small in amount and generally cover items such as tools and clothing. A list of these allowances can be obtained from any HMRC office.

17.4 Wrongful and unfair dismissal
17.4.1 Wrongful dismissal

There will be a wrongful dismissal if an employer breaches an employee's contract of employment when terminating it, for example, using shorter notice than the entitlement specified or in a way contrary to the terms set out. The normal remedy is for damages which are limited to the loss of earnings during the notice period required to terminate the contract, if it had been performed on the basis that the employer would have given proper notice. Common law rarely requires an employer to reinstate a wrongly dismissed employee. Moreover, there is no requirement of fairness in any such dismissal.

Generally, dismissal on due notice will not be a breach of contract. If there is a breach of contract, the employee is also under a duty to mitigate his loss in most circumstances, that is, take reasonable steps to find alternative employment.

Given the limited remedies available for wrongful dismissal, the statutory regime has created the separate concept of unfair dismissal.

17.4.2 Unfair dismissal

As previously mentioned in section 17.2.6 of this chapter, an employee has the right not to be unfairly dismissed by his or her employer under Section 94(1) ERA. In determining whether an employee's dismissal is fair or unfair, the employer must show the reason for the dismissal and that it is one of the potentially fair reasons prescribed by Section 98(2) ERA. The statutory provisions relating to unfair dismissal apply to all employees with continuous employment of 1 year or more. The six potentially fair reasons are:

- the capability or qualifications of the employee for performing work of the kind which he was employed by the employer to do;
- the conduct of the employee;
- retirement of the employee;
- redundancy of the employee;
- breach of some other legal requirement; or
- 'some other substantial reason' which justifies dismissal.

17.4.2.1 Capability

In most circumstances it will not be enough simply to assert that the individual is incapable of performing his or her job. In order for an employer to ensure that a dismissal is fair, it needs to demonstrate that it acted reasonably in the circumstances. In relying on capability as the reason for dismissal, the employee will need to be given a fair opportunity to improve, having been warned of the consequences of the failure to do so.

17.4.2.2 Conduct

General misconduct will not justify summary termination. Only gross misconduct of a nature which goes to the root of the relationship will do so. However, there must be a proper investigation of any allegations as to the individual's conduct, and he or she must be given a chance to make his or her case known. Again, dismissal must be a reasonable sanction. It must be made known that such conduct will constitute gross misconduct.

17.4.2.3 Retirement

Retirement will be the reason for dismissal where:

- the employee has no normal retirement age (NRA) and the operative date of termination falls on or after the date on which the employee reaches 65;

- the employee has an NRA of 65 or older and the operative date of termination falls on or after the date the employee reaches that age;

- the employee has an NRA below 65 and that retirement age has been objectively justified.

17.4.2.4 Redundancy

A redundancy situation arises where the employer ceases to carry on business for the purposes for which or in the place in which the employee is employed, or where the requirements of the business for employees to carry out work of a particular kind have ceased or diminished or are expected to cease or diminish. Before selecting an individual for redundancy, it is essential to establish the appropriate pool of workers from whom to select, using objective criteria to do so. The criteria must be explained and considered in the process of individual consultation with the individual. The individual must be consulted as to ways of avoiding redundancies. There is also a requirement to look for suitable alternative employment, if it exists. An individual has the right of a trial period of up to 4 weeks in suitable alternative employment. For those with over 2 years' continuous employment, there is a right to a statutory redundancy payment on a tax free basis, calculated by reference to gross weekly wage (which is currently capped at £380), length of service and with a multiplier factor for age.

17.4.2.5 Breach of another enactment

This applies where the continued employment of an individual would be in contravention of another statute. An example of this would be where a work permit was required but not held by the individual. An employer must, however, consider whether there were alternative roles to which the individual could be deployed before resorting to dismissal.

17.4.2.6 Some other substantial reason

This is a general catch-all, but does not justify dismissal on any reason whatsoever. It must be material to the business, and be for a very real need. Mere convenience will not suffice. For example, in a business reorganisation leading to change in working practices or where the relationship has completely broken down for reasons other than conduct, dismissal must still be a reasonable response.

17.4.3 Automatically unfair dismissals

There are some instances where the law states that there will be an automatically unfair dismissal, irrespective of length of service. Examples include those dismissed because of health and safety responsibilities, for trade union activities or pregnancy.

17.4.4 Reasonableness

While the law will not substitute its own judgment for that of a reasonable employer, an employer must demonstrate that it has behaved reasonably throughout. It will need to demonstrate that it has acted in accordance with the spirit of the Advisory, Conciliation and Arbitration Service (ACAS) Code of Practice on disciplinary practice and procedures in respect of such matters as communication of the procedures, incremental stages, warnings, the right of representation at hearings, and the right to respond to any case. In addition, an employer must show that the rules of natural justice have been satisfied.

17.4.5 Disciplinary and grievance process

Under the Employment Act 2008 the government completely overhauled the legal framework for disciplinary and grievance processes, and introduced a revised ACAS *Code of Practice on Discipline and Grievance* (ACAS Code), which is discussed later. Employees cannot bring a claim purely for breach of the relevant procedures and breach of the procedures will not automatically make a dismissal unfair. However, if in hearing a claim on most of the grounds over which it has jurisdiction, including unfair dismissal, the Employment Tribunal is satisfied that there has been a breach of the ACAS Code it may increase any award by up to 25%.

17.4.5.1 The current position

The Employment Act 2008 repealed all relevant provisions of the Employment Act 2002 and Section 98A of the ERA 1996 whereby dismissals that did not follow the procedure were automatically unfair. With the removal of the 'procedurally unfair dismissal' the law under the case of *Polkey v. A E Dayton Services* has been restored. In *Polkey*, the House of Lords stated that in instances of an unfair dismissal where a fair dismissal was likely to have occurred anyway a percentage reduction in any award should be applied to reflect this likelihood.

New provisions were also inserted into the Trade Union and Labour Relations Act 1992 that requires employers to comply with a 'relevant Code of Practice', which currently refers to the ACAS Code. Unreasonable failure by an employee to comply with the ACAS Code enables the tribunal to decrease an award by up to 25% where this would be 'just and equitable'; failure to comply by the employer allows the tribunal to increase the award by up to 25%.

The ACAS Code deals only with situations of misconduct and poor performance. The ACAS Code requires reasonable investigation by the employer prior to informing the employee of any alleged misconduct and/or poor performance. The steps to be taken by an employer are broadly the same as those described earlier, although there are some changes and more detailed guidance provided particularly in relation to investigations. The time limit in which an employee may bring a claim is not automatically extended even if an appeal is ongoing. The ACAS Code recommends two particular steps: (1) employers should go through the evidence gathered against the employee at the meeting and, (2) employees should be allowed to call witnesses to the meeting. Additionally, appeals should be allowed against warnings; as the ACAS code applies to suspension on full pay and formal warnings.

The employee should raise their grievance in writing and the employer should investigate the complaint and hold a meeting with the employee (to which he or she may bring a companion). The employee has the right to appeal the conclusions reached by the grievance investigation. Under the current law an employee who has not submitted a grievance is not barred from bringing a claim, additionally, submitting a grievance does not automatically extend the period of time in which a claim may be made.

17.4.6 Remedies

An employee who successfully claims unfair dismissal may seek the following remedies: compensation; reinstatement to his or her old job; or re-engagement to a different job but with the same employer or an associate employer. Compensation is the most popular remedy. A tribunal is entitled to make an award of compensation in two parts. Firstly, it may make a 'basic award', which is calculated on the basis of age, length of service and gross weekly wage (currently capped at £380) to a maximum of £11 400. In addition, the tribunal may make a compensatory award which is designed to compensate the employee for loss of salary and benefits to the date of the hearing, future loss of earnings and expenses incurred as a result of dismissal. The compensatory award is currently capped at £65 300.

Where a tribunal makes an order for reinstatement, but the employer fails to comply with it, the employee will be entitled to apply at a second hearing for further compensation, that is, an 'Additional Award', unless the employer can show that it was not reasonably practicable to comply with the order. An Additional Award will be valued at between 26 and 52 weeks' pay, subject to the current statutory limits.

17.4.6.1 Case study 4 – Capability?

A member of staff has, over a period of 2 years, not been performing at the level expected for the job. The employer conducts annual career development reviews with all staff. Each employee meets with a manager to discuss performance, future plans and training and career development. At the last two annual reviews for this individual, the employer has discussed the employee's underperformance with him and has recorded the issues on the relevant review forms. The employee has, however, never been warned that he may be dismissed or demoted if he does not improve his performance and the company's capability procedure has not been followed. After the second review, the employee is dismissed without any further meetings regarding his performance. The employee takes the case to tribunal and is successful in establishing that there was no fair reason for their dismissal, they win compensation on grounds of unfair dismissal which is increased to take account of the failure of the employer to follow the ACAS Code.

17.4.7 Taxation of termination payments

The taxation of payments to former employees in connection with termination of employment broadly falls into two categories: contractual payments, which will be subject to income tax and NICs in the normal way; and other payments, which will be taxable only to the extent that they exceed £30 000. The rules apply to benefits, as well as cash payments, for example the continuation of medical insurance or the use of a company car. If an employee has worked abroad, some tax relief may be available in relation to time spent outside the UK.

17.4.7.1 Payments arising out of the contract of employment

These will be subject to income tax and NICs as employment earnings. This category will include pay during a notice period, accrued holiday pay or any other contractual entitlements. In practice, most difficulties tend to arise where the notice period is not fulfilled and a payment is made in lieu of notice (PILON); the question arises whether the employer has paid damages for breach of contract (the first £30 000 of which is tax free) or has made a payment within the terms of the employment contract (which is taxable as set out earlier). PILONs will be considered to be contractual if the employer:

- is required to pay in lieu of notice if the contractual notice period is not honoured or

- has discretion to pay in lieu of notice and the employer exercised this right to make the payment (as opposed to paying damages for breach of contract).

In determining the content of the contract, it may be necessary to consider documents such as staff handbooks, where these form part of the employment contract. HMRC may seek to impute a contractual term by reference to past practice where an employer habitually makes payments in lieu of tax on termination of employment.

Whether an employer has exercised discretion or whether the payment represents damages for breach of contract, is a matter of fact. Where the amount is equivalent to pay for the notice period, HMRC is likely to tax it in full as a contractual reward. In contrast, where an employer can show that it has decided NOT to exercise its right, the payment may be viewed as damages (with the exemption for the first £30 000 compensation paid).

17.4.7.2 Other payments

Other payments in connection with the termination of employment which are not otherwise taxable, such as compensation for breach of contract or damages for wrongful dismissal, will generally be taxable under a separate charging provision, the first £30 000 of which will be tax free. Such payments will often be made under a statutory compromise agreement.

Redundancy payments are derived from an employee's employment law rights, rather than from the terms of the employment contract. Therefore the first £30 000 of any payment is tax free.

Payments to an employee for entering into restrictive covenants are, however, taxable in full. HMRC may examine a compromise agreement to check whether some or all of the payment made under the terms of the agreement is attributable to a restrictive covenant. Payments to a departing employee approaching retirement age will also be taxable in full if HMRC consider that they are paid as 'retirement benefits', rather than on a genuine redundancy. It is the employer's responsibility to determine whether a payment is taxable and HMRC will generally seek to recover any under-deduction of tax from the employer. In cases of uncertainty, HMRC may provide an advance ruling, which will only be binding if all relevant information is disclosed to it in that application.

17.4.8 Discrimination and dismissals

In the UK, it is unlawful for an employer to discriminate against employees and applicants for employment because of sex, marriage or civil partnership, pregnancy and maternity, gender reassignment, age, race, religion or belief, sexual orientation and disability.

The law relating to discrimination has developed in a piecemeal fashion and different pieces of legislation govern different types of discrimination. The long awaited Equality Act 2010 received Royal Assent on 8 April 2010 and the majority of its provisions came into force in October 2010. It brings all the different strands of discrimination law together in one place, whilst also adding a number of novel provisions to the law.

A claim for discrimination may be brought before a tribunal if the claimant has suffered direct discrimination, indirect discrimination, victimisation or harassment. Briefly, an employer directly discriminates against an employee if it treats him or her less favourably because of a protected characteristic, such as ethnic origin or sex. An employer discriminates indirectly against an employee where it makes that employee subject to a provision, criteria or practice (or, in some instances, a requirement or condition) which it applies equally to other employees, but which puts employees who share a protected characteristic and that employee at a disadvantage. An employer may defend a claim for indirect discrimination and direct age discrimination if it can show that the discrimination was objectively justifiable. A provision, criteria or practice is objectively justifiable where an employer can show that it was a proportionate means of achieving a legitimate aim. In *Bilka–Kaufhaus GmbH v. Weber von Hartz*, the European Court of Justice (ECJ) held that, in order to satisfy the test of justification, the measures taken by the employer:

- must correspond to a real need on the part of the employer;

- must be appropriate with a view to achieving the objectives pursued; and

- must be necessary to that end.

It is for the tribunal to decide whether the employer's actions were objectively justifiable.

Victimisation occurs when an individual subjects another individual (the 'victim') to a detriment because the victim has done a 'protected act' or the individual believes that the victim has done or may do a 'protected act'. An example of a protected act is the victim bringing a proceeding under the Equality Act 2010 or alleging that a person has contravened the Equality Act 2010 (or previous discrimination legislation).

Harassment occurs where, in relation to a relevant protected characteristic, an individual engages in unwanted conduct which has the purpose or effect of violating another individual's dignity or creating an intimidating, hostile, degrading, humiliating or offensive environment for that individual. The 'relevant protected characteristics' are age, disability, gender, reassignment, race, religion or belief, sex and sexual orientation.

If a claimant can show a *prima facie* case of any form of discrimination, the burden of proof will shift to the employer, who will be required to demonstrate that discrimination has not taken place. If an employer cannot provide a non-discriminatory explanation for its conduct, a court may draw an adverse inference and make a finding of discrimination. Compensation awards for claims of discrimination are unlimited in amount.

17.4.9 Collective consultation and dismissals

Under TULRCA, an employer must consult with trade unions or employee representatives when proposing to dismiss 20 or more employees at one establishment within a period of 90 days for a reason which is not individual, for example, redundancy. If the employer proposes to make between 20 and 99 employees redundant, it must start the consultation at least 30 days before the first proposed redundancy. If it proposes to make 100 or more employees redundant, the consultation must start at least 90 days before the first proposed redundancy. A failure to do so before any notices of dismissal are issued will almost certainly render dismissals unfair, and more particularly involves an additional penalty, namely a protective award of up to 90 days' uncapped pay for each affected employee. Where there is a duty to consult the Department for Business Innovation and Skills (BIS) should also be notified by the employer – failure to do this is a criminal offence.

Consultation should take place with trade union representatives if there is an independent recognised trade union, failing which the employer should invite the workforce to elect representatives. If the workforce fails to elect representatives, then the employer should nonetheless communicate on the issue of dismissal to all the employees on an individual basis.

Collective consultation is not the same as collective bargaining, but it is still necessary to consult with a view to seeking agreement, disclosing reasons for the dismissals, how they will take effect and considering ways of avoiding them.

Since April 2005, the duty to consult collectively must also be considered in light of any obligations the employer may have under the information and consultation of Employees Regulations 2004 (ICE Regulations). If those obligations arise, then the ICE Regulations allow employees in organisations with at least 50 employees to be

- informed about the business' economic situation;
- informed and consulted about employment prospects; and
- informed and consulted about decisions likely to lead to substantial changes in work organization or contractual relations, including redundancies and transfers.

In order to satisfy the requirements of the ICE Regulations, employers should set up information and consultation operations, such as staff forums and national works council, which enable the employer to consult the workforce. ACAS recommends that employers keep employees informed both face to face with one-to-one and team meetings or at arm's length using company handbooks, newsletters, notices and electronic methods such as emails and intranets. Managers should not rely on 'the grapevine' to pass on news and information accurately.

17.5 TUPE transfers

The TUPE Regulations 1981 (TUPE 1981) were introduced to protect the rights of employees on the transfer of an undertaking. On 6 April 2006, TUPE 2006 which implemented EC Directive 2001/23 came into force in the UK and repealed TUPE 1981.

Amongst other things, TUPE 2006 widened the scope of TUPE 1981 to cover more clearly outsourced and insourced services, as well as the assignment of services by a client to a new contractor.

17.5.1 When does TUPE apply?

TUPE 2006 applies to a 'relevant transfer', which means:

- a transfer of a business, undertaking or part of a business or undertaking where there is a transfer of an economic entity that retains its identity ('business transfer'). A part of a business can include just one employee as there is no specified threshold in terms of employee numbers; or
- a client engaging a contractor to do work on its behalf, reassigning such a contract or bringing the work in-house ('service provision change').

Relevant transfers may, however, be both a business transfer and a service provision change.

17.5.1.1 Business transfers

In order to establish whether a business transfer has taken place, it is necessary to consider whether:

- an economic entity is being transferred; and
- the economic entity retains its identity following the transfer.

TUPE 2006 defines an 'economic entity' as 'an organised grouping of resources that has the objective of pursuing an economic activity, whether or not that activity is central or ancillary'.

The definition is not limited to a going concern. To establish whether there is an 'economic entity', the Courts will consider a number of non-exhaustive factors, such as whether:

- physical assets are transferred;
- intangible assets, such as goodwill, are transferred and their value;
- staff are transferred;
- the customer circle remains the same;
- the business remains similar before and after transfer; and
- there was any interruption to the business, and, if so, its duration.

None of these factors will be independently conclusive.

In identifying whether an economic entity has been transferred, it is necessary to consider whether the economic entity still exists post-transfer. Consideration should be given to the following factors:

- has goodwill been transferred?
- who is servicing the seller's intangible assets?
- what activities were carried on before and after the transfer?

The importance of each factor will vary according to the nature of the transaction. A change in the way that the business of an economic enterprise is carried out does not necessarily prevent TUPE 2006 applying.

A transfer can happen in one stage, or involve a series of transfers.

17.5.1.2 Service provision changes

Where there is a change in service provider, there will be a transfer directly from the outgoing contractor to the subsequent contractor. TUPE 2006 sets out a detailed definition of a service provision change. It is necessary for one person to cease to provide the activities and for another to take them over. TUPE 2006 also specifies the situations in which there will not be a service provision charge, for example, when the client intends that the activities will be carried out in connection with a single specific event or task of a short-term duration.

Note, however, that employment tribunals will focus on the intention of the parties. It is unlikely that the effects of the legislation could be avoided by entering into a series of short-term contracts or deliberately rotating the employees who provide the service.

17.5.2 What are the consequences of TUPE 2006 applying?

All of the transferor's rights, powers, duties and liabilities under or in connection with the contract are transferred to the transferee, including any claims and liabilities arising before the transfer (with the exception of some provisions relating to pensions, see section 17.5.4). All those employed by the transferor transfer to the transferee on their existing terms of employment.

All terms and conditions involving benefits such as company cars, private health assurance, loans and life assurance will transfer. Where benefits cannot be identically matched, a similar benefit will have to be provided by the transferee. Failure to match existing terms risks claims by the employees concerned for breach of contract on the ground of unilateral variation of the contract without consent.

All collective agreements relating to the transferring employees automatically transfer, binding the transferee. Union recognition also transfers to the transferee, provided that the organised grouping retains a distinct identity after the transfer. The transferee may, however, de-recognise the union and bring the collective agreement to an end. Those terms which have been incorporated into the employee's contract will, however, continue to be effective.

17.5.3 Who transfers?

Where there is a TUPE 2006 transfer, those employees employed by the transferor and 'assigned to the organised grouping of resources or employees that is subject to the relevant transfer' will transfer to the transferee under their existing terms of employment and with their continuity of employment unbroken. Whether or not an employee is 'assigned to an organised grouping' is a

question of fact. If an employee is multi-skilled and has a range of functions, the law will consider to which undertaking, as a matter of fact, he or she can be said to be assigned.

TUPE 2006 does not transfer any employees who are only temporarily assigned. When determining whether or not an assignment is 'temporary', regard should be given to the length of the assignment and whether a date has been set for the employee's return.

The transferor must provide the transferee with certain 'employee liability information', on an accurate basis, before the transfer. If the transferor fails to do so it risks being liable to pay significant compensation to the transferee.

17.5.4 How does TUPE apply to rights under pension schemes?

Old age, invalidity and survivors' benefits under occupational pension schemes are excluded and do not transfer under TUPE 2006. An obligation for an employer to pay a percentage of salary into an employee's pension scheme will not fall within the aforementioned exemption and will therefore be covered by the automatic transfer principle. The Pensions Act 2004 places a duty on transferees to meet specified levels of pension provision for certain transferring employees. The exclusion does not, however, apply to other benefits under an occupational pension scheme.

Thus, if the transferor had an obligation to provide pension benefits to its employees, that obligation does not pass to the transferee following the relevant transfer, but remains with the transferor. However, because the employees now employed by the transferee cannot continue to accrue benefit under the transferor's pension scheme, it is usual for the transferor to require the transferee to offer comparable pension benefits for the employees who are transferred to it.

For this reason, business transfers on outsourcings will invariably involve the parties setting up pension arrangements for the transferring employees which are broadly equivalent to those they enjoyed with the transferor. This is done either by granting the employees the right to enter an existing pension scheme of the transferee or by the transferee creating a new scheme for the purpose. This is expected as standard practice by the government in transfers involving the public sector.

Employees who accept an invitation to join the pension arrangements of the transferee will usually also be given the opportunity to choose whether to have their rights earned in the transferor's pension scheme transferred to the transferee's scheme. If the employees choose to leave the rights with the transferor's scheme, they will on their ultimate retirement receive separate pensions from the transferor's scheme and the transferee's scheme in relation to their different service periods. If the employees do agree to the transfer of rights they will receive a single pension from the transferee's scheme which incorporates the entitlements earned in the transferor's scheme.

Early retirement benefits on the basis of redundancy or ill health do not fall within the exemption granted to occupational pension schemes by the Acquired Rights Directive. As indicated earlier, new contractors do not have to give employees who transfer to them equal pension rights to those they enjoyed under their previous employer but this means that a significant unfunded liability in an occupational pension scheme in the event of redundancy (or on retirement other than on the ground of reaching the relevant NRA) could transfer (as to which see subsequent section).

Since 6 April 2005, transferees have been obliged to provide pension benefits for transferring employees where:

- there is a TUPE transfer;

- the employee in question becomes employed by the transferee rather than the transferor;

- immediately before the transfer there is an occupational pension scheme in relation to which the transferor is the employer and the employee is either an active member of the scheme; or eligible to be such a member; or in a probationary period to become eligible to be a member.

Where the transferor's scheme is a defined benefit scheme, the transferring employee automatically qualifies for protection. Where the transferor's scheme provides money purchase benefits, the transferring employee only qualifies for protection if the transferor was required to make employer contributions. If the transferor was not required to make employer contributions, the transferring employee will qualify for protection if the transferor made at least one such contribution.

Where an employee qualifies for protection, it becomes a term of their contract with the transferee that the employee will be offered access to a money purchase scheme or a defined benefit scheme. The transferee may decide which arrangement to offer the new employees and is not obliged to match the type of scheme offered by the transferor. Where the transferee offers its new employees a money purchase scheme, it is required to match the employee's contributions up to a maximum of 6% of earnings per annum.

17.5.5 Varying terms and conditions

Under TUPE 2006 changes to terms and conditions are void if the sole or principal reason for the change is the transfer itself or a reason connected with a transfer which is not an economic technical or organisational (ETO) reason entailing changes in the workforce.

Changes may be made to employment terms before or after a transfer where the sole or principal reason is unconnected with the transfer or is connected with the transfer but is an ETO reason.

17.5.6 How are reorganisations and dismissals affected?

Dismissals of employees with continuous employment of a year or more will automatically be unfair where the sole or principal reason for dismissal is the transfer itself or a reason connected with the transfer which is not an ETO reason entailing changes in the workforce. The protection against dismissal applies to both those employees who transfer and any other employees who are dismissed as a result of the transfer. The rule can apply to dismissals by both transferor and transferee.

This defence is unavailable where there is a bare attempt to harmonise the terms and conditions of the transferring staff with those of the transferee's existing staff. It would, however, include a redundancy scenario after transfer. In such cases, the transferee or transferor would still have to follow a redundancy procedure and make the necessary payments. In addition, recent case law has thrown doubt on the ability of transferors to make employees redundant for a reason that only arises after the transfer.

17.5.7 What consultations have to take place?

Both the transferor and the transferee must consult with employee representatives prior to the transfer. TUPE 2006 also requires the transferor to provide certain information about the transferring employees, for example, the identity and age of the employees who will transfer and information on any collective agreements affecting those employees which will still have effect after the transfer. If there are recognised trade unions present, they must be used for the purposes of consultation with staff in the scope of recognition. Otherwise, elected representatives can be elected and consulted. If they are not, the employer has a defence if it gives out information on the transfer on an individual basis.

No specific timetable is laid down for the provision of information to the relevant trade union or employee, but particular terms and information must be provided, to the trade union or employee representatives, namely:

- the fact of the transfer, the reason for it being proposed, and when it is proposed that it will take place;

- the legal, economic and social consequences of the transfer;

- any measures proposed by the employer in respect of affected employees; and

- the transferor must state the measures which the transferee envisages it will take in relation to the transferring employees in connection with the transfer. If the transferee envisages taking no measures that fact should be stated or, if none, the fact that there are none.

Failure to comply with the obligations to inform and/or consult may result in the trade union or employee representatives, bringing a claim in the employment tribunal. If successful, the tribunal will make a declaration that the claim was well founded and will award compensation to the relevant affected employees of up to 13 weeks' uncapped pay each.

Under TUPE 2006, both the transferor and the transferee are jointly and severally liable for:

- any compensation awarded by a tribunal against the transferor for failure to inform and consult; and

- any failure by the transferor or transferee to pay compensation that has been ordered by the tribunal for a failure to inform or consult.

The representatives of the transferring employees will be able to bring a claim against either or both of the parties and the Tribunal will then apportion liability. Where the transferor establishes that it failed to inform or consult because the transferee failed to give it the relevant information, the tribunal may order the transferee to pay the compensation.

It is the employer's responsibility to ensure that the elections of employee representatives are fair and the employer must make sure that there are sufficient representatives.

17.5.8 Commercial context

As an indication only, commercial negotiations and agreements should consider:

- as a condition of any agreement, identifying which employees are transferring, and their terms and conditions, by way of due diligence and disclosure;

- warranties as to the accuracy of such information;

- indemnification for liabilities before and after transfer, in other words the transferor indemnifying the transferee for liabilities before transfer when the transferor is in control and the transferee indemnifying the transferor for liabilities arising after transfer when the transferee is in control;

- treatment of occupational pensions and benefits will require detailed consideration and implementation of similar schemes;

- consultation with the staff by both transferor and transferee;

- if it is an outsourcing or joint venture, since these will not last forever; what happens on exit, that is, whether staff retransfer.

17.5.9 Right to object

Transferring staff have a right to object to their transfer. If an employee informs either the transferor or the transferee of their wish to object, his/her employment with the transferee is treated as terminating with effect from the transfer date. Since there will have been no dismissal or resignation, the employee would not be entitled to any statutory or contractual compensation on termination. An individual is not, however, prevented from maintaining that he or she has been constructively dismissed, as such a claim is not precluded by exercising the right to object.

17.6 Working time regulations

What follows is a brief summary of the WTR, which came into force on 1 October 1998, to implement the EC Working Time Directive. The WTR take advantage of a number of 'derogations', that is, permitted exceptions to the Directive's application. Employers should consider which exceptions, if any, are available to them.

17.6.1 Meaning of 'working time' and record keeping

'Working time' is defined as any period during which the worker is working, carrying out his duties or is at the employer's disposal; any period during which the worker is receiving 'relevant training'; or any additional period which is agreed in an agreement (such as an employment contract or workforce agreement) to be 'working time'. Sensible employers will define 'working time' by agreement from the outset. Records must be kept of time worked. Failure to do so will be a criminal offence, as well as depriving an employer of evidence in disputes with employees. Records need not be kept in relation to those 'opting out' (see section 17.6.3), but it is prudent to keep such records in case of any health and safety challenges from such individuals. Certain days are excluded from the calculation of working time, such as annual leave, sick leave and maternity leave.

17.6.2 Weekly working hours limits

The WTR set a limit of an average 48 hours per week over a standard averaging period of 17 weeks. That can be extended to 26 weeks if the workers are covered by derogations, or up to 12 months by collective or workforce agreement.

Individuals may voluntarily agree to disapply the weekly working hours limit by 'opting out'. They must do so in writing, and the opt-out can last for a fixed period or indefinitely. Any opted-out worker can cancel his or her opt-out by giving at least 7 days' notice, unless the opt-out agreement provides for longer notice, which cannot exceed 3 months.

17.6.3 Measures relating to night time working

The WTR make particular provisions for 'night workers', which limit their shifts and require employers to offer them regular health assessments. These limits are in addition to the limit on average weekly working time.

'Night work' is 11 p.m. to 6 a.m., unless defined by an employment contract, collective agreement or workforce agreement, then being at least 7 hours between 12 a.m. and 5 a.m. Night workers are subject to a limit of an average of 8 hours in each 24-hour period, again over 17 weeks, but this can be extended. Night workers whose work involves special hazards or heavy physical or mental strain are subject to an 8-hour limit for each 24-hour period (without averaging).

Adult night workers must be offered a health assessment (an adolescent worker a 'health and capacities assessment') before being required to perform night work, and periodically thereafter. Those with illnesses relating to night work may have to be moved.

In the case of *SiMap*, the ECJ held that, if there is a business and operational need for a worker to be present on-call at the premises and be available for the purpose of providing continuity of service, this should be viewed as working time.

17.6.4 Rest periods and breaks

Under the WTR, adult workers are entitled to 1 day off each week. Adolescent workers are entitled to 2 days off. Both are subject to derogations in certain circumstances.

Adult workers are entitled to 11 hours' consecutive rest per day. Adolescent workers are entitled to 12 hours' consecutive rest per day. Both are subject to derogations in certain circumstances.

Adult workers are entitled to a minimum 20 minute rest break if their working day is longer than 6 hours. Adolescent workers are entitled to a minimum 30 minute rest break if they work for longer than 4½ hours. Both are subject to derogations in certain circumstances. There is also a requirement to alleviate 'monotonous' work.

17.6.5 Paid annual leave

All workers (including temps) are entitled to 5.6 weeks' paid annual leave (this was increased from 4 weeks in October 2007). This is equivalent to 28 days for a full-time worker who works a 5-day week. No minimum period of continuous service is required to qualify for statutory annual leave.

Unless otherwise stated, for workers already employed on 1 October 1998 the leave year begins on 1 October each year and for workers who started work after 1 October 1998 the leave year begins on the date the employment commenced and each anniversary of that date. A worker whose employment begins part way through a leave year has a *pro-rata* statutory holiday entitlement for that year.

There cannot be payment in lieu except on termination. Employers can require employees to take or postpone leave in certain circumstances, and there are notice provisions for both sides. Where there are part-time workers, it is sensible to make clear how any payment entitlement will be *pro rata*.

Employers have made a number of attempts to 'roll up' holiday pay. Earlier case law laid down guidelines in which rolling up holiday was found to be lawful, however, in *Robinson-Steele v. P D Retail Services Ltd* ECJ held that rolled up holiday pay is unlawful but that any sums already paid to the worker under a rolled up holiday pay scheme could be set off against the holiday pay due to the worker, provided the arrangements are sufficiently transparent and comprehensive and the sums represent an addition to pay for work done. The UK government has not amended the WTR to reflect this decision. However, government guidance does state that rolled up holiday pay should not be made to employees and that contracts allowing it should be renegotiated. Despite this in *Lyddon v. Englefield Brickwork Limited* the EAT found that an employer could offset rolled up holiday pay against a worker's entitlement to annual leave under the WTR where this was transparent and agreed.

However, it is submitted that such decisions are unlikely to be repeated with frequency. In light of the ECJ judgment and government guidance employers are best advised to avoid rolling up holiday pay and adopt alternative arrangements for paying holiday pay.

17.6.6 Derogations

There are certain derogations (i.e. exceptions) to the requirements set out earlier which are summarised later.

(a) *Unmeasured working time*: exceptions from breaks, rest periods, the length of night shifts and the maximum working week. This covers workers whose working time is not measured and/or pre-determined or can be determined themselves. Examples include managing executives and family workers. Effectively these workers will only be subject to the paid annual leave provisions. Also, part of a worker's time (even if other time is fixed) can in certain circumstances be unmeasured where they undertake it voluntarily and not at the employer's direction; obviously, however, this would not include overtime.

(b) *Specified circumstances*: exceptions from breaks, rest periods, and the length of night shifts, as long as the workers receive compensatory rest. The specified circumstances include security and surveillance activities, activities involving the need for continuity of service of production (such as dock work, hospital services, the provision of utilities, civil protection services and agriculture) and where there is a foreseeable surge of activity such as in tourism. Other specified circumstances include the situation where the worker must travel long distances between a temporary place of work (e.g. a site) and home, and it is better to work longer hours for a shorter period to complete the work.

(c) *Force majeure*: where there are unexpected and unpredictable occurrences beyond an employer's control such as imminent danger. Compensatory rest must still be given.

(d) *Shift workers*: exceptions from daily and weekly rest periods exist for workers with a shift pattern where employees succeed each other, but compensatory rest must still be given.

(e) *Collective or workforce agreements*: exceptions from daily and weekly rest periods. Collective agreements can be made with an independent trade union. Workforce agreements can be made with workers where there is no recognised trade union. In the case of workforce agreements, the workforce can either sign the agreement individually (for small firms with under 21 employees) or the workforce can elect representatives to negotiate on their behalf. The WTR provide a mechanism for representatives to be chosen and detail how an agreement is to be reached.

17.6.7 Enforcement

The limits (e.g. which relate to weekly working time and night work) and the obligations to keep detailed records will be enforced by the health and safety enforcing authorities, for example, the Health and Safety Executive and local authorities.

17.7 Collective consultation and industrial relations

17.7.1 When is consultation required?

Collective consultation when there is a transfer of an undertaking or mass dismissals has already been described in sections 17.4.7 and 17.5.7 of this chapter, respectively. Where the employer proposes mass dismissals; for example, because of a tactic of dismissal and re-engagement on new terms to force through a variation of contract, aside from other consequences, the employer will need to consult collectively as if it were a redundancy approach, before any notices of dismissal can be issued. This is because the original European Collective Redundancies Directive, which was implemented in the UK by TULRCA, refers to mass dismissals unrelated to the individual workers, which is wider than the UK perspective of a 'redundancy'.

The ICE Regulations, as referred to in section 17.4.8, may also be applicable here.

Many employers nowadays embrace the notion of a staff council with elected representatives of the workforce. The aim is to provide a forum for consultation over changes, health and safety issues, proposed redundancies, and so on. A staff council does not, however, have a legal standing unless it is part of a European Works Council arrangement. It would not prevent claims for compulsory trade union recognition, as discussed subsequently.

17.7.2 Trade union recognition

The Employment Relations Act 1999 allows employees to have a trade union recognised by their employer where the majority of the relevant workforce wishes it, that is, where a majority of those voting and at least 40% of those eligible to vote are in favour of recognition. A trade union or union seeking recognition to be entitled to conduct collective bargaining for a bargaining unit of workers may make a request to the Central Arbitration Committee (CAC). The scope of collective bargaining is limited to pay, hours, conditions of work and holidays. The request must be preceded by a request to the employer. The employer must employ at least 21 workers when the request is made, or as an average over the last 13 weeks. In the first 10 working days, the employer can end the proceedings by agreeing to a bargaining unit and recognition. Failing that, the employer can indicate a willingness to negotiate for 20 working days after this first period, or longer if both sides agree. If the employer fails to respond or rejects the request in the first 10 working days, the application goes to the CAC. If the negotiations in the 20 working day period fail, the application goes to the CAC, unless the employer proposes that ACAS assist negotiations within 10 working days of stating a willingness to negotiate. In the latter case, the union is barred from proceeding if it rejected the proposal to use ACAS or failed to accept it.

17.7.3 Deciding the bargaining unit

Once an application is before the CAC, the parties must reach an agreement. If there is no agreement, then the CAC itself must decide the appropriate bargaining unit taking into account the following factors:

- the need for the unit to be compatible with the effective management; the views of the employer and the union(s);
- existing national and local bargaining arrangements;
- the desirability of avoiding fragmented bargaining within the undertaking;
- the characteristics of workers within the proposed unit and other employees whom the CAC considers relevant; and
- the location of workers.

17.7.4 Sufficient support

Once the bargaining unit is agreed or decided, the CAC must then decide whether the union is likely to have the support of the majority of the workers in the bargaining unit. If the union shows that the majority are members of the unions, the CAC must automatically award recognition.

Other than in cases of majority membership, the CAC can only proceed with an application by way of a ballot, and then only if at least 10% of the workers are members of the union and there is evidence that a majority would be likely to favour recognition for collective bargaining.

17.7.5 The ballot

The ballot will be conducted independently, with gross costs shared 50–50 between employer and the union. Provided that a majority of the workers voting and 40% or more of the bargaining unit are in favour, recognition will then be granted.

17.7.6 The consequences of recognition

Once recognition is granted, the parties will negotiate for 42 days to agree a method by which they are to conduct collective bargaining. Failing agreement, the CAC must specify a method. No model formula is set out. An agreement reached or specified will have legal effect, and the only remedy available will be specific performance, that is, a court order can compel either side to comply with the prescribed method of collective bargaining.

17.7.7 Derecognition

There is a similar procedure for derecognition. This largely mirrors the recognition procedure, for example, if the employer has less than 21 workers, or at least 10% of the workers favour an end to recognition and there is evidence that a majority would support derecognition. New recognition/derecognition applications to the CAC will only be allowed after 3 years.

Last, but not least, an employee campaigning for recognition will be protected against detrimental treatment. Also, if the employee were dismissed for campaigning, that would automatically be an unfair dismissal, irrespective of length of service, and any selection for redundancy on such a ground would also be unfair.

17.7.8 Existing voluntary trade union recognition

Training will not be automatically covered by an award of trade union recognition. Instead, employers must inform and consult about training with recognised trade unions. If an employer fails to comply, an employment tribunal can award up to two weeks' pay for each employee affected.

17.8 Legislation update: recent and forthcoming legislation

This section gives brief details of recent and forthcoming UK legislation that affects employment.

17.8.1 Recent legislation

17.8.1.1 The Social Security (Medical Evidence) and Statutory Sick Pay (Medical Evidence) (Amendment) Regulations 2010

The government introduced the 'statement of fitness for work', or 'fit note', on 6 April 2010. The regulations replaces 'sick notes' with 'fit notes' to describe when a person is well enough to return work or complete certain tasks.

17.8.1.2 Pension Act 2008

Creates an obligation on employers to enrol all employees in a personal accounts pension scheme or their own qualifying scheme and make minimum contributions. It is expected that most of the provisions will come into force in October 2012.

17.8.1.3 Apprenticeship, Skills Children and Learning Act 2009

The Act reforms the current law on apprenticeship, provisions on which are expected to come into force in 2013. A new right to request time of to study or train is also created has been in force for businesses with 250 or more employees since April 2010 and will be in force for all businesses from April 2011. However, this is under review and is likely to be abolished.

17.8.1.4 The Equality Act 2010

The Act aims to consolidate and simplify discrimination law; however, it also introduces a number of new provisions including:

- a duty on public bodies to reduce socio-economic disadvantage;

- a broadening of the scope for positive discrimination;

- duties on employers to be more transparent in relation to gender pay gaps;

- changes to the comparator in cases of disability discrimination and introduce indirect disability discrimination; and

- an extension of the provisions whereby individuals such as carers may claim 'associative' discrimination.

The majority of the Act's provisions came into force in October 2010.

17.8.2 Forthcoming legislation

17.8.2.1 The Additional Paternity Leave Regulations 2010 and Additional Statutory Paternity Pay (General) Regulations 2010

The regulations give employed fathers, or co-adopter, a new right of up to 26 weeks' additional paternity leave, some of which may be paid if the mother returns to work before the end of her maternity leave period. This will apply for parents of babies born on or after 3 April 2011.

17.8.2.2 Agency Workers' Regulations 2010

Political agreement on the Temporary Agency Workers' Directive was reached in June 2008. The Directive gives temporary agency workers the right to be treated in the same way as the client's workers from the start of their assignment with the client. In the UK agreement has already been reached to derogate from this and temporary workers will only be entitled to equal treatment after a 12-week qualifying period. Further, in the UK equal treatment will not extend to statutory sick pay and pension payments (although under the Pensions Act 2008 agency workers will be entitled to benefits from 2012). The Agency Workers Regulations 2010 are due to come into force in the UK on 1 October 2011.

References

Advisory, Conciliation and Arbitration Service. *Code of practice on discipline and grievance* – Code of Practice 1. TSO, UK, London, 2003. www.acas.org.uk/media/pdf/9/5/CP01_1.pdf (last accessed 18 September, 2010).

Referenced legislation, regulations and standards

Acquired Rights Directive. Council Directive 77/187/EEC of 14 February 1977 on the approximation of the laws of the Member States relating to the safeguarding of employees' rights in the event of transfers of undertakings, businesses or parts of businesses. *OJ* **L061**, 05/03/1977 pp.26–28

Additional Paternity Leave Regulations 2010

Additional Statutory Paternity Pay (General) Regulations 2010

Agency Workers' Regulations 2010

Apprenticeships, Skills, Childcare and Learning Act

Disability Discrimination Act 1995

EC Directive 2001/23/EC of March 2001 on the approximation of the laws of the Member States relating to the safeguarding of employees' rights in the event of transfers of undertakings, businesses or parts of undertakings or businesses. *OJ* **L82**, 22/03/2001. pp.16–20

Employees Regulations 2004 (ICE Regulations)
Employment Relations Act 1999
Employment Act 2002
Employment Act 2008
Employment Equality (Age) Regulations 2006 (Age Regulations)
Employment Equality (Religion or Belief) Regulations 2003
Employment Equality (Sexual Orientation) Regulations 2003
Employment Rights Act 1996
Equality Act 2010
Equal Pay Act 1970
Finance Act 2004
Fixed-term Employees (Prevention of Less Favourable Treatment) Regulations 2002 (Fixed-Term Regulations)
Health and Safety at Work etc. Act 1974
Income Tax (Earnings and Pensions) Act 2003
Intermediaries legislation 2000 (IR35)
National Minimum Wage Act 1998
National Minimum Wage Regulations 1999
Part-time Workers (Prevention of Less Favourable Treatment) Regulations 2000 (Part-Time Workers Regulations)
Pensions Act 2004
Posted Workers' Directive (POWD)
Public Interest Disclosure Act 1998
Race Relations Act 1976
Sex Discrimination Act 1975
Social Security Contributions and Benefits Act 1992
The Social Security (Medical Evidence) and Statutory Sick Pay (Medical Evidence) (Amendment) Regulations 2010
Trade Union and Labour Relations Act 1992
Trade Union and Labour Relations (Consolidation) Act 1992 (TULRCA)
Transfer of Undertakings (Protection of Employment) Regulations 1981

Transfer of Undertakings (Protection of Employment) Regulations 2006 (TUPE)
Working Time Directive. Council Directive 93/104/EC of 23 November 1993 concerning certain aspects of the organization of working time. *OJ* **L307**, 13/12/1993. pp.18–24 (Amended by Directive 2000/34/EC of 22 June 2000; integrated text in Directive 2003/88/EC of 4 November 2003)
Working Time Regulations 1998

Referenced cases

ADT Fire & Security plc v. Speyer
Bilka–Kaufhaus GmbH v. Weber von Hartz
Bleuse v. MBT Transport Limited and Tiefenbacker
Burke v. The British Council
Camerson v. NAAFI
Duncombe & Others v. The Secretary of State for Children, Schools and Families (formerly the Department for Education and Skills)
Lawson v. Serco [2005]
Lyddon v. Englefield Brickwork Limited
Polkey v. A E Dayton Services
Robinson-Steele v. P D Retail Services Ltd

Websites

Advisory, Conciliation and Arbitration Service (ACAS); www.acas.org.uk
Central Arbitration Committee (CAC); www.cac.gov.uk
Construction Industry Scheme (CIS); www.hmrc.gov.uk/cis/intro/whatis-cis.htm
Employment Appeal Tribunal (EAT); www.employmentappeals.gov.uk/
HM Revenue and Customs (HMRC); www.hmrc.gov.uk
HM Revenue and Customs (HMRC); www.hmrc.gov.uk/ir35/

Chapter 18

Intellectual property

Simon Barker Freeth Cartwright LLP, Birmingham, UK
with contribution from **Ian Rogers**, Arup, London, UK

This chapter introduces key intellectual property rights relevant in particular to the UK and the European Union. It comprises information relating to trade marks, copyright, designs, patents, the law of confidentiality and a note on digital media and the internet. In each case it includes a discussion about the scope of those rights, their registration (where applicable), the duration of the rights, how they are infringed, and some defences against infringement, together with an explanation of the remedies available if the rights are found to have been infringed. The principles are illustrated with practical examples relevant to the construction industry.

doi: 10.1680/mocl.40878.0277

CONTENTS

18.1 Trade marks

18.1.1 Introduction

Trade marks are a means of differentiating between one business and another. They designate the origin of goods or services and assist in advertising them. They can also communicate values such as quality, luxury, reliability or even price.

The power of trade marks is perhaps most apparent when considering some of the world's most famous brands. For example, what would Coca-Cola be without its name and distinctive Coca-Cola wave? What would Nike's sports clothing be without a Swoosh? And what do you think when you see the words Rolls Royce?

Whatever the brand conveys it becomes something which customers relate to and identify with in the marketplace.

It follows that trade marks are extremely valuable to business in building reputation and goodwill. Therefore the ability to control the use of trade marks provides an essential means of defending market share, protecting against unfair competition and damage to reputation.

Registering a trade mark offers the owner control by granting an exclusive right to use the mark in the course of trade on goods or services for which the mark is registered.

18.1.2 Registration requirements

In the UK it is possible to obtain protection by registering a trade mark at a national level and to obtain a British registered trade mark. The UK Intellectual Property Office is responsible for administering the UK system. An alternative is to register your trade mark at a European level so that the mark is protected across all Member States of Europe (currently 27 [2010]). This is called a Community Trade Mark (CTM) and these are administered by the Office of Harmonisation for the Internal Market (OHIM).

In this way, marks are territorial in nature. Therefore it is necessary to register marks in each of the territories or countries where protection is required. In the UK and other countries of Europe the CTM is a common alternative to

registering a national mark due to the wider geographical protection available.

This discussion will be restricted to considering the UK and the Community systems.

Before a mark can be registered it must satisfy certain criteria. Firstly it must be capable of being graphically represented and be distinctive. In other words it must be sufficiently certain and capable of distinguishing the goods of one undertaking from those of another. This is at the heart of what a trade mark does and means that descriptive signs or ones that indicate kind, quality or geographical locations are not effective as trade marks and cannot be registered. The rationale behind this is that such signs should be free for everyone to use.

Every trade mark application is examined against these criteria and may be refused on this basis.

Another problem that can affect the function of a trade mark is the possibility of earlier trade marks that conflict with the later mark. If someone else is already using a mark that is identical or similar to a proposed trade mark then the ability of the earlier mark to distinguish the goods or services of its owner may be adversely affected. Of course, this is likely where the goods or services are identical or similar. Therefore, trade marks are registered for specific goods and/or services, which are defined by classes according to the Nice classification system (see World Intellectual Property Organization (WIPO) website). For example, consultancy services relating to construction are categorised in Class 37 and building products are to be found in Class 19.

This provides a basis upon which registration may be challenged by the owners of earlier trade marks. However, refusal is not automatic at the time of examination by the UK Registry or OHIM, which means that the owners of earlier rights have to prove that there is a likelihood of confusion between their mark and the applicant's mark. Earlier rights holders are able to challenge applications for later marks by filing an opposition notice with the UK Registry or OHIM.

Owners of famous registered trade marks may also oppose applications on grounds that without due cause the mark applied for takes unfair advantage of and/or is detrimental to the distinctive character of their mark.

Perhaps more importantly though, any applicant for registration of a trade mark will want to ensure that there is no likelihood of confusion before they use a mark because any such use may amount to trade mark infringement (if the earlier mark is registered) or passing off (if unregistered). These issues are discussed in more detail later.

18.1.3 Duration

Registered trade marks may last indefinitely subject to payment of renewal fees every 10 years. However, it is important to note that registered trade marks will become susceptible to revocation if they are not used for a continuous period of 5 years in respect of the goods and services for which they are registered. Therefore in order to maintain trade mark protection the proprietor must ensure use of the mark on those goods and services for which protection is required.

18.1.4 Infringement

A person infringes a registered trade mark if he uses in the course of trade a sign that is identical to the registered mark in relation to identical goods or services, provided such use adversely affects the guarantee of origin (intrinsic to trade mark protection) or such other functions of trade marks that are discussed earlier, including its functions of communication and advertising. At the time of writing there is debate over these latter functions but what is important is that confusion of the public is not required to find infringement on this basis.

However, akin to the essential function of a trade mark, infringement will occur where a person uses in the course of trade a sign that is identical to or similar to the registered trade mark, in relation to identical or similar goods to those for which the trade mark is registered, where there is a likelihood of confusion on the part of the relevant public, or a likelihood of association with the trade mark owner. Such an association can be the suggestion of a business connection with the trade mark proprietor or an impression that the infringer is authorised or licensed by the proprietor to use the mark.

As can be seen from the above these are equivalent grounds to those upon which a trade mark proprietor may oppose registration of a later mark on the basis of its earlier rights. It will not be surprising then that the proprietor of a famous mark might also be able to establish infringement of its registered trade mark if, without due cause, a third party uses the mark or a similar mark in the course of trade (in relation to any goods or services) where such use takes unfair advantage of or is detrimental to the distinctive character of the mark. Taking unfair advantage is commonly referred to as free riding on the repute and prestige of the famous mark in order to obtain some commercial advantage. This type of infringement is the subject of much debate at the time of writing. Detriment to distinctive character, however, refers to the damage that may be done to

the trade mark's unique guarantee of origin and repute, which may be by dilution or tarnishing of reputation.

18.1.5 Defences

A registered trade mark will not be infringed by a third party if that person uses the mark to describe the kind, quality, intended purpose or other characteristics of the goods or where its use is necessary to indicate the intended purpose of a product or service (i.e. as accessories or spare parts), provided the use is in accordance with honest practices in industrial or commercial matters.

A British trade mark will not be infringed by the use of a sign which is registered as a British trade mark provided the mark is not invalid due to an earlier right. However, this defence is not available in respect of CTMs.

Also, if a person has used an unregistered mark continuously in relation to goods and services in the UK (or in the case of CTMs a substantial part of the European Union [EU]) then its use in relation to those goods and services will not infringe a later registered mark.

18.1.5.1 Remedies

In urgent cases, where a trade mark proprietor stands to suffer substantial financial damage or damage to reputation, it may be possible to obtain an emergency injunction restraining infringement of the trade mark pending determination of the dispute. In addition to injunctive relief other remedies will include an order for delivery up or destruction of the infringing goods (i.e. goods bearing the unlawful sign) and an order for an enquiry as to damages or an account of profits made from the unlawful activity. Typically, the measure of damages will include the lost profit on lost sales or if no lost sales then compensation on a royalty basis and damages for any other loss which may have been suffered, such as damage to reputation and so on.

18.1.6 Passing off

The law of passing off 'does what it says on the tin'. It is a common law action which has developed over the past 400 years (i.e. one which is not determined by statute) that can be used to restrain one man passing off his goods or services as those of another. Commonly, this occurs where the wrongdoer uses a sign which is identical to or similar to the complainant's mark and which is calculated to deceive the customer into believing that the goods or services originate from the complainant, or there is some association with him. The reader will immediately appreciate that conceptually this is not very different to the grounds for establishing trade mark infringement where there exists a likelihood of confusion and/or association with the registered trade mark proprietor. The key difference in this illustration lies in the fact that the sign used is not registered as a trade mark. This is why the law of passing off is sometimes referred to as the law relating to the use of unregistered trade marks.

However, strictly the law of passing off protects the misappropriation of goodwill and reputation in a business. Accordingly any misrepresentation which is calculated to deceive the consumer (i.e. causes or is likely to cause confusion) and which causes damage, such as lost sales or damage to reputation, will amount to passing off.

The misrepresentation may arise in a third party copying the look or feel of a product (sometimes referred to as 'get-up'). In the well known 'JIF Lemon case', *Reckitt & Colman* successfully sued Borden for passing off their product as JIF Lemon because they had sold lemon juice in a similar lemon-shaped plastic bottle.

The law has also been extended to cases where a third party presents the work of another as his own. This form of misrepresentation is sometimes referred to as 'reverse passing off' and was found in the case of *Bristol Conservatories* where the defendant in that case had presented customers with pictures of conservatories built by *Bristol Conservatories* as examples of their own work.

18.1.6.1 Remedies

The remedies available in a case of passing off are equivalent to those in a trade mark action. However, establishing passing off is generally more difficult than proving infringement of a registered trade mark. In a trade mark case the mere registration of the mark is enough to prove entitlement whereas in a case of passing off it is necessary to prove ownership of goodwill; often with evidence of substantial sales over many years in relation to the subject of the misrepresentation relied upon. Also, it is necessary to establish damage to actually succeed.

Therefore it is advisable for any business to consider carefully what marks can be protected by registering them as trade marks. The same is true in relation to intellectual property generally: the more consideration given to protection of such rights at the outset the better chance of enforcing them later. See **Box 1** for an example of trademarks and passing off in action.

18.2 Copyright

Copyright, put simply, is the right to make copies. It is not a registered right but one that arises automatically in relation to a particular copyright work and then only when that work is first written down or 'fixed' in a tangible form. What this means in practice is that copyright does not subsist in relation to the idea for a work (maybe a building or a new design for a wallpaper) but only in the expression of that idea, namely the resulting drawing or painting.

The scope of works that may be protected under the law of copyright are numerous and include literary works such as books, manuscripts and computer programs; artistic works such as paintings, drawings and photographs; musical works such as music and sound recordings; films and works of architecture. In the construction world copyright will be most relevant in relation to architects' drawings, architecture and models for buildings.

Box 1 Trademarks and passing off in action

A consultant decides to launch a software tool which may be used by engineers in pile re-use projects, to assess pile capacity. A decision is made to call the software 'Pile Capacity Predict'. The consultant contacts a trade mark attorney and his solicitor who both advise that the proposed mark is descriptive and a registration unlikely to be granted. The consultant still wishes to market the software under this name, and to confer a degree of uniqueness to his marketing, devises a logo involving a red arrow sitting on a black rectangle, all in a red triangle.

The Attorney applies to register the software in Class 9. A notice of opposition is received from an individual who has recently set up in business as a supplier of computer hardware into visual arts and theatre businesses. The individual argues that the mark is confusingly similar to his (unregistered) logo. The consultant refines his application to refer only to technical software for use in the construction industry.

The individual is satisfied by this amendment and agrees to withdraw his opposition provided that the consultant does not use the mark in relation to software for use in the visual arts and theatre sector.

There remains a danger that the hardware supplier will bring a claim in 'passing off', but as the area of business is different, and the hardware supplier has a small operation without an established reputation, that claim should not succeed. Nevertheless the consultant requests and the individual agrees not to sue for passing off as a result of the consultant's use of the mark, provided he does not use it in the visual arts and theatre sector. The opposition settles on this basis and the Trade Mark Registry is not asked to decide the matter.

Another qualifying criterion is that the work must be original. One might think this to be a difficult test given that the body of work in any particular field could be enormous, not least in the field of architecture. However, the threshold for originality is low. What is required is that the work is not copied and results from the skill, judgement and labour of its creator.

The first owner of copyright in a particular work will be its author except in the case of an employee where the first owner will be his or her employer. What this means is that it is important for a business to ensure that copyright in any work created by a subcontractor (i.e. non-employee) is properly assigned to the business.

In order to prove ownership and indeed subsistence of copyright it is also important to prove when the work was created, by whom, and in certain cases when it was first published in the UK.

Alongside copyright the authors of works have separate personal rights, known as moral rights. These include the right to be identified as the author and the right to object to derogatory treatment of a work. These rights may be asserted by authors except in the case of employees against employers. Once again, it may be important to ensure that any subcontractors waive their moral rights if the contractor wishes to take the work free of them.

18.2.1 Duration

In the UK copyright in literary, musical and artistic works (including works of architecture) lasts for 70 years from the end of the year in which the author dies. Therefore copyright has the potential to last for a long time.

18.2.2 Infringement

A person infringes copyright where, without the consent of the copyright owner, they copy a work, distribute copies to the public, communicate them electronically (e.g. over the internet), or possess or deal with infringing copies, when they know or have reason to believe that they are infringing. It follows therefore that copyright owners should ensure that all drawings are marked with a suitable copyright notice.

In the context of architectural plans, or designs for buildings, it is important to understand that infringement may arise by copying the plans as drawings and/or erecting a building in accordance with such drawings, where they are subject to copyright protection.

Copyright protection will apply generally to building designs, plot layouts and interior designs. However, where architects are involved in design of fixtures and fittings, furniture or storage solutions, these may fall outside the ambit of copyright and into the realms of design protection (see subsequently). The reason for this is that while design drawings are protected as artistic works copyright is only infringed by the manufacture of an article to the design if the article is itself an artistic work. Therefore unauthorised photocopying of a drawing for the design of a door handle (for example) would amount to an infringement of copyright in the drawing but making the door handle to the design would not infringe that copyright. Such articles can only be protected by registered design or design right law.

18.2.3 Licences of copyright

As with all intellectual property rights, copyright can be licensed on a formal basis allowing the copyright owner to exploit his rights in return for lump sum or continuing payments called royalties. In the case of architectural or building designs, particularly those commissioned by clients, there will usually be an implied licence of copyright in the absence of a formal agreement.

Difficulties arise where architects are unpaid for drawings or where there is a change in architect on a project, perhaps where there has been a change in ownership of the land in a development. In these circumstances the extent to which a new developer or architect can use existing drawings is often a question that is fought over. The answer will be a question of fact in each case, which is hardly satisfactory, and an architect in such circumstances may well find that he is left with only a right to sue for the cost of the plans rather than for infringement of copyright. Where licences are implied by the law they will invariably extend to successors in title and will allow for rights of repair. Therefore, it is usually important to consider any contractual arrangements at the outset and to deal specifically with some of these issues.

18.2.4 Defences

In the UK the defences to copyright infringement are few and are restricted to fair dealing for the purpose of news reporting and non-commercial research amongst other rather specific

defences, none of which are likely to have application in the field of construction.

18.2.5 Remedies

The usual remedies are available to a successful claimant and include an injunction, damages (or an account of profits), destruction or delivery up of infringing goods and additional damages if the infringement is flagrant and the defendant has benefitted.

18.2.6 Criminal sanctions

Although there are criminal offences relating to breaches of copyright it is unlikely that these will be relevant to readers interested in the construction field. Prosecutions are more likely in relation to counterfeit goods. See **Box 2** for an example of copyright in action.

Box 2 Copyright in action

An architect is commissioned to prepare designs for the masterplan of a prominent docklands site. The designs are innovative and as part of the commission, images are prepared in soft and hard copy format and delivered to the client, and incorporated on the client's website.

Later, the architect places the images on its website as examples of its work. The client objects, stating that it owns the copyright. The architect checks the appointment signed with the client and is reminded that it had assigned all intellectual property in deliverables to the client. This did not seem to be a major issue to the architect when he bid for the project.

An engineer, later commissioned by the client to undertake detailed engineering design for the site, includes the same images in his marketing brochures. The architect objects but is informed that the engineer's client has agreed to such use. The architect seeks legal advice and is informed that the only option he has is to require the engineer to identify him as author of the images on the basis of A's moral rights in the images.

If, as is often the case, the architect's appointment had required him to waive moral rights, he would have been left with no remedy. It is important that consultants consider the intellectual property clauses in the contracts they are asked to sign.

18.3 Registered designs and unregistered design rights

The law on designs protects the appearance of products. In a construction context the sort of designs that may be protected could encompass a very wide range of products indeed, such as designs for roof panels and other building products such as specialist fasteners or fixings, panels, door furniture, flooring, lighting, safety equipment, windows, doors and blinds to name a few.

There are a number of forms of protection that may be available for any one design. These include UK registered designs (UKRD), registered Community (EU wide) designs (RCDs), UK unregistered design right (UKUDR) and Community unregistered design right (CUDR). As with CTMs, RCDs and CURDs afford protection across all the member states of Europe.

18.3.1 Registered designs

18.3.1.1 Registered designs – requirements for registration

The law on RCDs arises from European Council Regulation No. 6/2002 on Community Designs and the law on UKRDs from the amended Registered Designs Act 1949. Subject to some small differences, the protection of designs under each of these laws is effectively the same now. Therefore RCDs and UKRDs are dealt with together in this section.

As with trade marks the Community registered design system is administered by OHIM and the UK Registered Design system is administered by the UK Intellectual Property Office.

Registered designs (both UKRDs and RCDs) protect the appearance of the whole or part of a product resulting from its lines, contours, colours, shape, texture or the materials of the product or its ornamentation.

In order to qualify for protection the design must be new and possess individual character.

A design will be new if no identical design (or one differing only in immaterial detail) has been made available to the public before the date the design is applied for. However, for these purposes any disclosure made by the designer up to 12 months preceding the date of application for protection will not be treated as being made available to the public. The practical effect is to grant the proprietor a 12-month grace period in which to file for design registration.

A design will possess individual character if its overall impression on an informed user differs from the overall impression produced on such a user by any design made available to the public before the date of application. The extent to which a design has individual character also depends on the design freedom of the designer creating it. However, protection will not extend to designs that are solely dictated by function or which must fit other products (except designs within a modular system, which might be the case for certain building products such as specially designed bricks).

Therefore, the protection of a design by registration will depend upon previous designs ('the prior art'), the character of the informed user in the relevant field and the designer's design freedom. Thus, if there is less design freedom then smaller differences may be afforded protection.

Although these are the requirements for protection, applications for registration are not slavishly examined against them. This means that there may be many design registrations in the UK and Community Registers which, if challenged, may fall foul of these provisions. This is in marked contrast to patent applications (see subsequently), which are examined more closely against earlier patent applications.

18.3.1.2 Registered designs – duration

Both UKRDs and RCDs are relatively cheap and quick to obtain. Both can last for up to 25 years from the date of registration, subject to renewal every 5 years. Therefore design protection can offer a simple and inexpensive way to supplement protection of a product in addition to brand (trade mark) protection.

18.3.1.3 Registered designs – infringement

Such protection affords the owner an exclusive right to use the design and any design which does not create on the informed user an overall different impression. What this means is that a person infringes the registered design if he does anything which is the exclusive right of the registered proprietor.

It is not necessary to prove copying of the design to establish infringement. Therefore, the knowledge of the infringer is irrelevant *except* that a claimant will not be entitled to damages where a defendant can prove that he was not aware and had no reasonable grounds for supposing that the design was registered. For this reason it is important that owners of registered designs ensure that designs (and packaging) are marked appropriately.

18.3.1.4 Registered designs – ownership

For the purposes of determining ownership the first owner will be the person who creates the design unless the design is created by an employee in the course of his or her employment, in which case the original proprietor of the design shall be his or her employer.

There is a further exception in the case of UKRD so that where a design is created in pursuance of a commission for money (or money's worth), the person commissioning the design shall be treated as the original proprietor. Therefore, in the context of a construction project the client could be entitled to any UKRD arising in connection with a project unless there is an agreement to the contrary. The position is different for RCDs where the creator of the design rather than a commissioner will be entitled to register the design.

The lesson, as with other intellectual property rights, is that in any collaboration it is important to agree (or at least understand) from the outset who will be entitled to ownership of any rights arising from the project. This applies to a construction project as it does to any other.

18.3.2 Unregistered design rights

Unregistered design rights arise automatically. One crucial difference with registered designs is the requirement to prove copying in order to establish infringement. This is not always easy and therefore the exclusive monopoly right afforded by registration is preferable to relying on unregistered rights alone.

18.3.3 UK unregistered design right

UKUDR protects original designs. A design is defined as meaning any aspect of the shape or configuration (whether internal or external) of the whole or part of an article. However, UKUDR does not subsist in methods or principles of construction, or designs which must fit or must match other articles, or designs which amount to surface decoration.

As with UKRDs, the owner of the UKUDR will be the designer (or his or her employer or commissioner if applicable).

UKUDR arises automatically on the making of an article to a particular design or by the creation of a design document by a qualified person (or by a person employed by a qualified person). A qualified person is a national or resident of the EU or other certain specified territories.

18.3.3.1 UK unregistered design right – duration

UKUDR continues either for 15 years from the end of the calendar year in which the design was recorded or an article was first made to the design, or for 10 years from the end of the calendar year in which articles made to the design were first made available for sale or hire provided that date is within 5 years of the end of the calendar year in which the design was first recorded or an article was first made to the design. Therefore depending on the relevant dates UKUDR will last for between (approximately) 10 and 15 years.

However, in the last 5 years of UKUDR any person is entitled to apply for a licence as of right and to have the terms of any such licence determined by The Comptroller-General of Patents, Design and Trade Marks, if terms cannot be agreed between the design right owner and the proposed licensee.

Therefore, it can be seen that there are limitations to the scope and duration of protection under the law of UKUDRs and that registration of designs will, in most cases, be a preferable form of protection.

18.3.3.2 UK unregistered design right – infringement

The owner of UKUDR has the exclusive right to reproduce designs for commercial purposes (i.e. with a view to the sale or hire of an article to the design). Reproduction of the design can be either by making articles to the design or by making design documents for the purpose of enabling such articles to be made. However, as discussed earlier, it is also necessary to prove copying of the design and to show that the article copied is either identical to the design in question or substantially the same.

A person may also be liable for secondary infringement if, without licence of the owner, he possesses, sells, hires or offers for sale or hire, or imports an infringing article, where he knows or has reason to believe that such article is an infringing article.

Infringing articles are those whose making is an infringement of the UKUDR or ones which are imported and their making to the design in the UK would have been an infringement of the UKUDR.

As with UKRDs, damages are not available in the case of innocent infringement where the defendant did not know and had no reason to believe that UK design right subsisted in the design. Otherwise the usual remedies of injunctive relief and delivery up of infringing articles or their destruction are allowed.

In cases where damages are appropriate the court may also award additional damages either because of the flagrancy of infringement or because of the benefit accruing to the defendant.

18.3.4 Community unregistered design right

CUDR arises automatically when the design is first made available to the public in the European Community and it lasts for 3 years from that date. The protected design may be the whole or part of any product (internal or external) resulting from its lines, contours, colours, shape, texture or the materials of the product or its ornamentation. However, for CUDR to subsist the design must fulfil the requirements of novelty and individual character as described earlier in relation to registered designs.

The benefit of this right is limited by its short duration. However, the scope of protection in terms of the aspects of a design which can be protected, such as texture, colours or materials, may make it more useful that UKUDR in the short-term and in the context of products one might find in the construction industry.

As with UKUDR the CUDR does not create a monopoly right as such, and in order to prove infringement it is also necessary to prove copying.

18.3.5 Defences generally

A common line of defence is to argue that the relevant design is not new or does not possess individual character (i.e. in the case of UKRDs, RCDs and CUDRs) or is commonplace (i.e. in the case of UKUDR) taking into account earlier designs. In other words it is argued that the rights claimed are either invalid because they do not meet the requirements for protection or in the case of unregistered design right because such a right does not subsist in the first place. Thus intellectual property rights may be subject to careful checks and balances to ensure that any monopoly is justly afforded.

18.3.6 Practicalities

Designers or those commissioning design will want to ensure that they are able to prove when a design was created, by whom and when, when products to the design were first marketed and where. Therefore it is important that they keep all design documents, showing the development of a design and have them dated, signed and kept for safe keeping either electronically or in hard copy. See **Box 3** for an example of registered and unregistered designs in action.

Box 3 Registered and unregistered designs in action

A specialist supplier of reinforced concrete beams identifies a new and improved way of connecting his beams to the columns in a pre-cast concrete car park. This involves modifying the shape of the ends of the beam. The new beams are widely accepted, and before long a rival supplier starts offering an identical product at a cheaper price.

The rival's new offering follows the departure of the supplier's technical director, who has set up a consultancy and is working for the rival, so the supplier concludes that the rival is copying his designs.

18.4 Patents

Patents protect inventions. One way to think of them is in terms of the way a product or a process works. So, whereas a method of construction may be excluded from protection as a design it might be protected under the law of patents.

Once granted patents offer the strongest monopoly right of all the intellectual property rights. This is owed in some part to the fact that each application is carefully examined against the criteria for protection.

18.4.1 Criteria for patentability

An invention may be protected by a patent if:

1. it is new;
2. it is not obvious to someone with a good working knowledge of the subject;
3. it is capable of being used in industry; and
4. it is not excluded from protection.

The novelty requirement is fundamental to anyone thinking about applying for patent protection. The reason for this is that a disclosure of the invention anywhere in the world to anyone (not bound by an obligation to keep the invention secret) will negate the novelty requirement and will leave any granted patent open to attack on grounds that the invention is not new. In the UK there is no grace period of 12 months as in the case of registered designs and therefore the novelty requirement is a strict one.

For these reasons it is important for inventors (and owners in rights to inventions) to ensure that any third parties to whom the invention is disclosed sign up to non-disclosure agreements (see subsequently).

Whether an invention is obvious may be a more difficult question and will depend upon what inventions there have been in the relevant field before (i.e. the prior art), and also what would be understood as common general knowledge by a person skilled in the relevant subject.

18.4.2 Ownership

As with the creation of designs and copyright works it is also important to ensure that there is a written agreement with any third party who is collaborating on a project that may result in a new invention or other intellectual property right. Such an agreement should ensure not only confidentiality (see above) but also deal with ownership of any resulting invention (and other intellectual property) in addition to the rights to apply for patents and designs.

Such agreements should extend to all third parties, including non-employee individuals. The reason for this is that, as with copyright and certain design protection, the inventor is the first person entitled to apply for a patent unless that person is an employee, and the invention was created in the ordinary course of his or her duties of employment, in which case the invention shall belong to the employer.

18.4.3 Duration

Once granted a patent affords a monopoly of 20 years from the date of filing the application for the patent, subject to payment of annual renewal fees.

18.4.4 Infringement

A person infringes a patent in the UK if in relation to the invention for a product he makes, disposes of, or offers to dispose of, uses or imports the product. If the patented invention relates to a process then a person infringes the patent by using the process or offering it for use when he knows or it is obvious to a reasonable person that use of the process would be an infringement of the patent. Infringement may also occur by possessing or offering to dispose of a product or importing a product made by means of a patented process or by providing someone with means relating to an essential element of the invention.

Whether a product or process comes within the scope of a patent is often the subject of much argument and will depend upon the way in which the monopoly is claimed in the patent.

The remedies for infringement are the same as with other intellectual property rights save that like UKRD there is a restriction on the recovery of damages against a defendant who proves that at the date of infringement he was not aware, and had no reasonable grounds for supposing that the patent existed. Accordingly patent owners should ensure that patented products and relevant information are marked with the relevant patent number and a notice referring to the fact that the product or process is covered by a patent.

18.4.5 Defences

In addition to various specific defences it is important to note that acts done privately and not for commercial purposes do not infringe a patent.

As in the case of designs another common form of defence is to attack the validity of the patent. Typically, this is done by citing pieces of prior art and alleging that the patent is invalid because it is not new or because it is obvious. For this reason careful consideration is required when applying for patent rights. Any patent owner will want to ensure that the invention claimed is as broadly defined as possible to catch infringers but not so broad that the patent will be vulnerable to attack on these grounds.

The law on patents is complicated and, as with other intellectual property rights, professional advice and assistance will be required. However, the UK Intellectual Property Office website has more information on the subject of patents and other rights for the interested reader.

See **Box 4** for an example of patents 'in action'.

Box 4 Patents in action

A lighting supplier is approached by a foreign university which has a suite of patents in the field of low-energy lighting for buildings. The university wishes to establish a joint venture company (JVCo), with each taking a 50% shareholding. The intention is that the university's contribution is an exclusive licence of its patents to JVCo, whilst the supplier is expected to contribute £1m in cash to the new company.

The supplier needs to know that the patents which are licensed are worth the £1m sought and initiates a due diligence exercise. What is he looking for? He needs to check that:

1. The University owns the patents in question (rather than the individual research students).
2. The patents are in force in the territories in which he wishes to do business.
3. The patents cover the target area of business. For example, the patents may describe technology which works on a domestic scale but not at higher powers associated with industrial use.
4. Each patent is robust, that is, the technology is new, not obvious, capable of industrial use and not excluded from registration (just because a local Patent Office has granted a patent does not mean it is incapable of later challenge).
5. Whether any other licences have been granted (such licensees could set up a rival business and undermine the value of the JVCo's licence).
6. The extent to which the JVCo has 'freedom to operate': what other organisations does the JVCo need to seek licences from in order to exploit its patents.

Such a due diligence exercise can take many months to finalise and may cost many tens of thousands of pounds. It is also unlikely to be conclusive; nonetheless, it can offer a measure of comfort as to the other party's contribution. The alternative would be to seek contractual warranties from the counterparty in the shareholder's agreement as to the validity of the patents. However, it is usual for such warranties to be resisted or qualified.

Any organisation wishing to become involved in such a venture needs to be aware of the time, cost and uncertainty associated with a due diligence exercise of this sort.

18.5 Law of confidentiality

The law of confidentiality is often the only way to protect information or materials which cannot be protected by intellectual property rights such as patents; for example, mathematical or business methods, both of which are excluded from patent protection. However, confidentiality is also important in protecting information which might be patentable because as explained earlier any disclosure which is not made in confidence has the potential to destroy the patentability of the product or process concerned.

The types of information that may be protected is very wide and will extend to all sorts of information: financial information; personal information; plans and drawings; formulae and recipes which are not capable of being analysed from the final

product; customer lists; and know-how in relation to industrial processes.

18.5.1 Principles of protection

To be protected the relevant information must (a) have the necessary quality of confidence; and (b) be disclosed in circumstances importing an obligation of confidence.

For the information to be confidential it must not be public or within public knowledge. Difficulties arise where information can be pieced together from information in the public domain, such as customer lists. In these cases the information may be confidential in nature if it has been developed as a product of the human brain that is worthy of protection. If information such as customer lists are not confidential then they may nevertheless qualify for database right protection (see subsequently).

An obligation of confidence in respect of confidential information arises in three ways:

1. it is imposed by a contract;
2. it is implied because of the circumstances of disclosure; or
3. it is implied because there is a special relationship between the recipient and the disclosing party, such as employee and employer.

The best way of ensuring that information is disclosed in circumstances importing an obligation of confidence is through a written contract. These are often referred to as confidentiality agreements or non-disclosure agreements. These enable the confidential information and the obligations of the recipient to be clearly defined.

To decide whether an obligation of confidence arises out of the circumstances of disclosure is more difficult and will depend upon whether a reasonable man in the place of the recipient would realise that the information was being given to him in confidence.

Therefore in circumstances where there is no special relationship, for example, when disclosing confidential information to contractors or subcontractors, it may be important for the disclosing party to ensure that an appropriate confidentiality agreement is reached.

The duration of protection will depend on the nature of the confidential information and on the basis for its protection. For example, an employee will generally only be bound for so long he or she is employed unless the information is a trade secret that is capable of being kept confidential forever. Confidentiality agreements will usually be limited in time and the information itself may no longer be confidential in nature after a period of time.

There are other limits to the protection of confidential information. For example, if disclosure is made to a public authority it may be subject to a request under freedom of information legislation, or be the subject of a court order requiring disclosure.

Therefore, a confidentiality agreement may not cover it and, in any event, may be useless if breached by a recipient who without financial means may not be able to pay damages in compensation of the breach.

Although the information in this chapter is concentrated on the law of England and Wales, it is also worth mentioning that foreign laws will treat the law on confidentiality differently so that in some jurisdictions a contract is strictly required and in others not.

18.5.2 Remedies

The usual remedies of damages or an account of profits are available if a breach of confidence is established and it can be demonstrated that losses arise from the breach. Injunctions may also be granted restraining the use of confidential information, particularly before any breach of confidentiality if the disclosing party hears of the recipient's intentions before they disclose the information. However, once information has been used or disclosed then an injunction will be of little use. Nevertheless, in some cases a court may be persuaded to grant an injunction for a limited period, where, for example, the use of the confidential information has enabled the wrongdoer to obtain a head start in a market or a 'springboard', as it is sometimes referred to.

18.5.3 Practicalities

The best way to protect confidential information is not to disclose it. Other ways to protect the information might be to limit its disclosure by restricting the number of recipients or by disclosing the information in parts over time.

Other practical measures include ensuring that drawings and documents are marked confidential and that they are kept securely.

18.6 Digital media and the internet

The advent of the internet and digital media has presented new challenges to the protection of intellectual property rights. In the digital world vast amounts of information can be stored, copied and transmitted anywhere in the world in a matter of minutes. The result is that it is easier than ever for copyists and counterfeiters to share information and turn out copied products or plagiarise content on the internet.

Many databases are now online making it easier for large parts to be copied electronically.

The worldwide web created a new market for the sale of goods and a new forum in which to trade off the goodwill of others. This has lead to various controversies, including complaints over Google's AdWord service, which permits the use of third party trade marks as key words. Domain names are another area of dispute, which if similar to others' trade marks can lead to confusion and complaint.

In response to (and some might argue in the spirit of) the internet certain groups have decided to embrace this new

environment. A good example is the increase in open source software and copyright licensing. However, it is important to realise that open source materials are not necessarily free to use in any way one might choose. They are subject to terms; so, for example, if open source code is incorporated into another computer program the licence might dictate that it is to be licensed on the similar terms and may not be sold commercially without payment of a fee.

See **Box 5** for an example of digital media and the internet 'in action'.

Box 5 Digital media and the internet in action

A consultant bids for an important piece of work. In preparing his bid he downloads maps and photographic images of the project site from Google Maps. The images are readily accessible and, apparently, freely available; the Google pages are not obviously restricted. The bid is submitted. Meanwhile his managing director (MD) attends a talk by a law firm in which the dangers of copyright infringement are described. The MD asks the consultant to check whether permission was required to include the maps and images in the bid. The consultant discovers that the licence he has quickly clicked through is for personal, that is, non-commercial, use only. Any commercial use is an infringement of the intellectual property rights of the copyright holder (Google in this example).

On learning this the MD applies for an 'Enterprise' licence from Google. This licence enables his firm to use copyrighted information from Google Maps, including, for example, StreetView photographic images, in future bids, reports and presentations and otherwise for the purposes of commercial gain.

18.6.1 Database right

In 1996, the EU Database Directive brought in a new form of protection for databases. Although databases are defined broadly and do not necessarily have to be electronic, the rules are nevertheless applicable to online databases as they are to other forms of database.

The right protects a database where there has been a substantial investment in obtaining, verifying or presenting the contents of the database. It does not extend to resources used to create the data within the database. What this means is that the content has to be independently created. Therefore, it is often difficult to establish the right where the content is created by the maker because it is difficult to show the necessary investment in presentation. Nevertheless, where content is created the database may qualify for copyright protection if it constitutes the author's own intellectual creation (i.e. as a result of real skill and knowledge).

The 'maker' of the database will be the first owner of database right and the right lasts for 15 years from the end of the calendar year in which the database was completed or first made available to the public.

A person infringes database right if they extract or re-utilise all or a substantial part of the database.

See **Box 6** for an example of database right 'in action'.

Box 6 Database right in action

As part of a private research project, a transport consultant employs 20 contract staff to count vehicle movements at a number of locations across a city. The movements are compiled into an extensive 'Excel' spreadsheet which the transport consultant later licenses to a developer for a fee. The Developer sells the site and emails the spreadsheet to the purchaser, who reproduces it as part of a planning application. The transport consultant is entitled to take action against the purchaser for infringement of his database right. The purchaser agrees to appoint the consultant for the project, paying him a fee which reflects the commercial value of the database.

18.6.2 Domain names

Domain names are electronic addresses on the internet for webpages. Most businesses have a website these days and the domain name will often reflect the name of the business or some aspect of it. Accordingly they can be a valuable asset to any business and can be bought and sold like any other property right.

Different domain names are administered by different Registries and registered by different Registrars. For example, Nominet is the Registry for .uk domain names.

Each Registry has a policy and a form of dispute resolution. Generally if a third party registers a domain name which is identical or confusing similar to a trade mark, with no legitimate right to the domain name, and the domain name has been registered and/or is being used in bad faith then it will be an abusive registration. An abusive registration will entitle the trade mark owner to request transfer of the domain name, subject to the Registry's domain name dispute resolution procedure.

In serious cases where use of the domain name infringes a person's registered trade mark or constitutes passing off (see above) then another option may be to issue proceedings in court and, if necessary, apply for an injunction restraining the infringement as well as transfer of the domain name and damages.

18.6.3 Content copying

Copying from a website might include any number of issues but is increasingly prevalent. If text or images are copied then there may be a claim for copyright infringement. If the website constitutes a look-a-like and uses third party trade marks then there may be passing off and trade mark infringement. However, in some cases the worldwide nature of the internet can mean that it is difficult or costly to get at the individuals concerned. In other cases, it will be appropriate to notify the

ISP responsible for hosting the website, and to put them on notice of the infringement.

References

Referenced legislation, regulations and standards

Council Regulation (EC) No 6/2002 of 12 December 2001 on community designs. *OJ*, **L3**, 05/01/2002, p.1), [amended by Council Regulation No 1891/2006 of 18 December 2006 amending Regulations (EC) No 6/2002 and (EC) No 40/94 to give effect to the accession of the European Community to the Geneva Act of the Hague Agreement concerning the international registration of industrial designs. *OJ*, **L386**, 29/12/2006, p.14)]

Directive 96/9/EC of the European Parliament and of the Council of 11 March 1996 on the legal protection of databases. *OJ*, **L077**, 27/03/1996, pp.20–28. (*EU Database Directive*)

Registered Designs Act 1949

Referenced cases

Bristol Conservatories Ltd v. Conservatories Custom Built [1989] RPC 455

Reckitt & Colman Ltd v. Borden Inc [1990] 1 All E.R. 873

Further reading

Irish, V. *Intellectual property rights for engineers, 2nd edition,* London, UK, The Institution of Engineering and Technology, 2005.

Stim, R. *Patent, Copyright & Trademark (Patent, Copyright & Trademark: A Desk Reference to Intellectual Property Law), 10th edition,* Berkeley, NOLO, 2009. [USA title].

The Institute of Trade Mark Attorneys publications on trade marks, copyright, designs and domain names; www.itma.org.uk/trademarks/brochures/publications/itma-publications-general-intere (last accessed 20 September, 2010).

Websites

British Library patents homepage; www.bl.uk/reshelp/findhelprestype/patents/index.html

Intellectual Property Institute (IPI); www.ip-institute.org.uk

JISC Legal, Intellectual property rights; www.jisclegal.ac.uk/Default.aspx?tabid=463

Nice classification system; www.wipo.int/classifications/nice/en/classifications.html

Nominet, registry for .uk domain names; www.nic.uk

Office of Harmonisation for the Internal Market (OHIM); www.oami.europa.eu

UK Intellectual Property Office; www.ipo.gov.uk

World Intellectual Property Organization (WIPO); www.wipo.int

Section 3: General law
Section editor: Sir Vivian Ramsey

Chapter 19

The law of contract

Patrick Clarke Atkin Chambers, London, UK
Martin Bowdery QC Atkin Chambers, London, UK

Contracts are formed by offer and acceptance where the parties intend to enter into a legal relationship where a promise is supported by consideration. Contracts may be oral or in writing, and the existence or terms of a contract may also be construed from the conduct of the parties. The terms of the contract will be those agreed by the parties but will be given meaning in accordance with established legal principles and may be construed by reference to terms implied by common law or statute. Parties are obliged to abide by the terms of contracts and are able to claim damages for breach of contract to put them in the position they would have been in if the contract had been performed by the other party. Other relief includes injunctions pursuant to which a party may be compelled to perform a contract and declarations, by which the parties' rights and obligations under a contract may be clarified. Contracts can come to an end by performance of them by the parties, by agreement or by repudiation of the contract by one of the parties that is accepted by the other.

doi: 10.1680/mocl.40878.0289

CONTENTS

19.1 Why bother?

Many engineers and engineering contractors have an attitude to contracts which can best be described as indifferent if not hostile. They remark 'contracts are a waste of time', 'we've never had any trouble because we know our customers and our contractors', 'if we needed to rely on a contract with a client we wouldn't deal with them', 'Lawyers just get in the way'. This attitude is confusing and misleading. It mixes up a contractual frame of reference with the use of the law in order to enforce rights. The legal system should be used, at best, as a last resort, to enforce self-regulation by contract. However, that does not mean that the self-regulation contained within the contractual agreement is unimportant in guiding or influencing contractual behaviour. The contract will still be used or misused as a point of reference during negotiations towards a compromise of disputes even though for good and sufficient reasons neither party has any intention of resorting to law.

To understand how the law of contract can govern commercial behaviour, it is important to identify not just the requirements for a valid contract but also why contracts are usually always incomplete. The four basic requirements for a valid contract are tediously well known:

- an agreement between the parties (which is usually but not invariably established by the fact that one has made an offer and the other has accepted it)

- an intention or commitment to be legally bound by that agreement (often called an intention to create legal relations)

- certainty as to the terms of the agreement

- consideration provided by each of the parties.

In addition, the parties must be legally capable of forming a contract and, in some cases, certain formalities must be complied with. It is not necessary for a contract to be in writing – a contract is an agreement not a piece of paper. A 'gentleman's agreement' is invariably neither an agreement nor an arrangement entered into by gentlemen.

Before considering in greater detail each requirement for a valid or complete contract it is appropriate to consider what an agreement does not necessarily usually include or why it is sometimes more important to review what a contract does not encompass rather than consider what it does.

Agreements are almost always incomplete; contract lawyers are employed ostensibly for two different tasks:

- to plan or to record a transaction

- to participate in dispute resolution.

Cynics may say that weaknesses in fulfilling the first function are more than amply compensated by taking part in the second function. However, when contract lawyers seek to translate the economic deal into a legally enforceable written agreement, they must acknowledge that, although they can plan or draft for various contingencies or risks through the terms of the contract, such planning can never be complete. The risk can never be fully identified or offloaded. Recognising this inevitable incompleteness and uncertainty in tying down contractual risks is as important as the tedious drafting of clauses to regulate the parties' rights and obligations.

Contractual documents often attempt to allocate all risks, no matter how unexpected the contingency, by general phrases such as 'the contractor will be responsible for all disruption howsoever caused'. However, general words may often fail to cover specific risks if such unexpected risks only occur outside the contemplation of the contractual documents.

In an uncertain world, with a complex and challenging construction or engineering project, the parties may acknowledge and accept that they will want to modify their arrangements over time in the light of changing market conditions, changing requirements or changing technologies. In these circumstances the contract lawyer in drafting the contract, should avoid tight or rigid commitments but emphasise the need for flexibility, discretion or the intervention of an outsider to regulate the parties' rights and obligations in the face of changing circumstances. The parties can then achieve flexibility in their contractual agreements albeit at the cost of contractual certainty.

Contract documents do frequently provide for dispute resolution procedures, such as arbitration and adjudication considered in the chapters *Arbitration*; *Adjudication* and *Alternative dispute resolution*. However, these procedures are generally only enforced by the courts to the extent that they provide for or result in a binding resolution. Agreements to enter into negotiations about disputes are generally not enforceable (as confirmed in the case of *Halifax Financial Services Limited v. Intuitive Systems Limited* (1999) CILL 1467); however, the courts will enforce agreements to participate in a defined dispute resolution procedure properly construed as a condition precedent to litigation (*Cable & Wireless Plc v. IBM United Kingdom Ltd* (2002) CILL 1930).

The gaps or holes in the contractual arrangements will pose difficulties when disputes or differences arise. The parties to the contract may quite sensibly refrain from addressing detailed problems of remote or unforeseen risks in their business deals. However, when their risks become eventualities, the parties must either negotiate a compromise to deal with such an event or the courts must intervene.

Traditionally, the courts have been biased towards a literal interpretation of the express obligations of the parties and have been biased against any argument that these obligations or risks can be re-allocated or allocated afresh in the light of the parties' expectations once that risk has become an eventuality. The critical question is how the parties, and, if necessary, the courts should resolve issues which arise during engineering projects where the contract has not precisely or clearly allocated these risks. Should these issues be resolved on the basis of:

(a) the contract documents, and/or
(b) the business deal and the context in which it was made.

Judicial intervention which leads to the judicial reallocation of risk is almost, but not wholly, foreign to the English courts. Under the relief offered by doctrines such as *force majeure*, frustration or commercial impracticability, the allocation of risk can sometimes be re-allocated by the courts so as to do justice between the parties.

Some might say that the courts should generally try to do justice between the parties rather than adjudicate as to which set of contract lawyers has been luckier in allocating risks within the thousands of pages of contract documents assembled within an imposed or unrealistic tendering timetable. Judges should attach less weight to the paperwork but concentrate their minds on a study of the background, context, market circumstances, assumptions and expectations of the parties to the contract.

Such investigations might lead to more judicial decisions that the contract documents so expensively and comprehensively prepared by the parties' contract lawyers fail to begin to grasp how risks arising from improbable contingencies should be allocated. Having grasped that the contract documentation is a servant and not the master of the parties' commercial expectations, the courts might become more enthusiastic in engaging in a judicial review of these documents.

Lord Diplock in *Pioneer Shipping Limited v. BTP Tioxide Ltd 'The Nema'* [1982] AC 724 suggested that the Court should, in that case, defer to

> A commercial arbitrator's findings as to mercantile usage and the understanding of mercantile men about the significance of the commercial differences between what was promised and what in the changed circumstances would now fall to be performed.

However, the English courts generally remain biased against allocating the consequences of unidentified risks other than by interpreting what the contract says even if, as a matter of logic, the contract has nothing to say about such risks. The courts should recognise that for good and sufficient reasons contracts are often left incomplete because the allocation of unforeseen risks can only be dealt with as they arise and, having arisen, can only be allocated on the basis of the circumstances within which they arose.

In seeking to regulate contractual agreements the legal system overemphasises the significance of the formal contractual documentation at the expense of the parties legitimate commercial objectives and at the expense of the parties own priorities which are often their long-term business relationships and the commercial success of the particular transaction they have worked together on. When enforcing the contractual agreement the courts will tend to ignore the parties' own view that the contractual documentation only provides a partial reflection of the parties' commercial expectations.

This refusal to acknowledge that we live and operate and endeavour to cooperate in an uncertain world is typified by the English courts' general refusal to acknowledge any obligation by a contracting party to act in good faith. As Bingham LJ stated in *Interfoto v. Stilletto Visual Programmes* [1989] 1 QB 433:

> In many civil law systems, and perhaps in most legal systems outside the common law world, the law of obligations recognises and enforces an overriding principle that in making and carrying out contracts parties should act in good faith. This does not simply mean that they should not deceive each other, a principle which any legal system must recognise, its effect is perhaps most aptly conveyed by such metaphorical colloquialisms as 'playing fair', 'coming clean' or 'putting ones cards face upwards on the table'. It is in essence a principle of fair open dealing … English law has, characteristically, committed itself to no such overriding principle but has developed piecemeal solutions in response to demonstrated problems of unfairness.

However, a specific (rather than general) duty to act fairly or in good faith has been held to apply by implication to certain contractual obligations such as those between an employer and employee and the exercise of a unilateral discretionary power where conferred on one party by the contract (*Paragon Finance v. Nash* [2002] 1 WLR 594 CA).

In endeavouring to summarise the law of contract in the remainder of this chapter, emphasis will be given to the formal requirements of a contract and to the formal rules adopted in construing contracts even though it is envisaged that a more flexible and purposive construction of complex and complicated contract will, one day, be adopted by the English courts.

19.2 Making a contract

There are four key elements to the making of a valid contract:

- an agreement between the parties
- an intention or a communication to be legally bound by that agreement
- certainty as to the terms of the agreement
- consideration provided by each of the parties.

The contract need not be in writing, save for a few exceptions such as a contract for a guarantee. A contract is an agreement not a piece of paper. However, when considering what is required to form a valid contract concerted efforts should be made to ensure:

- that the contract is reduced to writing
- that the parties do not stumble into an agreement without realising that they have in fact concluded an agreement
- that the parties do not leave loose ends during these negotiations which can be exploited later when the disappointed party runs claims based on misrepresentation, collateral contracts or on the basis of contentions that the contract was, in fact, made partly in writing and partly orally.

To avoid or limit such opportunism, negotiations leading up to an agreement can be marked 'subject to contract' and/or subject to any written contract being signed by both parties. The written contract should also contain an 'entire contract clause' which provides that the parties' rights and obligations are defined and are contained by the four corners of the written contract.

19.2.1 Unilateral or bilateral contracts

The classification of contracts into unilateral or bilateral is not helpful. The distinction means only that with a unilateral contract, just one party undertakes an obligation. Bilateral contracts, or synallagmatic contracts, are those under which both parties undertake obligations. A unilateral contract would be the offer of a reward for the return of property or lost cat. A bilateral contract comprises the exchange of a promise for a

promise such as 'I will find your cat if you promise to pay me £10'. A similar distinction rests between 'executory' consideration and 'executed' consideration. Consideration is called executory when a party's promise is made in return for a counterpromise from the other party. Executed consideration is when a party's promise is made in return for the performance of an act. So, a unilateral contract relies upon executed consideration. A mutual contract relies on executory consideration. Given that both types of contract are binding contracts, these distinctions identify differences of academic and limited interest.

19.2.2 Letters of intent

Documents described as letters of intent are often exchanged. Such a document usually expresses an intention to enter into a contract in the future. Each letter of intent must be construed in its own factual content. For example, it may be:

- just a letter of comfort intended to have no legal effect
- an intention to carry out work pending the formal agreement of a more complex contract for which one party will pay the other party a reasonable sum if the final agreement is not concluded
- an executory ancillary agreement entitling the recipient of the letter of intent to reasonable costs if the future complex contract is not concluded and imposing an obligation on the recipient of the letter regarding the quality and suitability of the work carried out pursuant to the terms of such a letter.

The uncertainty created by the wide use of such letters of intent in differing factual circumstances would be eliminated or at least reduced if the parties accepted that, pending the agreement of a formal executed contract, the parties entered into a separate contract, called a preliminary contract, which spelt out the rights and obligations of the parties pending the agreement of the formal contract and the rights and obligations of the parties if that formal contract cannot be agreed. The fact that the parties both anticipate that the letter of intent is to be superseded by a later, more complex formal contract does not of itself prevent the letter of intent being interpreted as a contract in itself. What is important is to achieve certainty in the terms of this preliminary or anticipatory simple contract and to agree what happens if the more complex contract cannot be agreed.

19.3 Offer and acceptance

Generally, for a contract to come into existence one party must make an offer which the other must accept. Once acceptance takes effect a binding contract exists. Complex rules of offer and acceptance have been developed by the courts in order to identify the precise moment in time when a series of often complex negotiations have reached the point where a contract has been concluded. These rules are complex and sometimes archaic because there can be no halfway house: there is either a binding contract or there is not and the parties' negotiations can continue.

Before examining these rules in further detail, a third way should be considered. Steyn LJ in *G. Percy Trentham v. Archital Luxfer* [1993] 1 LR 25 stated that a contract may come into existence even if there is no coincidence of offer and acceptance during and as a result of performance. This third way of determining when parties during the course of long and complex negotiations, often while work is being carried out pursuant to the letter of intent, slip into a binding contract has not been endorsed by many judges or commentators. For example, the editors of the Building Law Reports take a conservative position on this case and state that

> The proposition that a contract may come into existence even if there is no coincidence of offer and acceptance (by whatever means), 'during and as a result of performance', is one to be applied with care. The cases cited by Steyn LJ do not perhaps fully support all his propositions.

An alternative interpretation of the 'third way' is that a contract may come into existence by a coincidence of an offer that arises out of the conduct of the offeror followed by acceptance by the conduct of the offeree. In any event, for present purposes the old rules of offer and acceptance need to be understood.

19.3.1 Invitations to treat

Most complex transactions require a preliminary stage in which one party, or a representative of one party, invites the other to make an offer. This stage in the dance which leads to a concluded contract is called an invitation to treat. The distinction between an invitation to treat and an offer is that an invitation to treat cannot be made with the intention that it becomes a binding agreement as soon as the person to whom it is sent communicates agreement to its terms. A statement is obviously not an offer where it expressly provides that the person who makes the statement is not to be bound by the other party's ratification of their consent, but only when the statement maker has actually signed the document containing the statement.

However, the courts have had difficulty in distinguishing between invitation to treat and offer, and in certain circumstances a statement has been held to be an invitation to treat even though it contained the word 'offer', and a statement has been held to constitute an offer although it was expressed as an 'acceptance', or even where it required the person to whom it was sent to make an 'offer'.

As always, clarity and certainty should be created by the maker of the document. An invitation to treat or an invitation to tender for proposed works should not only state clearly that it is not an offer but that there will not be a binding contract until the person asking for the tenders accepts one of them and then, and only then, both parties sign the contract documentation.

19.3.2 Offer

An offer is an expression of being ready, willing and able to enter into a contract made with the intention, actual or apparent, that the terms of the offer will become binding on the person making it as soon as it is accepted unequivocally by the person to whom it is addressed. Under the objective test of construing agreements, an apparent intention is sufficient. A binding contract is made if a lawyer, having been instructed to settle a claim for £10 000, by mistake offered to sell it for the higher sum of £100 000, that is, it is not what the parties do rather than what they may have intended to do that matters. An offer, to be effective, must be

- clear and certain

- communicated before it is accepted.

However, an offer may be withdrawn at any time before it is accepted. An offer may expressly state the precise time within which it is open for acceptance. If that time expires without acceptance then the offer also expires. If no time is stated during which the offer must be accepted, the offer remains open for a reasonable time and on the expiry of that time the offer expires. What is a reasonable time depends on the facts of each case. To avoid uncertainty, each offer should contain a 'sell-by date' beyond which it cannot be accepted.

19.3.3 Acceptance

There can generally be an acceptance of an offer bringing a binding contract into existence only when the person to whom the offer is made responds with an unconditional acceptance. If any new terms are suggested or any proposed terms are revised in the letter of acceptance there cannot be an acceptance unless these new terms or revised terms are insignificant in the overall scheme of things. What the courts decide are insignificant terms or insignificant revisions of offered terms will depend on the facts of each case and are difficult to define.

If the parties wish to avoid, including contracts by playing an elaborate form of the children's card game 'snap', it would be sensible to agree that no agreement is concluded unless some condition, such as both parties signing the written contract documents, is fulfilled. In the absence of such a precondition being fulfilled, the parties must abide by the rules of offer and acceptance, which include the following:

- acceptance must be unconditional and correspond to the terms of the offer

- acceptance may be made by conduct

- acceptance must be communicated, although postal acceptance generally takes place when the letter of acceptance is posted not when it is received.

19.3.3.1 Problems of offer and acceptance

Most, if not all, legal systems with European origins play the elaborate game of offer and acceptance to determine when the parties conclude a contract. This game distinguishes an offer from a counter-offer and an invitation to treat and requires an acceptance in accordance with legal rules which demand an unequivocal communicated acceptance. These rules are not self-applying but are imposed by the courts on the basis of an objective investigation of what the court thinks that the parties agreed and not what the parties thought had been agreed. This formal, pedestrian enquiry is regimented by rules developed by commercial practices based on the nineteenth century not the twenty-first century. This pedantic approach to determining when parties reach a concluded agreement will fall out of use and be replaced by a more modern approach. It is already disintegrating, but before it is replaced by a more modern approach to contract formation based on modern communications, commercial sense and the parties expectations, these rules of offer and acceptance must be recognised and the parties must play this game by its rules to avoid drifting into agreement without realising that the time for negotiation has ended.

Where there has been no formal and delineated 'offer and acceptance' the courts will have to analyse what passes between the parties to see whether objectively they have come to agreement on all essential terms. In such circumstances a contract may come into existence in the course of protracted correspondence and discussions or in the performance or part performance of transactions. Such analysis can obviously create uncertainty in situations where one party considers the contract to have been concluded and the other party not. In those cases the point at which all essential terms were agreed and the agreed terms themselves will be determined, or not, by the courts as in the case of *Haden Young Limited v. Laing O'Rourke Midlands Limited (TCC) 8 May 2008* that applied the leading cases of *Pagnan SPA Feed Products Limited [1987] 2 Lloyds Rep 601* and *G Percy Trentham Ltd v. Archital Luxfer [1993] 1 Lloyds Rep 25*. Indeed it remains possible for a contract to be formed by the conduct of the parties without direct or express communication of offer and acceptance (see *Fisher v. Brooker and Others [2009] 1 WLR 1764 HL*).

19.4 Consideration

In English law, an agreement is not usually binding unless it is supported by what is called 'consideration'. This means that each party must give something in return for whatever is provided by the other party. You don't get 'owt for nowt'. Consideration is normally said to be something which represents either a benefit to the party making the promise or some sort of detriment to the person to whom the promise is made. This doctrine has been called upon in support of general proposition such as 'English law will enforce a bargain but not a gift (or a promise)'. This doctrine has also attracted a series of contractual or legal rules to assess the adequacy or sufficiency of considerations, such as:

■ consideration must be real or sufficient

■ consideration must be something additional to the parties' existing obligations

■ consideration must not be past consideration

■ consideration must be given in return for the promise or act of the other party – something given as promised beforehand will not count as consideration

■ consideration must be of economic value

■ consideration can be a promise not to sue

■ consideration must be from the person who wants to enforce the promise.

19.4.1 Problems with consideration

The requirement for consideration can enable parties who make promises that ought to be morally binding to avoid legal culpability. This has been one reason for a long legal tradition of judicial hostility to this doctrine. Lord Mansfield, at the end of the eighteenth century, held that a moral obligation could amount to consideration and for some 60 years that view effectively demolished the doctrine of consideration. In 1937, the Law Revision Committee proposed that:

■ a written promise should be binding with or without consideration

■ part consideration should be valid

■ consideration should no longer need to move from the promisee

■ performance of an existing duty should always be good consideration for a promise.

These reforms have not yet been implemented. As stated in *Chitty on Contracts* (Beale, 2009):

> The present position therefore is that English law limits the enforceability of agreements (and deeds) by reference to a complex and multifarious body of rules known as 'the doctrine of consideration'.

As the law of contract is modernised this will be one of the first doctrines to fall. However, at present, forming a binding agreement still requires consideration.

19.5 Construction of a contract

The terms of an agreement will describe the duties and obligations that each party has assumed under their agreement. When endeavouring to discover the meaning of a contractual term, the court will approach the task of ascertaining the intention of the parties objectively. The courts are not interested in what the parties may have meant or understood by the words used, but in the meaning which the document could convey to the reasonable person having all the background information available to the parties when the contract was concluded.

19.5.1 Expressed intention

Lord Hoffman, since joining the House of Lords, has, in a succession of cases, been considering the weight to be attached to the meaning of the words 'expressed intention'. In *Mannai*

Investment Co. Ltd v. Eagle Star Life Assurance Co. Ltd [1997] AC 749, Lord Hoffman stated that

> It is of course true that the law is not concerned with the speaker's subjective intentions. But the notion that the law's concern is therefore with the 'meaning of the words' conceals an important ambiguity. The ambiguity lies in a failure to distinguish between the meanings of words and the question of what would be understood as the meaning of a person who uses words. The meaning of words, as they would appear in a dictionary, and the effect of their syntactical arrangement, as it would appear in grammar, is part of the material which we use to understand a speaker's utterance. But it is only a part: another part is our knowledge of the background against which the utterance was made. It is that background which enables us, not only to choose the intended meaning when a word has more than one dictionary meaning but also to understand a speaker's meaning, often without ambiguity, when he has used the wrong words.

Lord Hoffman in *ICS Ltd v. West Bromwich BS* [1998] 1 WLR 912 gave perhaps a clearer and less convoluted structured analysis of how, over recent years, what he described as 'all the old intellectual baggage' of legal interpretation has been discarded. Lord Hoffman thus provided a summary of the principles to be applied when construing or interpreting contractual documents. These principles are as follows.

(a) Interpretation is the ascertainment of the meaning which a document would convey to a reasonable person having all the background knowledge which would reasonably have been available to the parties in the situation in which they were at the time of the contract.

(b) The background was famously referred to by Lord Wilberforce as the 'matrix of fact' but this phrase is, if anything, an understated description of what the background may include. Subject to the requirement that it should have been reasonably available to the parties and to the exception to be mentioned next, it includes absolutely anything which would have affected the way in which the language of the document would have been understood by a reasonable person.

(c) The law excludes from the admissible background the previous negotiations of the parties and their declarations of subjective intent. They are admissible only in an action for rectification. The law makes this distinction for reasons of practical policy and, in this respect only, legal interpretation differs from the way in which utterances are generally interpreted in ordinary life. The boundaries of this exception are in some respects unclear, but this is not the occasion on which to explore them.

(d) The meaning which a document (or any other utterance) would convey to a reasonable man or woman is not the same thing as the meaning of its words. The meaning of words is a matter of dictionaries and grammars; the meaning of the document is what the parties using those words against the relevant background would reasonably have been understood to mean. The background may not merely enable the reasonable person to choose between the possible meanings of words which are ambiguous but even

(as occasionally happens in ordinary life) to conclude that the parties must, for whatever reason, have used the wrong words or syntax; see *Mannai Investments Co. Ltd v. Eagle Star Life Assurance Co. Ltd* [1997] AC 749.

(e) The 'rule' that words should be given their 'natural and ordinary meaning' reflects the common sense proposition that we do not easily accept that people have made linguistic mistakes, particularly in formal documents. On the other hand, if one would nevertheless conclude from the background that something must have gone wrong with the language, the law does not require judges to attribute to the parties an intention which they plainly could not have had. Lord Diplock made this point more vigorously when be said in *Antaios Compania Naviera S.A. v. Salen Rederierna A.B.* [1985] AC 191, 201:

> If detailed semantic and syntactical analysis of words in a commercial contract is going to lead to a conclusion that flouts business commonsense, it must be made to yield to business commonsense.

So-called rules of construction can now be used to provide what is called a purposive construction of a contract document to reflect the parties' intentions and what they meant to agree, not what the courts think they did in fact agree to. This purposive construction approach was adopted in the case of *Fiona Trust & Holding Corporation and others v. Privalov and others* [2008] 1 Lloyds Rep 254 where the House of Lords considered the scope of an arbitration agreement. Previous authority drawing fine distinctions between the scope of clauses providing for disputes 'in connection with' or disputes 'arising out of' contracts were dismissed on the grounds that the proper approach was to determine whether the parties, as 'rational businessmen' intended for any of their disputes to be excluded from the agreement or for some of their disputes to be determined by arbitration and others to be determined before a different tribunal. Previous distinctions were described as reflecting 'no credit upon English commercial law' and a line was drawn under them. The House of Lords determined that any construction should start from the assumption that the parties intended that any disputes between them, arising out of or in connection with the contract that contained the arbitration agreement, would be decided by the same tribunal. On this basis the arbitration clause was construed to encompass all of the disputes between the parties.

The exclusion of the previous negotiations of the parties in construing the terms of a contract was considered and reaffirmed in *Chartbrook v. Persimmon Homes [2009] BLR 551*. In that case it was argued that the rule excluding pre-contract negotiations from consideration of the proper construction of the terms was illogical and inconsistent with the modern approach for the court to put itself in the position of the parties when the contract was made. It was held that there was a long and consistent line of authority excluding pre-contract negotiations that had been clearly reaffirmed by the House of Lords in *Prenn v. Simmonds [1971] 1 WLR 1381* that should not be departed from. Previous communications could be relied upon as part of the background to the contract to shed light on the meaning of the words used in the contract but reference to the negotiations themselves could not be used to interpret the contract ultimately entered into. Evidence of negotiations remains admissible for other purposes, including a claim for rectification or estoppel.

19.5.2 Rules of construction

Rules of construction, like many if not most rules, are there to be broken. Rules of construction are not rites of law. They are no more than guidelines to the interpretation of the English language. As Megarry pointed out in the Law Quarterly Review as long ago as 1945:

> The great truth about interpretation in England seems to be that the Bench has been provided with some degree of 'principles' from which a judicious selection can be made to achieve substantial justice in each individual case. From time to time all the relevant principles point in the same direction and leave the Court no choice but in most of the cases susceptible of any real dispute the function of counsel is merely to provide sufficient material for the Court to perform its task of selection.

In these circumstances, if the tribunal adopts a pick-and-mix approach to the rules of construction it is necessary to be familiar with the more popular so-called 'rules'.

19.5.2.1 Constructing the document as a whole

To determine the true meaning of a contractual document, a clause must not be considered in isolation but must be construed in the context of the whole document.

19.5.2.2 Internal consistency

A draftsperson is assumed to aim at a uniform consistency and the same words will be presumed to have the same meaning in different parts of the contract and different words are perceived to refer to different things or matters.

19.5.2.3 Giving a role to all parts of the contract

In construing a contract, all parts will be interpreted so as to be effective where possible and no part should be regarded as inoperative or surplus to requirements. Where a clause or sentence is ambiguous, a construction which will make that clause or sentence valid will be preferred to a construction which would make that clause or sentence void.

19.5.2.4 Written words prevail

Where there is a contract contained in a printed form with additional clauses added which are inconsistent with the printed words the general rule is as follows:

> The written words are entitled to have a much greater effect attributed to them than the printed words in as much as the written words were the immediate language and terms selected by the parties themselves for the expressions of their meaning. (Lord Ellenborough in *Robertson v. French* (1803) 4 East 130)

19.5.2.5 Express terms prevent the implication of terms

An express term in a contract excludes the possibility of implying any term dealing with the same subject matter as the express term.

19.5.2.6 A party should not be able to take advantage of its own wrong

A contractual document should be interpreted where possible in such a way that one party cannot take advantage of its own wrongful behaviour. This analysis can result in the implication of a term that prevents that result (*The Bonde* [1991] Lloyds Rep 136).

19.5.2.7 Presumption of impossibility

Courts will generally expect a party not to agree to do what is impossible and there is a general presumption of contractual interpretation that a contractual document will not require the performance of the impossible. As Sir John Donaldson MR said in *The Epaphus* [1987] 2 UR 213 that

> My starting point is that parties to a contract are free to agree upon any terms which they consider appropriate, including a term requiring one of the parties to do the impossible, although it would be highly unusual for the parties knowingly so to agree. If they do so agree and if, as is inevitable, he fails to perform, he will be liable in damages. That said, any court will hesitate for a long time before holding that, as a matter of construction, the parties have contracted for the impossible, particularly in a commercial contract. Parties to such contracts can be expected to contemplate performance, not breach.

19.5.2.8 The reasonableness of the competing constructions

Where there is doubt as to two or more possible constructions of a contractual document the reasonableness of the result of any particular construction is a relevant if not decisive factor in determining which construction should prevail. As Lord Reid stated in *Schuler v. Wickham Machine Tool Sales* [1974] AC 235

> The fact that a particular construction leads to a very unreasonable result must be a relevant consideration. The more unreasonable the result the more unlikely it is that the parties can have intended it, and if they do intend it the more necessary it is that they shall make that intention abundantly clear.

Considerations to be taken into account in determining whether or not a particular construction is reasonable will include the factual circumstances and commercial common sense (*Somerfield Stores Ltd v. Skanska Rashleigh Weatherfoil Ltd* (2007) CILL 2449).

19.5.2.9 Clerical or typographical errors

Where the contractual documentation contains an obvious mistake or error the court will recognise the mistake or error and should correct the mistake or error or construe the construction discussed as if the error or mistake had been corrected or eliminated.

19.5.2.10 Recitals to a contract document used only in cases of doubt

Recitals to a contract document are part of the introductory part of a document which tend to set out what the parties intend to achieve by their contract. If there is any doubt or ambiguity regarding what the effective part of the agreement is trying to achieve, the recitals can be considered to resolve that doubt or that ambiguity. However, in the absence of any such doubt or any ambiguity, the meaning of the document can only be defined by the operative parts of the agreement and not the recitals to the agreement.

19.5.2.11 Irreconcilable clauses

Where a tribunal cannot resolve an apparent inconsistency between two points of the contractual documentation it will endeavour to give effect to the contentions of the parties. If it is still unable to ascertain which claim should prevail it will reject the latter claim and give effect to the earlier claim.

19.5.2.12 The ejusdem generis rule

This rule is that where there are words of a particular class followed by general words, the general words are construed as referring to matters of the same particular class. A simple example is that of a ship being exempted from liability for non-delivery of a cargo if the destination of the cargo is unsafe 'in consequences of war, disturbances or any other cause'. It was held that danger from ice was not within the meaning 'any other cause' which must be limited to causes similar to 'war or disturbance'.

19.5.2.13 Construction against the grantor

Before reference to Latin phrases was forbidden by the courts, this rule used to be known as the *contra proferentem* rule. This expression is intended to mean that where there is an ambiguity in the contract documentation, as there are two alternative meanings to certain sentences, the tribunal should construe the words against the party who drafted or put forward the document. However, where the contract documentation has been drafted by representative bodies or committees such as the Institution of Civil Engineers (ICE) or the Joint Contracts Tribunal (JCT), the *contra proferentem* rules, as it used to be known, should not be applied. This seems particularly harsh if one has any sympathy with the views of the edition of Hudson which, at page 116, states that

> It has to be said that even modern standard forms, or modern amendments to earlier forms, are replete with obscure and unconsidered draftsmanship, often leaving, whether deliberately or not, immediately obvious questions unanswered. Examples might include the new ICE fifth edition provision for interest

to be payable on certificates, a new right to extension of time in the RIBA/JCT forms for failure to give possession, apparently failing to deal with possession of the site itself, the longstanding provisions in both the ICE and RIBA/JCT forms prohibiting 'assignment of the contract' without consent, a new and complicated redefinition, the purpose of which is left to speculation, of the provisions relating to the architect's satisfaction introduced into the RIBA/JCT contracts in 1977, and a new apparent finality accorded in that regard to the architect's final certificate, with an initial and, it is submitted, incorrect interpretation of the latter by the courts in 1992. These examples are quite apart from the well-known major gaps in RIBA/JCT standard form draftsmanship, such as the silence and unknown intentions of the RIBA/JCT pre 1980 contracts in regard to the consequences of nominated sub-contractor repudiations, or as to the allocation of responsibilities for nominated sub-contractor design or as to the availability of set-off to owners resisting payment of sums due under interim certificates, or as to extensions of time for variations ordered after the contractor is in delay. 'In addition, there are the cases where, presumably under combined producer and professional influence, the scope of contractors' financial claims for additional payment have obviously been deliberately left quite undefined and subject to the widest possible discretion by, ultimately, a court or arbitrator.' A further area where careless draftsmanship has gravely damaged the interest of owners lies in the failure to provide practical and necessary remedies where defects are discovered during construction.

All these factors make construction contracts eminently suitable for a liberal 'business commonsense' or 'genesis and aim' interpretative approach; but it has to be said that whereas that approach was often a characteristic of the nineteenth and early twentieth century judges, modern judges, and in particular the higher judiciary, have in recent years, perhaps aware of the difficulties caused by lack of knowledge of the background and the excessive complication and difficulty of the draftsmanship of the contracts, and in some cases at least expressing an exaggerated respect for the quality of the draftsmanship, have tended to fall back on a policy of 'literalist construction'. This has produced, in a noticeable number of cases, results at serious odds with the aim or purpose of the transaction viewed as a whole.

Whether the courts adopt a more purposive or 'business commonsense' construction to standard form contracts or whether standard form contracts are simplified and clarified so that the more arcane excrescences are removed may not much matter; however, a 'literal' construction of the present-day standard forms will continue to create unexpected and somewhat surprising judicial interpretations of how these contracts are intended to work.

19.5.2.14 Subsequent conduct of the parties

The conduct of the parties following the formation of it is not relevant to the construction of written contract terms but may be a relevant consideration in the construction of the terms of an oral or partly written/partly oral contract (*Brian Royle Maggs (T/A BM Builders) v. (1) Guy Anthony Stanyer Marsh (2) Mars Jewellery Co. Ltd* (2006) CILL 2369).

19.5.2.15 Implied or inferred terms

The implication of terms in contracts is another method by which the courts will give effect to the common intention of the parties, or by which statute will impose particular terms, and they will be construed in the same way as express terms in light of the commercial background to the agreement. For a term to be implied the following conditions must be fulfilled according to Lord Simon in *BP Refinery (Westernpoint) Pty Ltd v. Shire of Hastings* (1978) 52 AUJR 20.

(a) It must be reasonable and equitable.
(b) It must be necessary to give business efficacy to the contract so that no term will be implied into an agreement if the contract is effective without it.
(c) It must be so obvious that it goes without saying.
(d) It must be capable of clear expression.
(e) It must not contradict any express term of the contract.

There is some dispute whether conditions (b) and (c) are alternative or cumulative. The stronger view may be that:

■ implied terms are implied by reasons of business efficacy

■ inferred terms are inferred by reason of obvious inference.

so terms can be inferred and/or implied into a contract depending on the particular circumstances of each contract. However, implied terms can also arise by way of:

■ the operation of law

■ custom

■ statute.

Each is dealt with in turn subsequently.

19.5.2.16 Terms implied by law

The following terms are generally implied into any commercial agreement unless explicitly or implicitly excluded by the express terms of the agreement.

■ Neither party to an agreement shall prevent the other from performing their obligations arising out of the contract.

■ Where the performance of the contract cannot take place without the cooperation of the parties, it is implied that the parties will cooperate with each other.

■ Where a contract provides for continuing performance and does not provide for the expiry or determination, the term will be implied that the agreement can be determined after a reasonable period of time after a party has given reasonable notice.

■ Where there is no express time by which the parties should perform any contractual obligation the parties will perform their contractual obligations within a reasonable time.

■ Where there is no express agreement for the price to be paid for any contractual benefit the price to be paid will be a reasonable price for any such benefit.

Eventually, the English courts will imply a term that parties to a commercial contract will act in good faith. Some might say this is the very least one would expect from a commercial contract. Sadly, at present the English courts cannot go that far and do not expect or require parties to a commercial contract to act in good faith!

19.5.2.17 Terms implied by custom or usage

Where a term or provision would automatically be part of an agreement made by the parties involved in a particular trade or enterprise, such a term will be implied by the courts provided that there is no conflict between the usage and the terms of the contract. To be implied, such a usage must be notorious, certain and reasonable and not contrary to law. It must be something beyond a mere trade practice. These usages are incorporated on the basis that the courts are spelling out what both parties knew and would, if asked, unhesitatingly agree would be part of the bargain.

19.5.2.18 Terms implied by statute

Parliament, irrespective of which government is in power, increasingly seeks to interfere in the freedom of parties to agree the terms which govern their business relationships. The incorporation of compulsory payment provisions and adjudication into most engineering and construction contracts by the Housing Grants, Construction and Regeneration Act 1996 is a recent example of where Parliament predetermines what terms must be implied into commercial contracts. Further examples of terms implied by statute are to be found in the Supply of Goods and Services Act 1982. In a contract under which a person or party agrees to provide a service other than a contract of service or apprenticeship and certain other exempted types of agreements, the Supply of Goods and Services Act 1982 implies by statute, various terms. For example, by section 13 it is implied that the supplier will carry out the service contracted for with reasonable skill and care. By sections 14 and 15 under this 1982 Act where, under a contract for the supply of a service by a supplier acting in the course of the time for the service to be carried out or the price for the service being performed has not been fixed or agreed, there will be statutory implied terms that the supplier will carry out the service within a reasonable time and for a reasonable price. Furthermore, a term is implied into contracts for the supply of goods and services by the Late Payment of Commercial Debts (Interest) Act 1998 whereby any qualifying debt created by contract is to carry statutory interest subject to the terms of that Act.

19.5.2.19 Exemption clauses

Any commercial agreement would wish to cover what Americans might describe as the upside and the downside of any bargain. It is a common feature of most written standard contracts that the party offering the document will seek to limit its liabilities if the contract turns sour. The use of exemption clauses is an important tool in apportioning risk between the parties and determining which party should bear which risk and indeed which risks neither party should bear but which should be protected by insurance.

Exemption clauses fall into the following categories.

- Clauses which seek to exclude all liability for certain breaches are called exclusion clauses.

- Clauses which seek to limit or reduce what would otherwise be the defendant's duty: this would be done by expressly restricting a party's substantive obligations, for example, by excluding from the contract express or implied terms or by restricting liability to cover of wilful default.

- Clauses which seek to limit or reduce the obligations of the party in default to fully

- Indemnify or compensate the other party by limiting the damages recoverable against it or by providing a time limit within which claims must be instigated.

The modern approach to exemption clauses, including exclusion clauses, is not to construe the contract as if the clause did not exist and then to consider whether the clause provides an effective defence to the claim, but to construe the whole contract together with the exemption clause to discover the presumed intention of the parties as to whether a particular risk has been included or excluded as a potential liability. A commercial agreement, particularly a standard form entered into by two significant parties, may contain relatively ferocious exemption clauses which the courts will tend to uphold. The Unfair Contract Terms Act 1977 was intended to control the use of clauses excluding or limiting liability by breach of contract, particularly where one of the parties is a consumer. Where the contract imposes a 'business' liability, exclusions or exemptions clauses may have to satisfy the statutory test of reasonableness but, between two organisations of reasonably comparable negotiating strengths and weaknesses, any agreed apportionment of risk should be held to be reasonable by most tribunals.

19.5.2.20 Unenforceable terms

Adding terms to a contract by the operation of law or statute that did not form part of the agreement between the parties as described earlier, the courts will also decline to enforce certain terms that the parties may have agreed thereby depriving them of any meaningful effect. The courts will not enforce:

(a) agreements to agree or negotiate (but see the *Halifax* and *Cable & Wireless* cases referred to above). Such terms are also considered to be too uncertain to have binding force;
(b) 'unreasonable terms' are not enforced in certain circumstances pursuant to the provisions of the Unfair Contract Terms Act 1977;
(c) terms or contracts where the agreement or the performance of the same is or would be illegal by common law or statute.

19.6 Terminating or determining a contract

Crucial differences between determining a contract and terminating a contract can be confused. 'Determination' means the exercise of an agreed contractual machinery to bring to an end the parties continuing contractual obligation. 'Termination' means that the innocent party has accepted the repudiatory breach of the guilty party and terminates the agreement. All primary obligations are then discharged, to be replaced by the secondary obligations to determine what damages should be paid as a result of the wrongful repudiation of the contract.

19.6.1 Discharge by agreement

The editors of *Chitty on Contracts* (Beale, 2009) acknowledge that the law relating to the discharge of a contract by agreement is a subject of 'considerable artificiality and refinement'. This may be an understatement. The most obvious way in which a contract is discharged is if both parties fully perform their obligations under it. In most cases this should be quite simple. However, in a complex building or engineering project, parties may legitimately disagree as to whether each party has fully performed their obligations under the contract and as a result the law which the judges have to address is the question of what constitutes performance. In reality, agreements, particularly engineering or construction agreements, which require entire performance are the exception rather than the rule. The courts have adopted several methods to avoid the consequences of a rule that entire performance is required in all contracts. These methods include those presented subsequently.

19.6.1.1 Substantial performance

This doctrine provides that a party who has substantially performed their contract with only minor defects or deficiencies can claim the price of the work carried out less any sum the other party may have to spend to complete or remedy the minor defects or deficiencies which prevent the entire performance.

19.6.1.2 Severable rather than entire contracts

An agreement is said to be severable rather than entire when payment becomes due and owing at various stages during performance of the works. Most engineering and construction contracts will be severable rather than entire since instalments of the price become due as each stage of the construction are completed. Where the contract is a severable and not an entire contract, the price for each instalment is due when each instalment of the works is complete.

19.6.1.3 Rescission by agreement

Where a contract is executory on both sides and where neither party has performed the whole of its obligations, the agreement can be rescinded by mutual agreement, express or implied.

An agreement which is partially executed can only be rescinded by agreement provided that there are unfulfilled obligations on both sides. An agreement, once rescinded by agreement, is completely discharged and not capable of being revived.

19.6.1.4 Abandonment

A court can infer that the parties to a contract have agreed to abandon the contract because of delay or maturity. To prove abandonment the court must be satisfied on the facts of each particular case that the parties conducted themselves in such a manner that neither party was entitled to assume that the parties will have agreed that the contract had been abandoned.

19.6.1.5 Variations

The parties may effect a variation of the contract by commanding, allowing or modifying its terms by mutual consent. However, any agreement which varies the terms of an existing contract must be supported by considerations.

19.6.1.6 Waiver or forbearance

Where one party decides to accede to a request from the other party that a contractual obligation need not be performed, a court may hold that that party has waived any right to require that contractual obligation to be performed. Such a waiver may be in writing, may be oral or, indeed, may be inferred from conduct. This doctrine of waiver can be compared and contrasted with a variation of the contract in that there is no need for any consideration for the forbearance moving from the party to whom it is given. For this reason it may be simpler if this type of waiver is regarded as a form of estoppels which requires a change of position in reliance on any such act of forbearance.

19.6.1.7 Provision for discharge in the contract itself

Most engineering or construction contracts will have an internal machinery for one or other party to determine (not to terminate) the contract exercisable usually on a breach of contract, sometimes just on notice and, somewhat more rarely, at the sole discretion of the other party. What causes confusion and uncertainty is the fact that, even though one party may be entitled to determine the agreement, say, in the event of a particular breach of contract, that in itself does not prevent the other party from electing to treat the contract as having been terminated by reason of the other party's repudiatory breaches. When a major project goes seriously wrong there is often an unseemly jockeying for position by each party, with ever increasing numbers of technical advisers, all instructed to determine whether it is more advantageous to determine or to terminate the agreement. Where a party decides to rely on the procedure laid down in the contract and to determine the contract, it is necessary to comply with the strict procedure laid down in the contract. The advantages and disadvantages of determination and termination are as follows:

■ A contractual right to determine can be exercised even if the triggering event or breach of contract is not a repudiatory breach.

■ The consequences of determining the contract pursuant to the contractual machinery will restrict the party determining the contract to the remedies specified by the contract which may not include its loss of profit on the outstanding work.

■ A common law termination of the contract does not require notice or warning from the party wishing to accept the repudiatory breach or breaches of contract.

■ A repudiatory breach of contract is a breach which is difficult to define definitively. The breach must go to the root of the contract. The guilty party must have evinced an intention no longer to be bound by the contract. However, the consequences of terminating a contract by accepting a breach which a court, years later, finds not to be a repudiatory breach of contract, can be catastrophic.

19.6.2 Discharge by frustration

A contract may be discharged by frustration only when something occurs after the contract is concluded which renders the contract physically or commercially impossible or an event occurs which transforms the obligation to perform into a radically different obligation from that originally envisaged. This doctrine is concerned with the allocation of the risks flowing from an unforeseen event occurring which makes the originally envisaged contractual performance much more onerous, impracticable or impossible. The judicial basis of this doctrine is unclear. Some say it is based on some sort of implied term. The contract is discharged because by implication the parties have agreed that they will no longer be bound by the original terms of the contract if a frustrating event occurs. This theory has been analysed on the basis of the legal difficulty in seeing how the parties could, even impliedly, have provided for something which *ex hypothesi* they neither expected nor foresaw. An alternative theory is based on the 'just solution' theory which considers that the court will adopt the doctrine of frustration to impose a fair solution when unforeseen circumstances arise which are wholly different from those originally envisaged. The second theory, which disregards the parties' intentions but is based on the intervening court's wish to do justice between the parties, is probably the more fashionable justification for this doctrine.

However, the doctrine of frustration is examined by the courts with enormous circumspection. The courts are reluctant to rewrite bad or imprudent commercial bargains. The intervention of a frustrating event has always been much easier to plead than to prove.

It is also the case that most standard form of engineering and construction contracts make provision for the effect of various catastrophic frustrating events and, where express provision has been made in the contract itself for the otherwise frustrating event, then the contract cannot be discharged by frustration.

The Law Reform (Frustrated Contracts) Act 1943 provides for most of the legal consequences of frustration. The purpose of this Act is to prevent unjust enrichment of either party to the contract at the other party's expense. Its aim is not to apportion loss between the parties. Section 1(2) of the Act provides that

> All sums paid or payable to any party in pursuance of the contract before the time when the parties were so discharged (in this Act referred to as 'the time of discharge') shall, in the case of sums so paid, be recoverable from him as money received by him for the use of the party by whom the sums were paid, and, in the case of sums so payable, cease to be payable:
>
> Provided that, if the party to whom the sums were so paid or payable incurred expenses before the time of discharge in, or for the purpose of, the performance of the contract, the court may, if it considers it just to do so having regard to all the circumstances of the case, allow him to retain or, as the case may be recover the whole or any part of the sums so paid or payable, not being an amount in excess of the expenses so incurred.

This subsection should entitle a party to the contract to recover monies paid to another party to the contract. This Act modifies the common law position which held that rights which had not yet arrived at the time of frustration were unenforceable. The Act also goes beyond the common law position by providing that monies paid are recoverable even where there is only a partial failure of consideration and the payee may be entitled to set-off against a claim by the payer 'the amount of any expenses incurred before the time of discharge in or for the purpose of the contract'.

19.6.3 Discharge by breach

Any breach of contract will give rise to a cause of action but not every breach of contract gives a discharge from liability. To be relieved from further performance of the contract by the other side's breach of contract, the failure of performance must go to the root of the contract. In the case of *Rice v. Great Yarmouth Borough Council* (2003) TCLR 1 the Court of Appeal confirmed that there are three categories of breach of contract that are considered so serious as to justify the innocent party bringing the contract to an end:

(a) those cases in which the parties have agreed either that the term is so important that any breach will justify termination or that the particular breach is so important that it will justify termination;

(b) those cases where the contractor simply walks away from his obligations thus clearly indicating an intention no longer to be bound; and

(c) those cases in which the cumulative effect of the breaches which have taken place is sufficiently serious to justify the innocent party in bringing the contract to a premature end.

Once a repudiatory breach occurs, the contract is not automatically discharged. The innocent party can elect whether to accept the repudiatory breach and terminate the contract or the innocent party can affirm the contract and insist that the contract should continue. Where the innocent party elects to terminate the contract by accepting the repudiatory breach, the contract is terminated in that all primary obligations of both parties which remain to be performed come to an end and

there is then substituted by implication of law for those primary obligations of the party in default which remain unperformed, a secondary obligation to pay financial compensation to the innocent party for all losses sustained by it in consequence of the guilty party's non-performance in the future and, just as important in many cases, the unperformed primary obligations if the innocent party are discharged.

19.7 Disputes and remedies

Whereas litigation, arbitration or adjudication should not be used as an alternative to negotiation, the absence of efficient, economical and expeditious dispute resolution processes will turn any analysis of the appropriate remedies for breach of contract into an academic analysis. Without confidence in the dispute resolution process any analysis of the appropriate remedies for breach of contract will be an academic analysis. Without confidence in the dispute resolution process, parties can break or bend contracts believing that they are immune from any effective sanctions. In considering the appropriate remedies for any breach of contract it is just as important to consider that these remedies can or will be enforced. If the contract breaker believes that the innocent party does not have the time, resources or commercial incentive to enforce its contractual rights, then fair compensation for any inadvertent or deliberate breach of contract will not be negotiated or agreed.

19.7.1 Remedies for breach of contract

When considering how a party can be recompensed for any breach of contract the parties to the contract should focus on the following questions.

- What is the speediest, fairest and cheapest method of resolving disputes?

- Will proper or even punitive awards of interest be paid as a contractual right?

- Can the financial consequences of common breaches of contract be predetermined to avoid the consequences and cost of having to plead and to prove actual losses?

Two general principles underlie the law on loss and damage.

(a) 'The rule of common law is, that where a party sustains a loss by reason of a breach of contract, he is, so far as money can do it, to be placed in the same situation, with respect to damages, as if the contract had been performed' per *Parke B, Robinson v. Harman* [1848] 1 Exch 850, 855.

(b) As a general rule, damages for breach of contract should be assessed as at the date when the cause of action accrued (i.e. the date of the breach). This is not an absolute rule. The date for the assessment of damage can be varied if, in all the circumstances, it is appropriate to do so, so as to compensate the claimant for the damage suffered by reason of the defendant's wrong. See *Johnson v. Agnew* [1980] AC 367, 400(h)–401(b), summarised in *Smith New Court*

Ltd v. Scrimgcour Vickers [1996] 3 WLR 1051, 1059 (g–h). Certainly, this general rule is the appropriate one in circumstances in which the plaintiff's loss is capable of quantification all at once. See dicta of Lord Hoffmann, *Banque Bruxelles S.A. v. Eagle Star* [1996] 3 WLR 87, 101 (d–g):

On the contrary, except in cases in which all the loss caused by the breach can be quantified at once, calculation of damages is bound to be affected by the extent to which loss in the future still has to be estimated at the date of trial …

It is true that in some cases there is a *prima facie* rule that damages should be assessed at the date of breach … But the purpose of this prima facie rule is not to ensure that the damages will always be the same irrespective of the date of trial. It is because where there is an available market, any additional loss which the buyer suffers through not having immediately bought equivalent goods at the market price is prima facie caused by his own change of mind about wanting the goods which he ordered … The breach date rule is thus no more than a prima facie rule of causation. It is not concerned with the extent of the vendor's liability for loss which the breach has admittedly caused.

19.7.2 Calculating loss

Once it has been established that a loss is one for which the defendant is liable, the tribunal will calculate the damages; what amounts will compensate the claimant for the loss? In an influential article published in 1936, American academics Fuller and Perdue pointed out that there are two main ways in which the losses of a claimant in a contract action can be calculated.

■ *Loss of expectation (also called loss of bargain).* This is the usual way in which contract damages are calculated, and it aims to put claimants in the position they would have been in if the contract had been performed. It means, for example, that a claimant who was buying goods with the intention of selling them can claim the profit that would have been made on that sale; and that a claimant who is forced to sell goods at a lower price when the original buyer pulls out, can claim the difference between the contract price and the price at which the goods were eventually sold.

■ *Reliance loss.* There are some cases where it is difficult or even impossible to calculate precisely what position the claimant would have been in if a contract had been performed correctly, and in this case the courts may instead award damages calculated to compensate for any expenses or other loss incurred by the claimant when relying on the contract.

However, to recover any loss the claimant must have at all times acted reasonably and mitigated the loss.

19.7.3 Equitable remedies

Where damages would be an inadequate remedy to compensate the claimant, there is a range of equitable remedies provided only at the discretion of the contract taking into account the position of both claimant and defendant. The alternative remedies include the following.

19.7.3.1 Specific performance

Specific performance will not be applied to a contract which is uncertain as to the required performance and it will be subject to the principle of mutuality which means that it will not be ordered against one party where it could not be ordered against the other party. Furthermore, it should not be ordered in the case of a contract which contains a contractual right to determine the contract because once ordered the contract could be determined. However, a claim for specific performance, if available, may not be the subject of the usual contractual limitation period, or any limitation period (*P&O Nedllyod BV v. Arab Metals Co & Others* [2006] EWCA Civ 1917).

19.7.3.2 Injunctions

Before ordering a party not to do something, or in rare cases to do something, the court will apply a balance of convenience test and may refuse the application if the defendant could lose a lot more by restoring the previous position than the claimant would gain. In deciding whether to grant an injunction, the contract should take into account the nature of the breach, the circumstances which gave rise to the breach and whether damages by themselves would be an adequate remedy.

19.7.3.3 Declarations

In granting the aforementioned remedies the court, or other tribunal, will almost invariably be required to make some determination as to the construction, interpretation and effect of the terms of the contract. However, it is possible to make a claim limited to a declaration by the court of how the terms of the contract should be interpreted or how the contract should operate. The declaration may then assist the parties in the continuing operation of the contract or the resolution of further disputes concerning the consequence of the proper construction, however, determined. The prevalence of claims for declarations has increased with the introduction of adjudication provisions in contracts whereby the parties can seek a binding determination on the proper construction of the contract during the course of its performance. The obvious disadvantage of claims for declarations is that it remains possible that further proceedings would be required to secure one or more of the aforementioned remedies in any event.

References

Beale, H. (ed). *Chitty on contracts, 30th Edition*, UK, Sweet & Maxwell, 2009.
Hudson's building and engineering contracts, 12th edition, UK, Sweet & Maxwell, 2010 (current edition).

Referenced legislation, regulations and standards

Housing Grants, Construction and Regeneration Act 1996
Late Payment of Commercial Debts (Interest) Act 1998
Law Reform (Frustrated Contracts) Act 1943

Supply of Goods and Services Act 1982
Unfair Contract Terms Act 1977

Referenced cases

Antaios Compania Naviera S.A. v. Salen Rederierna A.B. [1985] AC 191, 201

Banque Bruxelles S.A. v. Eagle Star [1996] 3 WLR 87, 101 (d–g)

Brian Royle Maggs (T/A BM Builders) v. (1) Guy Anthony Stanyer Marsh (2) Mars Jewellery Co. Ltd (2006) CILL 2369

BP Refinery (Westernpoint) Pty Ltd v. Shire of Hastings (1978) 52 AUJR 20

Cable & Wireless Plc v. IBM United Kingdom Ltd (2002) CILL 1930

Chartbrook v. Persimmon Homes [2009] BLR 551

Fiona Trust & Holding Corporation and others v. Privalov and others [2008] 1 Lloyds Rep 254

Fisher v. Brooker and Others [2009] 1 WLR 1764 HL

G Percy Trentham Ltd v. Archital Luxfer [1993] 1 Lloyds Rep 25

Haden Young Limited v. Laing O'Rourke Midlands Limited (TCC) 8 May 2008

Halifax Financial Services Limited v. Intuitive Systems Limited (1999) CILL 1467

ICS Ltd v. West Bromwich BS [1998] 1 WLR 912

Interfoto v. Stilletto Visual Programmes [1989] 1 QB 433

Johnson v. Agnew [1980] AC 367, 400(h)–401(b)

Mannai Investment Co. Ltd v. Eagle Star Life Assurance Co. Ltd [1997] AC 749

P&O Nedllyod BV v. Arab Metals Co & Others [2006] EWCA Civ 1917

Pagnan SPA Feed Products Limited [1987] 2 Lloyds Rep 601

Paragon Finance v. Nash [2002] 1 WLR 594 CA

Parke B, Robinson v. Harman [1848] 1 Exch 850, 855

Pioneer Shipping Limited v. BTP Tioxide Ltd 'The Nema' [1982] AC 724

Prenn v. Simmonds [1971] 1 WLR 1381

Rice v. Great Yarmouth Borough Council (2003) TCLR 1

Robertson v. French (1803) 4 East 130

Schuler v. Wickham Machine Tool Sales [1974] AC 235

Smith New Court Ltd v. Scrimgcour Vickers [1996] 3 WLR 1051, 1059 (g–h)

Somerfield Stores Ltd v. Skanska Rashleigh Weatherfoil Ltd (2007) CILL 2449

The Bonde [1991] Lloyds Rep 136

The Epaphus [1987] 2 UR 213

Websites

Institution of Civil Engineers (ICE); www.ice.org.uk

Joint Contracts Tribunal (JCT); www.jctltd.co.uk

Royal Institution of British Architects (RIBA); www.architecture.com

Chapter 20

doi: 10.1680/mocl.40878.0303

Construction health and safety I: Enforcement, HSW Act and management duties

Donald Lamont Health and Safety Executive, Bootle, UK
Mike Appleby Housemans Solicitors, London, UK

Health and safety responsibilities stem primarily from the Health and Safety at Work etc. Act 1974, and are shared by various parties who may be connected with construction and engineering projects. This chapter explains the system of health and safety legislation in the UK and how it is enforced.

CONTENTS

20.1 The regulatory agencies

20.1.1 Health and Safety Executive

The Health and Safety Executive (HSE) and the Health and Safety Commission (HSC) existed as separate entities from their formation until 1st April 2008 when they amalgamated to form a single regulatory body the 'Health and Safety Executive' to discharge the functions which were formerly their individual responsibility. The HSC was established under section 10 of the Health and Safety at Work etc. Act 1974 (HSWA) with the HSE as the executive arm of the HSC, responsible for implementing the Commission's policies as well as enforcing health and safety legislation. The decision for the merger was reached after consultation with stakeholders and through the process determined by the Legislative and Regulatory Reform Act 2006. The new HSE remains part of the Department for Work and Pensions.

The HSE's primary function is to promote the cause of better health and safety at work. The Chair of the HSC has become the Chair of the Board of the new Executive. The potential size of the Board of the HSE will be no more than 11 members plus the Chair. Members are appointed by the Secretary of State. They represent employers, the trades unions and the public interest (through local authority members).

The HSE has a duty to bring forward proposals for regulations, power to undertake research and to disseminate information, power to direct investigations and inquiries into accidents and similar events. The HSE is advised by a number of industry advisory committees (see section 20.1.2 of this chapter). The HSE also retains a duty to enforce health and safety legislation.

Inspection of industrial premises and construction sites is achieved through a network of regional and area offices. Within that structure are specialist units providing engineering and scientific advice. Depending on the location of the construction work, other HSE inspectorates, including those for mines, explosives, nuclear installations or offshore safety may also have enforcement responsibilities over the site on which the construction work is being carried out. In respect of construction work on the railways enforcement of health and safety legislation is the responsibility of Her Majesty's Railway Inspectorate which transferred from the HSC/HSE to the Office of Rail Regulation (ORR) on 1st April 2006.

In addition to its enforcement role, the HSE operates various licensing and approval schemes, one of which in the construction sector licenses asbestos removal contractors. The HSE is also the enforcing authority under legislation implementing European Community directives dealing with machinery and equipment safety (see the HSE website and *Construction health and safety II*, this volume).

20.1.2 Construction Industry Advisory Committee

The Construction Industry Advisory Committee (CONIAC) till April 2008 advised the HSC on matters relating to the construction industry but now advises HSE. The Committee is representative of all sections of the industry. Members are appointed by the HSE normally for a period of 3 years. The CONIAC members principally represent employer organisations and employee organisations; however, in addition, the CONIAC includes representatives of the construction professions, client organisations, materials suppliers, the plant hire industry and the public interest.

The CONIAC commissions and publishes guidance and advises the HSE on legislation and accompanying Approved Codes of Practice (ACoPs) and guidance. The CONIAC is supported by a number of working parties dealing with specific topics, including training and education, occupational health and the particular problems of small businesses within the construction industry.

20.1.3 Health and safety legislation in Scotland and Northern Ireland

The HSWA applies only within Great Britain, that is, Scotland, Wales and England. Separate but similar construction health and safety legislation, enforced by a separate inspectorate (HSENI), exists in Northern Ireland. In addition, the Isle of

Man and the Channel Islands have their own health and safety authorities. Occupational health and safety is not a responsibility which has been devolved to the Scottish Parliament or the Welsh Assembly. Some EC directives in the construction sector affect Great Britain, some the UK as a whole.

The text of Acts and Regulations coming into force after 1988 can be found on the website of the Office of Public Sector Information.

20.1.4 Approved Codes of Practice and guidance

Much current health and safety legislation is supported by ACoPs and guidance. It is important to understand where ACoPs and guidance come within the hierarchy of legislation which follows from the general framework of legal requirements in the HSWA. An ACoP is a document which, following a period of consultation with all sides of industry, is 'approved' by the HSE under section 16 of the HSWA.

Apart from containing information amplifying and supporting the requirements of regulations, ACoPs have a unique legal status. When cited in support of a prosecution, the burden of proof passes to the defendant to show that what was done was at least as good in respect of health or safety as the work practices set out in the ACoP.

Guidance in documents such as HSE guidance notes come below ACoPs in terms of legal standing. The HSE guidance documents are statements of good practice and, as such documents are the subject of consultation with both sides of industry prior to publication, reflect a consensus view.

20.1.5 British and CEN standards

A number of safety-related British Standards (BS) and BS codes of practice on construction-related topics are published by the British Standards Institution. Although, in law, most BSs have only the standing of guidance documents, courts increasingly seem to be placing greater importance on them because of the consultative process under which they are drafted and the consensus within industry which they reflect.

The CEN – the European Standards organisation – had largely completed the harmonised standards required to support EC directives, for example, the Machinery Directive 98/37/EC; however, the adoption of a revised EC Machinery Directive 2006/42/EC, has resulted in a large number of machinery standards having to be updated to reflect the requirements of the revised directive.

Harmonised standards, which are common to all EC member countries, are a way of removing barriers to trade within the Community. The CEN standards are drafted by committees of experts representing the national standards bodies of member states and draft standards are consulted and voted on by all EC member states.

Most construction-related CEN standards fall into two broad categories – machinery safety standards and product standards. Construction machinery must conform to the essential safety requirements of the EC Machinery Directive. Self-certification of conformity with the relevant CEN standards, by the supplier of the machinery into the European Community, is the most common way of demonstrating conformity with the essential safety requirements of the Directive. While CEN standards are not mandatory, conformity with the Machinery Directive is mandatory, so the role of standards in demonstrating has increasingly made them regarded as quasi-mandatory by industry. Construction product standards perform a similar role for materials used in construction work in respect of the requirements of the EC Construction Products Directive.

20.2 Enforcement
20.2.1 Jurisdiction over work

Although the HSE is the principal body for enforcement purposes, the HSWA provides for a specific authority to be designated for the purposes of particular health and safety regulations and, more importantly, for local authorities to be responsible for enforcing statutory provisions in certain lower risk situations.

The local authorities have designated areas of responsibility under the Health and Safety (Enforcing Authority) Regulations 1998, and have jurisdiction over, for example, retail or wholesale distribution activities (subject to certain exceptions such as for supply of dangerous substances), office activities, catering and the provision of residential accommodation. This jurisdiction is usually exercised by local Environmental Health Officers acting with the same powers as HSE inspectors. These jurisdiction rules are, however, altered in relation to construction work. The 1998 Regulations provide that the enforcing authority role of local authorities reverts to the HSE in relation to the following activities carried on at any premises by persons who do not normally work in the premises:

(a) construction work if:
   (i) Regulation 21 of the Construction (Design and Management) Regulations 2007 (CDM 2007) (which requires projects which include or are intended to include construction work to be notified to the Executive) applies to the project which includes the work, or
   (ii) the whole or part of the work contracted to be undertaken by the contractor at the premises is to the external fabric or other external part of a building or structure, or
   (iii) it is carried out in a physically segregated area of the premises, the activities normally carried out in that area have been suspended for the purpose of enabling the construction work to be carried out, the contractor has authority to exclude from that area persons who are not attending in connection with the carrying out of the work and the work is not the maintenance of insulation on pipes, boilers or other parts of heating or water systems or its removal from them.

(b) the installation, maintenance or repair of any gas system, or any work in relation to a gas fitting;
(c) the installation, maintenance or repair of electricity systems;
(d) work with ionising radiations except work in one or more of the categories set out in Schedule 3 to the Ionising Radiations Regulations 1985.

The consequence of this is that Environmental Health Officers are responsible for enforcement of health and safety requirements in relation to minor internal works in shops, offices and other low risk premises.

20.2.2 Enforcement powers

Inspectors have available to them a wide range of statutory enforcement powers enabling them to undertake routine inspections and incident investigations, to stop contraventions of statutory requirements or positively require steps to be taken. The powers of inspectors are contained mainly in Section 20 of the HSWA and relate to powers of entry, seizure of evidence (documentary evidence and physical objects) and questioning witnesses. In circumstances where there has been no death, the investigation will by HSE (or other appropriate authority such as a local authority).

However, if a death occurs in the workplace then, under the *Work-related Deaths: A protocol for liaison* (HSE free leaflet MISC 491; Association of Chief Police Officers *et al.*, 2003) is implemented and the death is treated as a manslaughter investigation led by the police with the HSE providing technical assistance. If there is sufficient evidence to bring manslaughter charges the case will be prosecuted by the Crown Prosecution Service (CPS). If there is insufficient evidence for a manslaughter prosecution, the investigation is handed over to HSE to consider if there have been any breaches of health and safety legislation. If there is sufficient evidence the HSE will prosecute. It is therefore necessary to look at the enforcement powers of both HSE and the police.

20.2.2.1 Powers of inspectors
Powers of entry

Inspectors are empowered to enter any premises where they believe it is necessary to do so to carry out their duties. These visits can be by appointment, but they are usually made spontaneously at any reasonable time (or at any time at all if the inspector has reason to believe there is a dangerous situation). It is an offence to obstruct an inspector attempting to exercise these powers (see subsequent section) but an inspector may be required to supply identification and establish credentials as a duly appointed person before gaining entry or exercising any powers. Once on the site or other premises an inspector has various powers to carry out examinations, or require that evidence on site is left undisturbed while investigations continue, and to make various records of what is found, including taking photographs.

Seizure of evidence, taking samples and so on

Inspectors' powers in relation to the collection of physical evidence include the right to take samples, for example, of substances or items of equipment, or samples from the atmosphere to test for environmental hazards. They can also dismantle equipment, or take possession of it so that it can be preserved for use as evidence in proceedings. There are certain rules relating to the rights of persons under investigation to be present or to receive samples of their own when these powers are exercised.

Access to documentary evidence

The powers of inspectors to require production of documents are virtually unlimited. Save for material which is subject to legal privilege, they are entitled to access to any documents they deem necessary to see for the purposes of their investigations which may include not only formal records kept pursuant to statutory requirements (such as accident books) but also papers such as a company's correspondence and the internal memoranda of its staff, any reports on health and safety and minutes of board meetings. Confidentiality is not a ground for refusing to give an inspector such documents.

Interviews

There are three types of interview by an HSE inspector. These are

(1) an interview under caution. In terms of a company this will be of a 'company representative'. This can be anyone who is specifically authorised by the company to talk on its behalf. This might be a director or senior manager
(2) an interview by an HSE inspector using his powers under section 20(2)(j) HSWA (often referred to as a 'section 20 interview')
(3) an interview by an inspector of a potential witness where the witness will be asked to make a voluntary statement under section 9 of the Criminal Justice Act 1967 (often referred to as a 'section 9 statement')

An HSE inspector does not have the power of arrest. Thus the inspector cannot compel someone to attend an interview under caution. Any interview under caution is subject to the provisions of the Police and Criminal Evidence Act 1984 (PACE). However, section 34 of the Criminal Justice and Public Order Act 1994 (CJPOA) only applies where an interview under caution takes place. Thus no adverse inference can be drawn if a defendant (whether individual or a company) declines an invitation to attend an HSE interview under caution.

Under section 20(2)(j) HSWA an HSE inspector can require any person who he/she has reasonable cause to believe is able to give information relevant to the investigation to answer questions asked by the inspector that he/she reasonably believes are required as part of HSE's investigation. The person interviewed under this provision will be required to sign a declaration of truth of his/her answers.

It is an offence to refuse to answer the HSE inspector's relevant questions. However, any answers given by the person cannot be used in evidence against that person.

Anyone who gives a statement as a witness for the HSE (or the police) will be asked to give a statement in 'section 9' of the Criminal Justice Act 1967 form. This means that there is a declaration at the start of the statement which must be signed and dated by the witness and then the foot of each page should also be signed and dated. In this form, if the statement is uncontested then it can be read out at trial and accepted in evidence.

The declaration for a section 9 statement is

> This statement, consisting of [ ] page(s), each signed by me, is true to the best of my knowledge and belief and I make it knowing that, if it is tendered in evidence, I shall be liable to prosecution if I have wilfully stated in it anything which I know to be false or do not believe to be true.

In a section 9 interview the HSE inspector cannot insist on his/her questions being answered. However, this approach does not afford the interviewee the same protection as under section 20(2)(j) HSWA. If the inspector believes the person is incriminating him/herself then the interview should be terminated and the inspector must caution the interviewee.

Additional powers

The HSWA provides that inspectors can require any person 'to afford him such facilities and assistance … as are necessary to enable the Inspector to exercise any of the powers conferred on him …' and also to exercise 'any other power which is necessary …'. Thus, provided the inspectors are in the course of an investigation (which will not usually be difficult for them to show), there is in principle no limit to the powers they can take in addition to those already described earlier. In practice, this provision has not been used by inspectors to take draconian steps and, in fact, with their powers of entry, seizure and questioning there is little else they are likely to need in order to obtain all the evidence they require to satisfy themselves whether or not they need to take action.

There are further powers in section 25 of the HSWA enabling an inspector to seize and render harmless articles or substances where there is reasonable cause to believe that the product in question is a cause of imminent danger of personal injury (this is separate from the powers to take samples and detain objects referred to earlier). If the circumstances warrant it, these powers may extend even to destroying products in order to render them harmless with certain rules, enabling the person from whom they are being seized to be provided with samples and be given a report on the circumstances in which the seizure took place.

20.2.2.2 Powers of the police

The police's powers are set out in the Police and Criminal Evidence Act 1984 (PACE) and the Codes of Practice to the Act.

Power to search

Police have the power to enter and search any premises without a warrant in order to make an arrest or to search premises occupied or controlled by an arrested person providing the officer has reasonable grounds for suspecting there is evidence at the premises, other than legally privileged items, that relates to the suspected offence.

There is also power to search under a warrant. Searches can also be carried out with the consent of a person entitled to grant entry.

Power of seizure

The police have a general power in respect to the seizure of evidence. A police officer, who is lawfully on any premises has the power to seize anything he has reasonable grounds for believing is evidence in relation to an offence and it is necessary to seize it in order to prevent the evidence being concealed, lost, altered or destroyed. This extends to the seizure of computer records. Items seized can be retained for so long as it is necessary 'in all the circumstances'.

Interviews

The police have the power to arrest a person for any offence (providing the officer has reasonable grounds for doing so) and to interview them at the police station under caution. The caution given at the start of the interview is

> You do not have to say anything. But it may harm your defence if you do not mention when questioned something which you later rely on in court. Anything you do say may be given in evidence.

On being arrested, the person will be taken to the custody suit where he/she will be presented to the custody sergeant and the arresting officer will explain why the person has been arrested. The custody sergeant will then authorise detention at the station and will open a custody record. The person will be informed of their rights to have a legal representative (if he/she does not have a solicitor they will be informed of the duty solicitor scheme), a person informed of their arrest and to be able to consult the Codes of Practice. The person will then have his/her photograph, fingerprints and DNA sample taken.

If the person declines to answer the police's questions then an adverse inference might be drawn if the matter later comes to trial. Section 34 of the CJPOA states that a court, in determining whether a defendant is guilty or not may draw such inferences as appear proper from the evidence of silence either when the defendant was interviewed under caution or on being charged or officially informed that they might be charged, the defendant failed to mention any fact that they later rely on in court in their defence which in the circumstances existing at the time they could reasonably have been expected to have mentioned. Note that a defendant cannot be convicted upon an adverse inference alone.

20.2.3 Powers of inspectors

Enforcement notices

Inspectors have a large measure of discretion over how they deal with non-compliance with health and safety requirements. Very often their response is to issue warnings to the employer or other person concerned, usually confirmed in writing, and requesting that action be taken within a set time. They may at the same time advice on the shortcomings that they have discovered and suggest that certain actions be taken or refer the person concerned to ACoPs or relevant guidance. These actions do not involve the exercise of formal enforcement powers. However, where a situation is regarded as sufficiently serious, an inspector will issue one of two types of enforcement notice pursuant to powers under the HSWA.

Improvement notices

An Improvement Notice can be issued where an inspector is of the opinion that a person is contravening the statutory requirements or has contravened the statutory requirements in circumstances that make it likely that the contravention will continue or be repeated. These contraventions may consist of the failure to comply with one of the general duties of the HSWA, or contravention of health and safety regulations. An Improvement Notice has to meet a number of requirements laid down by the Act. It must

- specify the provision or provisions which the inspector believes are not being complied with
- give particulars of the reasons why the inspector is of that opinion
- specify the period of time within which the person is required to remedy the contravention, being a period of not less than 21 days

In addition, an inspector may add to a Notice a Schedule containing information about the steps which the inspector would regard as necessary to remedy the contravention.

Prohibition notices

Prohibition Notices differ from Improvement Notices in that they may take effect immediately and they require the recipient to the Notice to cease the activity in question. There is no requirement for an inspector to demonstrate that statutory requirements have actually been contravened. The requirement for a Prohibition Notice to be served is that the inspector should be of the opinion that the activity in question involved, or will involve, a risk of serious personal injury. Such a Notice can be served in anticipation that activities carried out will pose such a risk. A Prohibition Notice can be served in any circumstances where an Improvement Notice could have been used. In circumstances where to cease activity immediately would present additional risks, for example, shutting down a refinery process, the coming into effect of the Prohibition Notice can be deferred for a period specified in the Notice. An inspector attaches a Schedule setting out the steps which should be taken to remedy the contraventions.

Appeal procedures

There are procedures whereby the recipient of an Improvement or Prohibition Notice can challenge the issue of the Notice, or may seek to have the terms (e.g. the time limits allowed for improvements) varied. These appeals are dealt with by employment tribunals. An application to a tribunal has to be made within 21 days from the date of service of the Notice (subject to any further time the tribunal may allow). The effect of this procedure pending the hearing varies depending on the type of Notice:

- The operation of an Improvement Notice will be suspended until the proceedings are finished (either with a ruling by the tribunal or with the proceedings being withdrawn).
- The operation of a Prohibition Notice may also be suspended in the same way, but this will only be the case if there was an interim application by the recipient of the Notice and the tribunal agrees that the Notice should be suspended. (Even then, the Prohibition Notice is only suspended from the time the tribunal so directs.)

On the hearing of an appeal (which may be a matter of weeks after an appeal is lodged), the tribunal has various options available, including cancelling the Notice completely, affirming it unchanged or affirming with such modifications as it thinks fit. In such an appeal, the onus of proof lies with an inspector to demonstrate that the Notice has been validly served, which means that the inspector is required to show either the serious risk of personal injury or the contravention of statutory requirements as the case may be.

In *Chilcott v. Thermal Transfer Limited* [2009] EWHC 2086 (Admin) the High Court gave guidance upon the approach to be adopted when reviewing an inspector's decision to issue a prohibition notice. Mr Justice Charles held that an employment tribunal's role was not limited to reviewing the genuineness and/or reasonableness of the inspector's opinion but was required to form its own view taking account of the inspector's expertise. However, the decision should be viewed on what was known at the time the notice was issued and not what was learnt after.

Two particular limitations on the service of enforcement notices should be noted. First, where an inspector is proposing to serve an Improvement Notice relating to a contravention of statutory requirements applying to a building, the Notice cannot correct any measures to be taken to remedy the position that are more onerous than those that are necessary to secure conformity with the requirements of any Building Regulations that apply at the time and to which the building would be required to conform if it were being newly erected (unless, i.e. the health and safety requirements which the inspector has identified are themselves more onerous than the requirements of the Building Regulations). Second, before an inspector serves an enforcement notice affecting means of escape in case of fire, he or she must first consult the Fire Authority.

Details of an enforcement notice will be included in a public register (if not withdrawn or cancelled in consequence of an appeal) unless it relates solely to the protection of persons at work. (A notice covering risks to private citizens would be made public under the Environment and Safety Information Act 1988.) Details of the appeals procedure are usually given out by the inspector with the notice.

20.2.4 Prosecutions

If the police prosecute in relation to a work-related death they will prosecute an individual for manslaughter on the basis of gross negligence and a company for manslaughter under the new Corporate Manslaughter and Corporate Homicide Act 2007 (CMCHA) which is applicable for all work-related deaths that occur after 6th April 2008.

HSE increasingly prosecutes employers under the general duties of the HSWA (see section 20.3), often pursuant to section 2 HSWA, failing to ensure the health safety and welfare of an employee 'so far as is reasonably practicable' or section 3, failing to conduct his undertaking (i.e. business) so as to ensure, 'so far as is reasonably practicable' persons not in his employment are not exposed to risks to their health or safety as opposed to prosecuting for contravention of health and safety regulations reflecting the higher penalties available on conviction. Even if the failures of an employer are adequately covered by a specific regulation, this does not prevent HSE from prosecuting under the general duties (see *R. v. Bristol Magistrates' Court ex parte Juttan Oy* [2003] UKHL 53).

Individuals when prosecuted by HSE are usually prosecuted for a breach of section 7(a) HSWA (this covers employees and managers) or under section 37 HSWA (if a director or very senior manager).

Prosecution codes

Prosecutions by the police and HSE must satisfy the Code for Crown Prosecutors (which can be viewed online). It sets out two fundamental steps in deciding whether to prosecute: the evidential test and the public interest test.

The evidential test requires the prosecutor to be satisfied that there is enough evidence to provide a 'realistic prospect of conviction' against the defendant on each charge. They must consider what the defence may be and how that is likely to affect the prosecution case.

A realistic prospect of conviction is an objective test. It means that a jury or bench of magistrates, properly directed in accordance with the law, is more likely than not to convict the defendant of the alleged charge.

In relation to public interest the Code quotes Lord Shawcross's statement of 1951 on public interest when he was Attorney General when he said that 'It has never been the rule in this country – I hope it never will be – that suspected criminal offences must automatically be the subject of prosecution.' (House of Commons Debates, volume 483, column 681, 29th January 1951.)

Prosecutors are required to balance factors for and against prosecution '*carefully and fairly*'. Public interest factors that can affect the decision to prosecute usually depend on the seriousness of the offence or the circumstances of the offender. Some factors may increase the need to prosecute but others may suggest that another course of action would be better.

HSE also have an *Enforcement Policy Statement* (2009) which sets out the general principles and approach. The statement says that

> The appropriate use of enforcement powers, including prosecution, is important, both to secure compliance with the law and to ensure those who have duties under it may be held to account for failures to safeguard health, safety and welfare.

Paragraph 39 of the statement says that prosecutions will normally follow where one or more of the following circumstances apply:

- death was a result of a breach of the health and safety legislation

- the gravity of an alleged offence, taken together with the seriousness of any actual or potential harm, or the general record and approach of the offender warrants it

- there has been reckless disregard of health and safety requirements

- there have been repeated breaches which give rise to significant risk, or persistent and significant poor compliance

- work has been carried out without or in serious non-compliance with an appropriate licence or safety case

- a duty holder's standard of managing health and safety is found to be far below what is required by health and safety law and to be giving rise to significant risk

- there has been a failure to comply with an improvement notice or prohibition notice served by the enforcing authority; or there has been a repetition of a breach that was subject to a formal caution

- false information has been supplied wilfully, or there has been an intent to deceive, in relation to a matter which gives rise to serious risk

- inspectors have been intentionally obstructed in the lawful course of their duties

Prosecution of employers for breaches of their general duties under HSWA

The three general duties under the HSWA relevant to the construction industry are sections 2, 3 and 4 (see section 20.3). Each of these duties is qualified by the term 'so far as is reasonably practicable'.

An offence occurs under these general duties as soon as there is an exposure to health and safety risks. The exposure to risk can be over a period of time or can relate to a single incident. The prosecution must prove this exposure to the criminal standard, that is, so the court is sure ('beyond reasonable doubt').

Once the prosecution has proved that there has been an exposure to a health and safety risk it is for the defence (pursuant to section 40 HSWA) to prove that it did all that was reasonably practicable to control the risk.

Section 40 HSWA states that

In any proceedings for an offence under any of the relevant statutory provisions consisting of a failure to comply with a duty or requirement to do something so far as is practicable or so far as is reasonably practicable, or to use the best practicable means to do something, it shall be for the accused to prove (as the case may be) that it was not practicable or not reasonably practicable to do more than was in fact done to satisfy the duty or requirement, or that there was no better practicable means than was in fact used to satisfy the duty or requirement.

This defence has to be proved on a balance of probabilities, that is, not to the criminal standard.

The general duties impose 'strict liability' upon an employer, subject only to the defence reasonable practicability (see *R. v. British Steel plc* [1995] 1 WLR 1356, *R. v. Associated Octel Co Ltd* [1996] 4 All ER 846 and *R. v. Gateway Foodmarkets Ltd* [1997] 3 All ER 78). By strict liability this means that the prosecution does not have to prove any intent on the part of the defendant to commit an offence or any negligence.

In relation to section 2 HSWA it was said in *Lockhart v. Kevin Oliphant* [1992] SCCR 774 that once there is a 'prima facie' case against the employer that the health, safety and welfare of employees was not ensured, then the onus under section 40 was on the employer.

In *R v. Chargot Limited and others* [2008] UKHL the House of Lords upheld the approach adopted in the Court of Appeal in that case requiring the prosecution only to prove the existence of a state of affairs or 'result', that is, the exposure of employees or non-employees to a 'risk'.

This will usually be evidenced by the fact of an accident (but the Lords did say 'Even where injury has occurred it may not be enough for the prosecutor simply to assert that the injury demonstrates that there was a risk'). This was restated in the later Court of Appeal case of *R v. EGS Ltd* [2009] EWCA Crim 1942.

In *Chargot* he defence's assertion that the prosecution was under a duty to identify and prove particulars as to how the defendant was alleged to have breached its statutory duty under sections 2 and 3 was dismissed as representing an issue of prosecution practice. The House of Lords said that particulars may be required for reasons of fairness.

The term 'risk' is defined in the ACoP to the Management of Health and Safety at Work Regulations 1999 (HSC, 2000) as

the likelihood of potential harm from that hazard (which is defined ... [as] ... being something with the potential to cause harm) being realised. The extent of the risk will depend on:

(i) the likelihood of that harm occurring;

(ii) the potential severity of that harm, that is, of any resultant injury or adverse health effect; and

(iii) the population which might be affected by the hazard, that is, the number of people who might be exposed (Emphasis added).

'Risk' was widely interpreted in the Court of Appeal case *R. v. Board of Trustees of Science Museum* [1993] 3 All ER 853, a prosecution pursuant to section 3 HSWA where the issue concerned whether there had been exposure to risk from *Legionella* bacteria present in a cooling tower that was not in use. It was held that the possibility of danger was sufficient and that there was no need for the prosecution to show that there was an actual danger.

The following passage from the judgement explains what is meant by the 'possibility of danger':

The critical question of interpretation is as follows. Was it enough for the prosecution to prove that there was a risk that [the legionella bacteria] might emerge or did the prosecution have to go further and show that [the bacteria] did in fact emerge into the atmosphere and was available to be inhaled? Mr Carlisle, leading counsel for the prosecution, illustrated the problem with a simple example. Imagine, he said, a loose object on the roof near a pavement. In case A, the loose object is in a position in which it might fall off and hit a pedestrian. In that case there is a mere risk. In case B, the object in fact falls and exposes pedestrians to actual danger. In case C, the object falls and causes actual injury to a pedestrian. The prosecution submits that exposure to risk in case A constitutes a prima facie case under section 3(1). The defence submits that section 3(1) only covers cases B and C.

The Court of Appeal found in favour of the prosecution. Thus the possibility of danger is the risk.

In the recent case of *R. v. Porter* [2008] All ER (D) 249 (May) the Court of Appeal stepped back from such a wide definition saying the risk must be a 'real' risk as opposed to a 'fanciful or hypothetical' one. HSE were refused leave to appeal to the House of Lords in October 2008.

This case was followed by the House of Lords decision in *Chargot*. Lord Hope said that

...when the legislation refers to risk it is not contemplating risks that are trivial or fanciful. It is not its purpose to impose burdens on employers that are wholly unreasonable......The law does not aim to create an environment that is entirely risk free. It concerns itself with risks that are material. That, in effect, is what the word 'risk' which the statute uses means. It is directed at situations where there is a material risk to health and safety, which any reasonable person would appreciate and take steps to guard against.

The Court of Appeal *R v. EGS Ltd* unusually sought to explain what Lord Hope meant by material risk. In doing so it also confirmed that foreseeability is not part of determining the materiality of the risk. Lord Dyson said:

...it is not entirely clear to us why Lord Hope added [those] words....We think the explanation is that he considered that, in practice, any reasonable person would appreciate and take steps to guard against a risk which is more than trivial or fanciful..... The word 'risk' has been interpreted in Chargot as meaning a risk which is not trivial or fanciful, but that is not a qualification to the statutory provision. It is a question of fact and degree whether a risk is trivial or fanciful......The prosecution did not have to prove that the risk was appreciable or foreseeable. They had to prove that the risk was not fanciful and was more than trivial.

While foreseeability is not part of determining whether there is a risk it is relevant to what is reasonably practicable. In the case of *R. v. HTM* [2006] Crim 1156 it was said by the Court of Appeal that

> ... it seems to us that a defendant to a charge under section 2 or indeed sections 3 or 4 [HSWA], in asking a jury to consider whether it has established that it has done all that is reasonably practicable, cannot be prevented from adducing evidence as to the likelihood of the incidence of the relevant risk eventuating in support of its case that it had taken all reasonable means to eliminate it.

In the case of *R. v. Nelson Group Services (Maintenance) Ltd* [1998] 4 All ER 331 the Court of Appeal held an employer was not precluded from relying upon section 40 HSWA merely because an employee carrying out the work was careless or omitted to take precaution. The employer could show it had done all that was reasonably practicable by proving appropriate instruction and training had been given and that there was a safe system of work in place. It was held in the *HTM* case that the *Nelson* is still good law.

The Corporate Manslaughter and Corporate Homicide Act 2007

Prior to the CMCHA to convict an organisation of manslaughter following a work-related death, it had to be proved that someone senior in the organisation, often referred to as the directing mind, was also guilty of manslaughter. This made prosecuting large organisations difficult.

The new offence does away with the requirement for proving the guilt of a directing mind. In the future an organisation will be guilty of corporate manslaughter if death is caused by a gross breach of its relevant duty of care that is substantially due to senior management failure (see section 1 of the CMCHA). Now the failures of a number of senior managers can be added together.

The organisations that can commit the offence include

1. a corporation
2. a partnership
3. a local authority

The relevant duty of care is that owed by an organisation to its employees and non-employees arising out of its business. Thus the CMCHA does not impose any additional duties to those that exist under the Health and Safety at Work Act 1974 (HSWA). All that it changes is the mechanics of prosecution.

Section 2 of the CMCHA sets out the meaning of the 'relevant duty of care' and specifically states it includes '*the carrying on by the organisation of any construction or maintenance operations*'.

The breach of duty does not have to be the only cause or indeed the major cause of death, only one of the causes.

These are persons who play a significant role in the decision making or management of the organisation. Following the line of reasoning in *El Aljou v. Dollar Land Holdings plc* [1994] 2 All ER 685 (concerning the definition of a 'directing mind') it is possible a person may be deemed senior management for only part of their job function. The duties of various duty holders set out in the CDM 2007 may be relevant in a prosecution concerning a construction project to determining the relevant senior management for the purposes of the CMCHA.

A 'gross breach' is defined in section 1 CMCHA as conduct amounting to a breach of duty that '*falls far below what can reasonably be expected of the organisation in the circumstances*'.

A jury will be asked to consider how serious the organisation's failure was and how much of a risk of death it posed. The jury may also take into account (see section 8 CMCHA) the 'attitudes, policies, systems or accepted practices' of the organisation relevant to the failure (in other words 'safety culture') and relevant health and safety and industry guidance.

Mistakenly, people believe the new law means there will be no prosecutions of directors or senior managers. The CMCHA does not make provision for secondary liability (e.g. aiding and abetting) but it does not prevent a director or senior manager from being prosecuted either for gross negligence manslaughter and/or a breach of section 37 HSWA.

On 23 April 2009, the CPS announced details of the first prosecution under the new Corporate Manslaughter and Corporate Homicide Act 2007. Engineering company, Cotswold Geotechnical Holdings, based in Gloucester, is the company charged.

The prosecution follows the tragic death of an employee, junior geologist Mr Alexander Wright. Mr Wright was taking soil samples from inside a pit when it collapsed and crushed him.

Mr Peter Eaton, one of just two directors of the company, has also been charged with gross negligence manslaughter. The trial started on 22nd February 2010 but (at the time of writing) has been adjourned to October 2010. Given the facts of the case and the size of the company it will not really be a test of the new law as the case could have easily been brought under the old law.

Prosecution of individuals for breaches of HSWA

Section 37 HSWA states

> Where an offence under any of the relevant statutory provisions committed by a body corporate is proved to have been committed with the consent or connivance of, or attributable to and neglect on the part of, any director, manager, secretary or other similar officer of the body corporate or a person who was purporting to act in any such capacity, he as well as the body corporate shall be guilty of that offence and shall be liable to be proceeded against and punished accordingly.

Section 37 is concerned with the secondary liability of an individual, in certain circumstances, for the offence committed by a corporate body which is primarily liable. It is only relevant where a corporate body has committed a health and safety offence.

In order to prove the case against the individual, the prosecution must first prove the corporate body committed a health and safety offence and then that this breach was due to the defendant's consent or connivance or was attributable to the defendant's neglect.

Consent is where the defendant had knowledge of the risk being run by the company but consented to it nonetheless. Connivance is where the defendant once again has knowledge of the risk but 'turns a blind eye' to what is happening. In terms of the meaning of the word neglect in the Scottish case *Wotherspoon v. HM Advocate* [1978] JC 74 it was said 'in its natural meaning presupposes the existence of some obligation or duty on the person charged with neglect'. The case goes on to say that

> in considering in a given case whether there has been neglect within the meaning of HSWA 1974 s37(1) on the part of a particular director or other particular officer charged, the search must be to discover whether the accused has failed to take some steps to prevent the commission of an offence by the corporation to which he belongs if the taking of those steps either expressly falls within or should be held to fall within the scope of the functions of the office which he holds.

In terms of what is 'attributable' it was said in the same case that any degree of attributability was sufficient.

As for knowledge in the case of 'neglect' it was held by the Court of Appeal in *R. v. P Ltd and G* [2007] All ER (D) 173 (Jul) (CA) that if a director

> ... had no actual knowledge of the relevant state of facts, the question would always be whether, nonetheless, he should have been put on inquiry by reasons of the surrounding circumstances whether the relevant safety procedures were in place ...
>
> The prosecution case might be such that in order to establish a case to go before the jury, it had to establish that the [director] did know of the unsafe practices; however, it did not have to prove that, if it could prove that the circumstances ought to have put him on inquiry to the extent that there was a duty on him to act.

In *Chargot* the House of Lords also considered section 37. Their Lordships observed that

> The offences that are created by sections 2(1) and 3(1) are directed to the result that must be achieved by the body corporate. Where it is shown that the body corporate failed to achieve or prevent the result that those sections contemplate, it will be a relatively short step for the inference to be drawn that there was connivance or neglect on his part if the circumstances under which the risk arose were under the direction or control of the officer. The more remote his area of responsibility is from those circumstances, the harder it will be to draw that inference.

In relation to the definition of a 'manager' it was held In *R. v. Boal* [1992] 3 All ER 177, CA, a case on the almost identical wording of the Fire Precautions Act 1971, section 23(1), that

only those responsible for deciding corporate policy and strategy were 'managers'. Thus a defendant will have to in practice be a very senior manager to come within this definition.

Section 36 HSWA, like section 37, concerns secondary liability. It is committed when the commission of a health and safety offence by another person is due to the act or default of some other person, and that other person is also liable to be prosecuted for the offence. An example of a prosecution under this section is of Christopher Hooper, a health and safety consultant. He prepared an inadequate risk assessment upon a machine for a client on which an employee of that client was later injured.

Individuals can also be prosecuted under section 7(a) HSWA. This covers a wide range of employees from front line workers to fairly senior managers. It states that

> It shall be the duty of every employee while at work – to take reasonable care for the health and safety of himself and of other persons who may be affected by his acts or omissions at work.

This is somewhat of a grey area of law since the vast majority of cases are dealt with in the magistrates' courts and as a consequence there are very few reported cases.

For a frontline employee to be prosecuted, his or her actions normally have to be bordering on the reckless. An example is the prosecution of Mr Holland in 1998 who was an employee at a fertiliser company. As a practical joke he exposed a 17-year-old colleague to hydrochloric acid which resulted in the teenager being injured.

For a manager to be prosecuted, the negligence does not have to be so bad. A manager can be prosecuted if he or she has failed to carry out his/her job (or has violated procedures) so that health and safety standards are consequently significantly lowered.

Prosecution of individuals for manslaughter

In a work-related death incident the police will be considering manslaughter by gross negligence. The leading case on this area of law is *R. v. Adomako* [1995] 1 AC 171. To be guilty of gross negligence manslaughter the jury must be satisfied:

1. the defendant owed a duty of care to the deceased; and
2. he/she was in breach of that duty; and
3. the breach of duty was a substantial cause of death (i.e. something more than trivial); and
4. the breach was so grossly negligent that the defendant can be deemed to have had such disregard for life of the deceased that it should be seen as criminal and deserving of punishment by the State.

20.2.5 Sentencing
Penalties for health and safety offences
The Health and Safety (offences) Act 2008

This Act was passed on 16 October 2008. It took effect on 16 January 2009. The Act has resulted in the £20 000 maximum fine in the Magistrates' Court applying to most health and safety offences.

The Act does not affect the position in relation to fines for sentences imposed in the Crown Court where fines are unlimited.

The Act also provides the courts with the power to imprison individuals for many health and safety offences (including offences pursuant to sections 7(a) and 37 HSWA). The maximum term in the Magistrates' Court is 6 months and in the Crown Court 2 years.

Disqualification of Directors and Managers

If a defendant is convicted under section 37 HSWA, the prosecution can apply for his/her disqualification from acting as a director (and in a management position of a company) pursuant to the Company Directors Disqualification Act 1986. The maximum period in the Magistrates Court is 5 years and in the Crown Court 15 years. In recent times applications for disqualification orders have become more common.

The objects of sentencing: Section 142 Criminal Justice Act 2003

The objects of sentencing in criminal cases are set out in section 142 of the Criminal Justice Act 2003. It says any court dealing with an offender in respect of his/her offence must have regard to the following purposes:

(a) the punishment of offenders,
(b) the reduction of crime (including its reduction by deterrence),
(c) the reform and rehabilitation of offenders,
(d) the protection of the public, and
(e) the making of reparation by offenders to persons affected by their actions.

The Court of Appeal in *R. v. Balfour Beatty Rail Infrastructure Services Ltd* [2006] EWCA Crim 1586 observed that most of these can be applied in the case of a company, although there are 'obvious difficulties' in applying (c).

Fixing a fine: Section 164 Criminal Justice Act 2003

Section 164 of the Criminal Justice Act concerns the level of fine to be imposed for an offence. It applies equally to health and safety offences as well as to any other criminal conviction where the sanction includes a fine. It is particularly relevant to health and safety matters where an unlimited fine can be imposed. This section of the Act requires the following:

1. Before the amount of a fine is determined in relation to an offender who is an individual, then the court must enquire into the offender's financial circumstances.
2. The fine must reflect the court's view of the seriousness of the offence.
3. Where the offender is an individual or a company, when fixing a fine the court must take into account the circumstances

of the case, including, among other things, the financial circumstances of the offender 'so far as they are known, or appear, to the court'.
4. In taking into account the financial position of the offender this can have the effect of increasing or reducing the amount of the fine.

Sentencing an employer/company for health and safety offences

The Court of Appeal in 1999 in the case *R. v. Howe & Son (Engineers) Ltd* [1999] 2 CrApp R(S) 37 said the purpose of health and safety prosecutions is to achieve a safe environment for employees and non-employees who may be affected by the defendant's business activities. It said that the fine should be large enough to bring that message home and where the defendant is a company not only to the managers but also the shareholders.

The brief facts were that a 20-year-old employee of the defendant company was electrocuted and killed while cleaning his employer's factory which had shut down for this purpose.

An electric vacuum cleaner known as a 'Freddy' was being used to suck up water from the factory floor. The cable to the machine became trapped between the wheels and the floor. As a result the cable became damaged and 'live'. The deceased was holding the cable when he was killed.

For a number of technical reasons the company failed to ensure that the safety at work of its employees had been safeguarded 'so far as was reasonably practicable', and the lack of a system to check its electrical equipment fell far short of the appropriate standard. The court observed: '... the tragedy that befell [the deceased] was unfortunately an accident waiting to happen ... .'

A fine was imposed of £48 000 plus costs of £7 500. On appeal the fine was reduced to £15 000 but the order for costs remained unchanged.

The Court of Appeal said that it was

> ... impossible to lay down any tariff or to say that the fine should bear specific relationship to the turn over or net profit of the defendant. Each case must be dealt with according to its own particular circumstances.

The court also said that in its judgement magistrates should always think carefully before accepting jurisdiction in health and safety cases, where it is arguable that the fine may exceed the limit of their jurisdiction or where death or serious injury has occurred.

The court provided guidance as to the factors to be considered when sentencing employers for health and safety offences. These factors have been approved in a number of subsequent appeals against sentences imposed for health and safety breaches. First, the court pointed out the seriousness nature of breaches of sections 2 and 3 HSWA which it said should be seen as 'the foundations for protecting health and safety'. Second it set out a number of general factors that should be considered as either aggravating or mitigating. These are as follows:

Mitigating Factors
1. guilty plea or prompt admission of responsibility
2. previous good safety record
3. steps to remedy deficiencies after they have been brought to the defendant's attention.

Aggravating Factors
1. how far the defendant has fallen below the standard of care to be expected
2. death or serious injury resulting from the breach (the penalty should reflect the public disquiet at unnecessary loss of life)
3. where a deliberate breach has occurred with a view to cutting costs or maximising profits
4. the degree of risk and the extent of the danger created by the offence
5. any failure to heed warnings.

In the case of *R. v. Jarvis Facilities Ltd* [2005] EWCA Crim 1409, which concerned health and safety failures of a company carrying out maintenance on the railways, the Court of Appeal said a more serious view of a defendant's breaches can be taken where there is a 'significant public element', particularly where the defendant has been entrusted to carry out work competently and efficiently which affects the public's safety. The company's fine was, however, reduced from £400000 to £275000.

In *R. v. Transco* [2006] EWCA Crim 838 the Court of Appeal made the distinction between health and cases involving systemic failure and those that did not. This case concerned an incident in November 2001. Transco engineers were called to an old flour mill in Ashton-under-Lyme that had been converted into flats after gas had entered the property from a fracture in the gas main. All the residents were evacuated and allowed back into the building once the gas main had been repaired and the flats ventilated. Unfortunately the engineers had failed to notice a 2 metre void between the ceiling of one of the flats and the one above. A resident lit a cigarette and was killed in the resultant explosion.

The Lord Chief Justice pointed out that the *Howe* case involved a serious systemic fault, as do most health and safety prosecutions. This case on the other hand involved no systemic fault but merely a mistake on the part of individuals managing an emergency situation on the ground. The fine of £1 million was reduced to £250000.

Therefore where there is systemic failure on the part of an employer the guidelines in *Howe* apply. Where the failure is non-systemic and due to failings by frontline workers the *Howe* guidelines do not apply and the fine will be significantly lower.

In sentencing more than one defendant for health and safety breaches resulting from the same incident, it is not appropriate in the sentencing exercise to consider an overall figure for the

incident and then divide it between those defendants. In criminal trials, fines should not be apportioned between defendants in the same way as damages in a civil claim, nor should a sentence be apportioned as if it was the apportionment of liability.

R. v. Yorkshire Sheeting & Insulation Ltd [2003] 2 Cr.App.R. (S) 93 concerned a company that had acted as subcontractor to the main contractor of a company involved in converting premises. The company successfully appealed on the basis that the sentencing judge had attributed a greater degree of responsibility to it than was justified. The Court of Appeal said that

> … the approach adopted by the judge appeared somewhat to mask the true nature of the sentencing exercise. This was to assess the degree of culpability and criminality on the part of the appellant by reference to the offence charged and its failure to take steps to ensure, so far as is reasonably practicable, the safety of the roofers. The judge placed too much emphasis on seeking to apportion overall liability (by reference to the projected total figure) … on a percentage basis and not enough on assessing the appellant's own culpability in respect of the offence charged.

The duties upon an employer under sections 2 and 3 of the HSWA are non-delegable duties (see the House of Lords decision in *R. v. Associated Octel* [1996] 4 All ER 846. This is relevant when it comes to sentencing a company who has contracted out part of its undertaking (i.e. business).

In *R. v. Mersey Docks and Harbour Company* [1995] 16 Cr App Rep (S) 806 a harbour company had failed to take adequate precautions to avoid an explosion, which killed two men, on a vessel which had previously carried a dangerous cargo. The Court of Appeal stressed that the duty under section 3 HSWA was non-delegable and it was no mitigation for the company to say it had relied upon the master of the vessel to ascertain whether there were dangerous areas on the vessel. The Court of Appeal also said that where a company has this 'attitude' to discharging its duty then it is important that the courts impose a fine which leaves people like the harbour company *'in no doubt that it is their duty and they have to discharge it'*.

The largest fines to date, both in 2005, are £15m for Transco in Scotland relating to an explosion killing a family of four in their home, and a fine of £7.5m (reduced on appeal from £10m) of the maintenance arm of Balfour Beatty for its part in the Hatfield train derailment of 2000 which killed four passengers.

The Sentencing Guidelines Council has issued guidance to courts for sentencing in corporate manslaughter cases and health and safety cases where the breach has resulted in death. This applies to all sentences imposed after 15th February 2010.

In relation to the guideline states that

> The offence of corporate manslaughter, because it requires a breach at senior level, will ordinarily involve a level of seriousness significantly greater than a health and safety offence. The appropriate fine will seldom be less than *£500,000* and may be measured in *millions of pounds.*

In relation to health and safety breaches causing death it says that

> The range of seriousness involved in health and safety offences is greater than for corporate manslaughter. However, where the offence is shown to have caused death, the appropriate fine will seldom be *less than £100,000* and may be me measured in *hundreds of thousands of pounds or more*.

Given the terms of this guidance the increase in fines for health and safety offences is a trend that is likely to continue.

Compensation orders

Criminal courts have a general power to make a compensation order in favour of anyone who has been injured or suffered loss or damage as a consequence of the defendant's offence for which he/she has been convicted. The maximum that can be awarded in the Magistrates' Court is £5000 and in the Crown Court there is no limit. Such orders are rare.

Name and shame

The HSE website has a public record of health and safety convictions (*HSE public register of convictions*). The site gives details of all prosecution cases by the HSE which has resulted in convictions. This has become known as the 'name and shame' list. It seems that the list is becoming of interest to insurers when considering employers' liability insurance and public liability insurance.

Remedial orders

Both the HSWA and the CMCHA have provision form remedial orders to be made. Under the HSWA in the past these orders have been rarely used.

Sentencing an individual for health and safety offences

Often fines for section 7 HSWA breaches are dealt with in the Magistrates' Court and are below £1000, particularly if the Defendant is a frontline worker.

Fines for section 37 HSWA offences have been increasing in recent years and the average fine is now above £3000. The average for section 36 offences is around £1000. However, the case of Gillian Beckingham in 2006, acquitted of manslaughter but convicted of a breach of section 7 HSWA in relation to a *Legionella* outbreak, may be an indication that fines for directors and managers convicted of health and safety offences are also on the increase in line with fines for employers. She was fined £15000 representing 50% of her gross annual income.

In November 2006 at Preston Crown Court, George Ruttle, Managing Director of Ruttle Contracting Ltd was found guilty of breaching section 37 HSWA. He was fined £75000 and ordered to pay £103500 costs. The case concerned a worker who had died as a result of a truck overturning. On appeal the Court of Appeal said the fine was not excessive.

However, these cases were determined the Courts have now gained the power to imprison individuals convicted of health and safety offence under the Health and Safety (Offences) Act 2008 – see aforementioned section.

Manslaughter

If an individual is convicted of gross negligence manslaughter as a result of a work-related death, then, on the basis of past cases, he/she can expect a custodial sentence in the region of 18 months to 2 years. However, given that it is now possible to receive a custodial sentence for breaches of most health and safety offences by individuals, the indirect impact of this may be an increase in sentences for individuals convicted of manslaughter.

However, there are occasions when the sentence can be much greater than 2 years. Mark Connolly was convicted of gross negligence manslaughter at Newcastle Crown Court and imprisoned on 17th March 2006 for 9 years (later reduced to 7 years on appeal).

The case concerned an incident on the railways at Tebay in February 2004. A railway trailer heavily loaded with scrap steel freewheeled wholly uncontrolled at about 40 miles per hour for several miles until colliding with four workmen on the track killing them. Mr Connolly's business operated the trailers. He was convicted upon the basis that he had deliberately disabled the braking system of the trailers solely for profit.

It is very unlikely these days that the sentence will be suspended. This was confirmed in *A-G's Reference No. 89 or 2006 [2006] EWCA Crim 2570*, a case concerning a defendant who had pleaded guilty to gross negligence manslaughter. Here the Court of Appeal held it was unduly lenient to suspend a custodial sentence where an employee of the defendant had died due to a faulty machine.

A company convicted of manslaughter is liable to an unlimited fine which is the same as for a breach of the HSWA. As stated earlier, guidance has now issued by Sentencing Guidelines Council.

20.2.6 Funding

There are a number of policies that may cover representation of a company or an individual charged with health and safety or related offences.

The usual insurance policies to consider are outlined below.

Employers' Liability

This insurance is arranged to protect employers in relation to claims involving injury to their employees. It should be noted that this cover is required by law pursuant the Employer's Liability (Compulsory Insurance) Act 1969 and it is an offence not to have such cover.

Public Liability

This insurance is designed to protect against the risk of incurring legal liability, usually for negligence, to third parties. Cover can be offered as part of a general policy or alternatively it can be offered separately.

D&O Policy

Directors' and officers' liability and company reimbursement policies (often referred to as D&O policies) provide insurance for senior executives against legal bills arising from their corporate responsibilities. D&O policies are not compulsory.

Professional Indemnity

This insurance cover protects professional specialists such as physicians, architects, engineers and others against third party claims arising from activities in their professional field.

Insurance policies like public liability cover may cover not only the company itself but also named individuals and indeed even employees.

Legal defence costs insurance may be contained in a separate policy. Costs recoverable should include the costs of defending criminal proceedings and health and safety prosecutions. Legal expenses insurance, contractors' at risk and other specialised insurances may also be in a position to respond.

It is good advice to any company to check its insurance policies and when they respond before an incident occurs.

For further information on this insurance see *Professional indemnity insurance.*

20.2.7 Inquests and judicial reviews

An inquest, which is held before a coroner, is an inquisitorial hearing not an adversarial one (like a criminal trial). The purpose of an inquest is to determine (a) who the deceased was and (b) how, when and where the deceased died. In work-related death inquest the 'how' question has become extended to look into the circumstances of the deceased's death.

If the police prosecute for manslaughter there will be no inquest until the criminal proceedings have been concluded. However, if the police decide not to prosecute and pass the matter over to HSE then it is usual for the HSE prosecution not to be commenced until after the inquest. Thus the inquest can be instrumental in ascertaining HSE's approach to the issues and is an opportunity to test the evidence. Further it is possible that after the inquest the matter could be transferred back to the police, if there is a finding of 'unlawful killing'.

A judicial review is a form of court proceedings in the Administrative Court in which a judge reviews the lawfulness of a decision or action made by a public body. It is a challenge to the way the decision has been made, not to the decision itself.

In the recent past there have been examples where the family of a deceased has challenged the police's or the HSE's decision not to prosecute and the court have ordered the decision be reconsidered.

On 6th May 2008 at Cardiff Crown Court, Roy Clark, owner of North Eastern Roofing was sentenced to 10 months imprisonment for gross negligence manslaughter. This followed the death of Daniel Dennis, a 17-year-old worker, who fell through a fragile skylight in 2003.

The case is of note because of its route to trial.

The inquest did not take place until almost 2 years after the deceased's death. The inquest jury returned a unanimous verdict of unlawful killing.

In March 2006 the CPS concluded there was no realistic prospect that a criminal prosecution of Mr Clark (or any other person) would succeed stating '*the degree of negligence exhibited was not such as to amount to criminal negligence*'. The deceased's parents commenced proceedings to judicial review this decision.

Lord Justice Waller in December 2006 ruled the CPS should reconsider its decision not to prosecute concluding the CPS had failed to give sufficient consideration to the evidence that the deceased had been instructed to go on the roof as part of his duties, without any training or induction course, or any serious warning about roof lights, and had not been told not to do so prior to receiving such training. The judge observed that the file note of the CPS lawyer said the inquest verdict was perverse and contrary to the evidence.

Lord Justice Waller, whilst emphasising he did not wish to prejudge the issue, concluded it was '... *seriously arguable that a different decision might be made once account is taken of these issues*'.

On the eve of his trial, 5 years after the incident, Mr Clark pleaded guilty.

The Coroners and Justice Act 2009 received the Royal Assent on 12 November 2009. Section 47 of the Act, which came into force with immediate effect, introduces a statutory definition of an 'interested person.' An interested person is a party allowed by the coroner to ask questions at the inquest. The definition is slightly wider than previously and includes any person who the coroner 'thinks has a sufficient interest.'

Many of the other sections of the Act are yet to come into force on dates to be specified. These include

■ the creation of the post of Chief Coroner and the introduction of a right of appeal on certain matters to the Chief Coroner. Section 40 lists the types of decisions which may be appealed to the Chief Coroner. These include whether an inquest should be held; whether the case should be heard with a jury; and the final verdict.

■ coroners will have the power to require the disclosure of documents and the production of witness statements (see Paragraph 1 of Schedule 5).

■ Paragraph 7 of Schedule 5 sets out a coroner's powers to report the matter to persons who can prevent, or reduce the risk of, a recurrence. These powers are very similar to the powers of the coroner under Rule 43 of the Coroners Rules 1984, where the coroner may announce at the inquest that he/she is reporting the matter to the authorities, including the HSE, with recommendations for action to prevent the recurrence of similar fatalities.

20.3 The Health and Safety at Work Etc. Act 1974

The HSWA imposes a number of all-embracing 'general duties', and three of these duties in particular combine to impose obligations on everyone involved in a project. When the Act was proposed it was intended that these general duties would reflect the common law obligations of the parties, the difference being that under the HSWA regime these obligations could be enforced directly by inspectors, not just through the courts after an accident, but in anticipation of a danger that might arise from work being carried out. In the following paragraphs the main provisions of the relevant parts of the HSWA are outlined.

20.3.1 Section 2: general duties of employers to their employees

Section 2 of the Act provides as follows:

(1) It shall be the duty of every employer to ensure, so far as is reasonably practicable, the health, safety and welfare at work of all his employees.

(2) Without prejudice to the generality of an employer's duty under the preceding subsection, the matters to which that duty extends include in particular:

   (a) the provision and maintenance of plant and systems of work that are, so far as is reasonably practicable, safe and without risks to health

   (b) arrangements for ensuring, so far as is reasonably practicable, safety and absence of risks to health in connection with the use, handling, storage and transport of articles and substances

   (c) the provision of such information, instruction, training and supervision as is necessary to ensure, so far as is reasonably practicable, the health and safety at work of his employees

   (d) so far as is reasonably practicable as regards any place of work under the employer's control, the maintenance of it in a condition that is safe and without risks to health and the provision and maintenance of means of access to and egress from it that are safe and without such risks

   (e) the provision and maintenance of a working environment for his employees that is, so far as is reasonably practicable, safe, without risks to health, and adequate as regards facilities and arrangements for their welfare at work.

These obligations need to be viewed in light of the remaining provisions of section 2 dealing with requirements for written health and safety policies (see subsequent section), and also provisions which deal with the requirement for employers to consult with safety representatives and safety committees in certain circumstances. It is also important to note that each of the matters dealt with in aforementioned sub-paragraphs (a)–(e) are now expanded upon and subject to additional rules applicable to particular circumstances that are contained in numerous health and safety regulations.

Whatever the exact circumstances of a project, and whatever regulations apply, it needs to be borne in mind that the fundamental duty under Regulation 2(1) to ensure safety of employees will always exist and it is important to understand that

compliance with a particular regulation (e.g. the CDM 2007), does not necessarily discharge all an employer's responsibilities. There may be some residual area of risk or some interface with another employer on site which steps taken under such regulations do not adequately cover. In this case, the employer will remain potentially liable under the general duty of the Act.

There is no exact meaning or measure of what will be reasonably practicable in any given case. The test tends to be less strict than a requirement simply to do what is 'practicable', since the courts recognise that there may be practicable measures which are not reasonable to take. The classic definition of the phrase was given by Asquith LJ in the case of *Edwards v. National Coal Board* [1949] 1 KB 704 who said that

> Reasonably practicable is a narrower term than physically possible, and implies that a computation must be made in which the quantum of risk is placed in one scale, and the sacrifice, whether in money, time or trouble, involved in the measures necessary to avert the risk, is placed in the other; and that, if it be shown that there is a gross disproportion between them, the risk being insignificant in relation to the sacrifice, the person upon whom the duty is laid discharges the burden of proving that compliance was not reasonably practicable. This computation falls to be made at a point of time anterior to the happening of the incident complained of.

The lack of definition for the term 'reasonably practicable' was criticised by the Work and Pensions Committee in its 3rd Report of Session 2007–2008: *The Role of the Health and Safety Commission and the Health and Safety Executive in regulating workplace health and safety* (House of Commons 2008). It said that

> We are concerned that the test of 'reasonable practicability' introduces a lack of clarity that can increase the burden on employers in meeting their health and safety obligations. We recommend that the Law Commission reviews the test of 'reasonable practicability' and how it applies to the Health and Safety at Work Act 1974.

Although the reasonably practicable qualification is obviously of considerable importance in relation to section 2 (and the other general duties described later) it should be contrasted with the standard of care that arises under other health and safety regulations which are often stricter and not qualified in this way.

The courts construe the wording of section 2 as being of wide application to any works that it has undertaken. An employer will, for example, be subject to the duty where plant and equipment is not yet meant to be in use but it is nevertheless available. Section 2 also extends to situations where there are employees working in a situation where their safety may be dependent on the way in which activities of people working alongside them are conducted, for example, employees of a contractor who are on the premises. There may be a duty for the employer, in such circumstances, in ensuring a safe system of work for its own employees, to give information and instructions to the visiting workers or to coordinate their activities with the contractor (*R. v. Swan Hunter Shipbuilders Ltd* [1981] ICR 831).

20.3.2 Section 3: general duties of employers and self-employed to persons other than their employees

Section 3 states the following:

(1) It shall be the duty of every employer to conduct his undertaking in such a way as to ensure, so far as is reasonably practicable, that persons not in his employment who may be affected thereby are not thereby exposed to risks to their health or safety.

(2) It shall be the duty of every self-employed person to conduct his undertaking in such a way as to ensure, so far as is reasonably practicable, that he and other persons (not being his employees) who may be affected thereby are not thereby exposed to risks to their health or safety.

This section is treated as being of broad application to any 'undertaking', a word which means not just a business carrying out physical work, such as the construction process, but also the provision of services or trading. Even a business which is not operational, for example, while maintenance is being carried out, is still likely to be viewed as an undertaking (although this is a question of fact for the magistrates or jury to decide). It had been held in one recent case that an employer who employs an independent contractor to do work is not himself 'conducting his undertaking' in circumstances where the employer is under no duty to control the work of the independent contractor and does not actually exercise control. It was said that the mere capacity or opportunity to exercise control over an activity was not sufficient to be within the scope of section 3(1) of the HSWA. However, this has now been overruled by the House of Lords in *R. v. Associated Octel Co. Ltd* [1996] 4 All ER 846 which is considered further.

Section 3 is of particular importance to health and safety in construction as those 'other than their employees' includes members of the public, a small number of whom are killed or injured by construction activity each year. Also, in principle, anyone involved with the project is charged with this general duty.

20.3.3 Section 4: general duties of person concerned with premises to persons other than their employees

In view of the expansive approach taken by the courts to the scope of section 3 as described earlier, the rationale for a separate general duty dealing with control of premises is perhaps less clear now than it was to those drafting the legislation. As can be seen subsequently there are in fact, over and above section 3, additional obligations arising out of control of

premises imposed by section 4, and overall the effect of this section is to place liability primarily on the person directly controlling the premises, rather than those carrying on activities within them even if persons in the latter category have obligations of their own under section 2 or 3. Section 4 provides

(1) This section has effect for imposing on persons duties in relation to those who:
   (a) are not their employees; but
   (b) use non-domestic premises made available to them as a place of work or as a place where they may use plant or substances provided for their use there and applies to premises so made available and other non-domestic premises used in connection with them.

(2) It shall be the duty of each person who has, to any extent, control of premises to which this section applies or of the means of access thereto or egress there from or of any plant or substance in such premises to take such measures as it is reasonable for a person in his position to take to ensure, so far as is reasonably practicable, that the premises, all means of access thereto or egress there from available for use by persons using the premises, and any plant or substance in the premises or, as the case may be, provided for use there, is or are safe and without risks to health.

(3) Where a person has, by virtue of any contract or tenancy, an obligation of any extent in relation to:
   (a) the maintenance or repair of any premises to which this section applies or any means of access thereto or egress there from; or
   (b) the safety of or the absence of risks to health arising from plant or substances in any such premises; that person shall be treated, for the purposes of subsection (2) above, as being a person who has control of the matters to which his obligation extends.

(4) Any reference in this section to a person having control of any premises or matter is a reference to a person having control of the premises or matter in connection with the carrying on by him of a trade, business or other undertaking (whether for profit or not).

As with the previous duties, section 4 is capable of applying to more than one party, since it refers to control 'to any extent' and the courts may well find that, in the circumstances of works being carried out, control is shared. The only significant restriction on the application of this duty is in relation to domestic premises, but the duties nevertheless apply where work is being carried out in parts of premises which are not in private occupation (such as lifts and service areas). Section 4(3), by referring to any contract, extends shared responsibility within its duties to anyone managing or undertaking property maintenance, or installing or maintaining plant and equipment.

The leading case in this area is *Austin Rover Group Ltd v. HM Inspector of Factories* [1990] 1 AC 619 which concerned maintenance work being undertaken under contract by specialist industrial cleaners at a car assembly plant. The owners of the premises gave instructions as to precautions for work in a potentially flammable atmosphere, but the employees of the subcontractors did not follow these instructions and there was a flash fire. The House of Lords held that the occupiers of the premises had not contravened section 4(2); the words 'such measures as it is reasonable … to take …' require consideration to be given not only to the extent to which the person in question has control of the premises, but also to that person's knowledge and reasonable foresight at all material times. In making premises available for use by another, the reasonableness of the measures which the individual is required to take to ensure safety of premises have to be determined in the light of this knowledge and of the anticipated use for which the premises have been made available and of the extent of the individual's control and knowledge, if any, of the actual use thereafter. The word 'reasonable' in the context of section 4(2) relates to what is reasonable for the person concerned, and not the measures themselves. This latter question is something to be considered in the light of what is reasonably practicable which, as has been explained earlier, is a matter for the defendant to prove on the balance of probabilities. It now appears that the matter of foreseeability of risk is to be treated differently under section 4 to the way it is treated under section 3 (and, for that matter, section 2 in relation to the duty to ensure that persons are 'safe').

R. v. Associated Octel Petroleum Ltd [1996] 4 All ER 846

This case is of particular significance to the construction industry.

R. v. Associated Octel Petroleum Ltd has certain similarities in the facts of this case with those of the Austin Rover case described earlier, but the difference was that this prosecution was brought under section 3(1) of the HSWA. In the course of an annual shutdown for the cleaning and repair of the company's chemical plant by a specialist contractor there was a flash fire and explosion and the contractor's workman was badly burned. The investigating inspectors identified a number of aspects of the contractor's operations to clean a tank within the chlorine plant which were unsafe, including the storage of acetone in an open container, failure to use a safety lamp, and inadequate ventilation arrangements. Octel argued that it was not liable on account of the work being carried out by an independent contractor whose operations it did not actually control. This argument was put in terms that Octel did not 'conduct its undertaking' for the purposes of section 3(1) in relation to an operation which was essentially the conduct of the contractor's undertaking.

The Court of Appeal's view: The Court of Appeal heard Octel's appeal in 1994 and disagreed, holding that the activities of the contractor necessary for carrying on the employer's business are part of the employer's conduct of its undertaking for these purposes, imposing the duty on Octel under the contract whether it is done by its own employees or the independent contractor. Given that this was a 'risk' (as broadly defined

previously) it was not necessary to show that the employer had actual control over how the work was done.

The Court of Appeal held that the general principle of the law of tort, under which a person is not normally (subject to a number of exceptions) liable for the acts of independent contractors, was not mirrored in section 3(1), which was to be given a wider interpretation. The notion that actual control had to be exercised over the works for liability to arise under the HSWA was rejected (the Court at the same time overruling the decision in an employer's favour in *RMC Roadstone Products Ltd v. Jester* [1994] ICR 456 which also concerned safety of contractors). The Court of Appeal said that the degree of control was relevant to the issue of whether or not the employer had done what was reasonably practicable, that is, it was something for Octel to prove in its defence.

> The question of what is reasonably practicable is a matter of fact and degree in each case. It will depend on a number of factors so far as concerns operations carried out by independent contractors: what is reasonably practicable for a large organisation employing safety officers or engineers contracting for the services of a small contractor on routine operations may differ markedly from what is reasonably practicable for a small shopkeeper employing a local builder on activities on which he has no expertise. The nature and gravity of the risk, the competence and experience of the workmen, the nature of the precautions to be taken are all relevant considerations (Stuart-Smith LJ in *R. v. Associated Octel* (Court of Appeal)).

The company had elected not to give its own evidence on this point and had been convicted at trial.

Decision of the House of Lords The decision of the House of Lords affirmed the Court of Appeal, and its strict interpretation of the law has to be followed by all other courts. The key points of its analyses were as follows.

(a) An employer is free to engage either employees or independent contractors for any task.
(b) The control over – or 'independence' of – the contractor is not decisive for determining liability under section 3.
(c) The question is 'simply' [*sic*] whether the activity in question can be described as part of the employer's undertaking: in Octel's case its undertaking of running a chemical plant included 'having the factory cleaned' by contractors.

Lord Hoffman described the duty as regards risks that arise in such a situation in this way:

> If therefore the employer engages an independent contractor to do work which forms part of the conduct of the employer's undertaking he must stipulate for whatever conditions are needed to avoid those risks and are reasonably practicable. He cannot, having omitted to do so, say that he was not in a position to exercise any control.

The House of Lords rejected the HSE's argument for a wider interpretation that any 'works of cleaning, repair and maintenance necessary for the conduct of the employer's business' would be covered by section 3. They held that it is always a factual question to be considered in each case whether or not a contractor's work is on the one hand 'entirely separate' from the employer's undertaking, or 'an activity integrated with the general conduct of this business'.

In Octel's case, the integration of the contractor's work with its own was clear to the House of Lords. However, having equipment such as cars sent out for repair, or office curtains sent out for cleaning, was rejected as being within the scope of section 3. Although these off-site activities were viewed as not generally creating a statutory duty, 'the place where the activity takes place' regarded by Lord Hoffman as being 'very important and possibly decisive' is unlikely in future to prove workable as a determining factor in whether or not a duty exists. In particular, the situation described in the judgment is not wholly analogous to construction projects where the employer under the contract to build a new building may be a more remote figure for whom the project is itself the undertaking. No attempt is made in the Octel case to analyse the implications for new build.

20.4 Management duties
20.4.1 Written health and safety policies

The legislation contains a variety of obligations on employers to produce and operate a number of management tools to assist in meeting the wider statutory duties to minimise risks. In addition, a number of requirements of an administrative nature must be observed in day-to-day activities. Accidents, 'near-misses' and industrial diseases must be notified and records kept.

Every employer who carries on an undertaking employing five or more people must prepare a written statement of its safety policy to ensure that thought has been given to potential hazards and their management. These policies serve several purposes:

■ to state the undertaking's health and safety aims

■ to identify hazards and to avoid or reduce them and to control residual hazards

■ to increase employees' awareness of the arrangements made

■ to provide a vehicle for consultation and employees' involvement

■ to define clearly the claim of responsibility for safety from the directors downwards

■ to provide explicit statements which can be reviewed and brought up to date to respond to changing circumstances.

There are HSE guidance publications available on writing safety policy documents, and on devising effective management systems.

20.4.2 The Management of Health and Safety at Work Regulations 1999

These regulations which were most recently amended in 2006 supplement the existing requirements of the Health and Safety at Work etc. Act and specify a range of management exercises which must be carried out in all businesses. The aim is to map out the organisation of precautionary measures in a systematic way, and to make sure that all staff are familiar with the measures and their own responsibilities.

Risk assessment (Regulation 3)

Every employer is required to make a 'suitable and sufficient' assessment of risks to employees, and to other people who might be affected by the business, such as visiting contractors and members of the public. A comprehensive investigation of risks involved in all areas and operations is required, together with identification of who is affected, and definition of appropriate precautions.

The assessment must be written down (or recorded by other means, such as on computer) when there are more than five employees. The assessment needs to be reviewed and kept up to date.

Various other regulations contain hazard-specific or activity-specific risk assessment requirements (see **Table 1**). These do

Hazard/Activity	Regulations
Manual handling and lifting	Manual Handling Operations Regulations 1992
Suitability of personal protective	Personal Protective Equipment at Work Regulations 1992
VDUs and associated work stations	Health and Safety (Display Screen Equipment) Regulations 1992
Noise	Control of Noise at Work Regulations 2005
Vibration	Control of Vibration at Work Regulations 2005
Chemicals	Control of Substances Hazardous to Health Regulations 2002, 2003 and 2004
Asbestos	Control of Asbestos at Work Regulations 2006
Lead	Control of Lead at Work Regulations 2002
Design work for construction and engineering	Construction (Design and Management) Regulations 2007
Pregnant and new mothers	Management of Health and Safety at Work Regulations 1999, 2003 and 2006
Young persons	Management of Health and Safety at Work Regulations 1999

Table 1 Regulations containing hazard-specific or activity-specific risk assessment requirements

not need to be duplicated for the purposes of Regulation 3 of the Management of Health and Safety at Work Regulations when they have already been done – so long as they remain valid.

Formal arrangements for health and safety (Regulations 4, 5, 6, 8 and 9)

It is very important to remember that producing a risk assessment is not in itself the purpose of these Regulations. The assessment is only a tool by which risks arising from work activity can be identified, quantified and prioritised. Thereafter formal arrangements must be worked through (and recorded) for effective planning, organisation, control, monitoring and review of measures to reduce the risks identified through the assessment under Regulation 3. The implementation of these measures must be in accordance with the 'General Principles of Prevention' (in Schedule 1 of the Regulations):

(a) avoiding risks
(b) evaluating the risks which cannot be avoided
(c) combating the risks at source
(d) adapting the work to the individual, especially as regards the design of workplaces, the choice of work equipment and the choice of working and production methods, with a view, in particular, to alleviating monotonous work and work at a predetermined work-rate and to reducing their effect on health
(e) adapting to technical progress
(f) replacing the dangerous by the non-dangerous or the less dangerous
(g) developing a coherent overall prevention policy which covers technology, organisation of work, working conditions, social relationships and the influence of factors relating to the working environment
(h) giving collective protective measures priority over individual protective measures
(i) giving appropriate instructions to employees.

In appropriate circumstances, health surveillance of staff may be required – the ACoP describes more fully when this duty will arise.

Procedures must be established for dealing with serious and imminent dangers, including fire evacuation plans and contacts with emergency services.

Access to dangerous areas should be restricted to authorised trained staff.

Competent assistance (Regulation 7)

Every employer is obliged to appoint one or more 'competent persons' to advise and assist in undertaking the necessary measures to comply with the statutory requirements. They may be employees or outside consultants, but the regulations specify that the 'preference' shall be for the appointments to be made internally.

The competence of the people appointed is to be judged in terms of their training, knowledge and experience of the work involved; it is not necessarily dependent on particular

qualifications. These people have to be provided with adequate information, time and resources to do their jobs.

Information and training (Regulations 10, 13 and 15)

Information must be provided to staff on the risk assessment, emergency procedures, and the identity of the people appointed to assist on health and safety matters. Specific information requirements apply for temporary workers.

Adequate training should be provided to staff when they are recruited, and periodically afterwards, with more later if their work changes.

In entrusting work to an employee, account must be taken of the individual's capability to do the job safely.

Employees must be informed of certain standard information directly or by approved leaflets or posters under the Health and Safety Information for Employees Regulations 1989.

Shared workplaces and visiting workers (Regulations 11 and 12)

Shared workplaces When using shared workplaces:

(a) employers must cooperate so as to enable compliance with statutory requirements
(b) each employer's safety measures need to be coordinated with the others
(c) other employers concerned must be informed of risks to their employees' health and safety.

These rules apply whether the sharing is temporary or permanent. (See also Regulation 13 relating to giving safety information to temporary workers and their employers.)

Working in host undertakings: Host employers and the self-employed are required to provide the outside employer, and its employees, and every self-employed person who is working in the host undertaking, with comprehensible information concerning risks to health and safety. The outside employer, and its employees and the self-employed, also have to be told how to identify the person nominated by the host employer under the regulations to implement evacuation procedures.

These requirements are, in effect, the principles underlying the CDM Regulations, the latter expanding them to deal with the complexity, scale and inherent danger of construction and engineering work being carried out on sites requiring careful management of the various participants.

20.4.3 Employee consultation

These are two main sets of regulations on consultation, reflecting the historical development of legislation in this area and changing work patterns. In addition, other hazard or activity-specific regulations may have applicable provisions.

Safety Regulations and Safety Committees Regulations 1977 (as amended)

These regulations permit trade unions (where recognised by the employer) to appoint an unspecified number of safety representatives, who acquire rights of time off with pay to undertake their roles and to undergo training. Their functions include:

- consultations with the employer on the introduction of significant safety measures and appointments
- investigation of potential hazards, dangers, occurrences and causes
- carrying out inspections of the workplace and certain safety documentation
- investigation of complaints by employees
- making representations to employers about the aforementioned or safety matters generally
- representing employees in consultations with HSE/local authority inspectors and receiving certain information from them

A safety committee may be required on the request of at least two representatives and this committee's functions are to be agreed between the employer, representatives and relevant trade unions.

Health and Safety (Consultation with Employees) Regulations 1996 (as amended)

Where there are employees who are not represented by trade union safety representatives under the 1977 Regulations, employers are required to consult with them on significant health and safety issues. The consultation may be directly with individual employees, or with elected employee representatives: if the latter, they are entitled to time off with pay for carrying out their functions and undergoing training.

Construction (Design and Management) Regulations 2007

The Construction (Design and Management) Regulations 2007 have replaced the Construction (Design and Management) Regulations 1994.

In the construction and engineering construction sector, CDM 2007 placed an obligation on the principal contractor to ensure that workers (including the self-employed) were able to discuss and offer advice in safety-related issues and to ensure there are arrangements for coordination of the views of workers or their representatives.

20.4.4 The Working Time Directive

This measure, which the European Court of Justice has affirmed is a health and safety measure in spite of its essential characteristics being those of employment rights, is implemented in the UK by the Working Time Regulations 1998 (as amended). Responsibility for enforcement lies with HSE/local authority inspectors. The rules apply to 'workers', so freelancers and agency workers as well as direct employees will be covered by it. The key provisions of the Regulations are as follows:

- maximum working week of 48 hours, averaged over a reference period of 17 weeks subject to opting out provisions if employees agree
- minimum daily rest period of 11 hours

- minimum annual leave of 4 weeks
- minimum rest period of one day per week
- workers will qualify for annual paid leave after they have worked continuously for 3 months
- a worker's daily break must last at least 20 minutes and be taken away from the workplace where possible
- provided that certain conditions are met, employers may enter into agreements with their employees on an individual or collective basis in order to be able to take advantage of some derogations from the provisions of the Working Time Regulations
- there are special provisions relating to 16- and 17-year-old workers: they can only be assigned to work during the period between 10.00 p.m. and 6.00 a.m. after they have had a free assessment of their health and capacities; they are entitled to 12 consecutive hours' rest in each 24-hour period and to 2 days' rest in each 7-day period (which should be consecutive if possible); and they are entitled to a rest break of at least 30 minutes if they work more than 4 1/2 hours a day
- employees will be entitled to claim compensation in the Employment Tribunal if their 'entitlements', principally the entitlement to paid annual leave, are not granted to them

20.4.5 Notification of construction work

Quite separate from the notices that have to be given for the purposes of planning applications or any requirements relating to compliance with Building Regulations, construction work may be notifiable to the HSE.

Under CDM 2007, the notification is required to be sent to the relevant local HSE Area Office, and it has to be in writing, submitted as soon as practicable after the appointment of the coordinator. When some of the required particulars cannot be notified at that time, the remaining information has to be given as soon as practicable after the appointment of the principal contractor for the project, and in any event before construction work begins. The information required in the notification is set out in Schedule 1 of CDM 2007, as detailed subsequently.

(1) Date of forwarding.
(2) Exact address of the construction site.
(3) Contact details of the client.
(4) Contact details of the coordinator.
(5) Contact details of the principal contractor.
(6) Date planned for start of the construction phase, (j).
(7) Time allowed for the planning and preparation for construction work.
(8) Planned duration of the construction phase.
(9) Estimated maximum number of people at work on the construction site.
(10) Planned number of contractors on the construction site.
(11) Name and address of any contractors already appointed.
(12) Name and address of any designers already engaged.

There is no mandatory format for presenting this information but HSE Offices have available a standard form (form F10(rev)).

To be notifiable for these purposes a project is one where the construction phase will:

(a) be longer than 30 days, or
(b) will involve more than 500 person days of construction work for a client.

The construction phase for these purposes means the period of time starting when construction work starts and ending when the construction work in the project is completed. The task of giving the notification is that of the coordinator acting on behalf of the client who is appointed for the purposes of CDM 2007 (see section 20.5 of this chapter). Where works are being carried out for a domestic client (i.e. for private purposes), which do not require a coordinator, responsibility for the notification will lie with all the contractors. Notification will still be required under CDM 2007. The precise requirements will be set out in the Regulations.

20.4.6 Accident reporting and incident requirements

The Reporting of Injuries, Diseases and Dangerous Occurrences Regulations 1995 (RIDDOR) which are currently under revision require that certain events, accidents or illnesses that happen at work must be notified and/or also formally reported to the enforcing authority. Primarily, the duty to report lies with the employer of the employee injured or (if no employee is involved) the person having control over the premises. Reference should also be made to the Regulations for criteria determining who is the 'responsible person' for these purposes.

The incidents covered by RIDDOR include the following:

■ the death of any person as a result of a work-related accident

■ any fracture, other than to the fingers, thumbs or toes

■ dislocation of the shoulder, hip, knee or spine

■ any amputation

■ loss of sight (whether temporary or permanent); a penetration injury to an eye or a chemical or hot metal burn to an eye

■ any injury resulting from an electric shock or electrical burn leading to unconsciousness or requiring resuscitation or admittance to hospital for more than 24 hours

■ acute illness requiring medical treatment, or loss of consciousness, resulting from absorption of any substance by inhalation, ingestion or through skin

■ incapacitation for work of a member of staff for more than three consecutive days (including any days which would not have been working days but excluding the day of the accident)

In addition, the Regulations now contain a specific duty to report injuries to non-employees where the person injured is taken from the site of the accident to a hospital for treatment.

The notification and reporting requirements are illustrated in **Figure 1** of this chapter.

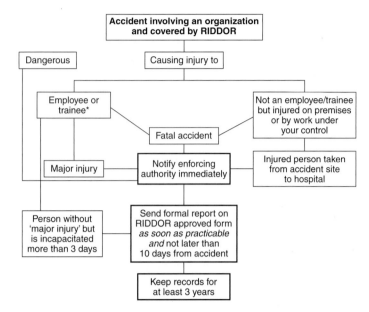

Figure 1 Notification and reporting requirements under RIDDOR Based on a chart in *Tolley's Health and Safety at Work Handbook.*

Diseases which have to be reported are listed in RIDDOR and are reportable if the person concerned has been involved with certain specified work. They include decompression illness, various skin and lung diseases as well as a number of forms of cancer.

In addition, a fire or explosion, or the collapse of any lifting machinery, scaffolding, floor, wall or other structure may in some circumstances be reportable as dangerous occurrences. There are various other circumstances in which matters are reportable and reference should be made to the Regulations themselves.

The manner of making the report is governed by the Regulations, and involves the use of approved forms (F2508 or F2508A or approved equivalents). However, where notification of an accident is also required this must be by the quickest practicable means which, in practice, is treated as a telephone call to the local office of the relevant enforcing authority. When someone dies or suffers a specified major injury or condition, or there is a gas incident covered by the Regulations, there is a duty to notify the HSE by the quickest practicable means, which will usually require telephone notification followed up by the requisite form. The RIDDOR also contains record-keeping requirements for particulars of accidents, dangerous occurrences and diseases, and the records must be preserved for at least 3 years. These records are in addition to the Accident Book records which are required to be kept for the Social Security (Claims and Payments) Regulations 1967.

20.4.7 First-aid arrangements

The extent of obligations in this area will vary according to the circumstances of the workplace: the principal requirements of the Health and Safety (First Aid) Regulations 1981 (as amended) for employers are

- to provide or ensure the provision of adequate and appropriate equipment and facilities

- to provide or ensure the provision of adequate and appropriate numbers of suitable persons as first-aiders (properly trained), unless the activities are so low risk that an 'appointed person' (see subsequent section) will be sufficient

- to make provision for temporary absences of first-aiders to be covered by a person appointed to take charge of situations when people may require medical assistance, including the use of first-aid equipment and facilities

- to inform employees of first-aid arrangements

- detailed guidelines on appropriate numbers and training of first-aiders and the provision of first-aid services are set out in the ACoP (L74 – *First aid at work*)

The provisions must take into account shift and weekend working, remoteness of the worksite, special hazards and so on.

The self-employed are under a lesser obligation to provide or ensure the provision of adequate and appropriate equipment to render first-aid to themselves while at work.

20.4.8 Employer's liability insurance

Except for certain government-related bodies, all employers are required to maintain cover in respect of their own employees by the Employers Liability (Compulsory Insurance) Act 1969. This must be an 'approved policy' which is not subject to conditions or exceptions prohibited by the Employers Liability (Compulsory Insurance) Regulations 1998 so that, for example, take notification of a claim under the policy would not invalidate the cover as it might under a normal policy. Under the 1998 Regulations the minimum cover requirement is for £5 million in respect of claims by one or more employees arising out of any one occurrence. (It is sufficient for a parent company to take out such cover on behalf of itself and its subsidiaries – see Regulation 3.)

20.5 Management obligations – construction and engineering projects

Employers and the self-employed have duties under section 3 of the HSWA in respect of ensuring the health and safety of those not in their employment but affected by their undertaking. These duties are particularly relevant in the construction industry due to the amount of subcontracting which is carried out and also because of the effects which construction operations can have on the general public. Each year a number of members of the public are killed by construction operations from hazards, including falling debris, construction plant, collapsing scaffolding, roadworks or inadequately guarded excavations.

Likewise, in the Management of Health and Safety at Work Regulations 1999, the requirement in Regulation 3 for risk assessment extends to risks to the health and safety of persons not in an employer's employment but affected by its undertaking. A similar duty is placed on the self-employed. By implication, the preventative measures required under Regulation 4 are similarly extended to non-employees.

20.5.1 Construction (Design and Management) Regulations (CDM) 2007

The Construction (Design and Management) Regulations 2007 (SI 2007 No. 320) came into effect on 6 April 2007. They replaced the 1994 Construction (Design and Management) Regulations 1994 (as amended in 2000).

The Regulations apply to construction projects and parties associated with them once a construction project exists. A project is deemed to exist as soon as a client has decided to proceed to design and construction.

As the EC directive which the CDM Regulations implemented (Temporary or Mobile Construction Sites Directive 92/57/EEC) has not been revised, the scope for change in the regulations is limited to a reworking of existing requirements. Another structural change in CDM 2007 is the incorporation of most of the requirements of the Construction (Health, Safety and Welfare) Regulations 1996 (CHSWR). The CHSWR requirements relating to work at height were revoked by and incorporated in the Work at Height Regulations 2005 (see *Construction health and safety II*).

There are probably more books and articles written about the CDM regulations in construction than all other construction-related regulations put together. Readers seeking in-depth information should consult publication catalogues of respected industry publishers such as Thomas Telford Publishing or the Construction Industry Research and Information Association (CIRIA).

Traditionally, parties to construction work in the UK have included a client, an engineer/architect responsible for design, and contractor(s). Construction-related health and safety legislation prior to the coming into force of the 1994 CDM Regulations predominantly placed duties on contractors only. The 1994 CDM Regulations changed this. The change has been continued in the 2007 regulations also along with the removal of the planning supervisor and the introduction of the coordinator.

There are duties on five key parties to a contract:

- client
- designer
- coordinator
- principal contractor
- contractors.

The client

The client who is considered by HSE to have a key role in ensuring proper attention is paid to health and safety matters has duties under these regulations. Clients must select and appoint a coordinator and principal contractor for the project. In making such appointments the client should be satisfied that the appointees for these roles are competent and will devote adequate resources to health and safety.

Similar duties apply to the client in respect of the appointment of designers and other contractors. Again, clients should ensure, so far as is reasonably practicable, that sufficient resources, including time, have been or will be allocated to enable the project to be carried out safely. Client duties do not apply to domestic householders when they have construction work carried out on their homes.

Before starting work, both designers and contractors must ensure the client is aware of his duties.

A client can no longer appoint an agent to act on its behalf.

The coordinator

The introduction of the planning supervisor brought a new role to the UK construction industry. This role has been redefined with the replacement of the planning supervisor by the coordinator. The coordinator has overall responsibility for coordinating the health and safety aspects of the design and planning phase, and for ensuring preparation of the early stages of the health and safety plan and the health and safety file.

The coordinator has to ensure that designers undertake their duty in respect of risk avoidance and reduction as well as cooperate with other designers over health and safety matters. When required to do so by the client, the coordinator should advise the client on matters relating to the competence of designers and contractors and on the adequacy of their resource allocation for health and safety as well as on the health and safety plans prior to the start of construction.

Coordinators have duties under the CDM Regulations to ensure notification of the project to the HSE and that the health and safety file is prepared. They are responsible for ensuring that other parties discharge their duties under the regulations, although they have no statutory powers to force these parties to act.

The designer

The designer has a key role under these regulations in contributing to health and safety. Designers have a duty to consider health and safety matters during development of their designs. They should ensure, as much as they can, that structures are designed to avoid or, if this is not possible, to minimise risks to health and safety while they are being built and maintained. Under CDM 2007 these duties are extended to the health and safety of those who will be using the structure – in particular to the aspects of the structure covered by the Workplace (Health and Safety) Regulations 1992, see *Construction health and safety II*. The definition of 'structure' is very wide and includes

tunnels, pipelines and earthworks in addition to more conventional structures. Where risks cannot be avoided, adequate information on residual risk has to be provided. The design should include adequate information on health and safety and this information should be passed to the coordinator for inclusion in the health and safety plan. Design is not limited to drawings but includes the preparation of specifications.

In addition, designers have a duty to ensure their design has with it, sufficient information about aspects of the design of the structure or its construction or maintenance to assist clients, other designers; and contractors to comply with their duties under these Regulations.

Where a project is notifiable, a designer shall not commence work on a project unless a CDM coordinator has been appointed for that project. The designer shall take all reasonable steps to provide the coordinator with sufficient information about the design of the structure, its construction or maintenance to assist the CDM coordinator to comply with his duties under CDM.

Designs prepared outside the UK but for UK structures must also comply with these regulations.

The principal contractor

The principal contractor should take account of the health and safety issues when preparing and assessing tenders or similar documents.

The main duties of the principal contractor under these regulations include the development, implementation and updating of the health and safety plan as well as the coordination of the activities of all contractors on site so that they comply with that plan. The principal contractor should also coordinate the activities of all contractors to ensure that they comply with health and safety legislation. Principal contractors have duties to ensure the provision of adequate information and training, including induction training, for employees and for consulting with employees and the self-employed on health and safety.

In particular, the principal contractor should plan, manage and monitor the construction phase in a way which ensures that, so far as is reasonably practicable, it is carried out without risks to health or safety. He should facilitate co-operation and coordination between other parties to the contract and generally apply the principles of prevention to construction of the structure.

The principal contractor should liaise with the CDM coordinator during the construction phase in relation to any design or change to a design. He should ensure that adequate welfare facilities are provided throughout the construction phase. Where necessary for health and safety, the principal contractor should draw up rules which are appropriate to the construction site and the activities on it and give reasonable directions to any contractor as necessary.

The principal contractor should ensure that every contractor is informed of the minimum amount of time which will be allowed for planning and preparation before construction work begins and where necessary, consult a contractor before finalising the part of the construction phase plan relevant to the work to be performed by him.

Every contractor should be given relevant information and sufficient time to prepare properly before he begins construction work and be given access to those parts of the construction phase plan relevant to the work to be performed by him.

In turn each contractor should provide promptly that information relating to his activity which is likely to be required by the CDM coordinator for inclusion in the health and safety file.

The principal contractor should ensure that the particulars required to be in the notice given under Regulation 21 are displayed in a readable condition in a position where they can be read by any worker engaged in the construction work and should take reasonable steps to prevent access by unauthorised persons to the construction site.

Contractors

Contractors, other than the principal contractor, and self-employed workers should cooperate with the principal contractor to provide relevant information on the health and safety risks created by their work and how these risks will be controlled. In addition, contractors have duties for the provision of other information to the principal contractor and to employees. The self-employed have duties similar to contractors.

20.5.2 CDM documentation and information transfer

The CDM Regulations require the provision of relevant information and the production of certain key documentation relating to the project – the construction phase plan and health and safety file.

The client is required to provide designers and contractors with relevant pre-construction information. The information provided is that in the client's possession or which is reasonably obtainable by the client, including any information relating to the site or the construction work, the proposed use of the structure as a workplace, the minimum amount of time before the construction phase which will be allowed to the contractors appointed by the client for planning and preparation for construction work and any information in any existing health and safety file. The purpose of this is to ensure so far as is reasonably practicable the health and safety of persons engaged in the construction work, of those liable to be affected by the way in which it is carried out, and who will use the structure as a workplace. This is to allow them to perform their duties under these Regulations and to determine the resources (see Regulation 9(1)) which they are to allocate for managing the project.

For notifiable projects, the client shall provide the CDM coordinator with the pre-construction information noted earlier along with any further information in his possession or which is reasonably obtainable, relevant to the CDM coordinator, including information on the minimum amount of time before the construction phase which will be allowed to the principal contractor for planning and preparation for construction work.

Also for notifiable projects, the client shall ensure that the construction phase does not start unless the principal contractor has prepared a construction phase plan which complies with the requirements of Regulation 23 and he is satisfied that the requirements for welfare facilities will be complied with during the construction phase.

A single health and safety file can relate to more than one project, site or structure but the client shall ensure that the information relating to each site or structure can be easily identified.

The client shall take reasonable steps to ensure that after the construction phase, information in the health and safety file is kept available for inspection by any person who may need it and it is revised as often as may be appropriate to incorporate any relevant new information.

A client who disposes of his entire interest in a structure should deliver the health and safety file to the person who acquires that interest and should ensure the purchaser is aware of the nature and purpose of the file.

The documents are to ensure the availability and transmission of key health and safety information between the parties to the project.

The construction phase health and safety plan is the foundation on which health and safety management of construction work should be based and should include arrangements for ensuring the health and safety of all who may be affected by the construction work, arrangements for the management of health and safety of the construction work, monitoring of compliance with health and safety law, and information about welfare arrangements.

The health and safety file is a record of relevant information for the client/end-user which tells those who might be responsible for the structure in the future of the risks that have to be managed during maintenance, repair or renovation. The planning supervisor has to ensure that it is prepared as the project progresses and given to the client when the project is complete. The client has to make it available to those who will work on any future design, building, maintenance or demolition of the structure.

To supplement the CDM legislation, there is an ACoP as well as a suite of guidance documents on managing health and safety in construction and guidance for designers.

The chapter *Construction Health and Safety II* describes the regulations which expand and elaborate on safety duties relating to projects and work on site and summarises a range of other detailed regulations that are likely to be encountered.

References

Association of Chief Police Officers, British Transport Police, Crown Prosecution Service, Health and Safety Executive and Local Government Association, *Work-related deaths: a protocol for liaison* (MISC 491), revised version, London, UK, HSE Books, 2003. Available online: www.hse.gov.uk/pubns/misc491.pdf (last accessed 18 September, 2010).

Health and Safety Commission. *Management of health and safety at work regulations 1999 Approved Code of Practice and guidance* L21, London, UK, HSE Books, 2000. Available for download from: http://books.hse.gov.uk/hse/public/saleproduct.jsf?catalogue Code=9780717624881 (last accessed 18 September, 2010).

Health and Safety Executive. *Enforcement policy document* HSE41(rev1), London, UK, HSE Books, 2009. Available online: www.hse.gov.uk/ pubns/hse41.pdf (last accessed 18 September, 2010).

Health and Safety Executive. *First aid at work. The health and safety (first aid) regulations 1981. Approved Code of practice and guidance.* (L74), London, UK, HSE Books, 2009. Available for download from: http://books.hse.gov.uk/hse/public/saleproduct.jsf?catalogueCode= 9780717662609 (last accessed 18 September, 2010).

House of Commons – Work and Pensions Committee. *The role of the health and safety commission and the health and safety executive in regulating workplace health and safety: HC 246-I, Third report of session 2007–08 – Volume I: Report, together with formal minutes*, London, UK, TSO, 2008. Available online: www.publications. parliament.uk/pa/cm200708/cmselect/cmworpen/246/246i.pdf (last accessed 18 September, 2010).

Shawcross, H. (Sir). *Prosecutions (Attorney-General's Responsibility).* House of Commons Debates (Hansard archive), volume 483, column 681, 29th January 1951, London, UK, UK Parliament, 1951.

Tolley's Health & Safety at Work Handbook, 22nd edition. Lexis Nexis, 2010.

Referenced legislation, regulations and standards

Company Directors Disqualification Act 1986

Construction (Design and Management) Regulations 1994 (as amended in 2000)

Construction (Design and Management) Regulations 2007 (CDM 2007)

Construction (Health, Safety and Welfare) Regulations 1996

Construction Products Directive – Council Directive 89/106/EEC of 21 December 1988 on the approximation of laws, regulations and administrative provisions of the Member States relating to construction products. *OJ*, **L40**, 11/02/1989, pp.12–26

Control of Asbestos at Work Regulations 2006

Control of Lead at Work Regulations 2002

Control of Noise at Work Regulations 2005

Control of Substances Hazardous to Health Regulations 2002

Control of Substances Hazardous to Health Regulations 2003

Control of Substances Hazardous to Health Regulations 2004

Control of Vibration at Work Regulations 2005

Coroners and Justice Act 2009

Coroners Rules 1984

Coroners (Amendment) Rules 2005

Corporate Manslaughter and Corporate Homicide Act 2007

Criminal Justice Act 1967

Criminal Justice Act 2003

Criminal Justice and Public Order Act 1994 (CJPOA)

Employer's Liability (Compulsory Insurance) Act 1969

Employers Liability (Compulsory Insurance) Regulations 1998

Environment and Safety Information Act 1988

Fire Precautions Act 1971

Health and Safety at Work etc. Act 1974

Health and Safety (Consultation with Employees) Regulations 1996 (as amended)

Health and Safety (Display Screen Equipment) Regulations 1992

Health and Safety (Enforcing Authority) Regulations 1998

Health and Safety (First Aid) Regulations 1981 (as amended)

Health and Safety (Offences) Act 2008

Ionising Radiations Regulations 1985

Legislative and Regulatory Reform Act 2006

Machinery Directive 98/37/EC – Directive 98/37/EC of the European Parliament and of the Council of 22 June 1998 on the approximation of the laws of the Member States relating to machinery. *OJ*, **L207**, 23/07/98, pp.01–46

Machinery Directive 2006/42/EC – Directive 2006/42/EC of the European Parliament and of the Council of 17 May 2006 on machinery, and amending Directive 95/16/EC (recast). *OJ*, **L157**, 09/06/2006, pp.24–86

Management of Health and Safety at Work Regulations 1999

Management of Health and Safety at Work Regulations 2003

Management of Health and Safety at Work Regulations 2006

Manual Handling Operations Regulations 1992

Personal Protective Equipment at Work Regulations 1992

Police and Criminal Evidence Act 1984 (PACE)

Reporting of Injuries, Diseases and Dangerous Occurrences Regulations 1995 (RIDDOR)

Safety Regulations and Safety Committees Regulations 1977 (as amended)

Social Security (Claims and Payments) Regulations 1967

Temporary or Mobile Construction Sites Directive 92/57/EEC – Council Directive 92/57/EEC of 24 June 1992 on the implementation of minimum safety and health requirements at temporary or mobile construction sites (eighth individual Directive within the meaning of Article 16 (1) of Directive 89/391/EEC). *OJ*, **L245**, 26/08/1992, pp.06–22

Working Time Directive – Directive 2003/88/EC of the European Parliament and of the Council of 4 November 2003 concerning certain aspects of the organisation of working time. *OJ*, **L299**, 18/11/2003, pp.09–19

Work at Height Regulations 2005

Working Time Regulations 1998 (as amended)

Workplace (Health and Safety) Regulations 1992

Referenced cases

A-G's Reference No. 89 or 2006 [2006] EWCA Crim 2570

Austin Rover Group Ltd v. HM Inspector of Factories [1990] 1 AC 619

Chilcott v. Thermal Transfer Limited [2009] EWHC 2086 (Admin)

Edwards v. National Coal Board [1949] 1 KB 704

El Aljou v. Dollar Land Holdings plc [1994] 2 All ER 685

Lockhart v. Kevin Oliphant [1992] SCCR 774

R. v. Adomako [1995] 1 AC 171

R. v. Associated Octel Co Ltd [1996] 4 All ER 846

R. v. Associated Octel (Court of Appeal)

R. v. Balfour Beatty Rail Infrastructure Services Ltd [2006] EWCA Crim 1586

R. v. Boal [1992] 3 All ER 177, CA

R. v. Board of Trustees of Science Museum [1993] 3 All ER 853

R. v. Bristol Magistrates' Court ex parte Juttan Oy [2003] UKHL 5

R. v. British Steel plc [1995] 1 WLR 1356

R v. Chargot Limited and others [2008] UKHL

R v. EGS Ltd [2009] EWCA Crim 1942

R. v. Gateway Foodmarkets Ltd [1997] 3 All ER 78

R. v. Howe & Son (Engineers) Ltd [1999] 2 CrApp R(S) 37

R. v. HTM [2006] Crim 1156

R. v. Jarvis Facilities Ltd [2005] EWCA Crim 1409

R. v. Mersey Docks and Harbour Company [1995] 16 Cr App Rep (S) 806

R. v. Nelson Group Services (Maintenance) Ltd [1998] 4 All ER 331

R. v. P Ltd and G [2007] All ER (D) 173 (Jul) (CA)

R. v. Porter [2008] All ER (D) 249 (May)

R. v. Swan Hunter Shipbuilders Ltd [1981] ICR 831

R. v. Transco [2006] EWCA Crim 838

R. v. Yorkshire Sheeting & Insulation Ltd [2003] 2 Cr.App.R. (S) 93

RMC Roadstone Products Ltd v. Jester [1994] ICR 456

Wotherspoon v. HM Advocate [1978] JC 74

Further reading

McAleenan, C. and Oloke, D. (eds) (2010) *ICE Manual of health and safety in construction,* London, UK, Thomas Telford Ltd.

Health and Safety Executive (2003) *Health and safety regulation... a short guide* HSC13(rev1), London, UK HSE Books. Available online: www.hse.gov.uk/pubns/hsc13.pdf (last accessed 18 September, 2010).

Websites

British Standards Institution (BSI); www.bsigroup.com

Code for Crown Prosecutors, CPS; www.cps.gov.uk/publications/code_for_crown_prosecutors/

Construction Industry Advisory Committee (CONIAC); www.hse.gov.uk/aboutus/meetings/iacs/coniac/

Construction Industry Research and Information Association (CIRIA); www.ciria.org

Coroners and Justice Act 2009; www.opsi.gov.uk/acts/acts2009/pdf/ukpga_20090025_en.pdf

Crown Prosecution Service; www.cps.gov.uk

Department for Work and Pensions; www.dwp.gov.uk

Health and Safety Executive (HSE); www.hse.gov.uk

HSE, Form F10(rev); www.hse.gov.uk/forms/notification/f10.pdf

HSE Public Register of convictions; www.hse.gov.uk/prosecutions

Health and Safety Executive Northern Ireland (HSENI); www.hseni.gov.uk

Legislation, at the Office of Public Sector Information (OPSI); www.opsi.gov.uk/legislation

Office of Rail Regulation (ORR); www.rail-reg.gov.uk

Sentencing Guidelines Council; www.sentencingcouncil.org.uk

Sentencing Guidelines Council, Corporate Manslaughter and health and safety offences causing death; www.sentencingcouncil.org.uk/professional/guidelines/homicide-related-offences.htm

Thomas Telford Publishing; www.icevirtuallibrary.com

ice | manuals

Chapter 21

doi: 10.1680/mocl.40878.0329

Construction health and safety II: Industry and hazard-specific regulations, work equipment and workplace safety

Donald Lamont Health and Safety Executive, Bootle, UK
Mike Appleby Housemans Solicitors, London, UK

CONTENTS

Health and safety responsibilities stem primarily from the Health and Safety at Work etc. Act 1974 (HSWA), and are shared by various parties who may be connected with construction and engineering projects. This chapter describes the regulations which expand and elaborate on safety duties relating to projects and work on site, and a range of other detailed regulations that are likely to be encountered are summarised.

21.1 Construction-orientated legislation

21.1.1 Construction (Design and Management) Regulations 2007

The requirements in respect of work at height are now contained in the Work at Height Regulations 2005; The Construction Health, Safety and Welfare Regulations 1996 have been revoked in full with most of their requirements transferred to Part 4 of Construction (Design and Management) Regulations 2007(CDM 2007).

The principal duty holders under Part 4 of CDM 2007 are employers and the self-employed, but Regulation 25 extends the duties to those who control construction work. Employees have duties under the regulations to carry out their individual task in a safe manner. Other organisational duties resulting from the regulations include one on those undertaking construction work to cooperate with others on health and safety matters.

The regulations are grouped into generally related topics as listed subsequently.

21.1.1.1 Safe places of work

There is a general requirement in the regulations to provide a place of work which is safe and without risk to health, so far as is reasonably practicable, and with sufficient working space at that place to do the work safely. Access to and egress from that place of work should also be safe and without risk to health. These requirements apply equally to work places below ground, at ground level and above ground.

21.1.1.2 Good order and site security

There is a requirement that every part of a construction site should be kept in good order and workplaces kept clean. In addition, the site perimeter should be identified and fenced off if the site poses a risk.

21.1.1.3 Unsafe structures or premature collapse

Employers must take steps to prevent the accidental collapse of structures under construction or of existing structures. Demolition and dismantling work should be carried out to a predetermined plan and in a safe manner under the supervision of a competent person.

21.1.1.4 Explosives

Explosive charges should only be fired if suitable and sufficient steps have been taken to prevent injury directly from the explosives or from flying material.

21.1.1.5 Excavations

Excavations, which include shafts and tunnels, should be supported as necessary and the support works carried out under the supervision of a competent person.

21.1.1.6 Cofferdams and caissons

Cofferdams and caissons should be of suitable and sound construction and of sufficient strength for their purpose.

21.1.1.7 Energy distribution installations

Energy distribution installations should be suitably located, checked and clearly indicated. Electric power cables should be directed away from the works area or cables should be isolated or earthed as necessary. Barriers or similar may be required to prevent vehicles striking overhead power lines.

Steps should also be taken to prevent risk from striking any buried service.

21.1.1.8 Avoidance of drowning

Employers must take steps to prevent people falling into water and drowning. In addition, the necessary personal protective equipment (PPE) should be provided and rescue equipment should be immediately available for use in the event of a fall.

Water-borne transport should be under the control of a competent person.

21.1.1.9 Traffic routes

Traffic routes throughout a site should be arranged to allow pedestrians and vehicles to operate without risk to people. Pedestrian and vehicle routes should be segregated. Unintended vehicle movements should be prevented and warning given of hazardous movements such as reversing.

21.1.1.10 Prevention and control of emergencies

The employer should take steps to prevent or control the risk from fire, explosion, flooding and asphyxiation. Emergency routes and exits should be available and procedures should be in place for dealing with emergencies. All necessary fire fighting, fire alarm and detection systems should be provided.

21.1.1.11 Welfare facilities

Welfare facilities should be provided by the employer, including all necessary sanitary, washing and rest facilities and facilities for changing and storing clothing.

21.1.1.12 Workplace environment

The employer's duties in respect of the workplace environment extend to ensuring that there is sufficient fresh air or ventilation, adequate temperatures in indoor workplaces, or facilities for protection against the weather and the provision of lighting. Emergency lighting may also be required. The site perimeter should be adequately fenced.

21.1.1.13 Training, inspection and so on

There are various obligations on employers to ensure that employees are adequately trained. Certain operations should either be carried out under the control of competent persons or be inspected prior to any work taking place by competent persons.

21.1.2 Confined Spaces Regulations 1997

These apply only to confined spaces as defined in the regulations. Confined spaces are defined as places which, by their enclosed nature, give rise to the risk of death or serious injury through lack of oxygen, the presence of toxic gas, fume or vapour, dust, drowning in liquid or free-flowing solid, fire or explosion or hot conditions.

The regulations do not contain specific requirements for the assessment of risks from the confined space but rely on Regulations 3 and 4 of the Management of Health and Safety at Work Regulations 1999 for this.

Once such an assessment has identified the risk from the confined space, the Confined Spaces Regulations 1997 require that work should only be carried out in the confined space if that work cannot reasonably be done from outside. In addition, if entry is unavoidable, the work should be done in accordance

with a safe system of work. Before any work in the confined space begins, appropriate emergency arrangements should be put in place to deal with foreseeable emergencies and the risk to those responding to the emergency must also be taken into account.

21.1.3 Work in Compressed Air Regulations 1996

21.1.3.1 General

These regulations set out requirements for the engineering, management and medical aspects of work in compressed air. They are supported by an extensive guidance document (L96; HSE, 1996). In 2001, oxygen decompression became mandatory from exposure pressures of 1.0 bar and over. At the time of writing, L96 is being revised and is expected to be republished in by the end of 2010.

The regulations apply to all work and all working in compressed air carried out in the course of construction work as defined in the CDM 2007.

There should be a competent 'compressed air contractor' who is central to the safe execution of the works and most of the duties in subsequent regulations are placed on this contractor. Often the compressed air contractor is the 'principal contractor' as defined in the CDM 2007.

The compressed air contractor must appoint a contract medical adviser, whose role is to advise on current best practice in all aspects of occupational health related to the work in compressed air. A number of new roles have been created, the most important of which is that of the hyperbaric supervisor. The hyperbaric supervisor is responsible for safety in the day-to-day running of the hyperbaric works.

Compressed air contractors are required to give 14 days' notification of work in compressed air to the Health and Safety Executive (HSE).

All work in compressed air should be carried out in accordance with a safe system of work. One aspect of the safe system of work is the involvement of a competent team to undertake the work and the guidance sets out the roles to be fulfilled. Another aspect is the provision of plant and equipment.

21.1.3.2 Medical surveillance

This is required for all people exposed to compressed air.

The regulations require that compression and decompression of persons be carried out in accordance with a regime approved by the HSE.

The regulations include extensive requirements for record keeping. 'Adequate facilities' for the medical treatment of decompression illness are also required.

Fire and flood are two of the major safety hazards associated with work in compressed air.

There are requirements for the provision of instruction and information about the specific hazards associated with work in compressed air.

Only persons fit for work in compressed air should be allowed through the airlocks.

21.1.4 Diving at Work Regulations 1997

These regulations apply to all diving projects in which at least one diver is at work either as an employee or as a self-employed person. The regulations place duties on all parties to the diving project from the client to the working diver. They should all ensure that the diving work is planned and executed safely. The regulations are supported by a series of Approved Codes of Practice (ACoPs) of which the one relating to commercial inshore diving is particularly relevant to construction.

The client has to appoint a competent diving contractor to carry out the work. In addition, the client should ensure that the diving site is safe and details of known hazards are identified to the contractor.

The diving contractor's duties include assessing the risks from the project and ensuring that a diving plan is prepared. In addition, the diving contractor should ensure that a diving team of sufficient size and competence is assembled and that the plan is known to the diving team. The diving contractor also has duties in ensuring that appropriate plant and equipment is available and in a suitable condition to be used.

Arrangements for first aid and medical treatment and the keeping of appropriate records are further duties of the diving contractor. Within the diving team is a diving supervisor on whom extensive duties are placed in respect of ensuring the safe conduct of the diving work in accordance with the diving plan.

Duties on the working divers generally relate to their possession of a certificate of competence to dive, a certificate of medical fitness to dive, a first-aid certificate and the keeping of personal exposure records, normally in a logbook. In addition, the diver should be competent for the work in hand and follow the instructions of the supervisor.

Extensive duties are placed on the diving contractor to ensure the safety of the diving project. These relate to the planning of the project, the appointment of competent supervisor(s) and the provision of sufficient other competent personnel, the provision of sufficient plant and equipment, and the communication of information on the project to those involved.

Diving contractors are required to notify the HSE of their trading as such.

21.2 Hazard-specific regulations: use of equipment

21.2.1 Provision and Use of Work Equipment Regulations 1998 (PUWER)

PUWER was most recently revised in 1998. They apply to any equipment which is supplied or controlled by the employer and used by employees at work. Duties on employers under PUWER also apply to equipment for use at work which is

provided by the employees themselves. 'Equipment' covers all machines, plant and equipment, tools including hand tools and so on for use at work. The 'use' of equipment includes starting or stopping, repairing, modifying, maintaining, servicing and cleaning the equipment, as well as transporting it.

There are also duties under the regulations on the self-employed if they supply equipment for use at work or control the use of equipment at work.

Employers and the self-employed must ensure that the work equipment is suitable for use and for the purpose and conditions in which it is used. Work equipment must be maintained in a safe condition for use so that the equipment itself does not present a risk to the health and safety of those using it. The regulations also contain requirements for the inspection of certain types of equipment.

Employers and the self-employed must also ensure that the risks arising from the use of work equipment are, where possible, eliminated or, if that is not possible, that the risks are controlled. Construction involves the extensive use of powered equipment and mobile machinery so in most cases it will not be possible to eliminate the risk. Control of the risks may in some cases be achieved by the provision of guards or other protective devices, for example, the provision of appropriate two-handed controls or emergency stop devices. With some equipment, risk control can be achieved by the use of a safe system of work accompanied by appropriate information, instruction and training with adequate supervision.

All employees must receive adequate information, instruction and training in the use of the equipment which they are using.

Mobile work equipment is used extensively in construction and there are additional duties in respect of such equipment arising from its mobility. Mobile work equipment which is used for carrying persons should be suitable for that purpose. There should be measures in place to ensure the safety of the operator and others on it from risks arising from the mobile nature of the machine. One such risk, particularly in construction, is overturning.

Plant hire companies may find it beneficial to seek expert advice on the application of these regulations to their business.

21.2.2 Lifting Operations and Lifting Equipment Regulations 1998 (LOLER)

These regulations consolidated the requirements in respect of lifting from legislation covering construction and other industries. They complement the requirements of the PUWER in that they cover requirements for equipment used for lifting at work.

The regulations apply to employers and the self-employed who provide lifting equipment for use, as well as to those who have control of lifting equipment.

The regulations require that lifting equipment provided for use at work is suitable, sufficiently strong and stable for the particular use. Lifting equipment includes any equipment used at work for lifting or lowering loads, including cranes, hoists and mobile elevating work platforms. Lifting accessories such as chains and slings are included. The load must also be suitable.

Lifting equipment provided by employees is also covered by the regulations.

The regulations require lifting equipment to be marked to indicate its safe working load. Lifting equipment should be positioned and installed to minimise risk. Lifting equipment should be used safely and, to achieve this, the lifting operation should be planned and carried out by people who are competent.

In addition, there are requirements for lifting equipment to be inspected and thoroughly examined. Where appropriate, lifting equipment should be thoroughly examined by a competent person before it is used for the first time and again at periodic intervals. The interval varies from 6 months for lifting accessories and equipment for lifting people, to annually for other lifting equipment. The precise interval should be set out in an examination scheme drawn up by a competent person. Reports of examinations and inspections should be submitted to the employer.

The duties in the regulations in respect of lifting operations require that lifting operations are carried out in a safe manner as a result of being planned and supervised by competent persons.

21.2.3 Electricity at Work Regulations 1989

These regulations set out the precautions to be taken against the risks to health and safety from the use of electricity at work. They place duties not only on employers and the self-employed but also on employees, including trainees. In quarry premises, duties are specifically placed on the quarry manager.

There is a fundamental requirement for all electrical equipment and systems to be constructed and maintained in a condition which prevents danger, and for associated systems of work to be safe.

Electrical equipment in use should be of sufficient strength and capability not to be exceeded in a dangerous way. Equipment should also be constructed or protected from foreseeable mechanical damage or hazardous environmental effects.

Among the technical requirements are those requiring live conductors to be either insulated or safe by position. Appropriate earthing should be provided. Joints and connections should be suitable for use and a means of protection from excess current should be incorporated in the system. In addition, there should be means of cutting off the supply and for isolating equipment.

The fundamental requirement for work on electrical equipment is for that equipment to be made dead prior to work being started; however, the regulations recognise that, in some circumstances, work on or near live conductors may be required. A further requirement for ensuring the safety of those working on electrical equipment is for there to be adequate access and working space around the equipment and for the equipment to be adequately lit.

Persons engaged in electrical work should be competent or, if trainees, under supervision.

The supply of electricity is regulated under the Electricity Supply Regulations 1998.

Although the Institution of Engineering and Technology (IET) produces so-called 'wiring regulations' (reproduced as a British Standard), these are non-statutory and have the status of guidance. Nevertheless, compliance with them should satisfy some technical aspects of the Electricity at Work Regulations in respect of electrical installations in the workplace.

21.2.4 Personal Protective Equipment at Work Regulations 1992

These regulations are linked with the regulations arising from the product directive relating to PPE. They place various requirements on employers in relation to the general provision, maintenance, storage and use of PPE.

They do not apply to the provision of PPE against certain specific hazards including lead, ionising radiation, asbestos, noise and head protection in construction works in respect of whether there are more specific statutory requirements for PPE.

The regulations place duties on employers to provide their employees with PPE which they have assessed as being suitable to protect them against residual risk to their health and safety. The self-employed are under similar duties in respect of their own health and safety.

The PPE supplied should be suitable for the risk against which it is intended to provide protection and under the conditions of expected use. It should take into account ergonomic requirements and be capable of fitting the wearer correctly. PPE should be designed and manufactured in accordance with the requirements in the Personal Protective Equipment (EC Directive) Regulations 1992 as amended.

Where people are exposed to more than one risk simultaneously, the various items of PPE required should be mutually compatible.

Employers are also required to maintain PPE and to make appropriate arrangements for its storage and maintenance, and for the provision of appropriate information, instruction and training for its safe use. Employers are further required to provide information instruction and training to ensure that employees properly fit and use the PPE issued to them. Employees are required to ensure that PPE issued to them is properly used, maintained and any loss or defect is reported to the employer immediately.

21.2.5 Construction (Head Protection) Regulations 1989

These apply to all construction activity and deal only with the control of risk of head injuries. The regulations apply to building operations and works of engineering construction as previously defined in the Factories Act, but not to diving operations. All employees should be provided by their employers with suitable head protection which shall be maintained and replaced as necessary. The suitability of the head protection has to be determined by an assessment of its characteristics and the perceived risk of head injuries as well as those of the situation in which employees are working. Self-employed persons must provide their own head protection.

The main duties of employers are to ensure that employees wear suitable head protection and that duty is extended to employees who have control over other persons. Hence, all supervisory staff should be ensuring that others wear head protection. These duties extend to the self-employed. Head protection is not required where there is no risk of head injury other than by persons falling over.

A further duty is placed on 'the person for the time being in control of the site' to make rules for the wearing of head protection in writing, and to bring the rules to the attention of the employees.

Employees and the self-employed are required to wear the head protection provided in accordance with the site rules. Employees are further required to take reasonable care of their head protection and to report any defect in it or the loss of it to their employer without delay.

21.2.6 Control of Noise at Work Regulations 2005

The Control of Noise at Work Regulations 2005 (SI No. 1643) revoke and replace the Noise at Work Regulations 1989 (SI 1989/1790), and implement in Great Britain the requirements of EC Directive 2003/10/EC, concerning minimum health and safety standards for workers exposed to noise. The Regulations impose duties on employers and on self-employed persons to protect both employees who may be exposed to risk from exposure to noise at work and other persons at work who might be affected by that work.

The 2005 Regulations impose more stringent limits on exposure. Lower exposure action values, upper exposure action values, and exposure limit values for daily or weekly personal noise exposure and for peak sound pressure (Regulation 4).

The regulations apply to virtually all work activity including construction.

Regulation 4 defines a number of exposure limit values and action values. The lower exposure action values are a daily or weekly personal noise exposure of 80 dB (A-weighted); and a peak sound pressure of 135 dB (C-weighted).

The upper exposure action values are a daily or weekly personal noise exposure of 85 dB (A-weighted) and a peak sound pressure of 137 dB (C-weighted).

The exposure limit values are a daily or weekly personal noise exposure of 87 dB (A-weighted) and a peak sound pressure of 140 dB (C-weighted).

There is a caveat for situations in which the exposure of an employee to noise varies markedly from day to day. In these circumstances an employer may use weekly personal noise exposure in place of daily personal noise exposure for the purpose of compliance with these Regulations (previous limits were a first action level of 85 dB (A), a second action level of 90 dB (A) and a peak action level of 200 Pa).

The employer is required under Regulation 5 to make an assessment of the risk to health and safety created by exposure to noise at the workplace. That assessment is required when the employee is liable to be exposed to noise at or above a lower exposure action value. Additionally the employer shall use the assessment to identify the measures which need to be taken to meet the requirements of these Regulations. In undertaking the risk assessment, the employer shall assess the levels of noise to which workers are exposed through observation of working practices; making reference to relevant information on the probable noise levels arising from the use of equipment and specific working practices and if necessary by the measurement of actual noise levels to which employees are likely to be exposed.

As a result of this assessment the employer shall assess whether any employees are likely to be exposed to noise at or above a lower exposure action value, an upper exposure action value, or an exposure limit value. Regulation 5 outlines additional factors to be considered in making the assessment. It further requires the risk assessment to be reviewed regularly, or immediately there is reason to suspect that the assessment is no longer valid or there has been a significant change in the work to which the assessment relates. Any changes in mitigation measures shown to be necessary must be made.

The employer must consult the employees concerned or their representatives and the employer shall record the significant findings of the risk assessment as soon as is practicable after the risk assessment is made or changed along with details of the mitigation measures taken.

The employer is required by Regulation 6 to ensure that risk from the exposure of his or her employees to noise is either eliminated at source or, where this is not reasonably practicable, is reduced to as low a level as is reasonably practicable.

If any employee is likely to be exposed to noise at or above an upper exposure action value, the employer shall reduce exposure to as low a level as is reasonably practicable by changing the system of work or by introducing technical measures, in accordance with the general principles of prevention set out in the Management of Health and Safety Regulations 1999, excluding the provision of personal hearing protectors. Examples of appropriate means of reducing exposure are given in the Control of Noise at Work Regulations.

If any employee is exposed or likely to be exposed to noise above an exposure limit value, the employer must reduce exposure to noise to below the exposure limit value, identify the reason for that exposure limit value being exceeded and modify the mitigation measures taken to prevent it being exceeded again.

Personal hearing protectors should be made available upon request to any employee who is exposed above a lower exposure action value. They should also be made available to an employee who is likely to be exposed to above an upper exposure action value but only if an employer is unable to reduce the levels of noise to which an employee is exposed by other means.

Any area of the workplace in which an employee is likely to be exposed to noise at or above an upper exposure action value should be designated a Hearing Protection Zone, demarcated and identified by means of appropriate signs and access to the area restricted to those wearing personal hearing protectors.

The employer shall be responsible for maintenance of personal hearing protective equipment.

If the risk assessment indicates that there is a risk to the health of his or her employees from noise exposure, the employer must arrange for his or her employees to be placed under suitable health surveillance, including testing of their hearing and maintenance of appropriate health records. Where, as a result of health surveillance, an employee is found to have identifiable hearing damage the employer shall ensure that the employee is medically examined if the damage is likely to have been the result of exposure to noise. The employer shall ensure that the employee is informed accordingly and the risk assessment and mitigation measures are reviewed.

Employees exposed to noise, and their representatives, are entitled to suitable and sufficient information, instruction and training on the nature of the risks, the mitigation measures being taken and the general results of health surveillance.

21.2.7 Safety of pressure systems and gas cylinders

The Pressure Systems Safety Regulations 2000 re-enact with amendments the Pressure Systems and Transportable Gas Containers Regulations 1989 ('the 1989 Regulations') as amended. The 1989 Regulations imposed safety requirements with respect to pressure systems which are used or intended to be used at work. They also imposed safety requirements to prevent certain vessels from becoming pressurised. The Regulations specified a number of exceptions.

Any person who designs, manufactures, imports or supplies any pressure system or any article which is intended to be a component part of any pressure system must ensure that the pressure system or component is properly designed and properly constructed from suitable material; that all necessary examinations for preventing danger can be carried out; that where the pressure system has any means of access to its interior, access can be gained without danger and the pressure system is provided with such protective devices as may be necessary for preventing danger and such device, designed to release contents, shall do so safely (Regulation 4).

Any person who designs or supplies a pressure system or component, shall provide sufficient written information

about its design, construction, examination, operation and maintenance to enable the provisions of the Regulations to be complied with. Similar information is required following modification or repair. Guidance on the information required is given in the regulations.

The employer of a person who installs a pressure system at work must ensure that it is not installed in a dangerous manner or in a manner which impairs the operation of any protective device or inspection facility.

Pressure systems must be operated within safe limits established by the user of an installed system or the owner of a mobile system.

Pressure systems must not be operated unless the user has a written scheme for the periodic examination, drawn up by a competent person, of all protective devices; every pressure vessel and every pipeline in which a defect may give rise to danger and those parts of the pipework in which a defect may give rise to danger.

The user of an installed system and the owner of a mobile system shall ensure that those parts of the pressure system included in the scheme of examination are examined by a competent person within the intervals specified in the scheme and, where relevant, before the system is used for the first time.

The competent person doing the examination must subsequently submit a report of his or her findings, the contents of which are specified in Regulation 9.

If the competent person carrying out the examination is of the opinion that the pressure system or part of it will give rise to imminent danger unless certain repairs or modifications have been carried out or unless suitable changes to the operating conditions have been made, he must immediately report that in writing to the user, identifying the band, the repairs, modifications or changes to be made.

The person operating the pressure system shall be provided with adequate and suitable instructions covering the safe operation of the system and the action to be taken in the vent of any emergency. It is the responsibility of the user of a pressure system to ensure that it is not operated except in accordance with the instructions provided.

The user should also ensure that the system is properly maintained in good repair, so as to prevent danger. The employer of a person who modifies or repairs a pressure system must ensure that nothing about the way in which it is modified or repaired gives rise to danger or otherwise impairs the operation of any protective device or inspection facility. The user of a pressure system must keep various records of its inspection.

The Carriage of Dangerous Goods and Use of Transportable Pressure Equipment Regulations 2004 (SI No. 568) amend the Pressure Systems Safety Regulations 2002 and impose requirements and prohibitions in relation to the carriage of goods by road or by rail and the use of transportable pressure equipment. They implement three EC Directives and also make other provisions in what are a complex and highly detailed set of regulations of only marginal interest in construction.

21.2.8 Manual Handling Operations Regulations 1992

These regulations as amended by the Health and Safety (Miscellaneous Amendments) Regulations 2002 (SI No. 2174) apply to manual handling operations in virtually all work activities, including construction. Manual handling includes all lifting, loading, pulling, pushing and carrying operations. The primary duty on an employer is to do what is reasonably practicable to avoid the need for its employees to carry out manual handling operations which give rise to a risk of injury to them, and, where that is not possible, the employer should assess the risk of injury to the employees and then take appropriate steps to reduce that risk to the lowest reasonably practical level. Although means of risk reduction are not specified in the regulations, it will normally be achieved by the use of mechanical handling equipment. In addition, where manual handling is undertaken, the employer should inform the employees of the weights of the loads being handled. Additional information has to be provided if the loads are of irregular shape.

Assessment made under these regulations should be reviewed as appropriate whenever any change in the operation is identified. Employees are under a duty to make use of any system of work provided to reduce the risk to them. Contrary to many people's belief, there are no minimum weights or loads specified in the regulations.

21.2.9 The Control of Substances Hazardous to Health Regulations 2002

The Control of Substances Hazardous to Health Regulations 2002 (SI No. 2677) (COSHH) as amended, are the most recent version of this set of regulations which implement the requirements of a number of EC Directives relating to hazardous substances. The Regulations impose duties on employers, employees and self-employed persons to protect their health from exposure to hazardous substances and prohibit the import of certain substances and materials.

These regulations apply to substances which are classified as 'very toxic, toxic, harmful, corrosive or irritant' under the Chemicals (Hazard Information and Packaging for Supply) Regulations 2002 along with certain biological agents and dusts above concentrations specified in the regulations as 'workplace exposure limits'. Lead, asbestos and radioactive substances are subject to separate regulation. Simple asphyxiants, flammable or explosive substances are not subject to COSHH. The control of exposure to a hazardous substance shall only be considered adequate if the principles of good practice for the control of exposure to substances hazardous to health are applied and any workplace exposure limit for that substance is not exceeded. For certain hazardous substances, including those causing occupational asthma, exposure should be reduced to 'as low

a level as is reasonably practicable'. There is extensive published guidance on compliance with these regulations – see, for example, the HSE website.

Employers' duties under COSHH begin with the need to identify the hazardous substances present in the workplace and the nature of the hazard and then make an assessment of the risk from those substances to the health of those exposed. Factors to be considered in making that assessment are set out in the Regulations. The assessment should cover all means of exposure, including ingestion, skin contact and inhalation. Having made the assessment and if there are risks to health, the employer should use the assessment to identify the measures needed to eliminate or control these risks. Principles of good control practice are set out subsequently.

Employers should take steps to ensure control measures are properly applied while employees must utilise the control measures provided. Employers must maintain and test control measures and undertake periodic monitoring of the workplace to demonstrate the ongoing adequacy of the measures.

Health surveillance should be carried out as appropriate and detailed requirements for that health surveillance are set out in Regulation 11. Employers should provide information, instruction, training and supervision. There are also requirements for employers to have in place arrangements to deal with accidents, incidents and emergencies involving the presence of the hazardous substance in the workplace.

The Principles of good practice referred to earlier are:

(a) design and operate processes and activities to minimise emission, release and spread of substances hazardous to health
(b) take into account all relevant routes of exposure – inhalation, skin absorption and ingestion – when developing control measures
(c) control exposure by measures that are proportionate to the health risk
(d) choose the most effective and reliable control options which minimise the escape and spread of substances hazardous to health
(e) where adequate control of exposure cannot be achieved by other means, provide, in combination with other control measures, suitable PPE
(f) check and review regularly all elements of control measures for their continuing effectiveness
(g) inform and train all employees on the hazards and risks from the substances with which they work and the use of control measures developed to minimise the risks
(h) ensure that the introduction of control measures does not increase the overall risk to health and safety

21.2.10 Control of Lead at Work Regulations 2002

The Control of Lead at Work Regulations 2002 (SI No. 2676) re-enact, with modifications, the Control of Lead at Work

Regulations 1998 (SI No. 543) which imposed requirements for the protection of employees who might be exposed to lead at work and of other persons who might be affected by such work and also imposed certain duties on employees concerning their own protection from such exposure.

Part of these Regulations implement in Great Britain, EC Directive 98/24/EC on the protection of the health and safety of workers from risks related to chemical agents at work insofar as it relates to risks to health from exposure to lead.

There is a complex series of prescribed limits set out in Regulation 2, depending on the nature of the exposure, the sex and age of the person exposed and whether a blood or urine sample is involved.

Under the Control of Lead at Work Regulations 2002, where there is a risk of exposure to lead, employers must carry out an assessment of the health risk to which employees or others affected by their work with lead (or certain lead compounds) are being exposed. Guidance of the factors to be covered in the assessment is given in the Regulations. Employers with five or more employees must record the findings of the assessment.

Every employer is required by Regulation 6 to ensure that the exposure of his or her employees to lead is either prevented or, where this is not reasonably practicable, adequately controlled. Possible control methods are set out in the regulations and the general principles of prevention are to be found in Schedule 1 of the Management of Health and Safety Regulations 1999. Employers should take steps to ensure that control measures are properly applied, while employees must utilise the control measures provided.

Because of the range of routes by which exposure to lead can occur, employers must ensure, so far as is reasonably practicable, that employees do not eat, drink or smoke in any place which is, or is liable to be, contaminated by lead, and employees must not eat, drink or smoke in any place that may be contaminated by lead.

Employers must maintain and test control measures and where the control measures include the use of PPE, the employer must have in place an adequate scheme for maintaining and decontaminating such equipment. Periodic air monitoring in the workplace to demonstrate the ongoing adequacy of the measures is also required.

Employers shall ensure that all employees who are or are likely to be significantly exposed to lead are subject to appropriate health surveillance, in particular where their blood-lead concentration or urinary lead concentration is measured and equals or exceeds the action levels detailed in the Regulations.

Employers should provide information, instruction, training and supervision. There is also a duty to ensure that the contents of containers and pipes for lead used at work are clearly identifiable.

There are also requirements for employers to have in place arrangements to deal with accidents, incidents and emergencies involving the presence of lead in the workplace.

21.2.11 Control of Asbestos at Work Regulations 2006

These Regulations revoke and replace the Control of Asbestos at Work Regulations 2002 (SI 2002/2675) and make changes to the Asbestos (Licensing) Regulations 1983 (SI 1983/1649) as amended and the Asbestos (Prohibitions) Regulations 1992 (SI 1992/3067) as amended.

They implement in Great Britain a number of EC directives, including 'the Marketing and Use Directive' 76/769/EEC as amended relating to restrictions on the marketing and use of certain dangerous substances, including asbestos. They also implement Directive 83/477/EEC as amended on the protection of workers from the risks related to exposure to asbestos at work.

Other directives which they implement include Directive 90/394/EEC on the protection of workers from the risks related to exposure to carcinogens at work insofar as it relates to asbestos and Directive 98/24/EC which requires protection of the health and safety of workers from the risks related to exposure to chemical agents at work, including asbestos.

Part 1 of the regulations covers application and definitions; Part 2 covers the practicalities of work with asbestos; Part 3 deals with prohibitions; whilst Part 4 sets out miscellaneous provisions.

Changes to existing requirements include a restriction on licenses of 3 years. Transitional arrangements for existing licences are set out in Regulations 32(1) and 35(1).

Part 2 of the Regulations replaces the Control of Asbestos at Work Regulations 2002 (SI 2002/2675) and makes a number of changes including additional definitions and a new control limit common to all types of asbestos which is lower than that applying previously; adoption of the 1997 World Health Organisation (WHO) procedure for the measurement of the control limit. It applies the duties in the regulations to all work with asbestos, apart from exceptions relating to licensing, notification, accident and emergency arrangements, asbestos areas and health surveillance in respect of sporadic and low-intensity exposure which is deemed to include textured wall coverings. The 2006 Regulations are disapplied in respect of ships other than naval ships.

The 2006 Regulations extend the list of topics on which information, instruction and training must be given to employees (Regulation 10(1)). Part 2 requires the provision of respiratory protective equipment so far as is reasonably practicable to any employee who is exposed to asbestos and requires that the control limit shall not be exceeded sets out the actions to be taken if this should occur. It provides that only competent persons should enter respirator zones or supervise employees in respirator zones and also in respect of competence, under Regulation 20(4), it provides for accreditation of persons who are requested to assess premises for the issue of a site clearance certificate for reoccupation. Labelling requirements are set out in Part 3. There is a duty to manage asbestos in non-domestic premises, along with requirements for the identification of the presence of asbestos are set out. Regulation 6 deals with the assessment of work which exposes employees to asbestos, the requirements for planning such work is set out in Regulation 7. Requirements for the licensing of work with asbestos are detailed in the Regulations. HSE must be notified of work with asbestos. Details of the information, instruction and training for those working with asbestos are set out in Regulation 10. In keeping with normal control principles, exposure to asbestos should be prevented if reasonably practicable or reduced if not. Reduction of exposure can be achieved by the use of control measures which once in place should be maintained. Employers have duties to provide and clean protective clothing and to make arrangements to deal with accidents, incidents and emergencies. Employers also have a duty to prevent or reduce the spread of asbestos. The cleanliness of premises and plant is covered under Regulation 17. Regulation 18 requires the employer to designate and enforce entry controls on areas where exposure to asbestos could occur along with respirator areas where exposure levels above the control limit could be experienced. Eating, drinking or smoking is not allowed in such areas. However, washing facilities are required. Control of exposure to asbestos is to be monitored through a programme of air monitoring with standards for analysis set out in Regulation 21. Successful completion of the work should be proved by air testing and the issue of a site clearance certification. As with regulations controlling similar occupations health hazards, health surveillance is required. Finally the regulations cover the storage, distribution and labelling of raw asbestos and asbestos waste.

21.2.12 Ionising Radiations Regulations 1999

The main application of these regulations within the construction industry is to the use of radioactive sources for instrumentation and testing purposes. The regulations themselves are divided into a number of parts. These deal with general matters including the cooperation between employers whose employees are likely to be exposed to radiation from the one employer's activities and notification of work with ionising radiations (IR) to the HSE.

Other parts of the Regulations deal with dose limitation, the regulation of work with IR, dosimetry and medical surveillance, arrangements for the control of radioactive substances, monitoring of IR and equipment safety.

Work with IR is limited to specialised applications in construction and any employer who intends to use IR or suspects that its employees may be exposed to IR should see more detailed HSE guidance for an in-depth description of these regulations.

21.2.13 Explosives

Legislation governing explosives is extensive and somewhat complex. There is separate legislation for the manufacture,

storage and transportation of explosives from that governing their use. The principal legislation governing the manufacture and storage was the Explosives Act 1875 and its subordinate legislation; however, significant changes came about with the coming into force of the Manufacture and Storage of Explosives Regulations 2005 (SI No. 1082). These Regulations set out requirements for licensing the manufacture and storage of explosives and for registration in respect of the storage of explosives. As such, they repeal a large number of provisions contained in the Explosives Act 1875 ('the 1875 Act') and its subordinate legislation.

Acquisition of explosives is governed by the Control of Explosives Regulations 1991 as amended by the Manufacture and Storage of Explosives Regulations 2005 which require persons acquiring explosives to obtain a certificate from the local police authority. These regulations also apply to the keeping and storage of explosives. The transfer of explosives and associated record keeping is also regulated by these regulations as well as the Placing on the Market and Transfer of Explosives Regulations. Transportation of explosives is regulated by the Packaging of Explosives for Carriage Regulations 1991, the Carriage of Explosives by Road Regulations 1996 and the Carriage of Dangerous Goods (Driver Training) Regulations 1996. Explosives are normally stored for use on site in a licensed store under the control of the local authority.

The use of explosives in construction works is regulated by the CDM 2007. Regulation 30 states:

(1) so far as is reasonably practicable, explosives shall be stored, transported and used safely and securely
(2) without prejudice to Paragraph (1), an explosive charge shall be used or fired only if suitable and sufficient steps have been taken to ensure that no person is exposed to risk of injury from the explosion or from projected or flying material caused thereby

The use of explosives in quarries is separately covered by the Quarries (Explosives) Regulations 1988 with further requirements for shot firers being set out in the Quarries Regulations 1999 (SI No. 2024).

A contractor wishing to store explosives requires a licence to do so. Where only a certain amount of explosives is to be stored, a person can apply to a licensing authority for registration in respect of that storage, instead of seeking a licence for it. The Police or Local Authority should be approached in advance to licence or register the intended place of storage. The Police are likely to be the licensing authority for storage for explosives for which an Acquire and Keep Certificate is required under the Control of Explosives Regulations which would include blasting explosives, accessories and detonators. The Police and Local Authority have powers to licence storage of up to 2 tonnes of explosives, but can only do so where certain conditions are met. It is important therefore to seek the view of the licensing authority for the intended place of storage well in advance of the need so that whatever arrangements are specified can be made.

The HSE issues licences for magazines for explosives which allow the keeping of amounts greater than 2 tonnes. Such a licence is not likely to offer advantage to a short-duration construction contract but would be more suited to an operation such as significant harbour, road or tunnel construction works which might be expected to last for periods running into years.

Explosives might be delivered to site with the intention of using them straight away, or for placement ready for use, as would occur, for example, in the charging of many holes in a large structure to be demolished. Explosives loaded into holes are not regarded as being in storage, but there should be maintained sufficient and adequate security to prevent their unauthorised removal. There is no bar to explosives being stored on behalf of the construction or demolition contractor by some third party at that third party's existing licensed storage place. This third party might be the explosives manufacturer. There would then need to be put in place arrangements for daily deliveries or some sort of call-off system so that explosives would be delivered to the site of intended use only at appropriate times. This would obviate the need for the construction site to be licensed to store explosives. When setting an explosives store, a specified separation distance must be maintained between the store and the buildings and other places not on the site where the storage takes place.

21.2.14 Work at Height Regulations 2005

The Work at Height Regulations 2005 (SI No. 735) (WAHR) amended in 2007 (but amendment not relevant to construction) impose health and safety requirements applicable to all work activity at height not just in the construction industry. Work at height can take place at any location either above or below ground level and includes temporary means of access to and egress from such work. The WAHR implement the requirements of EC Directive 2001/45/EC. The WAHR replaced the provisions in the Construction (Health, Safety and Welfare) Regulations relating to falls, fragile materials and falling objects, the latter set of regulations itself being replaced by CDM 2007.

The regulations impose duties on employers and the self-employed relating to the organisation and planning of work at height by employees, the self-employed and to persons under their control to the extent of that control. The Regulations require that work at height is properly planned, including the selection of the relevant equipment, appropriately supervised and carried out in a reasonably practicably safe manner. Planning must also cover emergency and rescue procedures. Avoidance of adverse weather conditions is a further matter to be covered at the planning stage.

Those working at height should be competent to do so. In accordance with the principles of prevention in Regulation 4 and Schedule 1 of the Management of Health and Safety at Work Regulations 1999, employers shall take cognisance of the risk assessment and shall seek only to carry out such work at height as cannot reasonably and practicably be done otherwise provided also that they take measures to prevent falls likely to lead to injury of the employee. Work at height should preferably be done from an existing workplace but if not with the use of work equipment capable of preventing a fall that failing through the use of equipment to minimise the consequences of this fall.

When selecting equipment for work at height, an employer shall consider the circumstances in which it will be used and give priority to collective protection measures such as the provision of a scaffold working platform over personal protective measures such as rope access equipment, and similarly in minimising the consequences of a fall shall favour collective measures such as a net or airbag over personal measures such as a harness. Detailed requirements for the respective types of equipment are given in Regulation 8 and in the schedules to the Regulations.

Employers are required to ensure that employees do not work on, near or pass close to fragile materials. When these conditions cannot be met, the employer must cover or guard the fragile material or, failing that, provide a means of minimising the consequence of any fall. Prominently placed notices must be posted at the approach to fragile materials or equivalent warnings given.

Employers must, in order of preference, take reasonably practicable steps to prevent objects or materials from falling and causing injury, or, failing that, to prevent injury from falling objects. Objects or materials should not be thrown from height where there is a risk of injury to a person below. Where by the nature of the work a person could still be injured by falling or from falling materials, access to that area should be prevented and the danger area clearly defined.

Safety critical work equipment and workplaces should be inspected once in position and before use and where degradation could occur, at periodic intervals thereafter. Appropriate records of inspections should be made and kept.

Those who work at height are required to report to their employer of any activity or equipment which is defective.

21.2.15 Dangerous Substances and Explosive Atmospheres Regulations 2002

The Dangerous Substances and Explosive Atmospheres Regulations 2002 (SI No. 2776) implement in Great Britain, Council Directive 98/24/EC which sets out requirements for the protection of the health and safety of workers from the risks related to chemical agents at work and Council Directive 99/92/EC on minimum requirements for improving the safety and health of workers potentially at risk from explosive atmospheres.

These Regulations impose requirements for the purpose of eliminating or reducing risks to safety from fire, explosion or other events arising from the hazardous properties of a 'dangerous substance' in connection with work.

'Dangerous substance' is defined by Regulation 2(1) and includes a substance or preparation which is classified as explosive, oxidising, extremely flammable, highly flammable or flammable under the criteria in the *Approved Classification and Labelling Guide* (HSE 2009) also any substance which because of its physical and/or chemical properties behaves as if it were explosive, oxidising, extremely flammable, highly flammable or flammable or any dust, whether in the form of solid particles or fibrous materials or otherwise, which can form an explosive mixture with air or an explosive atmosphere. Dangerous substances can be naturally occurring – for example, methane in a tunnel or other excavation sites.

The duties under the Regulations also extend to self-employed persons.

An employer is required to extend the risk assessment under Regulation 3 of the Management of Health and Safety at Work Regulations 1999 to include a suitable and sufficient assessment of the risks to his or her employees where a dangerous substance is or may be present at the workplace (Regulation 5). 'Risk' in this instance implies fire, explosion or other events arising from the hazardous properties of a dangerous substance.

Employers are required by these Regulations to eliminate or reduce risk so far as is reasonably practicable. Where risk is not eliminated, employers are required, so far as is reasonably practicable and consistent with the risk assessment, to apply measures to control risks and mitigate any detrimental effects.

The parts of the workplace where explosive atmospheres may occur must be classified as hazardous or non-hazardous. Hazardous places must be classified into zones on the basis of the frequency and duration of the occurrence of an explosive atmosphere. The Regulations also require that equipment and protective systems in hazardous places must comply with the requirements of Schedule 3 and, where necessary, hazardous places must be marked with signs at their points of entry in accordance with Schedule 4. The use of mining equipment in a non-mining application such as tunnelling is acceptable provided the dangerous substance (in this case methane) is the same as that for which the equipment was originally designed.

Employers are required to make arrangements for dealing with accidents, incidents and emergencies.

Employers also need to provide employees with precautionary information, instruction and training where a dangerous substance is present at the workplace.

Containers and pipes used at work for dangerous substances must, where not already marked in accordance with the requirements of the legislation listed in Schedule 5, have their contents clearly identified.

Where two or more employers share a workplace in which an explosive atmosphere may occur, the employer responsible for the workplace is to coordinate the implementation of the measures required by these Regulations.

21.2.16 Control of Vibration at Work Regulations 2005

The Control of Vibration at Work Regulations 2005 (CoVAWR) (SI No. 1093) implement in UK legislation, the requirements of the EC Physical Agents (vibration) Directive 2002/44/EC which sets minimum requirements for protecting worker health and safety against exposure to vibration. The Directive and CoVAWR cover exposure to both hand-arm vibration and whole body vibration.

Four 8-hour weighted (A(8)) exposure values are defined in Regulation 4 – for hand-arm vibration a daily exposure action value of $2.5\,m/s^2$ and a daily exposure limit value of $5\,m/s^2$ and for whole body vibration, a daily exposure action value of $0.5\,m/s^2$ and a daily exposure limit value of $1.15\,m/s^2$.

An employer whose employees are at risk from vibration must undertake a suitable and sufficient risk assessment to identify the extent of the risk and the protective measures which are required. Specific requirements for how the assessment is to be undertaken and what it should cover are also set out in this regulation. The assessment should be reviewed regularly and its findings recorded.

As with similar recent legislation, the action required of the employer is the elimination of exposure to the hazard (vibration) if reasonably practicable but if not, reduction of risk to as low a level as reasonably practicable. The latter should be achieved through a programme of organisational and technical measures in accordance with the principles of prevention (Schedule 1 of the Management of Health and Safety at Work Regulations 1999). Methods of reducing exposure suggested in the Regulations include changing the working method, shorter working shifts, task rotation, change of tool, better tool maintenance to reduce emission at source, additional rest periods and as a final resort the use of anti-vibration gloves.

The employer shall ensure that the employees are not exposed to vibration levels above the exposure limit value and, if they are exposed then immediate steps are taken to reduce that exposure to below the exposure limit value, the reason for the limit being exceeded is identified and steps are taken to prevent a recurrence. There is a relaxation for otherwise low-risk activities where vibration levels fluctuate widely, which allows vibration exposure to be averaged over a week rather than over 8 hours, provided additional health surveillance is undertaken.

All employers are required to provide health surveillance for those likely to be exposed above the exposure action value to prevent or to diagnose any vibration-related ill health. Health surveillance records must be kept and when evidence of vibration-related ill health is discovered, the employer should ensure the employee affected is appropriately advised of the situation, that he or she (the employer) reviews the risk assessment in conjunction with a source of occupational health advice, and he or she reassigns the employee affected to other, less hazardous tasks, where appropriate.

Regulation 8 covers the provision of information, instruction and training for those at risk from exposure to vibration.

21.3 Supply of work equipment and materials

21.3.1 Section 6 of HSWA – Other UK legislation relating to machinery

Section 6 of the HSWA has, from the time of its coming into effect, placed extensive duties on any person who designs, manufactures, imports or supplies any article for use at work to ensure that such articles are designed and constructed to be safe and without risks to health, while they are being set, used or maintained. Articles for use at work include plant, machinery or similar equipment. That person must also carry out such testing as may be necessary to meet the requirements of this section of the Act, and must provide all necessary instructional information to accompany the machine to ensure its safe use.

21.3.2 Supply of Machinery (Safety) Regulations 2008

The Supply of Machinery (Safety) Regulations 1992 (SI No. 3073) came into force on 1 January 1993 and implemented the requirements of the Machinery Directive 89/392/EC in UK law. A revised Machinery Directive (42/2006/EC) with a slightly enlarged schedule of essential safety requirements has now been adopted within the EC, and a corresponding revision of the regulations (Supply of Machinery (Safety) Regulations 2008 (SI 2008/1597)) came into force in December 2009.

The regulations incorporate the essential safety requirements of the directive as a schedule accompanying the regulations. The enforcing authority under these regulations in respect of machinery used at work is the HSE.

The regulations define what constitutes 'machinery' and 'partially completed machinery', for example, the base machine of an impact piling rig but without the hammer and leaders. They place duties on the 'responsible person', defined as the manufacturer of that machinery or the manufacturer's authorised representative in the EC or where the manufacturer is from outside the EC and has not appointed a representative within the EC, the person who first supplies the machinery within the EC (this could be a contractor).

The Regulations set out the duties on 'responsible persons', that is, those who place machinery or partly completed machinery on the market or put it into service. The key duties as far as the purchaser of machinery is concerned include ensuring the safety of the machinery which should be done by reference to the essential health and safety requirements contained in the Schedule to the Regulations, the compilation of a technical file and the provision of information necessary for its safe use. In addition, a conformity assessment procedure should have been followed before affixing the CE marking to the product.

Compliance with a relevant harmonised standard is an obvious and important way of demonstrating conformity.

Part 4 of the regulations make further provision about CE marking, whilst Part 5 is concerned with the activities of 'notified bodies', whose function is to assess the conformity of products with the Regulations.

Part 6 makes provision about enforcement.

The regulations make changes to the Lifts Regulations 1997 (S.I. 1997/831) along with consequential changes to avoid overlaps with other pieces of legislation, as well as rectifying some drafting defects in regulations implementing other New Approach Directives.

Requirements for mechanical and electrical equipment for use in potentially explosive atmospheres, such as in tunnels, can be found in the Equipment and Protective Systems Intended for Use in Potentially Explosive Atmospheres Regulations 1996.

21.3.3 Electromagnetic compatibility

Requirements in respect of electromagnetic compatibility (EMC) also arose from an EC product directive and have been incorporated into UK legislation. In the past, requirements in respect of EMC were contained in regulations made under the Wireless Telegraphy Act, until it became a topic related to machinery (product) safety under EC directives.

EMC relates to the electromagnetic disturbance caused by one electrically powered device on another. In general, the effect manifests itself as a malfunction in a control system or as interference in an electromagnetic transmission. Control system malfunction has obvious safety implications. The EMC issues, therefore, relate both to the effects of external electromagnetic interference on a machine and the unwanted electromagnetic disturbances generated by that machine.

EMC is regulated through the EMC Regulations 2005. These are technically complex and it is not intended to cover them in detail in this text. In general, the regulations make it an offence to supply electrical or electronic apparatus which does not conform to the specified protection requirements – essential requirements requiring the apparatus not to generate excessive electromagnetic disturbance or fall below a prescribed level of immunity to electromagnetic disturbance from an external source.

Machines conforming to relevant European CEN standards for machinery safety should already have been shown to conform to the EMC standards by the manufacturer.

21.3.4 Lifts directive

Lifts are frequently installed in buildings as part of construction work, in commercial premises such as offices, shops or healthcare premises, in an 'at work' situation or in private premises for domestic use. In both cases the supply of lifts (as defined in the regulations) is regulated under the Lifts Directive 95/16/EC which has been incorporated into UK legislation through the Lifts Regulations 1997. The Directive is a product directive so, again, the essential safety requirements relate to the safety of the product.

A lift is defined as an appliance serving specific levels and having a car moving along rigid guides or along a fixed course and inclined at an angle of at least 15 degrees to the horizontal and intended for the transport of persons and/or goods. The definition distinguishes lifts from other equipment for lifting persons or goods which is subject to the Lifting Operations and Lifting Equipment Regulations 1998.

The enforcing authority for the regulations is the HSE and otherwise the Department for Business, Innovation and Skills. The regulations came into force in July 1999 and apply to all lifts and safety components for lifts placed on the market from that date. Earlier legislation on lifts is revoked. There are transitional provisions in the regulations relating to lifts supplied under that earlier legislation.

The general duties under the regulations apply to the company which places the lift or safety component on the market or puts it into service and require conformity with the essential safety requirements, either directly or through conformity with the relevant harmonised CEN standards. There is a duty for the transfer of information between the lift installer and those responsible for construction of works into which the lift is to be installed. The regulations also set out procedures for assessing conformity with the essential safety requirements. Because of the somewhat complex nature of these requirements, anyone concerned with supplying or installing lifts is advised to consult the text of the regulations. Any overlap with the requirements in the PUWER should also be considered.

21.3.5 Construction Products Regulations 1991

The Construction Products Regulations 1991 as amended in 1994, and other 'product' regulations were made for the purpose of ensuring the free movement of goods within the European Community and not for worker protection purposes. The regulations are not enforced by the HSE but by local authority Trading Standards officers.

The safety of construction products – materials for permanent incorporation in both building and civil engineering works – is covered by the Construction Products Regulations 1991 as amended in 1994. The regulations apply to construction products which are products for incorporation in a permanent manner in construction work. The regulations also include provisions in respect of 'minor part products' which are products which play a minor part only in respect of health and safety.

One of the main requirements of the regulations is that it is an offence to supply a construction product (other than a minor part product), unless that product has such characteristics that the construction work in which the material is to be included if properly designed and built, satisfies the relevant essential requirements where and to the extent that the works are subject to regulations containing such requirements, for example, the Building Regulations. It is also an offence to supply minor part products which have not been manufactured in accordance with an 'acknowledged rule of technology' which essentially means

in accordance with currently agreed good practice which is taken to be the appropriate British or CEN Standard.

The essential requirements are set out in a schedule to the regulations and relate to the finished structure rather than the product as such. Despite this indirect way of referencing the essential requirements, any structure cannot meet the essential requirements unless its constituent products do so. The essential requirements of the structure include its mechanical resistance and stability under both construction loads and, when in use, safety in case of fire which covers both fire resistance and durability. Further requirements include the need for the construction work not to present a risk to health or hygiene through the emission of toxic or otherwise hazardous material from the construction work. The construction work must not pose a risk of accidents during service, such as slipping, falling or electrocution. The construction works must be designed and built in such a way that noise emissions are not a nuisance or a risk to health and that energy requirements for heating and cooling are minimised.

Construction products intended for export outside the European Community and products which are not supplied new are excepted from the requirements.

All products bearing the CE mark are deemed to be supplied lawfully and there are extensive requirements for procedures to be gone through before this mark can be affixed by the manufacturer. These procedures include compliance with relevant national standards (BS) or European technical approval or an appropriate attestation procedure.

There are requirements in the regulations relating to the CE marking of construction products. Such marking is not compulsory. It is an offence to supply products which are CE marked but do not confirm to the requirements of the regulations.

The enforcing authorities have a range of powers in respect of non-conforming products. They can issue suspension notices prohibiting the supply to the market of products which do not satisfy the requirements of the regulations. Similarly, a supplier can be required to publish a public warning in respect of a product which does not satisfy the regulations.

21.3.6 Low voltage directive

This product directive applies to the safety of electrical equipment supplied for normal industrial and domestic use and which is designed for use between 50 and 1000 volts ac (75–1500 volts dc). It is implemented in the UK through the Electrical Equipment (Safety) Regulations 1994.

The regulations apply to anyone who supplies electrical equipment in the course of business. The fundamental requirement is for electrical equipment, when connected to the electricity supply system, to be safe through being constructed in accordance with good engineering practice and in accordance with the 'safety objectives' specified in the directive and regulations. In addition, equipment should be CE marked, which can only be done after the appropriate declaration of conformity and technical documentation have been compiled.

21.3.7 Registration of tower cranes

Following a number of recent spectacular crane collapses, regulations have been introduced – the Notification of Conventional Tower Cranes Regulations 2010 (as amended 2010) to establish a statutory register of tower cranes. They came into effect in April 2010. The requirements apply to 'conventional tower cranes' as defined in the Regulations. These requirements are restricted to requirements on the employers of those using the crane about notifying HSE of basic information about the location, ownership and the employer using the crane within 14 days of the initial thorough examination on erection and following any subsequent thorough examination of the crane. In addition HSE should be notified of any defects identified during these examinations.

21.4 General workplace safety requirements

21.4.1 Workplace (Health, Safety and Welfare) Regulations 1992

These regulations which, in addition to transposing an EC Directive, consolidate a considerable number of former parts of health and safety legislation, apply to all work premises except construction sites at which the CDM 2007 apply, means of transport and sites where minerals extraction or exploration are carried out. (Agriculture and forestry are exempt from most requirements.) The regulations are concerned with good housekeeping and have many practical provisions. Whilst they do not apply to construction sites, the CDM 2007 extend designers duties to cover the health and safety risks arising from the aspects of workplace safety relating to the internal environment set out in the Workplace Regulations.

The following provisions regulate the internal environment.

- Ventilation must be effective in enclosed areas, and any plant used for this purpose must incorporate warning devices to signal breakdowns which might endanger health or safety.

- Lighting must be suitable and sufficient.

- A reasonable temperature must be maintained.

- Room dimensions have to allow adequate space to work in and to move about freely.

- Suitable arrangements must be made, including adequate seating, in the places where employees carry out their work.

21.4.1.1 Accident prevention

The following provisions relate to the prevention of accidents.

- Safe passage of pedestrians. and vehicles must be arranged.

- Windows and skylights must open and close safely, and be arranged so that people may not fall out of them. They must be capable of being cleaned safely. Windows and transport doors and partitions must be appropriately marked and protected against breakage.

- Doors, gates and escalators have to be of sound construction and fitted with appropriate safety devices.

- Measures must be taken to prevent people falling, and to guard against them being hit by falling objects.

- Floors and other surfaces need to be even, free of obstructions and not prone to slipping.

21.4.1.2 Provision of facilities

The regulations require the provision of various welfare facilities including:

- toilets and changing rooms

- washing, eating and drinking facilities

- rest facilities, with arrangements made for non-smokers and pregnant women or nursing mothers

21.4.1.3 Maintenance

Maintenance is also covered by the Regulations.

- Workplaces, furniture and fittings have to be kept clean.

- Waste materials must not be allowed to accumulate.

- Premises, plant and equipment are to be subject to suitable maintenance regimes.

21.4.2 Health and Safety (Display Screen Equipment) Regulations 1992

The regulations apply wherever there is a 'user' who operates 'display screen equipment'. The statutory definitions of these terms are important.

- 'User' means an employee who habitually uses display screen equipment 'as a significant part of his normal work'. (Self-employed users are termed 'operators' for these purposes.)

- 'Display screen equipment' means equipment used for the display of text, numbers or graphics.

Employers therefore need to make an initial determination whether staff do carry out work which is covered by these terms. If so, the requirements summarised later will need to be met.

21.4.2.1 Analysis of workstation

The regulations use the term 'workstation' to mean the display equipment itself, any optional accessories that go with it, any keyboard, disc drive, telephone, modem, printer, document holder, work chair, desk, work surface or other peripheral item, and – in very general terms – the immediate working environment around the equipment.

Workstations must be analysed for any risks to health and safety they might present to users, or other operators, and the analysis must be reviewed and up-dated where appropriate. (The HSE Guidance Note discusses the possible risks, and concentrates on visual fatigue, stress and postural problems.) Risks identified are to be reduced to the lowest extent reasonably practicable.

21.4.2.2 Requirements for workstations

All workstations must meet the standards set out in a schedule to the regulations. Three main aspects are covered.

- 'Equipment': design and conditions of use of screens, keyboards, desks or work surface, and chairs.
- 'Environment': space requirements, lighting, reflections, glare, noise, heat, humidity and radiation.
- 'Interface between computer and operator/user': suitability of software and systems.

21.4.2.3 Welfare of users

Work routines of users are to be planned to provide periodic interruptions of display screen equipment work by breaks or changes to different activities.

Staff are entitled to have (at the employer's expense) initial eye and eyesight tests, and subsequent tests at regular intervals or when experiencing visual difficulties associated with work on display screen equipment. Employees are entitled to receive special spectacles where these are needed to correct vision defects at the viewing distance used for the work involved and when their normal spectacles cannot be used.

21.4.2.4 Information and training

Appropriate health and safety training has to be given to existing users and to employees who are going to become users: modifications to a workstation may necessitate additional training.

Information on safety measures is to be given to users and operators, including information about entitlements to free testing and special spectacles.

21.4.3 Fire safety

Fire legislation was extensive and was located in numerous statutes and statutory instruments. Information on requirements could be found under the Buildings Regulations, fire certification requirements under the Fire Precautions Act 1971. Fire regulation was reviewed to simplify and consolidate the various requirements and the result of that review is the Regulatory Reform (Fire Safety) Order 2005 (SI No. 1541).

This reforms the law relating to fire safety in non-domestic premises in England and Wales only. It replaces fire certification under the Fire Precautions Act 1971 with a general duty to ensure, so far as is reasonably practicable, the safety of employees, a general duty, in relation to non-employees to take such fire precautions as may reasonably be required in the circumstances to ensure that premises are safe and a duty to carry out a risk assessment. The Order imposes a number of specific duties in relation to the fire precautions to be taken. The Order provides for the enforcement of the Order, appeals, offences and connected matters. It amends or repeals other primary legislation concerning fire safety to take account of the new system and provides for minor and other consequential amendments, repeals and revocations. The Order also gives effect

in England and Wales to a number of EC Directives including Directive 89/391/EEC on the introduction of measures to encourage improvements in the safety and health of workers at work ('the Framework Directive'). The Order applies to most non-domestic premises. The main duty-holder is the 'responsible person' as defined in article 3. The duties on the responsible person are extended to any person who has, to any extent, control of the premises to the extent of their control (article 5).

Part 2 imposes duties on the responsible person in relation to fire safety in premises. Article 23 imposes various duties on employees.

Part 3 provides for enforcement. The enforcing authority is defined in article 25. Articles 27 and 28 set out the powers of inspectors. Articles 29 to 31 provide for the service of alterations, enforcement and prohibition notices in certain circumstances.

Part 4 (articles 32 to 36) provides for offences and appeals. Part 5 (articles 37 to 53) provides for miscellaneous matters, including fire-fighters' switches for luminous tube signs (article 37), maintenance of measures provided to the ensure the safety of firefighters (article 38), civil liability for breach of statutory duty by an employer (article 39), special requirements for licensed premises (article 42) and consultation by other authorities (article 46).

Schedule 1 sets out the matters to be taken into account in carrying out a risk assessment (Parts 1 and 2), the general principles to be applied in implementing fire safety measures (Part 3) and the special measures to be taken in relation to dangerous substances (Part 4). Schedule 2 amends various enactments, including amendments to limit the scope for other public authorities to attach conditions to licences in respect of fire precautions to be taken in premises and amendments to local acts to remove reference to fire safety. The remaining amendments in Schedule 2 and those in 3 are minor or consequential. Schedules 4 and 5 contain repeals and revocations.

The Fire (Scotland) Act 2005 received Royal Assent on 1 April 2005. Parts 1, 2, 4 and 5 of the Act commenced in August 2005. Part 3 introduces a new fire safety regime for non-domestic premises and came into force on 1 October 2006. It replaced the Fire Precautions Act 1971 and the Fire Precautions (Workplace) Regulations 1997, as amended. Fire certificates are no longer required and the fire safety regime is based on the principle of risk assessment (similar to the Fire Precautions (Workplace) Regulations).

Construction sites may be subject to two, and in some cases, more, enforcing authorities. HSE will be responsible for the enforcement of the Regulatory Reform (Fire Safety) Order 2005 and the Fire (Scotland) Act 2005 in relation to general fire precautions within the curtilage of the site. Fire & Rescue Authorities will enforce the rules for accommodation (e.g. site offices and sleeping accommodation) not within the site curtilage. General fire precautions and fire risks that arise from the construction process are dealt with under the CDM 2007. Duty holders are required to ensure suitable and sufficient steps (so far as is reasonably practicable) are taken to prevent the risk of injury to any person during construction work from fire and explosion. Measures must be taken to reduce the likelihood of fire due to work process, including storage. Duty holders are also required to have, in the event of danger:

- a means of raising the alarm

- means of fire fighting

- a means of escape that is clear from obstruction, have emergency lighting and protected where necessary

- and have emergency procedures and training

The Regulatory Reform (Fire Safety) Order 2005 and the Fire (Scotland) Act 2005 have revoked the Fire Certificates (Special Premises) Regulations.

The chapter *Construction health and safety I* explains the system of health and safety legislation in the UK and how it is enforced.

References

Health and Safety Executive. *A guide to the Work in Compressed Air Regulations 1996. Guidance on regulations* (L96), London, UK, HSE Books, 1996. Available for download: http://books.hse.gov.uk/hse/public/saleproduct.jsf?catalogueCode=9780717611201 (last accessed 21 September, 2010).

Health and Safety Executive. *Approved classification and labelling guide. Chemicals (Hazard Information and Packaging for Supply) Regulations 2009 (CHIP 4). Approved Guide.* (L131), London, UK, HSE Books, 2009. Available for download: http://books.hse.gov.uk/hse/public/saleproduct.jsf?catalogueCode=9780717663705 (last accessed 21 September, 2010).

World Health Organisation. *Determination of airborne fibre concentrations. A recommended method, by phase-contrast optical microscopy (membrane filter method)*, Geneva, WHO (World Health Organisation), 1997.

Referenced legislation, regulations and standards

Asbestos (Licensing) Regulations 1983
Asbestos (Prohibitions) Regulations 1992
Carriage of Dangerous Goods and Use of Transportable Pressure Equipment Regulations 2004
Carriage of Dangerous Goods (Driver Training) Regulations 1996
Carriage of Explosives by Road Regulations 1996
Chemicals (Hazard Information and Packaging for Supply) Regulations 2002
Confined Spaces Regulations 1997
Construction (Design and Management) Regulations 2007 (CDM 2007)
Construction (Head Protection) Regulations 1989
Construction (Health, Safety and Welfare) Regulations 1996
Construction Products Regulations 1991 as amended in 1994
Control of Asbestos at Work Regulations 2002
Control of Asbestos at Work Regulations 2006
Control of Explosives Regulations 1991
Control of Lead at Work Regulations 1998

Control of Lead at Work Regulations 2002
Control of Noise at Work Regulations 2005
Control of Substances Hazardous to Health Regulations 2002
Control of Vibration at Work Regulations 2005
Dangerous Substances and Explosive Atmospheres Regulations 2002
Directive 76/769/EEC of 27 July 1976 on the approximation of the laws, regulations and administrative provisions of the Member States relating to restrictions on the marketing and use of certain dangerous substances and preparation. *OJ*, **L262**, 27/09/1976, pp.201–203 (*Marketing and Use Directive*)
Directive 83/477/EEC of 19 September 1983 on the protection of workers from the risks related to exposure to asbestos at work. *OJ*, **L263**, 29/08/1983, pp.25–32
Directive 89/391/EEC of 12 June 1989 on the introduction of measures to encourage improvements in the safety and health of workers at work. *OJ*, **L183**, 29/06/1989, p. 1–8. (*Framework Directive*)
Directive 90/394/EEC of 28 June 1990 on the protection of workers from the risks related to exposure to carcinogens at work. *OJ*, **L196**, 26/07/1990, pp.1–7
Directive 95/16/EC of 29 June 1995 on the approximation of the laws of the Member States relating to lifts. *OJ*, **L213**, 07/09/1995, pp.01–31 (*Lifts Directive*)
Directive 98/24/EC of 7 April 1998 on the protection of the health and safety of workers from the risks related to chemical agents at work. *OJ*, **L131**, 05/05/1998, pp.11–23
Directive 98/37/EC of the European Parliament and of the Council of 22 June 1998 on the approximation of the laws of the Member States relating to machinery. *OJ*, **L207**, 23/07/98, pp.01–46 (*Machinery Directive*)
Directive 1999/92/EC of the European Parliament and of the Council of 16 December 1999 on minimum requirements for improving the safety and health protection of workers potentially at risk from explosive atmosphere. *OJ*, **L23**, 28/01/2000, pp.57–64
Directive 2002/44/EC of the European Parliament and of the Council of 25 June 2002 on the minimum health and safety requirements regarding the exposure of workers to the risks arising from physical agents (vibration). *OJ*, **L177**, 06/07/2002, pp.13–19. (*EC Physical Agents (vibration) Directive*)
Directive 2003/10/EC of the European Parliament and of the Council of 6 February 2003 on the minimum health and safety requirements regarding the exposure of workers to the risks arising from physical agents (noise). *OJ*, **L42**, 15/02/2003, pp.38–44
Directive 2006/42/EC of the European Parliament and of the Council of 17 May 2006 on machinery, and amending Directive 95/16/EC (recast). *OJ*, **L157**, 09/06/2006, pp.24–86 (*revised Machinery Directive*)
Directive 2006/95/EC of the European Parliament and of the Council of 12 December 2006 on the harmonisation of the laws of Member States relating to electrical equipment designed for use within certain voltage limits. *OJ*, **L374**, 27/12/2006, pp.10–19. (*Low Voltage Directive*)
Diving at Work Regulations 1997
Electrical Equipment (Safety) Regulations 1994
Electricity at Work Regulations 1989
Electromagnetic Compatibility Regulations 2005
Equipment and Protective Systems Intended for Use in Potentially Explosive Atmospheres Regulations 1996
Explosives Act 1875

Factories Act 1961
Fire Precautions Act 1971
Fire Precautions (Workplace) Regulations 1997
Fire (Scotland) Act 2005
Health and Safety (Display Screen Equipment) Regulations 1992
Health and Safety (Miscellaneous Amendments) Regulations 2002
Ionising Radiations Regulations 1999
Lifting Operations and Lifting Equipment Regulations 1998 (LOLER)
Lifts Regulations 1997
Management of Health and Safety at Work Regulations 1999
Manual Handling Operations Regulations 1992
Manufacture and Storage of Explosives Regulations 2005
Noise at Work Regulations 1989
Notification of Conventional Tower Cranes Regulations
Packaging of Explosives for Carriage Regulations 1991
Personal Protective Equipment at Work Regulations 1992
Personal Protective Equipment (EC Directive) Regulations 1992 as amended
Pressure Systems and Transportable Gas Containers Regulations 1989
Pressure Systems Safety Regulations 2000
Pressure Systems Safety Regulations 2002
Provision and Use of Work Equipment Regulations 1998 (PUWER)
Quarries (Explosives) Regulations 1988
Quarries Regulations 1999
Regulatory Reform (Fire Safety) Order 2005

Supply of Machinery (Safety) Regulations 1992
Supply of Machinery (Safety) Regulations 2008
Wireless Telegraphy Act 2006
Work at Height Regulations 2005 (amended in 2007)
Work in Compressed Air Regulations 1996

Further reading

Health and Safety Executive. *Ionising Radiations Regulations 1999. Approved code of practice and guidance* (L121), London, UK, HSE Books, 2000. Available for download: http://books.hse.gov.uk/hse/public/saleproduct.jsf?catalogueCode=9780717617463 (last accessed 21 September, 2010).

McAleenan, C. and Oloke, D. (eds). *ICE manual of health and safety in construction,*, London, UK, Thomas Telford Ltd, 2010.

Websites

British Standards Institution (BSI); www.bsigroup.com
Department for Business, Enterprise and Regulatory Reform (BERR); www.bis.gov.uk
Health and Safety Executive (HSE); www.hse.gov.uk
HSE, COSHH; www.hse.gov.uk/coshh/
HSE, Radiation protection publications; www.hse.gov.uk/radiation/ionising/publications.htm
Institution of Engineering and Technology (IEE); www.theiet.org
World Health Organisation (WHO); www.who.int

Chapter 22

Insolvency in construction

Richard Davis Pinsent Masons LLP Solicitors, London, UK
Alison Cull Pinsent Masons LLP Solicitors, London, UK

Insolvency law is concerned either with a structured approach to business recovery or with the distribution of a debtor's estate among its creditors as a general body. There are two main corporate procedures: administration provides a breathing space for the company to consider its options free from creditor pressure; liquidation is the classic insolvency procedure whereby a company is closed down and ultimately dissolved. Insolvency law lays down an order of priority for payment of creditors. Secured creditors with a fixed charge are entitled to enforce their claims against the secured assets outside the formal procedures. Insolvency is not normally regarded as a breach of contract. In construction, potential damage resulting from insolvency is managed by the extensive termination clauses in the standard forms and security required from companies in the supply chain. Some protection is also available through contract terms dealing with set-off and title to goods. Insolvency practitioners often facilitate the completion of contracts by procuring novations whereby a contractor enters into a new contract on similar terms to that of the insolvent party. The principal sources of law are the Insolvency Act 1986 and the Insolvency Rules 1986 both of which have been heavily amended. The Rules are to be consolidated in 2011.

doi: 10.1680/mocl.40878.0347

CONTENTS

22.1 Informal insolvency

Insolvency means the inability to pay debts. It can be formal or informal. Formal insolvency means the implementation of one of the recognised procedures, which are considered later. Informal insolvency occurs when a person fails one of the statutory tests. These vary depending whether the person is a company, an individual or a partnership.

22.1.1 Cash flow and balance sheet tests

There are two alternative tests of insolvency for limited companies. The first is known as the 'cash flow' test: 'A company is deemed unable to pay its debts … if it is proved to the satisfaction of the court that the company is unable to pay its debts as they fall due': Section 123(1)(e) of the Insolvency Act 1986, *Re Cheyne Finance (No. 2)* [2008] B.C.L.C. 741. The second is called the 'balance sheet' test: 'A company is also unable to pay its debts if it is proved to the satisfaction of the court that the value of the company's assets is less than the amount of its liabilities, taking into account its contingent and prospective liabilities': Section 123(2) of the 1986 Act, *BNY Corporate Trustee v. Eurosail* [2010] EWHC 2005. The balance sheet test adopts different criteria from those used on a statutory audit because full account is taken of liabilities which are 'contingent and prospective'. An example of a contingent liability is a guarantee given by a parent company: unless and until the subsidiary is in breach of contract with the beneficiary, the parent's liability remains contingent. Another could be a claim under a final account: *Hadden Construction v.*

Midway Services [2008] SLT (Sh Ct) 12. A prospective liability might be a claim for damages for defective work. The test requires that an estimate be made of both liabilities however difficult this may be.

Even if a company fails one of the tests, it may be able to trade out of its difficulties and return to solvency. For example, a property developer may fail the balance sheet test if its portfolio is re-valued downwards but remain able to pay its debts as they fall due with the support of its bankers. It can then wait until the market improves and its properties can be re-valued upwards. Similarly, a company with temporary cash flow difficulties might be supported by its lender or by its creditors agreeing an informal moratorium to allow its cash flow to be restored. On the other hand, informal insolvency may simply be the prelude to a formal insolvency procedure. The key to avoiding formal insolvency is to continue to pay debts as they fall due.

22.1.2 Statutory demands

A creditor can prove informal insolvency by serving a statutory demand at the registered office of the company. If payment is not received within 21 days and the debt cannot be disputed *bona fide* on substantial grounds, the debtor is deemed to be insolvent under Section 123(1)(a) of the 1986 Act. Even in the absence of a statutory demand, the mere fact of non-payment can give rise to the inference of inability to pay unless the debtor has a *bona fide* defence: *Re Taylor's Industrial Flooring* [1990] BCC 44. That case concerned a claim by a plant hire company for recovery of invoiced amounts from a subcontractor who argued that the money was not due as its credit period had yet to expire. This defence was rejected on a finding of fact and a winding up order was made. Otherwise the creditor will have to bring evidence that the debtor is unable to pay its debts or ask the court to infer insolvency from the surrounding facts: see for example *MacPlant Services v. Contract Lifting Services* [2009] SC 125.

An individual is insolvent under Section 267 of the 1986 Act where he or she owes a liquidated sum payable immediately or at some certain, future time and it is a debt which the individual appears either to be unable or to have no reasonable prospect of being able to pay. Inability to pay can be proved either after service of a statutory demand or where execution has been levied on a judgment and returned unsatisfied: Section 268 of the 1986 Act.

A partnership can be wound up as an unregistered company on the ground that the partnership is unable to pay its debts under Section 221(5) of the 1986 Act. Pursuant to the Insolvent Partnerships Order as amended 1994, a partnership can also go into administration or enter a voluntary arrangement. A partnership cannot, however, be placed in administrative receivership although individual partners can be made bankrupt or agree an individual voluntary arrangement (IVA) with their creditors.

22.2 Formal insolvency

The most common procedures of formal insolvency for companies are liquidation, administration, and company voluntary arrangement (CVA); and for individuals, bankruptcy and IVA.

22.2.1 Liquidation

Liquidation is of two kinds: voluntary and compulsory. There are two types of voluntary liquidation: members' and creditors' (see **Figure 1**).

22.2.1.1 Members' voluntary liquidation

A members' voluntary liquidation is not strictly an insolvency procedure. It is most often used on group reorganisations for tax reasons. The directors have to swear a statutory declaration that the company will be able to pay its debts in full with interest within a maximum of 12 months after the start of the

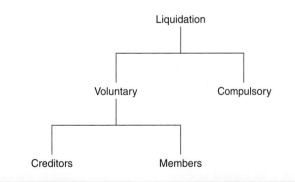

Figure 1 Forms of liquidation

liquidation. The shareholders, also known as members, can then pass a resolution to wind up the company and appoint a liquidator. If it turns out that the company cannot pay its debts in full within that time, the members' voluntary liquidation will be converted into a creditors' voluntary liquidation (*Re William Thorpe* (1989) 5 BCC 156), and the directors can be liable for a fine or even imprisonment if their original statutory declaration was not made on reasonable grounds: Section 89(4) of the 1986 Act. Members' voluntary liquidation is usually excluded from the list of insolvency events entitling the parties to terminate a construction contract.

22.2.1.2 Creditors' voluntary liquidation

Creditors' voluntary liquidation is the most common form of winding up. It is initiated by the directors convening a board meeting at which they resolve that the company should cease trading and call separate meetings of shareholders and creditors under Section 98 of the 1986 Act. The shareholders then pass a resolution that the company be wound up and appoint an insolvency practitioner as liquidator. The directors prepare a Statement of Affairs for the creditors who may either confirm the shareholders' nominee or appoint another insolvency practitioner as liquidator instead. Voting for this purpose is carried out by reference to the amount of the creditors' debts. In construction cases, this can be a contentious area since the directors may feel that a creditor's claim is invalid or that the company has a cross-claim which equals or exceeds it. Where the creditor's claim is unliquidated, it is the duty of the chairman of the creditors' meeting to place an estimated value on it for voting purposes. Not uncommonly, the estimated value is set at a nominal sum.

22.2.1.3 Compulsory liquidation

Compulsory liquidations are commenced by the issue of a winding up petition against the company. A petition will usually be filed by a creditor, but it is also open to the company, certain shareholders or the directors to do so. A petition can be presented on the ground that a company is unable to pay its debts. This can be shown by failure to comply with a statutory demand for payment of a debt exceeding £750 or by showing that a company's liabilities exceed its assets. The consequences of a winding up petition being filed are that disposals of property will be invalid from the date of filing the petition if a winding up order is ultimately made (see section 22.4.7). Hence, a company's bank account will be frozen and cheques dishonoured immediately.

22.2.1.4 Winding up procedure

The procedure is relatively simple. The petition is listed for hearing on a date about 6 weeks after presentation at court and is served at the registered office of the company. The petitioning creditor must allow at least 7 business days to expire after service of the petition before arranging for it to be advertised in the *London Gazette*. The advertisement must be placed at least 7 business days before the hearing. The court is prepared to waive procedural defects in certain circumstances. Other creditors are entitled to serve notice on the petitioner indicating their intention to support or oppose the petition. Where the petition is opposed, it is usually adjourned so as to allow adequate time for submissions to be made. Where the debt can be disputed *bona fide* on substantial grounds and the company is not insolvent, the court may be prepared to grant an injunction restraining the advertisement of the petition, or preventing it being issued in the first place. Even where the debt is disputed, the court has jurisdiction to make a winding up order in exceptional circumstances: *Lacontha Foundation v. GBI Investments* [2010] EWHC 37, which concerned the construction, financing, maintenance and operation of an underground gas storage plant. In that case the company was not trading and could not suffer prejudice by being placed in liquidation.

22.2.1.5 Conduct of the liquidation

On a winding up order being made, the Official Receiver (a government official) assumes office as liquidator. Where there are assets, a meeting of creditors will be convened to consider whether an insolvency practitioner should be appointed in his place. An insolvency practitioner can also be appointed where a creditor obtains an order that the company should be placed in provisional liquidation pending the hearing of the petition. This occurs where the court is satisfied that the company's property would otherwise be seriously prejudiced. A compulsory liquidation follows the same course as a creditors' voluntary liquidation.

The directors are replaced by a liquidator who acts as an agent for the company. Any receivers appointed before the liquidation remain in office but they can no longer act as the company's agent. The role of the liquidator is primarily to:

- identify and safeguard the assets of the company
- deal with property claims by third parties, for example, where goods are supplied subject to retention of title
- value and sell the company's property
- invite creditors to submit details of their money claims (known as 'proofs of debt') and adjudicate them
- distribute the net proceeds of sale to the creditors in accordance with an order of priority known as 'the statutory scheme'.

In addition, the liquidator will investigate the conduct of the directors and, if appropriate, file a report on their fitness to act as such in the future and pursue claims to recover any property of the company misappropriated in the run up to the liquidation. A liquidator can also compel the production of documents and obtain an order for the oral examination of the directors in court: Section 236 of the 1986 Act.

22.2.1.6 Dissolution

When the liquidation process has been completed, the liquidator files a final account and return with the Registrar of Companies

and the company is deemed to be dissolved 3 months later: Section 201 of the 1986 Act. It is possible for the liquidator or an interested person to apply to the court under Part 31 of the Companies Act 2006 for an order restoring the company to the register in certain situations, for example, where an asset comes to light after the dissolution. On dissolution, any property which had not been distributed by the liquidator is forfeited to the Crown as *bona vacantia*. Such property automatically revests in the company if the dissolution is set aside and the company restored to the register.

22.2.2 Administration

Administration provides a breathing space for the company to consider its options: usually the objective is to rescue the business by keeping the company and its undertaking intact wherever possible. An administrator can be appointed by:

- the company or its directors,
- the holder of a qualifying floating charge (QFC), or
- the court.

22.2.2.1 Appointment by the company

The directors or the company must give 5 business days' prior written notice of their intention to appoint an administrator to any QFC-holder and to other prescribed persons (such as a sheriff charged with execution or other legal process against the company, a person who is known to have distrained against the company or its property and the supervisor of a CVA). Although the holder of a QFC can no longer prevent the appointment of an administrator by the court, he can prevent the appointment of an administrator by the company or its directors, as after receiving their notice of intention to appoint out of court, he can pre-empt them by himself appointing an administrator (or, if he has a QFC predating the Enterprise Act 2002, an administrative receiver).

A company or its directors may not appoint an administrator if:

(1) within the previous 12 months:
  (a) an administration of the company at the instance of the company or its directors has come to an end;
  (b) a voluntary arrangement has ended prematurely (for example, because the company has defaulted in making payments due under the voluntary arrangement); or
  (c) a moratorium under Schedule A1 of the Insolvency Act 1986 has ended without a voluntary arrangement having been approved; or
(2) a winding up petition or administration application is pending; or
(3) an administrative receiver is in office.

22.2.2.2 Appointment by a QFC-holder

A QFC is defined as a floating charge over the whole or substantially the whole of the company's property which is created by a document which states that paragraph 14 of Schedule B1 to the Insolvency Act 1986 applies or which purports to empower the charge holder to appoint an administrator or an administrative receiver of the company. The holder of a QFC must give 2 business days' prior written notice of its intention to appoint an administrator to the holder of any prior ranking QFC, unless the holder of that prior charge consents in writing. A QFC-holder may not appoint an administrator if the charge is not enforceable or either a provisional liquidator or an administrative receiver has already been appointed to the company.

Schedule B1 of the Insolvency Act 1986 prescribes the formalities which must be followed in order to appoint an administrator without a court order, whether by the holder of a QFC or the company or its directors. These formalities relate largely to the giving of notice and to the filing, form and contents of supporting documents. If the company or its directors are proposing to appoint an administrator, the directors must swear a statutory declaration that the company is, or is likely to become, unable to pay its debts. This does not apply to an appointment by a QFC-holder.

22.2.2.3 Appointment by the court

The court may only appoint an administrator if satisfied that the company is, or is likely to become, unable to pay its debts and that the administration order is reasonably likely to achieve the statutory purpose of administration set out in paragraph 3 of Schedule B1 to the Insolvency Act 1986. The applicant must notify any person who has appointed or is in a position to appoint an administrative receiver or any person who could appoint an administrator of his intention to appoint an administrator.

22.2.2.4 Criteria for appointment

The relevant test which must be satisfied before an administrator can be appointed (whether the appointment is to be made by court order or one of the out-of-court routes described earlier) can be sub-divided into three parts: the primary purpose, the secondary purpose and the fallback purpose.

The primary purpose is to rescue the company as a going concern and not to sell the company's business and assets to a third party. The secondary purpose is to achieve a better result for the company's creditors as a whole than would be likely to be achieved on a winding up (for example, by the administrator effecting a sale of the company's business and assets to a third party). The administrator can seek to achieve the secondary purpose if he believes that the primary purpose is not reasonably practicable or that the secondary purpose would achieve a better result for the creditors as a whole. The fallback purpose is to realise the company's property in order to make a distribution to one or more of the company's secured and/or preferential creditors. The fallback purpose will only apply if the administrator believes that neither the primary nor the secondary purpose is reasonably practicable and that no unnecessary harm will be caused to the interests of creditors as a whole. In practice, the secondary purpose is the most commonly used.

22.2.2.5 Consequences of appointment

After a company enters administration, the company cannot be wound up, legal proceedings cannot be taken against it, and a receiver cannot be appointed by any charge holder or other steps taken to enforce security without the consent of the administrator or permission of the court. Permission to bring proceedings is unlikely to be granted in the absence of special circumstances: *Re Atlantic Computers* [1992] 1 All ER 476. It has been held that adjudication is a 'proceeding' within Section 11(3) of the Act: *Straume v. Bradlor Developments* [2000] BCC 333.

22.2.2.6 Powers and duties of the administrator

Once an administrator has been appointed he will take over the day-to-day management of the company from the directors. Alternatively, he may immediately complete a pre-packaged sale. The term refers to 'an arrangement under which the sale of all or part of a company's business or assets is negotiated with a purchaser prior to the appointment of an administrator, and the administrator effects the sale immediately on, or shortly after, his appointment' (*Statement of Insolvency Practice 16* (SIP16), para.1). SIP16 lists seventeen categories of information which ought to be disclosed to creditors in cases of pre-packaged sales. It has been approved judicially: *Re Kayley Vending* [2009] BCC 578. The administrator needs to be satisfied that the value obtained is higher than realistically achievable under any other scenario. This can be difficult as, by definition, he is not able to test the market to establish the true level of interest.

Trading with a company in administration is not entirely free from insolvency risk. It is advisable to take precautions by minimising credit. In most cases post-administration liabilities to creditors will have priority in a subsequent liquidation. Rent falling due during the period of the administration has, for example, been treated as an administration expense: *Goldacre v. Nortel Networks* [2010] BCC 299. Problems may arise, however, in the event that there are not enough assets from which to meet all post-administration claims in full. An administrator has wide powers of management, including the power to terminate ongoing contracts, provided he acts in the interests of the creditors as a whole: *BLV Reality v. Batten* [2009] EHWC 2994.

An administrator has the same powers as a liquidator to call for the production of documents from company officers. In *Cowlishaw and Wong v. O&D Building Contractors* [2009] EWHC 2445 the administrators of a property developer largely failed in an application under section 236 of the Insolvency Act 1986 for production of a range of documents from the contractor. Before the administration, the contractor had suspended work for non-payment and obtained an adjudication decision. There had as yet been no termination. Simplifying the facts, the partly built property was the employer's only significant asset. The administrators claimed they needed access to the documents to help them decide whether to sell the development in its incomplete state or to build out. The documents requested were planning related to determine whether consent had been obtained to vary the original design; lists of subcontractors and professionals so the administrators could make direct contact with them; drawings and specifications to assess the scope of the completion contract; all internal information relevant to the question how much work had been done; health and safety files; and collateral warranties and guarantees given by the contractor, subcontractors and professionals which might be directly enforceable by the owner of the property from time to time. Understandably the contractor relied on its copyright in the documents and denied that the developer was entitled in the absence of payment to any licence to use them. As built drawings and operating manuals would be handed over on completion but the works were suspended. The judge held that he had jurisdiction to make the order sought but refused to exercise his discretion in the administrators' favour. They had made no enquiries of the planning authority which might have given them some of the answers they needed. He was not sure how the administrators could make use of the documents without breaching the contractor's copyright. More fundamental was the contractor's objection that the administrators were unjustly trying to take advantage of its work without paying for it. The court did not consider the contractor to be unfairly exploiting the insolvency of the employer. In the end, the court ordered only the production of warranties and guarantees and to the extent they were already in force and capable of benefiting the employer and its successors in title.

22.2.2.7 Exit routes from administration

It is not the usual role of an administrator to distribute assets to creditors except where he is seeking to achieve the fallback purpose (having determined that the primary and secondary purposes are not achievable and creditors as a whole will not be unnecessarily harmed). The forum for distribution of assets will normally be a voluntary arrangement, a scheme of arrangement under Part 26 of the Companies Act 2006 or liquidation. However, there is now provision for the company to move automatically from administration to creditors' voluntary liquidation in certain circumstances and an administrator may apply to the court for permission to distribute the assets to the creditors.

22.2.3 Company voluntary arrangement

A CVA is a statutory procedure enabling a company to propose a composition with its creditors whereby they accept a dividend in full settlement of their debts. The directors make the proposal to an insolvency practitioner who files a report at the court stating whether a creditors' meeting should be called to consider it. All creditors receiving notice of the proposal and entitled to vote on it are bound by the arrangement irrespective of how they vote, provided at least 75% in value of creditors attending the meeting vote in favour. A CVA does not prejudice the rights of secured or preferential creditors. It is fundamental that the creditors are realistic when considering the company's proposal (especially in relation to the percentage of their debt to be written off), and that the company is realistic when proposing the dates by which sums will become payable. The CVA will set out the means by which payments are to be funded, for example, the disposal or refinancing of assets, a management buy out, other external finance or from future profits. Aside from these formal procedures, there are number of informal ways in which companies can be restructured, while presenting a normal face to the world. Section 1A of the Insolvency Act 1986 provides for a moratorium similar to that which applies on an application for an IVA but the section is only in force in respect of 'small companies' (as defined in the Companies Act 2006). As a company proposing a CVA has no automatic protection from creditors, companies will apply for administration to obtain protection from creditors while a CVA is being proposed.

22.2.4 Receivership

Receivership is a remedy afforded to creditors who have obtained a charge over the whole or part of the company's property as security for payment. In the event of default of payment, the creditor can appoint a receiver to sell the charged property (see **Figure 2**).

The court has jurisdiction to appoint a receiver, for example, where a creditor has a charge but the document is defective in some way (Lightman and Moss, 2007). Most receivers are appointed out of court pursuant to a fixed or a floating charge or a combined fixed and floating charge.

22.2.4.1 Fixed charge receivership

Only the holder of a fixed charge takes priority under the 'statutory scheme' over preferential creditors (see section 22.2.6). As its name suggests, a fixed charge prevents any dealing with the charged property without the holder's consent: *National Westminster Bank v. Spectrum Plus Ltd* [2005] 2 AC 680. Such charges are usually taken over assets which the borrower does

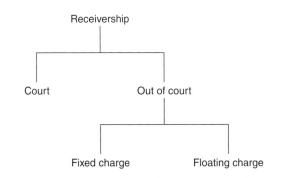

Figure 2 Forms of receivership

not need to deal with as part of its business such as land or fixed plant and equipment. A 'fixed charge receiver' has power under Section 109 of the Law of Property Act 1925 to receive rents and profits if appointed over land and other powers granted by the charge, for example, to complete building work on the land.

22.2.4.2 Administrative receivership

By contrast, an 'administrative receiver' (i.e. appointed under the terms of a floating charge over the whole or substantially the whole of the assets and undertaking of the business), has full power to carry on the company's business, including the right to bring or defend proceedings in the company's name and collect and get in the company's property (Schedule 1 to the Insolvency Act 1986). This includes the power to form a subsidiary for the purpose of completing a construction contract: *The Royal Bank of Scotland v. Chandra* [2010] EWHC 105. A floating charge has been defined as a security which charges assets present and future, allows the assets to change from time to time and allows the company to dispose of them in the ordinary course of business: *Re Yorkshire Woolcombers* [1903] 2 Ch 284. A document containing fixed and floating charges will identify which assets are caught by which charge.

As a result of changes made by the Enterprise Act 2002, a charge holder can only appoint an administrative receiver if the charge was created prior to 15 September 2003. Such a charge holder now has the ability to appoint an administrator if his security comprises a qualified floating charge ('QFC'), on which see section 22.2.2. There are certain limited exceptions where the holder of a floating charge created after the introduction of the Enterprise Act is entitled to appoint an administrative receiver (for example, in connection with a public-private project with step-in rights), but as a result of the 2002 Act administrative receivership will rarely be encountered in future.

22.2.4.3 Relation to other procedures

Given their different functions, a receivership, whether under a fixed and/or floating charge, can exist at the same time as the company is in liquidation. For example, a company might have granted separate fixed charges to project financiers over sites being developed. An unsecured creditor might petition to have the company wound up, the holder of the floating charge may appoint an administrative receiver and the holders of the fixed charges may each appoint a different fixed charge receiver all at the same time. The exception is administration since there can be no receivership or liquidation of any kind when an administration is in force.

22.2.5 Bankruptcy and individual voluntary arrangements

Bankruptcy applies only to individuals. A bankruptcy petition can be presented and issued by a debtor, a creditor or a supervisor under an IVA. The minimum sum on which a petition can be based is £750. There are several different forms of statutory demand for debts owed by individuals.

A statutory demand served on an individual as a means of enforcement of an adjudication award is liable to be set aside under r.6.5(4) Insolvency Rules 1986 if the individual asserts that he has a cross-claim, even though it would not be sufficient to prevent summary judgment being entered against him: *George Parke v. The Fenton Gretton Partnership* [2001] CILL 1712, *Shaw and Shaw v. MFP Foundations & Piling* [2010] EWHC 9. The court has power to dismiss the petition if it can be shown that the individual can pay his debts or has made an offer to secure or compound the debt on which the petition was brought that the acceptance of that offer would have required the dismissal of the petition and the offer has been unreasonably refused: Section 273 of the Insolvency Act 1986.

Until the bankruptcy order is discharged, a bankrupt cannot incur credit exceeding £500 without disclosing his status (Section 360 of the Insolvency Act 1986) or act as a company director (Section 11 of the Company Directors Disqualification Act 1986). A bankrupt is entitled to keep the 'tools of his trade' (which include items such as computers) and other property of a personal nature (Section 283(2) of the Insolvency Act 1986). The creditors submit proofs of debt and, if there are sufficient assets, receive a dividend from the trustee.

In most cases individuals will be discharged from bankruptcy no later than 12 months after commencement. The Official Receiver may file a notice at court effecting earlier discharge once his investigations are completed. However, if a bankruptcy restriction order is made, the bankruptcy period can be extended by a further 2 to 15 years. The procedure is similar to directors' disqualification proceedings and agreed undertakings may be given *in lieu* of a hearing.

The trustee in bankruptcy must take steps to realise the bankrupt's interest in the principal residence of the bankrupt or his spouse within 3 years from the date of the bankruptcy otherwise it will cease to form part of the bankrupt's estate and automatically revert back to the bankrupt. The bankrupt will continue to make payments where his or her income exceeds that required for his and his family's reasonable needs after discharge for a period of up to 3 years from the commencement of the bankruptcy. An income payment agreement may be entered into which will avoid the need for a hearing.

An IVA is an increasingly popular alternative to bankruptcy. It involves the individual making a formal proposal to his or her creditors and applying to the court for an interim order. The granting of an interim order prevents further proceedings being taken or judgments executed pending a report from an insolvency practitioner on whether the debtor's proposal is such as to make it worthwhile summoning a meeting of creditors. If a meeting is held and more than 75% in value of those voting are in favour, the IVA is approved and binds all creditors present at the meeting or who received notice of it. An IVA is a practical way out for both debtor and creditors: the debtor avoids bankruptcy and the creditors stand to receive a higher dividend than they might have done on a bankruptcy.

22.2.6 Company insolvency priority of payments

It is a fundamental principle of insolvency law that creditors who have not taken security in respect of the sums due are treated *pari passu* (literally 'with the same step'). Unsecured creditors receive as a dividend the same percentage of their debts. Where a creditor proves that certain goods are subject to retention of title or a valid trust, they do not form part of the property of the company available for distribution to creditors (e.g. Section 283(3) of the Insolvency Act 1986 for individuals). Where property is subject to a fixed charge, provided that the charge has been properly registered under Part 25 of the Companies Act 2006, assuming the charge is registrable, that property will also fall outside the scheme.

The Insolvency Act 1986 lays down the following order of priority for the payment of debts:

(a) Debts secured by fixed charges and the costs of realising fixed charged assets. These are payable out of the proceeds of sale of the asset. Any surplus will go back into the general pot for creditors; any shortfall will be unsecured debt.
(b) The expenses of the winding up. The liquidator's own expenses are not payable in priority to floating charge debts.
(c) Preferential debts consisting of certain limited employee claims and other debts. Note that debts owed to HM Revenue & Customs are no longer preferential debts.
(d) Debts secured by floating charges (with the exception of 'the prescribed part', a small percentage of floating charge realisations withheld for the benefit of the unsecured creditors).
(e) Unsecured debts.
(f) Interest on preferential and unsecured debts.
(g) Debts or other sums due from the company to its members, for example, unpaid dividends.
(h) Any surplus is distributed among the members in accordance with their respective rights and interests.

Each class of debt (save for the 'prescribed part') must be satisfied in full before assets are applied towards the following class. If there are insufficient assets to satisfy a class in full, each creditor's claim abates rateably.

22.3 Insolvency set-off

Set-off functions informally as a kind of security. For example, if A and B owe debts to each other, A can be said to have security for the debt owed by B to the extent that A can set off its cross-claim. Outside insolvency, the purpose of set-off is one of convenience, to prevent the need for A and B to issue proceedings against each other.

22.3.1 Liquidation set-off

If A or B were to go into liquidation, the general law or the parties' own contractual set-off arrangements are replaced by Rule 4.90 of the Insolvency Rules 1986. The key provisions are as follows:

(1) This Rule applies where, before the company goes into liquidation there have been mutual credits, mutual debts or other mutual dealings between the company and any creditor of the company proving or claiming to prove for a debt in the liquidation.

(3) An account shall be taken of what is due from each party to the other in respect of the mutual dealings, and the sums due from one party shall be set off against the sums due from the other.

...

(8) Only the balance (if any) of the account owed to the creditor is provable in the liquidation. Alternatively the balance (if any) owed to the company shall be paid to the liquidator as part of the assets except where all or part of the balance results from a contingent or prospective debt owed by the creditor and in such a case the balance (or that part of it which results from the contingent or prospective debt) shall be paid if and when that debt becomes due and payable.

The purpose behind liquidation set-off is to do justice between the parties: otherwise if A and B owed debts to each other and A went into liquidation, the liquidator could recover in full from B, but B would only have an unsecured claim for a dividend. 'Debt' is defined very widely and includes a liability which is present or future, certain or contingent, liquidated or unliquidated: r.13.12 of the Insolvency Rules 1986, as amended by r.498 of the Insolvency (Amendment) Rules 2010. Set-off in liquidation is therefore much wider than the general law.

The requirement for mutual credits, debts and dealings is normally satisfied in a construction contract: *Willment v. North West Thames RHA* (1984) 26 BLR 51, 62. The set-off is compulsory and cannot be excluded by agreement: *Halesowen Presswork v. National Westminster Bank* [1972] AC 785. The set-off is self-executing: *Stein v. Blake* [1996] AC 243. The account is taken as at the commencement of the liquidation. Until the works have been completed and the balance ascertained, the employer remains a contingent creditor. The creditor's proof of debt will be valued by the liquidator under r.4.86 of the Insolvency Rules 1986 or, in the event of a dispute which could impact on the recovery of other creditors, by the court.

Since only the balance is provable, it is not possible for the liquidator to assign the debt owing to the company without taking into account liabilities owed by the company: *Stein v. Blake* [1996] AC 243. In *Enterprise Managed Services v. Tony McFadden* [2009] EWHC 3222, a subcontractor in liquidation assigned for value any balance due after the account had been taken of mutual dealings between itself and the contractor under r.4.90. The assignee obtained an adjudication decision for what it asserted was the balance but Coulson J. held that the adjudicator had acted outside his jurisdiction, the power to take the account being reserved to the court, and refused to enforce the decision. This was because there was a 'fundamental clash' between liquidation set-off as a final process subjecting all mutual claims to judgment and adjudication as a procedure for the temporary resolution of single disputes (Para.70).

Contingent and future debts owing to and by the insolvent company are to be set-off provided they arise out of obligations incurred before the start of the liquidation. Debts acquired by way of assignment under an agreement entered into after the commencement of the liquidation cannot be taken into account.

There is a tension between the insolvency legislation and the Housing Grants, Construction and Regeneration Act 1996. Where a claimant in an adjudication is in liquidation and the defendant asserts a cross-claim which might qualify for set-off under r.4.90, the court ought not to grant summary judgment to enforce an adjudicator's decision as the proper forum (assuming the liquidator does not admit the cross-claims) is the Companies Court where the matter would proceed as an appeal against the liquidator's rejection of the defendant's proof of debt: *Bouygues v. Dahl-Jensen* [2000] BLR 522. In that case, the claimant went into liquidation the day before the adjudicator's decision was issued but liquidation set-off was not raised in argument by the defendant at the enforcement hearing. As a consequence, the Court of Appeal ordered summary judgment but granted a stay of execution until after the expiry of the time for lodging an appeal in the Companies Court or until after the outcome of any appeal.

22.3.2 Administration set-off

By contrast, set-off against a claim made by a company in administration is governed by the common law. This is because the administrator does not usually make distributions to creditors or accept proofs of debt. Payment of dividends is left to a subsequently-appointed liquidator or a supervisor under a voluntary arrangement. The appointment of an administrator is therefore a neutral event as far as rights of set-off are concerned.

The position is different where the administrator gives notice that he proposes to make a distribution to creditors under r.2.85 of the Insolvency Rules 1986. In that event, provisions in virtually the same terms as liquidation set-off come into play and will apply to the distribution.

22.4 Insolvency claims

An insolvency practitioner has wide powers to investigate the background to the company's insolvency and the conduct of the directors. If there is evidence, and funding available, he may pursue any of the following claims:

22.4.1 Fraudulent trading

Where any business of the company has been carried on with intent to defraud creditors of the company or creditors

of any other person or for any fraudulent purpose, the court has power under Section 213 of the Insolvency Act 1986 to order anyone knowingly a party to the carrying on of the business to contribute to the company's assets. The Singaporean case of *Tong Tien See Construction v. Tong* [2002] 3 SLR 76 is a recent example of a successful claim in the industry. In *Goldfarb v. Higgins* [2010] EWHC 613, it was held that the cause of action arose on the making of the winding up order rather than on presentation of the petition or the appointment of a provisional liquidator. The court will apportion liability between multiple defendants by taking into account the degree of control exercised by each party over the affairs of the company and the extent to which they benefited from the fraud. 'Fraudulent trading' is also a criminal offence under Part 30 of the Companies Act 2006 whether or not the company is in liquidation.

22.4.2 Wrongful trading

In order to provide liquidators with a more effective remedy than fraudulent trading, Section 214 of the Insolvency Act 1986 introduced a cause of action known as 'wrongful trading'. This is a civil claim requiring proof on a balance of probabilities and can be made against a director or a shadow director (defined by Section 251 as 'a person in accordance with whose directions and instructions the directors of the company are accustomed to act'). The liquidator has to show that the director allowed the company to continue to incur liabilities to creditors after the point had been reached when it was known or should have been known that there was no real prospect of the company avoiding insolvent liquidation. The director can be made personally liable for the amount of credit incurred after formal insolvency became inevitable. The claim is unusual in applying both a subjective test of whether the director acted properly in the light of his or her own abilities and an objective test of whether the director acted as a person with his or her role in the company ought to have done. A higher standard is expected from a director of a large company with sophisticated accounting procedures than a small company in a modest way of business: see *Re Produce Marketing* (1989) 5 BCC 569. It is not necessary to prove dishonesty.

In *Re DKG Contractors* [1990] BCC 903, a husband and wife acting as directors of a ground works subcontractor were held liable for wrongful trading and ordered to contribute £400,000 to the company's assets representing credit incurred between April and December 1998, when the company actually went into liquidation. The company was set up in parallel to a business carried on by one of the directors personally. An important factor is that the directors took no independent advice, whether from an auditor, a lawyer or a specialist insolvency practitioner. Wrongful trading is particularly relevant where a company is informally insolvent and the directors are trying to persuade the creditors not to enforce their rights, while a rescue package can be put together.

22.4.3 Preference

Under Section 239 of the 1986 Act, a preference occurs if a company does or suffers anything to be done which has the effect of improving the position of a creditor or a guarantor over that which would have obtained on the company's liquidation. It has to be shown that the company was 'influenced in deciding to give it by a desire' to produce the preference. In *Re Parkside International* [2008] EWHC 3654 it was held that in order for a company to 'suffer' something to be done, it must permit something to happen which it has power to stop or obstruct. Accepting or remaining passive in reaction to an event over which the company has no control does not amount to 'suffering' within the section. A claim can only be brought in respect of a preference made no more than 6 months before the start of the liquidation or 2 years where the creditor is a connected person. The most common situation arises where a director makes a personally guaranteed payment into the company's overdrawn bank account. The liquidator can make the preference claim against the bank and/or the director. The interrelation between preference and guarantee was considered in *Wilson and Oxford Pharmaceuticals v. Masters* [2009] 2 BCLC 485.

The need to establish motivation is troublesome. For example, pressure applied by the creditor can negative a preference (Totty, Moss and Segal, 1986; Para. H4.06). Hence, where a creditor is offered a settlement at a time when the company appears to be insolvent, it is important that the creditor asserts its rights (e.g. to petition to wind up the company) so that any payment can be viewed in the light of the creditor's pressure rather than simply the director's subjective desire to improve that creditor's position. Commercial considerations did not, however, save the director from liability for preference in *Re DKG Contractors* [1990] BCC 903 considered earlier. Much depends on how the transaction is structured and the precise words used.

22.4.4 Transactions at an undervalue

Under Section 238 of the 1986 Act the court has power to set aside a transaction entered into at an undervalue, that is, where the company receives no consideration or the value given is significantly more than that received. An example is the giving of a guarantee by a subsidiary on behalf of a parent company for no apparent benefit: *Phillips v. Brewin Dolphin* [2001] 1 WLR 143. The company must have been insolvent at the time or have become so as a result but this is presumed where the transaction is with a connected person, such as a director, or a company controlled by that connected person. There is a defence that the transaction was entered into in good faith for the purpose of carrying on the company's business and there were reasonable grounds for believing that it would benefit the company. It must have taken place within 2 years before the start of the insolvency procedure and the court has power to make such order as it thinks fit to restore the *status quo*. An

industry example is *Buildspeed Construction v. Theme* [2000] 4 SLR 776 where the novation of a contract by an insolvent contractor to a new company owned and operated by its directors was held to be a transaction at an undervalue.

22.4.5 Transactions to defraud creditors

Where a person enters into a transaction at an undervalue, the court may make an order under Section 423 of the Insolvency Act 1986 to restore the position to what it would have been if the transaction had not been entered into, and to protect the interests of persons who are victims of the transaction. The court must be satisfied that the transaction was entered into for the purpose of putting assets beyond the reach of a person who is making, or may at some time make, a claim against him, or of otherwise prejudicing the interests of such a person in relation to a claim. See *Re Ayala Holdings* [1993] BCLC 256 for an industry example. There is no fixed period within which a transaction must have occurred nor is it necessary for the company to have begun any insolvency process for a transaction to be liable to be set aside under this section. For example, in *Dornoch v. Westminster International* [2009] 2 Lloyd's Rep 420 the transferor company was not insolvent but the court still found that the transaction was at a undervalue under Section 423. This is in contrast to the position under Section 238.

22.4.6 Breach of duty

Section 212 of the 1986 Act provides for a remedy against directors and other officers and persons involved in the promotion, formation or management of a company who have been 'delinquent'. It creates no new liability against directors but provides a quicker procedure for enforcing certain rights which might have been enforced by an ordinary action before winding up.

If any of the directors or any of the other persons referred to in Section 212 has misapplied, retained, become liable or accountable for any money or property of the company, or has been guilty of misfeasance, breach of fiduciary duty or any other duty in relation to the company, the Official Receiver, liquidator, creditor or any contributory standing to benefit is allowed to recover money or damages for the benefit of the company in liquidation. The court may examine the conduct of such persons and compel them to repay or restore the money or the property with interest or to contribute money to the assets of the company by way of compensation.

Section 212 covers a variety of wrongs, including the improper payment of dividends, the application of moneys for *ultra vires* purposes, and any unauthorised loans or payment of unauthorised remuneration to directors: see *Re ED Games* [2009] EWHC 223. Construction examples include misappropriating money and cheques belonging to the company: *Re DKG Contractors* [1990] BCC 903; diverting tender enquiries for personal use: *Schott Kem v. Bentley* [1990] 3 All ER 850; and using company resources for building work to a director's home without paying for it: *Halls v. O'Dell* [1992] 2 WLR 308.

22.4.7 Post-petition disposition

Any disposition by a company after a winding up petition has been presented is void unless validated by the court under Section 127 of the Insolvency Act 1986. In the industry, this could invalidate a direct payment made to a nominated subcontractor: *Re Right Time Construction* (1990) 52 BLR 117. An application for validation can be made before or after the disposition is made: *Re Tain Construction* [2003] 2 BCLC 374 (validation refused).

22.4.8 Unregistered charges

Certain charges granted by a limited company must be registered with the Registrar of Companies within 21 days of their creation otherwise they will be void against a liquidator, administrator or creditor of the company under Part 25 of the Companies Act 2006. These are listed in Section 860 and include a charge on land or an interest in land, a charge on book debts, a floating charge, and a charge created or evidenced by an instrument which, if executed by an individual, would require registration as a bill of sale.

A power of sale in respect of plant and equipment contained in the termination clause of the ICE Conditions (5th Edition) was held to be a floating charge and invalid for want of registration as against an administrator appointed over the contractor in *Smith v. Bridgend County Borough Council* [2002] BLR 160. Other types of security used in the industry may not be registrable. For example, a trust of the contract sum was held not to be a floating charge or a charge on book debts in *Lovell Construction v. Independent Estates* [1994] 1 BCLC 31, and an assignment by way of legal mortgage of a management contract was a formal security but did not require registration: *L/M International v. The Circle* (1995) 48 Con LR 12.

22.4.9 Contravention of the pari passu rule

'Once the Insolvency Act regime has come into effect a contractual provision which seeks to remove property out of the estate and to vest it in a third party cannot override the provisions of the Act' (*Perpetual Trustee v. BNY Corporate Trustee* [2009] EWCA 1160, per Patten LJ at para.163). That case concerned two appeals, the second of which is particularly relevant to the construction industry. It concerned a joint venture agreement between Woolworths and the BBC by which, on the happening of an insolvency event, the BBC could buy the shares of the JV company at 'fair value', in effect at market value. The agreement also provided for automatic termination on insolvency if BBC served notice on Woolworths requiring it to sell its shares. The Court of Appeal reviewed the case law on attempts to avoid the 'anti-deprivation rule' that the parties cannot contract out of the *pari passu* distribution of the estate of an insolvent debtor and concluded that the forced sale

provisions were valid. Patten LJ stated that one had to consider first the nature of the property in question and then to see whether the parties have attempted to deal with it in a manner inconsistent with the *pari passu* rule (Para.123).

The rule has been applied to the industry in a number of situations. In *Re Harrison, ex parte Jay* (1880) 14 Ch D 19 the court struck down a term which forfeited a builder's plant and materials in the event of his bankruptcy. A direct payment clause allowing an employer to pay subcontractors after a contractor's liquidation has been declared invalid by reason of the employer's claim to set off the amount of the payment from sums otherwise due to the contractor, that is, its property: *Mullan v. Ross* (1996) 86 BLR 1 (see the discussion in McCormack, 1997). As an administrator or a liquidator takes property subject to any powers of termination attached to it, the inclusion of a mere power to terminate for insolvency is not likely to infringe the rule. Similarly, a liquidator is bound by a contractual bar on assignment: *Ruttle Plant v. Secretary of State for the Environment* [2008] EWHC 238.

22.5 Termination of contracts

Most of the value of a contractor consists in its receivables: debtors, retention, work in progress, claims. Where the contractor becomes insolvent before completion, its insolvency practitioner will if possible wish to see its contracts completed in order to recover the receivables, for example, by novating them to another contractor with the employer's consent. The problem is that construction contracts almost invariably provide for termination in the event of the contractor's insolvency. The reason why these clauses are included is that insolvency is not normally a breach of contract. The only exceptions are where the contract contains a covenant not to become insolvent or where the insolvency event or the surrounding circumstances amount to an 'anticipatory breach'.

'Anticipatory breach' is a term of art used in the law of contract. In construction, it could be an act by the contractor which, although not itself a breach, is such as to entitle the employer to conclude that the contractor will be unable to perform its side of the contract when the time for performance arrives. Insolvency is not an anticipatory breach of contract in the absence of special circumstances (*Re Agra Bank, ex parte Tondeur* (1867) LR 5 Eq 160), nor is administrative receivership (*Laing and Morrison Knudson v. Aegon Insurance* (1997) 86 BLR 70 at 91). Even the possibility of treating administrative receivership as an anticipatory breach cannot arise where the contract has excluded the common law: *Perar v. General Surety* (1994) 66 BLR 72. It follows that any discussion of the options following the insolvency of a party to a project must involve a careful review of all the circumstances, including the terms of any termination clause and the relationship between that clause and the common law.

22.5.1 Termination under the contract

Against that background, it is not surprising that the engineering standard forms have developed express terms providing for termination on insolvency. For example:

- They identify specific events which trigger the power to terminate on notice, normally by reference to formal insolvency procedures, although informal insolvency may also be included.

- The termination clause provides for the contractor's exclusion from site to enable the employer to engage an alternative contractor to finish the work. This power is expressed in different ways: terminating the contract, taking the works out of the contractor's hands, terminating the contractor's obligation to provide the works and so on.

- The employer's duty to make any further payment to the insolvent contractor, even if accrued due at the date of termination, may be expressly suspended and postponed until after the works have been completed: *Melville Dundas v. George Wimpey* [2007] BLR 257.

- Some forms entitle the employer to make direct payments to suppliers and subcontractors and deduct the amount of such payments from sums due or to become due to the contractor.

- A contractual set-off is made between what would have been due to the contractor had it performed the contract and the actual cost incurred by the employer in having the work completed, together with any loss resulting from the termination.

Before activating the termination clause it is essential to analyse its terms and be clear on how they relate to the contract as a whole. Some forms, such as NEC3, do not confer a right of direct payment and there can be discrepancies and omissions in the list of relevant insolvency events. The NEC3 form includes liquidation and administration as termination events in Clause 91, but it refers to 'an administration order' rather than simply administration. It is arguable that a contractor would not be able to rely on this ground where the employer entered administration voluntarily: compare *William Hare v. Shepherd Construction* [2010] EWCA 283 in which a pay when paid clause triggered by the making of an administration order was held not to take effect where the administrators were appointed by the company. As Clause 91 allows the employer to terminate 'for any reason' it would be able to repossess the site on that ground alone but would not be contractually entitled to use the contractor's equipment or deduct its additional costs of completion.

22.5.2 Termination at common law

It may be necessary to rely on the common law rather than (or in addition to) an express termination clause, for example:

(a) where the relief allowed by the termination clause will not enable the employer to recover its losses in full,
(b) where the employer fails to comply with an essential requirement of the termination clause, or

(c) it is unclear whether a contractual termination event has in fact occurred but there has been an anticipatory or repudiatory breach.

Provided common law rights have not been excluded, it may be possible both to terminate under the contract and accept a repudiation at common law: *Laing and Morrison Knudson v. Aegon Insurance* (1997) 86 BLR 70 (Davis, 2008 [Para.14–09]). In that case there was a contractual termination of 'the works'. This kept the contract alive, enabling the management contractor to have the remaining work completed and accept the works contractor's repudiation at a later date.

It remains a difficult question whether, and in what circumstances, a notice of termination under the contract can also serve as the acceptance of a repudiatory breach. In *Dalkia Utilities v. Celtech International* [2006] 1 Lloyd's Rep. 599, the contractor successfully invoked a clause, allowing it to terminate for 'material breach' where the employer had failed to pay three outstanding invoices. It was held that the non-payment was not repudiatory conduct, and that even if it had been, the notice of termination did not amount to an acceptance of the repudiation. The court stated, however, that such a notice could constitute an acceptance if it merely exercised the right to terminate without stating the ground or, where a contractual termination clause was referred to it was evident from the context that the party was not relying on it exclusively (Paras. 143–4). For more recent cases in this area see *Stocznia Gydnia v. Gearbulk* [2010] QB 27, *Shell Egypt v. Dana Gas* [2010] EWHC 465.

22.5.3 Novation

Novation is the procedure whereby an insolvency practitioner appointed over a contractor obtains value for the company's contracts by introducing a completion contractor to the employer. It differs from assignment in three important respects.

(a) Assignment is a transfer of rights under a contract which continues in being after the assignment, whereas novation brings the contract to an end and creates a new one in its place: *Scarf v. Jardine* (1882) 7 App Cas 345 at 351.
(b) Assignment transfers the benefit but not the burden of a contract, whereas a novation also transfers the burden with the consent of all parties; such a transfer is not an assignment of the burden but a novation of the contract.
(c) Consideration is not generally required for assignment but is necessary on a novation as a new contract is being formed.

Novation has been defined as 'the substitution of a new contract for an old by the agreement of all parties to the old and the new' (*Tito v. Waddell* (No. 2) [1977] Ch 106 at 287). This usually consists in the release of one party and the introduction of a new party in substitution. Most of the reported cases concern implied rather than express novation. In order to establish a novation 'what the plaintiff has to prove is conduct inconsistent with a continuance of his liability, from which conduct an agreement to release him may be inferred' (*Rouse v. Bradford Banking* [1894] 2 Ch 32 at 54).

The case usually cited as an example of novation in the construction industry is *Chatsworth v. Cussins* [1969] 1 All ER 143. After practical completion a contractor assigned the benefit of the contract to a purchaser who undertook direct to the contractor to discharge all its liabilities. The purchaser then changed its name to that of the contractor. The employer issued proceedings against the purchaser in respect of defects in the works in the mistaken belief that it was the original contractor. The Court of Appeal held the purchaser liable to the employer on the basis of an implied novation. This case was recently followed in *Enterprise Managed Services v. Tony McFadden* [2009] EWHC 3222. By contrast in *Westminster City Council v. Reema Construction (No. 2)* (1990) 24 Con LR 26 the contractor became informally insolvent and hived down its assets to a purchaser but the employer failed in a claim based on implied novation. There was no evidence that the council was aware that the original contractor had hived down its assets or that the purchaser had agreed with the contractor to fulfil any unperformed obligations. It will be difficult to infer a novation if it would mean the employer losing the benefit of security for performance such as a cash deposit: *Aktion Maritime v. Kasmas* [1987] 1 Lloyd's Rep 283.

The law of novation has developed in cases involving the transfer of debts. In its simplest form, a novation of a debt owed by B to A occurs when, with the consent of A as creditor, B is replaced as debtor by C: see **Figure 3**.

The position is rather more complicated with a construction contract under which each party owes obligations to the other. A novation in this context has to take account of the benefit and burden of both A and B: see **Figure 4**.

Figure 4 assumes a straightforward novation whereby one contractor is substituted for another. There are four steps:

(1) the employer releases the contractor
(2) the contractor releases the employer
(3) the purchaser promises the employer to complete the contract
(4) the employer promises the purchaser to pay for the work.

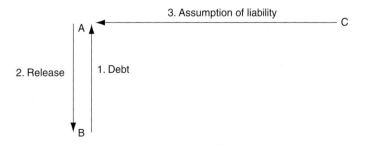

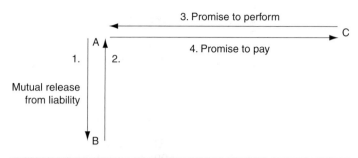

Figure 4   Novation: under a construction contract

The old contract is terminated by steps 1 and 2. The new contract is created by steps 3 and 4. For forms of novation agreement see Newman, 1992, and JCT Practice Note 24. Standard forms have been issued by the Construction Industry Council (2004), and the City of London Law Society (2004).

The agreement should deal with any changes necessary to the terms of the original contract. Such agreements normally provide that the purchaser assumes liability to the employer as if it had been a party to the original contract from the inception. The intention is that the purchaser becomes liable for any current breaches as if it had signed a contract with retrospective effect. In *Blyth and Blyth v. Carillion Construction* [2002] 79 Con LR 142 the Scottish Court of Session held that a contractor was not entitled to recover its own losses arising from an engineer's breach of contract where the breach occurred before the novation of the engineer's appointment to the contractor. This finding appears to be contrary to English authority on novation (*W&J Leigh v. CBI Nederland*, 20 June 1985, Otton J) but may be correct on the facts. The Court of Session seems to have viewed the arrangements between the parties as a merger of contracts for which novation (at least in the form of this case) was an inappropriate vehicle.

Other areas which are usually addressed include:

- pricing provisions
- scope of works
- the completion date
- liability for delay following the insolvency
- liability for patent and latent defects
- liquidated and ascertained damages already incurred
- availability of plant and materials on and off site
- retention of title claimants
- subcontractors' claims
- willingness of subcontractors and suppliers to novate their contracts
- bonds and guarantees
- the Transfer of Undertakings (Protection of Employment) Regulations 2006
- the availability of the professional team for novations.

22.6 Security for performance

Security for performance protects the paying party. It covers a very wide range of measures which can be taken:

(a) before deciding to enter into the contract
(b) by means of the contract terms
(c) by taking security outside the contract (see **Table 1**)

These are discussed in detail in Davis, 2008 (chapters 2, 6, 7, 10 and 19) and Newman, 1999. Termination, insolvency set-off and some aspects of formal security were considered earlier in this chapter. This section looks at title to materials, vesting of plant, and retention. Bonds and guarantees are discussed earlier in *Bonds, parent company guarantees and other security*.

22.6.1 Title to materials

Contractors often have few tangible assets on which a creditor can levy execution. Employers are therefore concerned to ensure that title to materials passes to them as quickly as possible.

Where the materials are fixed, they cease to be chattels and become part of the land by operation of law. This can cause hardship in cases where, unknown to the contractor, the employer is not the owner of the land or has mortgaged it. As a consequence, the contractor may be contractually obliged to continue to add to the value of the land even where the employer is informally insolvent because no event has occurred entitling the contractor to terminate. The construction process is such as to make it uncertain sometimes whether a chattel has become fixed. Where the object simply rests on the land by its own weight, the burden of proof is on the person asserting

Pre-contract	Prequalification
	Tender process
	Professional advice
	Financial modelling
Contract	Termination
	Set-off
	Vesting
	Indemnities
	Retention
	Conditions precedent
Security	Collateral contracts
	Suretyship
	Demand bonds
	Insurance
	Formal security

Table 1 Security for performance

that it has become part of the land. Where the item is fixed, even if only slightly, the burden of proof shifts to the person contending it is a chattel: *Holland v. Hodgson* (1872) LR 7 CP 328. The intention of the parties is relevant only insofar as it can be inferred from the degree and purpose of annexation: *Elitestone v. Morris* [1997] 2 All 513.

The second informal security arises from the linking of main and subcontracts. In the absence of any express provision, title to materials under a contract for goods and services will not pass until they are fixed to the land: *Tripp v. Armitage* (1839) 4 M & W 687. The mere fact that the value of materials is included in an interim certificate does not mean that title passes to the employer on payment. What is required is an express term that title to unfixed or off-site materials will become the property of the employer on payment to the contractor: see *Egan v. State Transport Authority* (1982) 31 SASR 481, not following *Banbury and Cheltenham Railway v. Daniel* (1854) LJ Ch 265.

Where materials are provided to the contractor pursuant to a sale of goods contract, and the employer pays the contractor for them in good faith and without notice of any retention of title clause in the supplier's terms and conditions, the employer can claim ownership of the materials under Section 25 of the Sale of Goods Act 1979. The section only applies where the goods are transferred to the employer under a 'sale, pledge, or other disposition'. It was impliedly held in *Archivent v. Strathclyde General Council* (1984) 27 BLR 111 that payment of a certificate which had specifically referred to the goods in question amounted to a 'disposition' within the section. Had the contract not specifically provided for title to pass on payment of a certificate, however, then the section could not have applied: *P4 Ltd v. Unite Integrated Solutions* [2006] EWHC 2640.

22.6.2 Plant and equipment

On some contracts, it is particularly important that plant and equipment is not removed from site by the contractor until after completion, for example, where it is designed specifically for the contract, or specially imported, is in short supply or simply to prevent the contractor prejudicing the programme by diverting resources to another contract. These availability risks are met in part by terms which prevent the contractor from removing the plant from the site without the engineer's consent and special provisions known as 'vesting clauses' that confer a proprietary right or a security interest in the plant in the employer until completion. There is considerable variety in these clauses and it is hard to generalise on their effect. The only recent English authority is *Smith v. Bridgend County Borough Council* [2002] BLR 160, which is the starting point on any discussion of vesting clauses and their effect. Broadly, the relevant principles are as follows:

(a) If the contract says that title passes on delivery of the plant to site, it will be treated as an absolute transfer to the employer: *Bennett & White v. Municipal District of Sugar City* [1951] AC 786.

(b) If the contract 'deems' the plant to be the employer's property for the purposes of the contract, the contract will be treated as ambiguous and subject to rules of construction: *Re Cosslett Contractors* [1997] 4 All ER 117.

(c) If the court concludes that, notwithstanding the ambiguity, the parties did intend to create a proprietary right, it will so hold: *Brown v. Bateman* (1867) LR 2 CP 272.

(d) Otherwise, the provision will be treated as having no legal effect, leaving it to the employer to rely on the termination clause: *Re Keen & Keen, ex parte Collins* [1902] 1 KB 555.

In *Re Cosslett Contractors* the court had to consider Clause 53 (vesting) and Clause 63 (termination) of the ICE Conditions (5th Edition). It held that the vesting clause was too uncertain to pass title and that the power of sale in the termination clause constituted a floating charge, which was not binding on the administrator of a contractor for want of registration. Nevertheless, the termination clause remained contractually binding on the contractor and the employer was entitled to use the plant to have the works completed. The employer sold the plant to the completion contractor and the administrator obtained substantial damages in conversion: *Smith v. Bridgend County Borough Council* [2002] BLR 160. In the ICE Conditions (7th Edition) the vesting clause has been dropped but the power of sale of plant on termination has been replicated in Clause 65(2) almost unchanged.

Other standard forms have subtly different provisions (Barber, 1998; Calnan, 1997). Vesting clauses have been challenged in various situations, for example, where termination is disputed, as a penalty, as an infringement of the *pari passu* rule, or where a claim is made in conversion, but not, it seems, on the ground that the clause is invalid as an unregistered bill of sale: see *Reeves v. Barlow* (1884) 12 QBD 436.

22.6.3 Retention

Retention is an informal security protecting the employer against the contractor's default. Some contracts restrict the cross-claims which the employer can make against retention while others preserve it as an asset of the contractor freely available for set-off by the employer on whatever ground. Retention accrues gradually as the contract proceeds until half is released at substantial completion and the balance paid to the contractor on at the end of the maintenance period. Where the employer agrees not to withhold retention in consideration of the contractor procuring a retention bond in the on demand form, the contractor obtains the benefit of improved cash flow but at some risk to itself. For example, the amount of the bond may not accrue gradually but be for the whole retention from the outset. Also, any contractual limitations on the employer's right of set-off against retention are not likely, in the absence of express provision, to restrict the employer's rights to make demands under the bond: *Costain International v. Davy McKee* (unreported, 25 November 1990, CA). Conversely, where retention is withheld but made subject to a trust in favour of the contractor,

the court has, in some cases, construed the employer's rights of set-off as restricted in scope to such amount of the retention as represents money earned by the contractor as opposed to proportions attributable to work done by subcontractors: *Harrington Contractors v. Co Partnership Developments* (1998) 88 BLR 44.

22.7 Security for payment

A study carried out in 1998 found that only 6% of contracts had any form of security for payment. The authors concluded that

> [Security for payment] would reduce risk and uncertainty in the industry and, consequently, lead to greater efficiency. It is likely that it would reduce the number of insolvencies or at least ensure that those who became insolvent did so from their own fault rather than the fault of those who employed them … Perhaps the industry should be less defensive about performance protection and more pro-active about security for payment. (Hughes, 1998)

Even where the contract obliges the employer to provide security on request, the contractor may not ask for it in order to avoid upsetting the employer.

Security for payment takes various forms depending on whether the mechanism is intended as the primary means of payment or as secondary protection against non-payment: see **Table 2**. Letters of credit are used in construction, especially on international projects. They entitle the beneficiary to payment on production of specified documents. Problems occur where the issuer of the document is the supervising officer under the contract and he or she has not been paid or where his or her duty to issue the document is not laid down in the contract. Other difficulties arise where the issuer is beyond the control of the employer.

Similar problems occur where the employer agrees to pay the contract sum into a bank account subject to specific terms for its release as the works proceed (escrow account) or to its being held in trust on specific terms (trust account). The

Secure means of payment	Letter of credit
	Escrow account
	Trust for part of contract sum
	Project bank account
	Special purpose trusts
Protection against non-payment	Third-party bond or guarantee
	Parent company guarantee
	Charge over land, cash at bank or debts
	Contractual term (set-off, suspension, termination)

Table 2 Security for payment

difference between the two is that failure to operate an escrow account gives rise to a claim for damages for breach of contract whereas a beneficiary under a trust has access to equitable remedies of tracing and breach of trust extending beyond the parties to the contract.

Ideally, the precise terms of the arrangement will be carefully negotiated and properly drafted. They can either be contained in a separate agreement or included in the contract, but whichever approach is taken it is essential that the operation of the account be fully integrated with the contract terms for payment. In *Lovell Construction v. Independent Estates* [1994] 1 BCLC 31 the employer's agreement to channel payment of the contract sum through a trust account was evidenced partly by a separate agreement and partly through amendments to the payment and termination clauses of JCT 81 and a letter from the employer and the contractor to their respective solicitors who were to act as trustees of the account. The employer went into liquidation and the contractor successfully claimed payment from the account. One of the difficulties stemmed from the fact that, after the contract had been terminated, the trust agreement required the contractor to produce a certificate from the architect of the amount it was entitled to claim, but the parties had failed to confer the power to issue such a certificate under the contract. The liquidator also argued that the arrangement amounted to a floating charge over the account which was invalid for want of registration. The court held that the trust account was the means of payment rather than a security for payment and therefore did not require registration.

Using a trust as the means of payment can have a further advantage in addition to conferring the right to equitable tracing. This appears from *Rafidain Bank v. Saipem* (unreported, 2 March 1994, CA) which concerned a contract between an Italian consortium and the Iraqi government which, in essence, was a barter of construction services in return for oil. The contractor built a pipeline for one agency of the Iraqi government who then supplied oil to another state agency who sold it to an associated company of the contractor who paid for the oil in U.S. dollars by remitting payment to an escrow account in London, from which the contractor was paid on production of documents to the trustees of the account. Among other things, these documents consisted of tax clearance certificates which the contractor had to obtain from yet another Iraqi state authority. After completion, the contractor sought payment of the second half of retention but, before the certificates could be issued, the Gulf war broke out and the pipeline was destroyed.

It appears that the employer did not dispute that the work had been properly done and local taxes paid, but the contractor could not obtain the relevant certificates. The court took a two-stage approach. First, it examined the position in contract. It found that the production of the certificates was a condition precedent for payment from the account and the contractor's claim would fail if that were its only ground. It then asked whether the imposition of a trust made any difference. The court held that, since the contractor had obtained

an immediate equitable proprietary interest in the account, the production of the certificates was just an administrative detail. Payment from the account in London was ordered notwithstanding the absence of the certificates. The case shows how overlaying a trust over the contractual matrix can enlarge the court's jurisdiction to deal with what is essentially a contractual claim.

In June 2008, the NEC Panel issued a new Clause Z3 with associated precedent documents for the use of a project bank account with the NEC3 form. It appears to be intended as a safe channel for payment: funds will be paid in by the employer and disbursed by the bank to the contractor and named suppliers as soon as practicable. Payment from the account is treated as payment by the employer or the contractor as the case may be. The contractor has to 'top up' the account if the employer fails to pay in sufficient to pay named suppliers in full the amounts shown as due to them in the contractor's application for payment, presumably on the basis that the shortfall is attributable to the contractor's default for which the suppliers should not be penalised. The account is held by the employer and the contractor on trust for the contractor and named suppliers in proportions ascertainable from the contractor's application for payment.

Where money is advanced to a contractor for the specific purpose of enabling it to pay its creditors and the contractor fails to do so, the money is held on resulting trust for the employer: see, for example, *Re Niagara Mechanical Services International* [2000] 2 BCLC 425. In that case a contractor went into administration and the employer agreed to make a payment to the contractor to pay a specialist subcontractor to procure the commissioning of air conditioning equipment. Instead of paying the subcontractor, the administrator accepted the money on account of sums due but had to repay it later to the employer.

Where the account is not intended as the means of payment, it will probably be regarded as a form of protection against non-payment. It is possible for the employer to offer formal security for payment using one of the recognised devices of mortgage, charge, lien or pledge. Of these, the most often encountered is the charge, often a second or third charge over the site being developed. A more practical alternative is for the employer to procure a bond or guarantee from a third party, such as a bank or a specialist insurance company, or a parent company guarantee. Otherwise the contractor has to rely on its normal contractual terms for protection, for example, rights of set-off, suspension or termination.

References

Barber, P. 'Title to Goods, Materials and Plant under Construction Contracts' in Palmer, N. and McKendrick, E. (eds.) *Interests in goods*, 2nd edition, London, LLP, 1998.

Calnan, R. *Property, Security and Possession in Insolvency Law*, Re Cosslett (Contractors) Ltd, (1997) 11 JIBFL 530.

Davis, R. 'Payment Issues and Legislation' in Davis and Odams (1996).

Hughes, W. *Financial protection in the UK building industry*, London, E & FN Spon, 1998.

Joint Contracts Tribunal/Society of Practitioners of Insolvency. *Practice Note 24: for use by Employers in the event of the insolvency of the Main Contractor*, London, RIBA Publications, 1992.

Lightman, G. and Moss, G. *The law of administrators and receivers of companies*, 4th edition, London, Sweet and Maxwell, 2007, Ch. 29.

McCormack, G. *Proprietary claims and insolvency*, London, Sweet and Maxwell, 1997.

Newman, P. *Insolvency explained*, London, RIBA Publications, 1992.

Newman, P. *Bonds, guarantees and performance security in the construction industry*, London, Jordans, 1999.

Totty, P., Moss, G. and Segal N. *Insolvency*, London, Sweet and Maxwell, 1986, (looseleaf), Ch. H19.

Referenced legislation, regulations and standards

Companies Act 2006
Enterprise Act 2002
Insolvency Act 1986
Insolvent Partnerships Order 1994
Insolvency Rules 1986
Law of Property Act 1925
Sale of Goods Act 1979

Referenced cases

Aktion Maritime v. Kasmas [1987] 1 Lloyd's Rep 283
Archivent v. Strathclyde General Council (1984) 27 BLR 111
Banbury and Cheltenham Railway v. Daniel (1854) LJ Ch 265
Bennett & White v. Municipal District of Sugar City [1951] AC 786
Blyth and Blyth v. Carillion Construction [2002] 79 Con LR 142
Bouygues v. Dahl-Jensen [2000] BLR 522
Brown v. Bateman (1867) LR 2 CP 272
Buildspeed Construction v. Theme [2000] 4 SLR 776
Chatsworth v. Cussins [1969] 1 All ER 143
Costain International v. Davy McKee (unreported, 25 November 1990, CA)
Cowlishaw and Wong v. O&D Building Contractors [2009] EWHC 2445
Dalkia Utilities v. Celtech International [2006] 1 Lloyd's Rep. 599
Dornoch v. Westminster International [2009] 2 Lloyd's Rep 420
Egan v. State Transport Authority (1982) 31 SASR 481
Elitestone v. Morris [1997] 2 All 513
Enterprise Managed Services v. Tony McFadden [2009] EWHC 3222
George Parke v. The Fenton Gretton Partnership [2001] CILL 1712
Goldacre v. Nortel Networks [2010] BCC 299 (currently under appeal)
Goldfarb v. Higgins [2010] EWHC 613
Hadden Construction v. Midway Services [2008] SLT (Sh Ct) 12
Halesowen Presswork v. National Westminster Bank [1972] AC 785
Halls v. O'Dell [1992] 2 WLR 308
Harrington Contractors v. Co Partnership Developments (1998) 88 BLR 44
Holland v. Hodgson (1872) LR 7 CP 328
L/M International v. The Circle (1995) 48 Con LR 12
Laing and Morrison Knudson v. Aegon Insurance (1997) 86 BLR 70 at 91

Locontha Foundation v. GBI Investments [2010] EWHC 37
Lovell Construction v. Independent Estates [1994] 1 BCLC 31
MacPlant Services v. Contract Lifting Services [2009] SC 125
Melville Dundas v. George Wimpey [2007] BLR 257
Mullan v. Ross (1996) 86 BLR 1
National Westminster Bank v. Spectrum Plus Ltd [2005] 2 AC 680
P4 Ltd v. Unite Integrated Solutions [2006] EWHC 2640
Perar v. General Surety (1994) 66 BLR 72
Perpetual Trustee v. BNY Corporate Trustee [2009] EWCA 1160
Phillips v. Brewin Dolphin [2001] 1 WLR 143
Rafidain Bank v. Saipem (unreported, 2 March 1994, CA)
Re Agra Bank, ex parte Tondeur (1867) LR 5 Eq 160
Re Atlantic Computers [1992] 1 All ER 476
Re Ayala Holdings [1993] BCLC 256
Re Cosslett Contractors [1997] 4 All ER 117
Re DKG Contractors [1990] BCC 903
Re ED Games [2009] EWHC 223
Re Harrison, ex parte Jay (1880) 14 Ch D 19
Re Kayley Vending [2009] BCC 578
Re Keen & Keen, ex parte Collins [1902] 1 KB 555
Re Niagara Mechanical Services International [2000] 2 BCLC 425
Re Parkside International [2008] EWHC 3654
Re Produce Marketing (1989) 5 BCC 569
Re Right Time Construction (1990) 52 BLR 117
Re Tain Construction [2003] 2 BCLC 374 (validation refused)
Re Taylor's Industrial Flooring [1990] BCC 44
Re William Thorpe (1989) 5 BCC 156
Re Yorkshire Woolcombers [1903] 2 Ch 284
Reeves v. Barlow (1884) 12 QBD 436
Rouse v. Bradford Banking [1894] 2 Ch 32 at 54
Ruttle Plant v. Secretary of State for the Environment [2008] EWHC 238
Scarf v. Jardine (1882) 7 App Cas 345 at 351
Schott Kem v. Bentley [1990] 3 All ER 850
Smith v. Bridgend County Borough Council [2002] BLR 160
Stein v. Blake [1996] AC 243
Stocznia Gydnia v. Gearbulk [2010] QB 27, *Shell Egypt v. Dana Gas* [2010] EWHC 465
Straume v. Bradlor Developments [2000] BCC 333
Tito v. Waddell (No. 2) [1977] Ch 106 at 287
Tong Tien See Construction v. Tong [2002] 3 SLR 76
Tripp v. Armitage (1839) 4 M & W 687
W&J Leigh v. CBI Nederland, 20 June 1985, Otton J
Westminster City Council v. Reema Construction (No. 2) (1990) 24 Con LR 26
William Hare v. Shepherd Construction [2010] EWCA 283
Willment v. North West Thames RHA (1984) 26 BLR 51, 62
Wilson and Oxford Pharmaceuticals v. Masters [2009] BCLC 485

Further reading

Davis, R. *Construction insolvency: security, risk and renewal in construction contracts*, 3rd edition, London, Sweet & Maxwell, 2008

Goode, R. M. *Principles of corporate insolvency law*, 3rd edition, London, Sweet and Maxwell, 2005

Hayton, D. J. 'The Significance of Equity in Construction Contracts,' *Construction Law Yearbook*, 1994, 2 Construction Law Yearbook 19.

Hopper, R. 'Construction Sector Retention Survey' in Davis, R. and Odams, A. M. (eds.) *Security for payment*, London, Construction Law Press, King's College London, 1996.

Latham, M. *Constructing the team,* London, HMSO, London, UK, 1994.

Oditah, F. Assets and the treatment of claims in insolvency, *Law Quarterly Review*, 1992, 108, Law Quarterly Review 459.

Sealy L. and Milman D. *Annotated guide to the insolvency legislation*, 13th edition, 2 vols, London, Sweet & Maxwell, 2010

Websites

Association of Business Recovery Professionals; www.r3.org.uk

British and Irish Legal Information Institute; www.bailii.org. Gives free access to law reports world wide.

City of London Law Society; www.citysolicitors.org.uk

Construction Industry Council (CIC); www.cic.org.uk

Institution of Civil Engineers; www.ice.org.uk

Joint Contracts Tribunal; www.jctltd.co.uk

London Gazette; www.london-gazette.co.uk

Office of Government Commerce; www.ogc.gov.uk. Has a draft trust deed annexed as Appendix A [project bank account] to the *Guide to Best 'Fair Payment' Practices* (2007)

New Engineering Contract; www.neccontract.com

The Insolvency Service; www.insolvency.gov.uk. A government resource with a searchable register of disqualified directors. The website makes available the government's recent review on pre-packaged sales in administration: *Report on the Operation of Statement of Insolvency Practice 16.*

Chapter 23

Law of tort

Graham Chapman Four New Square, London, UK
Emilie Jones Four New Square, London, UK
Tom Asquith Four New Square, London, UK

doi: 10.1680/mocl.40878.0365

The law of tort is concerned with the imposition of duties and liabilities as between parties. It has particular relevance for those working in the construction industry. Liability in tort may arise in a number of ways. Liability may arise in the tort of negligence. This requires an examination of the circumstances in which a duty of care will be found, the issue of breach of duty, whether a breach can be said to have caused loss, what losses may be recoverable by the injured party, and possible defences. Liability may also arise in nuisance (private, public and statutory), as well as under the principles of liability for the escape of dangerous substances established by the case of *Rylands v. Fletcher*. A party may be liable to another in tort for breach of a statutory duty owed by it; statute also imposes duties on those whom the law terms occupiers to visitors, under the Occupiers' Liability Act 1997, and on those undertaking work in connection with a dwelling, under the Defective Premises Act 1972. Finally, liability may arise in the tort of trespass, including trespass to the subsoil or airspace of a neighbouring property.

CONTENTS

23.1 Introduction

The law of tort, much like the law of contract, imposes obligations on individuals towards other individuals giving rights to the latter against the former. These rights and obligations arise independently of any contract but instead are derived in the main from the common law (the product of decisions by the court) or alternatively from statute law enacted by Parliament.

The law of tort is broad in its compass and covers a wide spectrum of wrongs including trespass, assault, libel and statutory torts. Some civil torts are also criminal offences. A criminal offence will arise from obligations that are owed to the state at large and proceedings are usually brought by the state. The civil wrong, in contrast, arises from obligations owed by certain individuals to certain other individuals or groups of individuals. The wronged individual is usually the person who brings proceedings against the wrongdoer or 'tortfeasor' in respect of the 'tortious' duty or obligation that is said to have been breached. This chapter examines the various areas of tortious liability and types of tortious duty in so far as they impact on the construction industry.

23.2 Negligence

The tort of negligence gives rise to the widest range of tortious duties. For a cause of action in negligence to arise:

(a) there must be a duty of care owed by the tortfeasor to the injured person;

(b) a breach of that duty of care must have taken place; and

(c) that breach must have caused the injured person to suffer loss.

The word 'injured' is used here to signify that the person has suffered some form of loss or damage and is not intended to suggest that tortious duties are in any way limited to the realm of personal injury. Indeed, the range of duties in tort is vast and, given this, it might be thought strange that until 1932 a single tort of negligence did not exist. Liability for negligent conduct was recognised only in discrete categories where particular circumstances were said to give rise to a 'duty of care'. Often these situations were readily identified as being akin to those where a contract would be said to arise. Today, identifying when a duty of care will arise can still be a difficult exercise.

23.2.1 Duty of care

The origin of the modern law of the tort of negligence is the decision of the House of Lords in *Donoghue v. Stevenson* [1932] AC 562. In this case, which famously concerned a snail in a bottle of ginger beer, the House of Lords sought to set out a single theory of negligence. This was based on what became known as the 'neighbourhood principle':

> The rule that you are to love your neighbour becomes in law, you must not injure your neighbour; and the lawyer's question, who is my neighbour? receives a restricted reply. You must take reasonable care to avoid acts or omissions which you can reasonably foresee would be likely to injure your neighbour. Who, then, in law is my neighbour? The answer seems to be – persons who are so closely and directly affected by my act that I ought reasonably to have them in contemplation as being so affected when I am directing my mind to the acts or omissions which are called in question (Lord Atkin at 580).

In other words, a duty of care (on the facts of *Donoghue* not to cause personal injury to others) is owed by an individual to other persons whom that individual ought to foresee might be injured by a particular act or omission. Thus, the establishment of a duty of care was founded on the reasonably foreseeable consequences of an individual's acts and omissions and the test of 'reasonable foreseeability' became known as the touchstone of liability in negligence. However, the *Donoghue* case did not lead to an explosion of litigation or a rapid and extensive expansion in tortious liability. Rather, new areas or 'pockets' of liability were established by the courts on a case-by-case basis with each new area being relatively confined to specific factual scenarios.

Then, in *Anns v. Merton London Borough Council* [1978] AC 728, the House of Lords attempted to lay down a simple two-stage test for the existence of all liability in negligence. The leading judgement was given by Lord Wilberforce who set out the test as follows, at 751, 752:

> ... the question has to be approached in two stages. First one has to ask whether, as between the alleged wrongdoer and the person who has suffered damage, there is sufficient relationship of proximity or neighbourhood such that, in the reasonable contemplation of the former, carelessness on his part may be likely to cause damage to the latter – in which case a prima facie duty of care arises. Secondly, if the first question is answered affirmatively, it is necessary to consider whether there are any considerations which ought to negative, or to reduce or limit the scope of the duty or the class of person to whom it is owed or the damages to which a breach of it may give rise.

Thus, the two elements for the establishment of a duty of care were:

(i) reasonable foreseeability of the type of loss suffered; and
(ii) the absence of any consideration of public policy to negative or limit the scope of the duty or the class of person to whom it was owed.

This test was criticised for essentially establishing a presumption of liability where the defendant ought to have foreseen injury to the claimant, unless public policy dictates otherwise. Not surprisingly, the scope of the tort of negligence widened as a result of the decision and new areas of liability were established. Still less surprising is that in the face of these developments the courts have retreated from the *Anns* approach.

In *Murphy v. Brentwood District Council* [1991] AC 398 the House of Lords effectively overturned *Anns*, particularly in so far as it applied to duties of care owed by local authorities. Lord Keith expressed the view that Lord Wilberforce's test should not be treated as being definitive, and emphasised the importance of finding a relationship of 'proximity'. In *Caparo Industries plc v. Dickman* [1990] 2 AC 605, a three-stage test was established.

What emerges from *Caparo* is that, in addition to the foreseeability of damage, necessary ingredients in any situation giving rise to a duty of care are that there should exist between the party owing the duty and the party to whom it is owed a relationship characterised by the law as one of 'proximity' or 'neighbourhood' and that the situation should be one in which the court considers it fairness, justness and reasonableness that the law should impose a duty of a given scope on the one party for the benefit of the other (per Lord Bridge at 617, 618).

Therefore, the three elements for finding that a duty of care is owed were established as being:

■ foreseeability

■ proximity

■ fair, just and reasonableness

However, as Lord Bridge himself admitted, such concepts should not be treated as a rigid formula and are, in fact, no more than 'useful labels' employed by the courts when examining the policy considerations of whether or not to impose a duty of care in a given case. Such policy considerations are not limited to the effects of the imposition of the duty as between the two parties before the court, but include the effect of imposing a duty of care on all other members of society in the same position as the parties currently before the court.

Importantly for the construction industry, the courts have encountered less difficulty in imposing duties of care in situations where physical loss – be it to person or property – has been caused than where only financial or purely economic loss has been suffered. It is in this latter area that policy considerations have particularly exercised the courts, which have adopted a more cautious and restrictive approach so as to limit the boundaries of liability. This is based on the fear that a less restrictive approach would open the 'floodgates' of liability such that tortfeasors would be flooded with substantial claims for pure economic loss (for example, loss of profits) by others which would be difficult to bear.

It is still arguable (despite a recent willingness by the courts to allow the recovery of economic loss) that the general rule is that pure economic loss is not recoverable in an action for negligence, or at least is not as readily recoverable as personal injury or property damage losses. The application of this rule is most readily seen in the situation where the defendant's alleged negligence causes damage to property which does not belong to the claimant, but which, because of an interest which the claimant has in that property, causes the claimant loss.

Thus, in *Spartan Steel and Alloys Ltd v. Martin & Co. Ltd* [1973] QB 27 the defendant negligently cut through an electric cable which did not belong to the claimant, but which supplied the claimant with electricity for his metal processing plant. The claimant was not able to claim for the lost profits caused by closing his business for the day while the electricity supply was disrupted, but was able to claim for damage caused to the metal being processed at the time the electricity was cut off, this being economic loss flowing directly from damage to the claimant's property.

In the construction industry a more difficult case is where defects arise in products and buildings. The courts have held that, where a product or building is defective, and the only loss occasioned is the cost of repairing or replacing that property when the defect is discovered, this is irrecoverable on the basis that it is pure economic loss. The manufacturer, builder or designer of the product or building will not be liable (because it owes no duty to take care so as not to cause purely economic loss) unless the defect causes damage to other property, or personal injury (in respect of which a duty is owed). The application of this rule can be seen in *Murphy v. Brentwood District Council* [1991] AC 398 in which the claimant suffered loss because the foundations of his house were defective which led to subsidence and cracking. The loss suffered on the subsequent sale of the house was not recoverable because the damage had been caused to the building itself ('the defective product') and not to other property. (However, now see the Defective Premises Act 1972 which is considered in section 23.7 of this chapter.)

The 'other property' argument was argued in the case of *Baxall v. Sheard Walshaw* [2002] CILL 1837 but the decision in this case addressed general questions about duty of care and causation in negligence. In relation to duty of care, the Court of Appeal held that such a duty can be owed to future tenants of a building by the architects responsible for its design (See also *Turner v. Watkins* [TCC, 9 November 2001]). In this case, the claim was for damage to equipment inside a building due to two floods caused by leaking gutters and drains. Baxall, the current building tenant claimed that the original architect (Sheard Walshaw) owed all future owners a duty of care to design the drainage system so as to avoid damage to the contents of the building. The Court of Appeal found that a duty of this sort could be owed but its existence was negatived on the facts of the case because Baxall's surveyors (who Baxall had retained to inspect the premises prior to taking its lease) should have identified the defects in the gutters and drains. Thus, because Baxall could reasonably be expected to instruct its own surveyors to inspect the premises and did so, and because had those surveyors inspected the premises competently the defects would have been discovered, the architects were absolved from owing a duty of care to Baxall in respect of those defects.

More recently, however, *Baxall* was not followed in *Pearson Education Limited v. Charter Partnerships Limited* [2007] BLR 324 (a case summary of which appears below) and so it would now appear to be more difficult to show that a duty of care should be negatived on the basis of a claimant's opportunity to carry out an inspection as set out in *Baxall*.

A possible exception to the general rule that pure economic loss is only recoverable where damage has been caused to other property might be found in what has become known as the 'complex structure' argument. From one point of view this is not in fact an exception to the rule laid down in *Murphy* at all but an application of it as it rests on how 'other property' is defined. In short, the complex structure argument demands that a building be treated as being the sum of its many parts with each part being regarded as distinct so that damage caused by one part of the building to another part of the same building can be classified as damage to 'other property'. The origin of

this theory lies in *D & F Estates Ltd v. Church Commissioners* [1989] AC 177 but it has not been adopted and developed by the courts; indeed the Court of Appeal in *Warner v. Basildon* (1990) Constr LJ 46 has suggested that such a theory has no place in English law. However, this view was not expressed in *Murphy v. Brentwood* itself (which was decided the day after the Court of Appeal case) and four of their Lordships thought that such a theory might have some role to play in the future. At present, the theory seems unlikely to be allowed to develop as in *Tunnel Refineries v. Brya Donkin* (1998) CILL 1392 the Recorder held that he was bound by the Court of Appeal's decision in Warner, and in *Tesco v. The Norman Hitchcox Partnership* (1997) 56 ConLR 42 the judge refused to apply the theory. Nevertheless, it is as well for those in the construction industry to be aware that such an argument exists.

It has been argued that a further possible exception to the rule in *Murphy* can be found in *Junior Books v. Veitchi* [1983] AC 520. In this case, the defendants were found to have been negligent in laying a defective floor at the claimant's factory and were held liable in damages for the cost of re-laying the floor and also for consequential financial loss suffered by the claimant. However, it is difficult to reconcile this judgement with the reasoning in the later case of *Murphy* and the status of the decision is therefore uncertain. It is likely that *Junior Books* will be confined to its own facts and the decision justified on the basis that the relationship between the parties was so close as to be akin to contract.

The courts have exhibited a more relaxed approach to the recovery of economic loss outside the building sphere. In particular, the courts have been prepared to sanction the recovery of purely economic loss where it has been caused by a negligent statement (see *Hedley Byrne & Co Ltd v. Heller & Partners Ltd* [1964] AC 465 and *White v. Jones* [1995] 2 AC 507). It was thought that such a relaxed approach would not apply where the loss had been caused by negligent acts or the supply of negligent services. However, since *Henderson v. Merrett* [1994] 2 AC 145 it now seems clear that liability for negligent statements and liability for the performance of negligent services is governed by the same test: that of 'assumption of responsibility'. The impact of this might be particularly felt by professionals working in the construction industry such as engineers and architects who supply services rather than labour or materials.

It is certainly arguable that the three-stage *Caparo* test has now been left behind and that, motivated by a need to incrementally extend the boundaries of liability (particularly in the area of pure economic loss) without opening the floodgates, the courts have adopted a pragmatic approach which entails simply deciding whether it is fair to impose a duty on the facts of a particular case. This simple process is then screened by result-pulled reasoning that may or may not employ some of Lord Bridge's 'labels' to mask what is essentially a policy decision taken by the court. The current label that is most fashionably used by the courts is 'assumption of responsibility'. This may be a facet of proximity or reasonable foreseeability or both. In practice it does not really matter much as the courts will decide on the facts and having weighed questions of policy whether or not one party has assumed responsibility towards another.

So in what situations will a duty of care be imposed to take care not to cause purely economic loss? It seems that there are three such situations.

(a) 'Quasi-contractual': that is where a direct contractual relationship exists between the claimant and defendant or where the relationship between the two of them is such that it is at least quasi-contractual.
(b) 'Negligent misstatement': where the defendant has made a negligent statement to (or for the benefit of) the claimant in circumstances where the defendant knows that the claimant may rely on that statement to his or her detriment and the claimant does in fact so rely on the statement and sustains loss.
(c) 'Provision of services': where the defendant is retained by another party to provide (usually professional) services and is or should be aware that those services are for the benefit of the claimant third party (i.e. not a party to the contract) who is likely to suffer economic loss if the service is performed negligently (see, for example, *White v. Jones*).

It is in the last two of these three situations that the language of 'assumption of responsibility' is most often employed. In practice, whatever the language used, there is little to choose between the *Caparo* 'three-stage test' or the 'assumption of responsibility' test. However, the use of 'assumption of responsibility' in the last two situations serves to illustrate that for liability to arise in these circumstances there must be a readily identifiable assumption of responsibility on the part of the defendant. Put another way (or to use the *Caparo* test), there must be a very close relationship of proximity between defendant and claimant for a duty of care to be imposed. This will certainly be the case where the defendant undertakes to render a service or statement which is designed to confer on the claimant the economic benefit of which he or she has been deprived as a result of the defendant's negligence, or is designed to protect the claimant from the same kind of economic loss as has been suffered. In such circumstances, an assumption of responsibility on the part of the defendant will be readily identifiable. This type of assumption of responsibility now often provides the touchstone of liability at the frontiers of the law of tort where it is unclear whether a duty of care should be imposed.

In *Tesco Stores Ltd v. Costain Construction Ltd* [2003] EWHC 1487 (TCC); (2003) CILL 2062 the court found that a building contractor did owe a duty of care to his employer not to cause economic loss. *Tesco* clarifies what many have long suspected namely that:

(a) *Murphy v. Brentwood District Council* [1991] 1 AC 398 did not decide that a builder/contractor will never owe a duty of care not to cause economic loss to his employer/the building owner. To the extent that HHJ Humphrey Lloyd QC found to the contrary in *Samuel Payne v. John Setchell*

Ltd [2002] BLR 489 then he was wrong to do so and his judgement ought not to be followed.
(b) Rather, *Murphy* decided that a duty not to cause economic loss will not be owed in the absence of a special relationship between builder and employer.
(c) Such a special relationship will exist where the builder consciously undertakes a responsibility for design under the terms of his contract: *Storey v. Charles Church Developments Ltd* (1996) 12 Const LJ 206.
(d) In fact, where a party undertakes by contract to perform a service for another upon terms, express or implied, that the service will be performed with reasonable skill and care, it will also owe a duty of care to like effect to the other contracting party which extends to not causing economic loss. There is no reason for the law not to apply this general principle to the case of a builder or a designer of a building (The court also suggested obiter relying on *Bellefield Computer Services Ltd v. E. Turner & Sons Ltd* [2000] BLR 97 that the duty may also be owed to a subsequent building owner).

Thus Costain (the building contractor) was found to owe to Tesco a duty to take reasonable skill and care not to cause economic loss in respect of both physical works of construction and design work which Costain itself undertook pursuant to its contract with Tesco.

This decision was based squarely on the development of the law following *Henderson v. Merrett Syndicates Ltd* and *Stovin v. Wise* [1996] AC 923. It would seem to follow that, even where a builder's contract provides for him to build only and not to design but where the builder voluntarily undertakes works of design, he will owe a duty of care to his client (and arguably, following *Bellefield*, to a subsequent purchaser too) in respect of both the construction and the design work which he himself undertakes.

Importantly, Costain's duty of care was found not to extend to work which Costain did not undertake itself but which (to the knowledge of all parties) was performed by others (The court distinguished the un-loved decision of HHJ Stabb QC to contrary effect in *Cynat Products Ltd v. Landbuild (Investment and Property) Ltd* [1984] 3 All ER 513). This demonstrates the important effect of the contractual matrix that exists between the parties on the scope of any duty of care in tort that may be found to be owed.

Case Summary: Tesco v. Costain

Tesco Stores Ltd v. Costain Construction Ltd & ors. [2003] EWHC 1487 (TCC)

C, a contractor, and P, a firm of architects, were involved in the construction of a Tesco superstore which was subsequently damaged in a fire which broke out during the course of later works by other contractors. Tesco (T) contended that the spread of the fire was due to the absence of proper fire stopping measures at the store.

As against C, it was contended that the contractor had acted in breach of the contract by which it agreed to design and construct the store; that it had been negligent in failing to provide appropriate fire stopping and inhibiting measures within the store as constructed; and that it had been negligent in relation to a later inspection and report into the adequacy of the fire stopping and inhibiting measures in place. C denied that it had entered into any concluded contract with T for the construction of the store, but admitted that it had in fact constructed the store; it denied that it owed the tortious duties to T contended for, and in particular denied that it owed any duties in respect of the design of the store; it contended that the subsequent inspection of the store's fire stopping and inhibiting measures had been carried out competently; and it argued that T's claims were statute barred (as to which see Section 23.2.6 of this chapter). As against P, it was common ground that the firm owed express contractual duties in relation to the construction of the store as set out in an agreement between T and P, and that P owed T a duty of care in tort to perform its obligations under that agreement with the care and skill to be expected of reasonably competent architects. P denied, however, that it owed any implied contractual duties save for a duty to exercise reasonable skill and care, arguing that the contract was comprehensive. P also ran a limitation argument (as to which, again, see section 23.2.6 below). P denied any involvement in the later inspection of fire stopping and inhibiting measures at the store, which involvement was only contended for by C.

In a lengthy judgement, His Honour Judge Seymour QC considered certain preliminary issues as to the alleged contractual and tortious liability of C and P. The duties found to have been owed by C in respect of the initial construction of the store are of most interest in the context of this chapter. As to this issue, it was held on the facts that a contract was entered into as a result of the counter-signing by C of a 'letter of intent' sent to it by T. The terms of that letter and therefore that contract were simple, with C only expressly agreeing to undertake the work which it was to undertake (either itself or by subcontractors) in relation to the store. This did not include design work which others had already undertaken or had contracted directly with T to undertake. It was, however, an implied term of the contract that C would perform any construction work which it undertook under the contract in a good and workmanlike manner and that, insofar as any design decision in relation to the store was made by C, the element designed would be reasonably fit for its intended purpose. C also owed T a duty of care in tort, but this too was limited to a duty to execute any building or design work which C in fact carried out itself (in respect of which such design work the judge gave the example of a carpenter choosing which nail or screw to use) with the care and skill to be expected of a reasonably competent building contractor so as not to cause damage to person or property or economic loss.

While the decision in *Tesco* provides helpful guidance, the existence of a duty of care will still turn on the facts of each particular case and, in particular, on the contractual context in which a duty of care in tort is also said to arise. Generally speaking, a duty of care in tort will not be found to exist where its existence would conflict with the contractual regime put in place by the parties.

A good example here is the decision in *Robinson v. PE Jones (Contractors) Ltd.*

Case Summary

Robinson v. PE Jones (Contractors) Ltd [2010] EWHC 102 (TCC)

J, a builder, built and sold a house to R. Twelve years later, a gas service engineer discovered and advised that one of the gas fires in the property had a 'poor flue run'. A surveyor then investigated and found that the flues had not been constructed in accordance with good building practice or the applicable Building Regulations. Two years after that, R brought a claim against J. Since a claim for breach of contract would have been statute barred (as to which see the section on Limitation at section 23.2.6 below), R opted to pursue his claim in tort, contending, in reliance on s.14A of the Limitation Act 1980, that that tortious claim was not statute barred because it was brought less than 3 years after he first acquired knowledge of the defect in question. J argued that R should have had the fires serviced annually, or at least much earlier than he did, such that he should be deemed to have acquired the requisite knowledge of the defect more than 3 years before the commencement of the action.

The court considered as preliminary issues (i) whether J owed a duty of care in tort to R, and (ii) whether R's claims in tort were statute barred. In relation to issue (i), the court considered whether a builder could owe his client a duty of care in tort in respect of economic loss concurrent with his contractual duty. It was held that, in principle, he could. A builder did not generally owe a duty of care to a subsequent owner or occupier of a property who had suffered economic loss, but that did not apply where the owner in question was the original client who had entered into a contract with the builder and with whom the builder therefore had a special relationship of proximity. Amongst other cases, the court considered the decision in *Tesco v. Costain* (above). However, on the facts of the case, it was found that J did not owe a duty of care in tort to R. The building conditions annexed to the contract which they had entered into provided that J would not be liable to R for a defect except during the period provided for by the NHBC's standard form of agreement which they had entered into, and that period had now elapsed. There was no good basis for challenging that exclusion clause: it actually operated to prevent a tortious duty arising, and did not fall to be struck through pursuant to the Unfair Contract Terms Act 1977 (as to which see section 23.2.6 of this chapter). Accordingly, no tortious duty could be relied on by R. As to issue (ii), limitation (as to which again see section 23.2.6 below), the court found that, if J had owed a tortious duty of care to R, his claim would not have been statute barred as R did not have either actual or constructive knowledge of the defect more than 3 years before proceedings were issued. R had been entitled to take the view during the first 12 years after construction of the property that the gas fires were simple appliances which did not require servicing but only repair as and when it became necessary.

What then, is the current approach for determining if a duty of care is owed in a novel situation? In such circumstances, the Court is effectively presented with a variety of analytical approaches from which it may choose in assessing whether or not a duty should be owed. The approaches are the 'assumption of responsibility', 'three-stage test' and 'the incremental approach'. Recent guidance on the interrelationship between these approaches was given by the House of Lords in *Her Majesty's Commissioners of Customs and Excise v. Barclays Bank plc* [2006] UKHL 28; [2007] 1 AC 181 where Lord Mance said this:

> [93] This review of authority confirms that there is no single common denominator, even in cases of economic loss, by which liability may be determined. The three-fold test of foreseeability, proximity and fairness, justice and reasonableness provides a convenient general framework although it operates at so high a level of abstraction. Assumption of responsibility is particularly useful as a concept in the two core categories of case identified by Lord Browne-Wilkinson in White *v.* Jones (at p. 274B-C), when it may effectively subsume all aspects of the three-fold approach. But if all that is meant by voluntary assumption of responsibility is the voluntary assumption of responsibility for a task, rather than of liability towards the defendant, then questions of foreseeability, proximity and fairness, reasonableness and justice may be very relevant. In White *v.* Jones itself there was no doubt that the solicitor had voluntarily undertaken responsibility for a task, but it was the very fact that he had done so for the testator, not the disappointed beneficiary, that gave rise to the stark division of opinion in the House. Incrementalism operates as an important cross-check on any other approach.

This tends to suggest that whichever approach is employed (or a combination of them) the same result ought to be reached. For recent applications of *Caparo*, see *Van Colle v. Chief Constable of Hertfordshire* [2008] UKHL 50; [2009] 1 AC 225, *Jain v. Trent SHA* [2009] UKHL 4; [2009] 1 AC 853 (para. 27), *Mitchell v. Glasgow City Council* [2009] UKHL 11; [2009] 1 AC 874, *Stone & Rolls v. Moore Stephens* [2009] UKHL 39; [2009] 1 AC 1391.

The courts have recently had to grapple with a number of cases where it was alleged that a provider of information or the maker of a statement owed a duty of care to a recipient of that information or statement who had acted upon it. Thus, in *The Law Society v. KPMG* [2000] Lloyds Rep PN 929 (paras [12]–[13]) in which Lord Woolf held that accountants retained by solicitors to prepare an annual report to the Law Society owed a duty of care to the Law Society:

> 12. [Sir Richard Scott V-C, the judge at first instance] applied the three criteria which must be met for there to be a duty of care identified by Lord Bridge of Harwich in Caparo Industries plc *v.* Dickman [1990] 1 All ER 568 at 573–574, [1990]

2 AC 605 at 617–619, namely: (a) reasonable foreseeability of damage; (b) a relationship of sufficient 'proximity' between the party owing the duty and the party to whom it is owed; and (c) the imposition of the duty of care contended for would be just and reasonable in all the circumstances.

> 13. Sir Richard Scott V-C also referred to the passage in the speech of Lord Oliver of Aylmerton in the Caparo Industries case. Based upon the decision of the House of Lords in *Hedley Byrne & Co Ltd v. Heller & Partners Ltd* [1963] 2 All ER 575, [1964] AC 465, Lord Oliver listed the circumstances which should exist in order to establish the necessary relationship of proximity between the person claiming to be owed the duty and the adviser:

> … (1) the advice is required for a purpose, whether particularly specified or generally described, which is made known, either actually or inferentially, to the adviser at the time the advice is given, (2) the adviser knows, either actually or inferentially, that his advice will be communicated to the advisee, either specifically or as a member of an ascertainable class, in order that it should be used by the advisee for that purpose, (3) it is known, either actually or inferentially, that the advice so communicated is likely to be acted upon by the advisee for that purpose without independent inquiry and (4) it is so acted upon by the advisee to his detriment. (See [1990] 1 All ER 568 at 589, [1990] 2 AC 605 at 638.)

In the Scottish case of *RBS v. Bannerman* [2005] CSIH 39 (para. 41), Lord MacFadyen, after a detailed review of the cases, concluded that there was:

> … a consistent line of authority that finds proximity in the act of making the information or advice available in the knowledge that it will be passed to the pursuer for a specific purpose and is likely to be relied on by him for that purpose.

While these dicta suggest that a duty of care may be imposed in favour of a third party recipient of information or advice in particular circumstances, it is right to acknowledge that these passages also indicate that in order for such a duty to be imposed there has to be a relatively close degree of proximity (to move from the incremental to the three-stage test) as between the information provider and the recipient of the information for a duty to be owed. The key to the imposition or otherwise of the duty is that the information provider should know (actually or inferentially) that the information it provides will be provided to a class (one might add 'identifiable' here) of potential recipients to which the third party claimant belongs and should know also that the information so-provided and received is likely to be acted upon.

What the Courts have been concerned to do is to limit those who can bring claims against the maker of widely published statements for fear of opening the flood gates to claims from an indeterminate number of claimants and thus giving rise to indeterminate liabilities. Thus, while a duty has been found to be owed in cases such as *The Law Society*, no duty of care was found to be owed by auditors of company accounts to investors who purchased shares in reliance on those accounts (*Caparo*, above) and no duty of care was found to be owed by a classification society which surveyed vessels for the purposes of maintaining class to a purchaser of the vessel who relied on the classification survey when completing the purchase ('The *Morning Watch*' [1990] 1 Lloyd's Rep. 547 and see also *Marc Rich & Co AG v. Bishop Rock Marine Co Ltd* [1996] AC 211). These examples show the importance of the purpose for which the information or advice is provided in considering whether a duty of care should be owed (to a third party recipient of that information or advice) (paras 2–116; Powell et al., 2007). Thus, the auditor producing audited accounts pursuant to statute owes no duty to the investor who purchases shares in the company whose accounts are being audited. Similarly, the classification survey is provided for the purposes of maintaining class and not for enabling a purchaser to decide whether or not to purchase the vessel.

While it is important to have these considerations and analytical approaches in mind, in the construction field the contractual matrix and relationships between the various parties will often prove to be determinative of whether a duty of care was owed.

23.2.2 Breach of duty

Once it has been established that a duty of care was owed by the defendant, the next question is whether the defendant has acted in breach of that duty. This requires an assessment of whether the defendant's conduct has fallen below the standard of care required by the duty. The standard of care is a question of law, but whether or not the defendant has failed to attain the requisite standard is a question of fact and so will depend on the circumstances of each case.

The standard of care is an objective standard which usually means that the defendant's conduct is measured against the conduct of the 'reasonable man'. In the past, this fictional reasonable man would take the form of the man on the Clapham omnibus, but it may be that the woman in the Ford Focus is a more appropriate test today.

If the defendant holds him or herself out as a person possessing a special skill he or she will not be judged against the 'reasonable man' but against the conduct of an ordinarily competent person possessing that special skill. Thus, an engineer will be judged against the conduct to be expected of the ordinarily competent engineer.

In addition to defendants possessing special skill, the standard required of the defendant may be modified by special circumstances in which the defendant acts (for example, the fact that the defendant is acting in an emergency situation and/or as a rescuer) and the legal capacity of the defendant (for example a child will be judged by the conduct to be expected of a child rather than an adult – see *McHale v. Watson* (1966) 115 CLR 866 as discussed and approved in *Orchard v. Lee* [2009] EWCA Civ 295).

Further, the court may consider the following matters when assessing the standard of care.

(a) Foreseeability of loss: defendants should take steps to guard against causing loss that is a reasonably foreseeable consequence of not acting as they should.
(b) Degree of risk: in short, the greater the risk, the more care should be taken (see *Glasgow Corporation v. Muir* [1943] AC 448 at 456 and *Bolton v. Stone* [1951] AC 850 at 860, both recently applied in *Whippey v. Jones* [2009] EWCA Civ 452).
(c) Degree of loss: the more dire the consequences of failing to take care, the higher the degree of care that should be taken to avoid causing it.

Against these three factors is weighed the expense and difficulty in taking care to avoid the risk. As Lord Reid put it

> … a reasonable man would only neglect a risk if he had some valid reason for doing so, e.g. that it would involve considerable expense to eliminate the risk. He would weigh the risk against the difficulty of eliminating it.
>
> *Overseas Tankship (UK) Ltd v. The Miller Steamship Co. Pty (The Wagon Mound (No. 2))* [1967] 1 AC 617 at 642. (and see *Grieves v. FT Everard & Sons Ltd* [2008] 1 AC 281 at para. 29).

As far as evidence is concerned, in *Bolam v. Friern Hospital Management Committee* [1957] 1 WLR 582 McNair J drew the distinction between, on the one hand, 'the ordinary case which does not involve any special skill' and, on the other hand, the 'situation which involves the use of some special skill or competence'. In the former case, negligence is judged by 'the conduct of the man on the top of the Clapham omnibus' and in the latter case 'the test is the standard of the ordinary skilled man exercising and professing to have that special skill'. Accordingly, in cases where the defendant has exercised a special skill then it will usually be sufficient for the defendant to show that he or she acted in accordance with the way that a recognised body of those in that particular field would regard as reasonable. This 'Bolam' test has been qualified, however. In *Bolitho v. City of Hackney Health Authority* [1998] AC 232, it was held that it is not always the case that an opinion held by a recognised body can withstand logical analysis and therefore be relied upon. Also, in *Nye Saunders & Partners v. Alan E Bristow* (1987) 37 BLR 92 it was held that expert evidence given to the court of other professional opinion was just the personal view of the expert rather than the view held by a recognised body.

23.2.3 Duties in the construction industry

Having reviewed these basic concepts in the tort of negligence it is worth considering a few examples of how these can operate in a construction environment.

Contractor

A contractor will owe a duty not to cause physical damage (be it to property or person) to those whom it can reasonably foresee might suffer loss as a result of negligence on the contractor's part. Following the decision in *Tesco*, a duty not to cause economic loss may well be imposed particularly where such a duty is concurrent, and co-extensive in scope, with contractual duties owed by the contractor. Further, where a contractor undertakes design functions under a design and build contract a claimant may well be able to show that there has been such an assumption of responsibility, at least in so far as design is concerned, that a duty of care will be owed.

Construction professional

A construction professional will owe a client a duty to employ a reasonable standard of skill and care in carrying out a retainer as would be expected of an ordinarily competent professional practising in the same discipline. The scope of this duty will often be determined by the contract between the professional and the client and, indeed, a term will usually be implied that the professional will exercise reasonable skill and care when performing the contract (Supply of Goods and Services Act 1982, s.13).

The existence of a contract will not prevent the existence of concurrent duties in tort (see *Henderson v. Merrett* and the discussion above). The claimant is entitled to rely on whichever action is the more favourable.

A key advantage of having the option to sue in tort as well as in contract is that the action in tort will benefit from more advantageous limitation periods. In contract law, time begins to run from the date of breach whereas in tort, time will not run until damage has been sustained. In addition, the tortious action benefits from the alternative limitation period provided for latent defects.

A construction professional, just like the contractor, will owe duties to take reasonable care so as to avoid causing damage to property or persons that is reasonably foreseeable. However, it seems unlikely that a construction professional will owe a duty to someone other than his or her employer (who may be able to show the requisite assumption of responsibility) in respect of purely economic loss (e.g. it is highly unlikely that a professional will be found to owe a general duty to the main contractor (who is not his or her employer) on a project to hold him harmless from economic loss). This will require exceptional circumstances and while there is no case where it has as yet been established, it is by no means impossible.

For a much more detailed discussion see Chapter 9 of Powell et al. 2007.

23.2.4 Causation

Once the claimant has been able to show that the defendant owed it a duty of care and has acted in breach of that duty, the claimant will then have to show that the breach caused the loss of which it complains.

The starting point for this inquiry is to ask: 'but for' the defendant's negligence, would the claimant have suffered the loss? (the so-called 'but for' test). A good example of this test in action is to be found in *Barnett v. Chelsea and Kensington*

Hospital Management [1969] 1 QB 428. Here the claimant's husband went to casualty complaining of feeling ill after drinking some tea. The doctor refused to examine him and sent him home. The gentleman then died of arsenic poisoning. The court held that the doctor's negligence did not cause the death because it would have been too late to treat the poison even if the doctor had seen him in the casualty department. That is to say, but for the negligence, the same harm or loss would have been suffered.

The 'but for' test can be difficult to answer. It frequently involves hypothesising about what someone would have done had the defendant not acted in breach of duty. For example, in a case where it is alleged that a defendant construction professional provided negligent advice, the claimant must be able to show that he would have acted differently, thereby avoiding the loss which occurred, if given proper advice. Cases where there is more than one potential cause of the claimant's loss also give rise to particular problems. Take for example the situation where there are four different possible causes of the loss, of which only one is attributable to negligence on the part of the defendant, and it cannot be ascertained which of the possible causes was in fact the cause of the claimant's loss. Each might have a 25% chance of causing the loss, but as a general rule it does not follow that the claimant will succeed on 25% of the claim. On the contrary, given that the claimant must prove the case against the defendant on the balance of probabilities (more than 50%) the claim will fail – see *Wilsher v. Essex AHA* [1988] AC 1074. However, there are certain circumstances in which the court is prepared to bridge the 'evidential gap' as to which of the potential causes in fact caused the claimant's loss. The claimant does not have to prove that the defendant's breach of duty was the sole, or even the main, cause of his loss provided that he can demonstrate that it made a material contribution to the damage. Moreover in some cases the court has been prepared to say that causation is established provided that the negligent act complained of materially contributed to the risk of damage. In *Fairchild v. Glenhaven Funeral Services Ltd* [2003] 1 AC 32, the House of Lords considered the situation in which an employee has been negligently exposed to asbestos while in the employ of a number of different employers, and has contracted mesothelioma. The mesothelioma has been contracted due to exposure to asbestos, but it cannot be determined in the employ of which employer the causative exposure took place. It was held that the claimant could succeed against a particular former employer even though he could not prove on the balance of probabilities that the exposure which caused the mesothelioma occurred during the period of employment by that employer. This is a complex area and the limits of the so-called 'Fairchild exception' remain somewhat uncertain. Further clarification of the position (and a further departure from *Wilsher*) was provided in the decision of the House of Lords in *Barker v. Corus* [2006] AC 572. This makes it clear that each defendant who is caught by the *Fairchild* exception is liable only in proportion to its own contribution to the injury or risk of injury.

There is also a difficulty with subsequent causes of the claimant's loss. For example, in *Performance Cars v. Abraham* [1962] 1 QB 33 the defendant negligently drove into the claimant's car which had been damaged by another driver just a few days before. Both collisions caused damage that required the car to be resprayed and the court held that, as a result, the defendant had not caused the claimant's loss – the car would have had to have been resprayed in any event.

However, in *Baker v. Willoughby* [1970] AC 467 the unlucky claimant had his leg injured by the defendant in a car accident. Subsequently, but before the case came to court, the claimant was shot in the same leg by an armed robber and the leg had to be amputated. This was a different case from *Performance Cars* as, here, the second tortfeasor (the robber) had made the situation worse. However, the House of Lords rejected the argument that the defendant should only be liable for the loss caused by the original injury up to the date of the shooting. The first injury was still a cause of the claimant's unfortunate condition, it had not been subsumed by the second, and the defendant's responsibility was to be assessed as if the second incident had never occurred.

It is perhaps not surprising that this reasoning has been the subject of criticism. In *Jobling v. Associated Dairies* [1982] AC 794 the claimant suffered an injury at work and then from a natural disease. The House of Lords upheld the decision in *Baker* on its facts and suggested that the reasoning in that case may be appropriate where there are two successive torts. This was easy to justify on the basis that if the first tortfeasor were not to remain liable then the claimant would be left under-compensated because the second tortfeasor would be able to rely on *Performance Cars* to escape liability. However, where the claimant has suffered first a tort and then the onset of a natural disease, the latter falls to be treated as a vicissitude of life and the defendant will only be liable up until the intervention of the disease. The disease is treated as the cause of the claimant's continuing condition. How far the reasoning in *Baker* can be sustained is open to real doubt, particularly in circumstances where a second tortfeasor has made a condition worse or where two torts combine to achieve a result that each on their own would not have caused. Certainly, the recent trend has been to follow the path established in *Jobling* and to distinguish and even to disapprove of the approach used in *Baker*: see *Gray v. Thames Trains Ltd* [2009] AC 1. This is of particular relevance in the construction industry where the possibility of multiple causes is high. For example, a defect in a building may have been caused by a combination of poor design and substandard workmanship; determining whether either or both of designer and builder should be liable will depend on the considerations discussed here.

Also important is the concept of a 'new intervening act' or 'new intervening cause' which may break the 'chain of causation' between a defendant's breach of duty and the claimant's loss. This concept is often referred to by its Latin name: a '*novus actus interveniens*'. The basic principle is that, in some cases, even though a breach of duty on the part of the defendant sets in motion a sequence of events which leads to the claimant's loss, things may have happened in the interim which make it unjust that the defendant should be held legally responsible for that loss. The intervening cause can be an act of nature, an act or omission by a third party, or an act or omission by the claimant himself, but in order to break the chain of causation the new intervening cause will need to be of such impact that it effectively eclipses the wrongdoing of the defendant. A classic example is the case of *Knightley v. Johns* [1982] 1 WLR 349. The first defendant's negligence caused the blockage of a road tunnel. The second defendant, a police officer, took charge. He did not immediately close the tunnel, which should have been standard practice. He later instructed the claimant, a police motorcyclist, to ride the wrong way back through the tunnel, to ensure that the tunnel was closed. The claimant was hit and injured by the third defendant who was driving too fast into the tunnel. The Court of Appeal found that the sequence of events subsequent to the original negligence eclipsed the first defendant's wrongdoing and he should not be held liable.

An interesting example in a construction context of how it might be argued that the chain of causation might be broken and the inter-play between such arguments and foreseeability of loss may be found in *Pearson Education Ltd v. Charter Partnership Ltd* [2007] B.L.R. 324.

Case Summary

Pearson Education Ltd v. Charter Partnership Ltd [2007] B.L.R. 324

A company of architects, C, had responsibility for the design of the rainwater system at a warehouse. The claimant, P, suffered financial loss when books that it owned and was storing at the warehouse were damaged in a flood. It was common ground that the cause of the flood was inadequate drainage capacity and that in specifying that capacity (75 mm rather than 150 mm) C had failed to exercise reasonable skill and care. Eight years before, there had been a previous flood which caused damage to property stored in the warehouse while it was leased to another company, I. After that incident, loss adjusters appointed by the insurers of I's books had discovered that the capacity of the rainwater system was inadequate, but that information was not communicated to I. C argued that the first flood brought its potential liability to an end. Its arguments, described by the Court as 'variations on a theme', were that: (i) it was not reasonably foreseeable that any further damage would flow from its defective design once the defect had led to a flood, since it was reasonable to expect that that first flood would lead to the identification of the defect; (ii) it was not fair, just and reasonable that C's duty of care should extend beyond the occurrence of the first flood; and (iii) the occurrence of the first flood broke the chain of causation between its negligence and the loss suffered by P. C also argued that P's claim was statute barred (as to which see section 23.2.6 of this chapter, below), relying on s.14B of the Limitation Act 1980, because the act or omission giving rise to the damage complained of had taken place more than 15 years prior to the claim being issued.

The Court of Appeal, dismissing C's appeal from the decision of the trial judge, held that there was no reason, when C specified the capacity of the rainwater system, for it to expect that an inspection would be carried out which would reveal any error it might make. It was reasonably foreseeable that, if C specified an inadequate drainage system for the warehouse, owners of property within the warehouse might suffer water damage to their property. The test of foreseeability in the context of duty of care did not require foresight of the precise sequence of events which resulted in damage. P did not know, and nor ought it to have known, about the first flood, so there was no reason why it should have carried out any investigation into the adequacy of the rainwater system. The Court could see 'no basis of principle or authority' why the fact that a latent defect had become known to a third party should be deemed to make the defect patent to others who neither knew nor ought to have known of it. The first flood and the inspection to which it gave rise did not place P outside the range of the duty of care owed by C, nor did it break the chain of causation between C's negligence and the damage caused to P's property. C's limitation defence also failed as its specification of a design capacity for the rainwater system which it ought to have known would be inadequate had occurred within the applicable limitation period.

What has also become clear in recent years is that a claimant must prove that his or her loss has been caused by the defendant in the sense that the type of loss caused was within the scope of the duty owed by the defendant to the claimant (see *South Australia Asset Management v. York Montague Limited* [1997] AC 191). A defendant may only 'assume responsibility' to the claimant for certain matters and so the defendant in breach of that duty will only be liable for loss that falls within the scope of the duty that he or she has assumed. This concept – called the SAAMCO principle (taking its name from one of the parties in the case) – influences considerations of duty, causation, remoteness and damages and so merits consideration in some detail. While SAAMCO impacts on each of these areas, Lord Hoffmann has taken the view that the principle is one of causation and so it is dealt with here. Nevertheless, SAAMCO should also be borne in mind in considering remoteness and damages (below).

SAAMCO was actually a number of joined appeals considered by the House of Lords. The common feature of the cases was that in each the plaintiff had instructed the defendant valuers to value properties which were to provide security for mortgage advances to be made by the plaintiffs. In each case, the defendants negligently overvalued the properties. The advances were made and, subsequently, the borrowers defaulted. The lenders were left with insufficient security to cover their losses. In the meantime, the property market had fallen sharply, thereby increasing the losses suffered by the lenders. The question that fell to be decided was to what extent could the plaintiffs recover the extensive losses that they had suffered?

The Court of Appeal ([1995] QB 375) held that in circumstances where the lender would not have entered into the transaction if the valuation had been accurate, the lender was entitled to recover from the negligent valuer the net loss of having made the advance. The Court of Appeal considered that the starting point for determining the measure of damages was that the damages ought, insofar as it was possible, to put the plaintiff in the position in which it would have been had it not suffered the wrong committed by the defendant. Lord Hoffmann, who gave the only speech in the House of Lords, disagreed ([1997] AC 191 at 211A–B):

> I think that this was the wrong place to begin. Before one can consider the principle on which one should calculate the damages to which a Plaintiff is entitled as compensation for loss, it is necessary to decide for what kind of loss he is entitled to compensation. A correct description of the loss for which the valuer is liable must precede any consideration of the measure of damages. For this purpose it is better to begin at the beginning and consider the lender's cause of action.

The starting point, then, must be the duty owed to the lender and its scope. Lord Hoffmann was at pains to suggest that such a duty does not exist in the abstract and that the lender must show that the duty owed was in respect of the kind of loss which it has suffered (see 211H). He then went on to set out the general principle (at 214C–F).

> It is that a person under a duty to take reasonable care to provide information on which someone else will decide upon a course of action is, if negligent, not generally regarded as responsible for all the consequences of that course of action. He is responsible only for the consequences of the information being wrong. A duty of care which imposes upon the informant responsibility for losses which would have occurred even if the information which he gave had been correct is not in my view fair and reasonable as between the parties. It is therefore inappropriate either as an implied term of a contract or as a tortious duty arising from the relationship between them.
>
> The principle thus stated distinguishes between a duty to *provide information* for the purpose of enabling someone else to decide upon a course of action and a duty to *advise* someone as to what course of action he should take. If the duty is to advise whether or not a course of action should be taken, the adviser must take reasonable care to consider all the potential consequences of that course of action. If he is negligent, he will therefore be responsible for all the foreseeable loss which is a consequence of that course of action having been taken. If his duty is only to supply information, he must take reasonable care to ensure that the information is correct and, if he is negligent, will be responsible for all the foreseeable consequences of the information being wrong.

The valuer had a duty to provide information and not advice. The consequence of the information being wrong was that the lender's security was worth less than the valuation suggested it was. The limit of the loss recoverable from the valuer was thus the difference between the valuation given and the true value of the property at the date of the valuation. Only loss that fell within this sum was loss properly referable to the valuer's duty.

This principle is perhaps best understood by looking at how it was applied to the facts of the cases under appeal in SAAMCO. In SAAMCO itself, the negligent valuation was £15 million. In fact, the actual value of the property at the time of the valuation was £5 million. Accordingly, the maximum liability of the valuers was £10 million. The lender had advanced £11 million and the sale of the property realised only £2.5 million. The total loss incurred by the lender was some £9.7 million. As Lord Hoffmann put it, at 222B–C:

> The consequence of the valuation being wrong was that the Plaintiffs had £10 million less security than they thought. If they had had this margin, they would have suffered no loss. The whole loss was therefore within the scope of the Defendant's duty.

In the other appeals, however, not all of the loss suffered by the lenders was within the scope of the valuer's duty. Thus, in *United Bank of Kuwait Plc v. Prudential Property Services Limited* the valuation was £2.5 million and the advance £1.75 million. The trial judge found that the correct value of the property had been between £1.8 million and £1.85 million. The lender's total loss as a result of the fall in the property market was quantified at £1.3 million and the trial judge awarded this sum in damages. Lord Hoffmann argued (at 222D) that this was wrong because:

> the damages should have been limited to the consequences of the valuation being wrong, which were that the lenders had £700 000 or £650 000 less security than they thought.

The lender's argument that the overvaluation increased the risk of default by the borrower was also rejected, with Lord Hoffmann saying this on the matter (at 222E):

> The greater risk of default, if such there was, is only another reason why the lender, if he had known the true facts, would not have entered into the particular transaction. But that does not affect the scope of the valuer's duty.

It is the scope of the duty of care that determines the extent of the valuer's liability and not whether the case is a 'no transaction' or a 'successful transaction'.

In the final appeal, *Nykredit Mortgage Bank Plc v. Edward Erdman Group Ltd*, the damages were again reduced to the difference between the negligent overvaluation and the true value of the property at the date of valuation. The lender in this appeal advanced one further argument which was that in this case the loan was made to a single asset company in order to finance the purchase and redevelopment of the property. The value of the property lay in its development value and the lender argued that if the valuation had been accurate, it would have appreciated that the development was not viable and that default was virtually inevitable. This argument was rejected by Lord Hoffmann, at 223F, as it was concerned with what the lender would have done if the valuation had been accurate, which was not the test of the valuer's liability.

Finally, it should be noted that Lord Hoffmann distinguished between the measure of damages in an action for breach of duty to take care to provide accurate information and that in an action for breach of a warranty that the information is accurate. In the former case, one must compare the loss which the claimant actually suffers with what its position would have been if it had not entered into the transaction and then ask what element of that loss is attributable to the inaccuracy of the information. In the latter case, the comparison is between the position in which the plaintiff finds itself and the position it would have been in if the information had been accurate (see 216D–F). Lord Hoffmann seems to have been moved by the idea that it would be strange, indeed unjust, if the measure in the former case were higher than in the latter; that liability for failing to take care could be more extensive than for giving an inaccurate warranty.

In general terms, the implications for the construction industry are likely to be that a greater emphasis will be placed on the extent and nature of the duty owed by the defendant to the claimant. It is therefore now even more important for those in the construction industry to be aware of the type and scope of the duties that they are assuming and to guard against 'assuming responsibility' for loss that they would rather avoid. The decision in SAAMCO is likely to be of most direct relevance to the industry in relation to the provision of information or advice (the distinction will be crucial) to a client which is used by him in deciding whether to proceed with a project. For example, in *HOK Sport Ltd v. Aintree Racecourse Co Ltd* [2002] EWHC 3094, it was held that the SAAMCO principle applied generally to claims against construction professionals and would be particularly important where (a) a professional is engaged to provide information for a specific project; (b) the client is to decide whether to proceed with the project; (c) the information to be provided by the professional is to be relied on by the client in the decision-making process; and (d) the decision is not participated in by the professional nor dependent upon his advice. In the HOK Sport case itself, the architect failed to warn the client racecourse owner that various design changes would result in fewer standing places than expected. The client therefore did not have an opportunity to redesign the project to remedy the loss of places. It was held that the architect's duty was to provide information as to the number of places which its design would provide; it was not to advise the client on whether it should postpone the project to allow for redesign. The loss which fell within the scope of the architect's duty was limited to the loss attributable to the racecourse owner's decision to proceed with the project on the incorrect assumption that a larger number of places would be provided (but cf. *Hancock v. Tucker* [1999] Lloyd's Rep. P.N. 814).

If, on analysis, what is provided is not merely information but advice as to whether to take a particular course then the defendant adviser is likely to be found to be liable for all the foreseeable consequences of that advice being wrong and the SAAMCO limiting principle will not apply: see *Aneco Reinsurance Underwriting Ltd v. Johnson* [2001] 2 ALL ER 929.

Issues of causation were considered in the case of *Baxall v. Sheard Walshaw* (see above), where the Court of Appeal considered whether the negligent designer can be liable for the losses caused by a defect after the owner should have known about the defect. The Court of Appeal answered this in the negative, reasoning that as soon as a defect becomes apparent ('patent') rather than hidden ('latent') then the owner must take steps to avoid the risk the defect presents. The Court of Appeal also said that where, as was the case in *Baxall*, the tenant did not know of the defect but *should have known*, then that defect becomes patent. The Court of Appeal also considered whether, where there are two defects in the design and one is hidden and one disclosed, the designer is liable for damage caused by the hidden defect if the damage in question would not have happened had the owner cured the disclosed defect. Again, and consistently, the Court of Appeal answered this in the negative. This would suggest that owners of new buildings should take care: it is not simply enough to say that you were not aware of a defect; if the defect was reasonably discoverable then you may fail on causation. However, note that *Baxall* was not applied in the recent case of *Pearson Education Ltd v. Charter Partnership Ltd* [2007] BLR 324 (a Case Summary of which is set out above). A firm of architects negligently designed a rainwater drainage system at a warehouse. This led to a flood which caused damage to property belonging to the claimant tenants. Eight years before this flood, when the warehouse was leased to a different company, there had been a previous flood. After that first flood, it had been discovered by loss adjusters that the capacity of the rainwater system was inadequate, but that information was not conveyed to the then tenants. The architects argued that the first flood brought their potential liability to an end in that it was not reasonably foreseeable that any further damage would flow from the defective design once it had led to a flood, as it was reasonable to expect that this would lead to the identification of the defect (see further below as to the concept of 'reasonable foreseeability'); that it was not fair, just or reasonable that their duty of care should extend beyond the occurrence of the first flood; and that the occurrence of the first flood broke the chain of causation between their negligence and the second flood. The Court of Appeal rejected this argument. There was no reason, when the architects specified the capacity of the drainage system, for them to expect that an inspection would be carried out that would reveal any error that it might make. The design shortcoming was truly latent: the claimants neither knew nor should have known of the first flood, so there was no reason why they should carry out any investigation into the adequacy of the drainage system.

Foreseeability and remoteness

The concept of foreseeability, as described above, plays an important role in determining whether a duty of care is owed, but it also has a role to play – once duty, breach and causation have been established – in determining whether the claimant can recover some or all of its loss. In short, the claimant must show that the loss which it has suffered was a reasonably foreseeable consequence of the defendant's negligence (*Overseas Tankship (UK) Ltd v. Miller Steamship Co. Pty (The Wagon Mound No. 2)* [1967] 1 AC 617). The test here is relatively easy to satisfy as even if the mere possibility of causing loss is contemplated by the defendant then this will be enough to fix the defendant with liability (*The Wagon Mound No. 2* [1967] 1 AC 617 and *The Heron II* [1969] 1 AC 350 at 385–389). If the loss is not reasonably foreseeable it is too remote and will be irrecoverable even though, as a matter of fact (though not law), the defendant has 'caused' the loss.

The claimant need not show that the extent of loss or the manner in which it suffered were foreseeable but simply that the type of loss suffered was a reasonably foreseeable consequence of the defendant's negligence (*Hughes v. Lords Advocate* [1963] AC 837). Thus, if personal injury is foreseeable it will not matter that the claimant has suffered more severe injuries than would otherwise be expected as a result of being particularly susceptible to that type of harm: the defendant must take the claimant as he or she is. This is the so-called 'egg-shell skull' rule and, while this is sometimes considered separately from the usual rules as to foreseeability and remoteness, the relationship between the concepts is clear.

23.2.5 Damages and the measure of loss

Damages in the law of tort are compensatory in nature and are designed, insofar as is possible, to put the claimant in the position it would have been in had the tort not been committed. Very rarely the courts will award exemplary damages which go beyond this and do more than compensate the claimant, although this is unlikely to occur in the construction context. This will usually involve a deliberate breach of duty by the defendant designed to result in a greater profit than any award of damages that the defendant will have to pay to compensate the claimant.

Broadly speaking, a claimant may suffer two types of loss: pecuniary and non-pecuniary. Where property is damaged, the usual measure of damages will be the cost of repair or the diminution in value of the property. The cost of repair will not be awarded if this would be unreasonable, for example, by being disproportionate to the value of the property in its repaired state; *Ruxley Electronics and Construction Ltd v. Forsyth* [1996] AC 344 (a case in contract but illustrative of the principle nevertheless).

Non-pecuniary loss most commonly arises in personal injury cases where the court will award damages in respect of the pain, suffering and loss of amenity caused to the claimant by his or her injuries. It is important to note that damages for disappointment and distress are not normally recoverable in either contract or tort, but where the claimant suffers anxiety and mental distress as a direct result of physical inconvenience caused by repairs to property, damages will be recoverable (*Watts v. Morrow* [1991] 4 All ER 937. Any award is likely to be modest and less than £1 000). This has particular relevance to the construction industry in the context of remedial works necessitated by faulty design or workmanship when the works were initially completed. Thus, the liability of the construction tortfeasor may not be limited merely to the costs of putting things right.

In recent years, an increasingly important remedy in terms of damages has been the development of the lost opportunity claim. In the ordinary course of events, in order to recover damages the claimant must prove on the balance of probabilities that it has suffered a loss. By way of contrast, in a lost opportunity claim, once the claimant has proved that it has lost an opportunity of some value the court may assess the value of the chance by making a series of deductions to reflect contingencies from the 'full' value of the chance had it materialised. This type of claim most often arises in the field of solicitors' negligence where, for example, by reason of the solicitor's negligence an otherwise good claim becomes statute barred (see below). The claimant in such circumstances cannot prove on the balance of probabilities that his or her claim definitely would have succeeded but instead can show that he or she has lost the chance of pursuing the defendant in the original action. If his or her claim was a good one, then the discount to be made to reflect, for example, the inherent risks of litigation and the chance of an early settlement of the claim at a figure below the full amount claimed, may be small, say 10–20%. This type of claim has an increasing relevance in the construction sphere. Thus, for example, in *Royal Brompton NHS Trust v. Hammond* [2002] 1 WLR 1397 the employer settled arbitration proceedings with the contractor and then brought claims against the professional team. Whereas the claim against the contractor was for delay in the completion of the works, the claim against the professional team was for the impairment of the employer's rights against the contractor.

23.2.6 Defences

There are several recognised defences to an action brought in negligence, the most common being voluntary assumption of risk, exclusions of liability and contributory negligence. The defence of limitation of actions is considered separately below.

Voluntary assumption of responsibility is a complete defence to an action brought in negligence – also known by the Latin maxim '*volenti non fit injuria*'. It will arise where the defendant can show that the claimant has freely assumed the risk of being harmed in the manner in which it has in fact been harmed by the defendant. The claimant must have acted freely and voluntarily in full knowledge of the risk it is agreeing to

run and accept that it is the claimant and not the defendant who is assuming responsibility for that risk. However, a claimant which exposes itself to risk in order to avert injury (be it to itself or others) is unlikely to be defeated by this defence. In the construction industry it is more likely that parties will have agreed to apportion the risk in respect of various types of loss between them. This may have the effect of excluding liability (see below) or simply meaning that a duty will not be owed in respect of the type of loss that is claimed.

It should be noted that, in practice, the defence of voluntary assumption only rarely succeeds, it being more common for a claimant to be found to have been only contributorily negligent and thus suffer a percentage reduction in damages rather than the claim failing altogether. This power is derived from the Law Reform (Contributory Negligence) Act 1945. Under Section 1(1) the court may reduce an award of damages to

> such an extent as the court thinks just and equitable, having regard to the claimant's share in the responsibility for the damage.

A claimant may not be 100% contributorily negligent as this amounts to a finding that the claimant rather than the defendant has caused the claimant's loss, and so the action against the defendant will fail completely.

It is important to bear in mind that the claimant is not under a duty to the defendant but to itself to take due care and that contributory negligence may arise even where the occasion of the claimant's loss is entirely a result of the defendant's conduct (an example being where the claimant fails to wear a seat belt and is involved in a collision caused by the defendant).

Turning finally to exclusions of liability, at common law a defendant could employ various devices in order to exclude or limit liability for negligence. For example:

(a) by an express contract with the claimant to that effect
(b) by giving the claimant notice that it was not accepting responsibility for harm caused to the claimant
(c) by issuing a disclaimer disclaiming responsibility for information or advice proffered to the claimant (as was the case in *Hedley Byrne v. Heller* [1964] AC 465)

However, the power of the defendant to do this is severely limited by the Unfair Contract Terms Act 1977 (UCTA). Section 2(1) prevents a defendant from excluding liability for personal injury and death. Nor can a defendant simply give the claimant notice excluding or restricting liability as the Act provides that mere awareness of the risk of harm on the part of the claimant is not effective to exclude liability on the part of the defendant. In all cases, liability can only be excluded in so far as the exclusion is reasonable (UCTA 1977, s.2(2)). Reasonableness is defined in Section 11 and Schedule 1.

Limitation

The defence of limitation is an important and useful tool for the defendant. A claimant must bring an action within a set period of time ('the limitation period') and failure to do so means that the action becomes 'statute barred'; that is barred by the Limitation Act 1980. The limitation periods for various different types of action are set out in the Act and the period for most torts, including negligence, is 3 years. It is important to note, however, that if the claim includes a claim in respect of personal injuries, then the period is 6 years.

Time, for the purposes of the limitation period, will begin to run when the claimant's cause of action accrues. Because a cause of action in negligence does not accrue until damage has been suffered, time will begin to run when the damage complained of occurs.

In the construction industry it will not always be easy to identify when damage has first been suffered. For example, in *Pirelli General Cable Works v. Oscar Faber and Partners* [1983] 2 AC 1 the House of Lords held that the cause of action for negligent advice in relation to the design of a building accrued when cracks were first visible rather than when the damage was reasonably discoverable. However, doubts have been raised concerning this decision (*Pirelli* was not followed by the Privy Council in *Invercargill City Council v. Hamlin* [1996] AC 624 but was followed by the Court of Appeal in *Abbott v. Will Gannon & Smith* [2005] PNLR 30 on the basis that it had not been overruled and could not be distinguished on the facts) and the position has in any event been altered by the Latent Damage Act 1986 which inserted Section 14A into the Limitation Act 1980. This section provides an alternative limitation period of 3 years from when the claimant had (or is deemed to have had) sufficient knowledge to enable the claim to be brought ('date of knowledge'). The relevant date of knowledge is when the claimant knew:

(a) that the relevant damage was sufficiently serious to justify proceedings;
(b) that the damage was attributable in whole or in part to an act or omission of the defendant; and
(c) the identity of the defendant.

These requirements mirror those of Section 14 which provides a similar alternative period for personal injury claims. In addition, for personal injury actions the court has discretion under Section 33 to, in effect, overlook the expiry of the limitation period if it considers it just and equitable to do so.

A further alternative limitation period is provided in Section 32 for cases involving fraud or deliberate concealment of facts relevant to the claimant's claim of 6 years from the date on which the fraud or concealment could, with reasonable diligence, have been discovered.

Finally, under Section 28, where the claimant is under a disability – that is an infant or of unsound mind – as at the date when the cause of action accrues, then time will not begin to run until such time as the disability ceases or when the claimant dies, whichever is the sooner.

Limitation is a substantial topic and further reference should be made to Chapter 33 of Clerk and Lindsell, 2006, and Chapter 5 of Jackson & Powell 2007.

23.3 Nuisance
23.3.1 Introduction
Nuisance divides into two categories: private and public. Apart from this distinction, commentators have found nuisance difficult to define. Possibly the best description is

> An act or omission which is an interference with, disturbance of or annoyance to, a person in the exercise or enjoyment of (a) a right belonging to him as a member of the public, when it is a public nuisance, or (b) his ownership or occupation of land or of some easement, profit, or other right used or enjoyed in connection with land, when it is a private nuisance.
>
> (Clerk and Lindsell, 2006; 20–01)

Nuisance and negligence share some of the same qualities, but there is an important difference between the two, namely that negligence is concerned with the protection of personal rights and nuisance is concerned with the protection of proprietary rights. However, both impose a similar standard of care on the potential tortfeasor and are subject to similar rules of causation and remoteness of damage. Damages for nuisance differ slightly to those for negligence because injunctive relief rather than damages is more often sought and gained.

Nuisance is an important factor in the construction industry because of the rules in relation to demolition and building and the effect they have on neighbouring land. It is also a factor to be aware of when planning new uses of land, for example a refinery or nuclear installation. In construction, knowing the restrictions in relation to nuisance may avoid unnecessary litigation at a later stage.

23.3.2 Public nuisance and statutory nuisance
Public nuisance has been described as 'an amorphous and unsatisfactory area of the law covering an ill-assorted collection of wrongs, some of which have little or no association with tort and only appear to fill a gap in the criminal law' (Deakin et al., 2008; p. 550). While this view may be a little extreme, it is true to say that there are very few similarities between public and private nuisance.

Public nuisance is actionable in both criminal and civil law. A person can sue for public nuisance without the requirement of an interest in land, unlike private nuisance.

A person can sue for public nuisance in civil law if it can be shown that he or she suffers special damage beyond inconvenience suffered by others who have also been affected (per Laurence LJ in *Harper v. Haden & Sons* [1933] Ch. 298 at 308). In order for an action to exist, the claimant must also show that a 'class' of people has been affected by the defendant's activities. The definition of a class has been held to be a matter of fact and degree.

Traditionally, public nuisance has been seen to cover the majority of 'highway' cases involving actions due to obstruction of the highway. This is particularly relevant to construction cases as building works will often affect the passage along highways or cause obstruction; for example, scaffolding on a building adjoining a busy main road.

In *Hubbard v. Pitt* [1976] QB 142 at 1491, the judge said:

> The vital characteristic of a highway is that it is land dedicated for a purpose; that purpose is for use by the public for passage to and fro.

At common law, the public have an implied easement of the right to access the highway. Any obstruction or prevention of access is actionable in tort as a public nuisance. Reasonableness of use will be taken into account in particular in access cases and courts will balance the competing interests of the ordinary member of the public and the user of the highway. So, for example, actions have failed where the court held that scaffolding erected for the construction of an additional storey to premises was a reasonable use (*Harper v. Haden & Sons*). In the recent case of *Hiscox Syndicates Ltd v. Pinnacle Ltd* [2008] EWHC 1386 (QB), when considering the variation of an injunction to enable, in effect, obstruction of the highway in connection with the construction of 'The Pinnacle' building in the City of London, Mr Justice Akenhead described it as 'eminently arguable that reasonable, temporary obstruction of the highway is or may be allowable before it becomes a public nuisance'; this will, however, be a matter of fact and degree.

Case Summary

Hiscox Syndicates Ltd v. Pinnacle Ltd [2008] EWHC 1386 (QB).

The claimant companies owned and occupied premises adjacent to the site on which the 'Pinnacle' building in the City of London was being constructed. The claimant had obtained injunctions against the defendants to restrict the blocking of access, vibrations and water penetration arising from the works. The defendants now sought variation of the injunction relating to access so as to enable the temporary blocking-up of some access and the provision of alternative access in the meantime.

Mr Justice Akenhead granted the defendants' application. He considered that the owner (or a leaseholder like the claimant companies) of land adjoining a highway had a right of access to the highway from any part of his premises, but that the private right ceased as soon as the highway was reached and any subsequent interference would be a public nuisance if it was a nuisance at all. However, it was 'eminently arguable' that a reasonable, temporary obstruction of the highway was or might be allowable before it became a public nuisance. Since there was therefore a reasonably arguable claim and a reasonably arguable defence, it was necessary for the purposes of determining whether the injunction should be varied to consider the balance of convenience as between the parties. In light of the defendants' intention to provide alternative access routes, and subject to their obtaining (and providing confirmation of) suitable insurance to satisfy, and giving adequate security in respect of, any significant business interruption claim by the claimants, the balance of convenience permitted variation of the injunction.

Distinguishable from, but similar to, public nuisance is statutory nuisance. Those working within the construction industry should be aware of the relevant legislation, in particular the Environmental Protection Act (EPA) 1990 which covers emission of noise and fumes among many other things. Statutory nuisances are often nuisances which would be actionable as public nuisance if not for the relevant statute.

Environmental protection legislation is discussed in the chapter *Environmental issues*. In essence, prior to the EPA 1990, a range of statutes covered the different nuisances actionable by statute. The EPA 1990 consolidated many of these, introducing streamlined procedures. Statutory nuisances under the EPA 1990 are actionable by local authorities and, in some cases, by individuals. Part III of the EPA 1990 defines statutory nuisance widely, including the state of any premises, smoke emitted from premises, emission of fumes, gas, dust, steam or other effluvia arising from an industrial trade or business premises and any other matter declared by enactment to be a statutory nuisance.

Moreover, Part IIA of the EPA 1990 creates a regime specifically aimed at the contamination of land, which will be relevant to any case where a nuisance is alleged to have been caused by an escaping contaminant. Any party that knowingly permits potential contaminants to come onto, or remain on, their land will be liable under Part IIA of the EPA 1990 if doing so leads to the contamination of land. Under s.78A(9) 'any natural or artificial substances, whether in solid or liquid form or in the form of a gas or vapour' are covered by the Part IIA of the EPA 1990 if they have caused contamination of land.

In practice, where a substance has escaped from a party's land and caused contamination of land, the relevant local authority is under a duty to serve a 'remediation' notice on him or her requiring the cleaning up of the contaminated land. The land must be restored so that it is again suitable for use. The polluter is generally required to pay for the cost of such remediation, even where it is arranged by the Local Authority.

23.3.3 Private nuisance: who can sue?

Lord Evershed MR in *Thompson-Schwab v. Costaki* [1956] 1 WLR 335 at 338 divided private nuisance into three categories:

(a) causing an encroachment on another's land;
(b) causing physical damage to another's land or building works or vegetation upon it; and
(c) unduly interfering with the comfort and convenient enjoyment of another's land.

In the case of *Hunter v. Canary Wharf* [1997] 2 WLR 684, the House of Lords took the opportunity to reaffirm this area of law. The Lords restated that the tort of nuisance is a tort directed against the plaintiff's enjoyment of rights over land and, accordingly, an action in private nuisance will only lie at the suit of a person who has a right in the land affected.

This is an example of a major difference between nuisance and negligence, nuisance being concerned with protection of rights over land and negligence being more concerned with the rights of the individual.

It was thought that the law was moving away from this stance in the case of *Khorasandjian v. Bush* [1993] QB 727. Here, the plaintiff was the daughter of the freeholder of the property and successfully sued the defendant for harassment in the form of telephone calls. The Court of Appeal held that it was sufficient that the property was her 'home' even though she had no formal proprietary interest. This decision was overruled by the House of Lords in *Hunter v. Canary Wharf*. The House upheld the traditional test of possession and occupation (see *Malone v. Laskey* [1907] 2 KB 141, CA) and refused to distinguish the right to sue in cases of direct physical damage to or encroachment on neighbouring land from situations involving interference with enjoyment. The reaffirmation appears perfectly logical when one works from the premise that the tort of nuisance is concerned with the rights of land. A possible reason for the departure from stated law in *Khorasandjian* is that, at that time, the law did not recognise a remedy for personal harassment not resulting in financial or other loss. This is no longer the case after the Protection from Harassment Act 1997.

Case Summary

Hunter v. Canary Wharf Ltd. [1997] A.C. 655.

The plaintiffs were several hundred individuals who occupied and/or had a legal interest in homes in the Docklands area of London which had been designated by the Secretary of State for the Environment as an urban development area and enterprise zone. They claimed damages for negligence and nuisance in respect of (i) interference with the television signals in their homes allegedly caused by the presence of a very large building erected by the defendants pursuant to planning permission granted by the enterprise zone authority, and (ii) deposits of dust in their properties caused by the construction of a link road.

The House of Lords considered the questions (i) whether interference with television reception was capable of constituting an actionable nuisance, and (ii) what (if any) interest in property was necessary in order for a party to claim in private nuisance. On issue (i), it was held that it was a long-standing principle that a property owner was entitled to build on his own land as he wished, subject to the system of planning controls in place, and was not generally liable, in the absence of a relevant easement or agreement, if his building interfered with his neighbours' enjoyment of their land. Therefore, since the interference with the plaintiffs' television reception was the result simply of the presence of the building on the defendants'

land, no action in private nuisance could succeed in respect of that interference. On issue (ii), a majority of their Lordships held that, generally, only a person with an interest in the land affected could sue in private nuisance. A mere licensee of land would not have sufficient standing to sue.

Hunter was applied in *Dobson v. Thames Water Utilities Ltd* [2009] EWCA Civ 28; [2009] 3 All ER 319, a case concerned with the nuisance caused by the operation of a sewage treatment works.

When must the potential claimant's interest in the land have been acquired in order to give rise to an entitlement to sue? It might have been thought that the claimant must have had the relevant interest when the damage caused by the nuisance was suffered. However, this does not now appear to be the case. In *Delaware Mansions v. Westminster City Council* [2001] 3 WLR 1007 (HL) the successful claimant brought an action against the defendant local authority in respect of damage to a mansion block caused by tree roots. The claimant acquired its interest in the property at a time after the damage, or at least much of it, had already been suffered. The House of Lords held that the nuisance was a continuing one and that the claimant had acted reasonably in carrying out the remedial works that it did. What seems to have been important was that the nuisance was a continuing one. The position may well have been different had the nuisance ceased and the damage been suffered prior to the claimant's acquisition of an interest in the property.

23.3.4 Public nuisance – who can sue?

In public nuisance, there is no qualification as to proprietary rights. A claimant must show that he or she has been affected by the nuisance caused. Public nuisance is generally constituted by acts which hinder the public from exercising their rights.

At common law, it is necessary to show that a class of person has been affected, although it is not necessary to prove that every member of that class has been injuriously affected and it is a matter of fact whether the number of persons affected is large enough to term the nuisance public.

Apart from the statutory remedies available, if public nuisance is governed by statute, the Attorney General may bring an action for an injunction on his or her own initiative or on the part of another person or a local authority, who will then be joined as co-claimant (see *A. G. v. Logan* [1891] 2 QB 100).

Finally, it should be noted that damages for personal injury can be recovered in public nuisance notwithstanding the indication in *Hunter* (above) to the contrary effect in the context of private nuisance: see *In re Corby Group Litigation* [2009] QB 335.

23.3.5 Who can be sued?

The general rule is that the actual wrongdoer is liable for the nuisance caused, whether or not he or she is in occupation of the land (see *Hall v. Beckenham Corp.* [1949] 1 KB 716). This means that, in construction, a contractor will be liable if it is employed to erect a building and that building becomes a nuisance (*Thompson v. Gibson* (1841) 7 M&W 456; also *Wilcox v.*

Steel [1904] 1 Ch. 212). Even if the contractor moves away from the nuisance, if the nuisance continues and even though the contractor is no longer in control to prevent it, it will be liable. A person taking over the land and continuing the nuisance will also be liable for carrying on that nuisance and therefore the claimant will have a choice of defendants. It will often be easier to pursue the current landowner who may be more readily available than the person or body originally responsible, who may have moved away. Therefore, purchasers of new developments should be wary as they may face a claim from a party affected by nuisance which they did not create.

An individual may also be liable for nuisance created by servants and agents as well as personally. In the case of independent contractors, whether the employer is liable for nuisance depends on whether it could reasonably have foreseen that the work instructed was likely to result in a nuisance (see *Bower v. Peate* [1876] 1 QB 321). If the nuisance was reasonably foreseeable and the employer did not take steps to prevent it, then the employer is liable. Otherwise, the independent contractor will be considered liable.

A party may not be liable in nuisance if to impose such liability would be inconsistent with statute. This principle is demonstrated by the decision in *Marcic v. Thames Water Utilities* [2004] 2 AC 42 in which the House of Lords held that to render a statutory sewerage undertaker liable in nuisance for the discharge of sewage into the claimant's house caused by inadequate sewer pipes would be inconsistent with the statutory scheme imposed by the Water Industry Act 1991. The Act provided a comprehensive scheme governing the obligations of sewerage undertakers and it was not for the courts to add to these by imposing liability in nuisance. However, in the case of *Dobson v. Thames Water Utilities Ltd* [2008] 2 All ER 362, it was held at first instance that the decision in *Marcic* did not prevent certain causes of action in nuisance based on negligence existing alongside the duties under the Act, where the exercise of adjudicating on that cause of action was not inconsistent with the statutory process under the 1991 Act (and this part of the decision was not the subject of the later appeal: [2009] 3 All ER 319). There is an obvious parallel here with the effect of the contractual matrix on the scope of any duty of care in tort that may be owed by a party, discussed earlier.

23.3.6 Establishing liability and damages

In private nuisance, the claimant must be able to show that, as a result of the nuisance, damage has been caused. This can either be in the form of physical damage to land, encroachment on the claimant's land or inconvenience materially affecting the enjoyment of the land by the claimant.

The damage must be reasonably foreseeable for the claimant to have a successful claim. In *The Wagon Mound (No. 2) (Overseas Tankship (UK) Ltd v. Miller Steamship Co Pty* [1967] 1 AC 617), Lord Reid set out the generally accepted statement as to reasonable foreseeability. The defendant discharged inflammable oil

into Sydney Harbour. The trial judge held that the damage to the plaintiff's ships by fire from the ignited oil was not reasonably foreseeable and so damages were not recoverable for negligence, but that the defendants were liable in nuisance because nuisance liability did not depend on foreseeability. On the facts, the Privy Council decided that the damage was reasonably foreseeable and therefore the plaintiff was entitled to damages in negligence. On the question of nuisance, Lord Reid said that 'although negligence may not be necessary, fault of some kind is almost always necessary and fault generally involves foreseeability'. He went on to state that 'it is not sufficient that the injury suffered by the respondent's vessels was the direct result of nuisance if that injury was in the relevant sense unforeseeable'.

In the more recent case of *Cambridge Water v. Eastern Counties Leather* [1994] 2 AC 264, HL, the defendants were held not to be liable in nuisance for the pollution of an underground water supply on the ground that seepage was not reasonably foreseeable. Lord Goff stated that:

> by no means [should] the defendant be held liable for damage of a type which he could not reasonably foresee; the development of the law of negligence in the past sixty years points strongly towards a requirement that such foreseeability should be a prerequisite of liability in damages for nuisance.

See also *Arscott v. Coal Authority* [2004] EWCA Civ 892.

Private nuisance is a tort connected with land, therefore damage unconnected with land, for example, personal injury, is not recoverable: see *Hunter* above. The position would appear to be different as regards public nuisance: see *In Re Corby Group Litigation* (above).

Whether or not physical damage or encroachment has occurred is a matter of fact for the court to determine. Often, expert evidence will be required to show relevant causation in physical damage cases. In encroachment cases, the very fact of the encroachment, that is a cornice projecting over the claimant's garden, is sufficient.

In *St Helen's Smelting Co. Ltd v. Tipping* (1862) 11 HL Cas 642; 11 ER 1483, Lord Westbury drew a distinction between material damage to the claimant's premises and interference with the use and enjoyment of property.

In the case of interference with the use and occupation of land, there is no definite standard at which interference with enjoyment is considered a nuisance; it is very much a matter of the circumstances of the case. In deciding what constitutes interference the courts have had to strike a balance between the right of the defendant to use its property for its own lawful enjoyment and the right of the claimant to the undisturbed enjoyment of its property.

In *Bamford v. Turnley* 3 B & S 66; 122 ER 27, Bramwell B termed the courts' approach to the conflicting interests of the plaintiff and defendant as a 'rule of give and take, live and let live'. The court will look to the reasonableness of the plaintiff's enjoyment compared with the defendant's use of its land.

Various tests have been applied to determine whether the defendants' actions constitute a nuisance. In *St Helen's*, Lord

Westbury referred to whether 'the thing alleged is productive of sensible personal discomfort'. The test is flexible and in *Thompson-Schwab v. Costaki* [1956] 1 WLR 325 the court stated that whether or not a nuisance had been committed would vary according to the 'usages of civilised society at the relevant date'. The nuisance has to be considered substantial, not trivial, in the eyes of the reasonable man. Therefore, it was previously thought that the peculiarly sensitive claimant will not succeed on the basis that the activity offends his or her particular sensitivity. In *Robinson v. Kilvert* [1889] 41 ChD 88, the plaintiff did not succeed in his claim for damage to paper kept on his premises as the court held his trade to be 'exceptionally delicate'. The activities of the defendant would not otherwise affect an ordinary business. However, this decision was disapproved of by the Court of Appeal in *Network Rail Infrastructure Limited v. Morris (t/a Soundstar Studio)* [2004] EWCA Civ 172 where the Court of Appeal questioned whether there could be 'further life' in this rule of law.

The courts will also consider locality and have stood firmly by the principle that 'what would be a nuisance in Belgrave Square would not necessarily be so in Bermondsey' (*Sturges v. Bridgman* [1879] 11 ChD 852 per Thesiger LJ).

23.3.7 Planning permission

As set out earlier, the nature of the locality is relevant, and the nature of an area may change due to the grant of planning permission. In *Gillingham BC v. Medway (Chatham) Dock Ltd* [1993] QB 343, the court held that where planning permission has been given to change the use of an area, nuisance will 'fall to be decided by reference to a neighbourhood with that development and use and not as it was previously'.

This appears to sit uncomfortably with the landowner's right to enjoyment of his or her land as the landowner may not have a choice in the development of the area. In *Hunter v. Canary Wharf* (a Case Summary of which is set out above), the case concerned an action by a group of residents for damages due to, *inter alia*, interference to television reception between 1989 and 1991/2 caused by the building of the Canary Wharf tower.

While the issue of planning permission was considered, their Lordships ruled against the plaintiffs on the separate ground that the right to build on land is an immutable right in common law, only restricted by agreement. In other words, neighbouring landowners have no right to light or air unless otherwise agreed. In most situations this will be the case.

In *Hunter*, the House of Lords endorsed the concept that residents of an area have the opportunity to make representations at planning permission stage. In theory this should give residents the opportunity to ensure that the area use is not changed if they do not want it to be. However, on the facts in *Hunter*, the local residents in practice had very little choice but to accept the development as the Secretary of State had designated the area an enterprise zone with the effect that planning permission was deemed to have been granted for any form of development and no application for permission was necessary.

Lord Hoffman, at 712, justified this situation on the ground that Parliament had authorised the ordinary protections to the local residents to be removed on the ground that the national interest required the rapid regeneration of the Docklands area.

In *Gillingham* and *Hunter*, however, the courts did maintain the view that a planning authority 'has no jurisdiction to authorise a nuisance' (*Allen v. Gulf Oil Refining Ltd* [1980] QB 156). This is evidenced in the more recent case of *Wheeler v. Saunders* [1996] Ch. 19. There the plaintiffs sued the defendant on the basis that the smell from the defendant's pig farm constituted a nuisance. The defendant argued that as planning permission had been sought and gained and the plaintiff had had the opportunity to make representations at that stage, the plaintiff had no claim. The Court of Appeal stated that on the basis of *Gillingham* and *Allen*, notwithstanding the fact that planning permission had been granted, that permission did not license the nuisance. A distinction was drawn between a large-scale or strategic planning decision affected by considerations of public interest and permission to change the use of one small piece of land for the benefit of an individual.

23.3.8 Building and demolition

Building and demolition works will not generally be considered a nuisance as long as the builder ensures 'he uses all reasonable skill and care to avoid annoyance to his neighbour' (Vaughan Williams J in *Harrison v. Southwark and Vauxhall Water Co.* [1892] 2 Ch. 409). The builder should be able to show that it has taken all reasonable steps necessary to avoid noise, dirt and dust. Examples of other factors which a builder could put forward to discharge the burden are that the hours during which the work was done were restricted, limits placed on the amount of any particular types of work done simultaneously, or that a special arrangement has been entered into with the neighbour to suit the neighbour's particular needs. For more details see Wignall, 1998; p. 16.

The court will attempt to reconcile the interests of local inhabitants and the desirability of developing sites. In *City of London Corporation v. Bovis Construction Ltd* [1992] 3 All ER 697, Lord Justice Bingham (as he then was) recognised that while unreasonable and excessive noise has been recognised as capable of being a nuisance for many years, a balance must be struck between local inhabitants' interests and the general desirability of redeveloping sites of great economic value. In this case, Bovis were construction managers at the Beaufort House site in the City of London and subject to noise abatement notices which they contravened. The case concerns other principles (principally the responsibility of management contractors and the terms of injunctions) but Lord Justice Bingham's comments are of interest and develop the principle that building operations carried out inconsiderately will be stopped by injunction.

23.3.9 Building and the right to light

When deciding to construct a building in and around other buildings, the potential constructor/developer should take account of rights of light. Rights of light may be acquired by grant or prescription (long usage). In *Colls v. Home and Colonial Stores* [1904] AC 179 at 208, Lord Lindley stated that the owner of such rights to light (termed 'ancient lights') is entitled to:

> sufficient light, according to the ordinary notions of mankind, for the comfortable use and enjoyment of his house as a dwelling-house, if it is a dwelling-house, or for the beneficial use and occupation of the house, if it is a warehouse, a shop, or other place of business.

Sufficient light has been further defined as 'the amount of light left' and can vary depending on the nature of the occupation and in some circumstances, locality. It should be noted that interference with rights of light of the owner of such rights on adjoining land will not necessarily prevent planning permission being granted, but if a constructor/developer were to construct a building that interfered with ancient lights then it may be faced with the prospect of an injunction by the owner of those ancient lights. However, there is authority that damages may be granted instead of an injunction, depending on the facts of the case (see the recent cases of *Regan v. Paul Properties Ltd* [2007] Ch. 135 and *Tamares (Vincent Square) Ltd v. Fairpoint Properties (Vincent Square) Ltd* [2006] EWHC 3589).

23.3.10 Defences

The general defences available in tort are available for an action in nuisance (see section 23.2.6 of this chapter). In addition to these, there are some specific defences to an action in nuisance which should be considered, particularly in construction cases.

It is not a defence to an allegation of nuisance that an individual has taken all reasonable steps to prevent the activity becoming a nuisance (see Lindley LJ in *Rapier v. London Tramways* [1893] 2 Ch. 588).

Generally, no liability is imposed on the owner of land for nuisance caused by a trespasser or natural causes unless it can be shown that the owner had knowledge or means of knowledge of the nuisance and should have corrected or obviated the effects of the nuisance (see *Sedleigh-Denfield v. O'Callaghan* [1940] AC 880). This principle was considered in *Bybrook Barn Centre v. Kent County Council* 1 December 2000, CA. Here, Kent County Council (in its capacity as a highway authority) diverted a stream under a road through a circular section culvert in 1936. Sixty years later the culvert became overloaded, water backed up in the stream and it burst its banks, flooding a garden centre and causing substantial damage. At first instance Bybrook (the garden centre)'s claim was dismissed. However, the Court of Appeal firmly stated that if a person is able to regulate a nuisance emanating from his or her property then they have an obligation to take reasonable steps to abate it, even it is caused by a third party or natural causes. The Court found that the Council knew the stream was overloaded and the expenditure to remedy the problem was not excessive. The Council was therefore ultimately held liable.

It is generally a defence to show ignorance of the facts constituting the nuisance. This defence will not work if the ignorance is due to the omission to use reasonable care to discover the facts. However, in *Wringe v. Cohen* [1940] 1 KB 229 the court stated that if premises become dangerous due to the owner's actions, the owner is liable even if he or she did not know of the danger and was not negligent in not knowing. If the premises become dangerous because of the act of a third party or a latent defect, the occupier is not liable without proof of knowledge or the means of knowledge and failure to abate it.

A fourth defence to nuisance is that of contributory negligence. It is a defence to an action in nuisance, except where the consequences of the act were intended by the defendant.

It is not generally a defence to lay the blame for the nuisance at the foot of an independent contractor (see *Bower v. Peate*, considered in more detail above). Further, it is no defence for the defendant to claim that the plaintiff 'came to' the nuisance. In *Sturges v. Bridgman* (1879) L.R. 11 Ch. D. 852, the doctor plaintiff built up a consulting room against a wall which adjoined his neighbour's kitchen in which mortars were pounded between 10 a.m. and 1 p.m. The plaintiff was successful, the courts upholding the principle that a person cannot be deprived of the right to land and comfortable enjoyment of that land.

It may also be possible to defend a claim on the basis that it was not reasonably practicable to abate the nuisance. This has had particular relevance for statutory undertakers such as utility companies – see *Glossop v. Heston & Isleworth Local Board* [1879] 12 ChD 102.

23.3.11 Statutory authority

A further defence to consider, particularly in relation to public nuisance, is that of statutory authority. Where a statute has authorised the doing of a particular act, or the use of land in a particular way, which inevitably causes nuisance, it is not actionable provided that every reasonable step consistent with the exercise of the statutory powers has been taken to prevent the nuisance occurring. This is relevant to construction operations which may normally constitute a nuisance but which are permitted by statute.

For example, in *Allen v. Gulf Oil Refining Ltd* [1980] QB 156 the House of Lords construed the Act in question, authorising the construction of a refinery, as conferring immunity from an action in nuisance upon the company involved.

Each Act must be interpreted separately and the burden of proving that the nuisance is inevitable falls on those with the statutory authority. They must show that all reasonable care and skill, according to the state of scientific knowledge at the time, has been taken (see *Allen v. Gulf Oil Refining Ltd*). Statutes sometimes provide compensation for those affected but this is not always the case.

This defence can be successfully defeated if the plaintiff can show that any nuisance caused by the activities granted by statute exceeded that for which immunity was conferred or that the acts authorised by statute had been carried out negligently.

In *Allen v. Gulf Oil*, the court stated the plaintiff had no action provided the defendant company could prove that it was inevitable that, using all due diligence, neighbours should sustain the harm complained of, even though no compensation for that harm was directly given by the Act. The only remedy the plaintiff then had was for the extent that the nuisance exceeded that for which immunity was conferred.

If reasonable care is not taken then liability will arise. In *Tate & Lyle v. Greater London Council* [1983] 2 AC 509, it was held that the GLC had not acted with due diligence in exercising its statutory powers in relation to the construction of various ferry terminals in the Thames and consequently should pay three-quarters of the costs which the plaintiff had incurred in dredging, the remaining quarter being the amount of costs that would have been incurred if it had acted diligently.

In the recent case of *Andrews v. Reading Borough Council* (No. 2) [2005] EWHC 256, the claimant was awarded compensation for interference with his right to Private and Family Life under Art. 8 of the Human Rights Convention, due to an increase in traffic noise experienced in his house as a result of the defendants' road improvement scheme. The defendants argued, unsuccessfully, that the award of compensation was precluded since the claimant's situation fell outside the criteria stipulated by the Noise Insulation Regulations 1975. The court held that there was no indication in the Regulations that immunity was to be conferred upon highway authorities from any action by those not included within them. Note that in the case of *Dobson v. Thames Water* (see above) Mr Justice Ramsey considered that damages could be awarded under the Human Rights Act where such damages were necessary to afford just satisfaction.

It can be seen in these cases that it might be said that Parliament and the courts are trying to balance the public and the private interest.

23.4 Rylands v. Fletcher
23.4.1 Introduction

The rule in *Rylands v. Fletcher* (1866) LR 1 Ex 265 at 279; affirmed in HL (1886) LR 3 HL 330 is an offshoot of the law relating to nuisance. It encompasses 'escaping liability'. In construction this is often seen in the form of flooding from, for example, drainage to buildings which causes substantial damage. A question that arises in those cases is whether the flooding is due to defective design and often, therefore, breach of contract. However, another option to consider is tort liability under *Rylands v. Fletcher*. The main difference between private and public nuisance and *Rylands v. Fletcher* liability is that it was considered that the rule in *Rylands* imposed liability on defendants regardless of foreseeability of damage. The law has now been substantially reviewed in *Cambridge Water v. Eastern Counties Leather* (1994) 2 AC 264.

23.4.2 The rule in Rylands v. Fletcher

In *Rylands v. Fletcher* the defendants built a reservoir on their land. Water collected and flowed into the plaintiffs' mine causing damage. The defendants were held liable on the ground that they kept the water on their land at their own peril. Blackburn J said:

> the person who for his own purposes brings on his land and collects and keeps there anything likely to do mischief if it escapes must keep it in at his peril, and, if he does not do so, is *prima facie* answerable for all the damage which is the natural consequence of its escape.

In the House of Lords this was refined to bring in the concept of the 'non-natural user'. That is to say that the defendant must be using his or her land for a non-natural use. The rule was interpreted to impose strict liability, that foreseeability of damage was not necessary to establish liability. This principle has now been very much eroded.

In *Cambridge Water v. Eastern Counties Leather*, the defendants were leather manufacturers whose tanning chemicals had seeped through a concrete floor into the soil and subsequently into the plaintiff's underground watercourse used to supply the local public. The water was deemed unfit for human consumption. The seepage was unforeseeable and the plaintiffs attempted to establish liability on the basis of the *Rylands* rule. The House of Lords took a narrow view of the extent of strict liability and held that the defendants were not liable on the ground that the rule in *Rylands* did not apply.

The reasoning behind the decision is clearer. Their Lordships denied the existence of a general principle of strict liability and stated that, in the absence of negligence, liability would only be imposed in certain defined situations. The view was taken that the rule in *Rylands* should be no more than an extension of the law of nuisance to cases of isolated escapes. Lord Goff stated that instances of strict liability should be imposed by Parliament rather than by the courts. Parliament has not responded to this invitation. The courts' view is to some extent similar to that of Australia where it is considered that the rule in *Rylands* is absorbed by the law of negligence generally (see *Burnie Port Authority v. General Jones Pty Ltd* (1994) 120 ALR 42), although it should be noted that in the later case of *Transco v. Stockport MBC* [2004] 2 AC 1, in which the House of Lords endorsed its view in *Cambridge Water*, their Lordships denied that the principle had been absorbed by the tort of negligence (see also *LMS International Limited v. Styrene Packaging and Insulation Limited* [2005] EWHC 2065 [TCC]).

After an analysis of the judgement of Lord Blackburn in *Rylands*, Lord Goff (in *Cambridge Water*) concluded, at 302D, that

> the general tenor of his statement of principle is that knowledge, or at least foreseeability of the risk, is a prerequisite of the recovery of damages under the principle; but that the principle is one of strict liability in the sense that the defendant

may be held liable notwithstanding he has exercised all due skill and care to prevent the escape occurring.

This significantly waters down the original effect of the rule. Particularly as Lord Goff went on to hold, at 309E, that 'foreseeability of damage of the relevant type should be regarded as a prerequisite of liability in damages under the rule'.

It is worth noting that the courts are increasingly taking the view that the concepts of 'natural' and 'non-natural' use of land are unhelpful, and that an approach similar to the concept of 'reasonable user' in nuisance is more appropriate: see for example *Arscott v. Coal Authority* [2004] EWCA Civ 892, per Laws L.J. at 29.

23.4.3 Who can sue and who can be sued?

The person liable is the owner or controller of the dangerous thing. If he or she brings or collects it on land, he or she is liable even if that individual is not the owner or occupier of the land. Therefore, in construction a contractor bringing dangerous chemicals onto site may be liable for their escape and subsequent damage. The occupier will be liable as well in such a case if the dangerous thing is brought or collected on his or her land for the occupier's purpose or with his or her permission. The plaintiff need not have an interest in land affected to sue but must be affected by the escape. For example, in *Charing Cross Electricity Supply Co. v. Hydraulic Power Co.* [1914] 3 KB 772, a water company authorised by statute to carry water under the surface of a highway was liable for the escape of water from a broken main which damaged the cables of an electricity supply company which also ran under the highway.

It is very doubtful whether a claimant can recover damages for personal injury under the rule (see *Read v. J. Lyons & Co. Ltd* [1947] AC 156 at 169 and 173 and the obiter comments of the House of Lords in *Transco v. Stockport MBC* at 9 and 35).

There is no liability unless the thing which does the damage escapes from a place where the defendant has occupation or control over land to a place outside the defendant's occupation or control. In *Read v. J. Lyons & Co.* a worker in a munitions factory failed to recover when injured by a shell exploding within the factory on the basis that there had been no 'escape'.

23.4.4 Special rules for water, gas, electricity, fire, explosives, poisonous waste and oil pollution, aircraft and nuclear installations

As mentioned earlier, the *Rylands v. Fletcher* rule allows for particular exceptions which now are exceptions mainly because they impose strict liability! The exceptions are too numerous to detail here, but it is worth noting that in many cases there are specific statutes in place governing liability on a *Rylands* basis.

23.5 Breach of statutory duty
23.5.1 Introduction

Statute imposes numerous duties on many different organisations from local authorities and statutory undertakers to private companies. If any of these bodies breach their obligations under statute, then a claimant may have an action in tort against them for that breach.

23.5.2 Is the breach actionable?

In addition to showing that the obligations under the relevant statute have been breached and that the breach caused loss or harm to the claimant, the breach must be capable of being actioned. This area of law has been subject to much interpretation by the courts. The important point is that not all breaches of statutory duty can be actioned by a claimant in the civil courts. This is satisfactory if there are other remedies within the Act for a breach of obligations under the Act but much less satisfactory if there are no such provisions.

In addition to showing that the breach caused loss, the claimant must also show that the damage was of the type that the legislation in question was intended to prevent. Further a claimant must be within the category of persons that the statute was meant to protect. This area of law is governed by the common law.

In *Cutler v. Wandsworth Stadium Limited* [1946] AC 398 at 407, Lord Simonds stated that whether or not a breach was actionable 'must depend on a consideration of the whole Act and the circumstances, including the pre-existing law, in which it was enacted'.

In *Lonrho Limited v. Shell Petroleum Limited* [1981] 2 All ER 456, Lord Diplock in the House of Lords approved the general rule that 'where an Act creates an obligation, and enforces the performance in a specified manner … that performance cannot be enforced in any other manner'.

Lord Diplock recognised two exceptions to this rule. First, where the obligation or prohibition is imposed for the benefit of the protection of a particular class of individuals. Second, where the statute creates a public right and an individual member of the public suffers 'particular damage'.

Therefore, the general principles appear to be that if an Act provides for a penalty, that penalty is the only remedy, subject to the two exceptions. Sometimes if another common law remedy is available this may affect the decision of the court as to whether the breach is actionable in tort.

23.5.3 The two exceptions

The first question concerning the first exception is what is a class of individuals? The courts have made a distinction between a class and the public at large. For example, visitors to premises which are in breach of fire regulations due to the lack of an adequate fire escape are considered a class whereas the public using a highway are not (*Solomons v. Gertzenstein*

Ltd [1994] 2 QB 243; compare *Phillips v. Britannia Hygenic Laundry Ltd* [1923] 2 KB 832), although pedestrians using a pedestrian crossing are (*London Passenger Transport Board v. Upson* [1949] AC 155).

However, in the recent case of *X (minors) v. Bedfordshire County Council* (1999) 3 WLR 1252, the House of Lords held that the social services authority was not liable for breach of statutory duty in respect of child care legislation despite the fact that such legislation had been put in place for a limited class, that is to say, children at risk.

Lord Diplock's second exception comes into play when a statute creates a public right and an individual member of the public suffers 'particular damage'. The damage must be direct and substantial and different from that which was common to the rest of the public.

In considering the two exceptions, the first is by far the most important. In determining whether or not the statute was designed to protect a limited class of individuals, a broad analysis of the statute is required – see *Phelps v. Hillingdon LBC* [2000] 3 WLR 776 at 789E-H per Lord Slynn. Recently the courts have appeared reluctant to hold that the local authorities owe a duty of care in respect of the exercise of their statutory duties and powers for fear of challenging decisions of policy. However, a route to liability may be found in holding that the employees of the statutory body owe duties of care in discharging their functions. The statutory body is then vicariously liable (as employer) for any breaches of these duties: see *Phelps* (above). On this basis, it might be argued that a significant new extension to the potential liability of statutory bodies has been fashioned.

23.5.4 Construction and breach of statutory duty

The courts are more likely to infer a breach in cases of industrial safety legislation. Therefore those in the construction industry must be aware of such legislation and enforce it or be at risk of multiple actions by contractors, employees or other parties that may be affected. Some statutes will state expressly whether it is intended to create a right of action in favour of someone who suffers loss.

23.6 Occupiers' liability
23.6.1 Introduction

Occupiers' liability is governed by two statutes, the Occupiers' Liability Acts 1957 and 1984. The former is concerned with invitees coming onto the land and the 1984 Act is concerned, *inter alia*, with trespassers. In the context of construction, the 1957 Act is of more importance. For example, it governs the liability to and of independent contractors when carrying out work on another's land.

23.6.2 The Occupiers' Liability Act 1957

The main purpose of this Act was to replace the old common law duties with a standard duty of care. Prior to the Act, a fine

distinction was placed on the law relating to 'invitees' and the law relating to 'licensees'. The Act went some way in trying to level the standard of care owed and is now more akin to the law of negligence. Section 1(1) states:

> [the Act] shall have effect in place of the rules of the common law, to regulate the duty which an occupier of premises owes to his visitors in respect of dangers due to the state of the premises or to things done or omitted to be done on them.

23.6.3 The occupier

The Act does not define an 'occupier' and therefore one must look to the common law for a definition. 'Occupier' is a wide term encompassing anyone with a degree of control associated with and arising from his or her presence in and the use of the premises (*Wheat v. Lacon* [1966] AC 552). A contractor may be liable as an occupier (*Bunker v. Charles Brand & Son Ltd* [1969] 2 QB 480). For example, a builder may be considered an occupier if it is in control of part of the house even though it has no power to permit or prohibit the entry of other persons to the house. There may be multiple occupiers, in the case of the builder the householder may also be deemed to occupy. The owner is not always considered to be the occupier.

An interesting case in the context of building and the status of contractors and subcontractors is *Ferguson v. Welsh* [1987] 3 All ER 777. Here, a local authority subcontracted building work to an independent contractor. An express condition of the tender was that the work should not be subcontracted without the local authority's express permission. Despite this, the contractor subcontracted the works to a firm of builders which employed an unsafe system of work. This led to the collapse of a wall, injuring the plaintiff. The plaintiff sued the builders, the contractor and the council. It was most likely that the only party able to pay damages was the council.

The House of Lords upheld the Court of Appeal judgment that the council was not an occupier in relation to the 1957 Act. Both the contractor and subcontractor were deemed to be occupiers but the council had not invited the plaintiff onto the premises and had not delegated that right to the contractor. The House of Lords went on to state that an occupier would not usually be liable to an employee of a contractor employed to carry out work on the occupier's premises if the employee was injured as a result of an unsafe system of work used by the employer as it would not be reasonable to expect the occupier to supervise the contractor to ensure that the duty owed to employees to use a safe system of work was being carried out.

23.6.4 Visitors

Visitors under the Act are the same people who under the common law would be treated as licensees or invitees. Visitors have implied or express permission to come onto the land. Permission may be implied, for example in the public part of a shop, or when the public habitually uses the premises with the knowledge of the occupier and no steps are taken to prevent this. If visitors stray from the usual access then they become trespassers (discussed in section 23.8 of this chapter). Repeated trespass does not constitute a license to come onto the property (see *Edwards v. Railway Executive* [1952] AC 737).

The occupier's permission may be limited to only part of the property. A licence may be implied to enter only the parts of the property where the visitor may reasonably be supposed to go in the belief that he or she is entitled or invited to be there. Similarly, visitors may be limited to the time when they visit the property – for example a public house. Special considerations apply to children, however. The presence of an attractive but dangerous object on land may aid the inference of an implied licence (Cmd. 9305 [1955]). This is an important point for those with building sites which should be secured from children.

In the recent case of *Jolley v. Sutton LBC* [2000] 1 WLR 1082, the House of Lords upheld the plaintiff's appeal that liability under the 1957 Act can be very much a question of fact and circumstance, particularly in relation to children. In this case, the claimant was a 14-year-old boy who had been playing with an abandoned boat on the council's land when the boat fell on him and he suffered serious injury. The House concluded that the council was liable although on slightly differing grounds. Of interest is Lord Hoffmann's view in concluding that the accident had been reasonably foreseeable on the basis that the defendants had admitted they were negligent in failing to remove the boat and that, given these circumstances, the defendants were liable for 'the materialisation of even relatively small risks of a different kind'. Further, the judge stated that the ingenuity of children in finding different ways to do mischief should not be underestimated. Therefore builders who leave dangerous but attractive items on land should be careful if reasonable care demands that the item should be removed, otherwise the builder could be liable under the 1957 Act.

23.6.5 Duty of care

The duty of care imposed by Section 2 of the 1957 Act provides that it

> is a duty to take such care as in all the circumstances of the case is reasonable to see that the visitor will be reasonably safe in using the premises for the purpose for which he is invited or permitted by the occupier to be there.

The situation is one of fact to be determined with regard to all the circumstances of the case, for example, how obvious the danger is, warnings, lighting and fencing are all relevant. Also, occupiers must be prepared for children to be less careful than adults (Occupiers' Liability Act 1957, s. 2(3)(a), see also *Jolley v. Sutton LBC, supra*).

Further, the 1957 Act imposes a duty on the occupier not just in respect of negligent acts but also negligent omissions.

If the visitor enters under a contract then Section 5 of the 1957 Act states that the occupier owes that person the statutory duty of care. It is implied into the contract.

23.6.6 Entering the premises to carry out works

Section 2(3)(b) of the 1957 Act states that an occupier 'may expect that a person, in the exercise of his calling, will appreciate and guard against any special risks ordinarily incident with it'. For example, a scaffolder's work is inherently dangerous and it would be wrong to expect an occupier to take responsibility for factors inherent in the scaffolder's job. On the other hand, if the scaffolder were to be caused injury by a loose tile, then the duty of care owed by the occupier should bite. In *Clare v. Whittaker & Son Ltd* [1976] ICR 1, QBD the occupier of a building site was not liable to the experienced workmen of an independent roofing contractor for failing to urge them to use the crawling boards which had been provided for their protection.

23.6.7 Duty to warn

Whether or not the occupier has discharged his or her common duty of care to the visitor must be assessed in relation to all the circumstances of the case. Section 2(4) of the 1957 Act states that where damage is caused to a visitor by a danger about which he or she had been warned by the occupier, the warning ought not to be treated without more as absolving the occupier from liability unless in all the circumstances it was enough to enable the visitor to be reasonably safe. Therefore a warning is not an absolute bar to recovery. It should be borne in mind on building sites that warnings should be centrally placed and easily visible and specific as to the danger that may occur. It is not a defence that the visitor was merely aware of the risk.

23.6.8 Defences

The most common defence to a claim under the 1957 Act is *volenti non fit injuria* (that the risk was willingly accepted by the visitor). For example, in the case where a visiting rugby player injured himself it was held that he willingly accepted the risk of playing on a field which he knew had a concrete wall running at a distance of seven feet three inches from the touchline (*Simms v. Leigh Rugby Football Club* [1969] 2 All ER 923). Willingly accepting the risk usually means having knowledge of the precise risk in advance. Therefore, the spectator to motor racing who was catapulted into the air by safety ropes was held not to have willingly accepted the risk. The fault lay with the organisers' failure on safety arrangements (*White v. Blackmore* [1972] 2 QB 651).

Another defence is that of contributory negligence. The apportionment provisions of the Law Reform (Contributory Negligence) Act 1945 apply to an action in occupiers' liability.

A question asked by many in occupation of dangerous sites is whether they can exclude liability by notice or warning. Section 2(1) of the 1957 Act provides that the occupier owes any visitor the common duty of care 'except insofar as he is free to and does extend, restrict, modify or exclude his duty to any visitor or visitors by agreement or otherwise'. In practice, there are limits to how far liability can be excluded;

particularly as the Unfair Contract Terms Act 1977 (UCTA) limits the occupier's power of exclusion.

Exclusion by contract is relatively straightforward but is subject to the UCTA. Liability can also be excluded by a suitably worded notice, also subject to the UCTA. This is explained in law as conditional licence – the occupier allowing someone onto his or her land on the condition that the occupier is not liable for loss or damage. This is a common occurrence, for example, car parks and private parking areas often display such notices.

The power to exclude is wide. However, the notice must be sufficiently explicit in its terms. The question appears to be whether the occupier took reasonable steps to tell the visitor of the exclusion (Clerk and Lindsell, 2006; 12–47). One exception which has a limiting effect is if the claimant did not have a choice to enter the premises. It has been held that in such cases the occupier cannot exclude liability. It has also been suggested that this principle should be rethought, given its potentially damaging effect on the ability to exclude liability on the part of the occupier.

23.6.9 Liability of occupier for independent contractors

Section 2(4)(b) of the 1957 Act provides that where damage is caused by faulty construction, maintenance or repair by an independent contractor employed by an occupier, the occupier is not liable if in all the circumstances he or she acted reasonably in entrusting the work to an independent contractor and had taken such steps (if any) as ought reasonably to have been taken in order to satisfy him or herself that the contractor was competent and that the work had been done properly.

23.7 Defective Premises Act 1972

A wide range of tortious duties are now imposed by statute. These range from the wide number of health and safety related duties which are often derived from EC law to duties on occupiers and builders. For the construction industry one of the most important sets of statutory duties can be found in the provisions of the Defective Premises Act 1972.

The Act applies to 'dwellings' by which is meant residential, rather than commercial properties.

Section 1 of the Act imposes a duty to build dwellings properly:

(1) A person taking on work for or in connection with the provision of a dwelling (whether the dwelling is provided by the erection or by conversion or enlargement of a building) owes a duty – if the dwelling is provided to the order of any person, to that person; and without prejudice to paragraph (a) above, to every person who acquires an interest (whether legal or equitable) in the dwelling; to see that the work which he takes on is done in a workmanlike or, as the case may be, professional manner, with proper materials and so that as regards that work the dwelling will be fit for habitation when completed.

There is some doubt as to whether the final part of Section 1 (fitness for habitation) imposes a free-standing and separate duty from those relating to the work and the materials used. Certainly in the case of *Thompson v. Alexander & Partners* (1992) 59 BLR 81 it was thought that there was no separate duty and that the words simply explained or qualified the duty imposed earlier in the section.

The wide duty imposed by Section 1 applies to anyone who takes on the type of work described in the section and includes builders, subcontractors and even professionals such as architects and engineers. Section 1(4) extends the duty to developers and local authorities who organise the works. However, under Section 1(2) those working under the instructions of others will not be subject to the duty so long as they warn the person giving the instructions if the instructions themselves are defective.

The Act also applies to any failure to carry out remedial work as well as to carrying out such work badly (see *Andrews v. Schooling* [1991] 1 WLR 783, CA).

Any cause of action in respect of a breach of the duty imposed under Section 1 accrues when the building has been completed. However, if the person who has done the work returns to site after completion to do further work, then the cause of action accrues only once the further work has been completed. (Section 1(5) of the 1972 Act and section 23.2.6 of this chapter).

23.8 Trespass

This section considers trespass to land. This is most easily defined as the unjustified interference with the possession of land. Trespass is distinct from negligence in that it is actionable *per se* without proof of damage.

23.8.1 Intention

While the interference with the possession of the land must be intentional, this is readily established as the intention that is required to be shown is simply that the trespasser intended to enter upon the land. It is not necessary to show that the trespasser intended to trespass or even knew that he or she was in fact trespassing. This has particular consequences for the construction industry where, for example, a crane operator may intend to swing the crane over adjoining land (and indeed may have no choice but to do so) but possess no intention to trespass on that land. Nevertheless the operator may be liable in trespass.

23.8.2 Possession

It is not necessary for the complainant to have some legal title to the land, possession of which has been interfered with. Unfortunately, there is as yet no coherent theory of possession in this area of the law and whether or not a complainant has a sufficient possessory interest to bring proceedings for trespass depends on the facts of the case. Physical presence or even control of the land will not be sufficient to found an action for possession. This might have particular consequences in the construction industry, where it will be the employer rather than the contractor who will be able to bring the action.

In the landlord and tenant context, it will often be the tenant rather than the landlord who will be best placed to bring proceedings for trespass to the demised property while the landlord will be unable to do so save if the trespass has caused damage to his or her reversionary interest. However, a person who is entitled to immediately possess land (otherwise known as having 'constructive possession') will be able, having taken possession, to sue for trespasses committed after the right to possess had accrued but before he or she was in physical possession of the land.

23.8.3 Interference

Interference with the right to possess may take place in a number of ways. For example, it is possible to trespass not only to the surface of the land but also to its subsoil, which may be owned by different entities. Thus, a construction project that involves tunnelling may cause a trespass to the owners of the subsoil while not trespassing on the surface. In contrast, digging holes vertically will trespass on both the surface and the subsoil.

A particularly problematic area in the construction industry is that with regard to trespass to airspace. It is now clear that while aircraft flying several hundred feet above a property will not be deemed to trespass, a crane swinging above property can be trespassing (see *Woollerton & Wilson Ltd v. Richard Costain Ltd* [1970] 1 WLR 411 and *Anchor Brewhouse Developments v. Berkley House (Docklands Developments)* [1987] 284 EG 625).

It is also important to remember that trespass can be continuing, allowing several actions in respect of the same trespass to be brought. Thus, if bridge buttresses trespass on land and are not removed, actions in trespass can be brought for as long as the trespass continues (*Holmes v. Wilson* [1839] 10 A & E 50 and, more recently, *Field Common Limited v. Elmbridge Borough Council* [2008] EWHC 2079 where it was suggested that the trespasser may ask the landowner if he wants the trespassing material to be removed and, if the answer is 'yes' and the trespasser fails to remove it then there is a continuing trespass and, if the answer is 'no' then there is no continuing trespass [at least as long as that remains the landowner's position]).

23.8.4 Defences

The most useful defence to an action for trespass is justification. The alleged trespasser may have the right to interfere with possession of the land by reason of permission (a licence) or by operation of law. For example, police and bailiffs are given the power to enter premises to carry out certain of their functions. However, if a person who is justified in interfering with possession of the land – whether by licence or law – acts without the conferred authority then he or she will be treated as a trespasser from the moment of entering onto the land.

An important statutory defence insofar as the construction industry is concerned is the Access to Neighbouring Land Act 1992. This allows a court to make an order granting access to land for the purpose of carrying out works that are reasonably necessary to preserve adjoining land. The works must be substantially more difficult to carry out without trespassing to justify the trespass. Further, the court will not make an order if to do so would cause unreasonable hardship or permit unreasonable interference with the enjoyment of the land. The works can include alteration, adjustment, improvement or demolition but these must be incidental to the work required for preservation. Thus, an order will not be granted so as to allow development.

23.8.5 Remedies

A complainant may seek to re-enter his or her land so long as no more than reasonable force is used (it is outside the scope of this handbook to deal with trespass and squatters, where different considerations may apply). Alternatively, the complainant may seek an order for recovery of the land so as to eject the trespasser. In addition, the complainant may recover mesne profits for the damage suffered while he or she has been out of the land. However, in the construction industry the most important remedies will often be an injunction and damages.

In practice, to avoid having an injunction made against them, contractors may be forced to offer large sums in damages to those whose land may be affected by building works. This will prevent the landowners obtaining an injunction because they will have been offered an alternative remedy for any trespass caused by the works. This appears to be the approach adopted in the case of tower cranes which swing over land adjoining the site (see *Woollerton & Wilson Ltd v. Richard Costain Ltd* [1970] 1 WLR 411). Thus, the works will be able to proceed but only at the cost of paying sums to the adjoining landowners. In practice, it will be a case of weighing the risk of injunctive proceedings and the consequent costs incurred by the delay in the works against paying sums in compensation to the adjoining landowners.

References

Deakin, S., Johnston, A. and Markesinis, B. (2008) *Markesinis & Deakin's Tort Law*, 6th edn. Oxford University Press.

Dugdale, A. and Jones, M. A. (eds) (2006) *Clerk & Lindsell on Torts*, 19th Edn. Sweet & Maxwell.

Powell, J. L., Stewart, R. and Jackson, R.M. (eds) (2007) *Jackson & Powell on Professional Liability*, 6th Edn. Sweet & Maxwell.

Wignall, G. (1998) *Nuisances*. Sweet & Maxwell.

Referenced legislation, regulations and standards

Access to Neighbouring Land Act 1992
Defective Premises Act 1972
Environmental Protection Act 1990
Latent Damage Act 1986
Law Reform (Contributory Negligence) Act 1945

Limitation Act 1980
Occupiers' Liability Act 1957
Occupiers' Liability Act 1984
Occupiers' Liability Act 1997
Protection from Harassment Act 1997
Supply of Goods and Services Act 1982
Unfair Contract Terms Act 1977
Water Industry Act 1991

Referenced cases

A. G. v. Logan [1891] 2 QB 100

Abbott v. Will Gannon & Smith [2005] PNLR 30

Allen v. Gulf Oil Refining Ltd [1980] QB 156

Anchor Brewhouse Developments v. Berkley House (Docklands Developments) (1987) 284 EG 625

Andrews v. Reading Borough Council (No. 2) [2005] EWHC 256

Andrews v. Schooling [1991] 1 WLR 783, CA

Aneco Reinsurance Underwriting Ltd v. Johnson [2001] 2 All ER 929

Anns v. Merton London Borough Council [1978] AC 728

Arscott v. Coal Authority [2004] EWCA Civ 892

Baker v. Willoughby [1970] AC 467

Bamford v. Turnley 3 B & S 66; 122 ER 27

Barker v. Corus [2006] AC 572

Barnett v. Chelsea and Kensington Hospital Management [1969] 1 QB 428

Baxall v. Sheard Walshaw [2002] CILL 1837

Bellefield Computer Services Ltd v. E. Turner & Sons Ltd [2000] BLR 97

Bolam v. Friern Hospital Management Committee [1957] 1 WLR 582

Bolitho v. City of Hackney Health Authority [1998] AC 232

Bolton v. Stone [1951] AC 850

Bower v. Peate [1876] 1 QB 321

Bunker v. Charles Brand & Son Ltd [1969] 2 QB 480

Burnie Port Authority v. General Jones Pty Ltd (1994) 120 ALR 42

Bybrook Barn Centre v. Kent County Council 1 December 2000, CA

Cambridge Water v. Eastern Counties Leather [1994] 2 AC 264, HL

Caparo Industries plc v. Dickman [1990] 2 AC 605

Charing Cross Electricity Supply Co. v. Hydraulic Power Co. [1914] 3 KB 772

City of London Corporation v. Bovis Construction Ltd [1992] 3 All ER 697

Clare v. Whittaker & Son Ltd [1976] ICR 1, QBD

Colls v. Home and Colonial Stores [1904] AC 179

Court of Appeal ([1995] QB 375)

Cutler v. Wandsworth Stadium Limited [1946] AC 398

Cynat Products Ltd v. Landbuild (Investment and Property) Ltd [1984] 3 All ER 513

D & F Estates Ltd v. Church Commissioners [1989] AC 177

Delaware Mansions v. Westminster City Council [2001] 3 WLR 1007 (HL)

Dobson v. Thames Water Utilities Ltd [2009] EWCA Civ 28; [2009] 3 All ER 319

Donoghue v. Stevenson [1932] AC 562

Edwards v. Railway Executive [1952] AC 737

Fairchild v. Glenhaven Funeral Services Ltd [2003] 1 AC 32

Ferguson v. Welsh [1987] 3 All ER 777

Field Common Limited v. Elmbridge Borough Council [2008] EWHC 2079

Gillingham BC v. Medway (Chatham) Dock Ltd [1993] QB 343

Glasgow Corporation v. Muir [1943] AC 448

Glossop v. Heston & Isleworth Local Board [1879] 12 Ch. D. 102

Gray v. Thames Trains Ltd [2009] AC 1

Grieves v. FT Everard & Sons Ltd [2008] 1 AC 281

Hall v. Beckenham Corp. [1949] 1 KB 716

Hancock v. Tucker [1999] Lloyd's Rep. P.N. 814

Harper v. Haden & Sons [1933] Ch. 298 at 308

Harrison v. Southwark and Vauxhall Water Co. [1892] 2 Ch 409

Hedley Byrne & Co Ltd v. Heller & Partners Ltd [1964] AC 465

Henderson v. Merrett [1994] 2 AC 145

Her Majesty's Commissioners of Customs and Excise v. Barclays Bank plc [2006] UKHL 28; [2007] 1 AC 181

Hiscox Syndicates Ltd v. Pinnacle Ltd [2008] EWHC 1386 (QB)

HOK Sport Ltd v. Aintree Racecourse Co Ltd [2002] EWHC 3094

Holmes v. Wilson (1839) 10 A & E 50

Hubbard v. Pitt [1976] QB 142

Hughes v. Lords Advocate [1963] AC 837

Hunter v. Canary Wharf [1997] 2 WLR 684

In re Corby Group Litigation [2009] QB 335

Invercargill City Council v. Hamlin [1996] AC 624

Jain v. Trent SHA [2009] UKHL 4; [2009] 1 AC 853 (para 27)

Jobling v. Associated Dairies [1982] AC 794

Jolley v. Sutton LBC [2000] 1 WLR 1082

Junior Books v. Veitchi [1983] AC 520

Khorasandjian v. Bush [1993] QB 727

Knightley v. Johns [1982] 1 WLR 349

London Passenger Transport Board v. Upson [1949] AC 155

LMS International Limited v. Styrene Packaging and Insulation Limited [2005] EWHC 2065 (TCC)

Lonrho Limited v. Shell Petroleum Limited [1981] 2 All ER 456

Malone v. Laskey [1907] 2 KB 141, CA

Marc Rich & Co AG v. Bishop Rock Marine Co Ltd [1996] AC 211

Marcic v. Thames Water Utilities [2004] 2 AC 42

McHale v. Watson (1966) 115 CLR 866

Mitchell v. Glasgow City Council [2009] UKHL 11; [2009] 1 AC 874

'Morning Watch, The' [1990] 1 Lloyd's Rep. 547

Murphy v. Brentwood District Council [1991] AC 398

Network Rail Infrastructure Limited v. Morris (t/a Soundstar Studio) [2004] EWCA Civ 172

Nye Saunders & Partners v. Alan E Bristow (1987) 37 BLR 92

Nykredit Mortgage Bank Plc v. Edward Erdman Group Ltd [1997] AC 191

Orchard v. Lee [2009] EWCA Civ 295

Overseas Tankship (UK) Ltd v. The Miller Steamship Co. Pty (The Wagon Mound (No. 2)) [1967] 1 AC 617

Pearson Education Limited v. Charter Partnerships Limited [2007] BLR 324

Performance Cars v. Abraham [1962] 1 QB 33

Phelps v. Hillingdon LBC [2000] 3 WLR 776

Phillips v. Britannia Hygenic Laundry Ltd [1923] 2 KB 832

Pirelli General Cable Works v. Oscar Faber and Partners [1983] 2 AC 1

Rapier v. London Tramways [1893] 2 Ch. 588

RBS v. Bannerman [2005] CSIH 39

Read v. J. Lyons & Co. Ltd [1947] AC 156

Regan v. Paul Properties Ltd [2007] Ch. 135

Robinson v. Kilvert [1889] 41 Ch. D. 88

Robinson v. PE Jones (Contractors) Ltd [2010] EWHC 102 (TCC)
Royal Brompton NHS Trust v. Hammond [2002] 1 WLR 1397
Ruxley Electronics and Construction Ltd v. Forsyth [1996] AC 344
Rylands v. Fletcher (1866) LR 1 Ex 265 at 279; affirmed in HL (1886) LR 3 HL 330
Samuel Payne v. John Setchell Ltd [2002] BLR 489
Sedleigh-Denfield v. O'Callaghan [1940] AC 880
Simms v. Leigh Rugby Football Club [1969] 2 All ER 923
Solomons v. Gertzenstein Ltd [1994] 2 QB 243
South Australia Asset Management v. York Montague Limited [1997] AC 191
Spartan Steel and Alloys Ltd v. Martin & Co. Ltd [1973] QB 27
St Helen's Smelting Co. Ltd v. Tipping (1862) 11 HL Cas 642; 11 ER 1483
Stone & Rolls v. Moore Stephens [2009] UKHL 39; [2009] 1 AC 1391
Storey v. Charles Church Developments Ltd (1996) 12 Const LJ 206
Stovin v. Wise [1996] AC 923.
Sturges v. Bridgman (1879) L.R. 11 Ch. D. 852 per Thesiger LJ
Tamares (Vincent Square) Ltd v. Fairpoint Properties (Vincent Square) Ltd [2006] EWHC 3589
Tate & Lyle v. Greater London Council [1983] 2 AC 509
Tesco v. The Norman Hitchcox Partnership (1997) 56 ConLR 42
Tesco Stores Ltd v. Costain Construction Ltd [2003] EWHC 1487 (TCC); (2003) CILL 2062

The Heron II [1969] 1 AC 350 at 385–389
The Law Society v. KPMG [2000] Lloyds Rep PN 929
The Wagon Mound No. 2 [1967] 1 AC 617
Thompson v. Alexander & Partners (1992) 59 BLR 81
Thompson v. Gibson (1841) 7 M&W 456
Thompson-Schwab v. Costaki [1956] 1 WLR 335
Transco v. Stockport MBC [2004] 2 AC 1
Tunnel Refineries v. Brya Donkin (1998) CILL 1392
Turner v. Watkins (TCC, 9 November 2001)
United Bank of Kuwait Plc v. Prudential Property Services Limited
Van Colle v. Chief Constable of Hertfordshire [2008] UKHL 50; [2009] 1 AC 225
Warner v. Basildon (1990) Constr LJ 46
Watts v. Morrow [1991] 4 All ER 937
Wheat v. Lacon [1966] AC 552
Wheeler v. Saunders [1996]
Whippey v. Jones [2009] EWCA Civ 452
White v. Blackmore [1972] 2 QB 651
White v. Jones [1995] 2 AC 507
Wilcox v. Steel [1904] 1 Ch. 212
Wilsher v. Essex AHA [1988] AC 1074
Woollerton & Wilson Ltd v. Richard Costain Ltd [1970] 1 WLR 411
Wringe v. Cohen [1940] 1 KB 229
X (minors) v. Bedfordshire County Council (1999) 3 WLR 1252

ice | manuals

Chapter 24

Environmental issues

Adrian Hughes QC Thirty Nine Essex Street, London, UK
Tony Dymond Herbert Smith LLP, London, UK

doi: 10.1680/mocl.40878.0393

There have been a number of important changes in environmental law and regulation in recent years. Examples of new developments include the Environmental Permitting (England and Wales) Regulations 2010 which impose controls on a number of activities with the potential to pollute and the new environmental liability regime introduced under the Environmental Damage (Prevention and Remediation) Regulations 2009, which implemented the European Union (EU) Directive on Environmental Liability (2004/35/EC) in the UK. The Environmental Civil Sanctions (England) Order 2010 and Environmental Civil Sanctions (Miscellaneous Amendments) (England) Regulations 2010 allow the Environment Agency or Natural England to impose a range of civil sanctions instead of prosecuting for certain environmental offences. The final part of this chapter illustrates the far reaching effect of the Climate Change Act 2008 on the industry. A key method by which the government aims to meet its target to reduce greenhouse gas emissions by at least 80% by 2050 is through greater energy efficiency, this has led to a raft of policies and measures relevant to the construction industry being adopted or proposed. Environmental regulation is a constantly developing and important area for the construction industry.

CONTENTS

24.1 Introduction

This chapter will consider the principal features of environmental regulation in England. It focuses on those areas which are of particular relevance to the construction industry and therefore cannot be seen as a comprehensive guide. The legal position in Scotland, Wales and Northern Ireland may well differ from that in England and has not been covered in this chapter. Those responsible for any construction operation taking place in or near the borders of any of these areas will need to explore the relevant regulatory framework applicable. Regulatory bodies will also differ – for example, the Scottish Environmental Protection Agency carries out similar functions in Scotland to the Environment Agency (EA) in England.

24.2 Sources and enforcement of environmental law
24.2.1 Sources of law
24.2.1.1 Legislation

Legislation is the principal source of environmental law in the UK. The main Acts of Parliament include a framework of broad principles and the rules needed to implement the principles set out in the acts are often provided in 'secondary' or 'delegated' legislation. This generally takes the form of:

- statutory instruments – generally referred to as 'regulations'
- by-laws – not frequently used but may be applicable (e.g. by-laws of the British Waterways Board related to canals)

In addition, there may be relevant guidance published by regulators.

Much of UK environmental law implements European environmental legislation.

24.2.1.2 Case law

Case law has traditionally played an important role in environmental law in the UK. Civil actions dealing with nuisance, negligence and trespass have created a significant body of the UK case law addressing the common law principles relating to environmental law.

There is also an increasing body of case law based on administrative law, in particular judicial review of decisions taken by regulators (e.g. challenging a decision on the basis that the decision maker did not follow the correct process when making it). Some environmental legislation contains provision for an appeal to the relevant Secretary of State, for example, against refusal of authorisations and permits, and the grant of permits subject to conditions unacceptable to the holder. While each appeal needs to be determined on its merits, it can be relevant to review previous appeal decisions when considering launching an appeal. Time limits for commencing an appeal are set out in the legislation and need to be checked and strictly adhered to.

Most criminal prosecutions for breach of environmental laws take place in the Magistrates' Court. However, it should be borne in mind that most environmental provisions are 'triable' either way – in a Magistrates' Court or in the Crown Court. In a case where there has been major environmental damage, a fatality, or where the prosecuting authority considers the behaviour of the defendant to be so objectionable that a higher fine than that allowed in Magistrates' Court should be imposed, then the matter may be referred to the Crown Court.

Cases in the European Court of Justice (ECJ) can also assist in the interpretation of the law and what it obliges the UK regulators to do. Although not many cases actually make it to the ECJ, understanding those decisions is necessary in order to understand environmental law issues particularly where the law applicable in the UK derives from European law.

24.2.2 Environmental regulators

24.2.2.1 Environment Agency

The EA was created by the Environment Act 1995. It does not have a monopoly on regulation in the environmental field but does have a number of different functions.

In England and Wales, the EA's head office in Bristol is responsible for policies and standards, ensuring a consistent approach to environmental protection and financial control. The regional offices handle authorisations, licences, registration, regulation, monitoring and guidance, water management, pollution control and prevention, waste regulation and flood control. Some authorisations may be subject to a review by head office to ensure consistency of approval. The EA also has inspectors who investigate alleged breaches of the environmental law regime and decide on prosecutions, subject to the advice of the EA lawyers.

24.2.2.2 Local authorities

For the construction industry, the local authority will often be as important a regulator as the EA. Local authorities have particular responsibility for the statutory nuisance provisions contained in the Environmental Protection Act 1990 (EPA) as well as noise control under the Control of Pollution Act 1974. In England and Wales they also administer the air pollution control regime referred to as Local Authority Air Pollution Control (LAAPC) which is contained in the Environmental Permitting (England and Wales) Regulations 2010.

Since April 2000, the regulation of contaminated land has rested with local authorities, although in cases of certain types (known as 'special sites'), contamination responsibility shifts to the EA. These responsibilities are in addition to the responsibilities for town and country planning and building regulation.

24.2.2.3 Water and sewerage companies

The Water Industry Act 1991 sets out the duties of water companies in relation to water supply and sewerage. The privatised sewerage undertakers are the licensing body for discharges to sewers through the grant of trade effluent consents or agreements to discharge. Appeals against the decisions of the water company go to the Water Services Regulation Authority (Ofwat) which was set up by the Water Act 2003 and whose main functions relate to the regulatory control of the water industry.

24.2.2.4 Health and Safety Executive (HSE)

One of the functions of the HSE is to enforce safety legislation and to investigate accidents. The HSE also operates various licensing and approval schemes, for example, asbestos removal contractors. It is important to bear in mind that there can often be some overlap between environmental and health and safety duties and obligations.

24.3 Waste management
24.3.1 Waste management and recycling

UK and EU environmental legislation and case law are increasing the complexity of legal controls relating to waste. The cost of waste disposal, in particular to landfill, has also increased significantly. According to Defra, the construction, demolition and excavation sector generates more waste in England than any other sector, and is the largest generator of hazardous waste, around 1.7 million tonnes.

The construction industry, as with other industries, is subject to a statutory duty of care under the Environmental Protection Act 1990 as regards waste. An environmental permit is generally required to carry out waste management activities unless an exemption applies (in most cases, the exemption itself must be registered). There are complex and potentially very significant issues surrounding the re-use of excavated soils and other materials and their possible classification as waste and consequent liability for landfill tax. There may also be a need to register as a carrier of waste – carriers are exempt from registration if they are carrying waste they have produced themselves *unless* it is building or demolition waste.

If a waste is sufficiently hazardous to meet the definition of hazardous waste in the Hazardous Waste (England and Wales) Regulations 2005, then its handling and transport will attract additional procedural requirements and fees, and this usually means that permitting exemptions are not available. Disposal costs for hazardous waste are also higher because of the limited range of sites which are now licensed to accept it since the implementation of the Landfill Directive (1999/31/EC).

24.3.1.1 Site waste management plans

The Site Waste Management Plans Regulations 2008 require all sites with construction projects of an estimated cost of at least £300,000 to have in place a site waste management plan (SWMP). The aim of the regulations is to reduce the amount of waste produced on construction sites (by reduction, re-use etc.) and prevent fly-tipping.

A SWMP must be prepared prior to commencement of work and describe the amount and types of waste that will be produced and the actions proposed for the disposal of such waste, including recycling. There is no requirement for the SWMP to be approved by a regulator. For any project with an estimated cost greater than £500,000, the SWMP must be further reviewed every 6 months to reflect the progress of the project and record actual measures taken. If work begins without the SWMP being in place, both the client and the principal contractor are guilty of an offence.

24.3.1.2 What is waste?

Types of materials that may be classified as waste generally associated with construction activities include demolition, excavation, site and landscaping debris, contaminated soil and possibly equipment such as tanks or piping which has been removed.

The legal definition of waste is found in the Waste Framework Directive (2008/98/EC) (WFD): 'any substance or object which the holder discards or intends or is required to discard.' An identical definition has been in place for many years under previous framework directives. Its application can be confusing but, as a guiding principle, if the person producing or holding a material is getting rid of it, or intends or is required to do so, then you are probably dealing with waste. In situations where another party can re-use the material without having to treat or make any changes to it, then it may be possible to argue that the material is not waste, but this cannot be assumed to be the case (see the following text).

The ECJ and the UK courts have considered the definition of waste on many occasions. The over-riding principle established by the ECJ, set out in June 2000 in *ARCO Chemie Nederland Ltd etc* (joined cases C-418/97 and C-419/97), is that the definition of waste must be considered in the light of all the circumstances, regard being had to the aims of the WFD to protect human health and the environment and the need to ensure that its effectiveness is not undermined. This has resulted in a very expansive and inclusive approach to defining waste.

In April 2002, in *Palin Granit Oy v. Vehmassalon kansanterveystyon kuntayhtyman hallitus* (case C-9/00), the ECJ considered the position of leftover stone from quarrying which did not pose any real risk to human health or the environment. However, the fact that the holder of the stone had no particular plans to sell the leftover stone and stored it for an indefinite length of time meant that in that case, the leftover stone was waste. In September 2003, in *Avestapolarit Chrome Oy* (case C-114/01), the ECJ held that leftover rock was waste unless lawfully used for necessary works on site. Later ECJ case law (for example, *Niselli* (case C-457/02)) confirmed that production or consumption residues which can be or are re-used in a cycle of consumption or production may still meet the definition of waste.

Difficult issues arise where waste materials are transformed into a substance which is potentially not waste – when does it cease being waste? In June 2007, the Court of Appeal in *R (OSS Group Limited) v. Environment Agency (and others) and DEFRA* considered whether waste lubricating and fuel oils collected from garages and then converted into 'marketable fuel oil' remained waste. The court held that the fuel did not have to be treated as waste even though the garages had intended to discard it. The court focussed on whether the material needed to be treated as waste in order to provide the level of environmental protection required by the WFD finding in this particular case that the fuel could be used in exactly the same way as an ordinary fuel and with no worse environmental effects. These cases demonstrate that it may in certain circumstances be possible to argue that a re-used or leftover material is not waste.

In *Van de Walle* (case C-1/03), the ECJ ruled that soils contaminated by an oil spillage were waste, irrespective of whether the soils had been excavated. The effect of this decision was that owners of contaminated land, might, in theory, be reclassified as landfill operators and so would be subject to permitting and other controls pertaining to the keeping and disposal of waste. However, this approach was never adopted by the EA in its regulatory functions, and the WFD now clearly excludes unexcavated contaminated soils from the definition of waste.

24.3.1.3 Controlled waste

Some waste controls apply only to 'controlled waste' rather than simply waste. This distinction is rarely significant since the definition of controlled waste is wide. Controlled waste is defined in the EPA as 'household, industrial and commercial waste or any such waste'. This definition is expanded in the Controlled Waste Regulations 1992 to cover wastes arising from works of construction or demolition, including preparatory works. Such wastes are to be treated as industrial waste and therefore controlled waste. 'Construction' includes not only the building of new structures, but also improvement, repair or alteration of existing buildings and structures. The key wastes that are not controlled wastes are waste from explosives and radioactive waste to which specific controls apply.

24.3.1.4 Hazardous waste

The Hazardous Waste (England and Wales) Regulations 2005 (HWR) set out the definition of hazardous waste (previously referred to as special waste). Again, the underlying definition is found in EU legislation (the Directive on Hazardous Waste (91/689/EEC). Determining if something is hazardous waste can be a complicated process which may require technical assistance. Hazardous wastes are listed in the List of Wastes (England) Regulations 2005 and are marked with an asterisk. Hazardous wastes display a specified hazardous property, for example, being highly flammable, toxic, carcinogenic or ecotoxic. Of particular relevance to the construction industry is that contaminated soil excavated from a site can often be hazardous waste (although treatment may change its classification). Other hazardous wastes encountered on construction sites include asbestos (to which specific additional controls apply under health and safety legislation), some treated timbers, adhesives, paints, cleaners, bitumen-based waterproofers, certain compounds of lead, electrical equipment and insulation.

Since April 2005, producers of hazardous waste have been required to notify their premises to the EA unless they fall within the exemptions set out in the HWR. As a general rule, construction sites are not exempt from notification. The HWR also changed the requirements for consignment notes, including a consignment code based on a formula issued by the EA. They also include restrictions on mixing different categories of hazardous waste or mixing hazardous waste with non-hazardous waste. Notification of premises lasts for 12 months and a small fee is payable. The HWR prohibit any person, such as a waste carrier, from removing or transporting hazardous waste from premises that are either notified or exempt from the need to notify.

Failure to notify or comply with the other requirements of the HWR constitutes a criminal offence and there is also provision for a fixed penalty notice for failure to comply with, *inter alia*, the notification provisions.

24.3.1.5 Re-using construction materials

It is usual practice on construction sites for excavated material to be stockpiled and re-used as part of the development, for example, for landscaping or land-raising purposes. Quantities of this excavated material are often stored on site pending their use for these purposes. The government's Waste Strategy for England 2007 identifies the potential to increase resource efficiency in construction and reduce waste.

Whether or not excavated material constitutes waste must be considered on a case-by-case basis and, if the material does constitute waste, an environmental permit may be required and, potentially more significantly, landfill tax (see the following text) may be payable when it is re-used. In relation to uncontaminated excavated materials, the WFD excludes from the definition of waste 'uncontaminated soil and other naturally occurring material excavated in the course of construction activities where it is certain that the material will be used for the purposes of construction in its natural state on the site from which it is excavated'. Previous framework directives did not contain this exclusion, but it is broadly consistent with a position statement adopted by the EA in September 2008 which concludes that excavated material used for the development of land on the site where it was produced will not be waste when (a) it is used in appropriate amounts, (b) it is suitable for that use without further treatment and (c) its use will not cause harm to human health or the environment. The EA position statement indicates that the EA will also take account of *The definition of waste: development industry code of practice* published by the independent, not-for-profit body Contaminated Land: Applications in Real Environments (CL:AIRE) (an industry body which promotes sustainable remediation of contaminated land) in decisions whether to regulate excavated materials as waste. Clearly, both the position statement and the WFD allow for contaminated soils, or any materials used off-site, to still constitute waste, although there may be circumstances where it still is not waste, that is, the materials did not satisfy the discarded test set out in CL:AIRE's code of practice referred to above.

In *Environment Agency v. Inglenorth Limited* [2009] EWHC 670 (Admin) the High Court ruled that demolition material that had been transferred between sites was not waste as in the particular circumstances as there was a clear intention on the part of the holder to use it for construction. However, doubt was cast on this decision by the Court of Appeal in *R v. W, C and C* [2010] EWCA Crim 927. This case considered the use of soil and subsoil extracted from neighbouring farm land for the purpose of hard standing. The Court was not required to make any finding as to whether or not the material was waste, but ruled that whether the material will immediately be re-used is not, on its own, conclusive. Excavated soil that has to be discarded by the person who is, at that time, the holder of the waste can constitute waste, and 'in any individual case, ordinarily will be'. Confirming other case law, the court held that waste does not cease to be waste just because it might be re-used at some time in the future. However, the court did stress that if it is re-used, it may cease to be waste if consistent with the aims of the WFD; any environmental benefits resulting from the re-use are relevant considerations. The definition of waste and its application to the re-use of construction materials is likely to continue to remain problematic for the EA, the courts and the construction and development industries.

24.3.1.6 Environmental permits – waste operations and waste mobile plant

As a general rule, waste management activities need to be carried out in accordance with an environmental permit issued under the Environmental Permitting (England and Wales) Regulations 2010 (EPR). These activities were previously regulated by waste management licences, and continue to be so regulated in Scotland and Northern Ireland where the environmental permitting regime does not yet apply. Although the two regimes are similar, there can be differences in practice.

Treatment of excavated contaminated material will usually require an environmental permit. There are two types of permit – a permit authorising the carrying out of particular waste operations and a waste mobile plant permit authorising the recovery or disposal of waste using certain types of mobile treatment plant. The advantage of a waste mobile plant permit is that it is the plant and not the site at which the operations are carried out which is licensed. Environmental permits can be either 'standard' or 'bespoke'. Standard permits cover specified common activities and use a fixed set of conditions so they can usually be processed more quickly.

There are exclusions and exemptions to the general rule about when an environmental permit is needed. An exempt waste operation is a low risk waste operation listed in Schedule 3 Part 1 of the EPR. Before relying on an exemption, the wording should be checked carefully to ensure that all the specified criteria are, and continue to be, met. Reliance on many of the exemptions depends on notification (i.e. registration) with the EA every 3 years. Possible exemptions relevant to the construction industry include:

(a) use of waste in construction;
(b) sorting of mixed waste;

(c) disposal of waste by incineration;
(d) burning of waste in the open; and
(e) storage of waste in a secure place.

There are further exemptions relevant to the construction industry, mainly relating to the temporary storage of waste, that do not need to be registered. These include temporary storage for collection at the place the waste was produced as long as it is stored in a secure place for 12 months or less. An exempt waste operation must not (a) pose a risk to water, air, soil, plants or animals, for example, by causing water pollution, (b) cause a nuisance or (c) affect the countryside or places of special interest (such as a site of special scientific interest [SSSI]).

If a given material is not waste then there is no need for either an exemption or a permit. In practice, however, many people register an exemption because that may prove to be an easier course of action to enable schedules to be met rather than entering into long and inconclusive discussions with the EA as to whether a particular material is or is not waste. Landfill tax implications may, however, need to be assessed.

Application for an environmental permit should be a relatively straightforward process although it can be time consuming and may cause delay to a project if discussions are not initiated early enough with the EA. When deciding whether to grant a new permit, the EA is under an obligation to assess whether the operator is 'competent', which in practical terms means that the EA will have to decide whether the operator will be able to comply with the terms of the permit. A minimum of 4 months (or 3 months in the case of waste mobile plant) should be allowed for an application to be determined. The fee payable will depend upon the type of permit applied for.

In some projects, there may be no option but to apply for and obtain an environmental permit. However, it should be remembered that, once granted, an environmental permit for site activities can only be surrendered by the holder if the EA is satisfied that the necessary measures have been taken to (a) avoid any pollution risk resulting from the operation of the permitted activities and (b) to return the site to a satisfactory state, having regard to the state of the site before the waste operations were commenced. There may be concern that property which has been redeveloped but has an environmental permit associated with it will have commercial disadvantages. Even surrendering a permit for inert waste disposal (e.g. from road building) can be difficult. This makes a mobile treatment licence a much more attractive course of action where it is appropriate. The costs, including annual fees, of obtaining and maintaining an environmental permit will need to be factored into any budgets.

24.3.1.7 Landfill Directive

Implementation of the Landfill Directive (1999/31/EC) has resulted in there being far fewer landfill sites and the cost of landfill escalating. Certain specified wastes are not accepted in landfill – these include liquid wastes, explosive, corrosive, oxidising or flammable wastes, or used tyres (whole or shredded).

Any other waste material must be treated before being landfilled and only those within the numerical limits of the waste acceptance criteria (WAC) can be accepted for landfill. The WAC are specified in the EPR and are primarily intended to protect groundwater. It is very likely that testing of many wastes will be necessary to determine whether they are hazardous. Whilst inert demolition wastes will generally meet the WAC, the cost of disposal of inert material to waste has increased significantly.

24.3.1.8 Landfill tax

The Finance Act 1996 and the Landfill Tax Regulations 1996 introduced a financial levy on all waste that is disposed of by landfill. All such waste is liable to be taxed and operators of landfill sites are responsible for paying the tax. There are two rates of tax, depending on the type of waste deposited:

(a) lower rate: inactive or inert wastes listed in the Landfill Tax (Qualifying Material) Order 1996, that is, waste which does not give off methane or any other gas and does not have the potential to pollute groundwater – £2.50 per tonne
(b) standard rate: all other (i.e. active) waste – £48 per tonne

It was announced in the March 2010 Budget that the lower rate will be frozen until March 2012. The government is also considering changes to the definition of wastes that qualify for the lower rate. The Finance Act 2010 increases the standard rate to £56 per tonne from 1 April 2011 and DEFRA has indicated that this rate will continue to escalate by £8 per year until at least 2014/2015.

Where a consignment of waste to landfill contains both active and inactive materials, the whole load is liable for tax at the standard rate. However, as long as it does not lead to any potential for pollution, it is possible to ignore the presence of an incidental amount of active waste in a mainly inactive load, and the lower rate of tax applies. Unacceptable amounts of active waste in mixed loads would include a large piece of wood in a skip or lorry (e.g. a roof beam), rubble from the construction of a house containing mixed materials, including paint tins, unused tar and leftover plaster and a skip containing mixed waste unless it is clearly all inactive waste.

There are some exemptions from the tax set out in the Finance Act 1996, the Landfill Tax (Contaminated Land) Order 1996 and the Landfill Tax (Site Restoration and Quarries) Order 1999, including for waste arising from the reclamation of contaminated land (but this will be phased out from April 2012). For waste temporarily landfilled with the intention of later removing it for recycling, incineration or re-use (other than at a landfill site), the landfill operator can claim a tax credit at the time the materials are moved, provided that prior arrangement has been made with HM Revenue & Customs (HMRC).

The landfill tax can offer landfill operators an opportunity for cost effective spending on environmental objectives. Under the Landfill Communities Fund, a 90% tax credit, up to a ceiling of 5.5% of a licence holder's total annual landfill tax bill, will be given as contributions to approved 'environmental bodies'. The fund is administered by ENTRUST on behalf of HMRC.

24.3.2 Duty of care as respects waste

Section 34 of the EPA creates a statutory duty of care applicable to all persons who produce, keep, carry or treat or dispose of controlled waste and to any person who is a broker or has control of controlled waste. The duty of care is essentially a requirement to take all reasonable steps in the circumstances to ensure that waste is handled lawfully and safely. In most cases, a contractor will be acting as a producer of waste. All waste producers must follow the duty of care, under which they must take all reasonable steps to ensure that:

(a) waste consigned to a disposal contractor or transporter is accompanied by a detailed, written description containing information necessary for the safe handling, treatment and disposal of the waste;

(b) waste is consigned only to authorised persons, that is, registered waste carriers, licensed waste contractors, local authority waste collectors or persons dealing with waste in ways that are exempt from licensing;

(c) waste is securely contained to prevent it escaping into the environment both during storage and transit; and

(d) appropriate measures are taken to ensure that others involved in the handling and disposal of the waste do so in accordance with the law.

Defra published a Code of Practice in 1996 on the duty of care which provides guidance on how to comply with the duty of care. However, the Code does not meet every contingency and organisations should be aware that it is the failure to adhere to the duty of care, rather than to the Code, which is the offence. In April 2009, Defra launched a consultation on its proposals for a revised Code to ensure that it offers clear, fit for purpose and practical guidance. The finalised revised Code is still awaited in 2010. A SWMP must include a declaration from the client and principal contractor that they will take all reasonable steps to comply with the duty of care, that materials will be handled efficiently and that waste will be managed appropriately.

The construction industry has considerable experience with the duty of care. A construction company was convicted of a breach of the duty of care for failing to provide an adequate description of waste to be removed from one of its sites. The company described the waste as 'builders' waste' on the transfer note. At the bottom of the skip, covered with soil and rubble, were paint tins. The waste was transferred to a landfill which was not licensed to accept paint residues. The company unsuccessfully tried to argue that builders' waste could contain a wide range of materials. Similarly, a company was convicted for a breach of its duty of care in respect of a consignment described as 'general construction waste' which in fact contained asbestos pipe waste.

The duty of care is not an absolute one but does necessitate the taking of whatever steps are reasonable in the circumstances. In all cases this will involve all parties knowing who carries their waste, where it ends up and that the ultimate destination and all stops along the way are authorised to take that particular type and quantity of waste.

24.3.3 Penalties for breaches of waste management law

Penalties for an offence under the waste licensing or duty of care provisions can be, in the Magistrates' Court, a maximum of £50,000 and/or imprisonment not exceeding 12 months. In the Crown Court there is the potential for an unlimited fine and/or up to 2 years (5 years in the case of hazardous waste) imprisonment.

It will be a defence to a prosecution for failing to have an environmental permit or breaching it if it was an act done in an emergency in order to avoid damage to human health, provided that all reasonably practicable steps were taken to minimise pollution of the environment and harm to human health and the EA was informed as soon as reasonably practicable.

The EA is not under an obligation to prosecute when an offence has been committed and has an increasing range of enforcement options available to it. The EA can serve an enforcement notice if it believes an environmental permit has been or is likely to be breached. The enforcement notice must specify what steps the operator needs to take to remedy the breach and the deadline for doing so. If it believes there is a risk of serious pollution, the EA can serve a suspension notice requiring activities to be stopped. In April 2010, the EA became one of the first organisations to be granted new civil powers under the Regulatory Enforcement and Sanctions Act 2008 to complement existing regulatory powers. These include powers to issue fixed penalty notices. Fixed penalty notices issued by the EA have been provided for in previous legislation, including the HWR.

24.4 Water pollution
24.4.1 Summary

Discharges of polluting substances to inland waters, coastal waters and groundwater are now regulated under the Environmental Permitting (England and Wales) Regulations 2010. 'Water discharge activity' is defined in Schedule 21 of the regulations and includes discharge of poisonous, noxious or polluting matter, waste matter, trade effluent or sewage effluent. Water discharge activities also include the removal of certain accumulated deposits and the cutting of vegetation without removing it. A 'Groundwater activity' is defined in Schedule 22 and includes the discharge of a pollutant directly into groundwater and also discharges in circumstances that might lead to the indirect input of the pollutant into groundwater.

Some discharges, such as small sewage discharges, are exempt from permitting requirements.

24.4.2 Enforcement

It is an offence to engage in either a water discharge or groundwater activity without a permit or to breach a permit condition. Such an offence is punishable with a fine of up to £50,000 in the Magistrates Court and imprisonment of up to 12 months or both. In the Crown Court the offence is punishable with an unlimited fine, imprisonment of up to 5 years or both.

The EA is responsible for granting permits in relation to water and groundwater. If an operator is contravening a permit, the EA may serve an enforcement notice specifying the necessary steps to be taken by the operator, including steps to remedy any pollution. The EA can also suspend a permit if there is a risk of serious pollution.

In addition, the EA can carry out works itself under section 161 of the Water Resources Act 1991 if it appears that any poisonous, noxious or polluting matter or solid waste has entered or is likely to enter controlled waters (as defined in the Act). The cost of such works is recoverable from the person who caused the pollution. The EA can also serve an anti-pollution works notice on the person who has caused the pollution requiring him to carry out specified works. The Anti-Pollution Works Regulations 1999 give further detail as to the service of such notices.

24.4.3 Abstraction of water

The Water Resources Act 1991 requires those carrying out water abstraction or works to enable abstraction in England and Wales to have an abstraction licence granted by the EA. Abstraction licences must be applied for by the owner of the land. Licence conditions will govern the quantity which may be taken and possibly other matters such as when water may be taken and means of measurement. There is a right to abstract small quantities of water (not exceeding 5 m³) if the abstraction is not a continuous operation. Consent may also be given for abstraction of quantities not exceeding 20 m³, again provided that the abstraction does not form part of a continuous operation. Abstraction for fire fighting and for certain scientific experiments does not require a licence.

Abstraction may well be restricted at certain times of the year. Abstraction licences now have a limited duration and abstraction charges apply.

24.4.4 Disposal to public sewers

If trade effluent is to be discharged to a public sewer then the consent of the relevant water company (in England and Wales) will be needed. Consents to discharge will contain conditions relating to the volume and quantity of the effluent, and trade effluent charges can depend on effluent quality. Consents to discharge certain particularly hazardous substances (set out in the Trade Effluents (Prescribed Processes and Substances) Regulations 1989 (SI 1989 No. 1156) must be obtained from the EA, although the consent is ultimately issued by the water company. If it is intended to put material into a public sewer

during development, then a trade effluent consent will be needed. For existing premises there may already be a trade effluent consent in place, but the source of the permitted discharge will need to be checked.

24.5 Contaminated land

Contaminated land is an area of particular relevance to the construction and development sectors. On 1 April 2000, new statutory provisions regarding clean up and liability for contaminated land came into effect in England. Comparable provisions are also in effect in Scotland and Wales, but not yet in force in Northern Ireland.

A new environmental liability regime was introduced under the Environmental Damage (Prevention and Remediation) Regulations 2009, which implemented the EU Directive on Environmental Liability (2004/35/EC) in the UK. This new regime does not impact on the existing UK contaminated land regime. New requirements to achieve good water body status contained within the Water Framework Directive (Directive 20/60/EC) may also result in more regulatory focus on remediation of groundwater.

Proposals for an EU Soil Framework Directive, which, at the time of writing, have not yet passed through the EU legislative process because of Member State opposition, have the potential to impact on the UK's contaminated land regime significantly if adopted in the future, by requiring more stringent standards of identification and remediation of contaminated land.

24.5.1 Summary

A number of existing Acts and Regulations, as well as common law, provide legal remedies and obligations in respect of contamination of land. EU case law on the subject (see *Van de Walle* (C-1/03) and section 24.3), has also impacted on the development of the legal regime applying to contaminated land. The statutory regime, introduced by the Environment Act 1995 as Part 2A of the Environmental Protection Act 1990, and the Contaminated Land (England) Regulations 2000 (SI 2000 No. 227), was specifically designed to ensure the identification, and ultimate remediation, of contaminated land. Other legislation, in particular that dealing with pollution of controlled waters and the waste provisions contained in Part 2 of the EPA may also be relevant to contaminated land liabilities. Other considerations include the land-use planning system and building regulations, health and safety legislation, statutory and common law nuisance and occupiers' liability legislation.

Other legal risks associated with contaminated land include potential civil liability for personal injury or damage caused by pollution migrating off-site, potential criminal liability for breaches of legislation (especially in relation to water pollution), and planning conditions or obligations associated with redevelopment requiring investigation, restoration or aftercare. Redevelopment controls may act as a constraint on the scope of development or involve expenditure, or cause valuation issues regarding the value of the property.

Although it is not unlawful to own or occupy contaminated land, action will need to be taken if the condition of the land is or begins to cause an unacceptable risk to human health or the environment, either on-site or off-site. In practice, many land-owners will take action voluntarily rather than wait for a legal requirement to be imposed on them.

Many construction projects will involve planned remediation of land in order to enable development to proceed. In other cases, it may be the construction personnel on site who discover unknown contamination which needs to be dealt with immediately. Those on site need to be aware of these possibilities and understand what steps to take in such event.

This chapter deals with environmental requirements, but it should be borne in mind that occupational health and safety risks due to exposure to contaminated land are also important; for more on health and safety risks see the chapters *Construction health and safety I* and *II*.

24.5.2 What is 'Contaminated Land'?

As a general principle, land can be contaminated by having substances under, on or in it which may represent a hazard to people or to the environment. The statutory definition of contaminated land in Part 2A of the EPA is more specific, generally addressing cases of significant risk. Not all land with contaminants present will therefore meet this statutory definition. However, it should be noted that even if the land does not meet the statutory definition there may nonetheless be very good reasons for remediating contamination.

The statutory definition of 'contaminated' land as set out in Part 2A of the EPA is land which appears to the local authority to be in such a condition, by reason of substances in, on or under it that either:

(a) significant harm is being caused or there is a significant possibility of such harm being caused ('harm-type' contaminated land); or
(b) pollution of controlled waters is being caused or is likely to be caused ('water pollution-type' contaminated land). (Although the word 'significant' has been inserted in this definition by the Water Act 2003, that change has not yet been brought into effect in England.)

Part 2A now also applies to radioactive contamination, although this has only been the case since August 2006.

Under Part 2A of the EPA local authorities are under a duty to inspect their areas from time to time for the purpose of identifying 'contaminated land'. In doing this they must have regard to the 'statutory guidance'. For England and Wales this guidance is contained in Defra Circular 01/2006, titled 'Environmental Protection Act 1990; Part 2A, Contaminated Land' (the Guidance). The Guidance explains what harm is to be regarded as 'significant', what degree of possibility of harm is to be regarded as 'significant' and whether pollution

of controlled waters is being or is likely to be caused. The Guidance incorporates the 'source pathway receptor' model of risk assessment – in relation to 'harm-type' contaminated land, there are tables showing which level of harm to which kinds of receptor will count as 'significant harm', and which risks of such damage occurring will count as a 'significant possibility' of such harm.

As 10 years have now passed since this Guidance was introduced, Defra is now reviewing the current Guidance, in light of experience gained in delivering the regime to date. Defra will be launching a formal consultation on proposed changes to the Guidance. It should therefore be borne in mind that the sections which follow below on exclusions and remediation notices, which are largely based on the current Guidance, may be subject to change following this review.

In some cases of 'contaminated land' the local authority will decide if the land should be designated as a 'special site'. If so designated, all enforcement responsibilities are taken over by the EA. The categories of 'special site' are set out in the Contaminated Land (England) Regulations 2006 and are intended to cover sites with particularly difficult contaminants and sites with significant water pollution issues. Land designated as special sites will be entered on the public registers. The principles of liability are not changed by designation as a special site.

Defra and the EA have published a series of non-binding Soil Guideline Value (SGV) reports. The SGV reports provide threshold values to assess if land meets the statutory definition of contamination. As a result of stakeholder consultations and publications of various reports from 2006–2009, the EA has been in the process of updating its technical guidance, including the SGV reports. 15 updated SGV reports are expected to be available by the EA by the end of 2010.

In 2009, Defra published a new Soil Strategy for England, which aims to protect and sustainably manage soils. The strategy focuses on four key themes that include dealing with existing contamination. Defra has indicated that in pursuing its aims under the Strategy it will carry out further research on the impacts from contaminated land on human health and the environment and more sustainable methods of remediating contaminated land. Findings from this research could impact on the review of the Guidance, referred to above.

Part 2A does not apply in certain circumstances. Of particular relevance to construction projects, and in evaluating which controls might be applicable, are the following:

■ Part 2A does not apply to contamination of land in respect of which there is a current environmental permit, if that contamination was caused by the regulated activities or by breach of the permit conditions. Part 2A will apply to contamination on that land if it pre-dated or is otherwise unrelated to the regulated activities;

■ Part 2A cannot be used where action may be taken under Section 59 of the EPA to deal with controlled waste which has been unlawfully deposited (for example, fly-tipped) on land; and

- Part 2A cannot be used so as to prevent or impede an environmental permit to carry out water discharge activities issued under the Environmental Permitting Regulations 2010.

The Environmental Damage (Prevention and Remediation) Regulations 2009 also introduce obligations on owners and operators of sites in danger of causing imminent environmental damage (or which have already caused such damage) to notify the EA of this immediately (unless it is an imminent threat which has been eliminated). These Regulations only apply however to damage caused or threatened by contamination after 1 March 2009. Personnel on site faced with a situation where the local authority or EA intends to take immediate action need to be aware of the appropriate response.

Where the enforcing authority decides that the contaminated land is in such a condition that there is imminent danger of serious harm or serious water pollution being caused then it can take immediate action and subject to taking account of hardship considerations then seek to recover its costs.

Since August 2006, most of the statutory nuisance provisions in Part 3 of the Environmental Protection Act 1990 do not apply to matters which consist of or are caused by land 'being in a contaminated state'. Statutory nuisance therefore no longer applies to sites which meet the definition of contaminated land but may continue to apply to some contamination situations which are less serious.

24.5.3 Who is responsible for remediation?

Primary responsibility for remediation of contamination rests with what the Guidance calls 'the Class A Liability Group': every person who caused or knowingly permitted the contaminating substances to be in, on or under the land. Class A liability can only make persons responsible for remedial action which is referable to substances which they caused or knowingly permitted to be present. Whilst there are arguments that construction personnel are not persons who caused or knowingly permitted contamination on site, there could certainly be an argument that once contaminated soil has been moved within the site, the construction personnel are responsible for 'causing' that new situation. Responsibility to address contamination may also have been imposed by contract and such contractual assumptions of responsibility will have a bearing on whether the contractor is responsible under Part 2A. All persons who caused or knowingly permitted the presence of the relevant substances will be in Class A unless they specifically benefit from an exclusion test (see the following text).

If, after reasonable enquiry, no Class A person has been found the current owners and occupiers are liable (the 'Class B Liability Group') for remediation in respect of 'harm-type' contamination (i.e. contamination set out in s78A(2)(b)), even if they have not caused or knowingly permitted the substances to be in, on or under the land. However, there is no Class B liability for 'water pollution-type' contaminated land.

In an appeal decision, *Circular Facilities (London) Ltd v. Sevenoaks District Council [2005] All ER (D)* 126, [2005] EWHC 865 (Admin) the Administrative Court considered an appeal from a decision of the Magistrates' Court about whether the developer, Circular Facilities (London) Ltd ('CFL'), should have been the recipient of a remediation notice served by the council.

The site, which had been used for residential purposes for approximately 20 years, was an infilled clay pit. In 2002, the council discovered contamination sufficient to justify it being designated as contaminated land. CFL's role in the development of the site involved acquiring the site and developing it for housing. The issues in the case turned upon what information CFL had available to it that supported a finding that CFL was aware of the contamination at the time it redeveloped the property and allowed the contamination to remain underneath the houses. The District Judge found that the existence of a technical report was enough to impute knowledge of the contamination to the developer. This decision makes it less likely that developers in the future who have access to technical reports will be able to argue they are not liable for remediation as they did not know and there was no reason why they should have known of the presence of contamination.

Case law on the statutory contaminated land regime has been slow to develop, partially because of the complex nature of the regime and partially because much remediation has occurred through the planning process or voluntarily, rather than through the serving and enforcement of remediation notices. Nonetheless, the recent High Court case of *Crest Nicholson Residential Ltd (R on the application of) v. Secretary of State for Environment, Food and Rural Affairs* [2010] EWHC 561 (Admin), serves as a useful reminder of the strict liability and remediation standards that exist under the regime and which can be used as regulatory tools to require clean-up of sites. The case involved a remediation notice being served on a development company for contaminants released as a result of historical works which caused pathways to be opened. The notice was confirmed by the court as having been properly served (and therefore not subject to judicial review) on the developer, as they caused the contamination to be present on the site, even though they did not originally introduce the substances to the site. The case is also useful in covering division of liabilities between Class A group members, highlighting the retrospective nature of the regime and reminding developers of the need for careful preparation and site management in ensuring their works do not result in contamination.

24.5.3.1 Class A persons

Where there are two or more persons in a liability group the enforcing authority must first apply the exclusion tests set out in Chapter B of the Guidance. The application of the tests may exclude members of the Class A group from liability provided that there is always at least one Class A person left, or, as the legislation states, a Class A person 'can be found'. There are six exclusion tests contained in the Guidance which the authority must apply sequentially to any Class A liability group.

Of most relevance to the construction industry is Test 1 ('excluded activities') which potentially transfers the liability of persons who could conceivably be described as having caused or knowingly permitted the presence of substances, but whose involvement is peripheral. This includes lenders, insurers, authorities who have granted permission for the polluting activity, consultants, other advisers and, in some cases, the landlord and contractors. The contractor exclusion applies to those performing a contract by providing a service or supply of goods where the contract is made with another person who is also a member of the relevant liability group. The exclusion will not apply if the contractor was not acting within the terms of the contract, if the contract was made with a body corporate or an officer of the body corporate, or if the contractor consented to or had knowledge of the acts or omissions of the other appropriate person which gave rise to their liability to remediate. The exclusion also includes providing legal, financial, engineering, scientific or technical advice or services to another person ('the Client') for the purpose of assessing the condition of the land (e.g. if it might be contaminated), establishing what remediation may be required or in relation to acts or omissions by the Client which have led to Part 2A liability arising.

Test 2 ('payments made for remediation') excludes any liability group member who has paid another group member a sum to cover the cost of remediation. The regulatory authority should consider whether the payment made is adequate to cover the costs of the remediation required.

Test 3 ('sold with information') transfers liability from those group members who have sold the land to a person who has been given adequate information about the contamination. Large businesses or public authorities buying from other group members since 1990 will normally be presumed to have known about the contamination if they were given an opportunity to carry out site investigations; it is irrelevant whether or not they actually did so. Where this test does apply so that the seller is excluded, the buyer inherits the seller's liability as well as keeping its own.

Tests 4, 5 and 6 ('changes to substances', 'escaped substances' and 'introduction of pathways or receptors') each apply where one or more group members has caused or knowingly permitted substances to be present, but it was the later conduct of another group member which created the problem that caused the land to qualify as 'contaminated land'. Test 6 may be of particular relevance in the redevelopment of land. A typical Test 6 scenario would be where several persons have caused or knowingly permitted contaminants to be present on land which, perhaps being a vacant brown-field site, for example, does not present sufficient risk to qualify as 'contaminated land'. One of those persons then converts the land to residential use without adequately dealing with the contaminants. If the new use increases the risk posed by the contaminants sufficiently to render the

land 'contaminated land' then Test 6 transfers liability of all Class A group members other than the person who converted the land to that use to that person, assuming they can be found.

If Tests 1–6 leave more than one person in the Class A liability group then liability will be apportioned between them according to rules which are intended to equate to the respective contribution to the problem.

24.5.3.2 Class B persons

Exclusion in relation to the Class B liability group is much simpler but applies only when there are no relevant Class A persons for the relevant contamination. The basic principle is that every person in a Class B liability group (the current owners and occupiers of the land) is 'innocent' because otherwise they would be in Class A. The remediation can be expected to increase the capital value of the land, and its costs should therefore have a relationship to rights in the land and be borne in proportion to the group member's respective shares in that capital value. Accordingly, there is one exclusion test which will apply to those occupying the land under an agreement with no marketable value or which cannot be assigned and to rack rent tenants, who have no share in the capital value. If this leaves more than one group member, liability is apportioned between them according to their respective shares in the capital value of the land.

It should always be borne in mind that 'remediation' covers not only actual clean up, but also prior investigation to assess the condition of contaminated land and subsequent ongoing monitoring. The authority cannot use a remediation notice to require investigation to establish whether or not land is 'contaminated land'. It must already have satisfied itself that the land is 'contaminated land'. It can then use a remediation notice to require further characterisation of the problem in order to determine what (if any) clean up is reasonable for it to require by way of further notice.

24.5.3.3 Local Authorities

A recent High Court case, *Corby Group Litigation v. Corby DC* [2009] EWHC 1944 (TCC), determined that a local authority owed a duty in tort to apply skill and care when carrying out works on sites it owns or operates so as to prevent harm to local residents from exposure to contaminants. The court held that the local authority had failed in its duty when mud and dust from local land reclamation sites spread so as to cause birth defects in pregnant women. The authority was also found liable for causing nuisance in allowing or permitting the dispersal of the contaminants and was found to have breached its statutory duty of care with regard to waste under s34 of the EPA. Whether this case will open the floodgates for communities in similar situations to bring claims for negligence is questionable. As pointed out by the judge in this case, there are very few UK sites as large, contaminated and close to residents as the Corby site was. Nevertheless, it serves as a reminder of the importance of ensuring proper remediation standards and best practice techniques are adhered to in the redevelopment of contaminated sites.

24.5.4 Remediation notices

If the local authority has identified land as 'contaminated land' then it must notify the owner of land, any apparent occupier of the land, every person who appears to be an 'appropriate person' to remediate (i.e. a member of the relevant Class A or Class B liability group) and the EA. Before serving a remediation notice, the authority must reasonably endeavour to consult the person on whom the notice is to be served, the owner and any apparent occupier, concerning what is to be done by way of remediation. A 3-month period must be allowed for such consultation before any remediation notice is served. Any construction project commencing during this consultation period should take into account the likelihood of some form of remediation being required. Where contamination is discovered during construction activities and notified to the local authority, it is conceivable that in the absence of a suitable voluntary proposal, a local authority could seek to serve a remediation notice during the construction phase.

Where the local authority is satisfied that appropriate measures are being or will be taken, then it should not serve a remediation notice. The appropriate person responsible for bearing the remediation liability can also enter into a written agreement with the relevant authority for them to carry out the remediation at the appropriate person's expense.

When the authority is satisfied that there is nothing reasonable which can be done by way of remediation, it should not serve a notice. In considering what is reasonable, the authority should have regard to the likely cost involved, the seriousness of the harm or pollution of controlled waters in question and the Guidance, focusing on the concept of 'best practicable technique of remediation'. Only remediation actions which meet these tests can lawfully be required.

Where land has been identified as contaminated or designated as a special site, unless one of the restrictions referred to above on service of a remediation notice applies, the enforcing authority is under a duty to require remediation of contaminated land by serving a remediation notice.

A remediation notice can require a party to carry out works which the party served might otherwise have no right to carry out (e.g. where the works are to be carried out on someone else's property) and any person (e.g. the landowner) whose consent is required for the works to be carried out must give the necessary consent, in return for statutory compensation if suitable compensation cannot be agreed.

There is a right of appeal to the Secretary of State against a remediation notice within a period of 21 days of service. An appeal automatically suspends the effect of a remediation notice until the appeal is determined or abandoned.

If a remediation notice is complied with, that will be the end of the matter. The person complying with it may give notice to the authority of the remediation measures carried out. That notice must be placed on the public register. However, in placing these facts on the register, the authority does not represent that the remediation has been carried out, or has been carried out adequately.

If, without reasonable excuse, the remediation notice is not complied with, then the authority may prosecute under s78M for failure to comply.

Non-compliance with a remediation notice can result in a maximum fine of £20,000, plus a daily fine of one-tenth of the amount of the fine for each day that the notice is not complied with. The only defence in relation to non-compliance (apart from 'reasonable excuse') is if the defendant is only liable for a proportion of the cost of the remediation required by the notice, and the defendant has not complied with the notice because of the refusal or inability of one or more of the other persons who are responsible for the rest of cost to bear their proportion.

There are provisions for action to be taken by the authority itself and for it to recover its costs. Cost recovery is qualified by the obligation to take into account two factors: the hardship which this would cause to the appropriate persons and the Chapter E Guidance on cost recovery. The Guidance emphasises that an authority should normally recover its reasonable costs in full, but draws attention to various cases where the authority should consider recovering none or only a proportion of its reasonable costs (such as where the appropriate person is a charity or registered social landlord, or where full cost recovery could lead to a company becoming insolvent). In relation to Class B appropriate persons, the Guidance suggests that an authority should consider waiving some or all of its costs where remediation costs would exceed the land value or where a person entered into ownership or occupation without knowledge of the contamination, despite having taken all reasonable steps to discover the contamination before doing so.

24.5.5 Other remedies which may be applicable to contaminated land

There may be other persons or regulatory bodies that should be consulted before planning or commencing work on contaminated land. These include:

(a) the local planning authority – conditions on the planning permission may require approval of the remediation or treating programme prior to commencement of development. Land-use changes resulting in the site accepting waste may also require planning permission
(b) HMRC – if seeking to dispose of contaminated soil to landfill, landfill tax will be payable
(c) the EA and local authority –if designing remedial measures then these bodies should be consulted to ensure they are happy with the proposed remediation strategy. Although not a positive obligation, it may avoid the possibility of costly changes to the remedial method being required in future to accommodate their requirements
(d) the EA – if hazardous waste is being removed from the site as part of the clean up, procedural requirements including

notifying the EA of its removal will need to be complied with under the Hazardous Waste (England and Wales) Regulations 2005. A consignment note will be required to accompany the moving of any hazardous waste. Pre-notification is still required if the waste is being moved into or within Scotland or Northern Ireland

(e) environmental consultants, who may have prepared a remediation plan based on site investigations.

24.5.6 Contaminated land and environmental permitting

Typically, when remediating contaminated land on site, contaminated soil is excavated, treated and then returned to its point of origin or placed elsewhere on site. The excavated material is considered to be waste. Therefore, its keeping, treating or handling may require an environmental permit or the registration of an exemption (see section 24.3).

A useful discussion on guidance and the UK approach to safe development of housing on land affected by contamination has recently been published by the EA and the National House Building Council. The report, titled *Guidance for the safe development of houses affected by contamination*, takes into account the Part 2A statutory provisions on contaminated land and includes references to the Guidance and EA model procedures on assessing contaminated land. In addition to sections on risk assessment and evaluation and a section on remedial measures, there are a number of useful appendices. These deal with items such as key contaminants associated with industrial uses of land, key methodologies for risk estimation, background information on key contaminants, a summary of methods available for remedial treatment of contaminated land for housing developments and technology summaries for remediation of contaminated land. CL:AIRE also provides useful guidance on this topic on its website.

24.5.7 Contaminated land and planning

Planning Policy Statement PPS 23 deals with contaminated land and links the evaluation of contaminated land under a planning permission into the process of risk assessment defined in Part 2A. It is a requirement that a developer must undertake any works necessary to ensure that after development, the site cannot be determined as contaminated under Part 2A. If a planning authority does not consider that adequate information has been submitted in support of this, or an application showing that the contamination risks can be properly evaluated have been submitted in support of this, the guidance states they should refuse the application rather than granting a conditional approval.

24.6 Air pollution

Concerns in relation to air pollution and construction are widespread, especially pollution of the air by smoke and dust. There are a number of legislative controls over air emissions of which

anyone operating on a construction site must be aware. These include provisions dealing with asbestos removal. Odour complaints may also arise from excavation, particularly in the case of remediation of contaminated land. Use of finishers and paints, especially those with a solvent base, also often lead to odour complaints. Prosecutions of members of the construction industry have followed the burning of materials on site.

24.6.1 Clean Air Act 1993

This Act restricts emissions of dark smoke from chimneys and industrial and trade premises. Causing or permitting emissions of dark smoke from the construction or demolition site can be an offence. Burning on site will almost inevitably generate dark smoke. There is an exemption for burning timber and other waste matter resulting from demolition or clearance of the site in connection with any building operation or work of engineering construction, but only if certain conditions are met. In practice, it will be extremely difficult to meet these conditions which include the *proviso* that there was no other reasonably safe practicable method of disposing of the matter. There is a defence in relation to dark smoke if the emission was inadvertent and that the best practicable steps were used to prevent it.

Dark smoke is defined by reference to the British Standard Ringelmann chart (BS 2742C:1957). In relation to night-time emissions where it is not easy to prove that it was 'dark smoke' the authority will only need to prove that material was burned in circumstances where it would be likely to give rise to an emission of dark smoke. Local authorities and the Secretary of State can declare 'smoke control areas' within which smoke emissions are strictly controlled pursuant to this legislation.

24.6.2 Local authority air pollution control

This section discusses only the air pollution activities that continue to be regulated by the local authority – referred to as Part A(2) and B installations.

It is an offence to operate an installation or mobile plant which requires an environmental permit without having such a permit or otherwise than in compliance with it. For example, crushing grinding or other size reduction of bricks, tiles or concrete, with machinery designed for that purpose is a Part B process and will require a permit, although crushing of limited quantities may be exempt under Schedule 3 of the Environmental Permitting (England and Wales) Regulations 2010. The permit must contain conditions to ensure that the installation or mobile plant is operated in such a way that:

(a) all the appropriate preventative measures are taken against pollution, in particular through application of the best available techniques (BAT)
(b) no significant pollution is caused.

BAT guidance continues to be contained in Process Guidance notes issued by the Secretary of State. For example, concrete crushing using mobile plant is dealt with by Note PG3/16 (04).

It sets out what the Secretary of State considers to be BAT for the process and includes provisions dealing with matters such as use of water suppression to minimise dust emissions, prohibition of open storage except in certain circumstances and internal transport of materials. Authorisations for mobile plant will also normally include a requirement to notify the local authority in advance if it is proposed to relocate the plant.

On conviction in the Magistrates' Court for operating without or in breach of a permit a maximum fine of £20,000 is available. On conviction in the Crown Court an unlimited fine or prison sentence not exceeding 2 years may be imposed.

24.6.3 Statutory nuisances

Part III of the Environmental Protection Act 1990 gives local authorities powers to deal with a wide range of statutory nuisances, including odour, fumes and dust emissions. This legislation has been in place in virtually the same form for more than a century and is something which local authorities are very familiar with. Statutory nuisance is potentially a very powerful remedy and is one which is frequently utilised by residents aggrieved by construction or demolition projects.

In the case of a statutory nuisance, the key concept is that the smoke, dust, steam, smell or other *effluvia* or any accumulation or deposits are 'prejudicial to health' or a 'nuisance'.

If the local authority is satisfied that a statutory nuisance exists or is likely to occur, it is under a positive obligation to serve an abatement notice on the party responsible for the nuisance. Where that party cannot be found, the notice should be served on the owner or occupier of the premises. Identifying the appropriate party to receive the abatement notice may be a difficult question on a particular construction site, but there is a myriad of circumstances where the contractor could be a legitimate recipient.

Once an abatement notice has been served by the local authority (or if the Magistrates' Court has made an order regarding abatement), then failure to comply with the notice or order will be an offence. The abatement notice may require abatement of a nuisance, prohibit its recurrence or occurrence or require the carrying out of works and other steps to abate it.

There is a defence in relation to prosecution for breach of an abatement notice or court order for the categories of statutory nuisance relevant to air pollution. This is that the best practicable means were used to prevent or counteract the effects of a nuisance.

The abatement notice is served by the local authority on the party responsible for the nuisance. That party is the party to whose act, default or sufferance the nuisance is attributable. The notice does not now need to specify in detail how the nuisance is to be abated – that can be left to the recipient to sort out. A contractor in control of the site which creates a statutory nuisance by virtue of the construction activities taking place would clearly be a person responsible and an appropriate recipient for an abatement notice. However, where the nuisance has not yet occurred or the party responsible cannot be found,

then the abatement notice should be served on the owner or occupier of the premises.

The Magistrates' Court can make an order requiring abatement of a statutory nuisance when a claim has been made by a private citizen. It can also impose a fine. Individuals who fail to persuade the local authority that a statutory nuisance exists or that enforcement action should be taken in relation to an abatement notice will often consider an application to the Magistrates' Court.

On conviction in the Magistrates' Court for breaching an abatement notice a maximum fine of £20,000 is applicable, as is a daily fine of up to £500 for each day after conviction for which the nuisance continues.

24.7 Noise
24.7.1 Generally

Noise can be particularly difficult to regulate because of the subjective element introduced by the differing reactions of people to the same levels of noise. Nonetheless, noise is reported to be the most frequent cause of complaint to local authorities and is an issue with which the construction industry has grappled for many years.

Noise from construction sites is regulated by Sections 60 and 61 of the Control of Pollution Act 1974. Control of occupational noise and vibration which might affect employees is regulated by the Health and Safety at Work etc. Act 1974 and the Control of Noise at Work Regulations 2005. Noise levels may also be prescribed in conditions in planning permissions for development and there may well be a condition prohibiting noise above a certain level at the site boundary. Noise is also a statutory nuisance for the purposes of Part III of the Environmental Protection Act 1990 and abatement notices can be served in relation to construction site noise.

24.7.2 Control of Pollution Act 1974, Sections 60 and 61

Section 60 of the Control of Pollution Act 1974 allows the local authority to serve a notice on a party carrying out work or otherwise responsible for it regarding the emission of noise from construction activities. The party responsible for the work could be a main contractor or subcontractor as well as the employer. The local authority notice may specify the plant or machinery to be used, hours of work and noise levels. In serving the notice, the local authority is required to have regard to the need for ensuring that the best practicable means are utilised to minimise noise. 'Practicable' means reasonably practicable having regard to local conditions and circumstances, current state of technical knowledge and the financial implications. This test of best practicable means applies only so far as compatible with any duty imposed by law.

Further, in issuing a notice, the local authority should also have regard to the relevant provisions in any code of practice approved by the Secretary of State (see BS 5228), before specifying any particular methods or plant or machinery, and should have regard to: (i) the need for ensuring that the best practicable means are used to minimise noise; (ii) specifying any particular methods, plant or machinery in the interests of the recipient of the notice; and (iii) the need to protect persons in the locality from noise. Some local authorities will have their own 'Code of Practice' regarding noise. The type of works for which a Section 60 consent can be issued are:

(a) the erection, construction, alteration, repair or maintenance of buildings, structures or roads;
(b) breaking up, opening or boring under any road or adjacent land in connection with the construction, inspection, maintenance or removal of works;
(c) demolition or dredging works; and
(d) any work of engineering construction.

It is possible to appeal against a Section 60 notice within 21 days of its receipt. Grounds of appeal are limited and include the following facts:

■ the service of the notice was not justified

■ the notice contains a defect or irregularity

■ the notice gives inadequate time for compliance

■ the local authority acted unreasonably in refusing to accept alternative proposals

■ the notice was served on the wrong person.

It is a criminal offence, without reasonable excuse, to contravene a requirement of a Section 60 notice. It is a defence against a statutory nuisance action brought by a local authority that the noise emitted was in accordance with a Section 60 consent.

A contractor can avoid potential prosecution by applying to the local authority for a 'prior consent' governing work on the construction site, and adhering to the conditions set. These are referred to as Section 61 notices. The local authority must grant a consent if it is satisfied that the application contains sufficient information to enable it to assess the noise control requirements and that it would not serve a Section 60 notice if the works were carried out in accordance with the application. The local authority must have regard to the statutory codes of practice (BS 5228), whether the best practicable means are being used to minimise noise, and a need to protect any persons in the locality from the effects of noise. Some notices will include fixed noise levels rather than a general best practicable means approach. Care should be taken where this is the case.

It is possible to appeal against the conditions on a Section 61 consent or against a refusal to grant a consent. The appeal is to the Magistrates' Court and must be made within 21 days after the expiry of 28 days from the date the local authority receives the application.

Local authorities generally base the noise limits in consents or abatement orders on BS 5228: *Code of practice for noise*

and vibration control on construction and open sites. The standard consisted of the following five parts:

■ Part 1: Code of Practice for basic information and procedures for noise and vibration control.

■ Part 2: Guide to noise and vibration control legislation for construction and demolition including road construction and maintenance.

■ Part 3: Code of Practice for noise control applicable to surface coal extraction by open-cast methods.

■ Part 4: Code of Practice for noise and vibration control applicable to piling operations.

■ Part 5: Code of Practice applicable to surface minerals (excluding coal) extraction.

In January 2009 Parts 3 to 5 were withdrawn and superseded by revised versions of Parts 1 and 2; see British Standards Institute website for further information):

■ BS 5228–1:2009 Code of Practice for noise and vibration control on construction and open sites. Noise.

■ BS 5228–2:2009 Code of Practice for noise and vibration control on construction and open sites. Vibration.

The Noise Emission in the Environment by Equipment for use Outdoors Regulations 2001 (SI 2001/1701) implement Directive 2000/14 and make provision for equipment to comply with certain noise emission standards, labelling requirements and so on.

It is possible for an injunction, based on a private nuisance, to be granted by a court in the case of noise nuisance on a construction site and some councils make it clear that they will take proceedings in the High Court where a serious nuisance occurs. The Court of Appeal decision in *City of London Corporation v. Bovis Construction Limited* [1992] confirmed that injunctions are available provided it can be shown that no other remedy will stop the nuisance.

24.8 Asbestos

There remains a considerable amount of asbestos in buildings, notwithstanding the fact that it is now unlawful to use it for these purposes. However, it remains the case that, provided that asbestos is in good condition, it does not need to be removed.

The Control of Asbestos Regulations 2006 (SI 2006/2739) regulate the identification and control of asbestos in non-domestic premises and the protection of workers from exposure.

24.9 Nature conservation

The law regulates the conservation of nature mainly by the protection of individual plants and animals and by general habitat protection through the designation of key sites. The principal sources of legislation in this area are the Wildlife and Countryside Act 1981 and the Conservation of Habitats and Species Regulations 2010 (which implement in England and

Wales the Birds and Habitats Directives). The Countryside and Rights of Way Act 2000 extended rights of access to the countryside and the Natural Environment and Rural Communities Act 2006 amended nature conservation legislation (as well as amending the law relating to public rights of way) but the essential prohibitions on damaging or destroying protected species or their habitats remained with enhanced penalties – including increased fines and imprisonment for certain offences. Public authorities are also now under a duty to have regard, when exercising their functions, to the purpose of conserving biodiversity.

Probably the most important statutory designation for securing conservation interests is the SSSI provided for in the Wildlife and Countryside Act 1981. Natural England advise on wildlife cases in England and are required to identify and notify SSSIs on the basis that their flora and fauna, and their geological, physiological or biological features. When notified of an SSSI designation on their site, owners and occupiers will be given a list of operations which Natural England considers are likely to damage the special interest on the site. Owners or occupiers will then be required to consult them before undertaking any of the listed operations. If working in an SSSI or adjacent to an SSSI it is important to be aware of any listed operations.

It is also essential to be aware of whether or not there are any planning conditions regarding nature conservation.

Nature conservation orders (NCOs) made by the Secretary of State, pursuant to the Conservation Regulations, are similar to SSSIs but provide even greater protection for sites of national importance. These are made where it is necessary to ensure the survival of any plant or animal or to comply with an international obligation. Where an NCO is made, a wider range of people than owners or occupiers may be prosecuted for carrying out damaging operations without consent and a wider range of sanctions is available. Natural England administers compliance with these orders in England.

24.10 Environmental permitting

Many polluting activities now require a permit under the Environmental Permitting (England and Wales) Regulations 2010. The EA grants permits for activities with the potential to pollute most seriously including large combustion plants and heavy industrial processes. Local authorities also grant permits, generally for smaller scale activities.

Activities now included in the permitting regime include discharges to water, water abstraction, waste activities (permitting requirements referred to at section 24.3) and landfill (permitting requirements referred to at section 24.5). Permits will govern emissions to air and water and will also deal with waste disposal and will aim to take an integrated approach to pollution with the application of requirements based on the best available techniques. Certain permits are in standard form and require compliance with conditions which are set out in

the regulations. Other permits will be 'bespoke' and tailored to the individual activity. Provisions in the regulations allow the regulator to take action to enforce compliance with the permit and to take steps to prevent pollution if necessary. Guidance on environmental permitting in available on the Defra website.

24.11 Environmental liability

The Environmental Damage (Prevention and Remediation) Regulations 2009 implement the Environmental Liability Directive in England. They apply to 'operators' of economic activities, and to damage to biodiversity, water and land as defined in the regulations. If damage is caused by any of the activities listed in Schedule 2 to the regulations, then there is liability without the need to show fault on the part of the operator. In addition, operators of any other activity can be liable for damage to biodiversity if the damage is intentional or negligent. The regulations impose a duty on operators of activities to take steps to prevent damage, or if it is being caused, to take steps to prevent the damage becoming worse. Operators may then be required to clean up any damage they have caused. The Directive introduced some new concepts, such as the requirement to carry out not only primary remediation (broadly, to clean up the damaged site) but also complementary and compensatory remediation. Complementary remediation can be required where primary remediation is incapable of bringing the damaged site back to the state it would have been in had the damage not occurred, and may consist of action taken at an alternative site. Complementary remediation may also take place at an alternative site and is to compensate for the loss of environment suffered pending full primary and/or complementary remediation.

Clearly, the cost of this remediation may be substantial and it is therefore very much in the interests of operators to make sure that they do not cause damage in the first place. Operations taking place in or near an SSSI or other sensitive habitat will need to take particular care. Operations which have the potential to pollute water or land are already subject to regulation as explained elsewhere in this chapter, but, if appropriate, will be regulated as an alternative under the Environmental Damage Regulations which may result in more onerous remediation requirements.

24.12 Civil sanctions

The Environmental Civil Sanctions (England) Order 2010 and Environmental Civil Sanctions (Miscellaneous Amendments) (England) Regulations 2010 have been made under powers in the Regulatory Enforcement and Sanctions Act 2008. These provisions allow the EA or Natural England to impose a range of civil sanctions instead of prosecuting for certain environmental offences. Civil sanctions include fixed penalties, variable monetary penalties, remediation and compliance notices and undertakings. Guidance published by Defra and additional guidance from the regulators themselves will explain the considerations to be taken into account in deciding whether or not to adopt any of the available civil sanctions. Offences which are relevant to the construction industry might include those to do with hazardous waste, packaging waste, water pollution and wildlife offences.

24.13 Environmental management systems

Environmental management systems are increasingly being adopted by many industries. The two best known schemes are as follows:

ISO 14001 – written by the International Organization for Standardization, it has been adopted as a European standard by CEN. It is structured around five core principles: policy, planning, implementation and operation, checking and corrective action, and review. Emphasis is on compliance with relevant legislation, pollution prevention through avoidance, reduction and control and commitment to continual improvement of the system. Registration is by the company.

EMAS – the Eco-Management and Audit Scheme is based on EEC Regulation EEC/1836/93. Registration is achieved by establishing environmental policies, programmes and management systems in relation to sites, systematically, objectively and periodically auditing their performances, and providing information on environmental performance to the public in an environmental statement. Registration is by site and not by company.

A number of companies in the construction industry and building products industry have gained accreditation under ISO 14001 although take up by the industry as a whole has been relatively limited. Due to the site-specific nature of EMAS, it has been less widely adopted by the construction industry although companies in the building products industry have registered various sites.

24.14 Sustainable construction, climate change and energy efficiency

24.14.1 The Climate Change Act 2008

The statistic that constructing, occupying and operating buildings accounts for almost half of all greenhouse gas emissions and water consumption, and a third of all landfilled waste, in the UK is not entirely surprising. Whilst the construction sector has recognised and is managing the issue of climate change and energy efficiency of buildings, issues such as flood protection and drainage and building maintenance are also critical.

The Climate Change Act 2008 imposes a binding target on the UK government to reduce greenhouse gas emissions by at least 80% by 2050. A key method by which the government aims to meet this target is through greater energy efficiency, (mainly though improved design, materials and construction methods in buildings). A raft of policies and measures relevant to the construction industry have already been adopted or proposed.

24.14.2 Sustainable construction

In June 2008, the government and the construction industry jointly published the *Strategy for sustainable construction,* which argues that there is a strong business case for adopting sustainable construction. It identifies 11 areas for which targets and policy measures are proposed including: climate change, water, biodiversity materials, and waste. Many of the proposed measures and targets focus on climate change mitigation by reducing emissions from buildings. The most important of these measures, including zero carbon buildings proposals and the CRC Energy Efficiency Scheme, are summarised subsequently and could have a significant impact on the current and future design, specification and construction of many building projects.

The strategy also seeks to promote climate change adaptation to be included in design and construction methods to take account of likely changes such as rising sea levels and increasing water stress. It proposes a target for the construction industry to reduce waste by 50% by 2012. Further, by this date, 25% of materials should be responsibly sourced and all construction materials should have the least environmental and social impact as is feasible.

Some of the proposals are being implemented through changes to planning policies. In December 2007, the Department for Communities and Local Government (DCLG) published a Planning Policy Statement on Climate Change which significantly requires new developments to include a significant amount of on-site or near-site renewable or low-carbon energy generation (commonly known as the 'Merton rule').

It is becoming increasingly common for planning authorities to require commercial developments to achieve a Very Good or Excellent rating in a Building Research Establishment Environmental (BREE) Assessment Method (BREEAM) sustainability assessment. The Joint Contracts Tribunal (JCT) has recently drafted general sustainability provisions to add to its suite of contracts and has published a guidance note on sustainability, *Building a sustainable future together.*

24.14.3 Energy Performance of Buildings Directive

The Energy Performance of Buildings Directive (2002/91/EC) aims to improve the energy efficiency of all buildings and requires new buildings, and large buildings which are subject to major renovation, to meet certain energy performance standards. The Directive requires an energy performance certificate (EPC) to be made available to prospective buyers and tenants, and regular inspections of boilers and air conditioning systems.

The Directive is partly implemented in England and Wales through amendments to Part F and Part L to Schedule 1 of the Building Regulations 2000 requiring the government to approve minimum energy performance requirements for new buildings in the form of target carbon dioxide emission rates.

The requirements of the Directive in relation to EPCs have been implemented under the Energy Performance of Buildings (Certificates and Inspectors) (England and Wales) Regulations 2007. Revised regulations are currently before Parliament and will introduce a new duty to commission an EPC before marketing a property. Since October 2008, occupiers of certain large public buildings have been required to show a display energy certificate (DEC) in a prominent place to enable the public to compare the energy performance of public buildings and to promote improved energy use.

Proposals to amend the Directive are currently being negotiated. Amendments have been proposed by the European Parliament that would require all buildings in the EU built from 2019 to source all of the energy they need using on-site renewable energy technologies, although it is questionable whether this amendment will be ultimately adopted. Further clarity on the proposals is expected during the course of 2010.

24.14.4 Domestic proposals relating to energy-efficient buildings

In December 2006, the government proposed that all new homes should be 'zero carbon' by 2016, all new public buildings by 2018, and all new non-domestic buildings by 2019 (although the latter two targets have since been described by the government as 'ambitions' rather than targets). The Welsh Assembly government has stated that it wants all new domestic and non-domestic buildings to be zero carbon by 2011.

A 'zero carbon' building is one which has no net emissions of carbon dioxide resulting from energy use over the course of a year, inclusive of the energy used to heat and light the building. This definition requires energy used in the building to come from renewable sources. The main method for meeting the 2016 target is a gradual tightening of the requirements of the Building Regulations 2000, which are detailed in *Forward look,* published by DCLG in July 2007. The government has also introduced stamp duty tax relief for new zero carbon homes although this is currently due to expire in September 2012.

In November 2009, DCLG launched a consultation, *Zero carbon for new non-domestic buildings: consultation on policy options.* This document contains proposals for non-domestic buildings which closely follow the approach taken to homes. In December 2007, the UK Green Building Council published a report, commissioned by DCLG, on meeting the zero carbon emissions target in new non-domestic buildings, which estimated that the cost of meeting the target would range from 5% to over 30% of current baseline construction costs.

There have also been a number of industry led developments. In April 2007, *The Code for Sustainable Homes* was published by the BRE (revised in 2009 – CLG, 2009). It adopts a six level star rating system assessed against a series of design standards across nine categories (including energy efficiency) and is intended to complement the system EPCs for new homes. A level 6 rating is equivalent to a zero carbon home. A revised Code is due to be introduced in October 2010. In December 2009, the BRE published *Smart home systems and the code for sustainable homes* which provides guidance on how different technologies can deliver benefits in meeting the targets set out in the Code.

24.14.5 CRC Energy Efficiency Scheme

The CRC Energy Efficiency Scheme (CRC) is a mandatory emissions trading scheme that commenced on 1 April 2010. Commercial and public sector organisations that were supplied with at least 6000 MWh of electricity through half hourly meters during 2008 (roughly equivalent to an electricity bill of over £500,000) must participate. Many organisations in the construction sector will meet this threshold.

The main requirement of the CRC on participants is to purchase sufficient carbon allowances to cover carbon dioxide emissions resulting from their consumption of electricity, gas and other fuels from 1 April 2011 onwards. Allowances will be initially sold at a fixed price of £12 in unlimited number but from 2013 annual auctions will be conducted with the total number of allowances available subject to a decreasing cap. A key part of the scheme is the annual publication of a league table highlighting good and bad performance.

Unlike other emissions trading schemes, the CRC targets emissions at an organisation level, rather than a site or installation level. The CRC draws on the definitions of parent and subsidiary undertakings used in company legislation to define a participating organisation. This is relevant to the construction industry, where organisations often make use of subsidiaries to ring fence their liability. The determination of whether an undertaking is a subsidiary undertaking may be complex, particularly in joint venture, Public Finance Initiative (PFI) and Public Private Partnership (PPP) scenarios. In January 2010, Partnerships UK announced it would carry out a study to look at representative samples of PFI and PPP contracts to determine how the CRC affects common PFI and PPP structures.

In addition to a construction organisation's potential direct participation in the scheme, the CRC could impact many construction projects. The CRC should provide owners and occupiers of large buildings with an incentive to make their buildings more energy efficient, and may encourage greater use of energy efficiency requirements in project specifications. Construction organisations that are better placed to deliver cost effective energy-efficient buildings should enjoy a competitive advantage.

References

Communities and Local Government. *Building Regulations: energy efficiency requirements for new dwellings – A forward look at what standards may be in 2010 and 2013,* London, UK, DCLG, 2007. www.communities.gov.uk/publications/planningandbuilding/energyefficiencynewdwellings (last accessed 21 September, 2010).

Communities and Local Government. *Planning policy statement: planning and climate change – supplement to planning policy statement 1,* London, UK, DCLG, 2007. www.communities.gov.uk/planningandbuilding/planning/planningpolicyguidance/planningpolicystatements/planningpolicystatements/ppsclimate-change/ (last accessed 21 September, 2010).

Communities and Local Government. *The code for sustainable homes: technical guide – May 2009 Version 2,* London, UK, DCLG, 2009. www.communities.gov.uk/publications/planningandbuilding/codeguide (last accessed 21 September, 2010).

Communities and Local Government. *Zero carbon for new non-domestic buildings: consultation on policy options,* London, UK, CLG, 2009. www.communities.gov.uk/publications/planningandbuilding/newnondomesticconsult (last accessed 21 September, 2010).

Contaminated Land: Applications in Real Environments (CL:AIRE). *The definition of waste: development industry code of practice,* 2008. Available online at www.claire.co.uk (under 'Projects and Initiatives').

Defra. *Waste management the duty of care: a code of practice,* London, UK, Defra, 1996. www.defra.gov.uk/environment/waste/controls/duty.htm#code (last accessed 21 September, 2010).

Defra. *Defra Circular 01/2006. Environmental Protection Act 1990; Part 2A. Contaminated Land,* London, UK, Defra, 2006. www.defra.gov.uk/environment/quality/land/contaminated/documents/circular01–2006.pdf (last accessed 21 September, 2010).

Defra. *Waste strategy for England,* London, UK, TSO, 2007.

Defra. *Safeguarding our soils: a strategy for England,* London, UK, Defra, 2009. www.defra.gov.uk/environment/quality/land/soil/documents/soil-strategy.pdf (last accessed 21 September, 2010).

Environment Agency and Defra. *Soil guideline value (SGV) reports.* www.environment-agency.gov.uk/research/planning/33734.aspx (last accessed 21 September, 2010).

HM Government and Strategic Forum. *Strategy for sustainable construction,* London, UK, Department of Business Enterprise and Regulatory Reform, 2008. www.bis.gov.uk/files/file46535.pdf (last accessed 21 September, 2010).

National House Building Council (NHBC) and Environment Agency (EA). *Guidance for the safe development of houses affected by contamination,* UK, NHBC, EA and Chartered Institute of Environmental Health, 2008. www.nhbc.co.uk/Builders/Technicaladviceandsupport/Publications/ContaminatedLandDevelopment/ (last accessed 21 September, 2010).

Nicholl, A. and Perry, M. *Smart home systems and the code for sustainable homes: A BRE guide,* Bracknell, UK, IHS BRE Press, 2009

UK Green Building Council. *Report on carbon reductions in new non-domestic buildings: Report from UK Green Building Council,* London, UK, CLG, 2007.

Referenced legislation, regulations and standards

Anti-Pollution Works Regulations 1999

Birds Directive – *Directive 2009/147/EC of the European Parliament and of the Council of 30 November 2009 on the conservation of wild birds. OJ* **L20**, 26/01/2010. pp.7–25

BS 2742C:1957 Ringelmann chart

BS 5228–1:2009 Code of practice for noise and vibration control on construction and open sites. Noise

BS 5228–2:2009 Code of practice for noise and vibration control on construction and open sites. Vibration

Building Regulations 2000

Clean Air Act 1993

Climate Change Act 2008

Conservation of Habitats and Species Regulations 2010

Contaminated Land (England) Regulations 2000

Control of Asbestos Regulations 2006

Control of Noise at Work Regulations 2005

Control of Pollution Act 1974

Controlled Waste Regulations 1992

Countryside and Rights of Way Act 2000

Directive 2000/14 – *Directive 2000/14/EC of the European Parliament and of the Council of 8 May 2000 on the approximation of the laws of the Member States relating to the noise emission in the environment by equipment for use outdoors. OJ* **L162**, 03/03/2000, pp.1–78.

Directive 91/689/EEC – *Council Directive 91/689/EEC of 12 December 1991 on hazardous waste. OJ* **L377**, 31/12/1991, pp.20–27

EEC Regulation EEC/1836/93 – *Council Regulation (EEC) No 1836/93 of 29 June 1993 allowing voluntary participation by companies in the industrial sector in a Community eco-management and audit scheme. OJ* **L168**, 10/07/1993, pp.1–18

Energy Performance of Buildings (Certificates and Inspectors) (England and Wales) Regulations 2007

Energy Performance of Buildings Directive – *Directive 2002/91/EC of the European Parliament and of the Council of 16 December 2002 on the energy performance of buildings. OJ* **L1**, 04/01/2003, pp.65–71

Environment Act 1995

Environmental Civil Sanctions (England) Order 2010

Environmental Civil Sanctions (Miscellaneous Amendments) (England) Regulations 2010

Environmental Damage (Prevention and Remediation) Regulations 2009

Environmental Permitting (England and Wales) Regulations 2010

Environmental Protection Act 1990

EU Directive on Environmental Liability (2004/35/CE) – *Directive 2004/35/CE of the European Parliament and of the Council of 21 April 2004 on environmental liability with regard to the prevention and remedying of environmental damage. OJ* **L143**, 30/04/2004, pp.56–75

Finance Act 1996

Finance Act 2010

Habitats Directive – *Council Directive 92/43/EEC of 21 May 1992 on the conservation of natural habitats and of wild fauna nad flora. OJ* **L26** 22/07/1992. pp.7–50.

Hazardous Waste (England and Wales) Regulations 2005

Health and Safety at Work etc. Act 1974

ISO 14001 – BS EN ISO 14001:2004 Environmental management systems. Requirements with guidance for use.

Landfill Directive (1999/31/EC) – *Council Directive 1999/31/EC of 26 April 1999 on the landfill of waste. OJ* **L182**, 16/07/1999, pp.1–19

Landfill Tax (Contaminated Land) Order 1996

Landfill Tax (Qualifying Material) Order 1996

Landfill Tax Regulations 1996
Landfill Tax (Site Restoration and Quarries) Order 1999
List of Wastes (England) Regulations 2005
Natural Environment and Rural Communities Act 2006
Noise Emission in the Environment by Equipment for use Outdoors Regulations 2001
Site Waste Management Plans Regulations 2008
Trade Effluents (Prescribed Processes and Substances) Regulations 1989
Waste Framework Directive (2008/98/EC) – *Directive 2008/98/EC of the European Parliament and of the Council of 19 November 2008 on waste and repealing certain Directives (Text with EEA relevance). OJ* **L312**, 22/11/2008, pp.3–30
Water Act 1989
Water Act 2003
Water Industry Act 1991
Water Resources Act 1991
Wildlife and Countryside Act 1981

Referenced cases

ARCO Chemie Nederland Ltd etc (joined cases C-418/97 and C-419/97)
Avestapolarit Chrome Oy (case C-114/01)
Circular Facilities (London) Ltd v. Sevenoaks District Council [2005] All ER (D) 126, [2005] EWHC 865 (Admin)
City of London Corporation v. Bovis Construction Limited [1992]
Corby Group Litigation v. Corby DC [2009] EWHC 1944 (TCC)
Crest Nicholson Residential Ltd (R on the application of) v. Secretary of State for Environment, Food and Rural Affairs [2010] EWHC 561 (Admin),

Environment Agency v. Inglenorth Limited [2009] EWHC 670 (Admin)
Niselli (case C-457/02)
Palin Granit Oy v. Vehmassalon kansanterveystyon kuntayhtyman hallitus (case C-9/00)
R v. W, C and C [2010] EWCA Crim 927
R (OSS Group Limited) v. Environment Agency (and others) and DEFRA
Van de Walle (case C-1/03)

Websites

British Standards Institute (shop); http://shop.bsigroup.com/
CRC Energy Efficiency Scheme; www.decc.gov.uk/en/content/cms/what_we_do/lc_uk/crc/crc.aspx
Department for Communities and Local Government (DCLG); www.communities.gov.uk
Defra; www.defra.gov.uk
Eco-Management and Audit Scheme (EMAS); http://ec.europa.eu/environment/emas/index_en.htm
Environment Agency; www.environment-agency.gov.uk
Health and Safety Executive (HSE); www.hse.gov.uk
HM Revenue & Customs (HMRC); www.hmrc.gov.uk
International Organization for Standardization (ISO); www.iso.org
Joint Contracts Tribunal (JCT); www.jctltd.co.uk
Landfill Communities Fund; www.entrust.org.uk
Natural England; www.naturalengland.org.uk
Ofwat; www.ofwat.gov.uk
Process Guidance notes; www.defra.gov.uk/environment/quality/pollution/ppc/localauth/pubs/guidance/notes/pgnotes/index.htm
Scottish Environmental Protection Agency; www.sepa.org.uk

Section 4: Construction disputes
Section editor: Michael P. O'Reilly

ice | manuals

doi: 10.1680/mocl.40878.0415

Chapter 25

Administration of claims

Daniel Atkinson Daniel Atkinson Limited, Robertsbridge, UK

A claim may be made in a variety of situations, which commonly arise in construction. It is important to understand when claims may be made and on what basis. In this chapter a range of situations will be covered, including entitlements under the contract, claims in respect of breaches of contract. The circumstances will include claims for additional payment and for extensions of time. The basis upon which compensation is to be computed will be examined.

CONTENTS

25.1 Legal basis of claims

A legal basis for compensation may arise as follows:

(a) under contract
(b) at common law for breach of contract
(c) at common law for breach of a duty arising in tort
(d) in restitution.

Claims for breach of a duty arising in tort are not examined in detail here, but should be considered (see the chapter *Law of tort*).

Claims under the contract are claims for compensation for events for which specific provision is made within the conditions of contract. The claims at common law considered here are claims for damages for breach of contract. The two heads are entirely separate, although they may relate to the same event. If, for example, information is issued late there may be grounds for a claim under both heads. Of course, the claimant will not be able to recover twice for its loss. The measure of damages for breach will take into account the compensation received under the contract.

Some events which create an entitlement under the contract do not constitute a breach of contract; they are neutral events. The contract simply makes provision for compensation as a means of apportioning risk, there is no breach of a legal obligation. In some contracts this is the case with extensions of time for exceptional adverse weather conditions, for instance. Similarly, if a risk event of physical conditions or artificial obstructions causes the contractor to incur delay and extra cost, some contracts provide that the employer is liable for this risk. In neither case can it be said that the employer was in breach of an obligation with regard to the weather or physical conditions.

Therefore, in many situations there will be a choice, whether to pursue a claim under the contract and/or as an action for damages at common law. The use of the standard forms will not normally preclude the right to sue for damages for breach of contract at common law. In some cases a procedural failure, such as the lack of notice, may leave only a claim at common law if the procedure is a condition precedent to entitlement under the contract.

If the contract states that the contractual entitlement is an exhaustive remedy, then there will be no alternative remedy at common law since such suitably drafted clauses have been held to be enforceable. Lack of notice in that case will therefore exclude any contractual remedy for the particular event.

A claim in restitution is to be distinguished from a claim for contractual *quantum meruit*. The latter arises when the contract does not state the rate for the work carried out. It may also arise when the contract specifies that the valuation of a variation is to be at a reasonable rate, or such a term is implied by statute. A claim in restitution will not succeed when there is an agreement between the parties which covers the situation.

25.1.1 Claims under the contract

Presentation of a claim under the contract has the advantage that the procedure under the contract for compensation will in many cases be quicker and cheaper than coercive dispute resolution processes such as litigation or arbitration (see *Litigation for the construction industry* and *Arbitration*). A valid claim pursued under the contract has the following advantages:

(a) it will normally create a right to an interim payment
(b) it may create a right to an extension of time
(c) it may allow resolution of any resulting dispute or difference by statutory adjudication under the Housing Grants, Construction and Regeneration Act 1996 for agreements entered into after 1 May 1998.

25.1.2 Claims for breach of contract

25.1.2.1 Remedy of damages

The normal remedy for breach of contract is damages. Damages are intended to compensate the innocent party for the loss suffered as a result of the breach of contract. In order to establish an entitlement to substantial damages for breach of contract, the injured party must establish that

(a) actual loss has been caused by the breach; and
(b) the type of loss is recognised as giving an entitlement to compensation;
(c) the loss is not too remote; and
(d) quantification of damages to the required level of proof can be provided.

A breach of contract can be established even if there is no actual loss. In that case there will only be an entitlement to nominal damages.

In general, the claimant must prove its loss. This requires records to be kept during execution of the works so that loss can be established as a matter of fact.

A claim for damages is the means of putting the injured party back into the position in which it would have been but for the particular event complained of. Claims are not a means of turning a loss into a profit, or obtaining a windfall. The remedy for breach of contract is an award of damages. Damages at common law are intended to compensate the injured party for its loss, not to transfer to the injured party, if it has suffered no loss, the benefit which the wrongdoer had gained by its breach of contract.

Losses recoverable as damages are limited to those which are reasonably foreseeable. Recoverable losses are those which may fairly and reasonably be considered as arising naturally according to the usual course of events from the breach of contract. Losses are also recoverable when they may reasonably be supposed to have been in the contemplation of both parties at the time they made the contract, as the probable result of breach of the contract.

25.1.2.2 Measure of damages

There are two possible measures of loss:

(i) loss of bargain
(ii) wasted expenditure.

25.1.2.3 Loss of bargain

The normal measure for breach of contract is loss of bargain. This measure of damages is intended to place the injured party in the same situation, as far as money can accomplish this, as if the contract had been performed *Mertens v. Home Freeholds Co* (1921) CA. This principle arises from the nature of contracts. Contracts involve the making of bargains and create expectations on each side which are intended to be fulfilled by performance of the contract obligations. If, for instance, the contractor does not complete its part of the development, then the measure of damages in this case will be the cost of completing the project in a reasonable manner, less the contract price *Mertens v. Home Freeholds Co.* (1921) CA. This measure of damages therefore protects the expectations of the

parties arising from the contract. Allowance must be made for the expense which may have been saved by the contractor not having to complete its side of the bargain.

25.1.2.4 Cost of reinstatement

Where the breach of contract involves defective work, the normal measure of damages is the cost of reinstatement taken at the time when the defect was discovered *East Ham Corporation v. Bernard Sunley* (1966). The claimant will not necessarily lose its entitlement to damages if it waits for the outcome of the case before carrying out the remedial works, it all depends on the circumstances of the case *William Cory & Son Ltd v. Wingate Investment (London Colney) Ltd* (1980) 17 BLR 104 CA. An injured party will be entitled to the cost of making building works conform to contract unless that cost is significantly disproportionate to the benefit that is obtained from it *Roxley Electronics and Construction Ltd v. Forsyth* (1996).

The reasonableness of the pursuer's remedial works is not to be weighed in fine scales. *McLaren Murdoch & Hamilton Ltd v. The Abercromby Motor Group Ltd* [2002] Court of Session Outer House.

Where the cost of reinstatement is out of proportion to the claimant's real loss then some other measure should be used. This is the case where there has been a modest effect on the utility of the works and where it would be reasonable to assess the loss on the basis of diminution in value *Birse Construction Ltd v. Eastern Telegraph Company Ltd* [2004] EWHC 2512 (TCC).

25.1.2.5 Loss of market value

In some cases the measure of damages for defective work may instead be the reduction in market value of the development. This will be the case when it is unreasonable for the defects to be put right, particularly where the value of remedial works is out of proportion to the value of the development and only affects the 'amenity value' of the development.

A loss of use claim in a building case is not a claim for the loss of use of the purchase price of the property, or for the loss of the consideration received for that purchase price.

The loss of use element of the claim for general damages has often been dealt with as part of an overall claim for inconvenience and distress and only recoverable by a natural person *Bella Casa Ltd v. Vinestone* [2005] EWHC 2807.

25.1.2.6 Wasted expenditure

In some circumstances the claimant may have difficulty in proving loss of profit. It may then elect to claim for wasted expenditure, that is expenditure rendered futile by the defendant's breach. This can include expenditure incurred before the contract was made *CCC Films (London) v. Impact Quadrant Films* (1985); *Anglia Television v. Reed* (1972). It cannot claim this reliance loss if it has made a bad bargain since the courts will not put a claimant in a better position than it would have been in if the contract had been performed. However, it is for the defendant in breach to show that the claimant made a bad bargain since it is the defendant who has made the matter an issue by the breach.

The two measures of damage, loss of bargain and wasted expenditure, are alternatives and mutually exclusive, at least so far as to prevent double recovery.

25.1.3 Claims in restitution

25.1.3.1 Quantum meruit

The expression quantum meruit means 'the amount he deserves' or 'what the job is worth'. A claim for *Quantum Meruit* is a claim for payment for work carried out where the price has not been quantified and is usually a claim for a reasonable sum.

A *quantum meruit* claim may be based in contract or in restitution, although the term '*quantum meruit*' is frequently used to mean a claim in restitution only.

A claim for *quantum meruit* in contract is based on the agreement of the parties. It arises in two situations.

(i) In the first situation the contract is silent on the measure of remuneration for the services provided. In such a situation in construction, contract terms of payment of a reasonable remuneration will be implied by statute.
(ii) In the second situation the contract contains an express agreement to pay reasonable remuneration or similar terminology.

The above 'Contractual *Quantum Meruit*' claims are in fact simply claims in contract, so that the first issue is whether or not there is a contract which applies to the situation. If so, the main issue is then the measure of the reimbursement. In the second situation above the main issue will be the interpretation of a particular term of the contract.

Claims for *quantum meruit* in restitution seek to impose a right to payment by law arising from the circumstances of unjust enrichment by one party at the expense of another. The claim is occasionally referred to as a claim in quasi-contract. The issue in 'Restitutionary *Quantum Meruit*' is whether or not there is any entitlement at all in law. If so, then the second issue is how the reimbursement is to be measured.

The two types of claims are the extreme ends of a spectrum of circumstances – *Serck Controls Ltd v. Drake & Scull Engineering Ltd* [2000] (TCC) HH Judge Hicks QC.

The general principle is that a claim in restitution does not depend on an 'implied contract' theory and cannot be sustained if a contract already governs the situation – see Court of Appeal of New South Wales in *Trimis v. Mina* (2000) 2TCLR 346, *Mowlem plc v. Stena Line Ports Limited* [2004] EWHC 2206 (TCC) and *S & W Process Engineering Ltd v. Cauldron Foods Ltd* [2005] EWHC 153 (TCC).

25.1.3.2 Letters of intent and bare agreements

Many situations in which the claim for *quantum meruit* arises involve letters of intent or limited exchanges between parties

each followed by rapid commencement of the works. The issue in those cases is whether or not there is a contract and if so the meaning of the terms of payment. The claim in restitution is usually presented as an alternative claim if indeed there is no contract.

To establish a contract not only requires agreement by the parties on all the terms they consider essential, but also sufficient certainty in their dealings to satisfy the requirement of completeness. An intention to create a legally binding relationship must also be present.

Letters of intent which state an intention to contract in the future frequently fail on both requirements since they are usually incomplete statements preparatory to a formal contract. In such cases a letter of intent is binding on neither party *Turiff Construction Ltd v. Regalia Knitting Mills Ltd* (1971).

A contract may come into existence following a simple request to carry out work and may take one of two forms. It may be an ordinary executory contract. It may otherwise be an 'if' contract, that is a contract under which A requests B to carry out a certain performance and promises B that, if he does so, he will receive a certain performance in return *British Steel Corporation v. Cleveland Bridge & Engineering Co. Ltd* (1983). Terms may then be implied into that contract in accordance with normal principles.

In *Clarke & Sons v. ACT Construction* [2002] EWCA Civ 972 the judge at first instance held that there was no contract between the parties. He held that the parties' relationship was not a contractual one, with the consequence that the value of the work carried out by ACT could be recovered and paid for, but on the basis of a *quantum meruit*, a reasonable sum, a restitutionary basis in fact. The Court of Appeal disagreed and held that the proper conclusion was that there was 'a contractual *quantum meruit*'. It was observed that in focusing on the essential ingredients for 'a building contract of some complexity' the judge may have lost sight of the fact that even if there was no entire contract, and especially if there is no 'formal' contract, there may still be an agreement to carry out work, the entire scope of which was not yet agreed, even if a price has not been agreed. It was held that provided there was an instruction to do work and an acceptance of that instruction, then there was a contract and the law would imply into it an obligation to pay a reasonable sum for that work. It was held that was the situation in the instant case. It was observed that reversing the judgement on this point did not significantly advance either case.

Simply carrying out work is not sufficient to create a contract, all the necessary ingredients of contract must be present *Mowlem plc v. PHI Group Limited* [2004].

For a contract to arise in the case of a letter of intent (see *Tender process*, this volume), the letter must contain all necessary terms. Further, it must be plain that the unilateral contract is to govern the main contract work in the event that no formal contract is concluded *Monk Building and Civil Engineering Ltd v. Norwich Union Life Assurance Society* (CA) (1993).

Although a letter of intent may not govern the main contract works, the letter may relate to part or preparatory works and in that case may create a contract for those limited works, if all the necessary ingredients of contract are present. In *Turiff Construction Ltd v. Regalia Knitting Mills Ltd* (1971) the employer's letter of intent was a legally binding agreement to reimburse the contractor his expenses for preliminary design work and feasibility studies for a main contract which was not in the event concluded.

If work is carried out beyond the financial limit of the letter of intent, then there will only be an entitlement if the financial limit was not intended to prevent further payment. In *AC Controls Ltd v. British Broadcasting Corporation* [2002] EWHC 3132 (TCC) it was held that the spending cap was not intended to limit the amount that ACC could recover, but was intended to operate as a 'trigger' entitling the BBC to terminate the contract any time after the cap was reached. ACC was required to carry on working and was entitled to payment of a reasonable value for the work done.

Apart from the above particular circumstances, a contractor exceeding the financial limit will have great difficulty in establishing an entitlement to payment absent a clear instruction and acceptance that additional payment would be made *Mowlem plc v. Stena Line Ports Limited* [2004] EWHC 2206 (TCC).

25.1.3.3 Work outside the contract

In order to establish an entitlement to payment for work 'outside' the contract the necessary ingredients of either a collateral contract or restitution must be present. This may be difficult if the reason for the extra work not falling within the existing contract is the lack of a request for the work to be carried out or agreement to payment for the work.

In *Parkinson v. Commissioners of Works* (1949) 2 KB 632 the contractor agreed under a varied contract to carry out certain work to be ordered by the Commissioners on a cost plus profit basis subject to a limitation as to the total amount of profit. The Commissioners ordered work to a total value of £6 600 000 but it was held that on its true construction the varied contract only gave the Commissioners authority to order work to the value of £5 000 000. It was held that the work that had been executed by the contractors included more than was covered, on its true construction, by the variation deed, and that the cost of the uncovenanted addition had therefore to be paid for by a *quantum meruit*.

In *Costain Civil Engineering Ltd v. Zanen Dredging & Contracting Co.* [1997] 85 BLR 77 the instructions purported to be given under the subcontract did not constitute authorised variations of the subcontract works because the instructions required work to be done outside the scope of the subcontractor's obligations under the subcontract. The subcontractor was therefore entitled to payment on a *quantum meruit*. In measuring a fair remuneration an allowance was to be made for profit and consideration had to be given to the relationship of the parties and the competitive edge that the subcontractor had

by the significant advantage of having already mobilised his equipment.

In *S & W Process Engineering Ltd v. Cauldron Foods Ltd* [2005] EWHC 153 (TCC) HH Judge Peter Coulson QC considered that where there is a contract for specified work but the contractor does work outside the contract at the employer's request, the contractor may be entitled to be paid a reasonable sum for the work outside the contract: *Thorne v. London Corp* (1876) 1 Ap. Cas. 120 and *Parkinson and Co. v. Commissioners of Works* [1949] 2 KB 632. He observed that this will always turn on what is meant in any particular instance by 'outside the Contract'. He held that S & W would have to demonstrate that, in some way, Cauldron freely accepted services in circumstances where they should have known that S & W would expect to be paid for them. He considered that might be difficult where the item of extra work in dispute was not clearly requested or instructed or authorised.

A claim for *quantum meruit* in restitution may arise in the following situations:

(i) where the parties proceed on the mistaken basis that there is an enforceable contract, but there is no contract
(ii) one party requests services from the other which are not governed by a contract
(iii) where the contract is frustrated
(iv) where before completion the contractor accepts a repudiation by the employer as terminating the contract. The contractor can elect to sue for damages for breach of contract or *quantum meruit* in restitution for the work performed

In *Banque Financière de la Cité v. Parc (Battersea) Ltd* [1999] 1 AC 221 Lord Steyn identified four questions which arose in relation to any claim in restitution:

(i) Had the defendant benefited or been enriched?
(ii) Was the enrichment at the expense of the claimant?
(iii) Was the enrichment unjust?
(iv) Were there any defences?

If there has been a total failure of consideration in a contract, the injured part can then make a claim in restitution. So, for instance, if the subcontractor has not performed at all, the contractor can claim for the return of monies paid. If the subcontractor has been overpaid and has failed to complete, the contractor can recover the overpayment even if it has managed to have the work completed without, in fact, incurring any loss despite the overpayment.

Estoppel by convention can operate to prevent a claim to restitution of payment by mistake. If the money is spent in good faith, in reliance on the representation that there was an entitlement to it, then the order for repayment will create the detriment sufficient to found the estoppel.

25.1.3.4 Speculative work

If the parties enter on a speculative venture then it will be difficult to succeed in a claim in restitution for reimbursement of the expense incurred if the venture fails, absent express agreement to payment. The reasons for the failure are highly relevant as is the nature of the risk that that was accepted.

In *Easat Antennas Ltd v. Racal Defence Electronics Ltd* [2000] (ChD) Racal succeeded in a bid in which Easat agreed to and carried out considerable work, but did not award Easat the subcontract. Mr Justice Hart held that the work undertaken in order to obtain a contract does not give rise to a restitutionary remedy. The party providing the services is taken to have run the risk that the contract will not eventuate and he will not therefore be paid. In this case there was no dispute that Racal had received a benefit as a result of the services. Mr Justice Hart accepted that Easat only had an expectation of being rewarded for its work in the event of the bid succeeding and the conditions for placing the subcontract then being satisfied. However, while Easat was prepared to take the risk that Racal's bid would fail, it was not prepared to run the risk that, if Racal's bid succeeded, as it did, that it would not be rewarded. It was held that that was the whole purpose and underlying assumption of the agreement. On that basis the claim by Easat was held to be a good one.

In *Countrywide Communications Ltd v. ICL Pathway Ltd* [2000] CLC 324 a consortium assembled to make a bid involved the members in considerable work. When the bid was successful the consortium excluded one of the members.

Mr Nicholas Strauss QC considered whether the excluded member had a claim in restitution. He held that appropriate weight was to be given to a number of considerations:

(i) whether the services were of a kind which would normally be given free of charge

(ii) the terms in which the request to perform the services was made may be important in establishing the extent of any risk (if any) which the plaintiffs may fairly be said to have taken that such service would in the end be uncompensated. It may be important whether the parties are simply negotiating, expressly or impliedly 'subject to contract', or whether one party has given some kind of assurance or indication that he will not withdraw, or that he will not withdraw except in certain circumstances

(iii) the nature of the benefit which has resulted to the defendant and in particular whether such benefit is real (either 'realised' or 'realisable') or a fiction. There was more inclination to impose an obligation to pay for a real benefit, since otherwise the abortive negotiations would leave the defendant with a windfall and the plaintiff out of pocket. The performance of services requested may of itself amount to a benefit or enrichment

(iv) the circumstances in which the anticipated contract does not materialise and in particular whether they can be said to involve 'fault' on the part of the defendant, or to be outside the scope of the risk undertaken by the plaintiff at the outset maybe decisive

Mr Nicholas Strauss QC held that justice required that Countrywide should be appropriately recompensed. Countrywide had accepted the risk that its services would not be accepted for submission with the bid or that the bid might fail or that negotiations might fail. It had not accepted the risk that it would be dismissed after the final bid had been submitted because Pathway changed personnel. The measure for repayment was time spent with associated costs.

In *Stephen Donald Architects Limited v. Christopher King* [2003] EWHC 1867 (TCC) the parties were friends and King did not have the means to pay fees for redevelopment of the property until completion of the project. HH Judge Seymour QC considered that the nature and extent of the risk assumed by the party claiming payment on a *quantum meruit* basis in relation to the abortive transaction was a material consideration in determining whether an enrichment has been unjust. There was nothing unjust about being visited with the consequences of a risk which one has consciously run. The Architects took on the risk that King might decide not to proceed, either for insufficient funds or on terms perceived by King to be unsatisfactory. That was the risk that eventuated.

25.1.3.5 Measure of contractual quantum meruit

In the situation where there is a contract, then the issue in a Contractual *Quantum Meruit* claim is either the measure of the 'reasonable sum' or the interpretation of similarly wide express terms. The issue is whether the measure is on the basis of cost or market price. There appears to be no hard and fast rule.

The assessment of a *quantum meruit* in the case of an unquantified price was usually based on actual cost which would include on- and off-site overheads provided that it was reasonable and was reasonably and not unnecessarily incurred, plus an appropriate addition for profit *ERDC Group Limited v. Brunel University* [2006] (TCC).

In *Clarke & Sons v. ACT Construction* [2002] EWCA Civ 972 the issue was the assessment of the reasonable remuneration. The judge at first instance decided that it was cost plus 15%. The judge found that it was 'slightly higher' than the bracket of 5%–12% advanced by Clarke's expert but that that bracket was based on defined building contracts whereas dayworks were being charged for with higher uplifts in 1992/1994. He also took account of the higher percentages charged out and paid for pursuant to the earlier invoices.

The Court of Appeal held that there was no reason why the prices actually paid should not be factors to take into account in the instant case and stated that it should be very slow indeed to interfere with a judgement on such an issue made by an experienced judge in a specialist tribunal and upheld his finding that the uplift was 15%.

The express term for payment may yield a different result. Judge Bowsher QC in *Laserbore Ltd v. Morrison Biggs Wall Ltd* (1992) had to decide the meaning of the term 'Fair and reasonable payments for all works executed'. He considered that the costs plus basis was wrong in principle even though in some instances it may produce the right result. The appropriate approach was to adopt general market rates.

In *Robertson Group (Construction) Limited v. Amey-Miller (Edingburgh) Joint Venture)* [2005] CSIH89 the Inner House of the Court of Session considered the meaning of the phrase 'all direct costs and directly incurred losses shall be underwritten and reimbursed' in a letter of intent.

It was held that parties prospectively entering into a contract subject to JCT conditions could be expected to be familiar with the traditional loss and expense clause and the interpretation judicially placed on it. The phraseology used in the instant arrangement was different but similar. The adjective 'direct' qualified the word 'costs' and the phrase 'directly incurred' the word 'losses'. In the event (which occurred) of a formal contract not being entered into, Amey-Miller undertook that 'all direct costs and directly incurred losses' would be 'underwritten and reimbursed'. It was held that the first of the two verbs used ('underwritten') was, in its familiar sense of 'guaranteed', clearly wide enough to embrace elements beyond actual outlays. It was held that while the second verb ('reimbursed') might tend to suggest the making good of something expended, the phrase read as a whole did not have that restricted sense.

25.1.3.6 Measure in restitution

The practical issue is usually whether the measure of reimbursement is on the basis of cost incurred with contribution for profit and overheads, or whether it is to be based on market value. Where there is a contract with prices but which does not apply or an unconcluded contract with prices, this may be taken into account in considering the reimbursement. In some cases there will be little difference in the measure between cost and market value. It might be thought that a measure based on rates would always be higher than one based on costs. This may not always be the case where the rates are based on an unconcluded contract, since there are many commercial reasons for a contractor to bid low for a contract.

In the case of an express contract to do work at an unquantified price, the measure is the reasonable remuneration of the contractor. In the case of a benefit which it is unjust to retain the measure is the value to the employer normally the market value, namely the sum that would have been agreed including profit. In between there is a borderline, the position of which is debatable *Serck Controls Ltd v. Drake & Scull Engineering Ltd* (2000). The unconcluded contract may be good evidence of the appropriate measure.

In the measure of a fair remuneration and allowance for profit, consideration had to be given to the relationship of the parties and the competitive edge that the subcontractor had by the significant advantage of having already mobilised his equipment *Costain Civil Engineering Ltd v. Zanen Dredging & Contracting Co.* [1997] 85 BLR 77.

The contractor's offer in the unconcluded contract should act as an upper limit to the measure of the *quantum meruit*, even though that might lead the contractor to sustain a loss see Mr Recorder Colin Reese QC in *Sanjay Lachhani v. Destination Canada (UK) Ltd* (1997).

In *ERDC Group Limited v. Brunel University* [2006] (TCC) the circumstances were unusual in that there was a move from contractual to a non-contractual basis. Lloyd J held that it was not right to switch from an assessment based on ERDC's rates to one based entirely on ERDC's costs. The move was not marked at the time.

Some allowance must be made for work which is defective or work carried out inefficiently. The issue then is the standard to be adopted to establish the defect or inefficiency and the duty owed by the contractor for performance (if any in the absence of a contract). Since restitution is not based on implied contract theory there is no scope for reducing the measure by something like a set-off or cross-claim equal to the costs of putting the work right, except perhaps where as a result of the contractor's performance there is no benefit or value – *Sanjay Lachhani v. Destination Canada (UK) Ltd* (1997), *Serck Controls Ltd v. Drake & Scull Engineering Ltd* (2000) 73 Con LR 100 and *ERDC Group Limited v. Brunel University* [2006] (TCC).

25.2 Claims for extension of time
25.2.1 Purpose of extension of time clauses

Delays frequently occur on construction projects and so standard forms make provision for extension of the time for completion in certain events. Such extension of time clauses are not intended to provide the contractor with a completion date to aim for, but are to protect the employer's right to levy or deduct liquidated damages for late completion by the contractor. If the employer causes delay, by its breach, and there is no provision for extension of time due to its breach, then the liquidated damages clause is unenforceable. The employer is then left only with an entitlement to claim such common law damages as it is able to prove. Extension of time clauses in standard forms are therefore drafted to compensate not only for specific risk events but also for breaches of contract by the employer.

25.2.2 Parties' obligations as to time
25.2.2.1 Employer's duty to perform

The employer is required to complete its obligations specified in the contract, such as supplying information, giving possession, executing any work or providing any materials, at such times as to permit execution and completion of the works by the contractor at the times specified in the contract. If no such times are specified, the employer must carry out its obligations at reasonable times, having regard to the date of completion of construction, the provisions of any approved programme of work and the actual progress of the contractor. These obligations of the employer do not require that it should comply with the provisions of the approved programme of work, but only that it should not hinder the contractor from carrying out its obligations to complete the works at the times specified in the contract. It is only if no time is specified that the approved programme is relevant, and then only in establishing what are reasonable times. This, therefore, is not an obligation to positively co-operate with a contractor to complete prior to the date provided for in the contract. The situation will, however, be different if the programme is incorporated in the contract as a contract document or if the express terms of the contract state otherwise.

25.2.2.2 Contractor's obligations as to time

The contractor's obligations as to time will depend on the express terms of the contract and on the terms implied as a matter of business efficacy. In modern construction contracts there are usually three separate but interrelated express obligations. If the three obligations are not stated expressly then similar terms will not necessarily be implied into the contract.

The first obligation is usually that the contractor shall complete by a specified date or a specified period, and possibly with stage or sectional completion obligations.

In modern construction, the obligation to complete by a date is of little assistance to an employer or a contractor in a subcontract in the management of the project. In most cases the employer will wish action to be taken early to avoid late completion. This is the purpose of the second obligation in construction contracts. The second obligation is that the contractor shall progress the works regularly and diligently. In some subcontract forms the subcontractor's obligation to progress the subcontract works is stated in terms that progress must be in accordance with the progress of the main contract works. The third obligation relates to the means by which the employer monitors progress and the implementation of corrective measures. The third obligation is that the contractor prepares and works to an accepted programme, updates the programme when actual progress differs from the programme and revises the programme to include corrective measures to mitigate the effects of delays.

25.2.2.3 The obligation as to programme

If the contract requires the contractor to submit a programme in accordance with the requirements of the contract then the contractor's failure to do so will be a breach of contract. The contractor will then be liable for substantial damages if the employer can establish a loss. It is suggested that the employer will need to demonstrate:

- that the contractor was under an obligation to progress the works in accordance with the programme; and

- that the absence of the programme prevented the employer managing either the contract or other related work; so

- that as a result the employer suffered delay and/or loss which could have been avoided if the programme had been submitted.

In practice, establishing the necessary evidence is likely to be difficult. This is particularly so if the contractor has submitted a programme, but the extent of the breach is that the programme is not in accordance with the specified requirements.

25.2.3 Substantial completion

25.2.3.1 The use of the term 'completion'

The completion of an obligation by the contractor will usually mark the transfer of certain risks or the crystallisation of certain rights. The term 'completion' may therefore have a number of different meanings in a contract, depending on the obligation. For example, completion for the purposes of payment may differ from that defining the end of the construction stage, which in turn may differ from that defining the end of the defects correction period.

The term 'completion' may be used in different parts of a contract without identifying what state of completion is required. In terms of the whole works, completion may mean completion for the purpose of handover and commencement of the defects liability period. It may instead mean completion including the remedy of all defects and any outstanding work sufficient for the issue of a Final Certificate. The term 'completion' may also be used to determine the extent of the right to interim payment in cases of stage payments.

The meaning of 'completion' depends on the proper interpretation of the contract and the related obligation.

If the contractor is required to 'complete' the works in accordance with the contract before being entitled to payment, then the contract is said to be an entire contract (*Sumpter v. Hedges* [1898]). The rule is strict so that if work is completed but not in accordance with the contract no payment is due (*Bolton v. Mahadeva* [1972]).

In *Close Invoice Finance Limited v. Belmont Bleaching and Dying Company* [2003] Eaton's right of action had been assigned to Close. Eaton had given a quotation for the delivery, installation and commissioning of a machine known as a Stetner that set fabrics to a certain width. The quotation was accepted and the contract terms agreed including timescale and payment terms. Three sums were to be paid. The second of £12 000 on completion of erection and the third of £9 000 was payable once the Stetner had been commissioned and handed over. The issue was the whether or not the last two payments were due for payment.

Belmont argued that Eaton had contracted to perform entire obligations and were entitled to nothing until they completed a stage. Close argued that Eaton was entitled to be paid if they gave substantial performance of a stage.

HH Bowsher QC referred to *Hoenig v. Isaacs* [1952] 2 All ER 176 and held that Eaton was only entitled to be paid on completion of each stage. He held that Eaton had not completed either stage and therefore no payment was due other than for the supply of spare parts which was another issue.

Construction contracts involve the fixing and incorporation of the works on land, with the consequent transfer of ownership. The owner is therefore likely to receive substantial benefit even if the works are not entirely complete. The doctrine of substantial performance mitigates the harshness of the above rule and allows the contractor payment for work if substantially completed with an allowance for defects. It is a question of fact whether the contractor has substantially performed its obligations. The contractor cannot rely on the doctrine to seek payment for work carried out if it has abandoned the works. It applies where the work has been completed except for minor defects or minor outstanding works.

The requirements of 'completion' in relation to a time obligation are likely to be different than for the obligation for payment, particularly when the contract makes provision for the contractor to remedy defects and/or outstanding work in the defects liability or correction period. So, for instance, occupation by the employer may be good evidence of completion for payment purposes, particularly with the employer's exercise of the right of abatement of price. It will not necessarily be relevant evidence of completion of the time obligation.

The general meaning of 'completion' for the obligation to complete the construction or installation of the works is that the works should be free from known or patent defects and that any outstanding work is minor or *de minimus*, so that the use for the purpose intended is not affected or beneficial occupancy as intended is not prevented.

Standard forms of contract generally do not require complete performance by the date for completion of installation or construction, but allow a defects liability period for the correction of minor defects and defects which only become apparent later. Completion is normally identified by the date stated in a certificate by the A/E stating that completion has taken place. The date stated in the certificate will mark the end of the period for which the contractor is liable for liquidated damages, mark the change in responsibility to insure, require the release of retention and mark the commencement of the defects liability period.

In some standard forms 'completion' of the construction or installation stage is defined by achieving specified standards in tests. In other forms completion of construction is defined by the term 'substantial completion'. The ICE Form is such a form and provides for the contractor to apply for a Certificate of Substantial Completion together with an undertaking to carry out outstanding work in the defects liability period. It is suggested that the outstanding work may include the making good of defects identified before the issue of the certificate. In any event it is suggested that the ICE Form places an obligation on the contractor under Clause 49(2) to correct defects 'of whatever nature' which is wide enough to cover defects known at the date of the certificate. This is to be contrasted with the term 'practical completion' used in JCT Forms. Clause 17.2 of JCT 1998 for instance relates to the making good of defects that appear within the defects liability period. There is no power for the architect to issue instructions for the remedy of defects that were known or patent at the date of the Certificate of Practical Completion. As a matter of interpretation therefore the architect is not required to issue a certificate if there are known or patent defects. The contractor's obligation of practical completion is therefore different to the obligation of substantial completion under the JCT and ICE Forms respectively.

25.2.3.2 Legal definition of completion

There have been a number of decisions attempting a legal definition of the terms 'practical completion' and 'substantial completion'.

In *J. Jarvis and Sons v. Westminster Corporation* (1978) 7 BLR 64 HL, Lord Justice Salmon defined practical completion as completion for the purpose of allowing the employers to take possession of the works and use them as intended. He held that practical completion did not mean completion down to the last detail, however trivial and unimportant. Lord Dilhorne's definition was that practical completion meant almost but not entirely finished.

In *H.W. Neville (Sunblest) Ltd v.William Press and Son Ltd* (1981) 20 BLR 78, it was held that practical completion did not mean that very minor *de minimus* work had to be carried out, but did mean that if there were any patent defects the architect should not give a certificate of practical completion.

In *Emson Eastern Ltd v. E.M.E. Developments Ltd* (1991) 55 BLR 114, Emson were the contractors and E.M.E. developers under the JCT 80 Form. Practical completion was certified but some time after Emson went into administrative receivership and their employment in compliance with Clause 27.2 of the conditions of contract was automatically determined. The issue was whether Emson were entitled to further payment. The matter turned on whether completion under Clause 27 meant the same as practical completion, or whether it meant that all snagging and remedial works has to be made good at the end of the defects period before the works could be said to be complete.

His Honour Judge John Newey QC, in arriving at a decision, took account of what happens on building sites. He considered he should keep in mind that building construction is not like the manufacture of goods in a factory. The size of the project, site conditions, use of many materials and employment of various types of operatives made it virtually impossible to achieve the same degree of perfection as can a manufacturer. His view was that it must be rare for a new building to have every screw and every brush of paint correct. Further, a building can seldom be built precisely as required by the drawings and specification. Judge Newey, in considering the meaning of practical completion, thought he stood somewhere between Lords Salmon and Dilhorne in the Jarvis case. He concluded that there was no difference in meaning between completion and practical completion. Completion, he considered, was like practical completion, something which occurs before defects and other faults have to be remedied. Were it otherwise, the deduction of liquidated damages under Clause 24 would be unworkable, he considered. In view of this reasoning Judge Newey held that the contractor was entitled to be paid as practical completion had been achieved.

The Court of Appeal of Hong Kong in *Big Island Contracting (H.K.) Ltd v. Skink Ltd* (1990) 52 BLR 110 upheld the decision of the judge at first instance that in deciding practical completion account should be taken of the value of work outstanding and the importance of defects to the safety of the facility.

In *Voscroft (Contractors) Ltd v. Seeboard plc* (1996) 78 BLR 132, HH Judge Humphrey Lloyd QC was required to consider the operation of Clauses 14.1 and 14.2 DOM/2 (in this respect the same as DOM/1) Form of Subcontract. Clause 14.1 required the subcontractor to give notice when it considered practical completion of the subcontract works had been achieved. The Form made provision for the parties to agree the date of practical completion, but in the event of disagreement practical completion was deemed to be the date of practical completion of the main contract works. There was, however, no provision for the situation which occurred of the subcontractor not giving notice. It was argued that in that situation practical completion was a question of fact to be decided by an arbitrator.

It was held that, from the other provisions of the contract, the presumed intention of the parties was that there should be some definition and certainty attached to practical completion. Without a firm or contractually ascertainable date the parties' obligations as set out in the insurance and indemnity provisions became uncertain in duration, the extension of time clauses became in part unworkable and there was no certainty as to when a part of retention might be paid. The point of defining terminal dates would be lost if the effect of the subcontractor failing to give notice was to make practical completion a question of fact and would deprive the definitions of practical value.

It was held that a subcontractor who failed to operate Clause 14.1 could not achieve a result other than the one which would have been achieved had it given notice but not reached agreement. The subcontractor could not have the benefit of Clause 14 in establishing a date for practical completion other than the deemed date. The date of practical completion was therefore the date of practical completion under the main contract.

The standard forms adopt different procedures for the identification of completion. Generally a certificate is issued.

25.2.4 Time at large

In commercial contracts the parties usually intend the works to be completed by an agreed date. In many contracts the date for completion will be stated as an express term. The term 'time at large' is not a legal term, but describes the situation where there is no identified date for completion, either by absence from the contract terms or arising from events and the operation of law. Time is said to be 'at large' because the time or date for completion is not fixed before carrying out the work, but determined after the work has been completed.

The term 'time at large' is usually used in construction contracts in the situation where liquidated damages are an issue.

If time is 'at large' then it is argued liquidated damages cannot be applied, because there is no date fixed from which the liquidated damages can be calculated.

Time is made 'at large' in four situations:

(a) where no time or date is fixed by the terms of the contract by which performance must take place or be completed; and

(b) when the time for performance has been fixed under the contract, but has ceased to apply either by agreement or by an act of prevention (which includes instructed additional work) or breach of contract by the employer with no corresponding entitlement to extension of time; and

(c) where the employer has waived the obligation to complete by the specified time or date or where the employer, faced with a breach of contract by the contractor which would entitle the employer to terminate the employment of the contractor and/or to bring to an end the primary obligations of the parties to perform, instead elects to continue with the performance of the contract; and

(d) where the employer has interfered in the certification process to prevent proper administration of the contract.

25.2.4.1 No time or date fixed in contract

If no date or period is fixed by the contract then the objective intention of the parties must be ascertained. In the case of a contract under the Supply of Goods and Services Act 1982, if the date is not fixed by a course of dealing between the parties, a term will be implied that the contractor's obligation is to complete within a reasonable time (section 14(1)).

In *J. and J. Fee Ltd v. The Express Lift Company Ltd* [1993] 34 ConLR 147 there had been correspondence between the parties on the date of commencement and completion. The last correspondence from Express Lift stated that it could see little possibility of improvement on the dates previously given, but suggested that the situation be monitored and, if it became possible, reviewed. It was held that as a matter of construction of its express terms Express Lift made a contractual offer of the completion date which it consistently offered before and that offer was accepted. The last letter was not written in plain 'take it or leave it' terms but held out the possibility of bettering the completion date. Nonetheless, there were dates for commencement and completion as a express term of the contract. HH Judge Peter Bowsher QC stated that if he was wrong on that issue, then there was a term implied that Express Lift would complete within a reasonable time. He gave a provisional view, without deciding, that based on the documents before him that it would be impossible for Express Lift to contend that a reasonable time for completion of the works would be any later than the date they had consistently put forward.

In *Bruno Zornow (Builders) Ltd v. Beechcroft Developments Ltd* [1990] 51 BLR 16, Bruno as contractor entered into a contract with Beechcroft as employer for preliminary works and later varied by a further agreement by letter. The effect of the letter was to include additional work and to agree a programme for the additional work. There was no express term of the agreement stating that the additional work would be carried out by any completion date. The issue therefore was whether any such provision could be implied. The contract contained a date for completion before variation, when it was, relatively, a much smaller contract. HH Judge John Davies QC considered whether time for completion was to be left at large subject only to the implication that the works should be finished within a reasonable time. The alternative was to presume as necessary for business efficacy that the parties must have intended that it should continue to have a fixed date for completion. It was held that in a lump sum contract involving a commercial development with an attendant risk of an indeterminate loss of profits claim it was commercially unrealistic to suppose that the parties did not mutually intend that it should contain a date for completion linked to the liquidated damages provision which it contained already. Both provisions were interrelated and both were material elements, so far as the contractor and employer were concerned in deciding whether to enter into the bargain at all, and if so, what price. It was held that it was necessary to imply into the contract a date for completion. It was held that the parties intended that the date for completion would be the period which both parties had in mind for the whole of the works when the first tier tender was submitted. It was that date, as modified by extensions of time granted by the architect, that was the relevant date for the application of liquidated damages.

25.2.4.2 Time or date ceases to apply

In many situations where the issue of 'time at large' arises, the parties are concerned with the application of liquidated damages and whether or not the contract makes provision for extension of time for acts of prevention by the employer. Relevant decided cases are:

- *Wells v. Army and Navy Co-operative Society Ltd* [1902]
- *Peak Construction (Liverpool) Ltd v. McKinney Foundations Ltd* [1976] 1 BLR 114
- *Percy Bilton Ltd v. Greater London Council* [1982] 20 BLR 1
- *Bramall & Ogden Ltd v. Sheffield City Council* [1985] 29 BLR 73
- *Rapid Building Group Ltd v. Ealing Family Housing Association* [1985] 29 BLR 5
- *Davy Offshore Ltd v. Emerald Field Contracting Ltd* [1992] 55 BLR 1
- *Inserco Ltd v. Honeywell Control Systems* [1996].

In *Davy Offshore Ltd v. Emerald Field Contracting Ltd* [1992] 55 BLR 1, Emerald employed Davy to carry out design and provide certain facilities including a semi-submersible drilling rig and a floating storage unit together with the provision of subsea work. The contract terms were extensive and complex and HH Judge Thayne Forbes QC was asked an extensive list of preliminary questions. It was held that, under the contract, time only became at large when the failure to complete on time was due to an act or omission by Emerald. For one of the issues it was common ground that time was at large which, it was held, meant that Davy was obliged to complete the work within a reasonable time making allowance for the period of delay attributable to Emerald's default.

In *Inserco Ltd v. Honeywell Control Systems* [1996], Inserco contracted to complete all work by 1 April 1991. Due to additional and revised work, and lack of proper access and information Inserco was prevented from completing by 1 April 1991. There was no provision in the contract for extending the completion date and time was held to be at large.

25.2.4.3 Waiver or election

Time may become at large if the original obligation to complete is waived. In *Charles Rickards Ltd v. Oppenheim* [1950], a Rolls Royce motor car was not built by the agreed delivery date, but new dates were agreed. Eventually, Oppenheim gave written notice to Rickards stating that unless he received the car by a firm date, four weeks away, he would not accept it. The car was not delivered within the time specified and was not completed until some months later when Oppenheim refused to accept it. The Court of Appeal held that he was justified in doing so. After waiving the initial stipulation as to time, Oppenheim was entitled to give reasonable notice making time of the essence again, and on the facts the notice was reasonable.

This principle applies to construction contracts. If, because of waiver, time becomes 'at large', the employer can give the contractor reasonable notice to complete within a fixed reasonable time, thus making time of the essence again, *Taylor v. Brown* [1839]. The employer will have lost the right to liquidated damages so that if the contractor fails to complete by the revised agreed date the employer will be left with the remedy of general damages. It is not clear whether the employer can make time of the essence, if it was not previously so.

25.2.4.4 Failure of contractual machinery

If the time or date for completion is effected by events which entitle the contractor to an extension of time, but the contractual machinery can no longer operate, then time is at large. The circumstances will be rare.

In *Bernhard's Rugby Landscapes Ltd v. Stockley Park Consortium (No. 2)* [1998], BRL was awarded the contract for the construction of a new golf course on a reclaimed landfill site under an amended ICE 5th Edition. One issue was whether the contractual machinery had broken down and, if so, the effect. It was held that a breakdown of the contractual machinery occurs when, without material default or interference by a party to the contract, the machinery is not followed by the person appointed to administer and operate it and, as a result, its purpose is not achieved, and is either no longer capable of being achieved or is not likely to be achieved. HH Judge Humphrey Lloyd stated that this could for most practical purposes be equated to interference by a contracting party in the process whereby the other is deprived of a right or benefit. Examples were the failure of an employer to reappoint an administrator or certifier on the resignation of the previously appointed person or where that person fails or is unwilling to do his or her duty and the employer will not take steps to rectify the position. Reference was made to the decision in *Panamena Europea Navigacion v. Frederick Leyland Ltd* [1947]. It was held that non-compliance with the machinery by the administrator was not in itself sufficient: the effect must be that either or both of the parties to the contract do not in consequence of the breakdown truly know their position or cannot or are unlikely to know it. If the true position is or can be established by other contractual means then the breakdown is likely to be immaterial even when the result of the breakdown is that one party does not obtain the contractual right or benefit which would or might otherwise have been established by the machinery, provided that the true position can be restored by the operation of other contractual machinery.

25.2.4.5 Reasonable time

If time does become 'at large', the contractor's obligation is to complete within a reasonable time. What constitutes a reasonable time is a question of fact. The principles to be applied are those in *Pantland Hick v. Raymond & Reid* [1893]. What constitutes a reasonable time has to be considered in relation to circumstances which existed at the time when the contract obligations are performed, but excluding circumstances which were under the control of the contractor. In *British Steel Corporation v. Cleveland Bridge & Engineering Company* [1981] 24 BLR 100, Lord Goff applied these principles by first considering what in ordinary circumstances was a reasonable time for performance and then considering to what extent the time for performance of the contractor was in fact extended by extraordinary circumstances outside his control. Whether a reasonable time has been taken to do the works cannot be decided in advance, but only after the work has been done.

If time is at large because no time or date was fixed in the contract, then it is not clear whether the test of a reasonable time and the extent of control required is an objective or subjective test. It is suggested that since the obligation is an implied term, that the reasonable time must be determined from the objective intention of the parties. If the contractor has been specifically chosen then it will be a subjective test. If, as is likely to be more usual, the contractor has been selected in competitive tendering, then it will be an objective test of how a reasonably experienced contractor in the actual circumstances would have carried out the works.

If time is at large because the specified time or date no longer applies following an act of prevention or breach by the employer, the original completion date is good evidence of what is a 'reasonable time in ordinary circumstances'. The original completion date is not conclusive, it is suggested. Part of the ordinary circumstances will include the fact that a contractor would be expected to resource and plan the works in order to achieve the original completion date. The delay and disruption caused by the act of prevention or breach needs to be taken into account.

It is suggested that if time is at large by waiver or election that this does not mean, without more, that the employer has waived the right to damages for the breach of the obligation to complete.

In *Shawton Engineering Ltd v. DGP International Limited* [2005] EWCA Civ 1359 there were variations to the contract but there was no contractual mechanism for extending time on account of the variations. It was accepted that the effect in law of the variations was that DGP became obliged to complete their work within a reasonable time.

The Court of Appeal held that a reasonable time had to be judged at the time when the question arises in the light of all relevant circumstances. One of the circumstances was the original contract date, even if DGP had underestimated the work content. The nature of the variation was relevant.

The original completion dates, and, indeed, the original completion periods had ceased to be of any relevance because Shawton were not insisting on the stipulations as to time, nor were they insisting on any times or periods for completion. That overlaid to extinction any question of calculating time periods by reference to the original dates for completion and the work content of variations. In this case, a reasonable time for completion was literally at large.

25.2.5 Power of Architect/Engineer to grant extensions of time

The Architect/Engineer (A/E) cannot simply take a passive role in the examination of extension of time, without jeopardising the validity of his certificates *Holland Hannon Cubitts (Northern) Ltd v. Welsh Health Technical Services Organisation* (1981).

There are four issues to be considered in deciding on the time for exercise of the A/E power to grant extensions of time:

(a) The contract may contemplate the exercise of a power at once on the occurrence of the event causing delay, for example for non-continuing causes of delay such as the ordering of extras.

(b) The contract may contemplate the power being exercised only when the full effect on progress is known such as continuing causes of delays such as strikes, withholding of the site etc.

(c) The contract may contemplate exercise of the power at any time before issue of the final certificate.

(d) The contractor's entitlement to receive an early indication on request of the A/E's decision on individual grounds of extension as they arise.

It is necessary to examine the precise provisions of the construction contract in order to determine whether or not there has been a breach of contract in relation to granting of extension of time. The fourth issue is clearly important to enable the contractor to decide whether or not to incur possible substantial acceleration expenditure and avoid the prospect of paying liquidated damages *Perini Corporation v. Commonwealth of Australia* [1969] 2. N.S.W.L.R. 530.

The contractors actions particularly in providing particulars to substantiate the delays claimed may give rise to issues of waiver and estoppel which would prevent the contractor claiming that the employer is in breach of contract in not ensuring that the A/E granted extensions of time at the appropriate time.

In *John Barker Construction Ltd v. London Portman Hotel Ltd* [1996] it was held that the Architect's exercise of his judgement in assessing a fair and reasonable extension of time must be fairly and rationally based. In this case the Architect's assessment was fundamentally flawed. For instance, he had not carried out a logical analysis in a methodical way of the impact of the relevant matters on the contractor's planned programme. Instead he had made an impressionistic, rather than a calculated assessment of the time consequences. Being a JCT Contract the Architect had not paid sufficient attention to the contents of the bills of quantities.

In *Amalgamated Building Contractors Ltd v. Waltham Holy Cross Urban District Council* (1952) it was held that where the cause of delay operated partially but not wholly, every day, until the works were completed, then the Architect could not decide the extension of time until completion. The parties intended that the Architect could grant an extension of time retrospectively. It was also held that if the contractor has overrun the contract time without legitimate excuse and during that period an event occurred causing further delay, then if it was a qualifying event the contractor is entitled to extension of time for that further delay, which operates retrospectively.

In *Temloc v. Errill* (1987) it was held that the 12-week period in the JCT80 Form for reviewing the extension of time after completion was directly and not mandatory.

In *Fernbrook Trading Co. Ltd v. Taggart* (1979), it was held that the contractor must be informed of the new completion date as soon as reasonably practicable. If the entitlement to extension of time was the order of extra work then in the normal course extensions should be given at the time of the order. It is suggested, however, that if the fact of additional work can only be ascertained by measure of the drawings and comparison with the original definition of the work, then the assessment of extension of time may not be possible at the time of issue of the drawings.

It was held that if the cause of delay lies beyond the Employer, and particularly where its duration is uncertain, then the grant of extension of time should be given a reasonable time after the factors which govern the assessment have been established. Where there are multiple causes of delay, there may be

no alternative but to leave the final decision to just before the issue of the Final Certificate.

In *Perini Corporation v. Commonwealth of Australia* (1969) it was held that in the particular contract, there was an implied term which required extensions of time to be given within a reasonable time. The measurement of a reasonable time was a question of fact. The A/E must have sufficient time as is necessary to enable him to investigate the facts which are relevant in making the decision. When the investigation is complete then the decision must be made.

There is no reason why the A/E's failure to grant an extension of time within the specified time or a reasonable time as appropriate, should bring down the mechanism of liquidated damages. The remedy is to have the matter decided in arbitration or litigation, or adjudication if a construction contract. The extension of time provision is a means of apportionment of liability for delay and liquidated damages and not intended to give the contractor a date to aim for.

25.2.6 Omitted work

Whether the A/E is entitled to reduce the contract period or reissue an extension of time already granted but showing a shorter period when work has been omitted by a variation, depends on the terms of the contract.

25.2.7 Acceleration

25.2.7.1 The problem of deciding when to accelerate

'Acceleration' is not a legal term. Its natural and common meaning is to 'bring about in an earlier point in time' (Webster's dictionary), which is a comparative measure. There must be some benchmark against which to measure the acceleration. In construction, the main issue is the date against which progress is measured. There are two situations relating to the overall works as opposed to discrete areas or sections of work.

The first acceleration situation arises if the contractor is required to complete earlier than the contract date fixed for completion. The main issue will be whether this requirement is a variation to the contract. In practice, the issue will turn on whether it can be established that an instruction was given in those terms. A complication is whether the failure of the A/E to properly grant an extension of time, or simply the timing of the ascertainment of the extension of time due, together with pressure from the employer or its agents for the contractor to complete by the then fixed date for completion, is effectively an instruction to accelerate. This is the issue of the 'constructive order' and of 'constructive acceleration' examined below.

The second acceleration situation arises if the contractor is likely to complete later than the contract date fixed for completion due to reasons which may not entitle him to an extension of time. If the contractor is in default then the issue is whether it is under an obligation to reduce or avoid the effects of the delay including taking acceleration measures. If it is not clear whether the contractor is entitled to an extension of time, in practice the contractor is left with the same choice whether or not to accelerate. This is the 'temporary default' problem, in which the contractor, until the extension of time is granted, is in default or likely to be in default and may decide that the most reasonable action in its commercial interests is to take acceleration measures rather than incur potential liquidated damages. There is also the related issue of the extent of the contractor's obligation to take measures to mitigate the consequences of a delay for which the contractor may be entitled to an extension of time and the effect this has on any entitlement to extension of time and whether it can recover the cost of such measures and this is examined below.

25.2.7.2 Acceleration measures

Acceleration may be achieved by a change in the deployment of resources. In some cases it may be achieved by simply changing the order or sequence for carrying out the work and may therefore not cause additional cost. More usually, acceleration is achieved by adopting longer working hours or additional days of working with the same resources. In many cases acceleration involves employing resources additional to those originally planned either for the same hours or days of working, or in additional shifts or days of working.

The possible acceleration measures are summarised below.

(a) Increased resources to reduce the time taken for critical activities. The increase in resource may at some level have the effect of reducing productivity and thereby increasing unit cost of construction. There will normally be an optimum level of resource for any one activity.
(b) Increased man hours is a means of increasing resource input, but will introduce inefficiency and both quality and health and safety issues.
(c) Incentives will motivate labour to increase productivity.
(d) Changed methods of working may open up additional workforces or workplaces as well as introducing economies in the use of plant and equipment.
(e) Re-sequencing work is a fundamental part of managing the progress of the work and is why float is always required on most of the activities on a project.

25.2.7.3 Effect of acceleration

When tendering and planning for the efficient completion of the works, contractors can optimise resources and progress. The interface between different resources can be properly managed so that a pattern develops which the workforce can follow with reduced planning, so increasing productivity.

Most standard forms of contract allow the contractor to complete the works before the completion date. It is not unusual for a contractor to decide once work commences to adopt a different approach than assumed at tender. The contractor may see advantages in completing early due to factors which only come to light once more detailed planning is undertaken. In other words, the

contractor may decide to accelerate because it perceives a commercial advantage. This may create problems for the employer in supplying the relevant information or completing other works.

In *Glenlion Construction Ltd v. Guinness Trust* [1987] 39 BLR 89, Glenlion was contractor under JCT 63 for the construction of a residential development for Guinness in Bromley, Kent. The issue that arose was whether Glenlion was entitled to complete the works before the completion date. Glenlion had submitted a programme which showed early completion.

It was held that it was self-evident from Clause 21 of JCT 63 that Glenlion was entitled to complete before the date of completion. This was so whether or not Glenlion produced a programme with an earlier date and whether or not it was required to produce a programme.

While Glenlion was entitled to complete before the contractual completion date it was held that the Guinness Trust was not required to actively co-operate to enable the earlier date to be achieved but was only required not to hinder completion.

It is suggested that the situation will, however, be different if the programme is incorporated in the contract as a contract document or if the entitlement under the contract is bound up with the programme. If the employer does not wish to take possession of the works early, then this needs to be dealt with by amendment of the contract terms so that the contractor can price accordingly.

If acceleration is adopted as a reaction to events which have caused delay, rather than a planned strategy for optimisation of resources, then this will normally result in additional costs. The late or unplanned timing of acceleration measures will normally mean that the resources deployed are different to the resources planned, due to lack of availability. The available additional equipment may operate at less than full capacity, being overcapacity for the work intended but with the additional hire costs involved. The need to use material more quickly than planned may result in a reduced number of uses such as formwork, which will increase unit costs. The change in the sequence of working may result in an increased number of moves and/or distances for plant, such as cranage in piling. Additional resources and out of sequence working will place additional burden on the management to order materials and consumables, and increase the supervision required.

Acceleration will affect the pattern of work, and has an effect on efficiency, material delivery, equipment availability and therefore the cost of the work. In most situations acceleration will mean carrying out the work at a rate that is less than optimum in terms of cost. Acceleration in many situations will disrupt the works, affecting smooth trade interfaces and increasing interference between follow-on operations. In some cases it will mean unplanned access to working areas, reduced productivity and increase in defects as well as stoppages.

The additional payments for overtime or weekend working do not necessarily result in increased productivity. Indeed extended overtime and long hours will usually reduce efficiency. Additional shifts are not always productive. Evening or back shifts and night shifts are more likely to be less productive than day shifts, and may create more defects and less safe working. The out-of-hours working may increase the cost of delivery of materials, together with the additional cost of larger stockpile areas. New suppliers may need to be found for the increase in consumption, which may involve increase in unit costs.

25.2.7.4 Obligation to accelerate

The employer's remedy for the contractor's breach of contract in failing to complete by the completion date will be damages, whether general damages or liquidated damages. Many standard forms require the contractor not only to complete by the completion date but also to proceed regularly and diligently. Many standard forms provide a power for acceleration to be ordered in the event of the contractor's default in progressing with due diligence, without additional payment. Many standard forms also provide a power for ordering the contractor to adopt acceleration measures if it is considered that progress is not in accordance with the programme, if due to the contractor's default. Such powers do not normally extend to agreeing to accelerate in the absence of the contractor's default, which requires a separate agreement. If such an agreement is entered into it is important to ensure that the terms relating to liquidated damages still operate.

In *John Barker Construction Ltd v. London Portman Hotel Ltd* [1996] 83 BLR 35, John Barker were building contractors carrying out refurbishment of works to the London Portman Hotel. The contract was the JCT 80 Form with quantities. The contract provided for completion of floors 9 to 11 on 16 July 1994, floors 5 to 8 by 29 July 1994 and floors 2 to 4 by 14 August 1994. Clause 24 provided that liquidated damages would be paid at £30 000 per week for each section of the contract which was not completed by the specified date. Delays occurred and it was apparent to all concerned that John Barker was entitled to extensions of time. After negotiations it was agreed that the work would be accelerated so that all the work would be completed by 14 August 1994 and John Barker would receive additional payment.

After the acceleration agreement there were further delays and further instructions from the architect. One of the issues which arose was the effect of the acceleration agreement on the sectional completion provisions of the contract in relation to liquidated damages.

John Barker argued that the effect of the acceleration agreement was to dispense with all the provisions of the sectional agreement supplement, including the provisions for liquidated damages. It was argued that the substitution of a single date was logically inconsistent with such provisions having continuing contractual force. This was not accepted. It was common ground that at the time of the acceleration agreement no one raised the question of abandoning the liquidated damages provisions. It was held that it was neither intended by the parties nor logically necessary that the liquidated damages would

no longer apply. It was held that the provisions of the sectional completion supplement regarding liquidated damages were capable of continuing to have contractual force by merely substituting the new date of 26 August 1994 for completion of each section. The parties' intention did not go beyond that.

In *Ascon Contracting Limited v. Alfred McAlpine Construction Isle of Man Limited* [1999] there had been delays due to a number of causes and Ascon, the concrete subcontractor, claimed extension of time. It was held that, in considering the subcontractor's entitlement to extension of time, it could not be refused or reduced because of the possibility of future acceleration. That would impose an obligation on the subcontractor to incur expense in order to mitigate the consequences of the contractor's breaches of contract.

It would also deprive the subcontractors of the opportunity, knowing how much of the current delay had been allowed, of assessing whether it was necessary to consider incurring additional expense in accelerative measures in order to reduce its potential liability in damages for any disallowed balance, and if so to decide for itself how far it was in its own interests to incur that expense in the absence of instructions to do so as a variation. Accordingly Ascon was awarded an extension of time.

It was not in dispute that Ascon was also entitled to damages to the extent of any recoverable loss which could be established as caused by the period of delay, and a sum was awarded.

Ascon also claimed for loss caused by acceleration measures it had undertaken. HH Judge Hicks QC stated that acceleration had no precise technical meaning. Acceleration which was not required to meet a contractor's existing obligations was likely to be the result of an instruction from the employer for which the employer must pay. On the other hand, pressure from the employer to make good delay caused by the contractor's own default was unlikely to be so construed. There was no instruction in this case. Ascon was under pressure from McAlpine to accelerate the works to recover the time lost, but was insisting that it was not going to pay for acceleration. Ascon's claim on that basis did not therefore succeed.

Ascon claimed that it allocated additional resources, worked longer hours, worked 7 days per week and purchased and supplied duplicate plant and equipment. Ascon claimed that these acceleration measures were taken in order to mitigate the delays caused.

It was held that there could not be both an extension to the full extent of the employer's culpable delay, with damages on that basis, and also damages in the form of expenses incurred by the way of mitigation, unless it was alleged and established that the attempt at mitigation, although reasonable, was wholly ineffective. Ascon had not put its case in that way. It contended that the work was indeed completed sooner than it would have been in the absence of the accelerative measures. The mitigation claim wholly failed at the outset and the acceleration claim also failed.

In *Motherwell Bridge Construction Limited v. Micafil Vakuumtecchnik* [2002] TCC 81 ConLR 44 the issue of acceleration was addressed in a long and complicated judgement by Judge Toulmin CMG QC.

Motherwell was a subcontractor to Micafil for the construction of an autoclave for the employer BICC under modified FIDIC Forms of contract. The autoclave was a large steel vessel used in the manufacture of high quality power cables. There were a large number of claims by Motherwell.

One of two claims was for acceleration costs for the work in relation to on site fabrication for hours worked by Motherwell's staff in excess of 46h for the period from 8 October 1998 to March 1999. Micafil raised the defence that a term of the contract provided that if unexpected delays and difficulties occurred, Motherwell was required to provide additional personnel at no extra cost at the request of Micafil in order to meet the required completion date. It was held that the delays and difficulties came within the definition of 'unexpected'. There was no dispute that Micafil constantly urged Motherwell to increase its resources to meet the requested completion date. Accordingly, Judge Seymour held that Motherwell could not succeed in recovering damages for this item.

The second acceleration claim is examined below.

25.2.7.5 Acceleration agreements

Some standard Forms make provision for the parties to agree to accelerate the works. Even without such clauses, it is always possible for the parties to agree to vary the contract to their mutual benefit. If the acceleration is necessary solely due to the contractor's default, it may be argued that the agreement to accelerate has no legal effect for lack of consideration, since the employer will simply obtain that which it is already contractually required to receive.

In *Lester Williams v. Roffey Brothers & Nicholls (Contractors) Ltd* [1989] 48 BLR 69 Roffey was the main contractor for the refurbishment of a block of flats known as Twynholm Mansions. Williams was a carpentry subcontractor providing labour for the roof and first and second fix to the flats with a total price of £20000. The price was too low and a reasonable price should have been £23783. This was further aggravated by Williams failing to supervise his men adequately, which reduced productivity. Williams therefore were experiencing financial difficulties.

In April 1989 Roffey agreed to pay Williams an additional £10300 at the rate of £575 for each completed flat in order to have Williams continue with the works and complete on time. The carpentry work was on the critical path of Roffey's global operations so that failure by Williams to complete the work in accordance with the subcontract would lead to Roffey being liable for liquidated damages for delay under the main contract. The expected payments were not made by Roffey so that in May 1989 Williams ceased work. Roffey engaged other contractors to complete the work.

It was argued that the agreement to make additional payments was not legally binding on Roffey, since they had agreed to pay for work which Williams was already bound to carry out under the subcontract. There was no consideration.

There was some difficulty in finding consideration. It was held that in this case a benefit was derived from the agreement by each party and that was sufficient consideration for the promise to pay additional sums to be binding.

Although not referred to as such, it is suggested that the agreement was in the form of an acceleration agreement, the delay in this case having been caused by William's own default.

There may be considerable difficulties in evaluating the additional costs of acceleration and differentiating those costs from the costs of carrying out the works at the normal pace. Good records are vital, but it may be appropriate to simply take a broad approach.

In *Amec & Alfred McAlpine (Joint Venture) v. Cheshire County Council* [1999] BLR 303, Cheshire appointed the Joint Venture as contractor for construction of the Wilmslow and Handforth Bypass at Manchester under the ICE 5th Edition. By the end of 1994 there had been various delays for which the Joint Venture was not responsible. An acceleration agreement was entered into for which the Joint Venture was paid various sums for completing by 25 October 1995. Early in 1995 it became clear that there was likely to be another overrun and the Joint Venture was entitled to further extensions of time. An informal agreement was entered into in which the Joint Venture agreed to use its best endeavours to complete by 25 October 1995 and Cheshire would pay fair and reasonable recompense for the additional acceleration measures necessary. The date was achieved.

No specific method of valuation had been agreed and disputes arose as to the method of valuation, particularly because of delays for which Cheshire was not responsible and because of the difficulties of separating out the cost of work which the Joint Venture was already obliged to carry out under the original contract. A method of valuation was decided as a preliminary issue which was endorsed by the Court.

First, the Joint Venture's actual costs (X) were ascertained for the period of acceleration. The amount that the work carried out in the period of acceleration should have cost was evaluated (Y). The evaluation took into account all the events that had taken place before commencement of the acceleration period. The basic calculation of the acceleration costs was therefore $X - Y$. Further subtractions were made for factors and events for which the Joint Venture was liable (A). A further subtraction was the cost of variations ordered in the acceleration period (B) since these were included in X but not in Y. The *prima facie* entitlement was therefore $X - Y - (A + B)$ plus a reasonable amount for overheads and profit. This approach was adopted because of the difficulties of causation by analysis of particular items of work and of how time had been saved.

One issue before the Court was the adjustment to be made for payments received by the Joint Venture from their insurers for events during the acceleration period. The essential question was whether insurance payments should be taken into account in deciding a fair and reasonable remuneration. It was held that to allow a deduction would give Cheshire the full benefit of the insurance cover whereas it was primarily for the benefit of the Joint Venture and only incidentally Cheshire. Further, there would be no double recovery because the principles of indemnity which lie at the basis of insurance law would require the Joint Venture to be accountable to the insurers for the proceeds of amounts received from Cheshire of the relevant amounts.

25.2.7.6 Claims for acceleration

If the contract does not make completion by a particular date or time an obligation under the contract then the contractor will not be able to make a claim for the cost of acceleration measures. The only obligation will be to complete within a reasonable time which will involve optimisation of the resources for greatest efficiency and productivity. In most standard forms the contractor has an obligation to complete by a particular date or within a specified period. Even with such an obligation, the contractor will have some difficulty in pursuing the additional costs of acceleration where the contract entitles him or her to an extension of time for the delays which have occurred. In the case where the extension of time provisions are not properly operated, the contractor may consider a constructive acceleration claim, but this is not without its difficulties.

If the contractor is ordered to accelerate in the mistaken belief that the delay is due to the contractor's default, whereas the delay was the responsibility of the employer under the contract, then the contractor may be entitled to the acceleration costs.

25.2.8 Mitigation of delay

The issue of the contractor's right or obligation to reduce the effect of qualifying delays may arise in three ways.

(a) The contractor may be considered to have a right to choose how to deal with a qualifying delay and whether for instance to accelerate or not and to recovery on the basis of this right.

(b) The contractor may be considered to be entitled to extension of time and any associated loss only to the extent that it has mitigated the effect of the delays.

(c) The contractor may be under an obligation to progress the works including an express obligation to mitigate delays and the failure to do so prevents remedies of extension of time and associated losses and may make the contractor liable in damages.

These three possibilities are examined below. Since the issue of the contractor's right to choose is a positive aspect of mitigation it has been examined below with mitigation.

25.2.8.1 Mitigation of loss

The main remedy for breach of contract is damages. The measure of damages does not include losses caused by the injured party's failure to take reasonable steps to mitigate the loss.

There are three rules relating to mitigation for breach of contract. First, an injured party cannot recover damages for a loss which could have been avoided by reasonable steps. The injured party is not required to do anything other than in the ordinary course of business. Second, if the injured party takes steps which it could not reasonably have been required to do, and avoids the potential loss it cannot recover the potential loss as damages. Third, the injured party may recover its loss or expense in taking reasonable steps to mitigate the loss due to breach of contract. This is so even if the mitigation is unsuccessful and even increases the loss *British Westinghouse v. Underground Electric Railway* [1912].

Although the injured party must act with the other party's as well as its own interests in mind, it is only required to act reasonably and the standard of reasonableness is not high in view of the fact that the other party is the wrongdoer: *Dimond v. Lovell* [1999] approving the statement in McGregor on damages 16th Edition para 322.

In *White and Carter (Councils) Ltd v. McGregor* [1962] it was held that the rules of mitigation do not apply in the situation where the injured party has a legitimate interest in performing the contract rather than stopping and claiming damages. The injured party is not required in that case to discontinue performance even though the employer may no longer require him or her to continue.

Although commonly referred to as a 'duty to mitigate' the loss, it is not a duty but a principle adopted in the measure of loss: *The Soholt* [1983]. The onus of proving the failure to mitigate rests on the party alleging the failure: *Garmac Grain Co. v. Faire and Fairclough* [1968].

25.2.8.2 Mitigation of delay

The remedy of extension of time is a contractual remedy for acts of prevention and breach of contract by the employer and for events at the risk of the employer. It may therefore be thought that if the remedy of extension of time is based on causation, the principles referred to as the 'duty to mitigate' should apply. It is suggested that there are two situations to consider, first when the contractor responds positively and the second when the contractor takes no positive action.

In the first situation the contractor may react to the qualifying delay by making changes to its methods of working, or sequence of working, or even accelerate the work. The issue then is whether it is entitled to recover the loss incurred by this reaction and that depends on whether or not the contractor has a right to react as it did. This issue has been examined below. It is suggested that subject to the express terms of the contract, the contractor has no right to accelerate and is not entitled to recover additional costs incurred in acceleration measures to mitigate the effect of qualifying delays without an instruction from the employer. Since many contracts contain provisions for the grant of extensions of time and express terms for agreement of acceleration measures, the unilateral action by the contractor in giving priority to the fixed date for completion over the cost of working efficiently cannot bind the employer in those contracts. It is suggested that this interpretation can be expressed in terms of the reasonableness in mitigation. It is not reasonable when there are sufficient contractual remedies for the contractor to decide to accelerate the works. This interpretation must be examined in the context of express obligations to progress the works.

In the second situation the contractor may not react to the qualifying delay and the issue then is what minimum measures it is required to take in order to mitigate the effects of the qualifying delay and if it fails to take those measures whether this affects the extent of the contractor's entitlement to extension of time. It is suggested that the rules of mitigation do not generally apply to construction contracts in relation to time where there are extension of time provisions.

In *Ascon Contracting Limited v. Alfred McAlpine Construction Isle of Man Limited* [1999], HH Judge Hicks QC held that it was difficult to see how there could be any room for the doctrine of mitigation in relation to damage suffered by reason of the employer's culpable delay in the face of express contractual machinery for dealing with the situation of extension of time and reimbursement of loss and expense. This decision was made in relation a submission that the contractor should have incurred additional expenditure in accelerating the works to overcome the delay.

In *Motherwell Bridge Construction Limited v. Micafil Vakuumtecchnik* (2002) TCC 81 ConLR 44 the claim for acceleration costs of site works failed. There was a term of the contract that if unexpected delays and difficulties occurred, Motherwell was required to provide additional personnel at no extra cost at the request of Micafil in order to meet the required completion date.

25.2.8.3 Obligation to mitigate delay or to progress the works

It is suggested that although the rules of mitigation do not generally apply to construction contracts with extension of time provisions and provision for recovery of time-related losses, the contractor will have some obligation to progress the works which will involve an aspect of management of resources and planning of activities in the circumstances of actual events. Although a matter of interpretation of the terms of the contract, it is suggested that such an obligation will usually be intended by the parties to apply equally to events causing qualifying delays. The obligation to progress the works may, however, require the contractor to take some positive action, and a failure to do so may sound in damages measured by the liquidated damages for additional periods of overrun which could have been avoided but for the breach. Since the obligation to proceed 'regularly and diligently' means to proceed continuously, industriously and efficiently with appropriate physical resources so as to progress the works steadily towards completion, it is suggested this will include managing the effects of the delay.

It is suggested that, faced with delay, the contractor will not be able to claim extension of time for delays which could have been avoided by changing the planned sequences of working, unless the sequence is a specified sequence, so that the contractor could carry on with other work as best it could. It cannot be considered reasonable that a contractor should maintain a sequence of working, doing no further work and incurring delay when by changing the sequence it would be able to open up other areas of work and progress some of the works. It is suggested that the contractor is not required to take steps which would reduce productivity such as acceleration measures and increase direct costs by procuring additional plant or materials. It will usually be required to properly manage the progress of the works, including terms as to proceeding regularly and diligently as examined earlier. The obligation will apply to the consequences of the delay.

In *DSND Subsea Ltd v. Petroleum Geo-Srevices ASA and PGS Offshore Technology AS* [2000] the contractor was under an obligation to carry out and complete the work involving deep-sea diving in an expeditious and timely manner. The sequence of the phases of work was specified in a programme incorporated in a Memorandum of Agreement agreed by the parties as the way to deal with delays that had occurred. There were further delays. It was held that the obligation to progress the works in an expeditious and timely manner did not impose an obligation on the contractor to carry out the work in a different sequence and particularly to carry out deep-sea diving work before all other work specified to be carried out (the riser installations), had been completed. The contractor had carried out a significant amount of diving before the installation of the risers, but that was not something he was obliged to do. Since plant was on site it made sense for it to do some diving work as and when it was able to do so, but there was no obligation to do so.

It is suggested also that if the entitlement to extension of time is on the basis of what is fair and reasonable, that this must include consideration of the positive steps taken by the contractor to reduce the consequences of the delay, and the steps which could have been taken, without the expenditure of substantial sums.

It is because of these difficulties that many standard forms require the contractor to take steps to reduce the effects of delays, to mitigate the delay, but the extent of the obligation differs. Failure to comply with the obligation may reduce or even extinguish the contractor's entitlement to extension of time.

The most onerous obligation is that the contractor must use its best endeavours to reduce the delay. It is suggested that the obligation does not require the contractor to expend substantial sums to reduce the delay. In *Midland Land Reclamation Ltd v. Warren Energy Ltd* [1997] it was held that the best endeavours obligation was not the next best thing to an absolute obligation or guarantee. In *Terrell v. Mabie Todd and Co.* [1952] it was held that a best endeavours obligation only required a party to do what was commercially practicable and what it could reasonably do in the circumstances.

It is suggested that an express obligation to proceed regularly and diligently will include applying resources in such a way as to reduce the consequences of a qualifying delay, so that work is carried out efficiently. It is suggested that the reasonable steps to be taken by the contractor when faced with a qualifying delay is to provide the appropriate notices required by the contract together with the details required or requested by the A/E. It is also suggested that where a contractor takes reasonable steps to mitigate the effects of the delay and succeeds in reducing the effect of the delay, then its entitlement to extension of time is reduced accordingly. If the entitlement is based on actual delay evaluated retrospectively and if the contractor is entitled to recover losses due to the delay, then it is suggested that losses incurred in taking reasonable steps are part of the recoverable loss. If, on the other hand, the contractor is awarded an extension of time prospectively, there is then no reason to mitigate the delay, since it has been granted the compensation under the contract. Whether or not the contractor would be entitled in that case to recover its loss due to the delay depends on the terms of the contract.

25.2.9 Particulars

Many standard forms require the contractor to submit to the A/E particulars of the events complained of and the delays. Some standard forms require the A/E to ascertain the delay caused and the extension of time due, but in other forms the contractor is required to provide some analysis as part of the particulars submitted. Similarly, in coercive proceedings such as litigation or arbitration, the claimant is required to plead its case with particulars of the events and delays and, in a subsequent forum, to prove its case. It is suggested that in both processes a distinction needs to be made between the particularisation required to be submitted to establish a right to have the claim considered, and the ascertainment or proof itself. Whether sufficient particulars have been submitted is solely a question of fact and degree.

The contractor must set out a proper particularised case of those events complained of, such as late information or instructions, which gave rise to the delay and the reasons why they did so. This does not mean that the contractor must at that stage put a period of delay against each event, unless the contract so requires, but some indication must be given as to those matters which caused substantial delay and why that should have been the case. The basic purpose of particularisation and pleadings is to enable the A/E or other party to know what case is being made in sufficient detail to enable a proper answer or ascertainment to be made. The particulars must identify the events which give rise to the delay and which of these events were the fault of the employer.

It is suggested that proper particularisation of an event causing delay requires at least:

(a) particulars of the event describing the factors necessary for the event to be a qualifying event either under the contract

or as a breach of contract. So, for instance, if the complaint is that the specification was inadequate, the description and grounds of the inadequacy. If the complaint is that the information or instruction was late, then the particulars must identify when the information ought to have been given and when it was given

(b) demonstration of the link between the particular event and the particular trade or operation to show the nature of the work which was delayed and to show any ways in which the event caused or contributed to the delay

(c) the dates between which the delay occurred and whether such delay was continuous or intermittent.

25.2.10 Cause and effect

Causation is an issue of fact. A common-sense approach is required involving evidence from which it can be inferred that, more likely than not, the delay was caused by the event complained of, *BHP Billiton Petroleum Ltd v. Dalmine SpA* [2003] EWCA Civ 170.

The usual approach is to carry out a retrospective and dissectional reconstruction of events if appropriate day by day, and/or drawing by drawing, and/or information by information to show that the event complained of delayed or disrupted progress of the works. It will usually be necessary to examine events in addition to those complained of, if only to demonstrate that they could not have caused the delay.

The type of evidence and the extent of analysis required will depend on the particular circumstances, but will involve some or all of the following:

(a) a programme showing the planned construction process

(b) an as-built programme showing actual progress for the particular part of the work delayed

(c) documentary evidence of dates and progress such as diary extracts, progress reports, progress programmes, correspondence, photographs, video evidence, etc.

(d) network analysis normally showing construction logic links and identifying the delays

(e) evidence of witnesses and experts.

25.2.11 Concurrent delays

One particular problem in the analysis of cause and effect is the situation which arises when two events contribute to the same delay. So, for instance, the situation may be that the contractor has been delayed due to variations or late issue of information, both of which are the responsibility of the employer, but some if not all of the delay would have occurred in any event due to other factors, either neutral events or breach of contract which are the responsibility of the contractor.

Whether or not the contractor is entitled to an extension of time depends on the construction of the extension of time clause.

Several cases show the modern development of the interpretation of extension of time clauses under the JCT 80 Standard

Form in which extensions of time may be due only for 'Relevant Events' defined by the form.

In the case of *Balfour Beatty Building Ltd v. Chestermount Properties Ltd* (1993) 62 BLR 12 the Architect issued a variation (a Relevant Event) after the construction of the office block should have been completed and during a period of contractor's culpable delay. Was it the 'gross' method – an extension of time up to the date when the contractor completed the varied work? Was it instead the 'net' method. It was held to be the 'net' method, as this was fair and reasonable as required by the contract, an extension of time representing the additional delay caused by the Relevant Event. The 'net' approach left open difficult questions of causation, particularly where the Relevant Event could have been avoided if the contractor had not been late in the first place.

In the case of *Henry Boot Construction (UK) Ltd v. Malmaiston Hotel (Manchester) Ltd* (1999) 70 ConLR 32 completion of construction of the hotel was late. Although the Architect had granted some extensions of time for Relevant, this did not account for all the delay. Malmaiston therefore deducted £250 000 in liquidated damages. The parties agreed that if two events caused delay to completion and only one was the responsibility of the Employer, then the contractor was nonetheless entitled to an extension of time. The issue was how should the Architect establish whether an event was the cause of delay. It was held as a matter of interpretation of JCT 80 that the Architect was permitted to consider the effect of all events to establish whether the Relevant Event caused any delay to completion (i.e. that it was on the critical path) or whether another event actually caused the delay. This was the first time that the UK courts accepted the principle that the contractor is entitled to an extension of time in the situation of concurrent delays. Whether the principle applies to other forms of contract other than JCT 80 is yet to be decided.

In the case of *The Royal Brompton Hospital NHS Trust v. Watkins Gray International* (Dec 2000) the proper approach to the assessment of extensions of time for concurrent was considered. It was held that where a Relevant Event occurs during a period of contractor's culpable delay, which does not cause any further delay, then this is not a case of a concurrent event. No extension of time is due. On the other hand, where two events happen before either has caused delay and each would on its own have caused delay, then this is a real concurrency. If one of the events is a Relevant Event then the contractor is entitled to an extension of time. The decision confirmed and emphasised the need for proper analysis of the actual causes of delay. It was recognised that different methods may give different results. The case left open the development of methods of analysis.

In *Motherwell Bridge Construction Limited v. Micafil AG* [2002] HH Judge Toulmin QC examined concurrent delay and referred to and adopted the approach of Dyson J in *Henry Boot Construction (UK) Ltd v. Malmaison Hotel (Manchester) Ltd* [1999] which in turn adopted the approach in *Balfour Beatty Ltd v. Chestermount Properties* [1993] in relation to FIDIC conditions.

In some standard forms, the clause determines the matter of causation for concurrent causes of the same delay. Where it does not, the law on causation in contract is not clear. Until recently it was considered that the courts did not have inherent jurisdiction to apportion liability for truly concurrent causes, and so various theories have been adopted to establish liability.

The dominant cause approach avoids the issue of concurrency and is difficult to apply in delay situations. Nonetheless this is an important part of the process of analysis. A close examination of *H Fairweather and Co Ltd v. London Borough of Wandsworth* (1987) 39 BLR 106, shows that the case is not authority against the dominant cause theory.

In *Great Eastern Hotel Company Ltd v. John Laing Construction Ltd* [2005] EWHC 181 (TCC) it was argued that if it was established that some breach or breaches caused delay to an identified critical path, of itself that cannot establish the necessary causal link citing in support *Galoo Limited v. Bright Grahame Murray* [1995] 1 All Eng 16 and the dicta of *Glidewell LJ and Quin v. Burch Brothers (Builders) Limited* [1968] 2 All Eng 283 and the Australian case *Alexander v. Cambridge Credit Corporation* [1987] 9 NSWLR.

HH David Wilcox observed that in the cited cases the courts were considering the consequences of breach and were careful to distinguish between the consequence of merely giving rise to the opportunity or occasion of loss as opposed to causing it.

HH David Wilcox held that if a breach of contract is one of the causes both cooperating and of equal efficiency in causing loss to the Claimant the party responsible for breach is liable to the Claimant for that loss.

He held that the contract breaker was liable as long as his breach was an 'effective cause' of his loss and referred to *Heskell v. Continental Express Limited* [1995] 1 All Eng 1033.

He held that the Court need not choose which cause was the more effective. He referred to the approach of Devlin J in *Heskell* which was adopted by Steyn J (as he then was) in *Banque Keyser SA v. Skandia* [1991] QB and accepted by the Court of Appeal.

In the important part of the judgement in relation to the issue of concurrent delay, Judge Wilcox emphasised the importance of the terms of the contract. He held that each claim or group of claims must be examined on their own facts and in the context of the specific contractual provisions such as variations which may give rise to a consideration of the comparative potency of causal events and to apportionment.

He held that in the absence of such provision the appropriate test was that if a party proved the breach and the proven breach materially contributed to the loss then it could recover the whole loss, even if there is another effective contributory cause provided that there is no double recovery. This approach caused no injustice, because the Defendant who pays is protected, because it was open to him to seek contribution from any other contract breaker.

He held that on the basis of the evidence that the dominant cause of Trade Contractor delay was in fact the delay to the project caused by Laing's proven breaches.

In the Scots case of *John Doyle Construction Ltd v. Laing Management Ltd* [2004] it was stated that in determining what is a significant cause, the 'dominant cause' approach is of relevance. If an event or events for which the employer is responsible can be described as the dominant cause of an item of loss, that will be sufficient to establish liability, notwithstanding the existence of other causes that are to some degree at least concurrent.

It was held that if an item of loss results from concurrent causes, and one of those causes can be identified as the proximate or dominant cause of the loss, it will be treated as the operative cause, an the person responsible for it will be responsible for the loss.

The dominant cause theory is to be distinguished from the situation where one event caused by one of the parties influences the actions of the other party. So, for example, if the contractor is aware that the works are to be delayed due to matters which are the responsibility of the employer, it may delay the delivery of certain materials or the commencement of part of the works as part of efficient planning of the works. A retrospective analysis may show superficially concurrent causes of delay, whereas one event has, in fact, set the circumstances for the second event.

It now appears that where a defect was caused equally by the default of the plaintiff and the defendant and where each default was insufficient to cause the defect in the absence of the other, then the court is entitled to ascertain and exercise the jurisdiction to apportion where required to do justice. This is an example of 'composite' or 'compound' causation.

In *W Lamb Ltd v. J Jarvis & Sons plc* (1998) ORB the plaintiff subcontractor installed pipework to a petrol filling station for the contractor defendant. The pipework leaked and was replaced. The matter to be decided as a preliminary issue was whether the failure was caused by the faulty workmanship on the pipework by the plaintiff or acts or omissions in the construction of the concrete supports by the defendant. It was found that failure was caused equally by the plaintiff and the defendant. The defaults were each insufficient to cause the leaks in the absence of the other. It was held that following *Tennant Radiant Heat Ltd v. Warrington Development Corporation* (1988) 1 EGLR 41 that the court was entitled to ascertain and exercise the jurisdiction to apportion where required to do justice.

If this jurisdiction applies to the situation where each event would have caused the same delay in the absence of the other event, then apportionment will assist in resolving the problem of concurrent causes. In the Scots case of *John Doyle Construction Ltd v. Laing Management Ltd* [2004] it was stated that if it cannot be said that events the employer's

responsibility are the dominant cause of the loss, it may be possible to apportion the loss between the causes. The events for which the employer is responsible should be a material cause of the loss.

It was held that apportionment of loss between the different causes is possible where the causes of the loss are truly concurrent, in the sense that both operate together at the same time to produce a single consequence, for example late provision of information during a period bad weather might have prevented work for a part of the time. In such a case responsibility for the loss can be apportioned between the two causes, according to their relative significance.

25.2.12 Method of analysis

There are many methods of analysis to demonstrate entitlement to an extension of time. The choice of the appropriate analysis depends on the evidence available, the existing programme evidence, the particular circumstances and the terms of the extension of time clause. Whatever method is chosen, it should be sufficiently detailed to explain the situation convincingly but not so complex as to be difficult to understand.

In practice the method of analysis is a means of demonstrating causation and inevitably will be theoretical based on disputed facts and opinion. There are indeed only two methods, of which there are different variants and hybrids given different names (impact as-planned, as-planned *v.* as-built, as-built but-for, collapsed as-built, time impact method, window slice method).

The method of analysis using an as-built programme has the advantage that it creates an accurate record of actual progress if based on traceable evidence. In practice, it is necessary to focus the analysis on key areas of delay to avoid unnecessary expense. This makes the method iterative. It is not usually sufficient to simply compare the as-built programme to the planned programme without verifying the planned programme. It is necessary instead to prepare a construction logic which explains the sequence of events and the reasons for the actions taken and the delay caused.

The method of analysis using the time impact or snapshot approach requires the base programme initially adopted by the contractor to be updated for each event. The update requires the construction logic to be examined for any change with new activities created if necessary and the durations re-evaluated. This update may create a new critical path and an extended period. The updated programme is then updated for the next event and so on. If data is not available at the time of the delay then another method needs to be used. The advantage of this method is that it records the unfolding of events and places actions in context.

Whatever method is adopted, it is necessary that the expert preparing the programme understands the construction issues involved as well as the limitations of the particular programme software and the method. The expert must also be able to explain the analysis to allow the judge, arbitrator, adjudicator or A/E to understand.

25.3 Liquidated damages
25.3.1 Agreed value of damages

Damages is one of the most important remedies for breach of contract in the construction industry, but requires two significant legal hurdles to be overcome before there can be recovery. First, the injured party must prove he has incurred actual loss as a result of the breach. Second, the loss must not fall foul of the legal rules as to remoteness; *Hadley v. Baxendale* (1854); *Victoria Laundry (Windsor) Ltd. v. Newman Industries Ltd* (1949).

These rules prevent recovery of losses which arise from special circumstances, unless the circumstances are known and there is an implied acceptance that the contract was directed to these special circumstances. In practice this means that the injured party is faced with expensive legal action if he is to obtain compensation.

Liquidated damages (LD) clauses in a contract avoid these legal hurdles. Just as the parties at the time of contracting can agree their obligations under the contract, so they can agree the amount of compensation to be paid if the particular obligation is not performed. There is no need to look for an implied agreement to compensate for losses due to special circumstances. The liquidated damages clause is an express agreement, so compensation is payable whether or not the special circumstances which make the loss likely are known. In other words the parties are not bound by the rules as to remoteness for the particular breach specified; *Robophone Facilities Ltd v. Blank* (1966) 3 All ER 128 CA. By this mechanism of LD clauses, disputes are either avoided altogether or if there is a dispute the cost involved in proving damages is avoided.

There is no reason in public policy why the parties should not enter into an arrangement under which each know where they stand in the event of a breach and can avoid the heavy costs of proving the actual damage *Robophone Facilities Limited v. Blank* [1966] 1 WLR 1428.

Particularly in building and engineering contracts it is to the parties advantage that they should be able to know with a reasonable degree of certainty the extent of their liability and the risk which they run as a result of entering into the contract. Liquidated damages provisions enable the Employer to know the extent to which he is protected in the event of the contractor failing to perform his obligations *Philips Hong Kong Ltd v. The Attorney General of Hong Kong* (1993).

A liquidated damages provision is commercially very attractive to both parties, since it allows the Contractor to know when he tenders precisely the level of his liability for the risk inherent in the particular obligation and hence may allow the contractor to reduce the level of his bid. The reduced bid which may result from the adoption of liquidated damages clauses

benefits the purchaser, providing the extent of the risk which materialises is not greater than allowed for in the liquidated damages clause. If so, then the liquidated damages clause will have had the effect of passing part of the risk of the particular event from the contractor to the purchaser.

It cannot be assumed that the LD rate is the measure of the full loss likely to be suffered. The parties may deliberately have agreed to limit the financial loss recoverable *Bath and North East Somerset District Council v. Mowlem plc* [2004] EWCA Civ 115.

The parties might even agree that liquidated damages as '£ nil' per week as decided in *Temloc v. Errill Properties Ltd* (1987) 39 BLR 30 (CA).

If a contractor wishes to pass to a subcontractor the risk under the main contract of paying liquidated damages as a result of the subcontractor's breach, he may choose to do so either by a subcontract liquidated damages clause or by giving the subcontractor notice of the provisions of the main contract. In the latter approach, the rules of remoteness above will require the Subcontractor to acknowledge that any breach by the Subcontractor which may result in breaches by the Contractor under the main contract and other contracts made in connection with the main works, and that the consequent damages, including liquidated damages payable, are within the contemplation of the parties.

25.3.2 Types of LD clauses

Conceptually an LD clause could apply to any type of breach of contract, either a single event or a continuing breach. If the clause does not relate to a breach of contract then it simply operates to allocate risk and/or determine the measure of payment *Exports Credits Guarantee Department v. Universal Oil Products Company* [1983] 23 BLR 106 HL.

Failure to complete by a specified date is the most common breach of contract for which LD clauses are used in the construction industry.

The damages are usually expressed in Standard Forms as an amount per day or per week of delay to completion to be paid by the Contractor to the Purchaser. In some commercial developments there may be a critical delay beyond which the damages change – such as a critical date for supply or the date for opening a development. In such cases a limit is usually stated for the overall amount of LDs or another rate is stated to apply after the critical date. It may be necessary in specific situations to stipulate a maximum delay beyond which the LD provision is no longer an adequate remedy and the contractor's performance is considered and agreed as no performance at all.

If sections of the works have different importance to the Purchaser, sectional completion dates should be stated with different LD rates together with a rate for the remainder of the works.

Standard Forms usually allow the Purchaser the flexibility to take over parts of the works. The entitlement to LDs should be modified in that case to reflect the reduced damages for any delay caused by the contractor, so that the right to LDs for the remainder of the works is not lost.

25.3.3 Rules of penalty clauses

Although the rules on penalty clauses set out in *Jeancharm Limited v. Barnet Football Club Limited* [2003] EWCA Civ 58 are an anomalous feature of the law, there has been no abandonment of the rule that the clause must be a genuine pre-estimate of damage.

The test remained one of ascertaining whether the provision was a genuine pre-estimate of loss or was a penalty for non-performance of the contractual obligation. The first type of provision was essentially compensatory in nature. The second was there to deter the party in question from breaking the contract by providing for a punitive level of payment *Jeancharm Limited v. Barnet Football Club Limited* [2003] EWCA Civ 58.

So long as the sum payable in the event of non-compliance with the contract is not extravagant, having regard to the range of losses that it could reasonably be anticipated it would have to cover at the time that the contract was made, it can still be a genuine pre-estimate of the loss that would be suffered and so a perfectly valid liquidated damage provision *Philips v. The Attorney General of Hong Kong* [1993] 61 BLR 41.

There seem to be two strands in the authorities. In some cases judges consider whether there is an unconscionable or extravagant disproportion between the damages stipulated in the contract and the true amount of damages likely to be suffered. In other cases the courts consider whether the level of damages stipulated was reasonable. I accept, that these two strands can be reconciled. In my view, a pre-estimate of damages does not have to be right in order to be reasonable.

The test of genuine pre-estimate does not refer to the genuineness or honesty of the party or parties who made the pre-estimate. The test is primarily an objective one, even though the court has some regard to the thought processes of the parties at the time of contracting. There must be a substantial discrepancy between the level of damages stipulated in the contract and the level of damages which is likely to be suffered before it can be said that the agreed pre-estimate is unreasonable *Alfred McAlpine Capital Projects Limited v. Tilebox Limited* [2005] EWHC 281 (TCC).

A clause in a hire purchase agreement requiring the hirer to pay compensation for premature termination was a penalty since it provided a sliding scale which operated in the wrong direction. The less the depreciation of the vehicle, the greater was the compensation payable *Campbell Discount Co Ltd v. Bridge* [1962] AC 600 HL.

The amount stipulated as damages should be proportionate to the extent of the breaches. It is not unreasonable to take an overall figure for a failure to return all or a substantial part of the specified parts. Where the same sum was payable for failure to return even a few of some comparatively unimportant items, the sum was out of all proportion to any loss suffered

and was a penalty *Ariston SRL v. Charly Records Limited* [1990] Court of Appeal.

An agreement that if payment was late interest was to be paid at 5% per week was a penalty clause.

The 5% per week figure amounted to an annual rate of about 260% percent which was an extraordinarily large amount to have to pay for the suggested administrative costs, even if the sums involved were relatively small. It was purely a matter of speculation, and the clause went wider than that and covered comparatively large debts too.

The provision of graduated sums increasing in proportion to the seriousness of the breach was characteristic of a liquidated damages clause which was commonplace in commercial contracts *North Sea Ventilation Limited v. Consafe Engineering (UK) Limited* [2004].

A liquidated damages clause is construed on the basis that the amount stipulated as damages should be proportionate to the breach. If there was a substantial discrepancy between the level of damages stipulated in the contract and the level of damages which is likely to be suffered the liquidated damages would be unreasonable.

It is a strong indication of a penalty if the clause provides for a single sum to be payable on a number of different breaches, which may give rise to widely different amounts of damage. This can give employers difficulties, particularly when an LD clause is drafted in anticipation of the several different ways that the plant may not fulfil its performance requirements. Many separate performance criteria may need to be met if the intended overall plant performance is to be achieved. In practice, providing easily ascertainable sums as liquidated damages means that different performance criteria need to be grouped together, in order to assess the likely loss in production and increased costs due to their cumulative effect.

The liquidated damages should not be out of all proportion to any part of the range of losses, particularly where the range is broad. Special provision will need to be made for such parts of the likely losses otherwise the LD clause may be held to be a penalty. This means that there should not be too great a difference between the greatest and the smallest possible losses.

The LDs are not unenforceable simply because it is difficult to pre-estimate the loss from a breach. In such cases the courts will not become involved in examining different scenarios to find a likely loss less than the liquidated damages. This would effectively defeat the purpose of LD clauses in providing the parties with a level of certainty and a mechanism for avoiding disputes. Even if the liquidated damages are greater than the loss it would still be a genuine pre-estimate of the loss if it was not so great in relation to the range of losses that it could reasonably be anticipated it would have to cover at the time the contract was made.

The employer is not required to demonstrate that it has suffered loss as a result of the breach. Liquidated damages are enforceable even if in the event there has been no loss. If the actual loss is greater than the sum stated in the LD clause and the LD clause is enforceable, the stated sum is exhaustive of the employer's entitlement to damages. It cannot elect to sue for damages in addition to the sum stated in the LD clause.

If the LD clause is a penalty, then the injured party must then prove its loss in the ordinary way. The law is not entirely clear on whether the stated sum will limit the amount recoverable as damages. It has been argued that the sole purpose of the courts using their power to strike down a penalty clause is to provide relief against oppression. If, having struck down the clause, the courts then allowed recovery of a sum greater than the stipulated penalty, this would be productive of an injustice.

The agreement on liquidated and ascertained damages was not an agreed price to permit a party to breach its contract and did not preclude the Court granting any other relief that may be appropriate such as injuncture.

It may be significant in that case that the level of LDs was less than the anticipated loss and to show that it would not be adequately compensated if it were left to a claim in damages *Bath and North East Somerset District Council v. Mowlem plc* [2004] EWCA Civ 115.

25.3.4 Onus of proof

The onus of showing that an LD clause is a penalty clause falls on the party who is sued on the clause. If the contractor challenges the LD clause as being a penalty, then the contractor is required to prove that it is a penalty. In such a case, it is not for the employer to prove that the liquidated damages amount is a reasonable pre-estimate of loss *Robophone Facilities Ltd v. Blank* [1966] confirmed by the Court of Appeal in *Jeancham Ltd v. Barnet Football Club Ltd* [2003] EWCA Civ 58.

25.3.5 Contractor's failure to apply for extension of time

If the contractor loses the right to extension of time for the Employer's breach of contract, because he fails to provide effective notice, it has been argued that the Employer is not entitled to deduct liquidated damages for the delay caused by the breach. It is argued that the principle in *Alghussein* would to prevent the Employer benefiting from his own breach to the detriment of the contractor. This has been examined in two recent cases, one Australian and one Scottish.

It is suggested that the failure of the contractor to give notice condition precedent to an extension of time, will not prevent the Employer deducting LDs. The principle in *Alghussein* is a principle of construction of the contract. The presumption must be that a contractor will act to preserve his rights. His failure to do so will not prevent LDs being levied.

An extension of time notice provision in a JCT80 Contract did not impose any obligation on the contractor when he received an architect's instruction. It merely provided the contractor with an option to take certain action if he sought the protection of an extension of time in the circumstances in which the clause applied.

If the contractor failed to take action and the notice was condition precedent to an extension of time, the Employer was entitled to deduct liquidated damages for the contractor's failure to complete *City Inn Ltd v. Shepherd Construction Ltd* [2003] Inner House.

25.4 Claims for site conditions
25.4.1 Changed ground conditions

It is not possible to investigate every existing physical condition which will affect construction. The normal approach of both designers and contractors is to prepare a reasonable model of the conditions based on the limited information and engineering experience. The model will be the basis of the design and estimates or the basis of prices and the programme. It is when the model is found to be inaccurate that disputes and differences arise. The interaction of information, analysis and methods of construction which affect the model, means that the nature of the risk event will not be immediately clear.

The above interaction makes it difficult to define a risk event in a contract clearly so that when it occurs the allocation of liability for the consequences can be readily determined. Although the principles for allocation of risk are clearly understood, in practice, when a risk event occurs, the liability for the consequences of the risk event depends on such a number of interrelated factors, that inevitably the allocation of liability will involve a legal process of proof of legal obligation or entitlement. Any risk allocation will therefore create a substantial legal risk – the risk of disputes or differences. The management of the risk must recognise and cater for this aspect of the risk.

25.4.2 The nature of the risk

The claims, differences or disputes which arise in construction contracts have their roots in the incomplete information about the nature of the ground properties and in the misunderstandings which only become apparent after work has commenced. Apart from natural phenomena such as floods, earthquakes and adverse weather conditions, disputes about 'changed conditions' arise from the choices and judgements made by the contracting parties. In short, when a 'changed condition' arises, it is not the condition which has changed but the parties' perception of it.

The apportionment of risk between the parties to the contract must be accomplished through the terms of the contract against the background of the law of the contract. The complexity of the risk of 'changed conditions' means that it is difficult to fully place the risk with one party. In addition, the consequences of a risk event once it materialises will be determined by the actions already taken by the parties such as the issue of information, the selection of the method of construction or the selection of the payment mechanism, as well as the reaction of the parties to the risk event.

The complexity of the interacting factors means that clear and unambiguous allocation of liability for the consequences of 'changed conditions' cannot easily be achieved by drafting of contract terms. The major practical risk from 'changed conditions' in construction contracts is therefore the protracted resolution of the differences and disputes which subsequently arise. It is, however, precisely in this area that well drafted contract procedures for rational and logical dispute resolution can reduce the consequences of the legal risk. The aim must be to provide a mechanism for rapidly providing certainty in the interpretation of the various terms of the contract and in rapidly providing a practical evaluation of the technical, time and financial consequences of 'changed conditions'.

This conclusion appears to fly in the face of industry views of disputes on 'changed conditions'. It is often said that disputes should not be an inherent part of construction contracts. The resort to dispute resolution procedures is seen as a failure of management. It is suggested that this is to misunderstand the nature of the risk of 'changed conditions'. The risk is not solely a technical risk but is predominantly a legal risk involving proof of legal obligation or entitlement and which accordingly requires a management approach which recognises the legal nature of the risk.

25.4.3 Incomplete information – disclosure

The general principle, subject to the express terms of the contract, is that if a contractor has contracted to carry out the whole of the construction works, then it must satisfy itself as to the nature and condition of the site for the works. It cannot assume that the statements in the contract documents about the state of the site, or the extent of work involved are accurate. It cannot assume that the statements about the method of working are practical. The general principle is that the employer has not warranted the accuracy of the information or statements in the contract documents.

Information may be incomplete for a number of reasons. First, there may be insufficient site investigation. Experience shows that a proper site investigation is always an effective means of reducing the risk of 'changed conditions' since it provides the information necessary to create an accurate model of the conditions. Second, sufficient information may be available in the form of old maps, aerial photographs, previous site investigations and even public reports and articles. The incompleteness may arise from the failure of one or both parties to locate and take account of the information. Third, even though information is available and has been obtained, the model of the condition may be incomplete because the interpretation of the information or analysis of the information is incorrect. Finally, despite the collation and analysis of the information, the limitations of the information and analysis techniques do not allow the accurate position of probable features to be established. This is the case where the possibility of the occurrence of a feature is recognised but cannot be predicted in any tangible and practicable form. These four types of incompleteness are defined only in relation to the particular operation to be carried out in or on the ground. The extent and the nature of the site investigation required will depend on the method of working or the type of ground treatment to be carried out.

In many construction projects, the employer will have relevant information about the site which will not otherwise be available to the contractor. The contractor may not be aware that such information is available. The question which arises is whether the employer is under a legal obligation to disclose this information.

There is no general duty of disclosure in English law in commercial transactions such as construction projects. The mere non-disclosure of information does not, of itself, create a cause of action. In order to succeed, the contractor has to establish either a breach of contract or negligent misrepresentation which induced the contract. An action in negligent misrepresentation will require the contractor to show that the employer assumed or accepted responsibility for assembling and transmitting full and accurate information. The contractor will need to show that it relied on the employer assembling and transmitting the information. The success of such an action will depend on the circumstances, including the language of the contract, the specification relating to the site, the respective positions of the parties and their respective knowledge.

In normal circumstances, a person in pre-contract negotiations will not be under a duty to assemble or present information relating to the subject matter of the contract. Instead he or she is entitled solely to look after his or her own interests and make the best deal possible.

Some forms of contract recognise that the employer may have information not available from other sources and by various provisions encourage the employer to make full disclosure. The ICE 6th and 7th Edition Clause 11 is such a provision. The Engineering Construction Contract Clause 60 is another such provision.

The employer must, of course, ensure that its selection of information will not constitute misrepresentation, for example by only issuing one of a number of subsoil surveys for the site. For the same reason, the employer should ensure that advice or opinion given by the specialists carrying out the surveys are excluded from the information issued. It cannot be pretended that this is an easy matter. If this is carried too far, it may create the very risk of underpricing which the issue of information is intended to avoid.

If the employer does supply information, then it may attempt to exclude the information from the contract and/or exclude liability for the accuracy of the information. Whether such a disclaimer is successful will depend on the terms of the disclaimer and the circumstances.

If the employer is to rely on a disclaimer for information supplied to the contractor then it will need to be carefully drafted.

Inevitably, the definition of the information which the contractor is required to have obtained for itself is in terms which are open to interpretation.

25.4.4 Pricing mechanism

Even without a changed condition clause the pricing mechanism may in effect transfer the risk to the employer of the as-built quantities being greater than those estimated at tender. Depending on the method of measurement, the employer may still carry the risk of changed conditions, for example with regard to

■ longer piles in the event of deeper suitable bearing strata;

■ increased volume of unsuitable material and imported fill.

25.4.5 Reaction to risk events

One additional factor which may determine liability for the consequences of a risk event is the reaction of the parties to the risk event. Many standard forms with changed condition clauses have requirements for the issue of notices of both the risk event and particulars of measures to overcome the consequences. This is the case under ICE 6th and 7th Edition Clause 12. If the contractor fails to serve notice as soon as is reasonable, its entitlement to payment is limited to the extent that the engineer is prevented or prejudiced by the late notice in the engineer's investigation of the claim. In the ICE 4th Edition, Clause 12 included a requirement for the contractor to give notice and provided that the cost of all work done prior to the giving of such notice was deemed to have been recovered in the rates and prices under the contract. In such a case, the risk of the effect of the encountered conditions only passes to the employer after the notice is given, and the risk remains with the contractor until it is able to comply with the requirements relating to notice.

25.5 Financial claims

25.5.1 Payment

If the parties have not agreed a price then the contractor will be entitled to a reasonable price for the work. Some contracts only provide for payment from the time the works or services are substantially complete. If they are not substantially complete there is no entitlement to any payment. Many building contracts are lump sum or entire contracts under which the contractor undertakes to complete the whole of the works for an agreed sum. However, even for these arrangements, the forms will provide a mechanism under which the contractor's entitlement is calculated in the event of non-completion. In general, standard forms of contract normally provide for two types of payment, namely periodic payments on account or interim payments and the payment of the final price.

25.5.1.1 Interim payment

There is no common-law right to interim payment unless the parties have agreed. Generally, a party is entitled to payment only when it has completed its part of the contract, fully in accordance with the contract.

In construction contracts this is seen as creating substantial cash flow problems for smaller contractors. The normal practice in the industry has been for contracts to specify interim payment mechanisms which depend in some way on a certification process. This therefore creates a contractual right to interim payments. It is not clear whether a term will be implied in a construction contract for interim payments in the absence of an express term but it is suggested that a term will not be implied. There is no authority on this issue but there is the dicta of Lord Diplock in *Gilbert-Ash (Northern) Limited v. Modern Engineering (Bristol) Limited* [1974] AC 689 which suggest to the contrary.

Section 109(1) of the Housing Grants, Construction and Regeneration Act 1996 gives a party to a relevant construction contract (as defined by the Act) a statutory right to interim payments by implying such a term in the absence of an express term. This is an entitlement to payment by instalments, stage payments or other periodic payments for any work under the contract. There is no such right under a construction contract for short duration contracts as defined in the Act.

25.5.1.2 Abatement

Employers do not normally wish to pay the full payment requested by the contractor if the work carried out is defective, or if the employer has claims against the contractor. To do so increases the employer's exposure to the consequences of the contractor's possible insolvency. Instead, the employer will wish to deduct the cost of remedial works and the value of the claims from the amount due to the contractor.

The employer has the right at common law to raise a defence of abatement against any action for payment in full by the contractor This right of abatement only applies to defects which are patent at the time payment is due. The amount by which the employer might rightfully reduce the amount due to the contractor is limited to the cost which the contractor would have incurred in remedying any defect. Where the defects are the responsibility of the contractor and it does not carry out the remedial work within a reasonable time, then the employer is entitled to abate the amount otherwise due to the contractor, by the amount it would cost the employer to remedy the defect. This additional liability arises from the contractor's further breach of contract in not remedying the defect.

During the defects liability period, defects may be discovered. Once the contractor has remedied those defects which have appeared during the defects liability period, the A/E under many standard forms is required to issue a final certificate. Some standard forms provide that such a certificate is conclusive of certain matters and particularly that there are no other patent defects and therefore prevents operation of the right to abate the price.

25.5.1.3 Set-off

If the paying party has claims against the other party, in addition to or instead of claims of abatement, it will normally wish to make a deduction from the sums otherwise due for payment.

The deduction is known as set-off. For a deduction to amount to a valid set-off against the claim for payment, both the claim and set-off must arise out of and be inseparably connected with a single transaction. Where the parties have entered into two different contracts it is exceptional for one party to be allowed to use a claim arising under one contract as a set-off in response to a claim made against it on the other contract.

If the contract does not expressly state the right of set-off then the right to set-off is only for matters so closely connected to the demand for payment that it would be manifestly unjust to allow the enforcement of payment without taking set-off into account. There is a right of set-off unless expressly restricted or withdrawn by the terms of contract. Many standard form of subcontract include provisions which limited the main contractor's rights of set-off, by means of notice requirements. If these provisions are not complied with then there may be no right of set-off and it may then be easier to obtain summary judgement for the amounts due. Otherwise in practice it is difficult to obtain summary judgement for payment of amounts due when there is a claim of set-off.

Section 111(1) of the Housing Grants, Construction and Regeneration Act 1996 makes the giving of notice a condition precedent to a right to withhold payment beyond the final date for payment for construction contracts under the Act. Such rights may include the right of set-off and the right of abatement of price. Such a notice must specify the amount proposed to be withheld and the grounds for withholding payment, or if there is more than one ground, each ground and the amount attributable to it.

25.5.1.4 Retention

Many standard forms provide for the employer to retain a percentage of payments due until the contractor has completed the work. This percentage varies but is usually not more than 5% nor less than 3% of the sums due for payment prior to completion. Unless there are specific provisions in the contract which give the contractor a legally identifiable interest in retention money, then in the event of insolvency by the employer, the contractor joins the queue of unsecured creditors. The contractor should therefore seek terms in the contract that the retention is given the status of a trust fund. It is the duty of the trustee to keep the trust funds separate and, provided this is done, the fund cannot form part of the employer's assets in the event of insolvency. In that case, the contractor is entitled to an injunction ordering the employer to place the retention fund in a separate account. If the contractor acts too late to preserve the retention fund before the employer becomes insolvent, then it will be unable to recover the funds ahead of an insolvency hearing.

25.5.1.5 Discount

Many standard forms of subcontract allow for discount, typically of 22%. This can represent the difference between profit and loss for contractors, and so it is not surprising that disputes arise. Different terminology is used to describe discounts such as 'cash' or 'preferential' or 'trade' or simply 'discount'. The

key question in each case is whether the discount is entirely unconditional and therefore a reduction in the price or whether it is conditional, normally on prompt payment. In each case this will be a matter of interpretation of the contract. There is no presumption that the parties intend the discount to be dependent on prompt payment, and each contract is to be interpreted in the light of its own particular facts.

25.5.2 Certificates

Many standard forms of contract provide a certification system for payments. The amount stated in the certificate for payment by the employer depends on the A/E's assessment based on his or her personal opinion. The parties have agreed that the A/E will be the particular expert to carry out this function. The interim certificate states the amount due on account, but the actual determination of the contractor's entitlement is not made until the final certificate. Most standard forms make the issue of a certificate a condition precedent to the contractor's right to payment. Subject to express provisions, such interim payments are not usually binding on subsequent certificates, but allow the work to be revalued for each subsequent certificate as well as the final certificate.

Whether or not a certificate is condition precedent to the right to payment depends on the proper construction of the contract, read as a whole *Henry Boot Construction Ltd v. Alstom Combined Cycles Ltd* [2005] EWCA Civ 814 CA.

In *Brodie v. Corporation of Cardiff* [1919] AC 337 the House of Lords held effectively that it was a condition precedent to the right of payment for extra works that an order was given, or ought to have been given and the finding of the arbitrator took the place of the order that should have been given.

In *Prestige v. Brettell* [1938] 4 All ER 346 the Court of Appeal applied Brodie and Greer LJ explicitly acknowledged that certificates were a condition precedent to payment, but the arbitrator and the court had power to dispense with the condition where a certificate ought to have been issued.

In *Henry Boot Construction Ltd v. Alstom Combined Cycles Ltd* [2005] EWCA Civ 814 CA the contract incorporated ICE 6th Edition It was held that certificates were a condition precedent to Boot's entitlement to payment under Clause 60(2) and (4) and they were not merely evidence of the Engineer's opinion. The right to payment only arose when a certificate was issued, *or ought to have been issued*, and not earlier and not when the work was done (*although the doing of the work is itself a condition precedent to the right to a certificate*). From Clause 60(2) a sum was payable forthwith on the issue of an interim certificate.

The certificate had to be issued within 28 days of the delivery of the Contractor's statement which on the terms was at least 28 days after the end of the month to which the statement related or even later if the contractor took time to deliver the statement.

It was held that the absence of a certificate was not a bar to the right of payment since the decision of the Engineer in relation to the certification was not conclusive of the rights of the parties, unless they have clearly so provided.

If the Payment Certificate has not been issued due to wrongful interference by the Employer then the contractor may be entitled to payment even in the absence of the certificate *Panamena Europea Navigacon v. Frederick Leyland* [1974] HL.

The Employer may not interfere in the timing of the issue of any certificate, but is not in breach of contract if a particular certificate is not issued or is erroneous unless he is directly responsible for the failure. If and when it comes to the Employers notice that the Architect has failed to comply with his administrative obligations by, for example, failing to issue a certificate required by the contract, the Employer has an implied duty to instruct the Architect to perform that function in so far as it remains within the power of the Architect to perform it and the Employer is in breach the contract with the Contractor to the extent that he does not intervene to arrange for the correct or correcting step to be taken by the Architect. *B R Cantrell v. Wright & Fuller Ltd* [2003] EWHC 1545 TCC.

The Employer's duty to call the Architect to boot was part of the duty of cooperation since the contract was not commercially workable unless the certifier does what is required of him. *Penwith District Council v. VP Developments Ltd* [1999] EWHC 231.

The final certificate of payment certifies the total amount payable to the contractor under the contract. There is generally a special procedure set out in the general conditions which should be followed leading up to its issue. A contract may state that the final certificate of payment will be conclusive evidence that the works are in accordance with the contract, that the contractor has performed all its obligations under the contract, and of the value of the works. This means that neither the contractor nor the employer can allege that the work is incomplete or defective or that the true value of the work has not been reflected in the certificate once the certificate is issued. This would even apply to defects appearing after the issue of the certificate. The final certificate of payment will normally not be conclusive evidence if arbitration or other proceedings have been commenced, either before the issue of the certificate, or within a stipulated period of issue, in respect of the matters referred to arbitration. The final certificate of payment again will not normally be conclusive regarding any matter within it where that matter is affected by fraud or dishonesty.

In *Penwith District Council v. VP Developments Ltd* [1999] EWHC 231 (TCC), HH Judge Lloyd considered the final certificate provisions in the JCT 80 Form. He stated that the last act once the works are completed was the issue of the final certificate. It had a dual role, it ostensibly dealt only with the final accounting and arrive at the Adjusted Contract Sum and it is also deemed to express the Architect's satisfaction with the quality of the works and with apparent compliance with the contract. The intention was that with certain exceptions there should be finality on all matters and on all issues.

In *B R Cantrell v. Wright & Fuller Ltd* [2003] EWHC 1545 TCC, HH Judge Thornton again considered JCT 80. He held that when the Architect certified he was recording for the parties his professional, personal and objectively arrived at opinion that the fact situation recorded by the certificate was accurate at the time when the certificate was issued.

It is suggested that a Final Certificate must be assessed by examining the power of the certifier. The certificate is then only conclusive on matters which he has power to decide finally between the parties. This is unlikely to include latent defects, or the value of consequential loss. The certificate could, depending on its terms, be conclusive as to patent defects having been remedied, or the valuation of the Contract Sum being final or conclusive as to the certifier having been satisfied.

In *Colbart Ltd v. Kumar* [1992] the issue was the Final Certificate under Clause 4.7 of the JCT Intermediate Form. It was held to be conclusive not only on whether the quality of materials or the standard of workmanship was to the reasonable satisfaction of the Architect, but also on matters where the standard of the work was to the approval of the Architect.

In *Crown Estate Commissioners v. John Mowlem & Co Ltd* [1994] 70 BLR 1, CA the Final Certificate under Clause 30.9.1.1 of the JCT 1980 was considered. It was held that the certificate was conclusive not only on materials and workmanship expressly stated to be for the opinion of the Architect for approval of quality and standard, but also of all materials and workmanship where approval was inherently for the opinion of the Architect.

In *Matthew Hall Ortech Limited v. Tarmac Roadstone Limited* [1997] the main issue was whether the Final Certificate prevented claims for defects which were latent at the time of the issue of the certificate. The contract incorporated that IChemE Red Book 1981 revision.

It was also held that there was commercial justification for the Contract to provide a defined cut-off point for liability.

The Final Certificate therefore meant that the contractor had a complete defence to a claim for breach of contract.

In *B R Cantrell v. Wright & Fuller Ltd* [2003] EWHC 1545 TCC, HH Judge Thornton again considered JCT 80. He held that the Final Certificate need not be issued on the standard template produced by the JCT for a Final Certificate, but it had to make clear that it was a Final Certificate and the certifying process must have been undertaken in the manner required by the contract, to have taken into account all matters required of the certifier by the contract and must be the opinion of the certifier and not the opinion of some other person and in a form that shows that the opinion is that of the Architect.

In *B R Cantrell v. Wright & Fuller Ltd* [2003] EWHC 1545 TCC, HH Judge Thornton held that the time for issue of the Final Certificate and for payment of the certified sum under Clause 30.8 was mandatory. The mandatory timescales could be relaxed so long as the steps which were linked to the issue of the final or other certificate were still to be taken before it was issued late and the power to postpone the issue of the Final

Certificate was exercised reasonably and in accordance with any express or implied agreement of, or waiver by, the parties to relax the timetable for its issue.

Although the certifier has an implied power to issue certificates out of time, the power was limited by the requirement for the parties to be notified of the intended exercise and the parties should not be prejudiced by the exercise. The power must be used reasonably. The parties should be given advance notice of the intention to issue late and of the proposed contents of the certificate, the nature of which will depend on the circumstances.

To the extent that the adjudicator had decided a matter that was relevant to the final certificate, the architect was bound by the adjudicator's decision.

If new material had emerged since the date of the adjudicator's decision, the architect was entitled to take that into account in preparing the final certificate, or indeed any interim certificate, and to make any appropriate modification to the adjudicator's decision *Castle Inns (Sterling) Ltd v. Clark Contracts Ltd* [2005] CS OH178.

25.5.3 Variations

Work which needs to be carried out in order to fulfil existing obligations under the contract is not a variation to the contract. In a lump sum contract, works or materials which are necessary for completion of the contract do not constitute variations. This is so even if they are not described in the specification. If the contractor has contracted to achieve a particular result for a lump sum then, if it fails to do so, it will be liable in damages. This is so even if the contractor complies with the specification. If it uses additional material to achieve the result, the contractor cannot claim for that additional material. This is based on the contractor being obliged to achieve a particular result for a lump sum.

In the absence of express provisions in the contract, variation to the original contract requires the agreement of both parties. Without such a clause, the employer is under no obligation to pay for varied work carried out, unless it has previously consented. Conversely, without such a clause the contractor is not required to carry out work which constitutes a variation if ordered by the employer.

If there is a variation clause in the contract there will also normally be a variation payment clause. The practical question will therefore be whether the instructed work falls within the variation clause so that valuation is to follow the contract provisions or whether it falls outside the contract so that payment will have to be established by other principles. That is, whether the variation is within the contract scope of work.

If the additional or omitted work which has been ordered is of a character contemplated by the contract, it will fall within the conditions of the contract relating to the power to order variations. For instance, under the ICE 6th and 7th Edition the engineer has authority to order any variations to any part of the works that may in his or her opinion be necessary for the completion of the works and shall have power to order any variation that, for any other reason, shall in his or her opinion be desirable for the satisfactory completion and functioning of the works. The engineer's authority is therefore limited.

25.5.4 Omitted work

Many standard forms of contract include the omission of work in the definition of variations which can be ordered under the contract. Despite this, the employer does not have a right to omit work from the contract and give it to another party in the absence of express terms to that effect. This is a breach of contract *Carr v. Berriman Pty Ltd* (1953).

A contract for the execution of work confers on the contractor not only the duty to carry out the work but the corresponding right to be able to complete the work which it contracted to carry out. To take away or to vary the work is an intrusion into and an infringement of that right and is a breach of contract.

Reasonably clear words are needed in order to remove work from the contractor simply to have it done by somebody else, whether because the prospect of having it completed by the contractor will be more expensive for the employer than having it done by somebody else, although there can well be other reasons such as timing and confidence in the original contractor. The basic bargain struck between the employer and the contractor has to be honoured and an employer who finds that it has entered into what he might regard as a bad bargain is not allowed to escape from it by the use of the omissions clause so as to enable it then to try and get a better bargain by having the work done by somebody else at a lower cost once the contractor is out of the way. *Abbey Developments Limited v. PP Brickwork Limited* [2003] EWHC 1987 (TCC).

There was no power to issue omission instructions which would detract from or change the fundamental characteristic of the works. *Trustees of the Stratfield Saye Estate v. AHL Construction Limited* [2004] EWHC 3286 (TCC).

The main contractor has a right to do that work which is set out in the contract documents for him to do, and it cannot be taken away from him in order that it be done by a nominated subcontractor. Conversely, if work is set out to be done by a nominated subcontractor, the main contractor cannot be forced to do it instead; nor, for that matter, can he resist on it himself (this was an important part of the ratio decidendi in the case *T.A. Bickerton & Son Ltd v. North West Metropolitan Regional Hospital Board* (1969) concerning the architect's obligation to nominate a new subcontractor under the JCT Form 63 Edition where the original nominee could not complete).

25.5.5 Measurement and valuation

Many standard forms of contract use bills of quantities to measure the value of the works. The bills are also used as a schedule of rates in order to value varied work and the effect of varied work on other work.

This dual function of the bills of quantities can give rise to considerable difficulty in the administration of the contract.

The normal starting point is that the contractor is entitled to assume that the bill of quantities has been prepared in accordance with the specified method of measurement. Standard forms normally make provision for the A/E to value corrections where the bill does not accurately describe the work shown Edition (Clause 55(2) of ICE 6th Edition). The work itself is not a variation since all that has happened is that the works have not been fully or properly set out in the bill.

Two main methods for valuation of variations are found in standard forms – evaluations based on rates and evaluation based on loss. Where the first method applies, most such standard forms adopt the following approach:

(a) valuation on the basis of bill of quantity rates or schedules
(b) valuation on the basis of rates analogous to (a) above
(c) valuation on the basis of fair or reasonable prices – fair valuation
(d) valuation on the basis of dayworks.

Whether bill of quantity rates or rates analogous thereto are used as the basis of the valuation will depend largely on the timing of the variation order, the location of the work, the quantity of the work involved and the circumstances in which the work is executed. If it can be established that these factors preclude the valuation on the basis of bill rates, then the valuation will be based on fair or reasonable prices. A fair valuation generally means a valuation which does not give a contractor more than its actual costs reasonably and necessarily incurred plus similar allowances for overheads and profit. Fairness is an objective test which takes into account the position of both parties.

25.6 Delay and disruption – financial claims

25.6.1 Causation

25.6.1.1 Tests for causation

When a failure occurs of either part or all of the works, it may be difficult to identify precisely the cause of that failure. It may be caused by a number of separate events, or by the unique combination of two or more events. This creates significant problems in deciding the liability for the failure. There are several possible tests to establish causation in fact and in law. English law prefers a simple approach.

In *BHP Billiton Petroleum v. Dalmine SpA* [2003] the Court of Appeal considered the issue of causation in relation to failure of a pipeline and observed that although it was a matter of common sense it could still be a difficult concept.

The cause of the loss was pipe failure solely where non-compliant pipe was in place. This was clearly an overwhelmingly important fact. The issue was whether the welding procedure as distinct from non-compliant pipe would have caused the loss of a hypothetical pipeline, even if that had been constructed solely out of compliant pipes. Dalmine argued

that the onus of proving that but for the incorporation of non-compliant pipes the pipeline would not have failed in any event rested on BHP. This was the 'but for' test of causation.

The Court of Appeal rejected an approach that was unrealistically theoretical. The Court of Appeal held that the role of the 'but for' test was not to be exaggerated. The purpose of that test was to eliminate irrelevant causes.

The Court of Appeal restated the general rule that proof rests on 'him who affirms not him who denies'. If Dalmine wished to show that a hypothetical pipeline made up only of compliant pipe, given more time and the operation of the pipeline at the ultimate working pressure, would have failed in any event, then it had the burden of proving that on the balance of probabilities. For these purposes, a mere possibility of such a failure would not be enough. The burden of proving Dalmine's negative hypothetical case rested on Dalmine.

25.6.1.2 Global claims

The process of construction can be a complicated interaction of activities. Normally a party making a claim must show a connection between the event and each item of loss. If the overall loss has been caused by the interaction of a number of events, and it is impossible to trace the connection between each individual event and the individual loss, then a global claim is often made. The loss is attributed to the list of events, without a connection between each part of the loss and each event.

It is clear that a global claim for loss may be advanced in certain circumstances: *L. B. Merton v. Stanley Hugh Leach, Wharf Properties Ltd v. Eric Cumine Associates, John Holland Construction v. Kvaerner R. J. Brown* (1996) 82 BLR 83 and, recently, *John Doyle Construction Ltd v. Laing Management (Scotland) Ltd* (2002).

However advancing a claim for loss in global form is a risky approach.

■ A global claim will fail if a material part of the cause of the loss was an event for which the other party was not liable and if the evidence disclosed no rational basis for the award of any lesser sum.

■ If a lesser claim is to be made out, that must be done on the basis of evidence which was properly led within the scope of the existing case as represented.

25.6.2 Head office overheads

If a claim is made on the basis of loss for delay then one head of loss is head office overheads. This is a claim that there has been an under-recovery of overheads due to the reduced volume of work caused by the delay. It is necessary to prove that loss has occurred and establish the reduction in contribution as a matter of fact.

This normally involves showing that adequate profit and fixed overheads could have been recovered in the prevailing market conditions if it had not been for the use of resources in the period of delay. It is usually necessary to show that the contractor's resources were limited or stretched until released from the delayed construction to such an extent that the contractor was unable to take on work elsewhere. However, it must be shown that there has been a reduction in volume of work overall. Variations may be a cause of the delay and the contribution of this additional work needs to be taken into account in measuring the supposed loss. If there is no reduction in overall turnover, so that the cost of the fixed overheads continues to be met from other sources, there will be no loss attributable to the delay.

Evidence has to be presented to prove that the contractor lost the opportunity of employing the workforce on another contract and that this alternative work would have funded the overheads during the period of delay.

Subject to such proof, the difficulties of evaluation allow a formula method to be adopted to ascertain the measure of the loss. One formula which has judicial approval is the Emden formula which is the ratio of the total overhead cost and profit of the contractor's organization to the total turnover as shown by the contractor's accounts for a fair annual average, multiplied by the contract sum and the period of delay in weeks, divided by the contract period.

The formula is used to solve the difficulties of establishing the measure of loss and not to avoid valuation if this should have been possible. So, for instance, contractors are expected to record managerial time spent on particular projects so that they can show evidence of the extent to which their trading routine was disturbed by the delay.

The evaluation of the loss of contribution needs to take into account the measure of contribution to overhead through the final account and recognition of the contribution from the project resources which have actually been deployed on other sites.

25.6.3 Finance charges

Finance charges are a measure of loss either as a result of the contractor having to borrow capital to make payments to progress the works or locking up capital in plant, labour and materials capital which it would have invested elsewhere. The loss is the interest which the contractor has to pay on the borrowed capital or the loss of interest on the capital which it is not able to invest.

The rate of interest premium for borrowed capital will depend on the contractor's arrangement with the lender. The premium is added to the basic lending rate set by the lender which will vary over time. The rate of interest earned on the contractor's own capital will usually differ from the basic lending rate by a margin which will depend on the amount deposited and the contractor's arrangement with the lender. The rest period for compound interest will vary, but interest is usually earned daily and capitalised either monthly or quarterly.

In *Amec Process and Energy Ltd v. Stork Engineers & Contractors BV* [2002] it was held that a claim for financing charges or interest on the amount awarded may be put forward on three alternative bases.

(a) Compound interest may be claimed as a contractual claim for financing charges for variations pursuant to the valuation provisions of the contract.
(b) Compound interest may be claimed as damages for breach of contract.
(c) Interest may be claimed on the basis of the discretionary power of the court or the arbitrator.

25.6.3.1 Contractual claim

The principles which apply to a contractual claim for financing charges are stated in the twin decisions of the Court of Appeal in *Minter v.WHTSO* [1981] 13 BLR 1 and *Rees & Kirby v. Swansea City Council* [1986] 30 BLR 1 restated in *Amec Process and Energy Ltd v. Stork Engineers & Contractors BV* [2002] as follows.

(a) Recovery, even for compound interest, is not intrinsically irrecoverable as being usurious or contrary to public policy.
(b) Whether such costs are recoverable as a contractual entitlement under the contract, is a matter for the parties and the terms of their contract.
(c) The expression 'direct loss and expense' under standard JCT Forms confers an entitlement for ascertainable loss caused by financing the expenditure for such parts of the period between the loss and expense arising and payment that are not directly excluded from an entitlement to payment by the terms of the contract. If the financing costs were not directly incurred as a result of the instructions of other causes which give rise to an obligation on the employer to pay but were incurred, instead, as a result of some other cause, these costs would not be recoverable as direct loss and expense.
(d) Interest reasonably paid on capital required to finance variations or work disrupted by the lack of necessary instructions was recoverable under 'direct loss and expense'.
(e) The cost of financing the necessary work for periods before any entitlement to payment arose under the contract would not ordinarily be recoverable.
(f) Any necessary notification procedures imposed on the contractor would need to be followed.

In order to succeed in a claim for financing costs it was necessary to show that:

(a) the contractor incurred the financing charges in question
(b) the basis of the relevant contractual evaluation was authorised by the terms of the contract
(c) compound interest was recoverable
(d) the relevant period was one for which the contractor may recover interest under the terms of the contract.

In *Amec Process and Energy Ltd v. Stork Engineers & Contractors BV* [2002], Stork had an obligation to agree or stipulate the basis of payment during the work. The contract allowed Stork to specify the basis of evaluation when instructing a variation. If an estimate was called for and not agreed then the basis of remuneration was reimbursable cost. Amec were required to give Stork access to its accounts and records. Stork had a contractual obligation to operate and give effect to the evaluation provisions of the contract such that the appropriate sum for variations would be determined, invoiced and paid within the timescales envisaged, being within 1 month from the execution of the work for invoicing and a 60-day further period for payment. In consequence, Amec became immediately entitled, once the variation work in question had been carried out, to payment on a reimbursable cost basis. The provisions of the contract were wide enough to embrace interest paid to enable the work to be financed. The costs arose because Stork varied the contractual arrangements for evaluating, invoicing and paying for these variations. Stork unilaterally decided not to reach agreement during the work or to issue stipulations or pay the sums being claimed. On that basis the claim succeeded.

ICE 6th Edition and MF/1 Edition 3 includes finance charges in the definition of the term 'costs'. The Engineering Construction Contract Schedule of Cost Components allows a cost component of finance charges in the evaluation of actual cost.

25.6.3.2 Damages for breach of contract

It is usually not possible to recover interest as damages where the relevant breach of contract has been non-payment of a debt. Interest may be awarded as the measure of damages for breach of contract under the second limb of *Hadley v. Baxendale* where such damages would also be recoverable under the first limb, *Wadsworth v. Lydall* [1991] CA, La Pintada [1985] HL and *President of India v. Lips Maritime Corp* [1988] HL restated in *Amec Process and Energy Ltd v. Stork Engineers & Contractors BV* [2002].

25.6.3.3 Discretionary interest by tribunal

The court has discretion to award simple interest under the Law Reform Act.

An arbitrator has discretion to award interest, whether simple or compound, under Clause 49 of the Arbitration Act 1996.

It is suggested that an adjudicator does not have the discretion to award interest absent an express power.

25.6.4 Constructive acceleration claim

25.6.4.1 Uncertainty due to absence of extension of time

A 'constructive acceleration' claim is an attempt by the contractor to recover its expenditure incurred due to the uncertainty created by the A/E's failure to grant extensions of time. This has been accepted in US courts but in English law there is little authority. The situation is characterised by the A/E's mistaken belief that no extension of time is due and the employer pressing the contractor to complete by the fixed date for completion.

The problem faced by the contractor is that in the absence of an extension of time it may be faced with the possibility of liquidation

damages being levied against it. The contractor has a stark choice. It can continue to work as planned and (presumably) efficiently in the hope that it can prove that it is entitled to an extension of time and that this will be granted by the A/E. Alternatively, the contractor can accept that it is in default, at least temporarily, and take steps to mitigate the consequences of this temporary default by increasing resources and reorganising the work.

This choice was recognised in *Ascon Contracting Limited v. Alfred McAlpine Construction Isle of Man Limited* [1999]. It was held that there was no obligation on the subcontractor to mitigate the consequences of the contractor's breaches of contract, since that would deprive the subcontractor of the opportunity, knowing how much of the current delay had been allowed, of assessing whether it was necessary to consider incurring additional expense in accelerative measures in order to reduce its potential liability in damages for any disallowed balance, and if so to decide for itself how far it was in its own interests to incur that expense in the absence of instructions to do so as a variation.

The decision in Ascon suggests that the choice of whether or not to accelerate is at the discretion of the contractor, but there is no obligation to do so. It is implicit in the decision that the contractor has a discretion in relation to its own culpable delay, but for delays for which the contractor is entitled to an extension of time it will not recover costs unless instructed to accelerate. The decision leaves open the issue whether there is any failure in the administration of the contract and particularly the extension of time provisions which would ever allow the contractor to recover acceleration costs in consequence.

The judgement to be made by the contractor is whether the additional costs of acceleration consequent on disruption are less than the liquidated damages which may be levied against it if it continues its normal sequence of working. The measure of acceleration costs is not always obvious so the choice is difficult. In addition, the contractor has to judge the real risk of levy of liquidated damages since it may eventually be granted an extension of time.

If the contractor is successful in accelerating the works then it may find that it has no or a reduced entitlement to an extension of time. The contractor will have succeeded in avoiding the levy of liquidated damages, but may find that this was not a risk in any event, because it had an entitlement to an extension of time.

In *Motherwell Bridge Construction Limited v. Micafil Vakuumtecchnik* (2002) TCC 81 ConLR 44 the issue of acceleration was addressed in a long and complicated judgement by Judge Toulmin CMG QC.

Motherwell was a subcontractor to Micafil for the construction of an autoclave for the employer BICC under modified FIDIC Forms of contract. The autoclave was a large steel vessel used in the manufacture of high quality power cables. There were a large number of claims by Motherwell.

One of two claims was for acceleration costs for the work in the shop for working night shift from 19 June 1998 to 11 September 1998 in order to keep the work to schedule as a result of additional substantial work due changes in design by

Micafil. Motherwell had requested an extension of time in its facsimile dated 11 May 1998, indicating that it was possible, at Micafil's expense, to work additional hours to reduce the over-run. In a facsimile dated 18 June 1998 Motherwell stated that it was considerably increasing its labour force and working night shift in an effort to meet the changes to the workscope. Motherwell recorded that it would record the costs associated with the work and sought recompense for acceleration of the programme. At a meeting on 23 and 24 June 1998, Motherwell stated that if Micafil was not prepared to acknowledge that there was an expanded contract, either Motherwell had to be compensated for accelerating the contract or granted an extension of time. At this point Micafil offered an extension of time of 3–4 weeks. The meeting finished without resolution with an action for Motherwell to prepare a substantial case for additional costs for acceleration. In a facsimile dated 25 June 1998 Micafil complained that Motherwell had still not increased their personnel resources on site. On 7 July 1998, Motherwell set out its claims which included additional costs for acceleration, and stated that if this was not acceptable that they would require an extension of time.

Judge Toulmin held that the costs were incurred by Motherwell in an attempt to recover time lost in completing the work in circumstances where Motherwell were subject to significant penalties for delay if they failed to complete the work in time. The causes were the restrictions encountered on site and the very substantial increased scope of the work. He held that Motherwell was entitled to additional costs, the quantum of which had been agreed by the parties. Motherwell was held also to be entitled to recover sums which were paid to their employees for work carried out at premium rates in order to keep to the required timetable. It was held that it was entirely reasonable for Motherwell to require its employees to work in excess of the hours allowed in its tender on order to try to keep to the time schedule which had been imposed on them and in respect of which they had not been given relief by Micafil to reflect the increase in work or the difficulties of working on site. Motherwell was also entitled to payment for the consequences of excessive overtime, which it was agreed resulted in a 10% loss of productivity equivalent to a delay in progress equivalent to 10% of the 'as planned' task duration.

The decision in Motherwell is a recognition of a constructive acceleration claim. It appears to be an important fact that Micafil complained that resources had not been increased and that it was accepted that Motherwell would prepare its acceleration claim. It is by no means clear from the judgement that Micafil insisted that Motherwell should keep work up to schedule, but it appears to have been sufficient that no extension of time was granted. Unfortunately, there is little in the way of legal analysis and it is suggested that the decision is very much on its own facts.

25.6.4.2 Nature of the problem

The difficulty faced by the contractor is that many standard forms of contract envisage several stages in the determination of extensions of time by the A/E. Many standard forms provide for the interim assessment of extensions of time followed by final review at some later stage. There would therefore appear to be a contractual remedy available to the contractor for the failure of the A/E to award the extension of time at the interim stage. In addition, there are remedies available in adjudication, arbitration and litigation. These remedies are of little help to the contractor at the time when it needs to make the decision whether or not to accelerate.

The essence of the problem is the exact nature of the 'temporary default', when the contractor may appear to be in breach of contract pending the final determination of extension of time. If the situation has been brought about by the employer's breach of contract in not ensuring that the contract is administered properly, then this may allow the contractor to recover acceleration costs. There are significant difficulties in this approach. First, it is difficult to establish grounds for such a breach and, second, even if such grounds can be established, acceleration measures are not so clearly the natural consequence of such a failure.

25.6.4.3 Employer's breach of contract

There are a number of cases which deal with the failure of the A/E to certify payment and the issue of whether this is can be a breach of contract by the employer.

In carrying out his or her role as a certifier, the A/E must act fairly, reasonably and impartially as between the employer and contractor, in exercising discretion and forming opinions. In *Hickman v. Roberts* [1913] the contractor was entitled to payment in the absence of a certificate because the architect had allowed himself to be influenced by the employer. In *Minster Trust Ltd v. Traps Tractors Ltd* [1954], Devlin J. held that there was an implied term that the parties would not do anything to prevent the certifier acting independently. *John Mowlem & Co. plc v. Eagle Star Insurance Co. Ltd* confirms that such a term will be implied into a contract if it is necessary having regard to the express terms of the contract. The fact that the A/E is employed by the employer does not in principle prevent him or her acting fairly between the parties. In *Panamena*, below, the certifying surveyor was the President of the employer company. This relationship was known to the contractor when the contract was made.

In *Panamena Europea Navigation Compania Limitada v. Frederick Leyland & Co. Ltd* [1947] the surveyor was required to certify the amount due to be paid under the contract. The issue of the certificate was a condition precedent to payment. It was found that the employer had hindered the proper execution of the certificate. It was held that, if the employer was aware that the certifier was failing to carry out his function properly, he was under a contractual duty to stop him and tell him what were his functions. The employer had failed to do so and it was held that the contractor was entitled to payment in the absence of a certificate. The decision was based on breach of a contractual duty implied as a term of the contract, and based on the principle that no person can take advantage of the non-fulfilment of a condition, if he or she has personally hindered the performance of it.

In *Lubenham v. South Pembrokeshire District Council* (1986) 33 BLR 46 the contract was a JCT Form. In contrast to *Panamena*, in this case the employer had not tried to influence its architect but had simply followed his advice. In addition, there was one fundamental difference between the JCT Form and the contract in *Panamena*. The JCT Form had a very wide arbitration clause which permitted arbitration on interim certificates before practical completion. There was no arbitration clause at all in the *Panamena* contract. Because of the arbitration clause there was no need nor any scope for the implication of a term as in *Panamena*. If the contractor wished to challenge any interim certificate, there was a simple remedy which did not require the implication of a term. The contractor could request the appropriate adjustment in another certificate or, if this was refused, go to arbitration and have the certificate corrected. It followed therefore that the responsibility on the part of the employer was merely to pay the amount certified even though he clearly knew the amount to be wrong.

In *Reed v. Van der Vorm* 33 BLR 140 (1985) the distinction between final and interim certificates was seen to be important. The contract was cost-plus. There was no arbitration clause. The employer agreed to pay the amount certified on a monthly basis. The works were not revalued as a whole each time a certificate was issued so that they were not interim certificates in that sense. It was held that since there was a mechanism chosen for payment, it was not open to the courts to reopen payments made on other past certificates.

On the basis of the above case law, there is no contractual duty implied as a term of the contract that the employer should oversee or supervise the A/E's functions of certification of payment under the contract. If the contractor wishes to challenge any interim certificate, it can request the appropriate adjustment in another certificate or, if this is refused, go to arbitration or litigation and have the certificate corrected.

In addition to the above cases dealing with certificates of payment, there are also cases which deal with the A/E's failure to grant an extension of time and the affect that this has on the liquidated damages provisions. There is an important distinction between the above cases and claims for damages for constructive acceleration. In the former, the claim is simply for payment of the contract price and the central issue is the avoidance of the need for the A/E certificate. Alternatively, the claim uses the failure of the A/E to operate the extension of time provisions to resist the levy of liquidated damages. In contrast, in acceleration claims the damages are claimed in addition to the contract price.

In the Australian case of *Perini Corporation v. Commonwealth of Australia* (1969) 12 BLR 82, McFarlin J. agreed that *Panamena* was authority for the proposition that in the case of a wrongful, in the sense of an unauthorised, exercise of powers by the certifier with the knowledge of the employer, the contractor was entitled to disregard the provisions of the contract with respect to time and either sue for price or resist a claim for liquidated damages. McFarlin held further, however, that it did not follow, nor had it been decided that if the contractor has otherwise suffered damage it was not entitled to sue on an implied term.

It was held in *Perini* that there was an implied term ('a positive implied term') in the contract that the employer would ensure that the A/E did his or her duty as a certifier. In *Perini* the equivalent of the A/E repeatedly refused to give a decision on a contractor's applications for an extension of time. The contractor accelerated in order to avoid liquidated damages being imposed and to meet the contractual completion date. McFarlane J. found in favour of the contractor but indicated clearly that this type of claim could only be sustained on the basis of some proven breach by the employer; the breach in this case being the refusal or failure of the certifier to give any consideration at all to the contractor's applications. The contract in this case contained an arbitration clause, and the fact that the contractor could have sought the resolution of the matter at an early stage did not appear to be significant, the issue does not seem to have been raised.

It would therefore appear that where it can be shown that the A/E has unreasonably or unnecessarily delayed the grant of extensions of time, there is little difficulty in establishing that this is a breach of contract by the employer. In cases which deal with the failure to grant an extension of time and the affect that this has on the liquidated damages provisions, it appears to be accepted that the said failure by the A/E is a breach of contract by the employer. It is suggested that a distinction needs to be made between an express refusal or continued failure to deal promptly with an extension of time application on the part of the A/E, and an honestly held view or assessment that no extension of time is due. The issue, however, is when can the A/E be considered to have unreasonably or unnecessarily delayed the grant of an extension of time.

25.6.5 Evaluation of disruption

The employer's breach of contract, such as late supply of information and late possessions, may disrupt the contractor's method of working. This may show itself as a loss of productivity with loss of motivation of the workforce due to the inability to offer incentive bonuses and the inability of management to plan properly due to the uncertainties caused by the breach.

The very fact of disruption may itself prevent the record keeping required to accurately evaluate the loss caused by disruption. A claim based simply on global overspend is unlikely to be sufficient to evaluate loss. Once liability and causation has been established, the courts will not allow the difficulties of proving exact measure of loss to prevent a contractor being compensated. So, the steps to establishing a claim for disruption are as follows.

(a) A breach of contract needs to be proved.
(b) A loss needs to be proved.

(c) The loss complained of needs to be proved to have been caused by the breach of contract – cause and effect.

(d) If some loss is shown as having occurred then several methods are available to quantify the loss:

  (i) a global claim may be sufficient but this will be unusual

  (ii) the adoption of norms will normally be sufficient based either on industry specific norms, contractor-specific norms or site-specific norms

  (iii) assessments may be sufficient if reasonable.

If it is possible to compare the productivity of the workforce before the disruption occurred with the productivity during the disrupted period, then the courts are willing to accept this as the basis for quantifying the loss. This method requires clear labour records, so that the area which the labour resources are working on can be identified.

It may not be possible due to the nature of the disrupting matters and the complexity of the project to employ the comparison of norms approach. There may be difficulties in isolating the additional hours of labour and plant which result from each and every disrupting event. It may be appropriate then to base the measure of loss on the rate which the contractor would have charged if the disruptive conditions had been known in advance. The rate must be shown to be a reasonable estimate.

Where there are competing causes, apportionment is possible in cases of disruption according to the relative importance of the various causation events in producing the loss.

The contractor should be able to recover for part of his loss and expense, and the practical difficulties of carrying out the exercise should not prevent him from doing so *John Doyle Construction Ltd v. Laing Management Ltd* [2004].

25.7 Management of claims

The main purpose of a claim is to present sufficient information to another party, to persuade them that there is an entitlement to the remedy sought and, together with information and experience they already have to decide the measure of that entitlement. In construction, most claims will require legal argument to be presented, even if in some cases this is only a statement as to the clause of the contract. In addition, the claim will be a statement of relevant facts with an explanation of the technical consequences of the facts in terms of engineering, and/or time and/or cost. The extent of analysis and explanation and the level of proof will depend on the experience of the other party as well as the forum in which the claim is presented.

A claim does not necessarily create a dispute, but some consideration must be given to the possibility that the parties will not be able to agree. Many costs incurred in preparing claims and resolving any disputes can be avoided if a structured approach is taken. The first consideration is the forum in which resolution is to be achieved. The level of proof, and therefore the cost, rises in proportion to the unwillingness of the other party to settle the claim or dispute at the level expected. Management of a claim means quickly establishing realistic levels of expectation of both parties. Understanding the other side's position is the key to a structured approach to disputes. It is necessary to know the restraints on, and the attitude of, the other side. In all cases dialogue is vital.

If the preparation of the claim and resolution of any dispute is to be managed efficiently, then it is necessary to manage both the technical and legal investigation. These two aspects are interrelated, and the process is essentially iterative. Such an investigation benefits from the type of project management approach adopted on construction projects themselves, but the skills required are different. A flexible approach is required. Because of the diverse disciplines normally involved and the commitment of the participants to existing tasks, some form of strategy plan, however short, will be required.

In order to prepare such a plan it will first be necessary to carry out an initial analysis so that the strategy for the claim can be established. In some claims this may simply be a short meeting with the manager of the project. On larger or complicated claims it may involve 3 or 4 days of intensive meetings with the team members led by a legally qualified facilitator experienced in the management of claims.

The plan addresses the main problems which will jeopardise the success of the process, such as the availability of evidence, both in terms of witnesses and documents, and the effort required to analyse the facts. The plan should identify the members of the dispute team, including witnesses of fact, the experts and their disciplines and any legal experts required. The plan will normally include a programme identifying the key elements of the investigation, the input required from witnesses and any experts, and the cost of the preparation of the claim.

The plan, which in many claims will be in the form of a network programme, is the main tool for reporting progress and managing the resources required. Efficient claims management requires the benefit or value of further investigation in increasing the chances of success, to be weighed against the cost of that further investigation. This is a form of claim value engineering but, to be effective, it must be based on the following:

(a) the loss incurred

(b) the loss likely to have been incurred by the other party

(c) the direct cost profile of the likely forum of dispute resolution

(d) the indirect cost profile of the likely forum of dispute resolution

(e) the likely range of levels of award.

Decision tree models can be constructed to allow analysis by computer of the various possibilities. While the necessary technology is available, in complex claims such models do not easily allow decisions to be made without a considerable investment in the construction of the model.

25.7.1 Management of evidence

Efficient fact management requires all data to be easily traced so that at any stage the relevant fact supporting a statement can be retrieved. Various systems can be adopted depending on the extent of information.

A system commonly used is electronic data management. This involves creating electronic copies of documents usually indexed initially by document type, date and reference number. As the investigation progresses the index is expanded by subject references. Once the documents have been scanned and the initial indexing completed, CD-ROMs are created. Some proprietary systems include on the CD all the software necessary to run the database of electronic documents from the CD. This is a significant benefit when the investigation involves team members in different geographic locations, since they can access the full evidence on the CD without needing to access the originals. If the full benefit is to be obtained, the integrity of the system needs to be protected and appropriate procedures followed.

References

Referenced legislation, regulations and standards

Arbitration Act 1996
Housing Grants, Construction and Regeneration Act 1996
Law Reform Act
Supply of Goods and Services Act 1982

Referenced cases

AC Controls Ltd v. British Broadcasting Corporation [2002] EWHC 3132 (TCC)
Abbey Developments Limited v. PP Brickwork Limited [2003] EWHC 1987 (TCC)
Alexander v. Cambridge Credit Corporation [1987] 9 NSWLR [Australia]
Alfred McAlpine Capital Projects Limited v. Tilebox Limited [2005] EWHC 281 (TCC)
Alghussein
Amalgamated Building Contractors Ltd v. Waltham Holy Cross Urban District Council (1952)
Amec & Alfred McAlpine (Joint Venture) v. Cheshire County Council [1999] BLR 303
Amec Process and Energy Ltd v. Stork Engineers & Contractors BV [2002]
Ariston SRL v. Charly Records Limited [1990] Court of Appeal
Ascon Contracting Limited v. Alfred McAlpine Construction Isle of Man Limited [1999]
B R Cantrell v. Wright & Fuller Ltd [2003] EWHC 1545 TCC
Balfour Beatty Building Ltd v. Chestermount Properties Ltd (1993) 62 BLR 12
Banque Financière de la Cité v. Parc (Battersea) Ltd [1999] 1 AC 221
Banque Keyser SA v. Skandia [1991] QB
Bath and North East Somerset District Council v. Mowlem plc [2004] EWCA Civ 115

Bella Casa Ltd v. Vinestone [2005] EWHC 2807
Bernhard's Rugby Landscapes Ltd v. Stockley Park Consortium (No. 2) [1998]
BHP Billiton Petroleum Ltd v. Dalmine SpA [2003] EWCA Civ 170
Big Island Contracting (H.K.) Ltd v. Skink Ltd (1990) 52 BLR 110
Birse Construction Ltd v. Eastern Telegraph Company Ltd [2004] EWHC 2512 (TCC)
Bolton v. Mahadeva (1972)
Bramall & Ogden Ltd v. Sheffield City Council [1985] 29 BLR 73
British Steel Corporation v. Cleveland Bridge & Engineering Company [1981] 24 BLR 100
British Steel Corporation v. Cleveland Bridge & Engineering Co. Ltd (1983)
British Westinghouse v. Underground Electric Railway [1912]
Brodie v. Corporation of Cardiff [1919] AC 337
Bruno Zornow (Builders) Ltd v. Beechcroft Developments Ltd [1990] 51 BLR 16
Campbell Discount Co Ltd v. Bridge [1962] AC 600 HL
Carr v. Berriman Pty Ltd (1953)
Castle Inns (Sterling) Ltd v. Clark Contracts Ltd [2005] CS OH178
CCC Films (London) v. Impact Quadrant Films (1985); *Anglia Television v. Reed* (1972)
Charles Rickards Ltd v. Oppenheim [1950]
City Inn Ltd v. Shepherd Construction Ltd [2003] Inner House
Clarke & Sons v. ACT Construction [2002] EWCA Civ 972
Close Invoice Finance Limited v. Belmont Bleaching and Dying Company [2003]
Colbart Ltd v. Kumar [1992]
Costain Civil Engineering Ltd v. Zanen Dredging & Contracting Co [1997] 85 BLR 77
Countrywide Communications Ltd v. ICL Pathway Ltd [2000] CLC 324
Crown Estate Commissioners v. John Mowlem & Co Ltd [1994] 70 BLR 1, CA
Davy Offshore Ltd v. Emerald Field Contracting Ltd [1992] 55 BLR 1
Dimond v. Lovell [1999]
DSND Subsea Ltd v. Petroleum Geo-Srevices ASA and PGS Offshore Technology AS [2000]
Easat Antennas Ltd v. Racal Defence Electronics Ltd [2000] (ChD)
East Ham Corporation v. Bernard Sunley (1966)
Emson Eastern Ltd v. E.M.E. Developments Ltd (1991) 55 BLR 114
ERDC Group Limited v. Brunel University [2006] (TCC)
Exports Credits Guarantee Department v. Universal Oil Products Company [1983] 23 BLR 106 HL
Fernbrook Trading Co. Ltd v. Taggart (1979)
Galoo Limited v. Bright Grahame Murray [1995] 1 All Eng 16
Garmac Grain Co. v. Faire and Fairclough [1968]
Gilbert-Ash (Northern) Limited v. Modern Engineering (Bristol) Limited [1974] AC 689
Glenlion Construction Ltd v. Guinness Trust [1987] 39 BLR 89
Glidewell LJ and Quin v. Burch Brothers (Builders) Limited [1968] 2 All Eng 283
Great Eastern Hotel Company Ltd v. John Laing Construction Ltd [2005] EWHC 181 (TCC)
H Fairweather and Co Ltd v. London Borough of Wandsworth (1987) 39 BLR 106

H.W. Neville (Sunblest) Ltd v.William Press and Son Ltd (1981) 20 BLR 78

Hadley v. Baxendale (1854)

Henry Boot Construction Ltd v. Alstom Combined Cycles Ltd [2005] EWCA Civ 814 CA

Henry Boot Construction (UK) Ltd v. Malmaiston Hotel (Manchester) Ltd (1999) 70 ConLR 32

Heskell v. Continental Express Limited [1995] 1 All Eng 1033

Hickman v. Roberts [1913]

Hoenig v. Isaacs [1952] 2 All ER 176

Holland Hannon Cubitts (Northern) Ltd v. Welsh Health Technical Services Organisation (1981)

Inserco Ltd v. Honeywell Control Systems [1996]

J. and J. Fee Ltd v. The Express Lift Company Ltd [1993] 34 ConLR 147

J. Jarvis and Sons v. Westminster Corporation (1978) 7 BLR 64 HL

Jeancharm Limited v. Barnet Football Club Limited [2003] EWCA Civ 58

John Barker Construction Ltd v. London Portman Hotel Ltd [1996] 83 BLR 35

John Doyle Construction Ltd v. Laing Management (Scotland) Ltd (2002)

John Doyle Construction Ltd v. Laing Management Ltd [2004]

John Mowlem & Co. plc v. Eagle Star Insurance Co. Ltd

L. B. Merton v. Stanley Hugh Leach, Wharf Properties Ltd v. Eric Cumine Associates, John Holland Construction v. Kvaerner R. J. Brown (1996) 82 BLR 83

Laserbore Ltd v. Morrison Biggs Wall Ltd (1992)

Lester Williams v. Roffey Brothers & Nicholls (Contractors) Ltd [1989] 48 BLR 69

Lubenham v. South Pembrokeshire District Council (1986) 33 BLR 46

Matthew Hall Ortech Limited v. Tarmac Roadstone Limited [1997]

McLaren Murdoch & Hamilton Ltd v. The Abercromby Motor Group Ltd [2002] Court of Session Outer House

Mertens v. Home Freeholds Co (1921) CA

Midland Land Reclamation Ltd v. Warren Energy Ltd [1997]

Minster Trust Ltd v. Traps Tractors Ltd [1954]

Minter v.WHTSO [1981] 13 BLR 1

Monk Building and Civil Engineering Ltd v. Norwich Union Life Assurance Society (CA) (1993)

Motherwell Bridge Construction Limited v. Micafil Vakuumtecchnik [2002] TCC 81 ConLR 44

Mowlem plc v. PHI Group Limited [2004]

Mowlem plc v. Stena Line Ports Limited [2004] EWHC 2206 (TCC)

North Sea Ventilation Limited v. Consafe Engineering (UK) Limited [2004]

Panamena Europea Navigacion v. Frederick Leyland Ltd [1947] HL

Pantland Hick v. Raymond & Reid [1893]

Parkinson and Co v. Commissioners of Works [1949] 2 KB 632

Peak Construction (Liverpool) Ltd v. McKinney Foundations Ltd [1976] 1 BLR 114

Penwith District Council v. VP Developments Ltd [1999] EWHC 231 (TCC)

Percy Bilton Ltd v. Greater London Council [1982] 20 BLR 1

Perini Corporation v. Commonwealth of Australia [1969] 2. N.S.W.L.R. 530 [Australia]

Perini Corporation v. Commonwealth of Australia (1969) 12 BLR 82 [Australian case]

Philips Hong Kong Ltd v. The Attorney General of Hong Kong [1993] 61 BLR 41

President of India v. Lips Maritime Corp [1988] HL

Prestige v. Brettell [1938] 4 All ER 346

Rapid Building Group Ltd v. Ealing Family Housing Association [1985] 29 BLR 5

Reed v. Van der Vorm 33 BLR 140 (1985)

Rees & Kirby v. Swansea City Council [1986] 30 BLR 1

Robertson Group (Construction) Limited v. Amey-Miller (Edingburgh) Joint Venture) [2005] CSIH89

Robophone Facilities Ltd v. Blank (1966) 3 All ER 128 CA

Roxley Electronics and Construction Ltd v. Forsyth (1996)

S & W Process Engineering Ltd v. Cauldron Foods Ltd [2005] EWHC 153 (TCC)

Sanjay Lachhani v. Destination Canada (UK) Ltd (1997)

Shawton Engineering Ltd v. DGP International Limited [2005] EWCA Civ 1359

Serck Controls Ltd v. Drake & Scull Engineering Ltd [2000] (TCC)

Stephen Donald Architects Limited v. Christopher King [2003] EWHC 1867 (TCC)

Sumpter v. Hedges (1898)

T.A. Bickerton & Son Ltd v. North West Metropolitan Regional Hospital Board (1969)

Taylor v. Brown [1839]

Temloc v. Errill Properties Ltd [1987] 39 BLR 30 (CA)

Tennant Radiant Heat Ltd v. Warrington Development Corporation (1988) 1 EGLR 41

Terrell v. Mabie Todd and Co. [1952]

The Royal Brompton Hospital NHS Trust v. Watkins Gray International (Dec 2000)

The Soholt [1983]

Thorne v. London Corp (1876) 1 Ap. Cas. 120

Trimis v. Mina (2000) 2TCLR 346 [Court of Appeal of New South Wales]

Trustees of the Stratfield Saye Estate v. AHL Construction Limited [2004] EWHC 3286 (TCC)

Turiff Construction Ltd v. Regalia Knitting Mills Ltd (1971)

Victoria Laundry (Windsor) Ltd. v. Newman Industries Ltd (1949)

Voscroft (Contractors) Ltd v. Seeboard plc (1996) 78 BLR 132

W Lamb Ltd v. J Jarvis & Sons plc (1998) ORB

Wadsworth v. Lydall [1991] CA, La Pintada [1985] HL

Wells v. Army and Navy Co-operative Society Ltd [1902]

White and Carter (Councils) Ltd v. McGregor [1962]

William Cory & Son Ltd v. Wingate Investment (London Colney) Ltd (1980) 17 BLR 104 CA

Useful websites

Institution of Civil Engineers; www.ice.org.uk

International Federation of Consulting Engineers (FIDIC); www.fidic.org

Joint Contracts Tribunal; www.jctltd.co.uk

NEC contracts; www.neccontract.com

Chapter 26

Litigation for the construction industry

Raymond Joyce Freeth Cartwright LLP, Birmingham, UK

The chapter is intended for those who need some knowledge of the litigation process in the courts of England and Wales and is not a substitute for specialist advice on any particular dispute. The chapter identifies the essential characteristics of litigation which set it apart from other forms of dispute resolution procedures. The courts and court system are described and the encouragement of the judicial system to explore and narrow the issues in dispute before commencing litigation proceedings is emphasised. All the steps from commencing litigation through to trial are set out with reference to the Civil Procedure Rules. Costs are discussed with reference to funding and award of costs.

doi: 10.1680/mocl.40878.0451

CONTENTS

26.1 Introduction

The procedural rules for civil litigation implemented the recommendations of Lord Woolf in his report, *Access to Justice* in July 1996 (Department for Constitutional Affairs, 1996) by means of the Civil Procedure Rules 1998 (CPR).

The CPR made pre-action conduct and protocols an important preliminary step, prior to the issue of proceedings in Court, obliging litigants to explore their respective positions giving rise to a dispute. By this means much litigation is now concluded, before the dispute is set out in a Claim Form.

A further important and influential preliminary concept set out in the CPR is the overriding objective which enables the Court to deal with cases justly (CPR 1.1).

Pre-action protocols and the overriding objective have revolutionised the day to day management of cases and has affected the culture and philosophy of litigation practice both before and after the commencement of proceedings.

Litigation practitioners spend much of their time trying to negotiate settlements before proceedings are commenced. Indeed, many litigation practitioners can spend most of their time concentrating on the pre-action issues and advising clients on the intricacies of funding cases and managing the risk of adverse costs orders. Knowledge of the CPR is essential for litigation practitioners and this chapter is not in any way to be construed as a substitute for having a detailed knowledge of the CPR and procedural law, but is intended to be an informative overview to assist construction professionals when they become involved in the litigation process. Moreover, understanding the boundaries between the bodies of law for other

means of resolving disputes is vital to ensure that a dispute is resolved without wasting costs and causing unnecessary delays.

26.2 Litigation infrastructure

Litigation is a dispute resolution procedure which involves the Crown as a third party, in the person of a judge, who is called upon to decide the merits of a case under the law. The state provides the infrastructure for resolving disputes including the judges, clerical support and the Court rooms. The administration of the civil justice system is the responsibility of Her Majesty's Courts Service which is an executive agency of the Ministry of Justice, one of the civil service departments.

The Courts within civil justice system include the County Court, High Court and the Court of Appeal. The Supreme Court, established by the Senior Courts Act 1981 in October 2009, replaced the House of Lords as the highest appeal Court in England and Wales.

Both the County Court and High Court are bound by precedents of the Court of Appeal and decisions of the Supreme Court bind the Court of Appeal.

26.3 Pre-action conduct and protocols

Lord Woolf recommended that parties to a dispute should embark upon meaningful negotiations as soon as the possibility of litigation was identified. The purpose of the CPR section

C on pre-action conduct and protocols is to promote the early settlement of disputes and avoid litigation altogether, if at all possible. The purposes of protocols are as follows:

i.   to focus the attention of litigants on the desirability of resolving disputes without litigation;
ii. to enable litigants to obtain information they reasonably need in order to reach an appropriate settlement;
iii. to make an appropriate offer (of a kind which can have cost consequences if litigation ensues); and
iv. if the pre-action settlement is not achievable, to lay the ground for expeditious conduct of proceedings.

Complying with the protocols is intended to benefit the parties and allow the Courts to deal with complex, difficult and intractable cases, as opposed to minor disputes.

The amount of work that the parties have to undertake to comply with the spirit and direction of the protocols can be substantial. This has led to the 'front loading' of costs in dealing with disputes. Importantly, although the claimant is encouraged to prepare and understand the case in detail before issuing proceedings, the costs that a claimant has incurred are not generally recoverable. The loss of entitlement to reimbursement of all its costs by the party which receives a settlement is supposedly set off by the saving made in avoiding the later costs and early receipt of settlement monies.

Inevitably, it is extremely unusual to have all the evidence at the very early stages of a dispute. However, this should not prevent a claimant (and defendant) from seeking to understand its case by analysing the strengths and weaknesses before the proceedings are commenced. The approach to assessing the strengths and weaknesses of a case should highlight the respective risks of handing the dispute over to the Court.

The Court will often consider the conduct of the parties before proceedings and any unreasonable behaviour or lack of co-operation by a party may be penalised by adverse costs orders. For example, when a claimant refused to adjudicate a building claim, refused to co-operate with the defendant's expert surveyor and failed to comply with the construction pre-action protocol, he was ordered to pay the defendant's costs on the indemnity basis (*Paul Thomas Construction Limited v. Hyland and Power 2002 18 CONST.L.J.345, 8 March 2000*). Indemnity basis means the costs are assessed as between the client and his own solicitor as opposed to on a standard basis where the costs awarded are typically ¼ to 1/3 below the costs actually incurred by a client.

The culture that is now encouraged is one of full disclosure of the key facts and supporting evidence at the outset.

The CPR encourages the parties to consider other alternatives to litigation for resolving a dispute. These might include a trade arbitration scheme, making a formal complaint to an industry membership organisation or ombudsman, applying dispute resolution procedures that had been agreed in the contract and whether an alternative dispute resolution mechanism might be appropriate. (For further detail on alternatives to litigation see the chapters *Arbitration*; *Adjudication*; *Alternative dispute resolution*.)

Making an offer to settle during the pre-action phase should be considered by the claimant as well as the defendant. Pre-action offers should be made in accordance with CPR 36.10. 'Part 36 offers', as they are known, can be used to tactical advantage by applying pressure to the other party knowing that it would have to pay the entire costs of an action, including the offeror's costs if the offer is rejected and later turns out to be more generous than the amount awarded at trial.

26.4 Pre-action protocol for construction and engineering disputes

The pre-action protocol for construction and engineering disputes can be found at CPR C5A – 001. The pre-action protocol applies to all professional negligence disputes and comprises a procedure which entails the claimant preparing a letter of claim to which the defendant has to prepare a response. The defendant should respond with the basis of his defence and any counterclaim, if appropriate. The exchange of correspondence effectively foreshadows the formal statements of each case which will be needed if the matter cannot be settled.

The pre-action protocol requires that there is a pre-action meeting between the parties. The purpose of this meeting is to focus on the issue at hand and ensure that the objectives of the Court are met to achieve the overriding objective, especially with regard to the proportionality of costs and Court resources prior to litigation.

The only situation in which the parties will be excused from complying with the pre-action protocol is where the claimant's claim may be time barred under any provision of the Limitation Act 1990. In such circumstances, a claimant who commences proceedings to avoid being out of time, must apply to the Court for directions as to the timetable and the form of procedure to be used, at the same time as he requests the Court to issue proceedings.

26.5 Commencement of proceedings

To commence proceedings, a Claim Form should be issued in either the County Court or the High Court. The Claimant has to make a decision in which Court to bring a claim. There are three main issues to consider, these are:

i.   the cause of action;
ii. the nature if the case; and
iii. the value of the dispute.

26.5.1 Cause of action

Many cases are suitable to be heard either in the County Court or in the High Court. Some specialist cases can only commence in the High Court such as applications for judicial review. Typical litigation in the construction industry, involving breach of contract and negligence claims, can commence in either the High Court or the County Court. However, the High Court is divided into specialist Courts and the Technology and Construction Court (TCC), which is a division of Queen's Bench, is staffed by judges who are familiar with the issues that affect the construction industry and the specialised documentation.

Examples of the types of claim which it may be appropriate to bring within the TCC are set out in CPR 2C-16.

26.5.2 Nature of the case
The factors to be considered in assessing the nature of a case include

i. financial value and the amount in dispute;
ii. the complexity of the facts, legal issues, remedies or procedures; and
iii. the importance of the outcome to the public in general.

26.5.3 Value of the dispute
The County Court has unlimited financial jurisdiction such that, subject to other factors, a claim of any value can start in the County Court. By contrast, the High Court has minimum financial thresholds:

i. personal injury claims with a value of £50 000 or more; and
ii. other claims with a value of more than £15 000.

The value of an action for a sum of money is the amount that the claimant reasonably expects to recover excluding any interest, costs and any reduction for contributory negligence or other sums as specified in CPR 16.3(6), which sets out in detail what to take into account when placing a value on a claim.

26.6 Claim form and statements of case
The Claim Form is a standard Court form which identifies the parties, the cause of action and a brief description of the facts, value, remedy sought and the case number when issued by the Court.

Most, if not all, construction claims will involve drafting Particulars of Claim. This is the first statement of case and sets out in detail the facts relied on to establish the claim, cause of action and the desired remedy or remedies.

The Defendant is obliged to prepare a statement of case in defence, unless the claim is admitted. The Defendant also has the opportunity of drafting a counterclaim which will mean that the Claimant has to prepare a further statement of case in defence to the counterclaim.

The exchange of statements of case is a succinct means to facilitate each party's understanding of the other's position.

There are many detailed rules about the service of the Claim Form and the subsequent statements of case especially with regard to time limits. To avoid prejudicing its' case a party has to ensure that it complies with all the time limits. If a defence is not served within the prescribed time limit, the other party has the opportunity to make an application to obtain judgement in default. This is a tactic that can apply pressure to the party in default but the Court will set aside a default judgement if the Defendant can show that he has a real prospect of successfully defending the claim, or there is another good reason why judgement should be set aside or the Defendant should be allowed to defend the claim.

At the end of all statements of case, it is a requirement that they are verified by a statement of truth. Signing is confirmation of the truth of the statement of case and the person signing may be liable for contempt if the Court finds that the signatory did not have an honest belief in the truth of the contents.

If a statement of case discloses no reasonable grounds for bringing or defending a claim, or it amounts to an abuse of the Court's process, or a rule or Court Order has not been complied with, it is open to one of the parties to make an application to the Court to have the statement of case struck out. Where a claim is entirely struck out, the case comes to an end.

One of the advantages of litigation is the ability of a party to bring other parties into the litigation. A Claimant can make a claim against more than one Defendant. The Defendant, as already identified, can make a counterclaim but may also want to make claims for contributions, indemnities or other remedies from other parties. Part 20 of the CPR deals with such claims and generically they are referred to as 'Part 20 claims'.

26.6.1 Case management
Judicial case management lies at the heart of the litigation process. The Court has a duty to actively management cases to further the overriding objective.

An important part of case management is the allocation of cases to tracks. There are three tracks referred to as the 'small claims track', 'fast track' and 'multi-track'. The tracks are designed to allow for the management of the case that is appropriate to its importance and complexity.

Once the defence has been filed, the case will be allocated to a particular track, usually after the parties have completed an Allocation Questionnaire. The basic distinctions between the tracks are as follows:

- The small claims track is generally for claims of less than £5 000.
- The fast track is generally for claims of less than £15 000 or for larger sums if the claims are relatively straightforward.
- The multi-track is usually reserved for claims of more than £15 000 or more complex cases.

There are different provisions regarding costs and timetabling for each of the tracks. For the majority of construction cases it would be unusual for such cases not to fall within the multi-track.

After allocation to the multi-track, the Court may decide to hold a case management conference. It is during the case management conference that the judge will ascertain from the parties what Directions are necessary to progress the case within a reasonable timetable.

The case management conference should ideally not be confrontational. It is usually in the interest of the parties to agree to most of the Directions beforehand. The Order for Directions will often provide a timetable for the steps in an action which are required up to the trial or to an earlier stage. If the case is very involved and complicated it would be unusual for the Court to establish a date for trial at this stage. However, matters concerning the drafting and serving of witness statements, disclosure, inspection of documents and matters concerning expert evidence are usually timetabled as part of the Order.

26.6.2 Is summary judgement appropriate?

One advantage of litigation is the opportunity to seek a summary judgement. Summary judgement is where a party can apply for an early judgement which, if successful, brings to a conclusion either issues of liability and/or quantum at an early stage. To be successful, a party has to show that the other has no real prospect of succeeding, subject to there being no other compelling reason why a trial should be held.

Applications for summary judgement are not inexpensive and should only be made if the party genuinely believes that the other either has no claim or has no defence as appropriate.

26.7 Evidence

Evidence is material put before the Court to enable the judge to decide the truth or probability of the matters alleged. The rules on evidence are complex but necessary to ensure that the parties are not treated unjustly and to enable the litigants and the Court to decide what evidence can be used and how.

26.7.1 Purpose of evidence

Any fact alleged in a party's statement of case needs to be proven, either on interim applications or at trial.

Some issues do not need to be proved by evidence. These include matters that are so well established that the Court does not require evidence of the, for example Christmas Day is always on 25 December. The judge is said to take 'judicial notice' of such matters.

There is a procedure for the parties to admit facts or allegations for the purpose of efficient litigation, which saves costs since they are no longer required to be proved.

In civil cases, the party which asserts a matter must prove its claim on the balance of probabilities. A judge will decide in favour of a party where the evidence is considered to be more probable than not on the facts.

It is for the claimant to prove the facts. The defendant whose defence is limited to denial of the claimant's case does not raise any new facts and therefore does not impose any burden of proof on the defendants.

26.7.2 Types of evidence

The Court will admit various types of evidence which includes:

i. oral testimony – this is evidence given by witnesses of fact or by an expert in Court
ii. written statements – these are often referred to as witness statements and in the case of experts, they are expert reports
iii. 'documents' – see section below on disclosure
iv. 'real evidence' – such evidence might include, for example, defective products with failed components that is materials from which the Court can draw conclusions or inferences by using its own senses. In the case of site visits by a judge to understand the physical characteristics of a site, this would be intangible evidence

26.8 Disclosure and inspection

Disclosure is the process of informing the other party, or parties, that a document exists or has existed. The disclosed documents are then available for inspection which takes place when the other party or parties inspects that documents in its original form or is given a copy of a disclosed document.

Deciding which documents to disclose will be part of a procedure known as standard disclosure unless the Court orders otherwise.

Standard disclosure is defined in CPR Part 31.6 as follows:

Standard disclosure requires a party to disclose only –

a. the documents on which it relies; and
b. the documents which:
    i. adversely affect his own case;
    ii. adversely affect another party's case; or
    iii. support another party's case; and
c. the documents which he is required to disclose by a relevant practice direction.

The identification and disclosure of documents is where costs can become disproportionate to a claim. It is important therefore that the documents identified for disclosure are relevant to the facts and allegations essential to a claim or defence.

Only those documents that are or were in a party's control need to be disclosed. This duty is set out as follows:

CPR 31.8(1) A party's duty to disclose documents is limited to documents which are or have been in his control
2) For this purpose, a party has or has had a document in his control if -
    a. it is or was in his physical possession;
    b. he has or has had a right to possession to it;
    c. he has or has had a right to inspect or to take copies of it.

Documents include the obvious paper-based records but now include in this digital age, video tape, computer hard disks, mobile phone memory, and so on.

26.8.1 The duty to search for documents

A litigant has a duty to make a reasonable search for documents that are relevant (CPR31.6(b) or (c)). The question is to what extent must the search be made. The factors to be considered are set out in CPR31.7(2) as follows:

The factors relevant in deciding the reasonableness of a search include the following:

a. the number of documents involved;
b. the nature and complexity of the proceedings;
c. the ease and expense of retrieval of any particular document; and
d. the significance of any documents which is likely to be located during the search.

Mindful of the overriding objective, the extent of the search must be proportionate to the value and importance of the claim and the complexity of the issues.

The disclosed documents are prepared in a list which will indicate the extent of the search made by the disclosing party. The duty of disclosure is a continuing duty and if relevant documents are found after the initial disclosure and throughout the course of the proceedings, these must still be disclosed as part of a continuing obligation of disclosure. Certain documents do not need to be disclosed and these include documents that are covered by legal professional privilege and without prejudice communications.

If there has been a failure to make a full disclosure the other party may apply for an order of the court compelling specific disclosure. Non-compliance with such an order will probably have a sanction which could involve having the statement of case struck out.

26.9 Costs

The subject of costs has become an increasingly significant issue between solicitors and their clients and consequently has become a much litigated topic in its own right since the introduction of conditional fee agreements and alternative means of funding.

A successful litigant will seek to recover their solicitor's costs from the losing party, but the amount awarded will be at the discretion of the court. Increasingly, it is becoming more difficult for solicitors to advise their clients as to cost consequences because costs are awarded at the discretion of the court, and the court uses its discretion to penalise unreasonable litigants.

There has been a general disquiet among the judiciary at the number of litigation cases that are solely about the allocation of costs and there has been considerable criticism that costs continue to be disproportionate to the value of a claim.

It is current practice for the courts, and in particular the TCC, to take an active role in limiting costs as a case progresses. Parties are required to submit final costs estimates to the court at various stages of the proceedings. It is not uncommon in large scale multi-party cases for Courts to impose a costs cap.

A review of costs has been undertaken by Lord Justice Jackson (Judiciary of England, 2010) in which he proposes a coherent package of interlocking reforms, designed to control costs and promote access to justice.

In respect of the TCC, the report recommends that the power of the Court disallows costs in respect of pleadings or witness statements which contain extensive, irrelevant or peripheral material and should be highlighted in the TCC guide.

Jackson also recommends that, at the pre-trial review, the focus should be on key issues rather than all issues in the case for the purposes of planning the trial. Jackson recommends that appropriate TCC cases can be allocated to the fast track. This would enable District Judges of appropriate experience to manage and try fast track TCC cases.

It is ironic that the severe cut back in the availability of legal aid which has seen the growth of 'no win no fee' agreements, has been a major contributor to disproportionate costs in civil litigation generally. The two key drivers that increase costs under such agreements are the lawyer's success fee and the after-the-event (ATE) insurance premium. Both the success fee and the ATE insurance premium are presently recoverable from the unsuccessful party.

In recent years, the no-win no-fee agreements, which are underwritten by insurance companies, have been used in commercial and construction disputes. If Jackson's recommendations are adopted, it will mean that the success fees and ATE insurance premiums will cease to be recoverable from unsuccessful parties in civil litigation.

Before-the-event (BTE) legal expenses insurance is available for legal expenses taken out before an event which gives rise to the litigation. Such insurance is commonly available with household policies but the market for small and medium enterprises has not been exploited to the same extent as ATE insurance.

If Lord Justice Jackson's proposals are implemented with the prospect that TCC cases are allocated to the fast track, there will be pressure for fees to be fixed with a financial limit on recoverable costs.

A key question for litigation practitioners from clients is always the cost of the case which, in turn, depends largely on its outcome. Both the judiciary and Parliament want to widen access to justice and this will be promoted under a regime recommended by Jackson where costs are not allowed to become disproportionate to the value of the litigation in dispute.

26.10 Enforcement

Most parties who have a court judgement against them do comply with the terms of that judgement. However, there are occasions when a party refuses to comply with a judgement or Order of the Court. There are a number of methods which are available to enforce a judgement CPR 70 contains the general rules about enforcement of judgements and orders.

The range of procedures involve further costs and applications to the Court.

An advantage of litigation is that the full range of the Court's powers can be invoked without delay. Enforcing the award of an arbitrator or an adjudicator will either involve the commencement of proceedings with a Claim Form or resorting to insolvency proceedings which will lead to bankruptcy of individuals or the winding up of limited companies or limited liability partnerships.

26.11 Appeals

The right to appeal is fundamental to the justice system, although it should be noted that appeals from expert determinations are usually prohibited because the determinations do not involve questions of law. The right to appeal in arbitration is very limited. Even within the Court system there are rules and procedures which limit the situations in which a party can challenge a decision of the Courts. A balance has to be struck between the need for incorrect decisions to be challenged as against the requirement of finality.

CPR 52 deals with the appeals in civil cases. A party will require permission to appeal against the decision of the Court. By this means, unmeritorious appeals are filtered out and avoid wasted costs.

The request for permission to appeal is either made immediately following the hearing in which the decision was made, or made alternatively, to the appeal Court, by way of an appeal notice, should the party be refused permission to appeal at the original hearing. Without permission a party cannot appeal.

CPR 52.3(6) provides:

(6) Permission to appeal will only be given where –
    (a) the Court considers that the appeal would have a real prospect of success; or
    (b) there is some other compelling reason why the appeal should be heard.

26.12 Pre-trial: checklists and review

On both the fast track and multi-track the Court will issue pre-trial checklists. The pre-trial checklists provide the Court with final information from the parties at least 8 weeks before the trial date. The Court can then give any further directions necessary and set a date for trial.

The pre-trial checklist deals with the following:

i. whether existing directions have been complied with and whether any further directions are required by the parties

ii. use and availability of experts for trial
iii. availability of lay witnesses for trial
iv. availability of legal representatives for trial
v. estimate length of trial

It is usual for the parties to agree to the content of their pre-trial checklist prior to filing at Court. Much of the information will have updated what was provided to the Court in the allocation questionnaire. At this stage, the parties must also file an estimate of their respective costs.

On the fast track, the Court will make the following directions after having received all relevant information:

i. necessary directions about evidence, including the use of expert evidence at trial
ii. a trial date or period, time estimate and timetable
iii. guidance for the preparation of the trial bundle
iv. any other direction relevant to the specific case.

On the multi-track the Court may make similar directions as above for the fast track. However, the Court will also consider whether this should be considered at a separate pre-trial review.

In complex multi-track cases where the trial is likely to involve a large number of witnesses and complex issues of law and fact, the Court may set a hearing for a pre-trial review of the case. This would normally take place within a matter of weeks before trial. Again, the Court will use this as an opportunity to give any final directions and set the trial timetable. The Court may make directions as follows:

i. necessary directions about evidence, including the use of expert evidence at trial
ii. a trial date, period of time estimate and timetable
iii. guidance for the preparation of the trial bundle
iv. any other direction relevant to the specific case.

The immediate preparations before a trial will have been determined by the pre-trial review or direction of the Court considering the responses to the Listing Questionnaire for trials of a few days in length.

It is the claimant's responsibility to file a trial bundle at Court which should include a copy of the following documents:

i. the Claim Form and all statements of case
ii. a case summary or chronology (if appropriate)
iii. requests for further information and responses to the requests
iv. all witness statements to be relied on as evidence
v. summaries of witness evidence
vi. any notice of intention to rely on hearsay evidence
vii. any notice of intention to rely on evidence such as plans, photographs, etc. which are not contained in witness statements, affidavits or expert reports
viii. any expert's reports and responses
ix. any order giving directions as to the conduct of the trial
x. any other necessary documents

The originals should be available at the trial and the trial bundle should be paginated continuously throughout as well as indexed.

It is usual for the contents of the trial bundle to be agreed between the parties. Mindful of the volume of documents that can be involved in the trial of a construction dispute, the parties may agree to have the trial bundle held as an electronic record which can be viewed during the trial by the Court and the parties online within a local network.

26.13 The trial

The general format for a trial is as follows:

i.   opening submission by the claimant's representative (if required)
ii. cross examination and re-examination of the claimant's witnesses
iii. cross examination and re-examination of the defendant's witnesses
iv. the closing submission by the defendant's representative
v.   closing submission by the claimant's representative
vi. judgement
vii. summary assessment of costs (where appropriate)

Note that the need for examination in chief of witnesses is now unusual because the written witness statements are intended to stand as the witness's evidence in chief.

A witness of fact may or may not attend Court voluntarily. This should not always be interpreted as hostile to the party relying on the witness because employers are reluctant to release witnesses for the purposes of giving evidence. Where a witness is unable or unwilling to attend Court voluntarily, a witness summons can be issued compelling his attendance at the trial, should his evidence be vital to the case.

The Court will often restrict the time during which a witness is examined or cross-examined.

After hearing all the evidence and the closing submissions, the judge has to make a decision. Judgements in the Courts are always given with reasons that support the overall decision. In small cases, the judgement will usually be given at the end of the trial. In more substantive cases where the judge has to consider the evidence that may have taken many days if not weeks to be presented, the judge may reserve judgement to be handed down at a later date.

A judgement or order takes effect from the date when it is given or made.

Interest on judgements usually run from the date that the judgement is given unless otherwise directed by the Court. The Court has the power to order interest to run from a date prior to the date of the judgement.

The parties have 14 days within which to comply with the judgement unless a different date is stated, or the Court has stayed the judgement.

26.14 IT and the Courts

The legal profession has embraced new developments in technology which is slowly turning a paper intensive profession into one where a paperless office is becoming a real possibility. By contrast, the Courts remain unable to deal consistently with the electronic submission of cases or the payment of fees by electronic means.

The rolling out of new technology in the Courts has been hampered by the scale of the task in question and inadequate infrastructure.

In an effort to push forward modernisation, the Ministry of Justice embarked on cutting the total number of IT suppliers to the Courts from six existing suppliers to just two. In 2007, the Ministry of Justice embarked upon £500 m of software and infrastructure improvements within the Courts across England and Wales. The idea was to create an all encompassing electronic working environment throughout the Court system.

This continuing investment can be expected to improve the Court's technological and case management systems. However, although the Ministry of Justice has stated that its objective is to begin modernisation of the Courts, there needs to be the acknowledgement that the sheer scale of the transformation required means only small incremental changes can take place.

With the recent economic crisis and substantial public sector debt, it remains to be seen whether the investment for such transformation continues to be made available for modernisation of the Courts.

References

Department for Constitutional Affairs (1996) *Access to Justice – Final Report* [online]. Available at: www.dca.giv.uk/civil/final/index.htm [Accessed: 15 April 2010]
Judiciary of England (2010) *Review of Civil Litigation Costs: Final Report* [online]. Available at: www.judiciary.gov.uk/about-judiciary/cost-review/jan2010/final-report-140110.pdf [Accessed: 15 April 2010]

Referenced legislation, standards and regulations
Limitation Act 1980

Referenced cases
Paul Thomas Construction Limited v. Hyland and Power 2002 18 CONST.L.J.345, 8 March 2000

Further reading
Waller et al. (2009) *Civil Procedure: Volumes 1 and 2*. Sweet & Maxwell, London.

Websites
Civil Procedure Rules; www.justice.gov.uk/civil/procrules_fin/
Her Majesty's Court Service; www.hmcourts-service.gov.uk/
Technology and Construction Court (TCC); www.hmcourts-service.gov.uk/infoabout/tcc/index.htm

Chapter 27

Arbitration

Sir Vivian Ramsey Judge in charge of the Technology and Construction Court, London, UK
Julian Critchlow Fenwick Elliott LLP, London, UK

doi: 10.1680/mocl.40878.0459

Despite the advent of adjudication, arbitration retains a pivotal role in the resolution of construction disputes. Not only does it remain for many contracting parties the preferred methodology (over litigation) for a final answer where one or other party is dissatisfied with an adjudicator's decision, but it is increasingly recognised as an appropriate first resort to decide those claims that the court itself has observed may be too complex to form the subject of an effective adjudication even as a first level process. Furthermore, its importance for the deciding of international construction disputes, where the parties are likely to require an independent tribunal and jurisdiction, remains unabated.

This chapter provides an overview of the entire arbitral process from commencement of a reference to challenging an award. It covers pre-arbitral proceedings, appointment of an arbitrator, preparing the case, the powers of the arbitrator, and enforcement. It does not neglect the international aspect.

CONTENTS

27.1 Introduction

Arbitration provides an alternative to the use of the court system as a method of resolving disputes. It depends on the consent of the parties. Therefore, before disputes can be referred to arbitration the parties to a dispute must make an agreement that it is to be resolved by arbitration. That agreement is usually contained in a clause of the contract between the relevant parties, for instance, the contractor and the employer or the employer and the engineer or between other participants in the construction process, for example, contractor and subcontractor. It is also possible, however, for the parties to agree that a dispute will be resolved by arbitration only when the dispute has actually arisen.

Arbitration has been referred to as litigation in the private sector. The arbitrator, like a judge, has to find the facts, apply the law and grant relief to one or both of the parties. The proceedings are usually less formal than court procedure but the arbitrator often follows a parallel procedure to that which applies in court. The arbitrator hears evidence, considers the arguments and evidence and then provides a written award which contains his or her decision on the matters to be determined.

27.1.1 The Arbitration Act 1996

Although arbitration arises out of the agreement of the parties, any arbitration based in England and Wales or in Northern Ireland is now subject to the provisions of the Arbitration Act 1996 (the 1996 Act). Scotland has a separate system. The 1996 Act provides a statutory framework for arbitration. It contains some mandatory provisions, some provisions which only apply if the parties have not agreed otherwise and some provisions which apply unless the parties expressly exclude them.

It contains provisions dealing with most aspects of procedure and practice in relation to the arbitration, together with provisions which regulate the relationship between the courts and the arbitration.

Prior to the 1996 Act, there was the Arbitration Act 1950 which still applies to arbitrations commenced prior to 31 January 1997. There are many changes in the 1996 Act and care should be taken in referring to any case decided under the provisions of the 1950 Act.

27.1.2 Arbitration procedure and rules

As the parties are free to agree many aspects of arbitral procedure, various institutions have introduced rules to be applied to arbitrations. Examples are the ICE Arbitration Procedure (2006), the Construction Industry Model Arbitration Rules (CIMAR), the Joint Contracts Tribunal (JCT) Arbitration Rules and, in the international context, the UNCITRAL Arbitration Rules, the International Chamber of Commerce (ICC) Rules and the London Court of International Arbitration (LCIA) Rules.

27.1.3 Advantages and disadvantages of arbitration

Why do parties choose arbitration in preference to court procedure? Very often the choice is made by the adoption of a standard form of contract which contains an arbitration clause, such as Clause 66 of the ICE 7th Edition.

Traditionally, the advantages of arbitration have been said to be speed, cost and privacy. In practical terms there is often very little difference in the time taken to resolve a dispute by arbitration compared to the courts, especially in the light of the Civil Procedure Rules for court proceedings. Equally, the arbitrator and the arbitration venue have to be paid for by the parties, while the judge and courts are made available out of public funds. This means that the overall costs of arbitration and court proceedings are, generally, not significantly different (Civil Procedure Rules). The advantage of privacy still remains. Many commercial organisations would prefer to have disputes resolved in private. The proceedings are protected, to a large extent, by confidentiality under English law: see *Hassneh Insurance v. Mew* [1993] 2 Lloyd's Rep. 243. The parties also see advantages in the fact that the arbitrator can be a construction professional or a lawyer with construction expertise. This may help to inspire confidence and assist in the resolution of issues related to construction practice.

The disadvantages of arbitration are that, unlike the court systems, the arbitrator may not be experienced in dealing with complex questions of law and procedure. In addition, there is an extent to which the arbitration procedure is dependent on the court, although this is much reduced under the 1996 Act. This is sometimes given as a reason for adopting the court system in the first place.

27.1.4 Domestic and international arbitration

Since construction disputes very often have an international element, either in the project being located abroad or one or both parties being foreign, many disputes are not domestic but have an international dimension. In such cases the Arbitration Act 1996 may not apply and questions arise as to the arbitration procedure, the arbitration venue and the law to be applied.

27.2 Commencing an arbitration

When a dispute arises between two parties to a contract containing an arbitration clause, the initial question is the method by which the arbitration is commenced.

27.2.1 The dispute

Before any arbitral process can commence it is necessary for there to be a dispute or difference. Under some arbitration rules there is a necessity to give a notice of dispute as a formal precursor to the commencement of arbitration.

In some cases there may be a doubt as to whether a dispute has arisen. While this may seem surprising, there are many cases in which, for instance, a contractor may have made a claim but there has been no formal response to or no rejection of the claim. In the ICE Arbitration Procedure Rule 2.1 provides, generally, that *'a dispute or difference is deemed to arise when a claim or assertion made by one party is rejected by the other party and that rejection is not accepted, or no response is received within a period of 28 days'*. That Rule still requires a rejection. In the absence of the rule, there is a dispute or difference when there is a claim and a rejection: see *Monmouthshire CC v. Costelloe & Kemple* (1965) 5 BLR 83.

27.2.2 Pre-arbitral procedures

Many arbitration clauses provide for a pre-arbitral process such as an engineer's decision or requirement for the dispute to be considered by a conciliator or mediator. In these cases, the wording of the clause needs to be scrutinised to see whether the process is a condition precedent to commencing arbitration or whether it provides an option, which may, if appropriate, be bypassed. In addition, many arbitration clauses in engineering standard forms of contract both make an engineer's decision a condition precedent to arbitration and also prescribe a limited time within which the arbitration must be commenced. If it is not commenced within that period, the decision of the engineer becomes final and binding. While there is an ability for the court to extend the time, the grounds under the 1996 Act are severely limited (Arbitration Act 1996, Section 12).

Before commencing an arbitration, it is necessary to confirm, therefore, that there is a dispute and that any mandatory pre-arbitral process has been complied with. The formalities for commencement of an arbitration depend first on the arbitration clause and any applicable arbitration rules. In the context of certain editions of the ICE Conditions of Contract and some subcontracts, the clause states that the arbitration 'may be' conducted in accordance with the ICE Arbitration Procedure. In addition, even where it says that it 'shall be' conducted in accordance with that Procedure, the version of the Procedure is, curiously, the version which applied at the date of the appointment of the arbitrator: see Clause 66(11)(a) of the ICE 7th Edition. This emphasises the need for care in considering whether rules do apply and, if so, which rules are the relevant ones.

In order to commence an arbitration under the ICE Arbitration Procedure it is necessary to give both a notice of dispute and a notice to refer.

27.2.3 Methods of commencing arbitration

If there is no express requirement within the arbitration clause or the applicable rules as to the method by which arbitration is to be commenced, then the provisions of Section 14 of the 1996 Act apply. That section requires a notice in writing and the contents of the notice depend on whether the arbitrator is named or designated in the arbitration agreement, is to be appointed by the parties or is to be appointed by a person other than one of the parties. While no particular form of notice is necessary, it is good practice to identify the dispute, identifying the relevant arbitration clause, set out the manner by which any pre-arbitral process has been complied with as well as dealing with the method by which the arbitrator is to be appointed. It is also advisable to date the notice and establish that the notice has been given by asking for acknowledgement or making delivering of the notice by a means which is recorded. While there is no objection to service by fax, it is generally preferable to ensure delivery of a hard copy.

27.2.4 Date of commencement of arbitration and the Limitation Acts

The date of the notice will, in the first place, be relevant to ensure that any time limits within the arbitration clause have been complied with. In addition, under Section 13 of the Arbitration Act 1996, the provision of the Limitation Acts apply to arbitral proceedings. This means that the arbitration must be commenced within a particular period (generally 6 years but with important exceptions) after the date on which a cause of action accrued. The provisions of Section 14 deal with the process by which arbitrations are commenced both for the purpose of any time limits provided in the arbitration clause and for the purpose of the Limitation Acts.

27.2.5 Method of appointment of arbitrator

The method of appointing the arbitrator depends on the terms of the arbitration clause and follows, in principle, one of the methods identified in Section 14 of the 1996 Act. Sometimes an individual is identified by name or is designated by an office. Often, however, domestic arbitration clauses require the parties to attempt to agree on a single arbitrator. There may be a default process in the absence of agreement, for example, nomination by the President of ICE under the ICE 7th Edition. In arbitration clauses in international contracts there is often the need to commence arbitration by filing a document with an organisation (for example, a request for arbitration with the ICC in Paris) and to name an arbitrator. Frequently, in such cases there are three arbitrators. However, in domestic arbitration there is, generally, a sole arbitrator. Section 15 of the 1996 Act states that there is a sole arbitrator, if the parties have not made an agreement as to the number of arbitrators. If there are any problems in appointing an arbitrator, Sections 15 to 21 of the 1996 Act contain detailed provisions including any necessary involvement by the court to resolve the difficulty.

27.2.6 Conflicts of interest and terms and conditions

Once an arbitrator has been agreed between the parties, or as part of the process of agreeing on the arbitrator, there are two matters to be considered. First, it must be confirmed that the arbitrator has no conflicts of interest. Second, the terms and conditions, including fees, must be agreed between the parties and the arbitrator, unless the method of appointment (for instance by the ICC or LCIA) deals with this aspect.

When the arbitrator has been agreed and the questions of conflicts of interest and of terms and conditions have been dealt with, the arbitrator normally makes a formal acceptance of the appointment. When the arbitrator has accepted the appointment, there are only limited grounds on which an arbitrator's appointment can be revoked or an arbitrator can be removed (see Sections 23 and 24 of the 1996 Act). Equally, there are limits on the arbitrator's ability to resign (Section 25).

27.2.7 Procedure after appointment

The arbitrator then, generally, fixes a preliminary meeting at which directions are given for the conduct of the arbitration.

Sometimes the directions can be agreed without the necessity of a meeting and under some rules, for instance, the ICC Rules, there may be a necessity for a formal signed terms of reference.

27.2.8 Representation in arbitration

While parties often choose to be represented by lawyers in arbitration proceedings, there is no requirement for that and anyone can represent a party to arbitral proceedings (see Section 36 of the Arbitration Act).

27.3 The arbitration process
27.3.1 General principles

The arbitrator will aim to lay down procedures suitable for the particular case, avoiding unnecessary delay or expense, so as to provide a fair means for resolving the dispute (Section 33(1)(b) of the 1996 Act). The arbitrator must act fairly, impartially and give each party the opportunity to put its case and deal with the opposing case (Section 33(1)(a)). The ability of the arbitrator to determine procedure is, however, subject to the parties' overriding entitlement to agree between themselves what the procedure should be. In a construction dispute involving significant sums, complex facts, and difficult legal issues, the appropriate procedure may not differ significantly from that of an equivalent case in the High Court. However, as in the High Court, the need to avoid unnecessary delay and expense requires the procedures to be proportionate to the importance of the case to the parties.

27.3.2 Defining the issues

At the first preliminary meeting the arbitrator will direct the manner in which the parties are to set out their cases and the time periods for doing so. The usual order is either for service of points of claim and defence or for statements of case and defence. Points of claim and defence set out the unadorned basis of the parties' cases, excluding matters of evidence and argument of legal points. Statements of case and defence, which seem to be becoming the preferred option, require the parties to set out their cases in greater detail, including the evidence and law relied on, and will generally be accompanied by copies of the most important documents that the parties wish the arbitrator to see. The claimant will usually be allowed to serve a reply to the defence. The arbitrator may also make provision for service of any counterclaim (provided that he or she has jurisdiction to do so within the terms of reference), defence to counterclaim and reply to defence to counterclaim.

If a party's case appears to be incomplete or ambiguous, the opposing party can request further information to enable it fully to understand the case it has to meet and, if the request is refused, the arbitrator may order the information to be produced.

27.3.3 Disclosure

The arbitral timetable will usually require the parties to list all those documents which are relevant to the dispute, that is which support or damage their own case or the case of the other party. Each party is then entitled to inspect the documents in the other party's list except where those documents are privileged. In broad terms, documents are regarded as privileged if they concern attempts between the parties to settle or have been generated in the course and for the purpose of conducting the dispute. Disclosure may not, however, be undertaken as an independent step in the process if the arbitrator has ordered the parties to serve the documents they wish to rely on with their statements of case. If a party considers that specific documents which are of relevance have been withheld, it can apply to the arbitrator for their disclosure.

27.4 Preparation of factual evidence

27.4.1 Documents

In construction disputes, especially those concerning delay or disruption, the parties' cases are likely to depend on a significant body of documentary evidence. Categories of document may include: pre-contract correspondence, documentation containing or evidencing the contract (articles, conditions, drawings, specification, method statement [if any], programme [possibly]), correspondence referable to the construction phase, site meeting minutes, site diaries, plant and labour returns, internal memoranda, board meeting minutes, and company accounts. Documentary evidence is usually fundamental to success in arbitration and participants in construction contracts are well advised to ensure that meticulous records are maintained from the invitation to tender stage through to completion and beyond – however amicable the parties' relationship might be at project commencement.

27.4.2 Witnesses

The timetable for directions will generally provide for the parties to exchange statements of evidence of witnesses as to fact after disclosure is complete (although some arbitrators favour the exchange of expert evidence before witness statements). Statements should be comprehensive as they may be ordered to stand as evidence-in-chief, that is be intended to deal with all the positive aspects of the case of the party on whose behalf the witnesses are called. Indeed, where there is not to be an oral hearing they will be the sole source of witness evidence (although it is rare in construction arbitrations for an oral hearing to be dispensed with where witness evidence is seriously in dispute). Preparation of witness statements is a less technical process than formerly, now that first hand hearsay (i.e. indirect) evidence is generally admissible (Civil Evidence Act 1995) and given that the arbitrator may, in any event, choose not to apply formal rules of evidence (Section 34(2)(f) of the 1996 Act).

27.4.3 Technical issues

The majority of construction arbitrations require the assistance of one or more technical experts who may give evidence as to liability, for example in respect of quality of workmanship or materials, or as to quantum. Traditionally, each party appoints its own experts and, having seen their statements and heard their cross-examination, the arbitrator decides which evidence he or she prefers. It is usual for the arbitrator to direct the opposing experts to meet before the hearing on a without prejudice basis (i.e. on terms that the deliberations are not discloseable to the arbitrator) to try to agree as many facts as possible and to narrow the differences in their opinions. Unless the parties agree otherwise, the arbitrator may appoint a technical assessor to provide assistance or may appoint an expert (possibly a legal adviser) to report both to the parties and to the arbitrator (Section 37 of the 1996 Act). The intention behind this provision is to avoid the duplication involved where each party appoints its own expert. However, use of the mechanism can sometimes cause problems. Thus, in practice, the parties may require their own experts to assist in evaluating their cases even before a reference is commenced, thereby reducing the cost advantages of a single expert. Furthermore, technical analysis can be stifled where an issue is susceptible to more than one technical viewpoint and the sole expert is not alive to all the possibilities.

27.4.4 Preparation for the hearing

In a reference of more than a moderate size, the arbitrator will generally order a pre-trial review to take place, usually some weeks (or even months) before the final hearing to ensure that all directions made up to that stage have been complied with and to finalise the details of pre-hearing preparation. Typical directions will include provision for the parties to prepare an agreed joint bundle of those documents they intend to rely on, sometimes together with a small core bundle of the documents they expect to refer to most frequently. The arbitrator will also require skeleton arguments to be submitted by the parties' representatives. The parties will need to ensure that all case reports and other references to legal authority are available for the use of the arbitrator at the hearing as they will not be readily to hand in the same way as in a courtroom. The arbitration room itself will also need to be reserved, usually at an agreed venue and with the claimant generally being responsible in the first instance for the cost of it (pending the final award on costs).

Each party's witnesses will need as much notice of the hearing as is realistic: if possible, the availability of the most important witnesses will be established before the date is fixed. Where a witness appears reluctantly it is prudent to apply to the court to obtain a witness summons requiring his or her attendance. Failure to attend when so summoned is a contempt of court.

Ensuring the availability of experts is also, of course, essential.

27.5 Presentation of the case to the arbitrator

27.5.1 Documents only or oral hearing

Depending on what has been ordered or agreed, the reference will proceed either on a documents only basis or with an oral hearing. Even in the latter case the arbitrator may, subject to any rules to which he or she is bound to the contrary, seek further clarification in writing or order a further meeting although, unlike an adjudicator under the Housing Grants, Construction and Regeneration Act 1996, the arbitrator may not communicate with one party privately to the exclusion of the other.

27.5.2 Oral hearings – the procedure

At an oral hearing the arbitrator is not generally constrained by any specific rules as to procedure other than the general obligations under the 1996 Act to act fairly and impartially and efficiently. It is, however, customary in the more complex sort of case to provide for the parties to commence with brief opening oral submissions followed by their leading of the substance of their cases, the claimant first and then respondent, and concluding with closing submissions. Frequently, the statements of witnesses and experts stand as evidence-in-chief and when they are called to give evidence it is usual, subject to any brief points of clarification, to move straight to their cross-examination. The arbitrator may direct that a party or witness is to be examined on oath or affirmation, which the arbitrator is empowered to administer (Section 38(5) of the 1996 Act).

Unless the parties agree otherwise, they may be represented both at the preliminary stages and at the hearing either by a lawyer or other person (Section 36 of the 1996 Act).

27.5.3 The involvement of the arbitrator

Traditionally, in the High Court, the judge allows the parties' representatives to present their cases largely uninterrupted, it being considered in the English tradition that 'an over-speaking judge is no well-tuned cymbal'. With the Civil Procedure Rules that tradition is changing and judges are encouraged to play a more interventionist role. Arbitrators, on the other hand, have historically tended to exercise greater direct control over the process, as an interventionist approach is necessary for the full advantages of procedural flexibility to be realised. It is noteworthy that, at least in theory, the entitlement of an arbitrator to intervene is now actually less than that of a judge because the judge can override even the joint views of the parties, whereas the arbitrator cannot (see Section 1(b) of the 1996 Act). In practice, however, the arbitrator is likely to have considerable discretion and, at the hearing, may exercise it by, for example, limiting the time made available to the advocates to present their cases or to cross-examine. An extreme example of such limitations occurs in the 'chess clock' sort of arbitration where each party is allotted a certain period to use as it considers appropriate. This has the advantage of keeping hearings to a minimum but can cause difficulties if one party is too prodigal of his time in the early stages and finds itself unable to lead or challenge important evidence towards the end. The validity of the award may be imperilled where an arbitrator refuses to extend a party's time in such circumstances.

27.6 The arbitrator's award

27.6.1 Effect of the award

The publication of the final award by the arbitrator brings his or her jurisdiction to an end. Except where the parties agree otherwise, the award will be final and binding, that is conclusive of the party's rights in respect of the dispute, subject to the limited rights to challenge referred to later.

27.6.2 Contents of the award

The parties may agree to the form of the award. Where (as is usual) they do not do so the award must (by Section 52 of the 1996 Act):

(a) be in writing and signed by the arbitrators or, where the decision is by a majority of a tribunal, by all those arbitrators who assent to it
(b) contain reasons
(c) state the seat of the arbitration, that is the place where the award was made or is deemed to have been made (e.g. England and Wales)
(d) state the date on which it was made.

The award must also deal with all the issues that were the subject matter of the dispute. Irrespective of the above, and again subject to the contrary agreement of the parties, the arbitrator may either on his or her own initiative or on the application of one of the parties, correct the award to rectify minor errors or ambiguities or to make an additional award to deal with an element of the dispute omitted from the main award (such as in respect of costs or interest). Subject to the arbitrator's entitlement to withhold the award until payment of the arbitrator's fees, he or she must give notice to the parties of the award by serving them copies.

27.6.3 Awards of interest

Except where the parties agree otherwise, the arbitrator may award either simple or compound interest at such rates as he or she considers just on the principal sum contained in the award. The arbitrator may also award interest on any amount paid by a party before the award was made, but only up to the date it was paid.

27.6.4 Awards of costs

Again subject to the parties' agreement, the award of costs is at the arbitrator's discretion. In exercising that discretion, costs must be awarded to the successful party unless there are unusual circumstances that would make it inappropriate to do so. The arbitrator must also set out the basis on which the decision has been reached (Section 63 of the 1996 Act) and specify each item of recoverable costs. The award should usually grant the receiving party a reasonable sum in respect of all costs reasonably incurred. Where there is doubt as to whether an item of costs is reasonable, the paying party should usually be given the benefit of the doubt. However, there can be an exception where the paying party has been guilty of improper conduct in the course of the proceedings, in which case the arbitrator can decide to give the receiving party the benefit of the doubt as to whether costs are reasonable. This effectively replicates the indemnity basis for costs in the equivalent High Court situation. It should be noted that what amounts to improper conduct for these purposes is a matter of some debate. It should also be noted that costs include the reasonable and appropriate fees of the arbitrator.

27.6.5 Enforcement of the award

The 1996 Act (Section 66) provides that the award may, subject to the leave of the court, be enforced in the same way as a court judgement or order. Application to the court is on affidavit attesting that the award was regularly arrived at. If the opposing party contends that the award is defective, it can object to leave being granted and the court will decide whether or not the award is formally correct – that is that there is no serious irregularity and that the arbitrator had jurisdiction to make it. Leave will not be granted for error of law – such error must be dealt with by appeal (see following text). Although not specified in the Act, proceedings can also be brought on the award as a breach of contract – it being an implied term of the parties' agreement to arbitrate that they will honour the final award.

If, once leave has been given to enforce the award, or a judgement has been given for failure to honour it, the defaulting party still fails to perform, all the usual enforcement processes of the court are available.

27.6.6 Challenges to the award

Awards may be challenged in the following ways.

(a) by application (pursuant to Section 67 of the 1996 Act) to set aside the award, or an application for a declaration that the award is of no effect, on the grounds that the arbitrator did not have jurisdiction to make it. This provision is most commonly invoked where there is a dispute as to whether there was ever a valid arbitration clause. The right to object may, however, be lost if a party has proceeded with the arbitration without lodging an objection at the time the issue could first have been raised

(b) by application to set the award aside for serious irregularity. Again, the right may be lost if not made timeously. Circumstances where such an application may succeed are where one of the following irregularities has caused or will cause substantial injustice to the applicant, namely (by Section 68 of the 1996 Act):

    (i)   failure by the arbitrator to comply with the general obligations of fairness and impartiality or failure to select appropriate proceedings

    (ii) the arbitrator exceeding his or her powers (otherwise than by exceeding the substantive jurisdiction)

   (iii) failure by the arbitrator to conduct the proceedings in accordance with any agreement to the parties

   (iv) failure by the arbitrator to deal with the issues put to him or her

    (v) an arbitral or other institution or person given authority by the parties in respect of the award exceeding its powers

   (vi) uncertainty or ambiguity as to the effect of the award

  (vii) the award's being procured by fraud or in a way contrary to public policy

 (viii) failure by the arbitrator to comply with the requirements as to the form of the award

  (ix) any irregularity in the conduct of the proceedings or in the award which the arbitrator (or an arbitral or other empowered person) admits.

Where serious irregularity is proved, the court can remit the award to the arbitrator for reconsideration, set the award aside, or declare it to be ineffective.

(c) by appeal on point of law (Section 69 of the 1996 Act). In order to seek leave, an applicant needs the agreement of the other party or the leave of the court, and the court will only grant such leave in restrictive circumstances. There are two tests for granting leave. Either the arbitrator's decision must be obviously wrong, or the point at issue must be of general public importance (e.g. because it relates to the interpretation of a standard form of contract) in which case the decision must be open to serious doubt. As such, the Act largely confirms the pre-1996 Act case law such as the *Nema* [1980] 2 Lloyd's Rep 83, 339, and the *Antaios* [1981] 2 Lloyd's Rep 284. Once leave to appeal has been granted, the court simply determines whether or not the award is legally correct – the applicant does not have to satisfy any higher legal test than does the respondent.

After hearing the appeal, the court may confirm the award, vary it, remit it to the arbitrator for reconsideration, or set it aside.

An application to set aside for lack of jurisdiction, serious irregularity, or by way of appeal, may not be brought more than 28 days after the date of the award. Since the arbitrator is entitled to withhold the award from the parties until the arbitrator's fees have been paid (by Section 56 of the 1996 Act) a party who believes it may need to appeal must consider paying the arbitrator's unpaid fees in full or, if it forms the view that the fees are excessive, apply to the court. In such circumstances, the court may order the award to be delivered on payment of the disputed fees into court, or arrange to determine what the fees should be. It should be noted that the 28-day time limit does not apply where a person has played no part whatsoever in the arbitral proceedings and then seeks a declaration or injunction challenging enforcement of the award on the basis that the arbitrator did not have jurisdiction.

27.7 Particular powers of arbitrators

It was observed earlier that the arbitrator has certain general obligations of fairness and impartiality, and to lay down appropriate procedures (by Section 33 of the 1996 Act).

To assist the arbitrator in fulfilling those obligations the Act gives certain express powers. Perhaps the most important power (which is also an obligation) is that contained in Section 34(1) which provides that the arbitrator is to decide the procedure (except to the extent that the parties reach agreement). Subsection 34(2) states that procedural and evidential matters include where to hold the proceedings, the language to be used (often important in international references), whether and what written statements of claim and defence are to be used, what documents should be disclosed by the parties, what questions should be put to the parties, whether to apply strict rules of evidence (or, more correctly, whether to apply rules of evidence strictly), the extent to which the arbitrator should take the initiative in finding out the facts and the law, and what written and oral evidence or submissions should be admitted. These provisions are intended to give the arbitrator an extremely broad discretion as to procedure so as to provide the flexibility required for laying down the most effective and efficient procedures for the particular dispute. In particular, except where the parties have agreed to limit this discretion, the arbitrator need no longer fear an application for his or her removal, or impeachment of award, on the grounds that he or she has adopted an inquisitorial methodology. Thus, he may ask his or her own questions and pursue a line of enquiry instead of merely assessing passively the evidence presented by the parties.

In addition, the arbitrator has certain other specific powers, again intended to promote the efficient running of the reference. Some of the most important are as follows, each of them being subject, however, to the ability of the parties by agreement between themselves to divest the arbitrator of these powers.

27.7.1 Jurisdiction (Section 30 of the 1996 Act)

The arbitrator may decide whether he or she has jurisdiction to determine whether there is a valid arbitration agreement, whether the tribunal is properly constituted, and what issues are properly included although, as seen earlier, this decision may be challengeable by one or other party.

27.7.2 Security for costs (Section 38(3) of the 1996 Act)

The arbitrator may require a claimant (or counterclaimant) to give security to the respondent for the costs which the arbitrator can show the claimant will incur in conducting the defence. This power is usually operated where a claimant's finances are so lacking in substance that it is probable that they will be insufficient to enable it to reimburse the respondent's costs if the defence succeeds.

27.7.3 Directions as to property (Section 38(4) of the 1996 Act)

The arbitrator has various powers in respect of property concerned in the proceedings including ordering its preservation, inspection, or sampling.

27.7.4 Provisional relief (Section 39 of the 1996 Act)

This power differs from the others mentioned here in that it has to be conferred on the arbitrator by agreement of the parties (which is unlikely after a dispute has arisen as its exercise is only of obvious benefit to claimants). However, where he or she has the power, the arbitrator may make a provisional order of anything which the arbitrator may finally order in the award, such as payment of money or disposition of property. The arbitrator may then confirm, vary, or reverse the provisional order in the award. It seems that provisional orders are intended to be made only where it is highly likely that the relief given will be confirmed at the hearing. The rationale is to ensure that a party with a good case is not kept out of its entitlement until the end of a long reference. This mitigates the absence of an entitlement to give a summary decision, that is to reach a final decision by use of a truncated procedure, for example on affidavit evidence alone, where the defence appears to be insubstantial.

27.7.5 Party default (Section 41 of the 1996 Act)

The arbitrator needs to be able to imbue the process with some discipline where one or the other party fails to comply with its obligations (which are expressed in Section 40(1) of the 1996 Act) to do everything required to enable the dispute to be dealt with efficiently and speedily. Accordingly, the arbitrator may dismiss a claim for a lengthy delay which prejudices the respondent or the possibility of a fair trial. Where a party fails to attend a hearing or make written submissions for a hearing the arbitrator may proceed to an award in their absence. Where a party defaults on any order, the arbitrator may make a peremptory order requiring compliance. If the default is continued, a range of options is available. If the failure is of a claimant to give security for costs, the arbitrator can dismiss the claim. In respect of other failures the arbitrator can prevent a party from relying on certain allegations or materials, draw adverse inferences, proceed to an award on the basis of such material as has already been submitted, or penalise the offending party in costs.

27.8 Particular problems
27.8.1 Relationship with the courts

In general terms, the policy of the Arbitration Act 1996 was to provide the arbitrator and the parties with more authority in the arbitration process and to reduce the extent to which the courts would be involved in that process.

The courts are now involved in a more limited way. The range of involvement is as follows:

- to stay legal proceedings where there is a relevant arbitration clause: Section 9
- to extend time for commencement of arbitration proceedings: Section 12
- to appoint arbitrators in default: Section 18
- to remove an arbitrator: Section 24
- to determine a preliminary point of jurisdiction: Section 32
- to enforce orders of the arbitrator: Section 42
- to order the attendance of witnesses or the production of documents by nonparties: Section 43
- to make orders, including granting injunctions in relation to or to aid an arbitration: Section 44
- to determine a preliminary point of law: Section 45
- to enforce an award: Section 66
- to consider a challenge to an award on the basis of substantive jurisdiction: Section 67
- to consider a challenge to an award on the ground of serious irregularity: Section 68
- to consider an appeal on a point of law: Section 69.

In each case, the ability of the court to be involved is very limited. However, subject to complying with the individual requirements in relation to each type of application, the court provides a function in both assisting the arbitral process and ensuring that serious miscarriages do not occur in arbitration.

27.8.2 Court proceedings commenced by a party to an arbitration clause

One particular aspect of the interrelationship between the courts and arbitration is the position where one party to an arbitration clause ignores that provision and commences proceedings in court.

In such circumstances, if the opposing party makes no objection, the court can proceed to consider the merits of the dispute as it would in any other case. At one time, it was thought that the powers of the court might be limited but that is not generally so. This was on the basis that arbitration clauses in standard engineering and building forms of contract often have an express provision that the arbitrator may open up, review and revise a certificate or decision of the engineer or architect. It was argued that the courts did not have that power and the Court of Appeal accepted that argument (*Northern Regional Health Authority v. Crouch* [1984] QB 644). That decision was later overturned and therefore the courts can now review the merits of any certificate or decision by the engineer or architect (*Beaufort Developments v. Gilbert Ash* [1998] 2 WLR 860).

However, if one party does commence proceedings in breach of the arbitration clause, it is open for the opposing party, provided that it does not take a step in the court proceedings to answer the substantive claim, to apply to the court to stay those proceedings to enable a dispute to be referred to arbitration. Under Section 9 of the Arbitration Act 1996 the court must stay the proceedings unless it is satisfied that the arbitration agreement is null and void, inoperative or incapable of being performed. This is markedly different from the 1950 Act under which the court had a discretion whether or not to stay the proceedings.

27.9 The international dimension

The provisions of the Arbitration Act 1996 generally only apply to arbitrations where the 'seat of the arbitration' is in England and Wales or Northern Ireland. Some provisions do apply to other international arbitrations, for instance, the seeking of attendance of witnesses: see Section 2.

27.9.1 Seat of arbitration

The seat (or place) of arbitration is defined as the judicial seat of the arbitration. It is generally determined by the parties. If there is no agreement then Section 3 of the Arbitration Act makes provision for it to be determined having regard to the parties' agreement and all relevant circumstances.

The relevance of the seat of the arbitration is that any mandatory procedural law applicable at that place will apply to the arbitration; a challenge might be made in the courts at that location and the award may be made or deemed to be made at that place. While the arbitration will frequently take place at the seat of the arbitration, by agreement between the parties, including the provisions of any agreed rules, hearings and deliberations of the tribunal may take place elsewhere. If that happens without such agreement, difficult questions may arise as to the effect of the arbitration taking place at a venue other than the seat of the arbitration.

27.9.2 The proper law

A different question arises as to the law to be applied to the merits of the disputes by an arbitrator or arbitrators, wherever the seat or place of arbitration may be. To determine the proper law, it is first necessary to see whether there has been agreement by the parties, then to see if the parties have designated a procedure by which the proper law is to be determined, for instance by the choice of particular rules. In the absence of any such procedure, the arbitrator will then have to consider whether there is any mandatory provision of the law at the seat of arbitration. If not, then the arbitrator will have to decide which rules of conflict to apply in deciding what is the proper law. Often the test will be the law with which the contract has the closest connection.

For an arbitration with its seat in England and Wales or Northern Ireland, Section 46(3) of the 1996 Act provides that if there is no choice or agreement on the substantive law, the tribunal shall apply the law determined by the conflict of laws rules which it considers applicable.

27.9.3 International arbitration rules

While in the domestic situation the court system and arbitration run in parallel, in the international context the choice may not, in reality, be available for a number of reasons. If, for example, an English contractor is carrying out work overseas, the overseas client may not be prepared to have any disputes resolved in the English courts and the English contractor may not be prepared to have these disputes dealt with in the courts of the country of the overseas client. It is in that context that international arbitration provides a necessary method of resolving disputes.

It is more common in that context for the parties to elect to have the arbitration made subject to the rules of an institution which administers the arbitration. The most common rules are those of the ICC in Paris or the LCIA in London. In addition, rules have been made, known as the UNCITRAL Rules, which can involve the administration of the arbitration.

The details of those rules are beyond the scope of this text but in general terms they provide an administration of the arbitration process. They do not act as a court in deciding any case. Rather they administer the appointment of the arbitral tribunal which then acts as any other arbitrator, but with the assistance of the relevant arbitral institution. The award given by the arbitral tribunal is then enforceable, as any other arbitration award made at the relevant seat of arbitration.

References

International Chamber of Commerce (1998; revised May 2010) *Rules of Arbitration*. ICC, Paris, France. www.iccwbo.org/uploadedFiles/Court/Arbitration/other/rules_arb_english.pdf

Institution of Civil Engineers (2006) *ICE Arbitration Procedure 2006*. Thomas Telford Limited, London, UK.

London Court of International Arbitration (1998) *LCIA Arbitration Rules*. LCIA, London, UK. www.lcia.org/Dispute_Resolution_Services/LCIA_Arbitration_Rules.aspx

Society of Construction Arbitrators (1998) *Construction Industry Model Arbitration Rules* (CIMAR). Society of Construction Arbitrators, UK. www.constructionarbitrators.org/cimar.htm

Society of Construction Arbitrators and Joint Contracts Tribunal (2005) *Construction Industry Model Arbitration Rules*. Sweet & Maxwell, London, UK. www.jctltd.co.uk/assets/JCT_CIMAR%2005.pdf

United Nations Commission on International Trade Law (1976) *UNCITRAL Arbitration Rules*. [online] www.uncitral.org/uncitral/en/uncitral_texts/arbitration/1976Arbitration_rules.html

Referenced legislation, regulations and standards

Arbitration Act 1950
Arbitration Act 1996
Civil Evidence Act 1995
Housing Grants, Construction and Regeneration Act 1996
Limitation Acts

Referenced cases

Antaios [1981] 2 Lloyd's Rep 284
Beaufort Developments v. Gilbert Ash [1998] 2 WLR 860
Hassneh Insurance v. Mew [1993] 2 Lloyd's Rep. 243
Monmouthshire CC v. Costelloe & Kemple (1965) 5 BLR 83
Nema [1980] 2 Lloyd's Rep 83, 339
Northern Regional Health Authority v. Crouch [1984] QB 644

Websites

Civil Procedure Rules; www.justice.gov.uk/civil/procrules_fin/
Society of Construction Arbitrators; www.constructionarbitrators.org
Institution of Civil Engineers (ICE); www.ice.org.uk
International Chamber of Commerce (ICC) – Arbitration; www.iccwbo.org/policy/arbitration/id2882/index.html
Joint Contracts Tribunal (JCT); www.jctltd.co.uk
London Court of International Arbitration (LCIA); www.lcia.org
United Nations Commission on International Trade Law (UNCITRAL); www.uncitral.org

Chapter 28

Adjudication

Adrian Hughes QC 39 Essex Street Chambers, London, UK
Ian Wright Crown Office Chambers, London, UK

This chapter provides an overview of the key features of adjudication as a means of dispute resolution for construction contracts in the UK, including the statutory requirements in the Housing Grants, Construction and Regeneration Act 1996 and in the Scheme for Construction Contracts.

doi: 10.1680/mocl.40878.0469

CONTENTS

28.1 Introduction

The objective of incorporating a mandatory right to adjudication in construction contracts in the Housing Grants, Construction and Regeneration Act 1996 (HGCRA 1996) was to provide a quick, low-cost and impartial means of resolving disputes during the course of a project with a particular view to protecting the cash flow of contractors (*Absolute Rentals Ltd v. Glencor Enterprises Ltd* (2001) CILL 17 Const LJ 322).

In an early case, HHJ Wilcox described the statutory process as follows:

> The purpose of the Scheme [Scheme for Construction Contracts] is to provide a speedy mechanism for settling disputes in construction contracts on a provisional interim basis and by requiring decisions of adjudicators to be enforced pending final determination of disputes by arbitration, litigation or agreement whether those decisions are wrong in point of law or fact, if within the terms of reference. It is a robust summary procedure and there may be casualties.
>
> Absolute Rentals Ltd v. Glencor Enterprises Ltd (2001) CILL 17 Const LJ 322

The first '*casualty*' to reach the Court of Appeal was *Bouygues (UK) Limited v. Dahl-Jensen* [2000] BLR 522 which showed just how '*robust*' the process could be. The Court enforced a decision which contained a plain and accepted error. By mistake, the adjudicator provided for early release of the 5% retention but the decision was enforced because the nature of statutory adjudication is that a decision can be wrong but is still enforceable on the basis that the parties subsequently have the opportunity to resolve any mistake by litigation or arbitration.

The scope and importance of adjudication have proved much wider than originally envisaged. An adjudication may be launched at any time, including after practical completion. In particular it may be launched in the middle of complex litigation and will take priority, sometimes causing considerable disruption. As May LJ pointed out in *Quietfield Ltd v. Vascroft Construction Ltd* [2006] EWCA Civ 1737, it can be problematic '*if huge disputes scarcely amenable to speedy, even temporary, determination are nevertheless referred wholesale for adjudication*' but there is no prohibition to the bringing of 'kitchen sink' disputes to adjudication as a matter of principle.

Adjudication may not be particularly inexpensive even by comparison with litigation or arbitration and it may not be particularly expeditious either. In *CIB Properties v. Birse Construction* [2005] BLR 173 adjudication proceedings took over a 100 days and the costs exceeded what would normally be expected of litigation or arbitration costs. Nor is adjudication limited to disputes about sums due under contracts. It is used in relation to disputes about damages and in particular disputes concerning allegations of professional negligence.

Adjudication may theoretically be binding only until a final decision in litigation or arbitration but common experience is that very often the adjudication is an end to the dispute. As Lloyd HHJ commented in *Balfour Beatty Construction Ltd v. London Borough of Lambeth* [2002] EWHC 597 (TCC):

> It is now clear that the construction industry regards adjudication not simply as a staging post towards the final resolution of the dispute in arbitration or litigation but as having in itself considerable weight and impact that in practice goes beyond the legal requirement that the decision has for the time being to be observed.

Within this expanded process, however, the courts have sought to introduce clarity to the process and have emphasised that it will only be in exceptional circumstances that successful challenges can be made to adjudication decisions. If the losing party does have a real challenge on the merits then the message is *'pay now in accordance with the interim decision, then argue in subsequent proceedings with the prospect of finality'*. On the other hand, where there is a plain case of apparent bias, breach of natural justice or of excess of jurisdiction then that can provide a ground for refusal to enforce but such cases will be rare.

The construction industry seems reasonably happy with the process, if judged by the number of adjudications; this stands at about 1 500 per year and is now fairly consistent. The parties are clearly attracted by the timescale, the cost and the ability to obtain an early decision albeit only of a temporarily binding nature. They then have the protection of being able to take their dispute further if they so need.

Given the importance of the process, the industry relies on the integrity and efficiency of the body of expert adjudicators. The importance of their task and the role that adjudicators play was emphasised by Chadwick LJ in *Carillion Construction Ltd v. Devonport Royal Dockyard Ltd* [2005] EWCA Civ 1358:

> The majority of adjudicators are not chosen for their expertise as lawyers. Their skills are likely ... to lie in other disciplines. The task of the adjudicator is not to act as arbitrator or judge. The time constraints within which he is expected to operate is proof of that. The task of the adjudicator is to find an interim solution which meets the needs of the case.

28.2 The origins and development of adjudication in the UK
28.2.1 The position prior to 1 May 1998
Adjudication as a means of dispute resolution has been available under standard form contracts for a number of years. Adjudication (in a limited form) was first introduced to standard form construction contracts in 1976 by amendments to the then 'Green Form' Nominated Sub-Contract under the 1963 edition of the Joint Contracts Tribunal (JCT) contract which incorporated provisions for an interim resolution of disputes involving amounts of set-off which were not agreed. Similar amendments were made at the same time to the 'Blue Form' of Domestic Sub-Contract. These subcontracts were subsequently replaced by subcontract forms NSC/4 and DOM/1 under JCT 80.

During the 1980s the draftsmen of standard form contracts sought ways of avoiding the costs and delays of the traditional forms of dispute resolution (arbitration and litigation) by introducing adjudication as a means of resolving a wider range of disputes. The second edition of the Association of Consultant Architects (ACA) form of contract, published in 1984, included

adjudication as one of its alternative procedures for dispute resolution (the British Property Federation version of the ACA Contract incorporated a mandatory provision for adjudication). The 1988 supplement to the JCT 1981 With Contractor's Design Contract included provisions for adjudication for certain types of dispute. The Institution of Civil Engineers (ICE) New Engineering Contract, First Edition, 1993 provided for adjudication as the primary form of first-stage dispute resolution for all disputes that arose. In 1997 the ICE Adjudication Procedure was published and in 1998 ICE introduced an amendment to the ICE Conditions 6th Edition (and other ICE forms) which provided for adjudication. The ICE Conditions 7th Edition, published in 2003, also incorporated a provision for adjudication but following several judicial decisions, in 2004 ICE published its 'recommended' amendments to the dispute resolution provisions in Clause 66 (ICE/Clause-66/July 2004) of the ICE Conditions of Contract (Measurement Version 7th Edition, January 2003; Term Version 1st Edition, September 2002; Ground Investigation 2nd Edition, November 2003). A common feature of the adjudication procedures is the referral of a dispute to a neutral third person, not the contract administrator, the Engineer or other certifier under the contract.

28.2.2 The position after May 1998
In the early 1990s, there was a significant decline in the construction industry in the UK. Although economic factors were a substantial cause of the decline, another factor was perceived to be the large number of conflicts on construction projects and that the construction industry was over-reliant on the use of litigation and arbitration to settle disputes and claims. The UK government and organisations within the construction industry commissioned Sir Michael Latham to conduct an enquiry to review procurement and contractual arrangements in the UK construction industry. The Latham Report (Latham, 1994; see also Egan, 1998), published in 1994, concluded that the industry's traditional methods of procurement and contract management and its adversarial culture caused inefficiency and ineffectiveness and criticised existing industry practices as 'ineffective', 'adversarial', 'fragmented', and 'incapable of delivering for its customers'. One of the report's recommendations was that adjudication should be the 'normal' form of dispute resolution.

The Latham Report led to the enactment of the HGCRA 1996, which includes mandatory provisions for adjudication. The HGCRA 1996 applies to 'construction contracts', as defined in the Act (Section 104 of the HGCRA 1996), from 1 May 1998. The Secretary of State made regulations concerning adjudication provisions under the powers conferred on him by the HGCRA 1996 (including sections 108(6) and 114 of the HGCRA 1996) in Statutory Instrument SI 1998 No. 649, titled *The Scheme for Construction Contracts (England and Wales) Regulations 1998*. A schedule in the Regulations is commonly known as 'the Scheme for Construction Contracts' (the Scheme) (see Regulation 4 of SI 1998 No. 649).

The HGCRA 1996 applies in England and Wales. Corresponding provisions apply in Scotland and Northern Ireland.

The intention of Parliament in enacting the HGCRA 1996 was to provide a cost-effective and fast procedure for settling disputes in construction contracts resulting in an interim remedy. A major concern was disputes between main contractors and subcontractors over amounts due under the subcontract and which adversely affected the cash flows of subcontractors. A particular problem had arisen where an arbitration clause in the subcontract provided that arbitration could not be commenced until the main contract works had been completed. The effects of such a provision were that a subcontractor on a major project might have to wait years before he could commence proceedings to recover a sum which was disputed by the main contractor (see *Macob Civil Engineering Ltd v. Morrison Construction Ltd* [1999] BLR 93 at 97 (TCC)) and the existence of the arbitration clause prevented him from seeking summary judgement in court even in cases where there was no arguable defence to his entitlement to the sum (Section 9 of the Arbitration Act 1996; *Halki Shipping Corpn v. Sopex Oils Ltd* [1998] 1 WLR 726 (CA)).

Many of the provisions for adjudication in earlier editions of standard form contracts did not comply with the requirements of the HGCRA 1996. After May 1998 standard forms were necessarily amended to incorporate provisions which complied with the HGCRA 1996 (for example, see amendment ICE/Clause-66/July to the ICE Conditions 7th Edition) and new standard form contracts incorporated provisions which were drafted to be compliant (for example, see Clause 9.2 of the JCT Standard Building Contract 2005).

The position is now that the majority of adjudications are conducted under provisions in contracts which comply with the requirements of the HGCRA 1996. Certain standard form contracts have incorporated the adjudication provisions of the Scheme (see, for example, the JCT Standard Building Contract with Quantities 2005). In the case of non-compliant contracts, the adjudication provisions of the Scheme apply.

28.2.3 Key features of a contract which complies with the HGCRA 1996

Key features of a contract which complies with the HGCRA 1996 are as follows:

- The construction contract (as defined in the Act) must provide a right to refer a dispute to adjudication 'at any time' (section 108(2)(a)).

- The adjudicator's decision will be binding until the dispute is finally determined in legal proceedings, litigation or by agreement (section 108(3)).

- The contract must be in writing (section 108(7)).

- Unless the duration of the work is to be less than 45 days, there is an entitlement to payment by instalments, stage payments or other periodic payments (section 109).

- There is a mechanism for determining what payments become due under the contract (sections 109 and 110).

- Unless appropriate notice is given within a prescribed time, a sum which is due may not be withheld (sections 110 and 111).

- There is a right to suspend performance in the event that a sum due is not paid and no effective notice to withhold payment has been given (section 112).

- There is a prohibition on conditional payment provisions (i.e. pay-when-paid clauses) (section 113).

In relation to adjudication, if the contract does not comply with the requirements of sections 108(1) to (4) of the HGCRA 1996 (see following text), the Scheme will apply (Section 108(5) of the HGCRA 1996).

An explanation of the policy and purpose behind the statutory provisions was given by May LJ in *Pegram Shopfitters Ltd v. Tally Weijl (UK) Ltd* [2004] BLR 65 (CA), paras 1 to 12.

It should be noted that certain provisions of the HGCRA 1996 are now amended by Part 8 of the Local Democracy, Economic Development and Construction Act 2009 (LDEDCA 2009). Although the LDEDCA 2009 became law on 12 November 2009, no order has yet been made for the commencement of Part 8 which is relevant to construction contracts and adjudication. The prospective version of Part 8 of LDEDCA 2009 published by the Office of Public Service Information affects the following sections of the HGCRA 1996: section 107 is repealed and sections 108, 109, 110, 111 and 112 are amended. The amendments are referred to under the relevant sections of the HGCRA 1996 below. Readers should be alert to the position that the Secretary of State may at any time make an order implementing Part 8 of the LDEDCA 2009.

28.3 The statutory right to adjudication
28.3.1 Introduction

The HGCRA 1996 requires a construction contract to incorporate, among others, terms which confer a right on a party to the contract to give notice of an intention to refer a dispute to adjudication at any time (Section 108(2)(a) of the HGCRA 1996), set out a timetable for the appointment of an adjudicator and the referral of the dispute to adjudication within 7 days (Section 108(2)(b) of the HGCRA 1996), and specify the period in which the adjudicator must reach a decision (Sections 108(2)(c) and (d) of the HGCRA 1996).

In order to have a valid adjudication decision under the HGCRA 1996, certain conditions must be satisfied. The contract must be a 'construction contract', made in writing on or after 1 May 1998, for the carrying out of 'construction operations' (Section 104(1) of the HGCRA 1996); and not be a contract to which Part II of the HGCRA 1996 does not apply. There must be a dispute in existence between the parties to the contract and the dispute must arise under the contract (Section 108(1) of the

HGCRA 1996). There must be a valid reference of the dispute to the adjudicator who must act within his/her jurisdiction and reach a decision within the prescribed time.

28.3.2 What constitutes a construction contract?

Construction contracts which confer a statutory right to adjudication are defined in Part II of the HGCRA 1996 (Section 104 of the HGCRA 1996). In general terms, construction contracts are agreements with a person for the carrying out of or arranging for the carrying out of or the provision of labour for the carrying out of 'construction operations'. It should be noted that the term 'construction contract' includes the appointments of professionals who provide design or advice in relation to construction operations.

A construction contract with a residential occupier is not within the definition in the HGCRA 1996. A provision for adjudication is viewed as 'onerous and unusual' in a construction contract with a residential occupier. If it is intended that a provision for adjudication should be incorporated into a contract with a residential occupier, at common law the provision must be brought to the attention of the residential occupier if it is to be validly invoked and not excluded as being unfair under the Unfair Terms in Consumer Contracts Regulations 1999. For example *Picardi v. Cuniberti* [2003] BLR 487 (TCC) HHJ Toulmin CMG QC. c.f. *Steve Domsalla (t/a Domsalla Building Services) v. Kenneth Dyason* [2007] EWHC 1174 (TCC) in which HHJ Thornton QC rejected submissions that the adjudication provisions were not binding on the employer and were unfair under the Unfair Terms in Consumer Contracts Regulations 1999 (although finding that provisions for withholding notices were unfair). However, where a residential occupier has access to professional advice or his/her agent proposes an adjudication clause for incorporation into the contract, the provision will be enforced. See *Lovell Projects Ltd v. Legg and Carver* [2003] BLR 452; *Westminster Building Co. Ltd v. Andrew Beckingham* [2004] BLR 265; and *Allen Wilson Shopfitters v. Buckingham* (2005) 102 Con LR 154.

Exclusion Order 1998 Statutory Instrument SI 1998 No. 648 excludes certain contracts from the ambit of HGCRA 1996 which would otherwise be encompassed by the Act. The excluded contracts include certain agreements under statute; private finance initiatives; Finance Agreements; and Development Agreements (the latter two as defined in the order).

28.3.3 The meaning of 'construction operations'

The activities which are, or are not, 'construction operations' within the meaning in the HGCRA 1996 are defined in some detail in section 105. However, notwithstanding the detail in the Act, a considerable body of case law has grown up on what falls within the meaning of construction operations. The cases below are given by way of examples only.

In *Nottingham Community Housing Association Ltd v. Powerminster Ltd* [2000] BLR 309 (TCC) the annual servicing and the provision of responsive repairs to gas appliances within a number of properties owned by the claimant was held to fall within section 105(1)(a) of the HGCRA 1996 (which defines construction operations as the 'construction, alteration, repair, maintenance, extension, demolition or dismantling of buildings, or structures forming, or to form, part of the land, (whether permanent or not)', and not section 105(1)(c) which expressly refers to systems of heating but is restricted to works of *installation* of such systems.

In *Staveley Industries plc v. Odebrecht Oil & Gas Services Ltd* [2001] 98(10) LSG 46 (TCC) it was held that the design, engineering, procurement, supply, delivery to site, installation, testing and commissioning of instrumentation, fire and gas, electrical and telecommunications equipment within modules intended for an oil rig to be fixed to a sea-based platform in the Gulf of Mexico did not form part of the land, as required by section 105(1)(c) of the HGCRA 1996. The main structure was to be founded on the sea bed below the low water mark, and such structures were excluded from the ambit of the HGCRA 1996.

Shop-fitting does not constitute construction operations unless the works consist of the construction of 'structures forming, or to form, part of the land, (whether permanent or not)', as required by section 105(1)(a), or 'installation in any building or structure of fittings forming part of the land' referenced at Section 105(1)(c). See *Gibson Lea Retail Interiors Ltd v. MAKRO Self-Service Wholesalers Ltd* [2001] BLR 407.

Clean-up operations on farm premises as a result of foot and mouth disease were within sections 105(d) and (e) of the HGCRA 1996. In addition, certain works carried out in relation to the provision of temporary or permanent offices, were held to be construction operations by virtue of section 105(a) of the HGCRA 1996 (*Ruttle Plant Hire Ltd v. Secretary of State for the Environment, Food and Rural Affairs* [2004] EWHC 2152 (TCC)).

In *Palmers Ltd v. ABB Power Construction Ltd* [1999] BLR 426 (TCC) scaffolding services for the provision of temporary access and support to a structural frame within which a boiler and its associated pipework were supported during erection (and where the scaffolding required almost constant modification while work was being carried out) constituted a 'construction operation' within section 105(1)(e) of the HGCRA 1996.

Section 105(2) sets out those matters that are **not** construction operations within the HGCRA 1996 Part II. The main categories of exempt operations are drilling for or extraction of oil or natural gas (section 105(2)(a)); extraction of minerals (section 105(2)(b)); assembly, installation or demolition of plant or machinery or erection of steelwork for the purposes of supporting or providing access to plant or machinery where the primary activity is nuclear processing, power generation, water or effluent treatment, or the production transmission processing or bulk storage of chemicals pharmaceuticals oil gas steel or food and drink (section 105(2)(c)); and the making of installation and repair of artistic works (section 105(2)(e)).

The manufacture and delivery (constituting supply only) of certain items, including 'building or engineering components or equipment, … materials plant or machinery or components for[mechanical and electrical services] systems' are not 'construction operations' unless the contract also provides for installation of the items (see section 105(2)(d) of the HGCRA 1996).

In *ABB Power Construction Ltd v. Norwest Holst* [2001] 77 Con LR 20 (TCC) a subcontract for the insulation of boilers, ducting, silencers, pipework, drums and tanks for the construction of heat recovery steam generator boilers as a part of a project to extend an existing power station was not a construction contract within the meaning in the HGCRA 1996: the work was necessary to achieve the aims or purposes of a power generation plant which is an exempt operation under section 105(2)(c) of the HGCRA 1996.

The words 'a site where the primary activity is …' in section 105(2)(c) of the HGCRA 1996 were considered in *ABB Zantingh Ltd v. Zedal Building Services Ltd* [2001] BLR 66 HHJ (TCC). It was held that the words had to be construed by reference to the whole site and that a generator surrounded by a security fence for the purposes of generating emergency power in the event of a Y2k problem commissioned by an organisation whose business was the printing of magazines, was not a 'site' where the primary activity was power generation and therefore not within the exemptions.

A hired item of plant, a mobile crane, plus a driver was held not fall within the exception in section 105(2)(d) of the HGCRA 1996 in that the activity was not one for the mere delivery of plant to the site but the contract was for the supply of plant and labour for use in construction operations on a building site and therefore was a construction contract within the meaning of section 104 of the HGCRA 1996 (*Baldwins Industrial Services plc v. Barr Ltd* [2003] BLR 176 (TCC)).

In *Conor Engineering Ltd v. Les Constructions Industrielle de la Mediterranee* [2004] BLR 212, the court held that determining what was the primary activity at a particular site was a question of fact and not necessarily determined by the primary *purpose* of that site. In *Conor* the primary activity was held to be the incineration of waste and not the generation of electricity, which was a mere spin-off, and a subcontract for boiler works was therefore a construction contract within the HGCRA 1996.

28.3.4 Agreement 'in writing'

The contract will not be a construction contract within the meaning in the HGCRA 1996 unless it is in writing, within the meaning in section 107. The provision includes agreements made in writing whether or not signed by the parties, agreements made by the exchange of written communications, agreements evidenced in writing and agreements made otherwise than in writing but by reference to terms which are in writing.

Subsection 107(5) contains an unusual provision that an exchange of written submissions in adjudication, arbitral or legal proceedings in which one party alleges the existence of an agreement otherwise than in writing and the response of the other party does not deny such an agreement will constitute, as between the parties, an agreement in writing. In *Grovedeck Ltd v. Capital Demolition Ltd* [2000] BLR 181 (TCC) it was held that subsection 107(5) only operates where the relevant exchange of written submissions has taken place in litigation or arbitration proceedings before the adjudication commenced.

In *Grovedeck* above HHJ Bowsher QC expressed the view that '[d]isputes as to the terms … of oral construction agreements are surprisingly common and are not readily susceptible of resolution by a summary procedure such as adjudication.'

The purpose of section 107 was considered by the Court of Appeal In *RJT Consulting Engineers Ltd v. DM Engineering (Northern Ireland) Ltd* [2002] 1 WLR 2344 (CA); [2002] BLR 217 (CA). Ward LJ (with whom Walker LJ agreed) said:

> Section 107(1) limits the application of the Act to construction contracts which are in writing or to other agreements which are effective for the purposes of that part of the Act only if in writing. This must be seen against the background which led to the introduction of this change. In its origin it was an attempt to force the industry to submit to a standard form of contract. That did not succeed but writing is still important and writing is important because it provides certainty. Certainty is all the more important when adjudication is envisaged to have to take place under a demanding timetable. The adjudicator has to start with some certainty as to what the terms of the contract are.

In *RJT Consulting* the majority of the Court of Appeal (Ward and Walker LJJ) held that on order for the contract to be 'evidenced in writing' all the express terms had to be evidenced in writing and that it was not sufficient that all terms material to the issues in the adjudication had been recorded in writing. Ward LJ also said that he did not think subsection 107(5) could dominate the interpretation of the section as a whole such as to limit what needs to be evidenced in writing simply to the material terms raised in the arbitration and emphasised that by virtue of section 107(1) the need for an agreement in writing is the precondition for the application of the other provisions of Part II of the Act, not just the jurisdictional threshold for a reference to adjudication. He concurred with Auld LJ and said he would regard it as a pity if too much 'jurisdictional wrangling' were to limit the opportunities for expeditious adjudication which had an interim effect only.

Auld LJ agreed with the decision but dissented on this point and said that what is important is that the terms of the agreement material to the issue or issues giving rise to the reference should be clearly recorded in writing, not that every term, however trivial or unrelated to those issues, should be expressly recorded or incorporated by reference and, by way of example, expressed the view that it would be absurd if a prolongation issue arising out of a written contract were to be denied a reference to adjudication for want of sufficient written specification or scheduling of matters wholly unrelated to the stage or nature of the work giving rise to the reference.

The narrow approach of the Court of Appeal has been applied consistently by the courts. In *Carillion Construction Ltd v. Devonport Royal Dockyard Ltd* [2003] BLR 79 (TCC) the court held that a statutory right to refer a dispute to adjudication could be lost where there had been an oral variation to a contract which had not been recorded in writing.

In *Trustees of the Stratfield Saye Estate v. AHL Construction Ltd* [2004] EWHC 3286 (TCC) Jackson J expressed the view that it was not possible to regard the reasoning of Auld LJ in *RJT Consulting* above as some kind of gloss upon, or amplification of, the reasoning of the majority; attractive though it was, it did not form part of the ratio in the case and concluded that an agreement was therefore only evidenced in writing for the purposes of subsections 107(2), (3) and (4), if all the express terms of that agreement were recorded in writing. See also *Hart Investments Ltd v. Fidler and Another* [2006] EWHC 2857 (TCC); *Mott MacDonald Ltd v. London & Regional Properties Ltd* [2007] EWHC 1055 (TCC); *Redworth Construction Ltd v. Brookdale Healthcare Ltd* [2006] EWHC 1994 (TCC).

The requirement that the terms of the agreement be in writing was designed to promote certainty and, to date, the courts have interpreted the provisions in section 107 strictly and rejected attempts to widen the application of the section.

The general purpose of Part II of the HGCRA 1996 was to facilitate and encourage the process of adjudication as a swift and summary process (see the time limits in section 108(2)) and one effect of the present provisions was that adjudicators were not required to decide disputes, which often arise as to the terms of an oral contract.

However, notwithstanding the element of certainty which written contracts bring to the adjudication process, section 139 of the LDEDCA 2009 repeals the entirety of section 107 of the HGCRA 1996 and thereby removes the requirement for the construction contract to be in writing. It is submitted that the removal of the requirement for the contract to be in writing may result in the need for more oral hearings in adjudications in order to test the evidence in cases where the formation and/or the terms of the oral contract are disputed.

28.3.5 The requirements to comply with section 108 of the HGCRA 1996

Section 108(1) of the HGCRA 1996 confers a right on a party to a construction contract to refer a dispute arising under the contract for adjudication under a procedure which complies with the section. Under the section a 'dispute' includes any 'difference'.

Sections 108(2) to (4) of the HGCRA 1996 set out requirements in relation to adjudication which a construction contract must contain if it is to be compliant with the Act. The relevant parts of section 108 are set out in full below.

(2) The contract shall—
  (a) enable a party to give notice at any time of his intention to refer a dispute to adjudication;

  (b) provide a timetable with the object of securing the appointment of the adjudicator and referral of the dispute to him within 7 days of such notice;
  (c) require the adjudicator to reach a decision within 28 days of referral or such longer period as is agreed by the parties after the dispute has been referred;
  (d) allow the adjudicator to extend the period of 28 days by up to 14 days, with the consent of the party by whom the dispute was referred;
  (e) impose a duty on the adjudicator to act impartially; and
  (f) enable the adjudicator to take the initiative in ascertaining the facts and the law.
(3) The contract shall provide that the decision of the adjudicator is binding until the dispute is finally determined by legal proceedings, by arbitration (if the contract provides for arbitration or the parties otherwise agree to arbitration) or by agreement.

The parties may agree to accept the decision of the adjudicator as finally determining the dispute.
(4) The contract shall also provide that the adjudicator is not liable for anything done or omitted in the discharge or purported discharge of his functions as adjudicator unless the act or omission is in bad faith, and that any employee or agent of the adjudicator is similarly protected from liability.
(5) If the contract does not comply with the requirements of subsections (1) to (4), the adjudication provisions of the Scheme for Construction Contracts apply.

Unless the parties are able to enter into a contract which does not constitute a construction contract within the meaning of the term in the HGCRA 1996, they cannot contract out of the right to adjudication.

If the contract does not provide for adjudication, or fails to include the requirements of section 108 (even if only in one respect), the adjudication provisions of the Scheme will apply as a whole (for examples, see *John Mowlem & Co. plc v. Hydra Tight & Co. plc* (2001) 17 Const LJ 358 (TCC); *Aveat Heating v. Jerram Falkus Construction* [2007] EWHC 131 (TCC); *Banner Holdings v. Colchester Borough Council* [2010] EWHC 139 (TCC) (obiter at paragraphs 42 and 43); *Yuanda (UK) Co Limited v. WW Gear Construction Limited* [2010] EWHC 820 (TCC) (at the time of writing possibly on appeal but on a different point) and take effect as implied terms of the contract (Section 114(4) of the HGCRA 1996).

The HGCRA 1996 only requires a contract to include a right to refer disputes to adjudication: there is no obligation on a party to do so. However, one effect of the statutory right is that, since 1998, adjudication has become the principal form of first-stage dispute resolution for construction contracts in the UK.

Part 8 of the LDEDCA 2009, when implemented, will amend section 108 of the HGCRA 1996. Section 140 of LDEDCA 2009 inserts a new section 108(3A) into the HGCRA 1996 which requires the construction contract to include a provision which gives the adjudicator power to correct clerical or typographical errors arising by accident or omission.

Section 141 of LDEDCA 2009 inserts a new section 108A into the HGCRA 1996 which provides that any contractual provision concerning the allocation of costs relating to the adjudication shall be ineffective unless either it is made in writing, is contained in the construction contract and confers power on the adjudicator to allocate his/her fees and expenses between the parties or it is made in writing after the giving of the notice of intention to refer the dispute to adjudication.

28.3.6 The existence of a dispute

A dispute must exist between the parties to the contract before it is capable of being referred to adjudication. Often a party will seek to challenge the jurisdiction of a tribunal on grounds that no dispute exists. Therefore it is important to know when a dispute exists. In *AMEC Civil Engineering Ltd v. Secretary of State for Transport* [2005] EWCA Civ 291; [2005] BLR 227 (CA) (in the context of adjudication see also the wide interpretation given to 'dispute' in *AWG Construction Services Ltd v. Rockingham Motor Speedway Ltd* [2004] EWHC 888 (TCC)) Jackson J summarised the law in relation to defining a dispute in seven propositions (see the chapter *Alternative dispute resolution*). The Court of Appeal accepted the propositions as 'broadly correct'.

In *AMEC* May LJ (with whom Hooper LJ agreed) and Rix LJ were prepared to go further than Jackson J at first instance and find that, in all the circumstances of the case, including the imminence of the end of the statutory limitation period for commencing an arbitration, there was a dispute or difference capable of being referred to the engineer at any time after a meeting at which AMEC had stated orally that it did not accept responsibility for defects ([2005] EWCA 291, para. 33).

In the context of the time constraints which occur in adjudication the part of Rix LJ's judgement which considers whether dispute or difference existed should be noted. First, Rix LJ said that he 'would be very cautious about accepting that either a "claim" or a "reasonable time to respond" was in either case a condition precedent to the establishment of a dispute.' Rix LJ then referred to adjudication as the *additional* provisional layer of dispute resolution, pending final litigation or arbitration' and to a 'legitimate concern to ensure that the point at which this additional complexity [the need for a "dispute" in order to trigger adjudication] has been properly reached should not be too readily anticipated'. He emphasised the difference between arbitration and adjudication in that adjudication is likely to occur at an early stage and expressed further concerns that 'the respondent should have a reasonable time in which to respond to any claim' otherwise the parties 'may be plunged into an expensive contest, the timing provisions of which are tightly drawn, before they, and particularly the respondent, are ready for it' ([2005] EWCA 291, paras 62–69). In the context of adjudication see also the wide interpretation given to 'dispute' in *AWG Construction Services Ltd v. Rockingham Motor Speedway Ltd* [2004] EWHC 888 (TCC).

Jackson J's propositions also received further approval by a different Court of Appeal in *Collins Contractors Ltd v. Baltic Quay Management (1994) Ltd* [2004] EWCA Civ 1757 (see also *Cantillon Ltd v. Urvasco Ltd* [2008] BLR 250 (TCC)). Clarke LJ (as he then was) endorsed, in particular, the general approach that, while the mere making of a claim does not amount to a dispute, a dispute will be held to exist once it can reasonably be inferred that a claim is not admitted and rejected earlier cases which suggested either that a dispute may not arise until negotiation or discussion have been concluded, or that a dispute should not be likely inferred. Negotiation and discussion are likely to be more consistent with the existence of a dispute, albeit an as yet unresolved dispute, than with an absence of a dispute. The court is likely to be willing readily to infer that a claim is not admitted and that a dispute exists so that it can be referred to arbitration or adjudication ([2004] EWCA Civ 1757 paras 63–64).

The Court of Appeal's wide approach to determining whether a dispute exists and the concerns of Rix LJ in *AMEC* are important in the context of the need to comply with the requirements of natural justice, for example, in circumstances where a dispute is referred to adjudication and the respondent has no prior knowledge of the detail of the claim and has little time to carry out its own investigations before being required to provide a response.

28.3.7 Dispute 'under' the contract

Section 108 of the HGCRA 1996 provides a right to refer a 'dispute arising under the contract' to adjudication. Based on earlier case law, the use of the word 'under' would limit the scope of the type of disputes which may be referred to adjudication in contrast to a wider dispute resolution provision using, for example, the words 'in connection with the contract' (for example, see amended Clause 66(B)(1)(a) of the ICE Conditions 7th Edition) and the statutory right would (probably) not include disputes about mistake, misrepresentation under the Misrepresentation Act 1967, negligent misstatement and rectification of the contract. For example, see *Ashville Investments Ltd v. Elmer Construction Ltd* [1988] 2 All ER 577 (CA) for the interpretation of 'in connection with the contract' in the context of an arbitration agreement.

However, in *Premium Nafta Products Limited and Others v. Fili Shipping Company Limited and Others ('Fiona Trust')* [2007] UKHL 40 the House of Lords was prepared to construe the term 'under the contract' widely in the context of international arbitration when determining a dispute over whether a contract could be set aside or rescinded for alleged bribery was within the scope of an arbitrator's jurisdiction. The House of Lords said that it was time to draw a line under the authorities to date concerning the construction of arbitration clauses and supported the view that arbitration clauses should be construed liberally, without making fine semantic distinctions between disputes 'arising out of', 'arising under' or 'in connection with' the contract. It is not yet clear whether this principle could also apply generally to adjudication clauses. However, in *Air Design (Kent) Ltd v. Deerglen (Jersey) Ltd* [2008] EWHC 3047 (TCC). Akenhead J appears to have accepted that, on the particular facts of that case, the principles in *Fiona Trust* did apply in adjudication.

It is submitted that there is no reason why the principles established in the *Fiona Trust* above should not have general application to adjudication clauses (following *Air Design* above). If the courts should adopt such an approach, the distinctions made in earlier cases between disputes 'arising out of', 'arising under' or 'in connection with' the contract should largely fall away. Earlier cases should now be read in the context of the *Fiona Trust* above.

However, the type of dispute which falls within the scope of an adjudication clause will continue to depend on the precise wording of the clause and the contractual and factual background in which the dispute has arisen.

A dispute about a settlement agreement fell outside section 108 of the HGCRA 1996 because it was not a 'construction contract'; and such a dispute did not arise 'under' the related construction contract. In addition, matters which preceded the making of a subcontract, such as questions as to whether a contract was entered into on a false basis, or as a result of a misrepresentation, or on the basis of promises which did not materialise, were not within the jurisdiction of an adjudicator required to resolve disputes 'under' the subcontract (*Shepherd Construction Ltd v. Mecright* [2000] BLR 489 (TCC)).

A claim for damages arising out of a repudiatory breach of contract is a matter arising under the contract and capable of being referred to adjudication (*Northern Developments (Cumbria) Ltd v. J&J Nichol* [2000] BLR 158 [TCC]; although in the absence of a notice to withhold, the claim was held to be outside the adjudicator's jurisdiction. The right to adjudication survives termination. See in the context of arbitration, for example, *Heyman and another v. Darwins Ltd* [1942] AC 356, HL. Also in relation to adjudication, see *A&D Maintenance and Construction Ltd v. Pagehurst Construction Services Ltd* [1999] CILL 1518 [TCC]). Over time the scope of adjudication clauses has expanded and are now not limited to disputes involving rights of set-off but include almost every kind of dispute that may arise 'under' a contract and, in certain contracts, also disputes arising 'in connection with' the contract and the carrying out of the works (for example, see ICE Conditions 7th Edition Clause 66B(1)(a)). In the latter case, the provision is probably sufficiently wide to cover virtually all disputes which arise, except a dispute as to the existence of the contract itself.

28.3.8 Notice of adjudication

The contract must enable a party to give written notice 'at any time' of its intention to refer a dispute arising under the contract to adjudication (Section 108(2)(a) of the HGCRA 1996). The party giving notice is the 'referring party' and the notice to commencing the adjudication proceedings is the 'notice of adjudication' and must be in writing.

The notice of adjudication is an extremely important document. It defines the nature and scope of the referring party's claim in the adjudication and, thereby, the jurisdiction of the adjudicator (i.e. the scope of the adjudicator's authority to decide the dispute which has been referred to adjudication). For examples, see *Ken Griffin & John Tomlinson t/a K&D Contractors v. Midas Homes Ltd* [2001] 78 Con LR 152 (TCC); *Jerome Engineering Ltd v. Lloyd Electrical Services Ltd* [2002] CILL 11827 (TCC); *KNS Industrial Services (Birmingham) Ltd v. Sindall Ltd* (2000) 75 Con LR 71 (TCC). Therefore the notice must be carefully drafted to ensure that the nature of the dispute and the remedy sought are clearly stated.

The courts have adopted a robust approach in interpreting the right to refer a dispute to adjudication 'at any time'. Any contractual provision which seeks to postpone an adjudication by requiring the prior operation of another form of dispute resolution and/or by deeming that no dispute has arisen until the other process has failed to result in a settlement, is contrary to section 108(2) of HGCRA 1996 and is not enforceable (at least prior to adjudication). For examples, see *R.G. Carter Limited v. Edmund Nuttall Limited*, 21 June 2000 Unreported (TCC): a provision that the parties would not resort to adjudication or arbitration unless attempts to reach a settlement by mediation had been unsuccessful undermined the right of either party to refer a dispute to adjudication 'at any time' and was not compliant with the HGCRA 1996; *John Mowlem & Co. plc v. Hydra Tight & Co. plc* [2001] 17 CLJ 358 (TCC): a subcontract incorporating the provisions of NEC (Option A) Y(UK)2 with amendments providing for service of a 'notification of dissatisfaction', the expressed purpose of which was to delay adjudication for 4 weeks to give the parties an opportunity to meet and resolve their difference, was held not to comply with section 108(2)(a) of the HGCRA 1996. Also, see also *Midland Expressway Ltd v. Carillion Construction Ltd (No.2)* [2005] EWHC 2963 (TCC). There is no time limit for referring a dispute to adjudication (*Connex South Eastern Ltd v. MJ Building Services Group plc* [2005] 201 (CA). The defendant's notice of adjudication was not an abuse of process and neither the HGCRA 1996 nor the Scheme gives an adjudicator the power to strike out or stay an adjudication for abuse of process) and the right to commence adjudication exists notwithstanding there are court proceedings pending in the same dispute (*Hershel Engineering Ltd v. Breen Property Ltd* [2000] 70 ConLR 1 [TCC]).

28.3.9 The appointment of an adjudicator

Section 108(2)(b) of the HGCRA 1996 states that the contract 'shall provide a timetable with the object of securing the appointment of the adjudicator and referral of the dispute to him within 7 days of such notice'.

After the notice of adjudication has been given, the parties may agree on a person who is to act as adjudicator or, in default of agreement, the referring party should send a request (which should be accompanied by a copy of the notice of adjudication) either to any person named as adjudicator in the contract or to a nominating body named in the contract to appoint an adjudicator. Adjudicator nominating bodies include ICE, Royal Institute of British Architects (RIBA), Royal Institution of Chartered Surveyors (RICS), Chartered Institute of Arbitrators (CIArb), Chartered Institute of Building (CIOB), Technology & Construction Bar Association (TECBAR) and Technology & Construction Solicitors' Association (TeCSA). Where neither of the above applies, or a person indicates he/she is unwilling or unable to act as an adjudicator, the referring party may request any adjudicator nominating body to appoint an adjudicator.

The timetable imposed by section 108(2)(b) of the HGCRA 1996 is extremely tight. Therefore a request for an appointment should be made at the earliest possible opportunity (at the time of giving the notice of adjudication), otherwise it may prove very difficult for the referring party to comply with the 7-day time limit for referring the dispute to the adjudicator.

Many standard form contracts contain provisions for the appointment of the adjudicator to be governed by a standard adjudication agreement (see, for example, Clause 41A.2.1 of JCT 1998 which requires the adjudicator to execute the 'JCT Adjudication Agreement' with the parties) or for particular adjudication rules and/or procedures to apply in the adjudication. See, for example, Clause 66B(1)(a) of the ICE Conditions 7th Edition which requires the adjudication to be conducted under 'The Institution of Civil Engineers Adjudication Procedure'.

28.3.10 The referral of the dispute to the adjudicator

Once a selection has been made, the next step will be to refer the dispute to the adjudicator. The document by which the dispute is referred to the adjudicator is known as the 'referral notice'. The referral notice is the document in which the referring party sets out the detail of its claim. The referral notice is to be accompanied by copies of relevant extracts from the contract and any other documents relied on by the referring party.

In practice, the referral notice is usually similar to a statement of case in litigation or arbitration with appendices containing extracts from the contract, any contemporaneous documents and other evidence relied on, which may include witness statements and experts' reports. However, it is important to note that it is the notice of adjudication which defines the dispute not the referral notice. Therefore the referral notice must not seek to extend the nature and scope of the dispute (for examples, see *KNS Industrial Services (Birmingham) Ltd v. Sindall Ltd* above; *Mecright Ltd v. TA Morris Developments Ltd* Unreported 22.06.01 (TCC)). The adjudicator and the responding party may need to be alert to any attempt by the referring party to do so. In particular, the adjudicator will not have jurisdiction to decide any claim which did not form part of the dispute encompassed by the notice of adjudication and the court will decline to enforce the decision.

The precise date of the referral is important as, subject to any agreement to extend time, the adjudicator is required to reach a decision within 28 days of the referral (Section 108(2)(c)). However, the wording of section 108(2)(b) of the HGCRA 1996 gave rise to a debate whether 'referral' meant the sending of the referral notice or its receipt by the adjudicator. Clarification was provided by in *Aveat Heating Ltd v. Jerram Falkus Construction Ltd* [2007] EWHC 131 (TCC), HHJ Havery QC:

> a thing is not referred to another unless that other person receives it … the word is unambiguous. Referral takes place upon receipt of the notice by the adjudicator.

The 7-day time limit imposed by section 108(2)(b) of HGCRA 1996 (and paragraph 7(1) of the Scheme) is tight and may give rise to difficulties if, for example, it is necessary to approach several adjudicators before one is able to act. The position remains unclear whether the 7-day time limit is directory or mandatory. One view is that, taking into account the wording of section 108(2)(b) of the HGCRA 1996, a referral made after the 7 days would not be fatal, provided it was made reasonably promptly in all the circumstances. This approach was endorsed in *The Mayor and Burgesses of the London Borough of Lambeth v. Floyd Slaski Partnership and Mastrandrea* Unreported, 2 November 2001 (TCC). Also in *William Verry Ltd v. North West London Communal Mikvah* [2004] BLR 308 (TCC), a distinction was drawn between the permissive language of section 108(2)(b) and the more rigid wording of section 108(2)(c). Clause 41A.4.1 of the JCT Standard Form of Building Contract 1998 Edition also relies on section 108(2)(b) as being directory and provides that, if the adjudicator is not agreed or appointed within 7 days of the notice of adjudication, the referral shall be made immediately on such agreement or appointment (the JCT 2005 family of contracts now incorporates the adjudication provisions of the Scheme).

However, a line of authority has developed more recently in which the 7-day time limit has been held to be mandatory. For examples, see *Hart Investments Ltd v. Fidler* [2006] EWHC 2857; [2007] BLR 30 (TCC) and *Cubitt Building & Interiors Ltd v. Fleetglade Ltd* (2007) 110 Con LR 36; [2006] EWHC 3413 (TCC), distinguishing *William Verry v. North West London Communal Mikva* above, which the judge said was a particular decision on its own facts. However, the decision in *The Mayor and Burgesses of the London Borough of Lambeth v. Floyd Slaski Partnership and Mastrandrea* above does not appear to have been cited in either *Hart Investments Ltd v. Fidler* or *Cubitt Building & Interiors Ltd v. Fleetglade Ltd* above.

In view of the conflicting authority, it is submitted that a prudent referring party should ensure that the referral notice is received by the adjudicator not later than 7 days from the date of the notice of adjudication.

28.3.11 The time for reaching a decision

Under section 108(2)(c) of the HGCRA the contract is to require the adjudicator to reach a decision within 28 days of referral.

The parties may agree to any extension(s) of the 28-day period but only after the dispute has been referred to the adjudicator (section 108(2)(c)). The adjudicator can extend the period above by 14–42 days but only with the consent of the referring party (section 108(2)(d)).

In larger adjudications the time limits for reaching a decision may cause difficulties for the adjudicator: for example there may be large volume of material which he must consider or it may be necessary to allow time for further submissions as the adjudication develops over the course of the 28 days. If it becomes apparent that further time will be required, the adjudicator should immediately seek an extension of time.

The Court of Appeal's view (*Carillion Construction Ltd v. Devonport Royal Dockyard Ltd* [2005] EWCA Civ 1358; [2006] BLR 15 (CA)) is that, because of the time constraints within which the adjudicator is expected to operate, the task of the adjudicator is not to act as arbitrator or judge but to find an interim solution which meets the needs of the case; the need to have the 'right' answer has been subordinated to the need to have an answer quickly and the scheme was not enacted in order to provide definitive answers to complex questions. However, if the parties refuse to extend time and an adjudicator is unable to deliver a fair decision within the time scale of the adjudication, it appears that 'an adjudicator ought not to make a decision at all and should resign'. *Balfour Beatty Construction Ltd v. Lambeth Borough Council* [2002] BLR 288 (TCC).

The adjudicator's decision must be reached within the prescribed 28-day period or any extended period which is agreed, otherwise it is a nullity. See, for example, *Ritchie Brothers (PWC) Ltd v. David Philip (Commercials) Ltd* [2005] BLR 384 [IH SC of Sess] adopted in *AC Yule & Son v. Speedwell Roofing and Cladding Ltd* [2007] EWHC 1360 (TCC).

28.3.12 The adjudicator's duties and powers

The overriding duties to be imposed on the adjudicator by the construction contract are to act impartially (Section 108(2)(e) of the HGCRA 1996) and to reach a decision within 28 days or such other time period as may have been agreed (Sections 108(2) (c) and (d) of the HGCRA 1996. Also, see *Ballast plc v. The Burrell Co (Construction Management) Ltd* 2001 SLT 1039). However, the adjudicator is not a party to the construction contract and therefore the duties must be incorporated into the adjudicator's appointment as express (or implied) terms.

28.3.13 Duty to act impartially

The contract must impose a duty on the adjudicator to act impartially (Section 108(2)(e) of the HGCRA 1996). It is implicit in this requirement that the adjudicator must apply rules of natural justice. It is submitted that the provision does not add to the common law position where a tribunal is required to act fairly and independently.

However, the HGCRA 1996 does not expressly provide for any practice or procedure which must be adopted in the adjudication. The contract may provide for particular rules or procedures to apply (see, for example, the detailed procedural rules in Clause 41.A.5 of the JCT 1998 Edition Private with Quantities standard form contract c.f. the later JCT Standard Building Contract 2005, which adopts the Scheme), otherwise the procedure to be adopted in a particular adjudication is left to the discretion of the adjudicator.

The meaning of 'impartially' in the context of adjudication was considered in *Glencot Development & Design Co. Ltd v. Ben Barrett & Son (Contractors) Ltd* [2001] BLR 207 (TCC) (an adjudicator had first conducted a mediation process which had failed to resolve the dispute. During the mediation the adjudicator had private discussions with both sides. The judge held that, on the facts as he found them, although the adjudicator was not biased, those facts would lead a fair-minded and informed observer to conclude that there was a real possibility or a real danger that he was biased). It was held that an adjudicator had to conduct the proceedings in accordance with the rules of natural justice or as fairly as the limitations imposed by Parliament permit (see also *Discain Project Services Ltd v. Opecprime Development Ltd* [2000] BLR 402 (TCC)).

In *Glencot* the judge concluded that the test for apparent bias was an objective test (i.e. the view of the adjudicator is irrelevant and not determinative), and the approach to be adopted by the court was to first ascertain all the circumstances which have a bearing on the suggestion that the tribunal was biased and it must then ask 'whether those circumstances would lead a fair-minded and informed observer to conclude that there was a real possibility, or a real danger, the two being the same, that the tribunal was biased'. See *In Re: Medicaments* [2001] 1 WLR 700 at 726–727 (HL); *Magill v. Porter* [2001] UKHL 67 at para. 103; and the earlier case followed in *Glencot: R v. Gough Director* [1993] AC 646 (HL). See also *General of Fair Trading v. Proprietary Association of Great Britain* [2000] All ER (D) 2425 (CA).

In an early case (*Macob Civil Engineering Ltd v. Morrison Construction Ltd* [1999] BLR 93 (TCC)) Dyson J (as he then was) acknowledged that the timetable for adjudication is 'very tight' and that this was likely to result in injustice but that Parliament must be taken to have been aware of this. He stated that if an adjudicator's decision on the issue referred to him is wrong because the adjudicator erred on the facts or the law, or there was a procedural error, this would not invalidate the decision. In addition, the judge's view was that if a party was able to simply assert there had been a breach of natural justice, this would substantially undermine the intention of Parliament that adjudication should provide a speedy mechanism for settling disputes in construction contracts. However, in later cases the courts have refused to enforce adjudication decisions in applications for summary judgement where there appears to have been a breach of natural justice. For examples, see *Woods Hardwick Ltd v. Chiltern Air Conditioning Ltd* [2001] BLR 23 (TCC); *Balfour Beatty Construction Ltd v. London Borough of Lambeth* [2002] EWHC 597 (TCC); *RSL (South West) Ltd v.*

Stansell Ltd [2003] EWHC 1390 (TCC); *Discain Project Services Ltd v. Opecprime Development Ltd* [2000] BLR 402 (TCC); *Glencot Development & Design Co. Ltd v. Ben Barrett & Son (Contractors) Ltd* [2001] BLR 207 (TCC).

After the decision in *Macob* some aggrieved parties sought to contend in enforcement proceedings that the adjudicator could act in breach of natural justice. This argument was raised in *Discain Project Services Ltd v. Opecprime Development Ltd* [2001] BLR 287 (TCC) and HHJ Bowsher QC robustly rejected submissions that *Macob* held that the rules of natural justice did not apply to adjudication and that a breach of natural justice was to be regarded as a 'procedural error'.

The first rule of natural justice was summarised (in the context of an adjudication case) in *RSL (South West) Ltd v. Stansell Ltd* [2003] EWHC 1390 (TCC):

> [t]he rules of natural justice require that a party to a dispute resolution procedure should know what is the case against him and should have an opportunity to meet it.
>
> HHJ Seymour QC

The manner in which a dispute may be referred and the time constraints of the adjudication process may create considerable difficulties for an adjudicator applying the first rule of natural justice. A referring party may have been preparing for the adjudication for some time and submit voluminous and detailed information with the referral notice. However, the responding party may not know the details of the claim but nonetheless must be given sufficient time to respond within the timetable in which the adjudicator is required to reach a decision. See, for example, the concerns expressed by Rix LJ in *AMEC Civil Engineering Ltd v. Secretary of State for Transport* [2005] EWCA Civ 291 1757, paras 62–69, that a respondent should have sufficient time to respond to a claim before any adjudication commences.

There will be a breach of the second rule of natural justice if either the adjudicator is biased or in the circumstances a fair-minded observer would consider there was a real possibility that the adjudicator was biased (notwithstanding any explanation advanced by the adjudicator).

After a series of first instance cases concerned with the enforcement of adjudication decisions, in *AMEC Capital Projects Ltd v. Whitefriars City Estates Ltd* [2004] EWCA Civ 1418 (Dyson LJ gave the leading judgement with which Chadwick & Kennedy LJJ agreed). The court restated the principles. The common law rules of natural justice or procedural fairness are two-fold. First, the person affected has the right to prior notice and an effective opportunity to make representations before a decision is made. Second, the person affected has the right to an unbiased tribunal. The Court of Appeal supported the position that a breach of natural justice invalidates an adjudicator's decision.

Adjudicators often reach provisional conclusions which represent an intermediate position for which neither party was contending. In *Carillion Construction Ltd v. Devonport Royal Dockyard Ltd* [2005] BLR 310 (TCC) Jackson J, endorsed (on this point) by the Court of Appeal on the application to appeal [2006] BLR 15 (CA), paras 53 and 84–87, Jackson J recognised that it will often not be practicable for an adjudicator to put his provisional conclusions to the parties and held that it will only be in an exceptional case that an adjudicator's failure to put provisional conclusions to the parties will constitute such a serious breach of the rules of natural justice that the court will decline to enforce the decision. In the Court of Appeal, Chadwick LJ said that in adjudication the need to have the 'right' answer has been subordinated to the need to have an answer quickly and that the statutory scheme was not enacted in order to provide definitive answers to complex questions.

Where the adjudicator fails to consider evidence, it may be extremely difficult to decide whether the omission constitutes a breach of natural justice. In *Kier Regional Ltd v. City & General (Holborn) Ltd* [2006] EWHC 848 (TCC) Jackson J held that the adjudicator made an error of law which caused him to disregard two pieces of relevant evidence in the form of experts' reports but in the light of the Court of Appeal's decision in *Carillion* above that error did not invalidate the adjudicator's decision.

It is important that the adjudicator and the parties are alert to circumstances which may give rise to a breach of natural justice. After the HGCRA 1996 was implemented there followed a large number of cases in which many of the provisions of the Act and the Scheme were considered by the courts, usually in the context of proceedings to enforce an adjudicator's decision. In the event, the courts adopted an extremely robust approach to the enforcement of adjudicator's decisions (see, for example *Bouygues (UK) Ltd v. Dahl-Jensen (UK) Ltd* [2000] BLR 49 (TCC) Dyson J (as he then was); [2000] BLR 522 (CA). The adjudicator incorrectly calculated that one party was to pay a balance due of approximately £200 000 whereas if the calculation had been properly undertaken a sum of £140 000 would have been due and payable by the other party. It was held that the award contained an error but the error was made within the adjudicator's jurisdiction. The adjudicator had answered the right question, albeit in the wrong way, and the decision was binding and a 'breach of natural justice' (or an 'excess of jurisdiction' on the part of the adjudicator) represent probably the only grounds left on which enforcement may now properly be resisted.

28.3.14 Taking the initiative in ascertaining the facts and the law

Section 108(2)(f) of the HGCRA 1996 requires the contract to include a provision which enables the adjudicator to take the initiative in ascertaining the facts and the law. The practical effect of this provision is important. The adjudicator may, for example, require the production of particular information, meet and question the parties, make site visits, obtain specialist assistance, research the law and issue directions relating to the conduct of the adjudication (also see, for example, paragraph 13 of the Scheme).

Although the HGCRA 1996 (and the Scheme) appear to confer wide powers on the adjudicator in using his/her initiative to ascertain the facts and the law, and appear to allow the adjudicator to adopt an inquisitorial approach (see however, *Costain Ltd v. Strathclyde Builders Ltd* 2004 SLT 102 in which it was held that adjudication was an adversarial, not an inquisitorial, process and that taking the initiative extended only to obtaining any further evidence which was necessary to decide the dispute), the powers are, in effect, limited by, among others, the nature and scope of the adjudication notice, which determines the adjudicator's jurisdiction and the matters which he/she has to decide and the limited time in which the adjudicator is required to reach a decision. The time limit gives rise to practical issues and means that the power must be exercised cautiously in that there will usually be insufficient time for the adjudicator to undertake lengthy investigations into matters which he/she believes may be relevant but which have not been raised by the parties. Such matters may include, for example, factual matters in relation to the cause of defects, contractual provisions relevant to the matters in dispute but on which neither party relies, or relevant case law which has not been cited by either party.

In practice the adjudicator will often be faced with having to decide whether to reach a decision based only on the submissions received to date or to bring additional matters which he/she considers relevant to the attention of the parties with the likelihood that further submissions (and possibly responses) from the parties will be required and the adjudicator will need further time to consider the submissions before reaching a decision.

In *Costain Ltd v. Strathclyde Builders Ltd* 2004 SLT (per Lord Drummond Young) it was held that adjudication was an adversarial, not an inquisitorial, process and that taking the initiative extended only to obtaining any further evidence that was necessary to decide the dispute.

It is submitted that in order to reach a fair decision, the adjudicator should bring the parties' attention to any matter identified by him/her, but not the parties, as relevant to the decision and, if necessary, seek additional time for further submissions and for reaching a decision.

Where, in reaching a decision, the adjudicator relies on information not provided by the parties or finds it necessary to adopt an approach not contemplated by either party, the rules of natural justice require the adjudicator to inform the parties and give them an opportunity to put forward their respective views before reaching a decision. For examples, see *Woods Hardwick Ltd v. Chiltern Air Conditioning Ltd* [2001] BLR 23 (TCC) where the adjudicator obtained additional information from one party and third parties but failed to inform the other party or give it an opportunity to comment on the information; *Balfour Beatty Construction Ltd v. London Borough of Lambeth* [2002] EWHC 597 (TCC) where the adjudicator adopted his own methodology and, in effect, made-good one party's case but failed to allow the parties to comment

on whether an as-built programme provided by a independent programming expert from whom the adjudicator had sought assistance was a suitable basis on which to base a retrospective critical path analysis; *RSL (South West) Ltd v. Stansell Ltd* [2003] EWHC 1390 (TCC) where the adjudicator failed to give the parties an opportunity to comment on the final report of an expert engaged by the adjudicator. c.f. *Multiplex Constructions (UK) Ltd v. West India Quay Development Company (Eastern) Ltd* [2006] EWHC 1569 (TCC) where the court rejected a submission that in the adjudicator's decision on an extension of time claim was based on a case not put to the adjudicator and the adjudicator had adopted an approach which the parties had not been given an opportunity to address on the grounds that, in contrast to the decision in *Balfour Beatty* above, the adjudicator had not adopted his own methodology.

Any breach of the rules of natural justice must be more than peripheral; they must be material breaches (*Cantillon Ltd v. Urvasco Ltd* [2008] EWHC 282 [TCC]). Breaches will be material in cases where the adjudicator has failed to bring to the attention of the parties a point or issue which they ought to be given the opportunity to comment on if it is one which is either decisive or of considerable potential importance to the outcome of the resolution of the dispute and is not peripheral or irrelevant.

An adjudicator's failure to consider a discrete ground of defence which is not advanced in the original claim but is subsequently raised in the adjudication may be a breach of natural justice and a significant jurisdictional error (*Quartzelec Ltd v. Honeywell Control Systems Ltd* [2009] BLR 328 [TCC]). An adjudicator must consider all defences properly put forward. It is within the adjudicator's jurisdiction to decide what evidence is admissible and even if, within his/her jurisdiction, the adjudicator decides that certain evidence is inadmissible, that will rarely, if ever, amount to a breach of natural justice even if the adjudicator's decision to disregard the evidence was wrong in fact or law (*Jacques (t/a C&E Jaques Partnership) v. Ensign Contractors Ltd* [2009] EWHC 3383 [TCC]).

28.3.15 Adjudicator's decision

Section 108(3) of the HGCRA 1996 requires the construction contract to provide for the decision of the adjudicator to be binding until the dispute is finally determined by legal proceedings, by arbitration (if the contract provides for arbitration or the parties otherwise agree to arbitration) or by agreement. This section also contemplates that the parties may agree to accept the decision of the adjudicator as finally determining the dispute. However, the parties cannot agree in the original contract that the adjudicator's decision shall being binding as this would be contrary to section 108(3).

The arguments as to whether a decision in an adjudication is binding or not have generally arisen in the context of the enforceability of the decision and, in particular, the adjudicator's jurisdiction. The position adopted by the courts from the outset has been that if the adjudicator answered the question which he/she was asked by the parties, it will not matter whether there were errors of fact or law in the decision, it will be enforceable. For examples, see *Macob Civil Engineering Ltd v. Morrison Construction Ltd* [1999] BLR 93 (TCC); *Bouygues (UK) Ltd v. Dahl-Jensen (UK) Ltd* [2000] BLR 49 (TCC); *London and Amsterdam Properties Ltd v. Waterman Partnership Ltd* [2004] BLR (TCC); *Carillion Construction Ltd v. Devonport Royal Dockyard Ltd* [2005] EWCA Civ 1358, [2006] BLR 15 (CA).

In *William Verry Ltd v. London Borough of Camden* [2006] EWHC 761 (TCC), Ramsey J considered section 108(3) and relying on *Ferson Contractors Ltd v. Levolux AT Ltd* [2003] BLR 118 (CA), in which the Court of Appeal had considered the effect of the word 'binding' in that section in the context of an attempt to set-off an amount against an adjudicator's decision, said that the Court of Appeal 'set out in clear terms the principle which applies to the implementation of the intention of Parliament … In my judgment, the effect of those statutory provisions and of the passages in *Levolux* is generally to exclude a right of set-off from an adjudicator's decision.'

The parties may agree to accept the adjudicator's decision as final by an express agreement or provide in the contract that the decision will become final if not challenged. Under the ICE Conditions 7th Edition the adjudicator's decision becomes final and binding unless the dispute is referred to arbitration within 3 months of the decision. Clause 66(9)(b) and amended Clause 66B(3). See also *Castle Inns (Stirling) Ltd v. Clark Contracts Ltd* [2005] ScotCS CSOH 178 for the effect of the final certificate under the JCT Conditions.

The Court of Appeal has repeatedly emphasised that adjudicators' decisions must be enforced, even if they result from errors of procedure, fact or law. For examples, see *Bouygues (UK) Ltd v. Dahl-Jensen (UK) Ltd* [200] BLR 49 (TCC), *C&B Scene Concept Design Ltd v. Isobars Ltd* [2002] EWCA Civ 46; *Ferson Contractors Ltd v. Levolux AT Ltd* [2003] BLR 118 (CA); *Carillion Construction Ltd v. Devonport Royal Dockyard Ltd* [2005] EWCA Civ 1358.

28.3.16 Adjudicator's immunity

Section 108(4) of the HGCRA 1996 requires the contract to provide that the adjudicator is not liable for anything done or omitted in the discharge or purported discharge of his functions as adjudicator unless the act or omission is in bad faith, and that any employee or agent of the adjudicator is similarly protected from liability.

The immunity contemplated by the HGCRA 1996 is contractual and binds the parties to the contract. In addition to the contract, an equivalent provision should be expressly incorporated into the adjudicator's appointment. However, in certain disputes the minimum statutory requirement for immunity will not be satisfactory: for example, in cases where the adjudicator's decision may affect the performance or safety of the works or third parties. Under section 2(1) of the Unfair Contract Terms Act 1977 (UCTA), a person cannot by reference to any

contractual term exclude liability for death or personal injury resulting from negligence. Therefore if the adjudicator gives a negligent decision, albeit in good faith, and the result of implementing the decision is death or personal injury to any of the parties, the adjudicator would be liable. Where other loss or damage occurs, liability may possibly be excluded provided the requirement of reasonableness is satisfied (section 2(2) of UCTA). Also, and importantly, the contractual immunity provided for in the HGCRA 1996 does not affect the rights of third parties who are not parties to the adjudication and it would not protect the adjudicator in the case of death or personal injury of third parties or physical damage to their property. Therefore, before accepting an appointment in a particular dispute, the adjudicator should assess the potential effect of any decision and, if necessary, ensure that his/her terms of appointment require the parties to the contract to indemnify him against liability to third parties, including negligent liability.

28.3.17 Construction contracts which do not comply with the requirements of subsections 108(1) to (4) of the HGCRA 1996

Section 108(5) of HGCRA 1996 provides that, if the construction contract does not comply with the requirements of subsections 108(1) to (4), the adjudication provisions of the Scheme apply.

A substantial body of adjudication case law developed following the introduction of HGCRA 1996 including many cases concerned with the enforcement of adjudication decisions and in which standard form and bespoke contracts were found by the courts not to comply with the provisions of the HGCRA 1996. The payment provisions of the HGCRA 1996 have also given rise to a considerable volume of adjudication case law in the context of enforcement proceedings.

28.4 Statutory payment provisions in the HGCRA 1996
28.4.1 Section 109 of the HGCRA 1996: entitlement to stage payments

Standard form construction contracts and bespoke contracts which are professionally drafted ordinarily contain provisions for stage payments to be made during the course of the works. Section 109(1) of HGCRA 1996 is designed to ensure that, subject to certain exceptions, all contracts incorporate provisions for stage payments. The exceptions under HGCRA 1996 are contracts in which it is specified, or the parties otherwise agree, that the duration will be less than 45 days. The parties are free to agree to the amounts of the payments and the intervals at which, or circumstances in which, the payments become due (section 109(2)).

Section 143 of the LDEDCA 2009 amends the reference in section 109 of the HGCRA 1996 to payments 'under the contract' to payments 'provided for by the contract'. This terminology in respect of payments is adopted in the other amendments which LDEDCA 2009 will incorporate into the HGCRA 1996.

28.4.2 Section 110 of the HGCRA 1996: mechanism for payments

Prior to HGCRA 1996 a major source of disputes was the proper amount of payments which had become due under interim certificates, even where certificates had been issued under contracts or subcontracts incorporating the provisions of standard form contracts. Often the contractor or subcontractor would expect to be paid a particular sum on a particular day, only to find on the day that the payment was due to be made, amounts were being withheld because of allegedly incomplete or defective work or other (often unmeritorious) reasons. One of the principal aims of the HGCRA 1996 was to ensure the payment of the proper sums due under the contract and at the proper time.

The purpose of section 110 of the HGCRA 1996 is to ensure that there is a clear mechanism for determining what is due and the date on which it is to be paid (Section 110(1) of the HGCRA 1996). Section 110(1) of HGCRA 1996 states that every construction contract must provide an adequate mechanism for determining what payments become due under the contract and when they become due; and must provide for a final date for payment in relation to any sum which becomes due. The parties are free to agree how long the period is to be between the date on which a sum becomes due and the final date for payment.

The HGCRA 1996 does not define an 'adequate mechanism'. However, the intention is that a construction contract will contain provisions under which there is a degree of certainty over the amount to be paid and how it is to be determined and the date on which such amount is to be paid.

Section 110(2) provides that every construction contract must provide for the giving of notice by a party not later than 5 days after the date on which a payment becomes due, or would have become due, from that party under the contract, specifying the amount (if any) of the payment made or proposed to be made, and the basis on which such amount was calculated. The circumstances in which the payments would have become due are defined: if the other party had carried out his obligations under the contract (subsection 110(2)(a)); and if no set-off or abatement was permitted by reference to any sum claimed to be due under one or more other contracts (subsection 110(2)(b)). See also *SL Timber Systems Ltd v. Carillion Construction Ltd* 2002 SLT 997 (Outer House SC of Sess); [2001] BLR 516.

If a contract does not contain provisions equivalent to sections 110(1) and 110(2), the provisions of the Scheme Part II apply (Section 110(3) and see the Scheme Part II paras 4 to 7 and 9).

In *Maxi Construction Management Ltd v. Mortons Rolls Ltd* [2001] ScotCS 199; [2001] CILL 1784 the contract had been amended to include two stages in the payment provisions: the first was the submission of the contractor's valuation for agreement by the employer's agent and the second provided for an application by the contractor for payment of the sum which had been agreed. Lord MacFadyen concluded that the regime was not in accordance with section 110(1)(a) of the HGCRA 1996 on the grounds that the contractor's 'Application for Payment' did not constitute a 'claim by the payee' within the meaning of paragraph 12 of the Scheme Part II, because it was an application for agreement of the pursuer's valuation in accordance with a provision in the employer's requirements, and not a claim for payment at all. In addition, the application did not comply with the requirements of paragraph 12 in the further respect that it did not specify the basis on which it was calculated.

In *Alstom Signalling Ltd v. Jarvis Facilities Ltd* [2004] EWHC 1285 (TCC) the payment terms in the subcontract between the parties provided that payment was to be made within 7 days of a certificate issued by Alstom's employer, Railtrack. The adjudicator found that the subcontract did not satisfy section 110(1)(b) of HGCRA 1996 because (on the adjudicator's finding) the final date for payment was capable of being unilaterally altered. The court rejected the adjudicator's analysis and held that there was sufficient certainty in a final date for payment which required the issue of a certificate by Railtrack. The judge said that the final date for payment remained as 7 days after the issue of the (Railtrack) certificate and emphasised the fact that a date was set by reference to a future event did not render it any the less a final date. He referred to the wording in section 110(1) which says 'very clearly' that '[t]he parties are free to agree how long the period is to be between the date on which a sum becomes due and the final date for payment.' The judge concluded that the 'event could be a stage, or milestone or completion, practical or substantial. It could be the result of action by a third party, such as a certificate under a superior contract or transaction, as is found in financing arrangements' and '[p]rovided that the event is readily recognisable and will produce a date by reference to which the final date can be set, there is no reason why it cannot be used'. Accordingly, the date in the subcontract provided for a final date for payment in accordance with section 110(1)(b) of the HGCRA 1996.

Sections 142 and 143 of the LDEDCA 2009 introduce various amendments to section 110 of the HGCRA 1996. Section 142 introduces a new subsection 110(1A) which includes, among others, a provision that the requirement for an adequate mechanism for payment is not satisfied where payment is conditional upon the performance of obligations under another contract or a decision by any person whether obligations under another contract have been performed.

Section 143 of the LDEDCA 2009 omits subsection 110(2) of the HGCRA 1996 and inserts new sections 110A and 110B. The new section 110A is titled 'Payment notices: contractual requirements' and includes, among others, a provision that a construction contract shall, in relation to payments 'provided for by the contract', require the 'payer' or a 'specified person' to give notice to the payee not later than 5 days after the payment due date of the sum due at the payment date and the basis on which such sum is calculated. Alternatively, the construction contract is required to include a provision requiring the 'payee' to give such notice. The terms 'payee', 'payer', 'specified person' and 'payment due date' are defined in the section. Section 110B provides that, in relation to any payment provided for by the construction contract, the payee may give a notice complying with the notice required under section 110A(3) to the payer where the payer or specified person is required to provide the requisite notice under section 110A(2) but fails to do so.

28.4.3 Section 111 of the HGCRA 1996: notice of intention to withhold payment

Section 111 of HGCRA 1996 arises out of one of the key concerns expressed in the Latham (1994) Report that contractors were wrongfully withholding payments due to subcontractors who had little recourse to a remedy. Prior to 1998 this practice was a common source of dispute. Section 111 of HGCRA provides the mechanism by which the payer under the contract must notify the payee that it intends to withhold payment and is linked to the mandatory requirements of section 110 above. In summary, there can be no withholding of 'a sum due under the contract' unless an effective notice of an intention to withhold payment has been served not later than the 'prescribed period' before the final date for payment. The notice must specify not only the amount which it is proposed to withhold but the reason or reasons for such amount being withheld. The prescribed period may be agreed by the parties. If the parties do not agree to the prescribed period, the Scheme Part II, paragraph 10 applies and the prescribed period is not later than 7 days before the final date for payment.

In *Palmers Ltd v. ABB Power Construction Ltd* [1999] BLR 426 (TCC) a contractor employing ABB as a subcontractor intimated that liquidated damages would be set-off against an amount due. ABB's view was that its subcontractor, Palmer, was responsible for the delay to completion of the work as a result of employing insufficiently qualified operatives and withheld payment from Palmer. ABB sought to rely on two letters to Palmer in which there were intimations of a set-off as being notices under section 111 of HGCRA. The court held that the letters did not constitute effective notices under section 111 since neither identified any amount that ABB proposed to withhold and that, since the final date for payment had passed and no effective notice could therefore be served, the sum that was due was payable without being subject to set-off.

On the other hand, as explained in the Scottish case of *SL Timber Systems v. Carillion Construction Ltd* [2001] BLR 516, it is open to the employer to challenge a payment application on the basis that at least some of the sums claimed were not due under the contract without the need to issue a section 111 withholding notice; this was not a question of withholding sums but of defending on the basis that sums were not due in the first place. Insofar as HHJ Bowsher's judgement in *Northern Developments (Cumbria) Ltd v. J&J Nichol* [2000] BLR 158 might have suggested that a withholding notice was required to raise such a defence this was (in the view of the Scottish court) too broad an interpretation of the requirements of section 111.

In *Melville Dundas Ltd and others v. George Wimpey UK Ltd and Others* [2007] UKHL 18 c.f. *Pierce Design International Ltd v. Johnston and another* [2007] EWHC 1691 (TCC) the House of Lords held (by a bare majority) that the HGCRA 1996 does not interfere with the freedom of the parties to make their own terms about interim payments. In *Melville Dundas* the absence of a notice under section 111 was held not to undermine the operation of standard contractual provisions on termination suspending an obligation to make further payment, even when that further payment had otherwise become due, since an appropriately worded provision was sufficient to remove any obligation on the part of the employer to pay any more money once determination had been effected.

Generally a party cannot use section 111 of HGCRA 1996 to set off or cross-claim payments against an adjudicator's decision either if there has been no effective withholding notice at all or if the notice is issued after the decision is issued. In *VHE Construction Plc v. RBSTB Trust Co. Ltd* [2000] BLR 187 (TCC) (also see *The Construction Centre Group Ltd v. The Highland Council* [2002] BLR 476 (OH SC of Sess) affirmed [2003] SLT 623; *Solland International Ltd v. Daraydan Holdings Ltd* (2002) 83 ConLR 109 (TCC); *Balfour Beatty Construction v. Serco Ltd* [2004] EWHC 3336 (TCC) c.f. *David McLean Housing Ltd v. Swansea Housing Association Ltd* [2002] BLR 125 (TCC), an adjudicator found a net sum due to the contractor. The employer notified the contractor that they intended to deduct the majority of the sum awarded by reference to their cross-claim for liquidated damages for delay. They paid only the difference and the contractor claimed the sum that had been deducted. The court held that section 111 precluded such an attempt to set off a cross-claim in the absence of an effective withholding notice.

It may be possible to set off or cross-claim against an adjudicator's decision if the contract incorporates terms in relation either to set-off (for example, *Parsons Plastics (Research and Development) Ltd v. Purac Ltd* [2002] BLR 334) or if it follows logically from the adjudicator's decision that an employer is entitled to recover a sum by way for example of liquidated and ascertained damages (*Balfour Beatty Construction Ltd v. Serco Ltd* [2004] EWHC 3336 (TCC) per Jackson J at para. 53; also see the detailed discussion at chapter 10 of Coulson, 2007), or if the decision does not have immediate effect (for example, is declaratory only) such as would permit the giving of an effective withholding notice after the decision is published.

The leading case on this area is still the Court of Appeal's judgement in *Ferson Contractors Ltd v. Levolux AT Ltd* [2003] EWCA Civ 11 which provides clear guidance as to the position when a party seeks to set off a cross-claim against an adjudicator's decision. The general principle is that a defendant cannot avoid the consequences of failing to provide a valid withholding notice if, by reference to the contractual provisions and on the facts of a particular dispute, the cross-claim required such a notice. To hold otherwise would obviate the requirement for the service of withholding notices. See also the decision of Akenhead J in *Letchworth Roofing Company v. Sterling Building Company* [2009] EWHC 1199 (TCC).

Section 144 of the LDEDCA 2009 substitutes a new section 111 titled 'Requirement to pay notified sum'. Under the new section 111 the payer must pay the 'notified sum' on or before the final date for payment. The 'notified sum' in relation to any payment provided for by the construction contract is the amount specified in the notice given under the relevant subsection in section 110A. The payer or specified person may give the payee notice of the payer's 'intention to pay less than the notified sum'. The notice must specify the sum the payer considers to be due on the date the notice is served and the basis on which such sum is calculated. The notice must be given not later than the 'prescribed period' before the final date for payment and 'may not be given before the notice by reference to which the notified sum is determined'. The 'prescribed period' is either such period as may be agreed of in the absence of agree, the period provided by the Scheme.

28.4.4 Section 112 of the HGCRA 1996: right to suspend performance

A contract may expressly provide for specific rights in circumstances where amounts due under the contract are not paid. However, in the absence of such provisions, there is often a misconception that a contractor has a general right to suspend work if a payment is not made. In fact, there is no general right at common law to suspend work even if a payment is wrongly withheld. See, for example, *Lubenham Fidelities v. South Pembrokeshire District Council* (1986) BLR 39 (CA), in which the Court of Appeal said that whatever the cause of undervaluation, the contractor's remedy was to request the architect to make an appropriate adjustment in another certificate or take the dispute to arbitration under the contract. Adjudication would now be available to the contractor under a construction contract. Section 112 of HGCRA 1996 provides a party to a construction contract with a statutory right to suspend performance of his obligations if a payment is not made by the final date for payment and no effective notice to withhold payment has been given. The exercise of the right requires 7 days notice of an intention to suspend work (see *Palmers Ltd v. ABB Power Construction Ltd* [TCC] on the importance of the notice provisions) and the notice must state the ground(s) relied on for the proposed suspension. The right ceases when the party in default makes payment in full. The period for which work is suspended is to be disregarded in calculating any contractual time limit for completion of work affected by the exercise of the right.

However, the exercise of the right of suspension will generally be a high-risk approach where there is a dispute over whether a payment is due. It may subsequently be decided that the payment was properly withheld and the suspending party may incur liability for damages for non-performance of the contract.

The LDEDCA 2009, at section 145, provides an amendment to section 112 which provides that the party in default shall be liable to pay the party suspending work the reasonable costs and expenses it has incurred in exercising its right to suspend performance.

28.4.5 Section 113 of the HGCRA 1996: prohibition on conditional payment provisions

Prior to HGCRA 1996 contractors would often make a subcontractor's entitlement to payment dependent on the contractor receiving payment. Section 113 of HGCRA was designed to prohibit such 'pay-when-paid' clauses. Under section 113 any provision which seeks to make a payment under the construction contract conditional on receipt of a payment from a third party is ineffective, subject to certain conditions; either that the third person is insolvent or that payment by another person is, under the contract, a condition of payment by the third person and the other person is insolvent.

28.4.6 Construction contracts which do not comply with the requirements of sections 109 to 111 and 113 of the HGCRA 1996

If the construction contract does not comply with the requirements of sections 109 to 111 and 113 of HGCRA 1996 the provisions of the Scheme apply.

28.5 The scheme for construction contracts
28.5.1 Introduction

Under Regulation 4 of Statutory Instrument SI 1998 No. 649, the Scheme for Construction Contracts (England and Wales) Regulations 1998, the Schedule to the Regulations above is 'the Scheme for Construction Contracts' for the purposes of section 114 of HGCRA 1996.

The Secretary of State intends to amend the Scheme following the review of the HGCRA 1996. However, although the amendments to provisions in the HGCRA 1996 relevant to adjudication and payments are available in the prospective version of Part 8 of the LDEDCA 2009, the intended amendments to the Scheme are as yet unknown.

After the introduction of the HGCRA 1996 adjudications under the Scheme usually resulted from a contract which did not comply with HGCRA 1996. However, certain standard form contracts now contain express provisions under which the adjudication procedures are to be those of the Scheme (see, for example, Clause 9.2 of the JCT Standard Form Contract 2005).

The Schedule forming the Scheme is in two parts: Part I contains provisions covering adjudication under the Scheme and Part II contains provisions for payment. Where the construction contract between the parties does not comply with the requirements of sections 108(1) to (4) of the HGCRA 1996, the adjudication provisions in Part I of the Scheme apply. Where the construction contract does not contain one or more of the provisions in the following sections of HGCRA 1996, namely 109 (payment provisions); 110 (dates for payment); 111 (notice of withholding payment); and 113 (prohibition of conditional payment provisions); or similar equivalent provisions, then by default, the provisions in Part II of the Scheme apply. Unless the Scheme is expressly incorporated into the contract, the provisions of the Scheme have effect as implied terms of the construction contract (Section 114(4) of the HGCRA 1996).

An issue which has arisen in many cases is whether the Scheme applies in its entirety to a contract which is non-compliant with section 108 of the HGCRA 1996 or only to the extent that it is necessary to replace parts of the contract which do not apply. The present position is that the TCC Judges have adopted a different approach from the Scottish Courts.

In *C&B Scene Concept Design Ltd v. Isobars Ltd* [2001] CILL 1781 (TCC) (first instance); [2002] BLR 93 (CA), the Recorder decided the whole payment provisions fell and were replaced by the Scheme. On appeal the Court of Appeal felt it was not necessary to decide whether that point was correct because the appeal could be decided without it, but was content to assume the Recorder was right.

In *John Mowlem plc v. Hydra-Tight & Co. Ltd* (2002) 17 Const LJ 358 (TCC) HHJ Toulmin CMG QC held that Clauses 90.1 to 90.4 of Option Y(UK) 2 of the NEC2 standard form did not comply with parts of section 108 of HGCRA 1996 and concluded:

I have considered whether, if some parts of the subcontract comply with the Act, they can be retained and the Act can be used in substitution for or to fill in those parts of the subcontract which are contrary to the Act. But the words of the Act are clear. Either a party complies in its own terms and conditions with the requirements of sections 108(1) to (4) of the Act or the provisions of the Scheme apply.

In *Aveat Heating Ltd v. Jerram Falkus Construction Ltd* [2007] EWHC 131 (TCC) HHJ Havery QC followed the approach in *Mowlem v. Hydra-Tight* above and concluded that the words of HGCRA 1996 were clear: either the terms agreed by the parties complied with the requirements of the HGCRA 1996 or the provisions of the Scheme applied wholesale.

However, the Scottish Courts have adopted a contrary approach. In *Ballast plc v. The Burrell Company (Construction Management) Ltd* [2001] BLR 529 [OH SC of Sess] an adjudicator had decided he was unable to reach a decision. The court held that the decision was a nullity and it was unacceptable for the adjudicator to refuse to decide the dispute. Lord Reid indicated in the course of his judgement that he considered adjudication might be governed in part by the contractual terms and in part by statute since the Scheme may fill gaps where there was non-compliance with sections 108(1), (2) and (4). In the later Scottish case of *Hills Electrical & Mechanical plc v. Dawn Construction Ltd* [2003] ScotCS 107 [OH SC of Sess] the court was concerned with payment provisions and held that the Scheme only applied to the extent that there were gaps in the express terms of the contract.

In *Banner Holdings v. Colchester Borough Council* [2010] EWHC 139 (TCC) Coulson J acknowledged the conflicting authorities and although on the facts of the case it was not necessary to decide the point, he expressed the following view:

I would offer the tentative view that, at least in relation to the adjudication provisions in s108, the wording of section 108(5) suggests that the whole Scheme replaces the express terms, regardless of how many (or how few) of those express terms fail to comply with the Act. More generally, I do not believe that it should be for the court to have to piece together a compliant set of provisions from two different sources. That would not make for certainty.

See also Coulson, 2007, paragraphs 3.01–3.10, and 3.97 which uses an analogy with the Unfair Contracts Terms Act 1977.

In *Yuanda (UK) Co. Limited v. WW Gear Construction Limited* [2010] EWHC 720 (TCC) Edwards-Stuart J considered all the authorities above and concluded:

Where non-compliance with the adjudication provisions arises, that is to say non-compliance with section 108 of HGCRA, the position seems to me to be reasonably clear. The words of the section should be taken to mean what they say, namely that if the contract does not comply – in any respect – with the requirements of subsections (1) to (4), the adjudication provisions of the Scheme apply... the adjudication provisions in the Scheme are those contained in Part I. So if there is any non-compliance, the adjudication provisions in Part I of the Scheme are brought in – lock, stock and barrel.

It is submitted that the approach adopted by the TCC judges in the aforementioned cases is wholly consistent with the wording of section 108(5) of the HGCRA 1996 and is to be preferred.

28.5.2 The Scheme Part I: adjudication

28.5.2.1 Notice of adjudication

The Scheme Part I paragraph 1(1) reflects section 108(2)(a) and any party to a construction contract may give written notice of its intention to refer a dispute arising under the contract to adjudication. The Scheme provides expressly that the notice of adjudication is to be given to every other party to the contract (Part I paragraph 1(2)). The minimum requirements to be set out in the notice are identified as the following: the nature and a brief description of the dispute; details of where and when the dispute has arisen; the nature of the redress sought; and the names and addresses of the parties to the contract (Part I paragraph 1(3)).

28.5.2.2 The appointment of the adjudicator

After the notice of adjudication has been given, and subject to any agreement between the parties on a person who is to act as adjudicator, the referring party must send a request (which is to accompanied by a copy of the notice) either to a person named as adjudicator in the contract to act as adjudicator or to a nominating body named in the contract to appoint an adjudicator (Part I paragraphs 2(1)(a) and (b)). Where neither of the above applies, or a person indicates he/she is unwilling or unable to act, the referring party may request any adjudicator nominating body (such as ICE, RIBA, RICS, CIArb, CIOB, TECBAR and TeCSA) to appoint an adjudicator (Part I paragraph 2(1)(c)).

The Scheme, like the HGCRA 1996, does not state a time in which the request for an appointment is to be made. However, if the request is not made at the earliest possible opportunity (as in contractual adjudications), it may prove very difficult for the referring party to comply with the 7-day time limit for referring the dispute to the adjudicator as required by Part I paragraph 7(1) (see further text).

A person proposed as adjudicator must indicate within 2 days of receipt of the request whether or not he/she is willing to act (Part I paragraph 2(3)).

No one who is an employee of one of the parties may act as adjudicator and any adjudicator must declare any interest, financial or otherwise, in any matter relating to the dispute (Part I paragraph 4).

Where the contract provides for the selection of an adjudicator by an adjudicator nominating body, the body must communicate its selection to the referring party within 5 days of receiving the request (Part I paragraph 5).

Many standard form contracts contain provisions for the appointment of the adjudicator to be governed by a standard adjudication agreement (see, for example, Clause 41A.2.1 of JCT 1998 which requires the adjudicator to execute the 'JCT Adjudication Agreement' with the parties) or for particular adjudication rules or procedures to apply in the adjudication (see, for example, Clause 66B(1)(a) of the ICE Conditions 7th Edition which requires the adjudication to be conducted under 'The Institution of Civil Engineers Adjudication Procedure'). Subject to compliance with the provisions of the Scheme, standard terms of appointment, rules and procedures may apply in adjudications under the Scheme.

Where the contract does not contain a valid mechanism for the appointment of an adjudicator, the Scheme will apply and the appointment will be in accordance with the implied terms of the contract. (*David McLean Housing Ltd v. Swansea Housing Association Ltd* [2002] BLR 125 (TCC)).

28.5.2.3 The referral of the dispute to the adjudicator

Once an adjudicator has been selected, as in contractual adjudications, the next step is to refer the dispute to the adjudicator

by the 'referral notice' (see earlier text). The Scheme states that the referring party 'shall' refer the dispute to the adjudicator in writing within 7 days from the date of the notice of adjudication (Part I paragraph 7(1)). The use of 'shall' in the Scheme contrasts with section 108(2)(b) of the HGCRA 1996 which states that the contract 'shall provide a timetable with the object of securing the appointment of the adjudicator and referral of the dispute to him within 7 days of such notice.'

The 7-day time limit in paragraph 7(1) reflects that in section 108(2)(b) and is tight. The position on whether the 7-day time limit in paragraph 7(1) may be directory or mandatory is discussed earlier in the context of section 108(2)(b) of HGCRA 1996. In view of the conflicting authority, it is submitted that a prudent referring party in any adjudication under the Scheme should (as in contractual adjudications above) ensure that the referral notice is received by the adjudicator not later than 7 days from the date of the notice of adjudication.

28.5.2.4 The time for reaching a decision

In line with section 108(2)(c) of HGCRA 1996, an adjudicator under the Scheme is required to reach a decision within 28 days of the referral (Part I paragraph 19(1)(c)). The adjudicator can extend the period above by 14–42 days but only with the consent of the referring party (Part I paragraph 19(1)(d)). The parties may agree to any extension(s) of the 28-day period but only after the dispute has been referred to the adjudicator (Part I paragraph 19(1)(c)).

In larger adjudications the time limits for reaching a decision may cause difficulties for the adjudicator: for example there may be huge volume of material which he must consider or it may be necessary to allow time for further submissions as the adjudication develops over the course of the 28 days. If it becomes apparent that further time will be required, the adjudicator should immediately seek an extension of time. If the referring party or, as the case may be, the parties do not consent to an appropriate extension and the adjudicator considers that it is not possible to reach a fair decision within the time limit, it may be necessary for the adjudicator to resign in accordance with the Scheme Part I paragraph 9. See *Balfour Beatty Construction Ltd v. Lambeth Borough Council* [2002] BLR 288 (TCC).

If the adjudicator fails to reach a decision in the time, the parties may commence a new adjudication (Part I paragraph 19(2)).

The adjudicator's decision must be reached within the prescribed 28-day period or any extended period which is agreed, otherwise it is a nullity. See, for example, *Ritchie Brothers (PWC) Ltd v. David Philip (Commercials) Ltd* [2005] BLR 384 [IH SC of Sess] adopted in *AC Yule & Son v. Speedwell Roofing and Cladding Ltd* [2007] EWHC 1360 (TCC).

28.5.2.5 The adjudicator's duties and powers

The principal duties of an adjudicator under the Scheme are to act impartially (the Scheme Part I para. 12) and to reach a decision within 28 days or such other time period as may have been agreed (the Scheme Part I para. 19(1)).

The Scheme Part I paragraph 9: resignation of the adjudicator

Paragraph 9(1) provides that an adjudicator may resign at any time on giving notice in writing to the parties of the dispute. An adjudicator must resign where the dispute is the same or substantially the same as one which has previously been referred to adjudication, and a decision has been taken in that adjudication (paragraph 9(2)). Where an adjudicator ceases to act under paragraph 9(1), the referring party may serve a fresh notice of adjudication.

Paragraph 9(4) provides that where an adjudicator resigns in the circumstances referred to in paragraph 9(2), or where a dispute varies significantly from the dispute referred to him in the referral notice and for that reason he is not competent to decide it, the adjudicator shall be entitled to the payment of such reasonable amount as he may determine by way of fees and expenses reasonably incurred by him. The parties are jointly and severally liable for any sum which remains outstanding following the making of any determination on how the payment shall be apportioned.

The Scheme Part I paragraph 12: duty to act impartially

The adjudicator must act impartially. The nature and extent of this duty is considered earlier under the requirements of the HGCRA 1996. However, the Scheme, like the HGCRA 1996, does not expressly provide for any particular practice or procedure to be adopted in the adjudication and this is left to the discretion of the adjudicator.

Paragraph 12 of the Scheme does, however, expand on the contractual requirement in section 108(2)(e) of the HGCRA 1996. In addition to providing that the adjudicator is to act impartially, paragraph of the Scheme states that the adjudicator is required to carry out his/her duties in accordance with any relevant terms of the contract and reach his/her decision in accordance with the applicable law in relation to the contract (Part I paragraph 12(a)). The adjudicator is also under a duty to avoid incurring 'unnecessary expense' (Part I paragraph 12(b)). It is submitted that the provisions under the Scheme merely set out duties which an adjudicator would have in an adjudication under contractual provisions.

The Scheme Part I paragraph 13: taking the initiative in ascertaining the facts and the law

The nature and extent of the initiative in ascertaining the facts and the law is considered above. Paragraph 13 of the Scheme expands on the contractual requirement in section 108(2)(f) of the HGCRA 1996 and sets out particular ways in which the initiative may be applied in adjudications conducted under the Scheme. It is submitted that the matters listed in paragraph 13 include those which an adjudicator in a contractual adjudication would also consider relevant to his/her investigations.

Where the adjudicator relies on information not provided by the parties or finds it necessary to adopt an approach not contemplated by either party, the rules of natural justice require the adjudicator to inform the parties and give them an opportunity to put forward their respective views before reaching a decision (see also section 28.3.14 above and *Woods Hardwick Ltd v. Chiltern Air Conditioning Ltd* [2001]; *Balfour Beatty Construction Ltd v. London Borough of Lambeth* [2002]; *RSL (South West) Ltd v. Stansell Ltd* [2003]; *Multiplex Constructions (UK) Ltd v. West India Quay Development Company (Eastern) Ltd* [2006]). The need to apply the rules in this context is expressly recognised in paragraph 17 of the Scheme which requires the adjudicator to make available to the parties any information which the adjudicator intends to take into account in reaching his/her decision.

The adjudicator may obtain such representations as he requires and, subject to notifying the parties of his/her intentions, may appoint experts, assessors or legal advisers (paragraph 13(f)).

In terms of procedure and the adjudicator's need to control the process in a Scheme adjudication within the limited time available, paragraph 13(g) is important. The provision allows the adjudicator not only to give directions as to the timetable for the adjudication but also provides expressly that he may impose any deadlines or limits on the length of written documents or oral submissions. However, although paragraph 13(g) does not expressly refer to evidence, it is submitted that, taking into account the time limit in which the adjudicator must reach a decision, it is arguable that the limits on written or oral submissions would apply to any evidence served in support of such submissions.

The Scheme Part I paragraph 14: the parties' obligations

Paragraph 14 requires the parties to comply with any request or direction of the adjudicator in relation to the adjudication.

The Scheme Part I paragraph 15: failure to comply with a direction

If, without showing sufficient cause, a party fails to comply with a request, direction or timetable of the adjudicator, paragraph 15 provides that the adjudicator may continue the adjudication in the absence of the party or of any document or statement which the adjudicator requested; draw such inferences from the failure as the adjudicator considers justified in the circumstances; and make a decision on the basis of the information available to him attaching such weight as he/she thinks fit to any evidence submitted to him outside any period he may have requested or directed.

The Scheme Part I paragraph 16: advisers or representatives

Subject to any agreement of the parties otherwise, a party may be assisted or represented by such advisers or representatives as the party considers appropriate. Where the adjudicator is considering oral evidence or representations, a party may not be represented by more than one person unless the adjudicator gives directions otherwise.

The Scheme Part I paragraph 17: the duty to consider relevant information

Paragraph 17 states that the adjudicator 'shall consider' any relevant information submitted to him. The provision is mandatory and, within the time limits of an adjudication, the requirement to consider any relevant information can give rise to practical difficulties for the adjudicator. In complex adjudications a large volume of material will often be submitted during the process. In every adjudication, there is a possibility that information will provided at a late stage in the timetable. The question which frequently arises is how can, or should, the adjudicator deal with the information provided within the time available?

In *CJP Builders Ltd v. William Verry Ltd* [2008] EWHC 2025 (TCC) Verry did not serve its response to the referral within the requisite 7-day period apparently prescribed in the subcontract (DOM/2 1981 Edition) or within an extension of time permitted by CJP. Verry was some 5 to 6 h late in serving the substantial part of its response. The adjudicator mistakenly decided that he had no discretion to permit any extension of time and, having told the parties of his views about this, he informed them that he could have no regard to the contents of the response. The adjudicator's decision ordered Verry to pay the full amount outstanding on CJP's valuation. It was held that the adjudicator had failed to apply the rule of natural justice that each party has a right to be heard and to have its evidence and arguments considered by the tribunal. It was necessary to consider the end result of what the adjudicator actually did, which is that Verry's response, both in terms of argument and evidence, was expressly and consciously not considered by the adjudicator. The breach was found to be material as there was a real possibility on the facts that the adjudicator could have reached a different decision. The fact that the adjudicator acted honestly and in an open way did not mean that there was no breach of the rules of natural justice.

There is no requirement that the adjudicator must hold some form of an oral hearing or meeting. In *Dean & Dyball Construction Ltd v. Kenneth Grubb Associates* [2003] EWHC 2465 (TCC) the court held that, provided that the rules of natural justice were complied with and each party to an adjudication knew the case which it had to meet and was given a proper opportunity to meet that case, an adjudicator need not necessarily hold a hearing or allow cross-examination of witnesses. If a hearing or meeting is held, the Scheme permits a party to have legal or other representation (see the Scheme Part I paragraph 16).

In *AWG Construction Services Ltd v. Rockingham Motor Speedway* [2004] 20 Const LJ 107; [2004] EWHC 888 (TCC) Rockingham served additional material, including a witness statement which raised new matters at a very late stage in the proceedings. It was held that there had been injustice in the procedure in that the adjudicator had failed to afford AWG a proper opportunity to give a fully considered response to the additional material which had been served at such a late stage and that AWG had been clearly prejudiced by its inability to do so. The judge said that this was demonstrated by the basis on which the adjudicator had made the findings in his decision, which had taken into account matters which Rockingham had raised in detail for the first time at a late stage and to which AWG had not had a proper opportunity to respond.

The Scheme Part I paragraph 18: duty of confidentiality

Paragraph 18 imposes a duty on the adjudicator and the parties not to disclose any information or document provided in connection with the adjudication where the party supplying it has indicated that it is to be treated as confidential.

The Scheme Part I paragraph 19: time for decision

Paragraph 19(1) reflects subsections 108(2)(c) and (d) of HGCRA 1996. The adjudicator must reach his/her decision not later than 28 days after the date of the referral notice or 42 days if the Referring Party consents to the extension, or in such further period as may be agreed between the parties. Paragraph 19(2) provides expressly that if the adjudicator fails to reach a decision within the prescribed time, a party may serve a fresh notice of adjudication. Under paragraph 19(3), the adjudicator must deliver a copy of the decision as soon as possible after he has reached the decision. For these purposes making a decision and delivering it have been treated as equivalent. See *Bloor Construction (UK) Ltd v. Bowmer & Kirkland (London) Ltd* [2000] BLR 314 (TCC). Also see *St Andrew's Bay Development v. HBG Management and Another* 2003 SLT 740 in which it was observed that the HGCRA 1996 is silent on the question of intimation or communication of a decision and the court concluded that a decision cannot be said to be made until it is intimated.

The Scheme Part I paragraph 20: the adjudicator's decision

Paragraph 20: The adjudicator must decide the matters in dispute. He/she may take into account any other matters which the parties to the dispute agree should be within the scope of the adjudication or which are matters under the contract which he considers are necessarily connected with the dispute. This provision, in effect, expressly defines the adjudicator's jurisdiction. In *Northern Developments (Cumbria) Ltd v. J&J Nichol* [2000] BLR 158 (TCC) it was held that the adjudicator would (had he otherwise had the relevant jurisdiction) have been entitled to take into account matters of allegations of defective work and delays as necessarily connected with applications for payment of outstanding monies.

Paragraph 20(a) provides an express power that the adjudicator may open up revise and review any decision taken or certificate given by any person referred to in the contract, unless that decision or certificate is declared by the contract to be final and conclusive. The adjudicator may also decide that any of the parties is liable to make a payment under the contract and when that payment is due and the final date for payment (paragraph 20(b)).

Paragraph 20(c) of the Scheme allows an Adjudicator 'having regard to any term of the contract relating to the payment of interest [to] decide the circumstances in which, and the rates at which, and the periods for which simple or compound rates of interest shall be paid'. There has been debate over an adjudicator's powers to award interest in the absence of an express contractual term. In *Carillion Construction Ltd v. Devonport Royal Dockyard Ltd* [2005] BLR 310 (TCC) (first instance); [2006] BLR 15 (CA) at first instance Jackson J held that paragraph 20(c) envisaged a free-standing power to award interest even absent any contractual provision for interest; not only was a power to award interest the more natural interpretation of the words used in this paragraph of the Scheme but it made obvious commercial sense for an adjudicator to have such power. However, the Court of Appeal did not agree with that interpretation. Chadwick LJ said:

> It is necessary to have regard to the structure of paragraph 20 as a whole. There are three sentences: (1) The adjudicator shall decide the matters in dispute; (2) [In deciding those matters] he may take into account other matters (which are specified); (3) In particular [in deciding those matters] he may (a) open up, revise and review decisions already taken or certificates already given (unless the contract otherwise provides), (b) decide that any of the parties is liable to make payment and if so when and in what currency and (c) decide the circumstances in which (and the rates at which and the periods for which) interest is to be paid. Within that structure effect has to be given to the words 'In particular' at the beginning of the third sentence. We can see no reason why those words should not bear their usual and natural meaning. What comes after them is intended to be a particularisation of what has gone before. What comes after elaborates and explains what has gone before; it does not add to what has gone before. So the adjudicator may decide questions as to interest if, but only if, (i) those questions are 'matters in dispute' which have been properly referred to him or (ii) those are questions which the parties to the dispute have agreed should be within the scope of the adjudication or (iii) those are questions which the adjudicator considers to be 'necessarily connected with the dispute'. Questions which do not fall within one or other of those categories are not within the scope of paragraph 20(c) of the Scheme. There is no freestanding power to award interest.

The Scheme Part I paragraph 22: requests for a reasoned decision

Paragraph 22 states that, if requested by one of the parties to the dispute, the adjudicator must provide reasons for his decision. However, the provision is silent on the time at which the request may be made. The timing of the request is important. For example, the adjudicator may have approached the adjudication on the basis that reasons were not required and if a request is made late in the proceedings, it may not be possible to provide a decision with reasons in the time available. Any request received after the decision has given and communicated to the parties is too late: the adjudicator's appointment has expired. Therefore, the requirement for decisions should be addressed at the earliest opportunity and a prudent adjudicator will, immediately after the referral, direct the parties to state within a specified period (probably not more than 7 days) whether or not reasons will be required.

The Scheme Part I paragraph 23: effects of the decision

Paragraph 23(1) provides that the adjudicator may, if he/she thinks fit, order any of the parties to comply peremptorily with his decision or any part of it. Paragraph 23(2) reflects the requirement in section 108(3) of the HGCRA 1996 that the contract must contain a provision that the decision of the adjudicator is binding on the parties, and they shall comply with the decision until the dispute is finally determined by legal proceedings, by arbitration (if the contract provides for arbitration or the parties otherwise agree to arbitration) or by agreement between the parties.

28.5.3 The Scheme Part II: payment provisions

28.5.3.1 General

The payment provisions in Part II of the Scheme represent the default position in circumstances where a construction contract does not comply with the payment provisions in HGCRA 1996. An overview of the payment provisions in the Scheme is set out here merely for ease of comparison with the payment provisions in the HGCRA 1996 above.

28.5.3.2 The Scheme Part II paragraphs 1–2: entitlement to stage payments

Paragraph 1 provides that where the parties to a relevant construction contract fail to agree to the amount of any instalment or stage or periodic payment for any work under the contract or the intervals at which, or circumstances in which such payments become due under the contract the relevant provisions of paragraphs 2 to 4 of Part II of the Scheme apply.

Paragraph 2 provides a method of calculating the amount of any payment by way of instalments or stage or periodic payments which includes, among other matters, the value of the work performed and the materials brought on to the site.

28.5.3.3 The Scheme Part II paragraphs 3–7: dates for payment

If a contract does not contain a provision equivalent to section 110, then Part II of the Scheme applies (Section 110(3) of the HGCRA 1996). Paragraphs 4 to 7 of the Scheme Part II contain provisions for the dates for payment.

Paragraph 3 states that where the parties to a construction contract fail to provide an adequate mechanism for determining either what payments become due under the contract, or when they become due for payment, or both, the relevant provisions of paragraphs 4 to 7 apply. Under paragraph 4, payments of the kind referred to in paragraph 2 become due on whichever of the following dates occurs later: the expiry of 7 days following the period relevant to the instalment or payment (i.e. the payment cycle) or the making of a claim by the payee.

Paragraph 5 provides that the final payment payable under a construction contract shall become due on the expiry of 30 days following completion of the work or the making of a claim by the payee, whichever is the later. The final payment is defined as the payment of an amount equal to the difference (if any) between the contract price and the aggregate of any instalment or stage or periodic payments which have become due under the contract.

Under paragraph 6, payment of the contract price under a construction contract (which is not a relevant construction contract) becomes due on the expiry of 30 days following the completion of the work or the making of a claim by the payee, whichever is the later.

Under paragraph 7 any payment other than the final payment under a construction contract becomes due on the expiry of 7 days following the completion of the work to which the payment relates or the making of a claim by the payee, whichever is the later.

28.5.3.4 The Scheme Part II paragraph 8: final date for payment

If a contract does not contain a provision equivalent to section 110, then Part II of the Scheme applies. In particular, paragraph 8 provides the final date for payment.

Where the parties to a construction contract fail to provide a final date for payment in relation to any sum which becomes due under a construction contract, the provisions of paragraph 8(1) shall apply. Under paragraph 8(2) the final date for the making of any payment of a kind referred to in paragraphs 2, 5, 6 or 7, is 17 days from the date that payment becomes due.

28.5.3.5 The Scheme Part II paragraph 9: notice specifying amount of payment

If a contract does not contain a provision equivalent to section 110(2), the provision in paragraph 9 of the Scheme Part II applies. Under paragraph 9 a party to a construction contract must, not later than 5 days after the date on which any payment becomes due from him, or would have become due, if the other party had carried out his obligations under the contract, and no set-off or abatement was permitted by reference to any sum claimed to be due under one or more other contracts, give notice to the other party to the contract. The notice must specify the amount (if any) of the payment the party has made or proposes to make and also specify to what the payment relates and the basis on which the amount is calculated.

28.5.3.6 The Scheme Part II paragraph 10: notice of intention to withhold payment

If the parties do not agree to the prescribed period in section 111 of the HGCRA 1996, the Scheme Part II, paragraph 10 applies, and the prescribed period is not later than 7 days before the final date for payment determined either in accordance with the construction contract, or where no such provision is made in the contract, in accordance with paragraph 8.

28.5.3.7 The Scheme Part II paragraph 11: prohibition of conditional payment provisions

The HGCRA 1996 prohibits conditional payments (i.e. pay-when-paid clauses). Paragraph 11 of the Scheme Part II provides that where a provision making payment under a construction contract conditional on the payer receiving payment from a third person is ineffective (as referred to in section 113 of the HGCRA 1196, and the parties have not agreed to other terms for payment, the relevant provisions in the Scheme apply.

28.6 Adjudication provisions in standard form contracts
28.6.1 The ICE conditions

The dispute resolution provisions in amended Clause 66B(1)(a) of the ICE Conditions 7th Edition provide for the referral to adjudication of *'any matter in dispute arising under or in connection with the Contract or the carrying out of the Works'* [underline added]. The nature and scope of the matters which may be referred under this clause is wider than adjudication under HGCRA 1996 and the Scheme, which provide a right to refer a dispute arising 'under' the contract. Disputes referable under Clause 66B(1)(a) would probably include all disputes except disputes as to the existence of the contract itself.

The ICE Adjudication Procedure 1997.

The adjudicator may rely on his own expert knowledge and experience (paragraph 1.4). It is submitted that, in the absence of relevant submissions from the parties, the prudent adjudicator will always disclose his reasoning and allow the parties an opportunity to respond.

The adjudicator may be named in the contract or agreed between the parties. ICE is named as the nominating body in default of agreement (paragraph 3.3); standard terms and conditions apply to the appointment (paragraph 3.4) and are annexed to the Procedure; the adjudicator has 'complete discretion' in the conduct of the adjudication (paragraph 5.5); the adjudicator is empowered to obtain legal or technical advice after notifying the parties (paragraph 5.6); there is provision for joinder if the parties agree (paragraph 5.7); the adjudicator is not required to give reasons (paragraph 6.1); the adjudicator may direct the payment of simple or compound interest (paragraph 6.2); the parties are to bear their own costs (paragraph 6.5); the parties are jointly and severally responsible for the adjudicator's fees, which may however be allocated between them by the adjudicator, failing which each party is responsible for half (paragraph 6.5); and the adjudicator has an express power to correct a clerical mistake, error or ambiguity in the decision within 14 days of notification of his decision (paragraph 6.9).

Paragraph 6.4 in the original version of the Procedure provided that if a decision not reached within the time limit it shall still be effective. This procedure does not comply with section 108(2) of the HGCRA 1996, which only permits an extension of the 28 day, or as the case may be, the 42 day period *after* the dispute has been referred to adjudication. Following the decision in *Epping Electrical Company Ltd v. Briggs and Forrester (Plumbing Services) Ltd* [2007] BLR 126 (TCC) (the court considered a similar provision in paragraph 25 of the Construction Industry Council (CIC) Model Adjudication Procedure and held that it was inconsistent with section 108(2) of the HGCRA 1996) the ICE removed paragraph 6.4 (and paragraph 6.6, which provided for the adjudicator to exercise a lien on his decision) from the ICE Adjudication Procedure 1997. Where old copies of the ICE Procedure are still being used, the ICE recommends that, at the outset of an adjudication under the ICE Procedure, the adjudicator makes it clear to the parties that Clauses 6.4 and 6.6 do not apply. The ICE decided that it would not publish a new edition of its adjudication procedure until the final outcome of the review of the HGCRA 1996 were known.

28.6.2 JCT Standard Building Contract 2005

The JCT 2005 family of standard form contracts has abandoned the bespoke adjudication provisions in the JCT 1998 editions and have adopted the provisions of the Scheme for adjudication.

28.6.3 JCT Standard Form Building Contract 1998

The 1998 Editions of the JCT family of contracts are still in use and typical provisions such as those contained in Clause 41A of the JCT Standard Form Building Contract 1998 Private with Quantities standard form are considered below.

The scope of the adjudication provision is limited to any dispute or difference arising 'under' the contract (Clause 41A.1).

No adjudicator may be agreed or nominated unless the adjudicator executes the JCT standard form of agreement for appointment of an adjudicator (Clause 41A.2.1). By contrast, failure by the parties to execute the agreement (or, indeed, to comply with the majority of the procedural requirements laid down in Clause 41A) will not invalidate the adjudicator's decision (Clause 41A.5.6).

The adjudicator is not obliged to give reasons for his decision (Clause 41A.5.4). It is submitted that an adjudicator should always be asked to provide a reasoned decision. However, Clause 41A.5.4 is not qualified by words such as 'subject to any request by the parties ...' Therefore, it would appear that, notwithstanding a request by one (or perhaps both) parties, in an adjudication under these JCT contractual provisions, the adjudicator would not be obliged to give reasons (c.f. the Scheme Part I, paragraph 22). It could, however, be argued that the adjudicator's appointment is contractual and therefore if both parties agree, the adjudicator can be required to give reasons for his decision.

Under Article 7A of the Contract the enforcement of a decision of the adjudicator is excepted from the arbitration agreement (if incorporated). It follows that, even where the final determination is by arbitration, the parties may take legal proceedings to enforce an adjudicators decision by summary judgement in the ordinary way.

28.7 Costs and fees
28.7.1 The parties' costs

In *Northern Developments (Cumbria) Ltd v. J&J Nichol* [2000] BLR 158 (TCC) each party had asked in writing through experienced representatives for their respective costs. It was held that there is no express provision in the HGCRA 1996 or the Scheme which gives the adjudicator power to apportion or order the payment of costs by one party to the other. It is not necessary to include a term for the purpose of making the adjudication procedure efficacious and therefore a term may not be implied.

The judgement in *Northern Developments* was, however, subsequently qualified by the Court of Appeal in *John Roberts Architects Ltd v. Parkcare Homes* [2006] BLR 106 (CA) para. 12 in which May LJ said, obiter, that the decision in *Northern Developments* was wrongly decided to the extent that the judge had decided that where each party claimed costs against the other they had given the adjudicator jurisdiction to decide costs by implied agreement.

An agreement for adjudication may expressly provide that the adjudicator is empowered to direct the payment of costs and expenses (for example, see *John Roberts Architects Ltd v. Parkcare Homes* above). The nature and extent of the adjudicator's jurisdiction will be determined by the rules which apply or any agreement by the parties.

In *Total M & E Services Ltd v. ABB Building Technologies Ltd* [2004] EWHC 248 (TCC) the court held that the costs of adjudication could not be recovered as damages: to allow the recovery of costs on that basis would be to subvert the Scheme.

28.7.2 The adjudicator's fees

The general principle is that the adjudicator is entitled to the payment of such reasonable amount as he/she may determine by way of fees and expenses (the Scheme Part I para. 25 expressly reflects this principle). However, the adjudication agreement should include provisions setting out the level of the fees and terms which attach to their payment.

The Scheme Part I paragraph 25 expressly provides that the parties are jointly and severally liable to pay the adjudicator's fees and expenses and that the adjudicator may determine the apportionment between the parties of the payment to be made in respect of fees.

Many of the standard form contracts contain adjudication agreements in which the procedures are usually identified by reference to the adjudication rules into which that form of contract is tied (for examples, see the ICE 7th Edition and the JCT 1998 Edition). These rules will typically deal with the basis of the adjudicator's fees, the responsibility of each of the parties for those fees; and the circumstances in which the adjudication agreement may be terminated and the consequences which arise on such termination. The Scheme also sets out the various circumstances in which an adjudicator may resign or otherwise cease to act and the way in which fees are to be determined in each case (see the Scheme Part I paras 8(4), 9(4), 11(1), 11(2)).

Paragraph 11(1) of the Scheme Part I entitles the adjudicator to his fees if the appointment is revoked by agreement. However, paragraph 11(2) provides, the adjudicator will not be entitled to his/her fees if the revocation is due to default or misconduct on the part of the adjudicator.

In respect of a decision, or part of a decision, which the adjudicator has no jurisdiction to make, it appears that the party which had originally sought adjudication will be liable for the adjudicator's fees because the responding had not caused the reference to the adjudicator of matters in respect of which there was no jurisdiction. For example, see *Ken Griffin & John Tomlinson t/a K&D Contractors v. Midas Homes Ltd* [2000] 78 Con LR 152 (TCC).

Some adjudicators seek security for their fees usually by way of a deposit advanced by each party shortly after the referral. This practice can lead to difficulty with the perception of the adjudicator's independence and impartiality in cases where one of the parties lodges its part of the deposit and the other does not. This situation is best avoided by the adjudicator not requiring deposits or, if deposits have been requested and only one is received, by returning that deposit. Also, adjudicators sometimes seek interim payments of fees, usually in circumstances where the adjudication lasts longer than 28 days. It is submitted that this practice can rarely be justified taking into account the timescale under which an adjudication is ordinarily concluded.

In order to ensure the prompt payment of their fees, adjudicators in the past adopted the practice common in arbitration of exercising a lien on their fees and withholding the decision until the fees were paid in full. However, unlike arbitration, in adjudication there is a statutory deadline for reaching and communicating the decision. The courts have indicated strongly that, taking into account the short period imposed by the HGCRA 1996 for reaching a decision, an adjudicator is not entitled to exercise a lien over his decision if to do so would delay the communication of the decision beyond the prescribed period. For examples, see *St. Andrews Bay Development Ltd v. HBG Management Ltd* 2003 SLT 740; *Epping Electrical Company Ltd v. Briggs and Forrester (Plumbing Services) Ltd* [2007] EWHC 4 (TCC), [2007] BLR 126; *Mott MacDonald Ltd v. London & Regional Properties Ltd* [2007] EWHC 1055 (TCC).

28.8 Enforcement of adjudication decisions and the role of the courts

28.8.1 Temporary binding nature of the adjudicator's decision

Under section 108 of the HGCRA, an adjudicator's decision is in principle binding upon the parties once it is made until finally determined by court or arbitration proceedings and no other steps are required. In the majority of cases however the decision will order one party to pay a sum of money to the other party and in practice the losing party will often refuse to pay thereby requiring the successful party to apply to court for summary judgement to enforce the decision.

28.8.2 Enforcement procedure in the TCC

The Technology and Construction Court (TCC) is the court in which enforcement of an adjudicator's decision and other adjudication business is normally undertaken. In addition to enforcement applications, declaratory relief is sometimes sought at the outset of an adjudication in respect of matters such as the jurisdiction of the adjudicator or the validity of the adjudication.

Unlike arbitration business there is neither a practice direction nor a claim form for adjudication business. Enforcement proceedings normally seek a monetary judgement so that Civil Procurement Rules (CPR) Part 7 proceedings are usually appropriate however Part 8 proceedings may be used where no monetary judgement is sought and there is no substantial dispute of fact. Following commencement of proceedings an immediate application will then be made for summary judgement under CPR Part 24. The Court has developed a procedure to deal promptly with enforcement applications. Section 9 of the TCC Court Guide (2005, revised 2007; further revision expected in 2010) sets out the procedure and Appendix F provides a template for Directions for Enforcement Proceedings. The assigned judge will normally provide directions within 3 days of a party's application and the enforcement proceedings will be heard within 28 days of directions being made. At this hearing the parties are invited to address the court on the limited grounds on which a defendant may resist an enforcement application.

Enforcement may also be attempted through different forms of application. A party might apply for declaratory relief following an adjudicator's decision for example to affirm an entitlement to an extension of time. The TCC's summary procedure would be followed in such cases. Technically it is also possible to seek to enforce an adjudicator's decision by a statutory demand followed by winding up proceedings but in practice such a demand would be set aside if the losing party had a genuine cross claim and such an approach is not recommended given the fact that the TCC has an expressly tailored procedure for enforcement (see, for example, the case of *Harlow & Milner Ltd v. Teasdale (No. 1)* [2006] EWHC 54 [TCC]).

Similarly, whilst an injunction could be used to enforce such a decision this approach has been rendered unnecessary by the TCC summary judgement procedure and was not endorsed in the early case of *Macob v. Morrison* [1999] BLR 93.

28.8.3 Using the court enforcement process for the final determination of a point of law

The courts will not be bound by a mistaken decision of an adjudicator in all circumstances despite the nature of the adjudication process. In *Geoffrey Osborne Ltd v. Atkins Rail Ltd* [2009] EWHC 2425 (TCC), the TCC confirmed that in a case in which an adjudicator had incorrectly decided a point of law and there were no disputed questions of fact, a losing party could in defending enforcement proceedings ask the court to make a final determination of the issue thereby substituting its decision for that of the adjudicator. The ability of the court to cut short the effect of an adjudicator's mistaken decision in such circumstances will only apply where there is no arbitration clause.

28.8.4 Grounds for resisting enforcement

The courts take a very robust approach to the enforcement of adjudication decisions in order to give effect to the policy behind the HGCRA and it is rare for challenges to succeed.

In the important case of *Carillion v. Devonport* in the Court of Appeal, Lord Justice Chadwick made quite clear the approach that the courts will take to such challenges:

> The objective which underlies the Act and the statutory scheme requires the Courts to respect and enforce the adjudicator's decision unless it is plain that the question which he has decided was not the question referred to him or the manner in which he has gone about his task is obviously unfair. It should only be in rare circumstances that the courts will interfere with the decision of the Adjudicator. The courts should give no encouragement to the approach adopted by (the challenging party) in the present case which … may indeed aptly be described as 'simply scrabbling around to find some argument, however tenuous, to resist payment…'. In short, in the overwhelming majority of cases, the proper course for a party who is unsuccessful in an adjudication under the scheme must be to pay the amount that he has been ordered to pay by the Adjudicator. If he does not accept the adjudicator's decision as correct (whether on the facts or in law), he can take legal or arbitration proceedings in order to establish the true position. To seek to challenge the adjudicator's decision on the ground that he has exceeded his jurisdiction or breached the rules of natural justice (save in the plainest cases) is likely to lead to a substantial waste of time and expense….
>
> Carillion Construction Limited v. Devonport Royal Dockyard [2005] EWCA 1358 (CA)

The potential grounds for challenge have been flagged in the earlier sections of this chapter on the jurisdictional requirements of the Act and the Scheme and the obligation upon an adjudicator to act impartially and to observe the requirements of natural justice.

28.8.4.1 Challenge on grounds of lack of jurisdiction

It will clearly be a defence if the adjudicator has not been properly appointed or, in the case of a statutory adjudication, if the class of contract does not fall within sections 104 to 107 of the HGCRA.

The courts will enforce decisions which are within the jurisdiction of the adjudicator even if plainly wrong (*Bouygues v. Dahl-Jensen* [2000] BLR 522), save in cases which can be finally resolved by the court at the enforcement stage (section 28.7.3 above). But decisions which fall outside the jurisdiction of the adjudicator will not be enforced. The adjudicator's jurisdiction derives from the adjudication notice and the scope of the referral. Resolution of a dispute that has not been referred to the adjudicator will be a nullity and unenforceable (see, for example, *C&B Scene Concept Design v. Isobars* (2002) 82 Con LR 154).

28.8.4.2 Challenge on grounds of breach of natural justice

The obligation of the adjudicator to comply with the requirements of natural justice set in the context of the adjudication process has been described at 28.3.13 above.

This has proved a fertile ground for challenge to adjudicator's decisions. Guidance as to the balance reached by the courts between allowing adjudicator's control over procedure in the context of a speedy and to some extent abridged process and the maintenance of minimum standards of fairness can be found in the cases.

The following is a summary of the approach of the courts insofar as possible using the two aspects of natural justice identified by Dyson LJ in *AMEC Capital Projects Ltd v. Whitefriars City Estates Ltd* [2004] EWCA Civ 1418.

First, a party is entitled to have his case heard by an unbiased tribunal. An adjudicator must act impartially. This will be judged using the test whether a fair-minded person would describe the proceedings as having been tainted with bias. Examples of conduct which have been held to be unacceptable include the following: The adjudicator must not communicate with one of the parties in the absence of the other (*Discain Project Services Ltd v. Opecprime Developments Ltd* [2001] BLR 285). It will not be acceptable for an adjudicator to have acted as a mediator in a dispute before then deciding it as adjudicator (*Glencot Development & Design Ltd v. Ben Barrett & Son (Contractors) Ltd* [2001] BLR 207).

Second, a party should be informed of the allegations against him and be given an opportunity to answer those allegations. A fair procedure will not however require the adjudicator to ask for the comments of the parties on all matters; fairness will be judged within the context of the available timescale, the volume of material and the respective importance of the matter of which complaint is made. Examples of procedural unfairness invalidating a decision include the following: Where an adjudicator has made his/her decision on the basis of an argument of his/her own upon which the parties have not been given the opportunity to comment (*Balfour Beatty Construction Ltd v. London Borough of Lambeth* [2002] BLR 288). Where the adjudicator has obtained assistance from an expert but not given the parties a chance to comment on the advice received (*RSL (South West) Ltd v. Stansell Ltd* [2003] EWHC 1390). Where the adjudicator fails to consider a party's submission on the mistaken basis that he/she could not extend time to do so (*CJP Builders Ltd v. William Verry Ltd* [2008] BLR 545).

28.8.5 Enforcing parts of decisions and the difficulty of multiple adjudications

It is common to find several disputes being referred to an adjudicator in a single adjudication and also to find parties to a single contract engaging in successive adjudications. Each of these situations can cause challenges in relation to enforcement.

Where an adjudicator's decision addresses several issues and where the decision is accepted in relation to some issues but not in relation to others, the current approach of the courts is that the fact that part of a decision is unenforceable does not preclude the decision being enforceable in relation to other issues (*Cantillon v. Urvasco* [2008] BLR 250, and *Bovis Lendlease v. Trustees of the London Clinic* [2009] EWHC 64).

Jackson J had addressed the court's approach to enforcement where the parties engaged in multiple adjudications in the case of *Interserve Industrial Services v. Cleveland Bridge* [2006] EWHC 741 holding that at the end of each adjudication, barring special circumstances, the losing party must comply with the adjudicator's decision and cannot withhold payment on the expectation of recovery under a subsequent decision. This approach has since been followed (for example, in *Hart v. Smith* [2009] EWHC 2223, per Toulmin HHJ).

28.8.6 Concern that the successful party is insolvent

A losing party may be concerned about the solvency of the successful party at the stage of enforcement on the basis that it might not be able to recover any ensuing payment following a final determination. The Court of Appeal in *Bouygues v. Dahl-Jensen* [2000] BLR 522 para. 35 per Chadwick LJ suggested that r.4.90 of the Insolvency Rules 1986, which provides for set-off of mutual credits and debits, might in appropriate circumstances support the refusal of summary judgement on an adjudication. This suggestion has not been followed but there have been cases, for example *Rainford House v. Cadogan* [2001] BLR 417, in which the court has granted a stay of execution pursuant to RSC Order 47 (CPR Schedule 1) in cases where there is credible evidence of insolvency or inability of a party to repay the adjudication sums.

The principles which are to be applied in an application for a stay of execution of a summary judgement of an adjudicator's decision have been established in recent cases (*Wimbledon Construction v. Derek Vago* [2005] EWHC 1086; *JPA Design and Build v. Sentosa (UK) Ltd* [2009] EWHC 2312). Whilst emphasising that the court will bear in mind the purpose of adjudication and the priority of not keeping a successful party out of its money: (1) the probable inability of a claimant to repay may constitute special circumstances within Order 47 rendering it appropriate to grant a stay; (2) if the enforcing party is in insolvent liquidation or there is undisputed evidence to this effect then a stay will usually be granted, unless its financial position is the same or similar to that at the time of making the contract or is due wholly or insignificant part to the defendant's failure to pay the sums awarded in the adjudication.

These principles were recently qualified in the case of *Mead General Building Ltd v. Dartmoor Properties Ltd* [2009] BLR 225 so that a judgement will not normally be entered if a company is in insolvent liquidation but that a judgement may be entered where the claimant is in administrative receivership and a stay can be granted where evidence shows that it would be unable to repay the relevant sums. The fact that a company is subject to a company voluntary arrangement (CVA) will be relevant but not of itself sufficient to warrant a stay.

28.9 The courts and management of adjudication
28.9.1 Stay for adjudication

Parties are entitled under the HCGRA 1996 to commence an adjudication at any time. Particularly in complex cases, parties will be litigating at the same time as referring their disputes to adjudication. The courts have to grapple with the difficulty of managing the two processes efficiently whilst allowing the parties their statutory rights.

The TCC judgement in *DGT Steel and Cladding Ltd v. Cubitt Building and Interiors Ltd* [2007] EWHC 1584 addressed a party's application for a stay of court proceedings commenced in breach of an agreement to refer disputes to adjudication. The court's approach was essentially that if a party can establish a binding adjudication agreement, the persuasive burden shifts to the other party to justify why the court should not exercise its inherent jurisdiction to order a stay of the court proceedings. The judge considered the relevant authorities and derived three principles:

(1) The court will not grant an injunction to prevent one party from commencing adjudication proceedings even if there are ongoing arbitration or court proceedings in respect of the same dispute. *Hershel v. Breen* [2000] BLR 272

(2) The court has an inherent jurisdiction to stay court proceedings issued in breach of an agreement to adjudicate. *Cape Durasteel v. Rosser & Russell* (1995) 46 Con LR 75

(3) The court's discretion as to whether or not to order a stay in such circumstances should be exercised on the basis that if a binding adjudication agreement has been demonstrated the persuasive burden is on the party seeking to resist the stay to justify why it should not be granted.

28.9.2 The courts and 'kitchen sink' adjudications

An obvious problem that the courts have had to consider is whether to interfere in circumstances in which the size and complexity of a dispute referred to adjudication is clearly of a scale beyond that envisaged by the summary statutory process. HHJ Wilcox commented in his judgement in *London and Amsterdam Properties v. Waterman Partnership Ltd* 2004] BLR 179 that:

> Even where an adjudicator is prepared to firmly and impartially exercise the powers given to him under the Scheme to investigate control and manage the hearing of a dispute there may well be cases which because of their complexity and/or the conduct of a claimant are not susceptible of being adjudicated under the Scheme fairly and thus impartially.
>
> [2004] BLR 179, paragraph 146

Similar concerns were expressed in *AWG Construction Services v. Rockingham Motor Speedway Ltd* [2004] EWHC 888, at paragraph 123. When addressing a ground of challenge alleging that the size and complexity of the dispute made it impossible for it to be resolved fairly by adjudication in the case of *CIB Properties v. Birse Construction* [2004] EWHC 2365, HHJ Toulmin emphasised that the test was not whether the dispute was too complicated to refer to adjudication but whether the adjudicator was able to reach a fair decision within the time limits allowed by the parties.

The perceived tactical advantage of referring a 'kitchen sink' final account dispute to adjudication whilst effectively ambushing the respondent with a large and complex claim my rebound against the referring party. In *William Verry (Glazing Systems) Ltd v. Furlong Homes Ltd* [2005] EWHC 138, the adjudicator found against the referring party on its claims for outstanding final account sums and extensions of time and the judge hearing the enforcement proceedings was disparaging about such tactics.

Although the courts have commented about the unsuitability of referring over-complex disputes to adjudication particularly in circumstances where there has been an effective 'ambush', the courts have not for that reason alone refused to enforce a decision. The validity of the adjudicator's decision has depended upon whether or not the adjudicator has been able to deal fairly with the dispute so referred in the context of the speedy and robust adjudication process.

Akenhead J endorsed an agreement between the parties in the case of *Bovis Lend Lease Ltd v. The Trustees of the London Clinic Ltd* [2009] EWHC 64 that amongst other principles listed to be applicable to a challenge for ambush there was a *'sensible school of thought'* that although an adjudicator did not have an express power to extend time without the agreement of the referring party, he could decline to accept the appointment on the grounds that justice could not be done unless the referring party agreed to extend time as necessary.

Interestingly, Coulson J recently held that the court would have jurisdiction to interfere by declaration in an ongoing adjudication in rare but clear-cut cases where there was a clear risk of a breach of natural justice which might include factors such as complexity and limitations on time, but he did not consider it necessary on the facts of the case before him:

> If an ongoing adjudication is fundamentally flawed in some way or maybe just about to go off the rails irretrievably, then it seems to me that it must be sensible and appropriate for the parties to be able to have recourse to the TCC; otherwise a good deal of time and money will be spent on an adjudication which will ultimately be wasted.
>
> Dorchester Hotel Limited v. Vivid Interiors Ltd [2009] BLR 135

The courts will maintain a watchful eye but are likely to give considerable discretion to the common sense and experience of adjudicators in carrying out their role in the swift and summary process that is adjudication.

References

Coulson, P. (2007) *Construction Adjudication.* Oxford University Press, Oxford, UK.

Egan, J. (1998) *Rethinking Construction.* HMSO, London, UK.

Institution of Civil Engineers (1997) *ICE Adjudication Procedure 1997.* Thomas Telford Ltd, London, UK.

Latham, M. (1994) *Constructing the Team.* HMSO, London, UK.

Technology and Construction Court (2005, revised October 2007) *The Technology and Construction Court Guide, Second edition; first revision.* www.hmcourts-service.gov.uk/docs/tcc_guide.htm

Referenced legislation, regulations and standards

Arbitration Act 1996

Exclusion Order 1998 (Statutory Instrument SI 1998 No. 648)

Housing Grants, Construction and Regeneration Act 1996

Local Democracy, Economic Development and Construction Act 2009

Misrepresentation Act 1967

Scheme for Construction Contracts (England and Wales) Regulations 1998 (the Schedule in Statutory Instrument SI 1998 No. 649)

Unfair Contract Terms Act 1977

Unfair Terms in Consumer Contracts Regulations 1999

Referenced cases

A&D Maintenance and Construction Ltd v. Pagehurst Construction Services Ltd (1999) CILL 1518 (TCC) HHJ Wilcox

ABB Power Construction Ltd v. Norwest Holst [2001] 77 Con LR 20 (TCC) HHJ Humphrey Lloyd QC

ABB Zantingh Ltd v. Zedal Building Services Ltd [2001] BLR 66 HHJ (TCC) Peter Bowsher QC

AC Yule & Son v. Speedwell Roofing and Cladding Ltd [2007] EWHC 1360 (TCC) HHJ (as he then was) Coulson QC

Absolute Rentals Ltd v. Glencor Enterprises Ltd (2001) CILL 17 Const LJ 322

Air Design (Kent) Ltd v. Deerglen (Jersey) Ltd [2008] EWHC 3047 (TCC)

Allen Wilson Shopfitters v. Buckingham (2005) 102 Con LR 154

Alstom Signalling Ltd v. Jarvis Facilities Ltd [2004] EWHC 1285 (TCC) HHJ Lloyd QC

AMEC Capital Projects Ltd v. Whitefriars City Estates Ltd [2004] EWCA Civ 1418

AMEC Civil Engineering Ltd v. Secretary of State for Transport [2005] EWCA Civ 291

AMEC Civil Engineering Ltd v. Secretary of State for Transport [2005] BLR 227 (CA)

Ashville Investments Ltd v. Elmer Construction Ltd [1988] 2 All ER 577 (CA)

Aveat Heating Ltd v. Jerram Falkus Construction Ltd [2007] EWHC 131 (TCC) HHJ Havery QC

AWG Construction Services Ltd v. Rockingham Motor Speedway Ltd [2004] EWHC 888 (TCC) HHJ Toulmin CMG QC

AWG Construction Services Ltd v. Rockingham Motor Speedway [2004] 20 Const LJ 107

Baldwins Industrial Services plc v. Barr Ltd [2003] BLR 176 (TCC) HHJ Frances Kirkham

Balfour Beatty Construction Ltd v. London Borough of Lambeth [2002] EWHC 597 (TCC) HHJ Lloyd QC

Balfour Beatty Construction Ltd v. Lambeth Borough Council [2002] BLR 288 (TCC) HHJ Lloyd QC

Balfour Beatty Construction v. Serco Ltd [2004] EWHC 3336 (TCC)

Ballast plc v. The Burrell Co (Construction Management) Ltd [2001] SLT 1039

Ballast plc v. The Burrell Company (Construction Management) Ltd [2001] BLR 529 [OH SC of Sess]

Banner Holdings v. Colchester Borough Council [2010] EWHC 139 (TCC) Coulson J

Bloor Construction (UK) Ltd v. Bowmer & Kirkland (London) Ltd [2000] BLR 314 (TCC)

Bouygues (UK) Ltd v. Dahl-Jensen [2000] BLR 522

Bouygues (UK) Ltd v. Dahl-Jensen (UK) Ltd [2000] BLR 49 (TCC) Dyson J (as he then was)

Bovis Lendlease v. Trustees of the London Clinic [2009] EWHC 64

C&B Scene Concept Design Ltd v. Isobars Ltd [2001] CILL 1781 (TCC)

C&B Scene Concept Design Ltd v. Isobars Ltd [2002] BLR 93 (CA)

C&B Scene Concept Design Ltd v. Isobars Ltd [2002] EWCA Civ 46

C&B Scene Concept Design v. Isobars [2002] 82 Con LR 154

Cape Durasteel v. Rosser & Russell (1995) 46 Con LR 75

Cantillon Ltd v. Urvasco Ltd [2008] EWHC 282 (TCC) Akenhead J

Cantillon Ltd v. Urvasco Ltd [2008] BLR 250 (TCC) Akenhead J.

Carillion Construction Ltd v. Devonport Royal Dockyard Ltd [2003] BLR 79 (TCC) HHJ Bowsher QC

Carillion Construction Ltd v. Devonport Royal Dockyard Ltd [2005] EWCA Civ 1358

Carillion Construction Ltd v. Devonport Royal Dockyard Ltd [2005] BLR 310 (TCC) Jackson J

Carillion Construction Ltd v. Devonport Royal Dockyard Ltd [2006] BLR 15 (CA)

Castle Inns (Stirling) Ltd v. Clark Contracts Ltd [2005] ScotCS CSOH 178

CIB Properties v. Birse Construction [2004] EWHC 2365

CIB Properties v. Birse Construction [2005] BLR 173

CJP Builders Ltd v. William Verry Ltd [2008] BLR 545

Collins Contractors Ltd v. Baltic Quay Management (1994) Ltd [2004] EWCA Civ 1757

Connex South Eastern Ltd v. MJ Building Services Group plc [2005] 201 (CA)

Conor Engineering Ltd v. Les Constructions Industrielle de la Mediterranee [2004] BLR 212

Costain Ltd v. Strathclyde Builders Ltd 2004 SLT 102

CJP Builders Ltd v. William Verry Ltd [2008] EWHC 2025 (TCC) Akenhead J

Cubitt Building & Interiors Ltd v. Fleetglade Ltd [2007] 110 Con LR 36; [2006] EWHC 3413 (TCC) HHJ (as he was then) Coulson QC

David McLean Housing Ltd v. Swansea Housing Association Ltd [2002] BLR 125 (TCC) HHJ Lloyd QC

Dean & Dyball Construction Ltd v. Kenneth Grubb Associates [2003] EWHC 2465 (TCC) HHJ Seymour QC

DGT Steel and Cladding Ltd v. Cubitt Building and Interiors Ltd [2007] EWHC 1584

Discain Project Services Ltd v. Opecprime Development Ltd [2000] BLR 402 (TCC) HHJ Bowsher QC

Discain Project Services Ltd v. Opecprime Development Ltd [2001] BLR 287 (TCC)

Discain Project Services Ltd v. Opecprime Developments Ltd [2001] BLR 285

Dorchester Hotel Ltd v. Vivid Interiors Ltd [2009] BLR 135

Epping Electrical Company Ltd v. Briggs and Forrester (Plumbing Services) Ltd [2007] BLR 126 (TCC) HHJ Havery QC

Epping Electrical Company Ltd v. Briggs and Forrester (Plumbing Services) Ltd [2007] EWHC 4 (TCC)

Ferson Contractors Ltd v. Levolux AT Ltd [2003] BLR 118 (CA)

Ferson Contractors Ltd v. Levolux AT Ltd [2003] EWCA Civ 11

Geoffrey Osborne Ltd v. Atkins Rail Ltd [2009] EWHC 2425 (TCC)

General of Fair Trading v. Proprietary Association of Great Britain [2000] All ER (D) 2425 (CA)

Gibson Lea Retail Interiors Ltd v. MAKRO Self-Service Wholesalers Ltd [2001] BLR 407 HHJ Seymour QC

Glencot Development & Design Co. Ltd v. Ben Barrett & Son (Contractors) Ltd [2001] BLR 207 (TCC) HHJ Lloyd QC

Grovedeck Ltd v. Capital Demolition Ltd [2000] BLR 181 (TCC) HHJ Bowsher QC

Halki Shipping Corpn v. Sopex Oils Ltd [1998] 1 WLR 726 (CA)

Harlow & Milner Ltd v. Teasdale (No 1) [2006] EWHC 54 (TCC)

Hart v. Smith [2009] EWHC 2223, per Toulmin HHJ

Hart Investments Ltd v. Fidler and Another [2006] EWHC 2857 (TCC)

Hart Investments Ltd v. Fidler [2007] BLR 30 (TCC) HHJ (as he was then) Coulson QC.

Hershel Engineering Ltd v. Breen Property Ltd [2000] 70 ConLR 1 (TCC) Dyson J.

Hershel v. Breen [2000] BLR 272

Heyman and another v. Darwins Ltd [1942] AC 356, HL

Hills Electrical & Mechanical plc v. Dawn Construction Ltd [2003] ScotCS 107 [OH SC of Sess]

In Re: Medicaments [2001] 1 WLR 700 at 726–727 (HL)

Interserve Industrial Services v. Cleveland Bridge [2006] EWHC 741

Jacques (t/a C&E Jaques Partnership) v. Ensign Contractors Ltd [2009] EWHC 3383 (TCC) Akenhead J

Jerome Engineering Ltd v. Lloyd Electrical Services Ltd [2002] CILL 11827 (TCC) HHJ Cockroft QC

John Mowlem & Co. plc v. Hydra Tight & Co. plc (2001) 17 Const LJ 358 (TCC) HHJ Toulmin CMG QC

John Roberts Architects Ltd v. Parkcare Homes [2006] BLR 106 (CA)

JPA Design and Build v. Sentosa (UK) Ltd [2009] EWHC 2312

Ken Griffin & John Tomlinson t/a K&D Contractors v. Midas Homes Ltd [2001] 78 Con LR 152 (TCC) HHJ Lloyd QC

Kier Regional Ltd v. City & General (Holborn) Ltd [2006] EWHC 848 (TCC)

KNS Industrial Services (Birmingham) Ltd v. Sindall Ltd (2000) 75 Con LR 71 (TCC) HHJ Lloyd QC

Letchworth Roofing Company v. Sterling Building Company [2009] EWHC 1199 (TCC)

London and Amsterdam Properties Ltd v. Waterman Partnership Ltd [2004] BLR 179 (TCC) HHJ Wilcox

Lovell Projects Ltd v. Legg and Carver [2003] BLR 452

Lubenham Fidelities v. South Pembrokeshire District Council (1986) BLR 39 (CA)

Macob Civil Engineering Ltd v. Morrison Construction Ltd [1999] BLR 93 (TCC) Dyson J (as he was then)

Magill v. Porter [2001] UKHL 67

Mayor and Burgesses of the London Borough of Lambeth v. Floyd Slaski Partnership and Mastrandrea Unreported, 2 November 2001 (TCC) Forbes J.

Maxi Construction Management Ltd v. Mortons Rolls Ltd [2001] ScotCS 199; [2001] CILL 1784

Mead General Building Ltd v. Dartmoor Properties Ltd [2009] BLR 225

Mecright Ltd v. TA Morris Developments Ltd Unreported 22.06.01 (TCC) HHJ Seymour QC

Melville Dundas Ltd and others v. George Wimpey UK Ltd and Others [2007] UKHL 18

Midland Expressway Ltd v. Carillion Construction Ltd (No.2) [2005] EWHC 2963 (TCC) Jackson J

Mott MacDonald Ltd v. London & Regional Properties Ltd [2007] EWHC 1055 (TCC) HHJ Thornton QC

Multiplex Constructions (UK) Ltd v. West India Quay Development Company (Eastern) Ltd [2006] EWHC 1569 (TCC) Ramsey J

Northern Developments (Cumbria) Ltd v. J&J Nichol [2000] BLR 158 (TCC) HHJ Bowsher QC

Nottingham Community Housing Association Ltd v. Powerminster Ltd [2000] BLR 309 (TCC) Dyson J (as he then was)

Palmers Ltd v. ABB Power Construction Ltd [1999] BLR 426 (TCC) HHJ Thornton QC

Parsons Plastics (Research and Development) Ltd v. Purac Ltd [2002] BLR 334

Pegram Shopfitters Ltd v. Tally Weijl (UK) Ltd [2004] BLR 65 (CA)

Picardi v. Cuniberti [2003] BLR 487 (TCC) HHJ Toulmin CMG QC

Pierce Design International Ltd v. Johnston and another [2007] EWHC 1691 (TCC)

Premium Nafta Products Limited and Others v. Fili Shipping Company Limited and Others ('Fiona Trust') [2007] UKHL 40

Quartzelec Ltd v. Honeywell Control Systems Ltd [2009] BLR 328 (TCC) HHJ Davies

Quietfield Ltd v. Vascroft Construction Ltd [2006] EWCA Civ 1737

R v. Gough Director [1993] AC 646 (HL)

R.G. Carter Limited v. Edmund Nuttall Limited, 21 June 2000 Unreported (TCC) HHJ Thornton QC

Rainford House v. Cadogan [2001] BLR 417

Redworth Construction Ltd v. Brookdale Healthcare Ltd [2006] EWHC 1994 (TCC)

Ritchie Brothers (PWC) Ltd v. David Philip (Commercials) Ltd [2005] BLR 384 [IH SC of Sess]

RJT Consulting Engineers Ltd v. DM Engineering (Northern Ireland) Ltd [2002] 1 WLR 2344 (CA); [2002] BLR 217 (CA)

RSL (South West) Ltd v. Stansell Ltd [2003] EWHC 1390 (TCC) HHJ Seymour QC

Ruttle Plant Hire Ltd v. Secretary of State for the Environment, Food and Rural Affairs [2004] EWHC 2152 (TCC)

Shepherd Construction Ltd v. Mecright [2000] BLR 489 (TCC) HHJ Lloyd QC

SL Timber Systems Ltd v. Carillion Construction Ltd 2002 SLT 997 (Outer House SC of Sess); [2001] BLR 516

Solland International Ltd v. Daraydan Holdings Ltd (2002) 83 ConLR 109 (TCC) HHJ Seymour QC

St Andrew's Bay Development v. HBG Management and Another 2003 SLT 740

Staveley Industries plc v. Odebrecht Oil & Gas Services Ltd [2001] 98(10) LSG 46 (TCC) HHJ Richard Havery QC

Steve Domsalla (t/a Domsalla Building Services) v. Kenneth Dyason [2007] EWHC 1174 (TCC)

The Construction Centre Group Ltd v. The Highland Council [2002] BLR 476 (OH SC of Sess) affirmed [2003] SLT 623

Total M & E Services Ltd v. ABB Building Technologies Ltd [2004] EWHC 248 (TCC) HHJ Wilcox

Trustees of the Stratfield Saye Estate v. AHL Construction Ltd [2004] EWHC 3286 (TCC)

VHE Construction Plc v. RBSTB Trust Co Ltd [2000] BLR 187 (TCC) HHJ Hicks QC

Westminster Building Co. Ltd v. Andrew Beckingham [2004] BLR 265

William Verry (Glazing Systems) Ltd v. Furlong Homes Ltd [2005] EWHC 138

William Verry Ltd v. London Borough of Camden [2006] EWHC 761 (TCC) Ramsey J

William Verry Ltd v. North West London Communal Mikvah [2004] BLR 308 (TCC) HHJ Thornton QC

Wimbledon Construction v. Derek Vago [2005] EWHC 1086

Woods Hardwick Ltd v. Chiltern Air Conditioning Ltd [2001] BLR 23 (TCC) HHJ Thornton QC

Yuanda (UK) Co. Ltd v. WW Gear Construction Limited [2010] EWHC 720 (TCC)

Yuanda (UK) Co. Ltd v. WW Gear Construction Limited [2010] EWHC 820 (TCC) Edwards-Stewart J

Further reading

Totterdill, B. (1998) *ICE Adjudication Procedure 1997: A User's Guide and Commentary.* Thomas Telford Ltd, London, UK.

Bartlett, A. (ed.) (2002) Part V: Dispute Resolution, Chapter 1: Adjudication, of *Emden's Construction Law.* Butterworths.

Ramsey, V. and Furst, S. (eds) (2006) *Keating on Construction Contracts, Eighth Edition.* Sweet & Maxwell.

Wilmot-Smith, R. (2010) Chapter 23 of *Construction Contracts, Second Edition.* Oxford University Press, Oxford, UK.

Websites

Adjudication.co.uk – a recognised adjudicator nominating body and the leading provider of adjudication services and information; www.adjudication.co.uk

Association of Consultant Architects (ACA); www.acarchitects.co.uk

British and Irish Legal Information Institute (BAILII); www.bailii.org

British Property Federation (BPF); www.bpf.org.uk

Chartered Institute of Arbitrators (CIArb); www.ciarb.org

Chartered Institute of Building (CIOB); www.ciob.org.uk

Civil Procedure Rules; www.justice.gov.uk/civil/procrules_fin/

Construction Industry Council (CIC); www.cic.org.uk

Institution of Civil Engineers (ICE); www.ice.org.uk

Joint Contracts Tribunal (JCT); www.jctltd.co.uk

Office of Public Service Information (OPSI); www.opsi.gov.uk

Royal Institute of British Architects (RIBA); www.architecture.com

Royal Institution of Chartered Surveyors (RICS); www.rics.org

Technology & Construction Bar Association (TECBAR); www.tecbar.org

Technology and Construction Court (TCC); www.hmcourts-service.gov.uk/infoabout/tcc/index.htm

Technology & Construction Solicitors' Association (TeCSA); www.tesca.org.uk

UK Statute Law Database; www.statutelaw.gov.uk

Chapter 29

Alternative dispute resolution

Ian Wright Crown Office Chambers, London, UK

This chapter provides a brief overview of the various alternative dispute resolution processes used in the construction industry and the court's approach to alternative dispute resolution including the extent to which contractual provisions for alternative dispute resolution may be enforceable.

doi: 10.1680/mocl.40878.0499

CONTENTS

29.1 Introduction

Construction projects give rise to a disproportionate number of disputes when compared to activities in other commercial sectors. In the past the traditional methods of resolving construction disputes were either litigation or arbitration. However, litigation and arbitration (even under the Arbitration Act 1996) are usually lengthy processes in which the costs are often disproportionate to the sum in dispute and divert key personnel away from profit-earning work. Adjudication is now established in the UK as an alternative dispute resolution process (see *Adjudication*). However, although adjudication may offer benefits, it has become increasingly legalistic and costly; and in many adjudications the 28-day time limit has to be extended. Also, an adjudication decision has merely temporary finality and the greater the amount in dispute, the less likely it is that the decision will be accepted as the final outcome. It is against this background that, alongside negotiations, other dispute resolution processes have gained increasing importance. These processes seek to provide more equitable, faster and cost-effective dispute resolution, and include the following:

- facilitative and evaluative mediation;
- conciliation;
- mini-trial;

- dispute review and dispute adjudication boards (DABs);
- early neutral evaluation (ENE);
- expert determination; and
- mediation–arbitration.

The processes listed above may be divided into three broad categories:

- processes in which the procedure and the outcome are wholly consensual (e.g. facilitative mediation and mini-trials);
- processes in which an independent third party or a board provides a recommendation which may be accepted or rejected by the parties (e.g. evaluative mediation, conciliation, ENE and dispute review boards [DRBs]); and
- processes in which an independent third party or a board issues a binding decision (e.g. expert determination and DABs).

In this chapter, 'alternative dispute resolution' is referred to by the commonly used abbreviation 'ADR'. However, the letter 'A' in ADR may be used elsewhere to mean 'amicable' or 'assisted' or 'appropriate', rather than 'alternative'. For examples, see amended Clause 66(A)(2) of the ICE 7th Edition; FIDIC 4th Edition; FIDIC 1999 and the International Chamber of Commerce (ICC) ADR Rules.

ADR has no precise meaning. It was originally used to refer to any alternative process to litigation. ADR is now often given a narrow meaning to include only consensual processes in which the parties participate in the process voluntarily, control the process and agree the outcome. The narrow meaning excludes all processes which result in a decision of a third party which is binding on the parties (see the definition of ADR given by ICC: proceedings which do not result in a decision or the award of a 'neutral' which can be enforced at law). However, expert determination and DABs may properly be included as processes within the ADR spectrum and in this chapter ADR is given a wide meaning to encompass all the processes listed earlier.

Certain standard form contracts provide for a decision by the engineer or the contract administrator which is binding on the parties, either finally or until opened up and revised in litigation or arbitration proceedings. This form of dispute resolution, referred to as 'the engineer's decision', is considered in the chapter *Administration of Claims*.

The use of formal ADR for resolving commercial disputes in the UK has grown since the late 1980s. In the English legal jurisdiction, the use of ADR (principally in the form of mediation) increased significantly after 1999 with the reforms to the civil justice system implemented by the then new rules in Civil Procedure 1998 (the CPR) which expressly encourage the use of ADR (Waller, 2010).

29.2 Negotiated settlements

A negotiated settlement is the least formal method of ADR and, importantly, is the process over which the parties have the greatest control.

When a dispute arises, most parties will initially seek to resolve it by negotiation: in effect, a process in which each party seeks to persuade the other to accept a particular outcome. In common with other consensual processes, a successful outcome will usually depend on each party being willing to move from a particular position and to compromise. Unfortunately, negotiations often fail because the parties do not pay sufficient attention to providing a formal structure to the negotiating process or the negotiators do not possess the necessary communication and/or negotiating skills to conduct the negotiations in a manner that enhances the prospects of a settlement.

Negotiations undertaken in a constructive manner and in a structured way can offer significant advantages in that they will often be conducted by persons who have direct knowledge of the subject-matter of the dispute, the parties are free to determine the form of the negotiations and outcome, and costs can be minimised.

However, it may also be disadvantageous to achieving a settlement if negotiators have been directly involved at an earlier stage of a dispute. If negotiations do not result in a settlement at an early stage, the dispute may become personalised and/or positions may become entrenched, which may prevent further effective communication or negotiation. In such circumstances the dispute will often be referred to persons at a higher level in the organisations (or lawyers) who have no direct knowledge of the subject-matter.

A decision must be made at an early stage on whether all or any part of the negotiations are to be conducted on a 'without prejudice' basis, which offers the parties an opportunity to explore proposals for settlement openly and without prejudicing either party's position.

At the conclusion of each stage of any negotiations it is beneficial to record any matters that have been agreed in the form of heads of agreement which each of the parties signs.

Constructive negotiation remains a highly effective tool for dispute avoidance or resolution. In recent research (Gould *et al.*, 2010) the sample of cases studied showed that traditional party-to-party negotiation was more common than mediation in leading to a settlement before trial.

29.3 Mediation

There is often confusion as to what is meant by the term 'mediation' because there are a variety of fundamentally different processes referred to as 'mediation' and, in addition, the terms 'mediation' and 'conciliation' are often used interchangeably. Therefore, if the term 'mediation' is being used in a particular context, it is important that the parties understand and agree the nature of the ADR process that the term is being used to describe.

Mediation may be defined as a dispute resolution process in which an independent third party (the mediator) intervenes in the dispute with the consent of the parties, facilitates negotiations and communications between the parties, with the objective that the parties will change their respective positions and reach an agreement. The assistance of a mediator is often viewed as 'adding value' to the negotiations and more likely to be effective in achieving a settlement than the normal process of negotiation by discussion and offer and counter-offer. See the court's view in *Hickman v. Lapthorn* [2006] EWHC 12 (QB) Jack J. c.f. The findings of the report by Gould *et al.* 2010, on the effectiveness of negotiations in achieving settlements.

The mediation process is ordinarily voluntary, non-binding, and held on a 'without prejudice' basis, the intention being that the parties will be open and frank, and more willing to move from their previously stated positions and explore potential areas of agreement. In contrast to litigation, arbitration and adjudication, in which the outcome is a formal determination by a third party, mediation allows the parties to settle their dispute by agreement and the form of the settlement is entirely within the parties' control.

29.3.1 The principal forms of mediation

The nature of the mediator's role in the mediation process determines the two principal types of mediation: either facilitative or evaluative. However, even within each of these broad types there may be further differences in the procedures adopted and in the role of the mediator.

29.3.2 Facilitative mediation

In a facilitative mediation the mediator does not express a view on the merits of the parties' cases, or attempt to provide advice or a recommendation, or impose a solution. The mediator will act as a communicator between the parties and endeavour to provide a background which enhances the prospects of settlement, and against which the parties can agree how a compromise can be reached. A facilitative mediation is, in effect, negotiations between the parties assisted by the mediator.

In the UK the term 'mediation' is associated almost exclusively with the facilitative approach, and in construction and other commercial disputes, mediation using the facilitative approach has almost become synonymous with the term ADR. This has come about, not because facilitative mediation is necessarily the appropriate form of ADR for every dispute (which often in practice it is not), but because certain commercial organisations have promoted mediation heavily using non-technical mediators (mainly lawyers) and it is usually lawyers who advise clients on the form of ADR to be used. Also, in the UK there has also been a general unwillingness to adopt, or even explore, other forms of ADR, for example, evaluative mediation or conciliation (see subsequently).

29.3.3 Evaluative mediation

In an evaluative mediation, the mediator will endeavour to evaluate the strengths and weaknesses of each party's case, and express a view on the merits of the dispute or make a recommendation for settlement. The reasoning behind this approach is that once the parties know the mediator's view or recommendation, they will review and change their respective positions, and this will progress resolution of the dispute.

The stage at which the mediator expresses a view or makes a recommendation will vary, and the appropriate time requires careful judgement on the part of the mediator. If the parties do not accept the mediator's initial evaluation, the mediator may often endeavour to establish a range of options within which settlement may be possible.

In many 'technical' disputes the evaluative approach may offer significant advantages over the facilitative approach, especially where expert evidence would normally be determinative of the issues and the mediator is competent and experienced in the field in which the dispute has arisen.

29.3.4 The mediation process

Once the parties have agreed to mediate their dispute, a mediator is appointed. Some contracts may already identify a mediator or an appointing organisation. A venue (preferably neutral) is then arranged at which to hold the mediation.

Prior to the mediation, each party usually submits a brief statement of its case to the mediator (often referred to as a 'position statement'). The parties may wish to have a legal representative present at the mediation. It is essential that each

party has a person present with authority to settle the case and the mediator should verify that such person is present.

There is no set procedure for mediation, although most organisations involved in ADR and the appointment of mediators have formal guidelines or protocols or codes of practice.

The mediation process normally begins with an 'open' joint session (sometimes referred to as a 'plenary' session) at which all parties are present, and during which the mediator makes an opening statement explaining the process and the ground rules for the mediation. After the mediator has answered any questions which the parties may have, each party is then given an opportunity to explain its case orally in the presence of the other party (or parties) in an 'opening statement'. A party's opening statement will usually include a summary of its contentions, reference to any key documents, and a brief description of the evidence on which it relies. Ordinarily there are no formal rules of evidence in a mediation.

After the joint opening session, the parties retire to separate rooms and the mediator then engages in a form of 'shuttle diplomacy' by holding a series of private meetings (sometimes referred to as 'caucuses') with each party in turn. During the private meetings the mediator will seek to clarify the issues between the parties; explore the strengths and weaknesses of the parties' respective cases and the parties' positions (often acting as 'devil's advocate'); seek to identify the parties' interests; and endeavour to find common ground which may assist the parties to reach a settlement. Matters discussed in these private meetings are confidential and, unless expressly agreed by a party, no information provided to the mediator by a party will be conveyed to the other party. If deemed appropriate by the mediator, or requested by the parties, further joint sessions may take place.

The private meetings with the parties are common to a facilitative mediation and the early stages of an evaluative mediation. However, once the mediator in an evaluative mediation is of the view that he/she has sufficient information to understand each party's case and position, the mediator will express a view on the merits or make a recommendation to the parties. Subsequent negotiations (if any) will progress in the context of the mediator's view or recommendation.

In both types of mediation, if the parties reach agreement, the mediator should summarise the nature of the agreement that has been reached at a joint closing session. The extent of the mediator's participation after an agreement has been reached will depend on the procedures agreed or the wishes of the parties. The mediator will usually assist the parties to formulate outline proposals for settlement. The mediator may also assist the parties to set down the agreement in writing, although opinions vary as to whether this is appropriate, particularly if parties are legally represented. Depending on the procedure adopted, the mediator's involvement will usually end either after agreement has been reached or after the mediator has assisted the parties to draw up the agreement.

If agreement is not reached in a facilitative mediation, or the parties do not accept the mediator's view or recommendation in an evaluative mediation, the mediation will usually end without a concluded agreement. However, in certain ADR processes which commence with mediation, the parties agree that, if an agreement is not reached at the end of the mediation stage, the process can progress to a further stage. For example, the process may change from a facilitative mediation to an evaluative mediation or to arbitration proceedings (see mediation-arbitration subsequently); or the parties may request the mediator to provide a written opinion on how the dispute may be resolved.

29.3.5 The final agreement

It is important to distinguish between the mediation process itself, which is voluntary and non-binding, and any agreement which may be reached. If the parties reach an agreement, then in the absence of express provisions to the contrary, such agreement will be binding on the parties as a matter of contract in accordance with the law governing the agreement, and will be enforceable in the courts (*Thakrav v. Ciro Citterio Menswear plc* [2002] EWHC 1975). For the avoidance of any doubt, the parties should expressly agree in advance that any agreement reached at the conclusion of the process is to be binding.

The ordinary rules of contract will apply to any agreement reached. If an agreement reached at the end of any ADR process involving 'negotiation', including mediation, is to be enforceable, the court must be able to identify its terms with certainty. Therefore, at the conclusion of a mediation, the parties should draw up and sign a document setting out all the matters on which agreement has been reached.

Although the mediator will have assisted the parties to formulate the proposals for settlement, and may assist in drawing up the agreement, the nature and form of the final agreement are matters solely for the parties. Contrary to some views, the mediator is not a party to, and should not sign, what, in law, is the parties' agreement.

If court proceedings have commenced, the final agreement is often drawn up in the form of a 'Tomlin' order comprising the order to be made by the court with the parties' consent with a schedule incorporated into the order setting out the matters agreed which form the basis on which the proceedings will be stayed. The order will be placed before the court for sealing.

An alternative method of achieving an enforceable agreement is for the parties to agree that the agreement reached shall be deemed to have the same effect as an award to which the Arbitration Act 1996 applies. If it became necessary, a party could then enforce the award in the courts under Section 66 of the Arbitration Act 1996.

In the context of an international dispute, having an agreement in the form of an arbitral award will allow it to be enforced in any state that is a signatory to the Convention on the Recognition and Enforcement of Foreign Arbitral Awards adopted by the United Nations Conference on International Arbitration on 10 June 1958, usually referred to as 'the New York Convention'.

If the settlement has been concluded during arbitration proceedings, the agreement may be incorporated into a consent award. In such circumstances the parties should also include a provision in the consent award conferring power on the arbitrator to make the award because after conclusion of an agreement there is no longer a dispute in existence, and the arbitrator will be *functus officio* (i.e. will no longer have power to act).

29.3.6 European Directive 2008/52/EC on the use of 'mediation'

The European Parliament and the Council resolved to approve a common position on ADR across the Member States of the European Union and in May 2008 issued Directive 2008/52/EC. The Directive encourages the use of 'mediation' in the Member States as a means of settling disputes in civil and commercial matters and encouraging the amicable settlement of disputes. The Directive applies to cross-border disputes in civil and commercial matters (with the exception of revenue, customs or administrative matters or the liability of the State for acts or omissions in the exercise of state authority). It does not apply in Denmark. The EC drew up a code of conduct for mediators in 2004. The Directive aims to make the legal status of certain principles of mediation practice uniform throughout the Member States.

The Directive included the following definitions:

'mediation': a structured process, however, named or referred to, whereby two or more parties to a dispute attempt by themselves, on a voluntary basis, to reach an agreement on the settlement of their dispute with the assistance of a mediator; and

'mediator': any third party conducting a mediation for the parties to the dispute, irrespective of his profession or title.

The Directive provides that, without prejudice to a Member States' own legislation making mediation compulsory, each state should authorise their courts to suggest mediation to the litigants, without, compelling them to use it. Mediation is not treated as an alternative to court proceedings but as 'one of the methods of dispute resolution available in modern society'. It should be noted that 'mediation' and the role of the mediator are both widely defined. In particular, 'mediation' would embrace other ADR processes, not merely facilitative and evaluative mediation described earlier.

The Directive recognises that settlement agreements reached through mediation are generally more likely to be implemented voluntarily, but requires all the Member States to make provision for enforcement of written agreements arising from mediation (providing both parties are agreeable) unless it is contrary to the law of the Member State, or the Member State does not provide for its enforceability by establishing a procedure under which an agreement in a mediation may, at the request of the parties, be confirmed in a judgement, decision or an 'authentic instrument' by a court or public authority. The purpose is to allow mutual recognition and enforcement of settlement agreements throughout the EU under the same conditions as those for court judgements and decisions.

Significantly, the Directive recognises limitation periods (see further) which may arise in the more formal means of dispute resolution (e.g. litigation and arbitration) and to encourage more effective use of mediation, the Member States must ensure that the parties are not subsequently prevented from initiating judicial proceedings or arbitration in relation to the dispute by the expiry of limitation or prescription periods during the mediation process.

Member States (excluding Denmark) are required to give effect to the Directive by 21 May 2011 and will need to enact their own laws and administrative processes to achieve the objectives of the Directive.

29.4 Conciliation

There are several fundamentally different processes which are referred to as 'conciliation'. These range from what should properly be called 'facilitative mediation', through 'evaluative mediation', to adjudicative procedures. In addition the terms 'conciliation' and 'mediation' are often used interchangeably.

There are formal conciliation processes with established rules and procedures (e.g. The ICE Conciliation Procedure 1999 [ICE, 2009]). However, where a formal procedure is not being adopted, it is important that the parties understand and agree the nature of the ADR process that is being referred to as 'conciliation'.

In this text, conciliation is used in the sense of an ADR process which involves referring the dispute to a neutral third party (the conciliator) who facilitates settlement by, if necessary, expressing an opinion or providing a 'recommendation', and does not act in an adjudicative capacity. The process remains consensual, and either party remains free to accept or reject the opinion or recommendation of the conciliator.

The conciliator's primary role is to assist in negotiations between the parties with the aim of achieving a settlement. The conciliation process is usually conducted on a confidential and without prejudice basis and, at the initial stages, there are similarities between the conciliator's role and a mediator's role in an evaluative mediation. However, there are usually formal procedures in conciliation which are not present in a mediation. For example, the conciliator may be given specific powers to request the production of documents or the attendance of parties (e.g. ICE, 1999; para. 4.5) or the rules may place an obligation on the conciliator to give a recommendation on a solution to the dispute if the parties do not reach an agreement. Certain rules permit the conciliator to change roles and act as an arbitrator if agreement is not reached during the initial stages of the process.

In the context of engineering contracts in the UK, conciliation is most commonly conducted under the Institution of Civil Engineers (ICE) Conciliation Procedure 1999, which is incorporated into the following ICE standard form contracts: the ICE Conditions of Contract 6th and 7th Editions (ICE 7th); the ICE Design and Construction Contract

2nd Edition 2001; the ICE Minor Works Contract 2nd Edition, and the ICE Conditions of Contract for Ground Investigation. The procedure is also incorporated into the standard form subcontracts published by the Civil Engineering Contractors Association, which complement the main contract forms listed earlier. The ICE Conciliation Procedure remains part of the dispute resolution regime in ICE contracts even after revisions to comply with the Housing Grants, Construction and Regeneration Act 1996 (HGCRA 1996) and incorporate a contractual right to refer a dispute to adjudication at any time (see subsequently).

In the international context, the 1988 ICC Rules of Optional Conciliation were superseded by the ICC ADR Rules (ICC, 2001) (see subsequently). Any request to the ICC for conciliation must now be formulated in accordance with the new ICC ADR Rules. Under Article 5 of the ICC ADR Rules, the Neutral and the parties are required to discuss and seek to reach agreement on the settlement technique to be used and discuss the ADR procedure to be followed. However, the ICC ADR Rules do not expressly provide for conciliation and in the absence of agreement by the parties on the ADR procedure, the rules state that the process shall be mediation. It follows that, where the ICC regime applies, conciliation will now only be available by agreement and the parties will also need to agree to the rules and procedure under which the conciliation is to be conducted.

29.5 Mini-trial

Mini-trials were first given formal recognition in commercial disputes in the United States in the late 1970s. Although referred to as a 'mini-trial', the process in fact uses structured negotiation to achieve a settlement and is not a trial within the normal meaning of the word. The mini-trial process is also referred to by other names including 'executive tribunal', 'supervised settlement' or 'modified settlement conference'. Several organisations publish procedural rules for mini-trials. For example, the Chartered Institute of Arbitrators has provided guidelines for mini-trials since 1990 in its publication *The Chartered Institute of Arbitrators: guidelines for supervised settlement procedure*.

The process begins with each party presenting its case to a tribunal usually consisting of a senior executive with authority to settle from each party, and often (but not always) a 'neutral', sometimes referred to as a 'neutral adviser'. The presentations of the respective cases may be made by the employees of the parties involved in the dispute, or other non-legal employees (generally not above middle management level), or the parties' legal representatives.

After the parties have presented their respective cases, the senior executives meet together privately and endeavour to negotiate a settlement. The role of the neutral varies. The person may act merely as chairperson or, subject to the discipline of the person appointed, he/she may assist the executives on technical or legal matters, or may express a view on the likely outcome if the dispute were to proceed further to litigation or arbitration.

The mini-trial process is flexible and the manner and scope of the presentation and the constitution of the panel may be tailored to match the nature of the dispute. The intention of the process is to have a short hearing to focus on the issues in dispute, followed by negotiation by senior management with a view to settling the dispute. At the hearing stage, this focus on the issues is likely to be lost, and the achievement of a settlement prejudiced, if the process is allowed to develop into a process akin to a formal trial with the calling of witnesses of fact, experts, and full legal submissions.

29.6 Dispute boards

Traditionally under standard form engineering contracts, such as the conditions of contract published by ICE and FIDIC, respectively, 'the Engineer' was given authority to provide a decision in the event of a dispute arising between the employer and contractor. Under certain engineering contracts a decision by the Engineer was required before a dispute was said to exist (e.g. Clause 66(3)(a) of the ICE 7th Edition [c.f. the amended Clause 66 of ICE 7th Edition {see subsequently}]), or a decision was a condition precedent to arbitration (see, *Monmouthshire County Council v. Costelloe & Kemple Limited* (1965) 5 BLR 83 (CA), a case which concerns an Engineer's decision under the 4th Edition of the ICE Conditions of Contract).

This decision-making role requires the Engineer to act impartially. However, the Engineer is usually paid by the employer and this can create difficulties with the perception of the Engineer's independence if a dispute arises and the Engineer's decision itself often resulted in a further dispute. Although traditionally the Engineer's decision was often effective in resolving disputes without recourse to arbitration, in recent years there has been an increasing difficulty in accepting that the Engineer can act impartially and credibility in the Engineer's independence has reduced. In order to avoid such difficulties provisions requiring disputes to be referred to a dispute board (DB) (sometimes referred to as a 'dispute resolution board') for resolution were incorporated into certain contracts, particularly in the international context.

DB is a generic term and there are two principal types: DRBs and DABs. DBs arise out of contract and their jurisdiction and powers to advise on and/or resolve a dispute are necessarily governed by the contractual provisions. The principal difference between the two types of DBs is the status of the determination made in respect of any dispute referred to it, which is either a 'recommendation' or a 'decision'.

A DRB issues a 'recommendation' (rather than a formal decision). The procedure is consensual as the parties are free to accept or reject the recommendation (usually within a prescribed time limit). Failure to express dissatisfaction with the recommendation within the time limit will often render it contractually binding (effectively converting it into a decision). If the recommendation is rejected, then subject to the terms of the dispute resolution procedure in the contract, the dispute may be referred to arbitration or the courts for final determination.

A DAB issues a 'decision'. The parties are contractually obliged to comply with the decision, which is ordinarily enforceable as a term of the contract. If a party expresses dissatisfaction with a decision, it is usually entitled to commence arbitration or court proceedings to finally resolve the dispute. The parties are, however, generally obliged to comply with the decision until such time as it may be revised in an arbitral award or judgement. If the decision is to be binding on the parties, whether finally or until reviewed in subsequent proceedings, the contractual provisions may require the decision of the board to be unanimous.

A hybrid of the aforementioned types is known as a Combined Dispute Board (CDB). A CDB may issue both recommendations (non-binding) and decisions (binding until revised in an arbitral award or judgement). The default position is that a CDB issues a recommendation. However, if one party requests a decision and the other party does not object, the CDB may, at its discretion, issue a decision. If the other party does object, the CDB has power to decide whether to issue a recommendation or a decision. Factors which the CDB may take into account in making such decision include whether, due to the urgency of the situation or other relevant considerations, a decision would facilitate the performance of the contract or prevent substantial loss or harm to any party; whether a decision would prevent disruption of the project; and whether a decision is necessary to preserve evidence.

DRBs originated in the United States in the 1970s on a number of large civil engineering projects. Although these DRBs gave only non-binding recommendations, it was found that, once a recommendation was made, most disputes settled; avoiding the time and cost of further proceedings. In addition, because disputes were resolved at an early stage, the parties were generally able to maintain a good working relationship.

The use of DBs, increased during the 1990s, particularly on large-scale international projects.

In this ADR process, disputes are submitted to a tribunal consisting of one person (from 2007 Caltrans (California Department of Transportation) has used a 'dispute resolution adviser (DRA)', in effect, a one-man DRB, on its major contracts) or, more typically, three (or sometimes five) members for a decision. The members of the DB are chosen from disciplines that are likely to be appropriate taking into account the nature of the project. The members may be all 'neutrals', and named in the contract documents. Alternatively, the members may be appointed after the contract has been awarded but before any dispute has arisen, in which case the tribunal usually comprises one (or possibly more) representative from each party and a third 'neutral' member, either agreed by the parties or appointed by a nominating body. The members of the board are paid by the parties. The ICE and ICC both publish rules for DBs.

In complex projects there may be several boards with each constituted to deal with disputes arising in a particular discipline or even at a particular stage of the project. For example, in the early stages of construction of a power station disputes may arise over the civil works, requiring a DB with expertise in the field of civil engineering, whereas in the later stages where the work involves the incorporation of plant, mechanical or electrical engineers may be more appropriate to sit on the board (on the Artery / Tunnel Project in the US city of Boston there were 47 separate DBRs in operation, each with a special expertise).

A significant difference between a DB and most other ADR processes is that a DB will usually be constituted at, or even before, the commencement of a project, before any dispute arises and, by undertaking regular visits to the site, it is actively involved throughout the project. The process is most effective if the DB members are provided with full details of the project at the time of their appointment, and are kept fully informed periodically of progress and other relevant matters during the course of construction. If a dispute arises, the board members have the background knowledge of the matters which have given rise to the dispute to assist them in making a decision. DBs have a high success rate in resolving disputes (Dispute Board Federation, 2008) which, it is submitted, may be attributed to the DB's direct involvement from the commencement of the project and its contemporaneous knowledge of the project.

Certain contracts (e.g. *The Conditions of Contract for Plant and Design-Build* FIDIC 1999 [the Yellow Book]) provide for an 'ad hoc' DB, which is constituted after a dispute has arisen. It is submitted that, although cheaper, this approach significantly undermines the usual advantage of the DB process where the board is actively involved throughout the project and before a dispute arises.

It is possible for parties to provide within a construction contract for adjudication by a DAB which would satisfy the statutory requirement for adjudication under HGCRA 1996. However, notwithstanding the recognised advantages and benefits of DAB process, and its success rate, the opportunity is rarely taken to incorporate this form of ADR into construction contracts in the UK.

Following the successful experience of DRBs in the United States, the World Bank adopted the use of DRBs and published documentation to be used in conjunction with FIDIC contracts which made the use of a DRB mandatory in projects funded by the World Bank. In 1996 FIDIC published a supplement to the FIDIC Conditions of Contract for Works of Civil Engineering Construction 4th Edition 1987 (commonly referred to as 'the Red Book') which included optional amendments for a 'DAB' as the decision-maker in place of the Engineer. In 1999 the old Red Book was superseded when FIDIC published an updated version of its contract, the FIDIC Conditions of Contract for Construction 1st Edition 1999 (FIDIC 1999) (also referred to as 'the Red Book') which incorporates provisions for the adjudication of disputes by a DAB as the standard procedure. FIDIC 1999 also includes an appendix containing 'General Conditions of Dispute Adjudication Agreement' and an annexe setting out 'Procedural Rules' for the DAB. In 2000, the World Bank made the use of a DAB, rather than a DRB, mandatory on projects funded by it. The use of the DAB for dispute resolution has been continued in the FIDIC Multilateral Development Banks Harmonised Edition of the Conditions of Contract for Construction (the MDB Edition), published in 2005, which was agreed with a group of development banks who have been licensed to include it in their procurement procedures.

29.7 Early neutral evaluation

ENE is designed to provide the parties with an independent assessment of the dispute, or of particular issues giving rise to the dispute, by a 'neutral' who may be a judge or lawyer, or an arbitrator, or an expert in a discipline relevant to the nature of the dispute. Each party presents its case to the neutral third party who provides a non-binding evaluation of the likely outcome if the matter were to proceed to court or arbitration.

The Commercial Court and the Technology and Construction Court (TCC) each provide a formal facility within the jurisdiction of the Court for ENE by a judge (*Commercial Court Guide:* Section G2 and the *TCC Guide* Section 7.5). If the judge is of the view that ENE is likely to assist in the resolution of the dispute, he/she may offer to provide the evaluation or arrange for another judge to provide it. If the parties agree to ENE, the judge undertaking the evaluation will give directions as to the form of evaluation that he considers appropriate, and the preparatory steps which the parties are to take. The process is ordinarily conducted on a without prejudice basis and is non-binding. Unless the parties agree otherwise, the judge providing ENE will take no further part in the case.

In disputes involving technical matters the parties may appoint an independent expert to provide an early evaluation of the case, which is non-binding (expert determination subsequently). This process is referred to as 'early expert determination'.

29.8 Expert determination

Expert determination is, in effect, an expert's 'opinion' on a specific issue or issues in a dispute. The parties agree to appoint an independent third party of a relevant discipline to give a decision on the matters in dispute. Alternatively, the contract may provide for the expert to be appointed by a professional body on the application of a party.

The expert is usually required to use his/her own skills and expertise and, subject to the evidence provided by the parties, may need to make necessary enquiries or conduct his/her own investigations (see *WallshireLtd v. AaronsI* [1989] 2 EG 81 and *CIL Securities v. Briant Champion Long* [1993] 42 EG 281). Subject to the procedure defined by the contract, the parties will usually have an opportunity to make submissions to the expert. The process ordinarily provides a fast, cost-effective and final solution to the matters in dispute and has been used successfully for many years in disputes involving technical issues and disputes concerning rent reviews and property valuations.

The terms of the expert clause, the expert's appointment and the relevant provisions of the contract will determine, as a matter of contract, the expert's jurisdiction, in particular, what the parties agreed to remit to the expert by way of expert determination and what the expert was appointed to do; and whether the expert has done what he/she was appointed to do (see *Halifax Life Limited v. The Equitable Life Assurance Society* [2007] EWHC 503 (Comm) Cresswell J. and *Thames Water Utilities Ltd v. Heathrow Airport Ltd* [2009] EWCA 992).

In expert determination there is, ordinarily, no right of appeal and there are limited grounds on which an expert determination may be challenged. The grounds include mistake, material departure from instructions, manifest error, lack of independence, unfairness in the procedure and in the decision itself, and fraud, dishonesty or collusion (see *Dixons Group plc v. Jan Andrew Murray-Oboynski* (1998) 86 BLR 16; *Jones v. Sherwood Services Ltd plc* [1992] 1 WLR 277; and *Veba Oil Supply and Trading GmbH v. Petrotrade Inc* [2001] EWCA Civ 1832, [2002] 1 Lloyd's Rep 295). However, except in the case of the last three, the grounds and the circumstances in which the court will intervene after a 'final' determination give rise to difficult issues of law which are outside the scope of this chapter (for a full exposition see Kendall, 2001, Chapter 15).

In view of the limited grounds on which an expert determination may be challenged, instructions to the expert must be drafted with particular care in order to set out fully and precisely the subject matter of the dispute and the issues to be determined. The instructions should also make clear that the person appointed is acting in the capacity of an expert. The expert does not ordinarily enjoy the immunity from suit of a judge or arbitrator, and may be the subject of a claim if he/she acts negligently (*CIL Securities v. Briant Champion Long* listed earlier).

29.9 Mediation–arbitration

Mediation–arbitration (sometimes abbreviated to 'med–arb') is in effect a two-stage dispute resolution process that commences with mediation. If no agreement is reached, the role of the neutral third party changes from mediator to that of arbitrator, and the dispute resolution process continues as an arbitration in which the third party gives a binding decision.

Arguments advanced in favour of mediation–arbitration are that at the first stage the parties have an opportunity to reach agreement by mediation but, if that fails, the mediator is familiar with the subject of the dispute and there will be a saving in costs by then appointing the mediator as arbitrator; and the parties also know from the outset that the dispute will be resolved one way or another by the end of the process.

However, the change in the role of the third party from mediator to that of arbitrator may give rise to difficulties. In the UK, an arbitrator must conduct the proceedings in accordance with the Arbitration Act 1996 and the common law, in particular the rules of natural justice. There is a significant risk that mediation of a dispute prior to giving an arbitral decision will give rise to a breach of the rules of natural justice because in the role of mediator, the third party would ordinarily be privy to information provided by the parties on a private or confidential basis. Also, if a party provides the mediator with information that is prejudicial to that party's case, the mediator is then required to act in an independent and impartial role as an arbitrator required to decide the proceedings judicially. The prospect of achieving settlement by mediation may also be prejudiced if a party is reluctant to disclose information during the mediation stage because it knows that the mediator may act in the subsequent stage as arbitrator.

Opinions vary on whether mediation–arbitration is an appropriate form of ADR because of the change in the role of the person initially appointed as mediator. However, the process is provided for under certain statutory provisions (see Section 27 of the Commercial Arbitration Act 1984 [New South Wales]) and is now more commonly accepted. For example, in China the combination of arbitration and mediation plays a significant role in formal dispute resolution for cultural reasons (Xuan, 2008): the parties commence arbitration and then during the proceedings the 'arbitrator' attempts to settle the dispute by mediation (or conciliation). Notwithstanding the potential difficulties with the process, in the UK the Court of Appeal has observed that mediation–arbitration is particularly apt for disputes about patent rights, where a 'mediator' trusted by both sides can be given authority to decide the terms of a binding agreement (*IDA Ltd v. University of Southampton* [2006] EWCA Civ 145; *The Times* 31 March 2006 (CA)).

A variation of the process, particularly in the United States, is to appoint different people to the roles of mediator and arbitrator. It is submitted that this modified approach negates most of the advantages that are normally advanced in support of the mediation–arbitration process.

29.10 'Staged' dispute resolution provisions

Many construction contracts incorporate provisions for 'staged' (also referred to as 'tiered' or 'step-by-step') dispute resolution. The intention is to resolve the dispute speedily and at the earliest opportunity by having an appropriate procedure in place at each stage. The ADR process is only taken to a higher level if the preceding process fails. The processes adopted in the earlier stages of staged procedures may include any or all of the following: negotiations, a decision by the engineer or contract administrator, mediation, conciliation and a recommendation by a DRB. The final stage is usually an adjudicative procedure which results in a final and binding decision but is intended to be used only if the parties fail to settle the dispute at one of the earlier stages.

However, in the UK contractual provisions for consensual ADR have been largely undermined by the requirement of HGCRA 1996 for construction contracts (see Section 104 of HGCRA 1996) to incorporate a right to refer a 'dispute' to adjudication 'at any time' (see Section 108 of HGCRA 1996). A party still has the option of whether to refer a dispute to adjudication or not but, notwithstanding any contractual provisions for staged ADR, a claiming party will usually view adjudication as the first stage of dispute resolution and exercise its right to refer the dispute to adjudication, and the other party will not be able to prevent the referral (see further on the enforceability of ADR clauses). Various standard form contracts incorporate staged ADR procedures. However, in contracts to which HGCRA 1996 applies, the operation of a staged procedure in which one or more of the consensual and/or non-adjudicative ADR processes precedes adjudication will, in practice, only be possible if the parties are willing to agree to follow the procedure and postpone a referral to adjudication.

29.10.1 The dispute resolution procedures in the ICE 7th Edition

Clause 66 of the ICE 7th Edition is entitled 'Avoidance and settlement of disputes' and in its original version is designed to provide staged dispute resolution. Clause 66(2) seeks at the first stage to avoid adversarial language by not referring to 'disputes or differences' between the parties but to 'matters of dissatisfaction'. However, the term 'matter of dissatisfaction' is contrived, with the intended purpose of preventing a 'dispute' arising until after the 'matter of dissatisfaction' has been referred to the Engineer and a decision has been given. Clauses 66(2) and 66(3), taken together, also seek to require an Engineer's decision (or a failure to give a decision) as a condition precedent to the existence of a dispute. Although the intention is to provide for staged dispute resolution procedures, Clauses 66(2) and 66(3) are contrary to the requirements of Section 108(2) of HGCRA 1996 and would be unenforceable, in circumstances where a party sought to exercise its right to adjudication before there has been an Engineer's decision (or failure to give the decision). See *John Mowlem & Co. plc v. Hydra Tight & Co. plc* [2001] 17 CLJ 358 (TCC) HHJ Toulmin CMG QC., in which a provision similar to Clause 66(2) of ICE 7th. Edition was held to be contrary to the requirements of Section 108(2) of HGCRA 1996. See also *R. G. Carter Ltd v. Edmund Nuttall Ltd* 21 June 2000 Unreported (TCC) HHJ Thornton QC.

However, if a party does not wish to refer a dispute to adjudication (probably rare in the current litigious climate), the referral of a 'matter of dissatisfaction' would remain the starting point for the contractual provisions for dispute resolution in the ICE 7th Edition.

The intention of the ICE 7th Edition is that the contractual, not statutory, provisions for adjudication should apply and in July 2004 the ICE published a significant amendment to Clause 66 (ICE/Clause-66 July 2004) which it recommends are incorporated into in the ICE 7th Edition (and other ICE contracts, including the Design and Construct 2nd Edition, the Term Version 1st Edition; the Ground Investigation 2nd Edition).

The amendment deletes the original Clause 66 and inserts new Clauses 66, 66A, 66B, 66C and 66D, which have been drafted to comply with the statutory requirement for adjudication in HGCRA 1996 and relevant case law. Although the amendment to Clause 66 is recommended, it (or a similar amendment) is necessary where contracts are required to comply with HGCRA 1996. The 2004 amendment has necessarily abandoned the sequential 'step-by-step' approach of the original ICE 7th Edition, and allows the parties to use the various procedures that are available in any order and, significantly, does not require any reference back to the Engineer for a decision as a condition precedent to the existence of a dispute. A new dispute avoidance provision has also been introduced.

The dispute resolution provisions in the amended Clause 66 of the ICE 7th Edition include the following:

(1) 'advance warning' (Clause 66(2);
(2) notice of a dispute (Clause 66A(1));
(3) 'amicable dispute resolution' (Clause 66A(2));
(4) adjudication (Clause 66B);
(5) arbitration (Clause 66C); and
(6) appointments (Clause 66D).

Although the provisions can provide for a staged dispute resolution procedure if the parties agree, a party has a right to give notice of adjudication at any time. Each of the clauses is considered further.

Clause 66(2): 'advance warning'. Once a party becomes aware of 'any matter which if not resolved might become a dispute', it is required to give a warning in writing to the other party, with a copy to the Engineer. The parties are required to meet within 7 days to try to resolve the matter. If the matter is not resolved within a 'reasonable period', the parties are required to define those parts of the matter that remain unresolved. The clause is designed to avoid a 'dispute' arising and although expressed in mandatory language, it is submitted that the provision is, in effect, consensual. (See Clauses 66A(1), 66A(2) and 66B, which all provide for the service of various notices 'at any time'.)

Clause 66A(1): 'Notice of Dispute'. This clause provides a procedure which seeks to define when a dispute comes into existence and the nature of the 'dispute or difference', by the service of a 'Notice of Dispute'. The notice is intended to establish a clear starting point for any further action. Clause 66A(1) expressly provides that a party may not serve the notice unless and until any steps required by procedures available elsewhere in the contract have been taken. Clauses which require particular steps to be taken would include Clause 12 (adverse physical conditions and artificial obstructions) and Clause 44 (extension of time).

In the majority of situations where differences arise, there are often lengthy discussions and/or negotiations preceding a full-blown dispute. One effect of the decision in *AMEC Civil Engineering Ltd v. Secretary of State for Transport* [2005] EWCA Civ 291, [2005] BLR 227 (CA) (see the discussion in Section 29.13.3) is that the narrow, but very clear, approach to defining a 'dispute' in the contractual dispute resolution procedures of the ICE Conditions has been severely eroded, if not entirely eliminated (it is submitted that *Monmouthshire County Council v. Costelloe & Kemple Limited*, earlier, no longer has general application). Taking into account the wider approach of the Court of Appeal in *AMEC*, as to when a 'dispute' has crystallised, in many projects it may be extremely difficult for the parties to say with any certainty whether a dispute has come into existence or not.

It remains an open question whether the courts will be prepared to enforce the requirement for service of a contractual Notice of Dispute before a dispute is said to come into existence, or whether the provision will be held to be contrary to Section 108(2) of HGCRA 1996 under which a party may give notice of adjudication 'at any time'. It is at least arguable that the procedure under Clause 66A(1), requiring service of a 'Notice of Dispute', seeks to increase the fairness of the procedure prior to any adjudication by providing a warning of the dispute to the responding party and, to an extent, avoiding an 'ambush' by the claiming party. In such circumstances, the court may be prepared to require compliance with the contractual requirement before a dispute is said to exist which may be referred to adjudication.

Clause 66A(2): 'amicable dispute resolution'. Either party may 'at any time' give notice in writing seeking agreement of the other party for a dispute described in the Notice of Dispute or any matter which, if not resolved, could become a dispute to be considered for resolution by negotiation, or by 'other means' including conciliation (under the ICE Conciliation Procedure 1999) or mediation (under the ICE Construction Mediation Procedure 2002). If such means are used, any recommendation or proposal arising from the procedure is only binding if incorporated into a written agreement signed by both parties.

Clause 66B: adjudication. Under Clause 66(B)(1)(a) either party has a contractual right to refer a dispute to adjudication at any time. The contractual provision seeks to comply with the requirements of HGCRA 1996. Adjudication is outside the scope of this section. However, in relation to the scope of the disputes which may be referred to adjudication, it should be noted that Clause 66(B)(1)(a) refers to 'any matter in dispute arising under or in connection with the contract or the carrying out of the Works'. Therefore, Clause 66(B)(1)(a) arguably confers a wider jurisdiction on an adjudicator than the statutory provision in Section 108 of HGCRA 1996. (Section 108 of the HGCRA 1996 provides a right to refer a 'dispute arising under the contract' to adjudication. However, in the context of arbitration clauses see *Premium Nafta Products Limited and Others v. Fili Shipping Company Limited and Others ('Fiona Trust')* [2007] UKHL 40 in which the House of Lords said that it was time to draw a line under the authorities to date concerning the construction of arbitration clauses and supported the view that arbitration clauses should be construed liberally, without making fine semantic distinctions between disputes 'arising out of', 'arising under' or 'in connection with' the contract. It is not clear whether this principle could also apply

generally to adjudication. In *Air Design (Kent) Ltd v. Deerglen (Jersey) Ltd* [2008] EWHC 3047 (TCC) Akenhead J. appears to have accepted that, on the facts of that case, the principles in *Fiona Trust* did apply in adjudication). The wider range of disputes would probably include disputes about mistake, misrepresentation, negligent misstatement and rectification of the contract (see *Ashville Investments Ltd v. Elmer Construction Ltd* [1988] 2 All ER 577 (CA) for the interpretation of 'in connection with the contract' in the context of an arbitration agreement).

Clause 66B(3) of the ICE 7th Edition provides that the parties are bound by the decision of the adjudicator until the dispute is finally determined by legal proceeding or by arbitration or by agreement. If a dispute is referred for adjudication under Clause 66(B)(3), the decision of the adjudicator will be final and binding in any event unless a notice to refer to arbitration has been given within 3 months of the decision. Therefore, unless an extension of this period is agreed, any ADR procedure in respect of a dispute over the adjudicator's decision will need to be commenced and completed within 3 months from the date of the decision.

Clause 66C: arbitration: provides for disputes to be finally determined by reference to arbitration. Arbitration is outside the scope of this chapter. However, it should be noted that, contrary to the procedures in earlier versions of the ICE Conditions, a Notice to Refer to arbitration no longer needs to await completion of any antecedent step, except (possibly) the Notice of Dispute. In the absence of a Notice of Dispute there would, arguably, be no dispute to refer to arbitration. However, it is not clear whether such a contractual notice may be necessary before a dispute can be said to exist which may be the subject of a Notice to Refer. See *AMEC Civil Engineering Ltd v. Secretary of State for Transport* listed earlier.

29.10.2 Dispute resolution procedures under the Engineering and Construction Contract June 2005 (with amendments June 2006) (NEC 3)

Core Clause 10.1 of NEC3 places obligations on the Contractor, the Project Manager and the Supervisor to act as stated in the contract and in a spirit of mutual trust and co-operation.

However, NEC3 does not incorporate any contractual provision for consensual or non-adjudicative ADR but requires any dispute to be referred to adjudication. Two options are given depending whether or not HGCRA 1996 applies to the contract. Any party dissatisfied with the adjudicator's decision may refer the matter in dispute to a 'tribunal' identified in the Contract Data. It is, of course, always open to persons drafting contracts to choose the final adjudicative process for dispute resolution. However, it is a particular feature of NEC3 that, compared to other standard forms, the final adjudicative process is left open and is to be inserted in the Contract Data. Therefore, rather than merely opting for the traditional process of arbitration or the courts, those drafting the contract are required to consider which process may be appropriate. It is submitted that for particular projects certain forms of ADR, for example, a DB or expert determination, may be more appropriate as the final adjudicative process.

29.10.3 The dispute resolution procedures under JCT Standard Building Contract With Quantities 2005, Revision 2 2009 (JCT 2005 Rev 2)

JCT 2005 Rev 2 incorporates novel (for JCT forms) dispute resolution provisions which place obligations on the parties to co-operate (similar to NEC3) and also to enter into negotiations to avoid disputes or endeavour to achieve early resolution of any dispute.

Schedule 8, titled 'Supplemental Provisions', at paragraph 1, provides '[t]he Parties shall work with each other and with other project team members in a co-operative, collaborative manner, in good faith and a spirit of trust and respect. To that end, each shall support collaborative behaviour and address behaviour which is not collaborative.'

Under Schedule 8, paragraph 6, 'with a view to dispute avoidance or early resolution of disputes or differences' (and subject to the contractual right to adjudication at any time under Article 7), there is an obligation on each party to give early notification of any matter that appears likely to give rise to a dispute and for senior executives, who are to be nominated in the Contract Particulars, to meet as soon as practicable and engage in 'direct, good faith negotiations to resolve the matter'.

The provisions in Schedule 8 apply unless specifically excluded by the Contract Particulars.

Clause 9.1 provides that, subject to adjudication (under Article 7), if a dispute or difference arises under the contract which cannot be resolved by direct negotiations, each party 'shall give serious consideration' to any request by the other to refer the matter to mediation. Clause 9.2 provides for adjudication and Clause 9.3 provides for arbitration under the JCT 2005 edition of the Construction Industry Model Arbitration Rules (CIMAR) as the final adjudicative process.

It is not clear how effective the provisions in JCT 2005 Rev 2 for co-operation and dispute avoidance or early dispute resolution may be or what sanctions the courts may adopt in the event of a party failing to comply with its obligations under paragraphs 1 and 6 of Schedule 8.

29.10.4 'Ad hoc' staged dispute resolution provisions

Staged dispute resolution procedures were used by the Hong Kong government on the contracts for Chek Lap Kok. Disputes were first submitted either to the engineer who had limited powers in respect of money claims or to a government representative who decided on the award of extensions of time. If a party disagreed with the engineer's decision, it had to serve

a notice of dispute requiring a further formal decision of the engineer within 28 days. If a dispute arose over a decision of the government representative or the engineer's formal decision, it proceeded to the second stage of mediation which was to be completed within 42 days. Only disputes relating to payment or extensions of time could be referred to the third stage of adjudication. The final stage was arbitration which, except in certain limited circumstances, could only take place after substantial completion. A panel of expert mediators and arbitrators was established at the beginning of the project.

In the early 1990s, the US city of Boston adopted a then radical approach to dispute avoidance and ADR for its Central Artery Tunnel / Highway Project. After the contract was awarded, and throughout the construction period, the employer's team, the designers, and the construction teams attended educational seminars conducted by people experienced in dispute avoidance and resolution, to encourage 'partnering' between all the parties involved in the project. Claims during construction were submitted to an 'authorised representative', identified in the contract, for a decision. If a dispute arose over the authorised representative's decision, it was referred to a DRB (47 separate DBRs were in operation, each with a special expertise), which comprised two technical members who selected a chairman experienced in dispute resolution. If the parties agreed, a dispute could be referred for mediation at any time after it had been submitted to the DRB and before the board had given a decision. Although, the contract price escalated very substantially during the course of the project as a result of ground conditions and design changes (and financial irregularities), and there was a significant delay in completion, the ADR procedures appear to have been successful in resolving, or at least minimising the effect of, disputes which might have further delayed the project.

In 2005, the San Francisco Public Utilities Commission adopted comprehensive new ADR procedures to encourage dispute avoidance and resolution on its major water system projects, including the appointment of a DRB; partnering between contractors and the contracting agency; comprehensive education in dispute resolution for project managers and construction managers, including training in the role of DRBs, partnering and non-adversarial negotiation techniques; and, significantly, more authority was given to resident engineers, project managers and construction managers in order to encourage dispute resolution at the lowest possible level.

Staged procedures for dispute resolution procedure have been set up for the projects of the 2012 Olympic Games in London. The first stage is an independent dispute avoidance panel (IDAP), comprising construction professionals and a chairman whose function is to find a solution to any problem which may arise before it becomes a dispute that could require lengthy resolution. Any dispute which has not been avoided through use of IDAP is to be referred to an adjudication panel of experienced adjudicators. If a party seeks to challenge an adjudication decision, the final tribunal is the TCC.

29.11 Amicable settlement

The term 'amicable settlement' has no precise meaning and generally refers to any ADR process which seeks to achieve a settlement amicably. Several standard forms expressly recognise an 'amicable settlement' approach to avoiding or resolving disputes. For examples, see amended Clause 66A(2) of the ICE 7th Edition which seeks to retain a consensual approach to dispute resolution using negotiations or 'other means', including conciliation or mediation and Schedule 8 of JCT 2005 Rev 2 which provides for 'direct, good faith negotiations' (para. 6) and mediation (para. 9.1).

FIDIC 4th Edition and FIDIC 1999 also provide expressly for 'amicable settlement', by allowing for a 'cooling-off' period in which to attempt to settle the dispute before the commencement of arbitration. Unless the parties agree otherwise, no arbitration may be commenced until at least 56 days from a notice of intention to commence arbitration (FIDIC 4th) or from a notice of dissatisfaction (FIDIC 1999). In both cases the ADR process is left to the parties.

29.12 Court settlement process

The TCC offers ADR services under its Court Settlement Process (a process similar to mediation). If the case management judge's view is that the parties should be able to achieve an amicable settlement, the judge can decide, either at his/her own initiative or at the request of the parties, to offer a Court Settlement Conference. At the conference the parties endeavour to agree a settlement with the assistance of the judge. The process is private and confidential, voluntary and non-binding and any communications and documents provided during the process are confidential and privileged. If a settlement is reached, the parties enter into and sign a Settlement Agreement. If the case does not settle, the judge may send the parties an assessment of the case, setting out his/her views on the dispute, including the prospects of success, either overall or on individual issues, the likely outcome if the case proceeds to trial and what would constitute an appropriate settlement. The judge's assessment is confidential to the parties and may not be used or referred to in any subsequent proceedings. If a settlement is not achieved, the judge will not take any further part in the case, which will be allocated to a different judge. Unless agreed otherwise, each party bears its own costs and shares equally the court costs of the process. The Court Settlement Process will be incorporated into the next edition of the TCC Guide (due to be published in October 2010).

29.13 The court's approach to ADR
29.13.1 ADR within the court process

Since the late 1980s Official Referees (the predecessors of the judges of the TCC) made orders requiring parties to explore means of settling cases using ADR, particularly in complex multi-party disputes. It has also been the practice of the Commercial Court to direct parties to consider the use of ADR.

In the English legal jurisdiction, the procedural rules in the CPR (Waller, 2010) which first came into effect in 1999, expressly endorse ADR and provide that parties to litigation should be given an opportunity to resolve their dispute by ADR.

Under the CPR the court's duties to manage cases include 'encouraging the parties to use an alternative dispute resolution procedure if the court considers that appropriate and facilitating the use of such procedure' (CPR rule 1.4(2)(e)) and 'helping the parties to settle the whole or part of the case' (CPR rule 1.4(2)(f)).

The CPR also acknowledges that the parties may wish to have an opportunity to attempt settlement by ADR. Before the court allocates the case to a particular 'track', each party is required to complete an allocation questionnaire and, when filing the completed questionnaire, a party may make a written request for proceedings to be stayed while the parties try to settle the case by ADR or by 'other means' (CPR rule 26.4(1)). Neither the form of ADR nor the 'other means' are prescribed by the CPR. Where the parties request a stay or the court considers a stay would be appropriate, the court will direct that proceedings be stayed (CPR Part 26.4(2)).

Case management directions since implementation of the CPR have reflected the courts robust approach that parties should try to resolve disputes using ADR, in particular mediation (see *R (Cowl) v. Plymouth City Council* [2001] EWCA Civ 1935; *Hurst v. Leeming* [2001] EWHC 1051 (Ch) and *Dunnett v. Railtrack plc* [2002] EWCA Civ 303). However, it remains the right of any legal entity in the English jurisdiction to bring an action in the courts, unless the contract provides otherwise (e.g. by incorporation of an arbitration clause which would entitle a party to a stay under Section 9 of the Arbitration Act 1996) and a question arose whether the court had jurisdiction to compel parties to use ADR to resolve a dispute.

The extent to which ADR could be ordered in ongoing litigation was eventually considered by the Court of Appeal in the 'test' cases of *Halsey v Milton Keynes General NHS Trust* [2004] EWCA Civ 576 and *Steel v. Joy and Halliday* [2004] 1 WLR 3002 (CA) (see also *England and Wales High Court (Supreme Court Cost Office Decisions)* [2004] EWHC 90; and Waller, 2010, Vol2, paras. 14–4 to 14–15). The court accepted the proposition that ADR procedures are entered into voluntarily and the outcomes are ordinarily non-binding until agreed otherwise by the parties. The court concluded that CPR rule 1.4(2)(e) does not expressly permit the court to direct that ADR procedures should be used and that it may only encourage and facilitate ADR.

The court was also of the view that it was likely that compulsion of ADR would be regarded as an unacceptable constraint on the right of access to the court and, therefore, a violation of Article 6 of the European Convention on Human Rights; and that even if (contrary to the court's conclusion earlier) the court did have jurisdiction to order unwilling parties to refer disputes to mediation, the court found it difficult to conceive of circumstances in which it would be appropriate to exercise it. In relation to case management, the court emphasised that the form of encouragement to use ADR may be 'robust' and that it would be appropriate to make ADR orders of the kind then used in the Commercial Court (see *The Admiralty and Commercial Courts Guide*, Appx. 7.) to encourage and facilitate ADR. The court provided the following additional guidance:

(1) All member of the legal profession who conduct litigation should now routinely consider with their clients whether their disputes are suitable for ADR.
(2) The court should not compel mediation although it could make orders encouraging parties to mediate; and where such an order has been made, the test for refusing to proceed to mediation will be higher.

In *Halsey* the Court of Appeal also considered the consequences in terms of costs at the end of the case, if a party had refused to participate in ADR. The court held that a party who refused to go to mediation should not automatically be penalised in costs if otherwise successful in the litigation and that the burden of showing that it was unreasonable for a successful party who had refused or failed to go to mediation to have all their costs should lie firmly with the party making the allegation. The court set out six factors (set out in the TCC Guide (para. 7.4.1). The TCC Guide also states that, at the end of a trial, there may be costs arguments on the basis that one or more parties unreasonably refused to take part in ADR and that the court will determine such issues having regard to all the circumstances of the particular case.) that may be relevant to the court's consideration of whether a party has unreasonably refused ADR:

(1) the nature of the dispute;
(2) the merits of the case;
(3) the extent to which other settlement methods have been attempted;
(4) whether the costs of the ADR would be disproportionately high;
(5) whether any delay in setting up and attending the ADR would have been prejudicial; and
(6) whether the ADR had a reasonable prospect of success.

The Court of Appeal emphasised that the factors listed earlier were not exhaustive and that in many cases no single factor would be decisive. See also the approach of the Supreme Court of Western Australia in *Capolingua v. Phylum Pty Limited* (1991) 5 WAR 137.

Since *Halsey* the courts have generally proceeded on the basis that they do not have power to order mediation against the wishes of a party but that they can impose sanctions where there is an unreasonable refusal of a party to proceed to ADR. In particular, a recalcitrant party may be penalised in costs,

even if successful at trial. For examples of the factors taken into account by the court, see *Halsey*; *P4 Ltd v. Unite Integrated Solutions Ltd* [2007] BLR 1 (TCC) Ramsey J; and *Bray (t/a the Building Company v. Bishop* [2009] EWCA 768. Also, see *Roundstone Nurseries Ltd v. Stephenson Holdings Ltd* [2009] EWHC 1431 (TCC) Coulson J in which a party unilaterally cancelled an imminent pre-action meeting.

However, members of the judiciary have expressed strong doubts about the correctness of the decision in *Halsey*. (e.g. *Mediation: An Approximation to Justice* Lightman J, at S. J. Berwin 28 June 2007; and *The Future of Civil Mediation*, Sir Anthony Clarke MR, at the Civil Mediation Council Conference, Birmingham, 8 May 2008: the approach in *Halsey* 'may have been over cautious'; 'there may well be grounds for saying that *Halsey* was wrong on the Article 6 point' and that 'despite the *Halsey* decision it is strongly arguable that the court has jurisdiction to direct mediation'). In particular, mediation is compulsory in other jurisdictions and therefore there is a question whether compulsion, of itself, would give rise to a violation of Article 6. In addition, European Directive 2008/52/EC on mediation includes a provision that nothing in the Directive should prejudice a Member State from making mediation compulsory. The Master of the Rolls also expressed the view that the court's present case management powers under CPR rules 1.4(2)(e) (see earlier section) and 3.1(2)(m) (The court may 'take any other step or make any other order for the purpose off managing the case and furthering the overriding objective' of the CPR) are sufficient to confer jurisdiction on the court to require parties to enter into mediation. Therefore, although *Halsey* remains good law, the decision should now be viewed in the context of the comments of the judiciary.

In addition to the CPR, the respective guides of the TCC and the Commercial Court recognise and encourage the use of ADR (e.g. The Admiralty and Commercial Court Guide, Section G; and the TCC Guide, at Section 7) and both courts have standardised directions which provide the parties with a time window in which to explore ADR.

The Pre-Action Protocol for Construction and Engineering Disputes (Waller, 2010, Vol.1, Section C), which applies to all construction and engineering disputes (including professional negligence claims against architects, engineers and quantity surveyors) recognises the importance of negotiations at an early stage in a dispute and requires a face-to-face meeting between the parties before the commencement of proceedings. At the time of writing, it is the only Protocol under the CPR that requires the parties to meet, the stated purpose being to identify the main issues and the 'root causes' of their disagreement. The TCC Guide (para. 7.2.2) states '[a]t this meeting, there should be sufficient time to discuss and resolve the dispute' and that the purpose of the meeting is to see whether, and by what means, the issues might be resolved without recourse to litigation or, if litigation is unavoidable, what steps should be taken to ensure that it is conducted in accordance with the overriding objective of the CPR. Also, at or following the pre-action meeting, the TCC Guide requires the parties to consider whether some form of ADR would be more suitable than litigation and if so, they should endeavour to agree which form of ADR to adopt (see TCC Guide para. 2.4.3). Unfortunately the pre-action meeting is often regarded as nothing more than a formality required to satisfy the Protocol, rather than an opportunity to resolve the dispute at an early stage.

The courts, however, accept that all cases may not be appropriate for ADR. In *Hurst v. Leeming*, referred to with approval in *Halsey*, Lightman J. rejected an application by the claimant for costs on the grounds that the defendant had unreasonably refused to mediate. The Judge held that the critical factor in that case was whether, objectively viewed, a mediation had any real prospect of success; and answered that question in the negative. The decision in *Hurst v. Leeming* turned on particular facts, including an acceptance by the claimant that his case was 'hopeless', and may not have general application. Although a party may believe that a case is 'watertight', it remains the position that such a belief will not be justification for a party refusing mediation and nor is it necessarily sufficient of itself that a full and detailed refutation of the opposite party's case has already been supplied, though this may be a relevant consideration (see also *McCook v. Lobo and Others* [2002] EWCA Civ 1760 in which the Court of Appeal found that mediation would have had no realistic prospect of success).

In *Hurst v. Leeming*, the Judge also expressed the view that 'alternative dispute resolution is at the heart of today's civil justice system' (para. 10). while emphasising that mediation is not in law compulsory. However, in the Fourth Keating Lecture, 19 May 2010, this view did not receive unequivocal support from Lord Neuberger MR who observed (extra-judicially) that, while ADR did have an important part to play, it should not be viewed as being 'at the heart' of the civil justice system.

It appears that a genuine, but incorrect, decision to withdraw from a mediation, and therefore not comply with the pre-action protocol, will not necessarily result in an order for costs to be paid on an indemnity basis (*Roundstone Nurseries Ltd v. Stephenson Holdings Ltd.*)

In summary, the position is now that, notwithstanding the judicial comments on *Halsey*, any party to litigation under the English jurisdiction which does not wish to agree to ADR must have careful regard to the guidelines in *Halsey*, otherwise there is a significant risk of being penalised in costs even if eventually successful in the litigation. For example, see *P4 Ltd v. Unite Integrated Solutions Ltd*, in which a party was refused costs as a result of its conduct during the pre-action process and refusal to mediate.

On effect of encompassing ADR within the CPR and the various court guides and protocols is that usually any ADR process, for example, mediation, is not viewed by the parties (or their advisers) as a wholly stand-alone process to be undertaken at the earliest possible stage, and before a claim is issued, but rather is seen as part of the overall court process and therefore usually delayed until after proceedings have commenced.

29.13.2 The legal effect of ADR clauses: to what extent are they enforceable?

In relation to the enforcement of ADR clauses the principal questions which arise are whether undertaking and completing an ADR process can be a condition precedent to commencing adjudicative proceedings and whether the agreement for ADR itself enforceable?

The courts do not readily relinquish jurisdiction and clauses in contracts that purport to oust or limit the jurisdiction of the court are strictly construed. Any agreement that ousts the court's jurisdiction entirely is contrary to public policy and void: see *Scott v. Avery* [1856] 5 HLC 811 (HL). The courts have, however, been prepared to require a party to comply with procedures that are a condition precedent to the commencement of litigation or arbitration proceedings. In *Scott v. Avery*, the House of Lords upheld an agreement under which the award of an arbitrator was a condition precedent to the right to bring an action on the contract. This type of clause is now known as a *Scott v. Avery* clause.

The court has a general power to stay proceedings under its inherent jurisdiction where an action is brought in breach of an agreement to have disputes decided by a method other than adjudication by a court: see *Channel Tunnel Group Ltd v. Balfour Beatty Construction Ltd* (1993) 61 BLR 1 (HL) in which the House of Lords provided unequivocal support for the court not interfering in dispute resolution procedures agreed by the parties. Lord Mustill (with whom the rest of the Judicial Committee agreed) said:

> …those who make agreements for the resolution of disputes must show good reasons for departing from them … (at p.22)
>
> I would endorse the powerful warnings against encroachment on the parties' agreement to have their commercial differences decided by their chosen tribunals …(at p. 26)

The House of Lords also confirmed the court's willingness to enforce agreements to resolve disputes which were outside normal litigation or arbitration clauses. In the *Channel Tunnel* case this was in an international context: dispute resolution was first by an expert panel and then, if there was still dissatisfaction (with a unanimous decision of the panel), by an ICC arbitration with the seat in Brussels.

Therefore, although the general jurisdiction of the court cannot be ousted, the commencement of litigation or arbitration proceedings may, in certain circumstances, be validly delayed to permit an ADR process (see the later case of *Cable & Wireless plc v. IBM United Kingdom Ltd* [2002] EWHC 2059 (Comm) which is discussed further). The court's general powers are now supplemented by the CPR which expressly provide for the court to facilitate ADR and to grant a stay to allow the parties to proceed to ADR (see CPR rules 1.4(2)(e) and 26.4(2)).

However, although a stay may be granted in litigation and arbitration proceedings, the position is significantly different in contracts to which the HGCRA 1996, Section 108(2) of

HGCRA 1996 provides that a party to a construction contract (see Section 104 of HGCRA 1996) has a right to refer a dispute arising under the contract to adjudication 'at any time'. For the purpose of the section 'dispute' includes any 'difference'.

The courts have adopted a robust approach to interpreting the right to refer a dispute to adjudication 'at any time'. Any contractual provision which seeks to postpone an adjudication by requiring the prior operation of another form of dispute resolution and/or by deeming that no dispute has arisen until the other process has failed to result in a settlement, is contrary to Section 108(2) of HGCRA 1996 and is not enforceable (at least prior to adjudication). See, for example, *R. G. Carter Limited v. Edmund Nuttall Limited*, in which the court refused to uphold a provision in an amended form of DOM/1 which sought to prevent the parties resorting to adjudication or arbitration unless there had been 'informal attempts to reach a settlement by way of mediation' and a settlement had not been reached. HHJ Thornton QC held that a provision that the parties would not resort to adjudication or arbitration unless attempts to reach a settlement by mediation had been unsuccessful undermined the right of either party to refer a dispute to adjudication 'at any time' was not compliant with the HGCRA 1998. See also *Midland Expressway Ltd v. Carillion Construction Ltd (No.2)* [2005] EWHC 2963 (TCC) Jackson J.

Also, in *John Mowlem & Co. plc v. Hydra Tight & Co. plc.* a subcontract incorporated the provisions of NEC (Option A) Y(UK)2 with amendments, which provided for service of a 'notification of dissatisfaction', the expressed purpose of which was to delay adjudication for 4 weeks to give the parties an opportunity to meet and resolve their difference. Under the provisions, the parties also agreed that, in the aforementioned period, a dispute had not arisen with the intended effect that there was no dispute which could be referred to adjudication. The Judge adopted the parties' agreement that, insofar as the subcontract required a notice of dissatisfaction to be served before a dispute was deemed to have arisen, it did not comply with Section 108 of HGCRA 1996.

It is, of course, open to parties to agree to any ADR procedure. However, if a dispute arises on a construction project in the UK, adjudication is now the process favoured by the majority of claiming parties because of its (often perceived) advantages. The effect is that, unless the parties can agree to postpone a reference to adjudication, contractual provisions for ADR (to the extent that the process is to be undertaken before adjudication) will not be effective or enforceable where a party seeks to exercise its right to refer a dispute to adjudication.

The right of a party to refer a dispute to adjudication at any time has become a major obstacle to the operation of contractual provisions for consensual ADR, at least at a stage when that form of ADR can be most effective. Provisions which seek to circumvent or even merely delay adjudication will not be upheld and the court will not grant a stay to allow consensual ADR (see *R G Carter Ltd v. Edmund Nuttall Ltd* ; *John Mowlem & Co. plc v. Hydra Tight & Co. plc*; and *Midland*

Expressway Ltd v. Carillion Construction Ltd (No.2)). It is submitted that the effect of Section 108 of the HGCRA 1996 has been to undermine or, in practice, negate the intended effect of many contractual provisions for consensual and/or non-adjudicative ADR (e.g. see original Clause 66 of the ICE 7th Edition c.f. the ICE amendments to Clause 66), particularly staged provisions; and the legislation sits uneasily with the CPR which expressly provide for the court to encourage and facilitate ADR and to grant a stay to allow it to take place (CPR rules 1.4(2)(e) and 26.4(2)).

It is ironic that, at a time when the courts are strongly encouraging parties to endeavour to resolve disputes by ADR, a consequence of the legislation conferring a right to adjudication at any time is that contractual ADR procedures for dispute avoidance or resolution will not achieve their objective (at an early stage or, possibly, at all) unless there is a willingness by both parties not to proceed to adjudication at the first stage of the dispute resolution process.

In the context of enforcement, clauses which refer to ADR processes which involve 'negotiation' may present a potential difficulty. Such processes are generally similar to negotiations in that they are consensual, non-binding and have the objective of achieving a settlement, the terms of which have yet to be determined. Under English law an agreement to negotiate is ordinarily not enforceable: see *Courtney & Fairbairn v. Tolaini Brothers (Hotels) Limited* [1975] 1 WLR 297 (CA) (and *Paul Smith Ltd v. H&S International Holding Inc* [1991] 2 Lloyd's Rep 127) in which the Court of Appeal rejected the argument that an agreement to enter into negotiations was enforceable:

> If the law does not recognise a contract to enter into a contract (when there is a fundamental term yet to be agreed) it seems to me it cannot recognise a contract to negotiate. The reason is because it is too uncertain to have any binding force ... per Lord Denning MR

The rationale of the court's approach is that there is an general lack of certainty in a mere undertaking to negotiate a contract or settlement agreement and also in an agreement merely to endeavour to settle a dispute amicably, because the court would have insufficient objective criteria to decide whether one or both parties were in compliance or breach of such a provision.

There are, however, fundamental differences that distinguish certain consensual ADR processes from merely direct negotiations between the parties. First, the parties submit the dispute to a process which is outside the parties' direct negotiations, and which involves an independent third party, for example, mediation. Second, the process itself will be governed (to varying degrees) by the role of the third party and by any protocol and/or rules that may apply to the process.

In *Cable & Wireless plc v. IBM United Kingdom Limited* the court provided guidance on its approach to the enforcement of ADR provisions which involved a 'consensual' process. The court reviewed the enforceability of bespoke 'escalating' dispute resolution provisions, which included ADR (in the form of mediation), where completion of the ADR process was a condition precedent to the commencement of legal proceedings. A dispute had arisen and IBM tried to proceed by way of mediation. Cable & Wireless refused, arguing that the ADR clause 'imposed no more than an agreement to negotiate … and an agreement to negotiate [was] not enforceable in English law'. The judgement of Coleman J recognised that the scope of remedies available in a mediation would not necessarily be available in the legal proceedings:

> … parties who enter into an ADR agreement must be taken to appreciate that mediation as a tool for dispute resolution is not designed to achieve solutions which reflect the precise legal rights and obligations of the parties, but rather solutions which are commercially acceptable at the time of the mediation.

However, the Judge then acknowledged the public policy position on the use of ADR:

> For the courts now to decline to enforce contractual references to ADR on the grounds of intrinsic uncertainty would be to fly in the face of public policy as expressed in the CPR and as reflected in the judgment of the Court of Appeal in *Dunnett v. Railtrack* ….(See *Dunnett v. Railtrack plc* [2002] 1 WLR 2434 (CA) at pages 2436–7, per Brooke LJ.)

In *Cable & Wireless* a factor which weighed heavily with the court in upholding the ADR agreement was the incorporation into the contract of provisions that could be analysed as requiring not merely an attempt in good faith to negotiate a settlement but the participation of the parties in a particular ADR procedure recommended by an established external organisation which provided dispute resolution services. The judge found that the parties' intended engagement of a recognised organisation to provide the mediator and their participation in the recommended procedure of that organisation, provided sufficient certainty for the court readily to ascertain whether the parties had complied with the dispute resolution provisions in the contract.

However, in addition to the form of the ADR process, the prospects of a claim succeeding may be a relevant factor in any application to enforce an ADR. In *Balfour Beatty Construction Northern Ltd v. Modus Corovest (Blackpool) Ltd* [2008] EWHC 3029 (TCC) Coulson J viewed the mediation agreement under bespoke amendments as 'nothing more than an agreement to agree' and, unlike the ADR agreement in *Cable & Wireless,* as too uncertain to be enforced by the court; and held that it could not be said that the party which commenced court proceedings had done so in breach of the agreement to mediate. The Judge continued that, even there had been a binding agreement to mediate, he would only have stayed the claim for mediation if he had concluded that the party making the claim was not entitled to summary judgement (i.e. the other party had an arguable defence which had a realistic prospect of success) and that the best way of resolving the dispute was a reference to mediation. He stated that if a party is entitled to summary judgement on a claim, it is because there is no defence to that claim, or at least no defence with a realistic prospect of success; and, in such circumstances, there is no proper dispute to be referred to mediation as the party bringing the (unanswerable) claim would be entitled to summary judgement.

In summary, the overall position is that the commencement of litigation or arbitration proceedings (but not adjudication under contracts to which HGCRA 1996 applies) may, in certain circumstances, be validly delayed to permit ADR provided there is a genuine dispute over the claim and the ADR process incorporated into the contract has formal and defined procedures.

29.13.3 What constitutes a 'dispute'?

Often a party will seek to challenge the jurisdiction of a tribunal on grounds that no dispute exists. Therefore it is important to know when a dispute exists. In the context of contractual ADR provisions, it is also important to know whether or not the matter of complaint constitutes a 'dispute'. If a dispute exists, a party may find it impossible to enforce the ADR procedures in the contract if the other party exercises its right to refer the dispute to adjudication (see listed earlier).

There is a large volume of case law concerning the meaning of 'dispute'. The majority of cases need to be considered on their own facts but (at least in relation to construction contracts) the courts previously tended towards a narrow definition of 'dispute' and to define precisely the time at which a dispute came into existence. For example, see *Monmouthshire County Council v. Costelloe & Kemple Limited*, in which the Court of Appeal considered the meaning of the words 'dispute or difference' under Clause 66 of the ICE 4th Edition, and held that a letter from the contractor to the engineer merely requesting comments on a claim was not a reference to the engineer, and a 'dispute or difference' only came into existence when the engineer formally rejected the claim. The provisions of subsequent editions of the ICE Conditions of Contract also made an engineer's decision a condition precedent to a dispute. However, it is submitted that *Monmouthshire County Council v Costelloe & Kemple Limited* no longer has general application following the decision in *AMEC Civil Engineering Ltd v. Secretary of State for Transport*. However, in recent years the courts have demonstrated a willingness to define 'dispute' more widely.

In *AMEC Civil Engineering Ltd v. Secretary of State for Transport* a dispute arose over remedial works to the Thelwall Viaduct. After the arbitrator had issued his award, AMEC appealed to the court, challenging the arbitrator's jurisdiction on, among other grounds, that there was no dispute capable of being referred to the engineer for decision. Jackson J dismissed the appeal and AMEC appealed to the Court of Appeal, which also dismissed the appeal. The Court of Appeal was principally concerned with the operation of the contractual machinery for referring disputed to arbitration and whether an engineer, asked to make a decision under Clause 66 of the ICE 6th Edition, was required to comply with the rules of natural justice.

On the question of whether a dispute had arisen, the Court of Appeal accepted as 'broadly correct' (but dependent on the facts of a particular case) seven propositions in the judgement of Jackson J, which may be summarised as follows:

(1) The word 'dispute' should be given its normal meaning. It does not have some special or unusual meaning conferred upon it by lawyers.

(2) Litigation has not generated any hard-edged legal rules as to what is or is not a dispute. The judicial decisions provide helpful guidance.

(3) The mere fact that one party notifies the other party of a claim does not automatically and immediately give rise to a dispute. A dispute does not arise unless and until it emerges that the claim is not admitted.

(4) The circumstances from which it may emerge that a claim is not admitted are 'Protean'; for example, express rejection; discussions from which objectively it is to be inferred that the claim is not admitted; the respondent may prevaricate, giving rise to the inference that it does not admit the claim; the respondent may simply remain silent for a period of time, giving rise to the same inference.

(5) The period of time for which a respondent may remain silent before a dispute is to be inferred depends upon the facts of the case and the contractual structure. If the gist of the claim is well known and it is obviously controversial, a very short period of silence may suffice to give rise to this inference. If the claim is notified to an agent of the respondent, who has a legal duty to consider the claim independently and then give a considered response, a longer period of time may be required.

(6) If a claimant imposes a deadline for responding, that will not have the automatic effect of curtailing what would otherwise be a reasonable time for respond. However, a stated deadline and the reasons for its imposition may be relevant factors when the court comes to consider what constitutes a reasonable time for responding.

(7) If the claim is vague and ill-defined such that the respondent cannot sensibly respond, neither silence nor even an express non-admission is likely to give rise to a dispute for the purposes of arbitration or adjudication. (Jackson J's propositions also received approval by the Court of Appeal in *Collins Contractors Ltd v. Baltic Quay Management (1994) Ltd* [2004] EWCA Civ 1757. See also *Cantillon Ltd v. Urvasco Ltd* [2008] BLR 250 (TCC) Akenhead J.)

In the Court of Appeal May LJ was prepared to go further than Jackson J at first instance and was prepared to find that, in all the circumstances of the case, including the imminence of the end of the statutory limitation period for commencing an arbitration, there was a dispute or difference capable of being referred to the engineer at any time after a meeting at which AMEC had stated orally that it did not accept responsibility for

the defects (Judgement para. 33). It is submitted that if merely an oral rejection of responsibility during the course of ongoing meetings to discuss a potential claim is sufficient to create a 'dispute', it may often be difficult for a party to decide with any certainty whether a dispute exists which is capable of being referred to adjudication or whether there is no dispute such that it may properly require the other party to comply with a contractual provision under which the parties have agreed to undertake a non-adjudicative ADR process.

29.14 The ICC ADR rules

Many international construction contracts provide for dispute resolution under the institutional framework of the ICC. The ICC publishes ADR rules (the ICC ADR Rules) which allow parties to settle their disputes or differences 'amicably' with the assistance of a third party, known as a 'Neutral'. The Neutral may be a person designated by the parties or appointed by the ICC. In the latter case, the parties may specify certain requirements with regard to the qualifications or expertise of the Neutral. The objective of the ICC ADR Rules is to make proceedings flexible, rapid and inexpensive. It is open to the parties to choose the ADR process which they consider most appropriate to the nature of their dispute from the processes offered: mediation; a mini-trial; or neutral evaluation. The common factor in all processes is that the outcome is not binding upon the parties. The parties may, however, agree in writing that they will comply with a recommendation or decision of the Neutral. The parties are not restricted to using one process. In the absence of an agreement of the parties on a process, mediation will be used.

29.15 Advantages and disadvantages of ADR

Appropriate forms of ADR can assist in dispute avoidance and prevent disputes proceeding to trial or arbitration. However, the success in recent years of formal ADR, in particular mediation, must be seen in context. Prior to the introduction of the CPR over 90% of the disputes in which court proceedings had commenced settled in any event and did not proceed to trial.

The primary benefits of ADR are that the processes are flexible, fast and ordinarily more cost-effective than the traditional forms of dispute resolution. Even in the most complex disputes, the majority of ADR processes may be completed in no more than 1 or 2 days. In addition, processes such as mediation may generally be arranged at the convenience of the parties. Although it is rarely the case in the UK, often lawyers need not be involved. In consensual processes, the outcome is agreed by the parties thereby avoiding the imposition of a decision by a third party.

The prospects of a successful outcome in ADR are high. For example, mediation is said to have a success rate in excess of 80%. Often cases which do not settle on the day of the mediation, will settle a short time afterwards.

A process that achieves an early settlement benefits all parties. For example, in a delay and disruption claim, early settlement may assist the contractor's cash flow and provide the employer with better prospects for completion on time, and at the same time avoid 'grumbling' disputes throughout the project.

The litigation and arbitration processes in the UK are adversarial. Adjudication is usually conducted in an adversarial way. In contrast, in consensual ADR processes the parties are able to control the outcome of the settlement and there is an opportunity to minimise confrontation and prevent (or at least limit) further deterioration in the commercial relationship between the parties.

Consensual ADR can provide a more certain outcome which is reached by agreement. In contrast, the outcome in litigation, arbitration and adjudication is dependent on the tribunal and its findings on evidence of fact and expert evidence. In addition, in consensual ADR the parties can agree solutions to the dispute that would not be available in court or arbitration proceedings. The outcome may often be 'interest-based' rather than being strictly based on contractual rights.

Litigation takes place in the public forum of the courts. Although initially arbitration is a private process, the cloak of confidentiality may be lost if an appeal is lodged and the matter moves to the courts. In any event, many construction arbitrations run for periods of weeks or months, rather than days, and the longer the period, the more likely it is that confidentiality will be lost.

In contrast, ADR is a private (and generally short) process, and confidentiality about the matters in dispute, or the dispute itself, may be maintained.

Communications between parties to a mediation and between the parties and the mediator ordinarily will remain private and confidential for reasons of public policy and the court will generally be willing to protect the confidentiality of the process by which any settlement is reached (see *Re D (Minors) (Conciliation: Disclosure of Information)* [1993] Fam 231 (CA) and *Halsey v. Milton Keynes General NHS Trust*, at para. 14. Also *Cumbria Waste Management Ltd and Anor v. Baines Wilson* [2008] EWHC 786 [TCC] HHJ Kirkham [sitting as a High Court Judge]). It is outside the scope of this chapter to discuss the different ways in which mediation communications are protected from disclosure and the circumstances in which the court may wish to investigate matters that would ordinarily be private and confidential in an ADR process but it may be important to recognise that the position with each of the following, namely confidentiality, 'without prejudice' privilege, legal professional privilege and any other privilege, may be different (see *Farm Assist Ltd (in liquidation) v. Secretary of State for the Environment, Food and Rural Affairs (No.2)* [2009] EWHC (TCC) Ramsey J.; Waller, 2010, Vol. 2, Section 14, paras 14–18 to 14–18.5; and the other cases there cited).

ADR also has certain disadvantages, and there may be risks inherent in certain of the processes.

Parties to litigation and arbitration are required to adopt an 'open' approach which includes the disclosure of all relevant documents, and the exchange of witness statements and experts' reports, the intention being that no party should be taken by surprise by the other party. In the majority of ADR processes there will be no general disclosure of documents or evidence. This means that a party may not be aware of the existence of a document or evidence which would be adverse, or even fatal, to the other party's case, if the matter were to proceed to court or arbitration.

Unless the contract provides a timetable, careful judgement may be needed as to the point at which ADR should be commenced – see *Nigel Witham Ltd v. Smith* [2008] EWHC 12 (TCC) in which Coulson J offered general guidance on the timing of ADR and observed: 'A premature mediation simply wastes time and can sometimes lead to a hardening of the positions on both sides which make any subsequent attempt of settlement doomed to fail …The trick in many cases is to identify the happy medium: the point when the detail of the claim and the response are known to both sides, but before the costs that have been incurred in reaching that stage are so great that a settlement is no longer possible'. While disputes may be, and often are, resolved before a party has all the available information, in certain disputes it may not be appropriate to enter into ADR before sufficient information is available to both parties to allow them to formulate the terms of a settlement.

If a wholly equitable settlement is to be achieved in certain disputes, full disclosure of documents may be required. This may prevent the use of ADR at an early stage and therefore limit the potential savings in costs.

Although ADR in the form of mediation is generally without prejudice and non-binding, a party may disclose information that the other party would not otherwise have obtained except for the mediation. If agreement is not reached, such information may be beneficial to the other party in assessing the merits of the respective cases if the dispute proceeds to a hearing.

ADR is an additional layer in the dispute resolution process. Although the costs of ADR are generally much lower than the costs of litigation and arbitration, in a complex case the costs of, say, a mediation are likely to be substantial. If the process is not successful, a large proportion of these substantial costs may be wasted and become an additional cost to those incurred in subsequent proceedings. Certain mediators now seek to incorporate a clause in their mediation agreement providing that, if no settlement is achieved, the costs of the mediation will be included in the costs of the main proceedings. It is submitted that this approach is contrary to the spirit of mediation as a voluntary and non-binding process.

ADR processes, including mediation, are not controlled by the courts. If a mediator is guilty of misconduct by, say, revealing information given in confidence by one party to the other party, and this only comes to light after a settlement has been reached, the aggrieved party cannot appeal to the court and may only have a remedy if it commences an action in negligence against the mediator.

29.16 Selecting an appropriate ADR process for construction disputes

Certain contracts provide for a specific form of ADR. For example, the ICE 7th Edition includes conciliation or mediation.

In the United Kingdom, facilitative mediation has become virtually synonymous with 'ADR'. The primary reason for this is that the use of ADR in recent years has been largely driven by the courts and by lawyers who have no technical expertise and by certain organisations which provide mediators, the majority of whom are lawyers. It is submitted that, if mediation is the appropriate form of ADR in a particular construction dispute, evaluative mediation with a competent person of the appropriate discipline as mediator may often be a more suitable process (see conciliation under the ICE Conciliation Procedure 1999).

Although mediation is arguably the most flexible of the ADR processes, it is important not to be prescriptive as other forms of ADR may offer a more appropriate process and/or be more cost effective for resolving specific types of dispute. Selected examples of types of dispute and possible forms of ADR which may be used are given subsequently.

- Contractual interpretation: the interpretation of contractual provisions may either be determinative of the dispute or may form part of a larger dispute. In either case a non-binding early expert evaluation by an independent lawyer is likely to assist the parties. Alternatively, if the parties are prepared to be bound by an expert determination by a lawyer, such determination may dispose of the dispute. In important cases, ENE by a judge of the TCC or Commercial Court may be justified.

- Claims relating to loss and expense, extensions of time, and the valuation of variations: these types of dispute are normally the most protracted and complex. If the parties can agree to a final and binding decision, expert determination by an independent engineer or a quantity surveyor (as appropriate to the form of contract) may offer an effective means of settling these types of dispute in terms of time and cost. However, conciliation or non-binding early expert determination by an independent engineer or quantity surveyor (as appropriate) may offer more acceptable alternatives to the parties.

- Defective construction work: expert determination or non-binding early expert evaluation by an independent building professional whose discipline is appropriate to the type of the work.

- Disputes between a purchaser and a regular supplier over the performance of plant and equipment: although early expert evaluation may be appropriate, the mini-trial process would enable the dispute to be resolved by senior management familiar with technical matters and trade custom and practice, and who wish to preserve the existing business relationship.

- Professional negligence: a non-binding early expert evaluation by an independent professional of the appropriate discipline will

allow the parties to review the merits of their respective cases at an early stage.

There are certain types of dispute in which ADR is unlikely to be appropriate, including disputes in which:

- a party seeks an injunction or declaratory relief which is only available in court proceedings

- the nature of the dispute is such that a party requires the court to establish a legal precedent, for example, over the interpretation of a clause in a contract

- a party is entitled to summary judgement under CPR Part 24 (*Balfour Beatty Construction Northern Ltd v. Modus Corovest (Blackpool) Ltd*)

- a local authority requires a decision based on contractual provisions to satisfy the district auditor

- a party to the dispute does not act in good faith (See, however, the guidelines in *Halsey*).

29.17 Limitation periods and contractual time limits

It is essential for a claiming party considering ADR to be aware of any potential difficulties which may arise by the expiry of any relevant statutory limitation period or contractual time limit while the ADR process is being undertaken. The *Limitation Act 1980* and the other legislation which defines limitation periods in which court proceedings or arbitration must be commenced are discussed earlier. EU Directive 2008/52/EC acknowledges that, while undertaking an ADR process, limitation periods may arise in the more formal means of dispute resolution. Member States must ensure that the parties are not subsequently prevented from initiating judicial proceedings or arbitration in respect of the dispute by the expiry of limitation or prescription periods during the 'mediation' process. However, at the time of writing it is not clear what amendments may be made to the relevant statutory provisions in the UK.

In addition to statutory provisions, certain standard form contracts impose time limits within the dispute resolution procedures (see Clause 66B(3) of the ICE 7th Edition and 28.7 of the JCT Major Project Construction Contract 2005). If limitation or contractual timetables are likely to be a problem, it is open to the parties to agree to postpone time running or to extend contractual time limits. However, in the absence of agreement, a claiming party will need to ensure that its rights are not prejudiced by the expiry of a particular time limit while ADR is undertaken.

In relation to any action which arises in connection with the enforcement of the agreement concluded at the end of the ADR process, a party's cause of action will accrue on the date of the other party's failure to fulfil its obligations under such agreement.

References

Chartered Institute of Arbitrators. *The chartered institute of arbitrators: guidelines for supervised settlement procedure*, London, UK, CIArb.

Commercial Court. *The admiralty & commercial courts guide, 8th Edition*, UK, 2009.

Dispute Board Federation. *The Dispute Board Federation (Geneva) 2008 International Survey*, 2008. www.dbfederation.org

Gould, N., King, C. and Britton, P. *Mediating construction disputes: an evaluation of existing practice*, London, UK, King's College London Centre of Construction Law & Dispute Resolution, 2010. www.kcl.ac.uk/content/1/c6/06/13/33/KCLMediatingConstructionPartsI-III.pdf (last accessed 21 September 2010).

Institution of Civil Engineers. *The ICE conciliation procedure 1999*, London, UK, Thomas Telford Ltd, 1999.

Institution of Civil Engineers. *ICE construction mediation procedure 2002*, London, UK, Thomas Telford Ltd, 2002.

International Chamber of Commerce. *ADR Rules*, Paris, France, ICC, 2001. www.iccwbo.org/uploadedFiles/Court/Arbitration/other/adr_rules.pdf (last accessed 21 September 2010).

Neuberger, L. *The fourth Keating lecture: equity, ADR, arbitration and the law: different dimensions of justice*, 2010.

Kendall, J. *Expert determination, 3rd Edition*, UK, Sweet & Maxwell, 2001.

Technology and Construction Court. *The technology and construction court guide, Second edition; First revision*, (2005, revised October 2007). www.hmcourts-service.gov.uk/docs/tcc_guide.htm (last accessed 21 September 2010).

The Times 31 March 2006 (CA)

Waller, Mr Justice (ed). *Civil procedure – 'The White Book'*, UK, Sweet & Maxwell, 2010.

Xuan, G.U. *The combination of arbitration and mediation in China: research paper on arbitration law*, Université de Genève and Université de Lausanne, 2008. www.unige.ch/droit/mbl/upload/pdf/Gu_Xuan__s_paper.pdf (last accessed 21 September 2010).

Referenced legislation, regulations and standards

Arbitration Act 1996

Commercial Arbitration Act 1984 (New South Wales)

Directive 2008/52/EC of the European Parliament and of the Council of 21 May 2008 on certain aspects of mediation in civil and commercial matters. OJ, **L136**, 24/05/2008, pp.3–8.

Housing Grants, Construction and Regeneration Act 1996

Limitation Act 1980

Referenced cases

Air Design (Kent) Ltd v. Deerglen (Jersey) Ltd [2008] EWHC 3047 (TCC)

AMEC Civil Engineering Ltd v. Secretary of State for Transport [2005] EWCA Civ 291, [2005] BLR 227 (CA)

Ashville Investments Ltd v. Elmer Construction Ltd [1988] 2 All ER 577 (CA)

Balfour Beatty Construction Northern Ltd v. Modus Corovest (Blackpool) Ltd [2008] EWHC 3029 (TCC)

Bray (t/a the Building Company v. Bishop [2009] EWCA 768

Cable & Wireless plc v. IBM United Kingdom Ltd [2002] EWHC 2059 (Comm)

Cantillon Ltd v. Urvasco Ltd [2008] BLR 250 (TCC) Akenhead J.

Capolingua v. Phylum Pty Limited (1991) 5 WAR 137 (Supreme Court of Western Australia)

Channel Tunnel Group Ltd v. Balfour Beatty Construction Ltd (1993) 61 BLR 1 (HL)

CIL Securities v. Briant Champion Long [1993] 42 EG 281

Collins Contractors Ltd v. Baltic Quay Management (1994) Ltd [2004] EWCA Civ 1757

Courtney & Fairbairn v. Tolaini Brothers (Hotels) Limited [1975] 1 WLR 297 (CA)

Cumbria Waste Management Ltd and Anor v. Baines Wilson [2008] EWHC 786 (TCC) HHJ Kirkham

Dixons Group plc v. Jan Andrew Murray-Oboynski (1998) 86 BLR 16

Dunnett v. Railtrack plc [2002] EWCA Civ 303

England and Wales High Court (Supreme Court Cost Office Decisions) [2004] EWHC 90

Farm Assist Ltd (in liquidation) v. Secretary of State for the Environment, Food and Rural Affairs (No.2) [2009] EWHC (TCC) Ramsey J.

Halifax Life Limited v. The Equitable Life Assurance Society [2007] EWHC 503 (Comm) Cresswell J

Halsey v Milton Keynes General NHS Trust [2004] EWCA Civ 576

Hickman v. Lapthorn [2006] EWHC 12 (QB) Jack J. c.f.

Hickman v. Lapthorn [2006] EWHC 12 (QB) Jack J.

Hurst v. Leeming [2001] EWHC 1051 (Ch)

IDA Ltd v. University of Southampton [2006] EWCA Civ 145

John Mowlem & Co. plc v. Hydra Tight & Co. plc [2001] 17 CLJ 358 (TCC) HHJ Toulmin CMG QC.

Jones v. Sherwood Services Ltd plc [1992] 1 WLR 277

McCook v. Lobo and Others [2002] EWCA Civ 1760

Midland Expressway Ltd v. Carillion Construction Ltd (No.2) [2005] EWHC 2963 (TCC) Jackson J.

Monmouthshire County Council v. Costelloe & Kemple Limited (1965) 5 BLR 83 (CA)

Nigel Witham Ltd v. Smith [2008] EWHC 12 (TCC)

P4 Ltd v. Unite Integrated Solutions Ltd [2007] BLR 1 (TCC) Ramsey J

Paul Smith Ltd v. H&S International Holding Inc [1991] 2 Lloyd's Rep 127

Premium Nafta Products Limited and Others v. Fili Shipping Company Limited and Others ('Fiona Trust') [2007] UKHL 40

R (Cowl) v. Plymouth City Council [2001] EWCA Civ 1935

Re D (Minors) (Conciliation: Disclosure of Information) [1993] Fam 231 (CA)

R. G. Carter Ltd v. Edmund Nuttall Ltd 21 June 2000 Unreported (TCC) HHJ Thornton QC.

Roundstone Nurseries Ltd v. Stephenson Holdings Ltd [2009] EWHC 1431 (TCC) Coulson J

Scott v. Avery [1856] 5 HLC 811 (HL)

Steel v. Joy and Halliday [2004] 1 WLR 3002 (CA)

Thakrav. Ciro Citterio Menswear plc [2002] EWHC 1975

Thames Water Utilities Ltd v. Heathrow Airport Ltd [2009] EWCA 992

Veba Oil Supply and Trading GmbH v. Petrotrade Inc [2001] EWCA Civ 1832, [2002] 1 Lloyd's Rep 295

Wallshire Ltd v. AaronsI [1989] 2 EG 81

Further reading

Booen, P.L. (2000) *The FIDIC Contracts Guide*. FIDIC, UK.

Brown, H. & Marriott, A. (1999) *ADR Principles and Practice* (2nd Edition). Sweet & Maxwell, UK.

Chern, C. (2007) *Chern on Dispute Boards.* Wiley-Blackwell Publishing, UK.

Civil Procedure 2010; Volume 1: para., C5–001: *The Pre-Action Protocol for Construction and Engineering Disputes.*

Richbell, D. (2008) *Mediation of Construction Disputes.* Blackwell Publishing, UK.

Technology and Construction Court Guide, 2nd Edition; Section 7: ADR.

Totterdill, B.W. (2006) *FIDIC user's guide. A practical guide to the 1999 red and yellow books.* Thomas Telford Limited, London, UK.

Websites

British and Irish Legal Information Institute (BAILII); www.bailii.org

Chartered Institute of Arbitrators (CIArb); www.ciarb.org

Civil Engineering Contractors Association (CECA); www.ceca.co.uk

Civil Procedure Rules; *www.justice.gov.uk/civil/procrules_fin/*

Dispute Board Federation; www.dbfederation.org

International Federation of Consulting Engineers (FIDIC); www.fidic.org

Institution of Civil Engineers (ICE); www.ice.org.uk

International Chamber of Commerce (ICC); www.iccwbo.org

Joint Contracts Tribunal (JCT); www.jctltd.co.uk

New Engineering Contract (NEC); www.neccontracts.com

Technology and Construction Court (TCC), Court Settlement Process; www.hmcourts-services.co.uk/docs/tcc_court_settlement_process.pdf

The New York Convention; www.newyorkconvention.org/

Table of Statutes and Statutory Instruments

Table of European Legislation

Table of cases

Index

alternative dispute resolution *(cont.)*
  limitation periods and contractual time
    limits, 517
  mediation
    European Directive 2008/52/EC, 502–503
    evaluative, 501
    facilitative, 501
    final agreement, 502
    forms, 500
    process, 501–502
  mediation–arbitration, 506
  mini-trials, 503–504
  negotiated settlement, 500
  selection of appropriate, 517
  staged, 506–509
  use for formal, 500
alternative investment market (AIM), 170, 173
AMEC Civil Engineering Ltd v. Secretary of State for Transport, 514
Anchor Brewhouse Developments v. Berkley House (Docklands Developments), 389
Ancient Monuments and Archaeological Areas Act 1979 (AMAAA 1979), 15
ancillary construction contracts, 55, 119
Andrews v. Schooling, 388
annual general meeting (AGM), 168
Antaios Compania Naviera S.A. v. Salen Rederierna A.B., 294
appeals, 307–308
  enforcement, 13–14, 307
  heritage protection of listed buildings, 17
  litigation, for construction industry, 456
  against non-compliance with health and safety requirements, 307–308
  planning. *see* planning appeals
  planning applications, 13
  Secretary of State for Communities and Local Government (SSCLG), 13
Apprenticeship, Skills Children and Learning Act 2009, 274
Approved Codes of Practice and guidance (ACoPs), 304
arbitration
  advantages and disadvantages, 459–460
  Arbitration Act 1996 (the 1996 Act), 459, 466
  arbitrator's award, 463–464
  domestic and international, 460
  international dimension, 466–467
  powers of arbitrators, 465
  preparation of facual evidence, 462
  presentation of the case to the arbitrator, 463
  problems, 465–466
  procedure and rules, 459
  process
    conflicts of interest and terms and conditions, 461
    date of commencement, 460–461
    defining the issues, 461
    disclosure, 462
    dispute, 460
    general principles, 461
    lawyer representation in, 461
    method of appointing the arbitrator, 461
    methods of commencement, 460
    pre-arbitral process, 460

Architects Code: Standards of Conduct and Practice, 243
architectural competitions, 37
Areas of Archaeological Importance (AAIs), 5, 15
Arup's joint venture with Worsley Parsons, 177
Association for Consultancy and Engineering (ACE)
  agreements, 220–221
    consulting engineers' professional services contracts, 220–221, 227–228
    year 2009, 229
  PI insurance, 244
  Schedule of Services, 218
Association of Consultant Architects (ACA), 69
association of persons (AOP), 182
A.Straume (UK) Ltd v. Bradlor Developments Ltd, 148
Atkins, 178
audit committee, 172
Austin Rover Group Ltd v. HM Inspector of Factories, 317
Authority Requirements document, 22

Balfour Beatty Construction Northern Ltd v. Modus Corovest (Blackpool) Ltd, 514
Banbury and Cheltenham Railway v. Daniel, 359
bank funding, 23
  drawdowns, 23
  interest rate, 23
  prepayment, 23
  term loan, 23
Banque Bruxelles S.A. v. Eagle Star, 301
Banque Financie`re de la Cite´ S.A. v. Westgate Insurance Co. Ltd, 131
Banque Saudi Fransi v. Lear Siegler Services, 152
Bates, Sir Malcolm, 49
BCCI v. Ali, 151
Beaufort Developments v. Gilbert Ash, 466
benchmarking, 75–76
  benchmarker organization, 76
  in FM contracts, 75–76
Bennett & White v. Municipal District of Sugar City, 359
best and final offer (BAFO) submissions, 118
BHP Billiton Petroleum Ltd v. Dalmine SpA, 432
BHP Billiton Petroleum v. Dalmine SpA, 443
bid bond, 143, 152
bid-rigging, of construction contracts, 125
bilateral contract, 291
Blackpool and Fylde Aero Club Limited v. Blackpool Borough Council, 124
Blyth and Blyth v. Carillion Construction, 358
Blyth & Blyth v. Carillion Construction Ltd [2001] 79 ConLR 142, 84
board meetings, 167
board of directors, 171
bond financing, 23
  collateral deed, 29
  degree of control, 29

financial close, 30
guaranteed bond issue, 29–30
offering circular, 29
rating, 29–30
role of the guarantor, arranger and bond trustee, 29
timetable for a bond issue, 30
types, 29
unwrapped bond, 29
verification of, 29
bonds and guarantees, in construction projects
  advance payment bonds/repayment guarantees, 143, 152
  aim, 143
  bid bond, 143, 152
  characteristics of a contract of guarantee, 144
    contractual promise of a Guarantor, 144
    entitlement to notice, 144
    liability of the Guarantor, 144
    measure of damages, 144
    recovery of damages, 144
    seeking of an injunction in appropriate cases, 144
  conditional/performance bond, 147–148
  contract of guarantees, 143–145
  and contractor or consultant, 143
  defects liability bonds, 143, 153
  enforcing of guarantees, 145–146
    beneficiary's remedy for any failure, 145
    challenging, 146–147
    insolvency reason, 145–146
    power purchase agreement, 146
  on-demand bond, 148–149
    bad faith, 152
    challenging, 150–152
    evidence of fraud, 151–152
    invalidity, 151
    making a, 149–150
  performance bond/guarantee, 143, 153
  Principal to the Beneficiary, 143
  retention money bonds, 143, 152
  security of, 143
  selecting and drafting, 153
  suretyship, 143
Bouygues v. Dahl-Jensen, 354
breach of contract, 105
  and insolvency, in construction, 355
  and insurance, 132–133, 137–138
  recovery of damages from guarantor, 144
  remedies for, 124
Bribery Act 2010, 125
Bristol Conservatories, 279
British Institute of Facilities Management, 67
British Property Federation (BPF) collateral warranties, 233–234
British Steel Corporation v. Cleveland Bridge Engineering Company Limited, 119–120
Brown v. Bateman, 360
Builders Accident, Reliance and the Independent Insurance Company, 133

Corporate Manslaughter and Corporate Homicide Act 2007 (CMCHA), 308
Costain International v. Davy McKee, 361
costs and cost analysis
    control in design and build procurement method, 86
    facilities management contracts, 75, 77
    latent defects insurance, 139
    litigation, for construction industry, 455
    planning appeals, 12
    private financing initiative (PFI)
        of capital, 48
        risk allocation, 52
    Target, 82
    tendering
        in a design and build contract, 105
        overheads, 105
        recovery of, 123–124
        risks in, 116
    traditional contracting, 81–82
        actual cost method, 82
        cost plus reimbursement, 82
        Guaranteed Maximum Price (GMP), 82
        lump sum method, 81
        with quantities, 81
        reimbursements, 82
        re-measurement contracts, 81–82
        without quantities, 81
Court of Appeal, 514
Court of Appeal of New Zealand, 124
cover pricing, 125
Cowlishaw and Wong v. O&D Building Contractors, 350
CRC Energy Efficiency Scheme (CRC), 409
Credit Guarantee Finance, 48
Criminal Justice Act 1967, 306
Criminal Justice Act 2003, 312
Criminal Justice and Public Order Act 1994 (CJPOA), 305
Crown Prosecution Service (CPS), 305
Cutler v. Wandsworth Stadium Limited, 385

Dalkia Utilities v. Celtech International, 357
Dangerous Substances and Explosive Atmospheres Regulations 2002 (SI No. 2776), 338–339
decennial liability, 201
Defective Premises Act 1972, 388
Defective Title, 134
defects liability bonds, 143, 153
deliverability, consultant contracts, 109–110
Department for Business, Innovation and Skills, 341
Department for Communities and Local Government (DCLG), 4
    Circular 02/2006, 6
    Circular 03/09, 12
    Circular 11/95, 10
Department for Environment, Transport and Regions (DETR), 4
Department of Health's Standard Form of Project Agreement, 60
design and build procurement method
    ab initio approach, 84

buildability, 85–86
contractor's submissions/proposals, 84
design responsibility, 83–85
familiarity, 87
fitness for purpose, 85
general structure, 83
'in house' design team, 83
novation of design team, 84–85
overview, 83
payment, 86
perceived advantages of, 86–87
perceived disadvantages of, 87
price certainty, 86
quality of design, 86
responsibility for employer's requirements, 84
timescale, 85–86
design-and-construct contract, 223
Design Build Finance and Operate (DBFO) project, 177
design contests, 37
developer, 22
development
    and certificate of lawfulness, 6
    and the need for planning permission, 5
    operational, 5
    permitted, 5–6
development plan
    primacy of, 8
Diamond Build Ltd v. Clapham Park Homes Ltd, 120
difference in conditions method (DIC), 135
directors, 173
    board of, 171
    duties of, 172
    executive, 172
    non-executive, 172
dismissal, in employment law
    automatically unfair, 265
    collective consultation and, 268
    disciplinary and grievance process, 265–266
    discrimination and, 267
    individual's conduct, 265
    lack of capabilities, 264–265
    reasonableness, 265
    redundancy situation, 265
    remedies, 266
    retirement, 265
    substantial reasons, 265
    taxation of termination payments, 266–267
    unfair, 264–265
    wrongful, 264
dispute boards, 504–505
dispute resolution provisions. *see also*
    alternative dispute resolution
    construction contract, 101
    consulting engineers' professional services contracts, 224–225
    joinder, 64–65
    and legal environment of a particular country, 201
    NEC Engineering and Construction Contract (EEC), third edition, 101
    procedures, 64
    use of law of contract, 290

dispute resolution provisions, in PFI transactions, 64–65
Diving at Work Regulations 1997, 331
doctrine of frustration, 299
drawdowns, 23
due diligence, 133
Dunlop Pneumatic Tyre Company Limited v. Selfridge & Co. Limited, 231
duty of care, 212, 228, 365–371, 387, 398
dynamic purchasing systems, 38

early works agreements, 55
e-auctions, 38
EC procurement rules
    common, 33
    directives, 34–35
    distinction between procurements of works, supplies and services, 35–36
    enforcement, 40–41
    equality of opportunity and transparency, 38
    EU public procurement markets, 34
    financial penalties or 'contract shortening,' 41
    legal framework, 34
    and market integration strategy, 34
    notices, 38–40
    problem areas
        changes to an existing contract, 44
        construction management, 42–43
        extension of contract, 42
        losing of paper, 42
        lottery funding, 43
        misapplication of the prequalification or selection criteria, 42
        mismatch between project described and contract, 41
        negotiations, 42
        non-compliance, 43
        reopening of a deal, 43–44
        speculative work, 43
        time limits, 41
        types of breach, 41–42
        wrong procedure, 42
    time limits, 38–40
EC Treaty, 33
Edward Owen Ltd v. Barclays Bank International Ltd, 148
Edwards v. National Coal Board, 316
Edwards v. Railway Executive, 387
EEC Directive (EIA Directive) 1985, 14
Egan v. State Transport Authority, 359
EIA application, 15
ejusdem generis rule, 296
El Aljou v. Dollar Land Holdings plc, 310
Electrical Equipment (Safety) Regulations 1994, 341
Electricity at Work Regulations 1989, 332
Elian and Rabbath v. Matsas, 152
Elitestone v. Morris, 359
Elpis Maritime v. Marti Chartering, 144
Employers Liability Compulsory Insurance Act 1969, 129
Employers Liability (Compulsory Insurance) Act 1969, 323

Solo Industries UK Ltd v. Canara Bank, 151
Somerfield Stores Ltd v. Skanska Rashleigh Weatherfoil Ltd, 295
Southmead Hospital project, 23
sponsors, 22
spot market, 22
Standard Bank London Ltd v. Canara Bank, 149
Standardisation of PFI Contracts Version 4(SoPC4), 49–52, 54–55, 58, 60, 62, 64–65
Standard JCT Form 2005 Edition, 83
Static Control Components (Europe) Ltd v. Egan, 151
Stein v. Blake, 353
step-in arrangements, project financing, 24
   PFI project, 62
step-in warranties, 97, 236
Strategic Environmental Assessment directive 2001/42/EC, 14
Straume v. Bradlor Developments, 350
Structural Latent Defect insurance policy, 140
sub-consultants, 204, 218–219
subcontractors
   ACE's Schedule of Services, 218
   agreements in construction contract, 96–97
   in consulting engineers' professional services, 212, 214, 218–219, 221–222
   design and build procurement method, 83, 85–86
   and insurance contracts, 131, 136, 138–139
   management contracting, 88
      insolvency risk of, 89
   partnering agreements, 93
   PFI project, 48, 50, 53–54
      allocation of liability for deductions, 60
      collateral warranties, 62–63
      compliance monitoring, 58–59
      design and technical documentation, 55–56
      direct agreements, 62
      FM, 56–57
      negotiations, 64–65
      Part II of the HGA, 63–65
      remedies for defects, 59–60
      security documentation, 54–55
      service commencement certificate, 60–61
   specialist, 80
   tendering
      problems, 111
      problems for main contractors, 110–111
      traditional, 110
   in traditional method of procurement, 79–80
   two-stage tendering, 87
subsidized contracts, 36–37
suite contracts, 100
supervision
   in consulting engineers' professional services contracts, 222–223
   as insurer's responsibility, 132
   joint ventures, 181
   PFI project, 58
Supply of Goods and Services Act 1982, 297
suretyship, contract of, 143

suspension of work
   facilities management, 73
sustainable construction, 408
sustainable development, 4–5

Tamares (Vincent Square) Limited v. Fairpoint Properties (Vincent Square) Limited (2006), 134
Target Cost, 82
tax system
   companies
      corporate tax, 168–169
      national insurance contributions (NICs), 169
      trading losses, 169
      VAT law, 169
   employment law
      allowances for clothing and tools, 264
      private travel, 263
      site-based employees, 263–264
      tax reliefs, 264
      traveling expenses and time, 263–264
      working rule agreements (WRA), 263
   insurance premium (IPT), 137
   international offices
      asset tax, 205
      choice of corporate vehicle, 207
      corporation tax or corporate income tax, 204
      dealing with non-UK tax authorities, 204
      delivery of salary and multiple employment arrangements, 208–209
      double taxation agreements, 205, 207
      employee issues, 208–210
      exchange control restrictions, 209
      form of taxable presence overseas, 205
      income tax for employees, 208
      local and municipal taxes, 205
      losses of overseas company, 207
      national insurance contributions/social security charges, 205, 209–210
      one-off projects, 207
      payroll and income taxes, 205
      pensions, 209
      of permanent establishment, 205–206
      religious tax, 205
      stamp duties, 205
      taxable profits of a non-UK entity, 208
      tax breaks, 208
      'tax equalisation' or 'tax protection' policies, 209
      value added tax/sales tax (VAT), 205
      withholding of taxes, 204–206, 208
   joint ventures, 182–183
   partnership
      assessment of taxable profits, 163
      corporation tax, 163
      individual tax returns, 163
      LLP, 163
      provisions of Part 41 of the 2006 Act, 163
      records, 163
      section 64 ITA 2007 loss relief, 163
      tax relief, 163

Technology and Construction Solicitors Association (TeCSA), 224
tendering
   abuses
      bribery and secret commissions, 125
      collusive tendering, 125–126
      recovery of costs, 123–124
      remedies for breaches, 124
   construction contracts
      appointment of contractor, 107
      basis of selection, 107
      clarification of issues, 107
      documentation, 105–106
      pre-qualification, 105
      principles of EU law for evaluating tenders, 106
      procurement routes and selection criteria, 107
      tender lists, 105
      tender receipt and evaluation, 106
      two-stage, 107
   in construction projects, 103
   consultant contracts
      deliverability, 109–110
      price *vs* value, 107–109
      selection, 110
      similarities/differences, 107
   conversion to contracts
      acceptance, 121–123
      execution of documents, 123
      letters of intent, 119–121
      phrase 'subject to board approval,' 122–123
      phrase 'subject to contract,' 122–123
   cost of, 104–105
      in a design and build contract, 105
      overheads, 104
   and Freedom of Information Act 2000 (FOIA), 126
   guarantee, 152
   guidelines
      Codes of Practice, 112–113
      consultant selection, 113–114
      distinction between selection and award stages, 115
      for government, 111–112
      in-house tenderers, 112
      OGC guidance on 2009 Regulations, 115
      role of Construction Task Force, 112
      selecting a team, 114–115
      selection of main contractors, 112
      selection of subcontractors, 112
      standard forms of tender, 116
      tender assessment and acceptance, 113
      tender invitation and submission, 113
      tender list, 112
      use of e-tendering, 115–116
   laws in England, 104
   and partnering, 104
   PPP/PFI contracts
      evaluation, 118
      generic format, 117
      process, 117–118
   public sector, 116

Contents

Preface

Many texts on the market focus on the purely legal aspects of construction law – they are books on law for lawyers. *ICE manual of construction law* is different: our focus is to consider the practical and commercial implications of case law and legislation. This book is written primarily for those without a legal background; that is, for the construction industry and the professionals who work in it and with it.

Previously published as the annual *ICE construction law handbook*, *ICE manual of construction law* has been thoroughly revised and extended to become the latest addition to ICE's successful manual series. The ICE manuals series provides construction professionals with core knowledge in key areas within civil engineering; across the series each volume is split into easily digestible chapters, available in print, and online at www.icemanuals.com.

ICE manual of construction law covers the range of legal issues most commonly encountered on a construction project. The topics are split across four sections and are presented in the order they would usually arise in the course of a typical project: from planning, finance and procurement, through operational issues and general law, to the administration of claims and dispute resolution. The result is an essential reference for all construction professionals seeking to increase their understanding of the legal principles behind their practice and a valuable tool to help assess when expert advice is required.

For this first edition of *ICE manual of construction law* we have had the pleasure of working with many of the same construction law handbook contributors, as well as several new contributors. All are acknowledged experts in their fields and we would like to thank them for their commitment and hard work in creating this authoritative and reliable text.

We hope that you will find this manual a valuable reference in your work. We are always keen to receive feedback and welcome suggestions for the next edition. Please address any comments to the publisher, who will forward them on to us.

Sir Vivian Ramsey, Technology and Construction Court, London

Ann Minogue, Ashurst LLP, London

Jenny Baster, Arup, London

Michael O'Reilly, Adie O'Reilly LLP, Lincoln

List of contributors

SECTION EDITORS:

J. Baster, Arup, London, UK
A. Minogue, Ashurst LLP, London, UK
M. P. O'Reilly, Adie O'Reilly LLP, Lincoln, UK
V. Ramsey, Judge in charge of the Technology and
    Construction Court, London, UK

CONTRIBUTORS:

R. Abigail, Arup Group Limited, London, UK
M. Appleby, Housemans Solicitors, London, UK
T. Asquith, Four New Square, London, UK
D. Atkinson, Daniel Atkinson Limited, Robertsbridge, UK
L. Baker, Horwath Clark Whitehill LLP, London, UK
S. Bamforth, Griffiths & Armour, Liverpool, UK
S. Barker, Freeth Cartwright LLP, Birmingham, UK
R. Barnes, Beale & Company, London, UK
N. Beedle, Ashurst LLP, London, UK
M. Bowdery QC, Atkin Chambers, London, UK
S. Carey, Speechly Bircham LLP, London, UK
G. Chapman, Four New Square, London, UK
P. Clarke, Atkin Chambers, London, UK
A. Crawshaw, Addleshaw Goddard LLP, London, UK
J. Critchlow, Fenwick Elliott LLP, London, UK
A. Cull, Pinsent Masons LLP Solicitors, London, UK
R. Davis, Pinsent Masons LLP Solicitors, London, UK
N. Downing, Herbert Smith, London, UK
T. Dymond, Herbert Smith LLP, London, UK

J. Exten-Wright, DLA Piper UK LLP, London, UK
C. Fellowes, Mayer Brown LLP, London, UK
N. Glover, Horwath Clark Whitehill LLP, London, UK
I. Griffiths, Thring Townsend Lee & Pembertons LLP, Bristol, UK
D. Hayhow, Lockton Companies International Ltd, London, UK
P. Henty, Speechly Bircham LLP, London, UK
A. Hughes QC, Thirty Nine Essex Street, London, UK
E. Jones, Four New Square, London, UK
R. Joyce, Freeth Cartwright LLP, Birmingham, UK
H. Lal, Jones Day, London, UK
D. Lamont, Health and Safety Executive, Caldy, UK
D. Marks, CMS Cameron McKenna LLP, London, UK
C. Marsden, Alan Baxter & Associates LLP, London, UK
J. Marshall, EC Harris LLP, Birmingham, UK
A. Minogue, Ashurst LLP, London, UK
J. Moore, Wren Managers Limited, London, UK
F. O'Farrell QC, Keating Chambers, London, UK
M. O'Neill, Allen & Overy LLP, London, UK
M. P. O'Reilly, Adie O'Reilly LLP, Lincoln, UK
M. Ramphul, Herbert Smith, London, UK
V. Ramsey, Judge in charge of the Technology and
    Construction Court, London, UK
I. Rogers, Arup, London, UK
J. Scriven, Allen & Overy LLP, London, UK
M. Tomlin, Speechly Bircham LLP, London, UK
W. Wastie, Addleshaw Goddard LLP, London, UK
I. Wright, Crown Office Chambers, London, UK

Introduction

Having spent the better part of forty years in the construction industry, I realize that I have taken the phrase 'Construction Law' for granted. When every aspect of our lives is touched by some aspect of law, what is special about construction that it should have its own body of law?

The truth is that there is no particular area of law that applies solely to construction, although part of the regulatory framework within which the industry operates is specific. It is simply that in relation to many industries, such as construction, shipping and insurance, the law has developed and adapted as the industry itself has evolved and grown. Construction law is simply the amalgam of all those parts of the common law and regulation that apply to the construction industry and those who work in it.

Even the word 'construction' must be taken in its widest sense. The term covers the whole of our built environment and all of the processes that contribute towards creating and maintaining that environment, including acquisition of land, planning, project financing, procurement procedures, project and professional insurance and facilities management. It covers all of the aspects of the construction process itself, including the contracts between the various parties, collateral warranties, contract administration, claims and dispute resolution. And finally, it covers the environmental impact of construction and the health and safety of those involved in the process. All of this and more is covered in this manual.

Isambard Kingdom Brunel was a brilliant engineer and entrepreneur, but other aspects of his work might have benefited from modern law and regulation. He was not quick to recognise contractual entitlements and in one instance the contractor had to fight through the courts for 28 years to get his money. Over one hundred men are said to have died during the construction of his Box Hill railway tunnel. Nowadays, the legal and regulatory framework governing the construction industry is enormous and the rate of expansion shows no signs of slowing as society increasingly expects individuals to take responsibility for their actions and as we follow the US trend of pursuing through the courts those who have caused us loss. This pattern has been reflected in the increased amount of law taught in engineering courses over the last few decades. The law component of my own civil engineering course in the early 1970s was minimal. In recent years, the number of engineers going on to take a master's degree in construction law or even a degree in law has steadily increased. With these changes, the requirement for engineers and other construction professionals to have a working knowledge of the legal issues relevant to their work is absolutely crucial.

Globalisation has also affected construction law as firms have increasingly become international operators. They face differing legal and regulatory systems and complex issues of conflict of laws, as well as the difficulties of securing payment or enforcing rights in foreign jurisdictions. In Europe, the lofty ambition of harmonising law for consumers and business has resulted in the publication of a European Commission Green Paper on 1 July 2010 on policy options for progressing towards a European Contract Law. We will have to wait and see whether anything useful eventually emerges from this initiative. In the meantime, our own familiar mix of common law and legislation will continue to form the backdrop for construction activities in the UK.

This manual provides an essential guide to that legal backdrop. It is not intended to be a definitive statement of the current law on each topic covered. Rather it is intended to be a desktop reference book for all engineers and other construction professionals who need to have a working understanding of the law as it affects their area of practice. And that means virtually everyone.

The manual deals with key areas of relevant law in four themed sections. The first covers the construction and operation of an asset, from inception through obtainment of planning permission, acquisition of finance including through public-private partnerships, to procurement and tendering, including the particular EC regulations that apply to public projects. It also deals with alternative contractual arrangements for the construction stage, insurances, financial security for the funders including bonds and guarantees and lastly arrangements for operating and maintaining the completed asset.

The second section deals with the operational issues relevant to anyone seeking to conduct business or already conducting business in the construction industry. Valuable guidance is provided on possible legal structures for professional trading (from sole practitioner to company, to LLP), joint ventures, issues related to working internationally, contracts for engineering services including the engineer's legal obligations and payment for services, collateral warranties and professional indemnity insurance. This section also contains useful guides to employment law and intellectual property.

The third section of the manual covers those areas of the common law and regulation that apply to everyone but have particular relevance for engineers and other construction professionals. The initial chapter focuses on contract law and covers topics such as contract formation, interpretation of terms and terms that are implied into a contract by law. There is a chapter on the law of tort, which is a broad and amorphous subject encompassing negligence and nuisance, as well as tortious duties that are imposed by legislation, such as the Occupiers' Liability Act 1957 and the Defective Premises Act 1972. Further chapters deal with insolvency and environmental issues and, finally, two are devoted to health and safety regulations, which are vital reading for all.

The fourth and last section covers disputes. Most construction projects involve some tough talking about matters of payment and occasionally these talks turn into disputes. Many construction professionals will at some stage find themselves in the process of making or administering claims, and a good understanding of the law in this area will help avoid a situation where the parties have to turn to legal procedures to resolve the issues. However, in some instances legal intervention cannot be avoided; hence the section also includes chapters on all the main forms of dispute resolution, including ever popular adjudication, as well as an explanation of all the different forms of alternative dispute resolution including mediation, which is rapidly being adopted in the construction industry.

All in all, this manual is an essential desk reference book for all engineers and other professionals engaged in the process of procuring, designing, building or operating assets.

John Marshall BSc CEng FICE FCIArb MAE
Partner, EC Harris LLP, Birmingham, UK
Chairman, ICE Advisory Panel for Legal Affairs

Section 1: Legal issues arising during the course of the construction project
Section editor: Ann Minogue

Chapter 1

The planning system

Michael P. O'Reilly Adie O'Reilly LLP, Lincoln, UK

Planning is an essential prerequisite to most construction work. This is an area of significant complexity and generally speaking for major projects specialist planning consultants will be engaged for what is commonly a lengthy process involving considerable public consultation. In this chapter an overview of the process will be provided, including an update on reforms projected by the incoming coalition government, including the impending abolition of the Infrastructure Planning Commission.

doi: 10.1680/mocl.40878.0003

CONTENTS

1.1 Introduction

1.1.1 The nature of planning law

Prior to the 19th century, landowners were entitled to use their land as they wished. Many of the developments of that century caused disquiet and attempts were made to impose some order on poor and unsanitary living conditions and unrestrained development.

In 1909, the UK saw the first attempt at a unified system of planning control in the form of the Housing, Town Planning etc. Act 1909. This enabled local authorities to prepare schemes for the laying out of their towns in a well-ordered manner. But it was not until 1947 that an effective regulatory system was put in place, designed to give some democratic control over development proposals and to prescribe suitable locations for certain types of development. Since 1947, development control has burgeoned and we now have a system of great complexity which applies to all, including, now, the Crown.

In more recent years, it has been recognised that the planning system can be used to promote economic, environmental and heritage sustainability. It can be a vehicle for seeking to ensure security of energy and water supply/distribution and transportation capacity for a growing population. This means integrating policies, such as energy supply and transportation into planning. To that end the Planning Act 2008 was introduced to provide more streamlined and coherent procedures for major infrastructure projects.

Those involved with major schemes will necessarily be working within a team, including lawyers, and hence this chapter is principally concerned with more routine planning matters, such as those which may be faced by engineers and architects on a daily basis.

In order to appreciate the law that applies to the modern planning system, the following should be understood first:

(1) The system of planning control is entirely statutory. The principal statute is the Town and Country Planning Act 1990 (TCPA 1990), which has been amended by various subsequent statutes. Whilst judicial decisions play a role in planning law, large swathes of the law remain untouched by reported cases.
(2) It is led by policy statements. In the case of nationally significant infrastructure projects, National Policy Statements (NPSs) apply. In the case of local projects, the Local Development Plan applies, to be read in accordance with national planning policies.
(3) The process is democratically driven. National planning is driven by national politicians and local planning is governed by local politicians, albeit to national criteria.

1.1.2 Nationally significant infrastructure projects

There are, in broad terms, two routes to obtaining planning permission. The route which applies depends on whether the application relates to a:

(1) nationally significant infrastructure project or
(2) any other project

In the case of the first, the regime is governed by the Planning Act 2008. Section 14(1) of the Planning Act 2008 provides that for the purposes of the Act a 'nationally significant

infrastructure project' means a project which consists of any of the following:

(a) the construction or extension of a generating station
(b) the installation of an electric line above ground
(c) development relating to underground gas storage facilities
(d) the construction or alteration of a liquified natural gas (LNG) facility
(e) the construction or alteration of a gas reception facility
(f) the construction of a pipe line by a gas transporter
(g) the construction of a pipe line other than by a gas transporter
(h) highway-related development
(i) airport-related development
(j) the construction or alteration of harbour facilities
(k) the construction or alteration of a railway
(l) the construction or alteration of a rail freight interchange
(m) the construction or alteration of a dam or reservoir
(n) development relating to the transfer of water resources
(o) the construction or alteration of a waste water treatment plant
(p) the construction or alteration of a hazardous waste facility.

These categories are subject to further definition. Thus, for example, not every highway falls within section 14(1)(h); section 22 provides that the construction of a highway will only be included if the highway will (when constructed) be wholly in England, and the Secretary of State will be the highway authority for the highway.

Where the project falls within the definition, the application will be made to the Infrastructure Planning Commission. In other cases the application is made to the Local Planning Authority (LPA; see the Planning Portal website).

Connected with the concept of a nationally significant infrastructure project are NPSs which set out national policy. Seven out of twelve planned NPSs have been published. This arrangement establishes a duty to consult pre-application so as to front-load the planning process.

On 29 June 2010 the new coalition government indicated that this Commission would be abolished but stated that it would continue until legislation was brought forward. The replacement is expected to be a Major Infrastructure Planning Unit in the Planning Inspectorate, controlled by ministers. During the interim, if an application reaches decision stage and the relevant NPS has been designated, the Commission will decide on the application; but if the NPS is not designated, the Commission will make a recommendation to the Secretary of State who will make the decision.

1.1.3 Local projects

Projects which are not designated as nationally significant – the vast majority – are dealt with in what may be described as the normal planning system. The primary national government department overseeing the planning system is the Department for Communities and Local Government (DCLG). Prior to

that it was the Office of Deputy Prime Minister (ODPM) and before that the Department for Environment, Transport and Regions (DETR). Many relevant documents were originally issued by the DETR or the ODPM. In relation to some matters, other government departments may be involved in planning: for example, the Department of Culture, Media and Sport is involved in listing buildings.

At the local level, the situation is somewhat confusing. 'Local planning authorities' (being the bodies to whom an application for planning permission is made, or who enforce planning control) are:

(1) in the metropolitan areas: the London boroughs and the metropolitan districts;
(2) in the country: either unitary authorities (where they exist) or (where they do not) district councils for all matters except those specifically reserved for the county council, such as waste management.

When dealing with local authorities, it is always advisable to call up the planning department to check in the first instance that one is dealing with the right authority. In some cases, more than one authority may have jurisdiction: for example, in relation to a waste transfer station, the county council and local district council may each have a role to play in relation to different aspects of any development.

1.1.4 Development plans

The planning system – whether nationally significant or local – is plan-led.

In the case of nationally significant infrastructure projects, the NPS sets out the relevant policies. These are designated through powers in Part 2 of the Planning Act 2008.

In the case of local projects, the development plan sets relevant criteria. Prior to 2004, the development plan typically involved a structure plan and local plan. The former gave broad policy direction at a county level; the latter gave more detail and, in some cases, individual sites or areas could be identified for development. In 2004, the Planning and Compulsory Purchase Act 2004 (PCPA 2004) introduced a new system which included a Regional Spatial Strategy (RSS) which would then inform the Local Development Framework (LDF) (see the Planning Portal website). However, the incoming coalition government has acted in July 2010 to abandon the RSS as part of the development plan.

As well as the local plan as disclosed in the LDF, regard must be made to national guidance set out in Planning Policy Statements (PPS) and Planning Policy Guidance notes (PPG) and Circulars (published on the DCLG website).

1.1.5 Sustainable development

Section 39 of the PCPA 2004 requires those responsible for preparing plans in England, to undertake these functions with

a view to contributing to the achievement of sustainable development through good design.

1.2 Development

1.2.1 Development and the need for planning permission

Section 57(1) of the TCPA 1990 provides subject to the following provisions of that section: 'planning permission is required for the carrying out of any development of land'. The definition of the term 'development' is central to the application of this part of the planning system.

Section 55(1) contains the primary definition of development: 'the carrying out of building, engineering, mining or other operations in, on, over or under land' or the 'making of any material change in the use of any buildings or other land'. Thus, planning permission is required whenever there is 'development'. Development may take one of two forms:

(1) operational development, and/or
(2) change of use.

The legislation attempts to keep the two forms of development separate. The main form of development with which readers of this manual will be concerned is operational development.

Some developments, however, need no specific permission because they are subject to a blanket permission in a development order – this is known as 'permitted development'.

It is, generally speaking, not directly a criminal offence to develop without permission (in the case of carrying out unauthorised work, for example, in Areas of Archaeological Importance (AAIs) or to a listed building and other particular cases, carrying out work can involve criminal liability), but the financial penalties can be severe, particularly if the LPA takes action to have the works stopped. It is therefore prudent to ensure that any necessary planning permission is obtained before starting work.

1.2.2 What operations constitute development?

We shall divide operational development into the four elements set out in section 55(1): (1) building operations, (2) engineering operations (3) mining and (4) other operations.

1.2.2.1 Building

Section 55(1A) of the TCPA 1990 provides that the term 'building operations', which includes:

(a) the demolition of buildings; (b) rebuilding; (c) structural alterations of or addition to buildings; and (d) other operations normally undertaken by a person carrying on business as a builder.

The definition of a building in the statute is wider than the everyday use of the word suggests: section 336(1) provides that

any structure or erection, or any part of a building, as so defined, but does not include plant or machinery comprised in a building.

So, for example, a mast may well be a building in this sense.

Conversely, there are works which would normally be undertaken by a builder but which are not development within the statute: section 55(2) provides that internal works which do not materially affect the external appearance are not development requiring permission, providing there is no enlargement of underground space or addition of mezzanine floors exceeding 200 m[2] in retail buildings. This latter provision has recently been introduced using powers under section 49 of the PCPA 2004 enabling the Secretary of State for Communities and Local Government (SSCLG) to issue a development order to restrict the operation of section 55(2).

Prior to the Planning and Compensation 1991 Act (PCA 1991), the definition of building did not include demolition, as it does now. Accordingly, there was significant confusion as to whether or not demolition required planning permission. There was a potential paradox in that structural alteration might require permission, but that total removal might not. In 1991, it was decided to extend the definition of building to include demolition; but the SSCLG has power to exclude certain demolitions from this provision and this has created yet further confusion because the exceptions created by the Town and Country Planning (Demolition – Description of Buildings) Direction 1995 involve almost all buildings. In the case of a dwelling house, the General Permitted Development Order Schedule 2, Part 31 provides that before demolition, an application must normally be made to the LPA for approval of the method of demolition.

1.2.2.2 Engineering operations

The legislation does not contain any definition of engineering operations. The matter has been raised in a decided case where the judge said that the term should be given its natural everyday meaning, being an operation upon which an engineer might be engaged. There are some excluded activities, including road and sewer, pipe or cable maintenance.

1.2.2.3 Mining

The removal of material for their economic value from a site is development: see also the Town and Country Planning (Minerals) Act 1981.

1.2.2.4 Other operations

The scope of this provision is very uncertain. It can, however, be said that it must mean an operation of the same scope and scale as the other operations which fall within the definition.

1.2.3 Permitted development

Many kinds of relatively minor works or changes of use enjoy deemed planning permission and form the category of what is known as 'permitted development'.

At the national level, there is the Town and Country Planning (General Permitted Development) Order 1995 (GPDO) which has been amended on a variety of occasions (five times in the period 2005 to 2010; reference should be made to the planning portal and DCLG websites for the most up to date list of permitted developments). Amendments include the much-heralded (Amendment) (No. 2) (England) Order 2008 which extends permitted developments in the case of dwellings, for example, making it easier to construct extensions without the need for permission; this came into force on 1 October 2008 and is expected dramatically to reduce the number of minor planning applications. At the local level, there is a new power which came into force in May 2006 enabling LPAs to issue equivalent provisions affecting the locality.

In relation to changes of use, reference should be made to the Use Classes Order (UCO) (Town and Country Planning (Use Classes) Order 1987) which establishes a series of use classes and provides for where a change in use is not considered to be a development. These rights can be constrained by agreement between the LPA and the developer. The UCO has recently been updated: see the amendments in SI 2005 No. 85 and SI 2006 No. 220 respectively explained in ODPM Circular 03/2005 and DCLG Circular 02/2006.

1.2.3.1 GDPO

Paragraph 3 of GPDO provides:

> Subject to the provisions of this Order... planning permission is hereby granted for the classes of development described as permitted development in Schedule 2.

There are exceptions and the SSCLG or LPA has power to constrain the development in individual cases.

Schedule 1 sets out the geographical areas to which the GPDO does not extend. This essentially includes National Parks, Areas of Outstanding Natural Beauty (and from October 2008 sites on UNESCO's World Heritage List ('World Heritage Sites') etc.).

Schedule 2 sets out a wide range of relatively minor developments in 42 parts. As examples, Part 1 relates to development within the cartilage of a dwelling house and Part 33 relates to the installation of closed circuit cameras. The other parts deal with minor developments, changes of use, temporary buildings, agricultural buildings and operations, forestry operations, industrial and warehouse development, repairs to unadopted streets, repairs to services, development by local authorities, highway authorities, drainage bodies, Environment Agency, sewerage undertakers, statutory undertakers, aviation-related developments, developments ancillary to mining (including waste tipping), electronic communications-related development, development at amusement parks, driver information, toll road facilities, demolition and development by schools, colleges, universities and hospitals, development by the Crown, aviation development by the Crown, Crown railways, dock-yards, and so forth and lighthouses, emergency development by the Crown, development for national security purposes, temporary protection of poultry and other birds, installation of microgeneration equipment, office buildings and shops or catering, financial or professional services establishment.

1.2.3.2 Local development orders

Sections 61A–61D, inserted by the PCPA 2004 provide LPAs with a power to issue a Local Development Order (LDO). By this means, certain developments may be granted planning permission without the need to make an application. There are restrictions as to what may be permitted by way of LDO. For example, there must be no blanket permission in the case of listed buildings or for development that requires an environmental impact assessment. LDOs will not avoid the need for a conservation area consent for development in those areas.

It is anticipated that LDOs will be used for (1) small domestic development to avoid the resources spent on routine applications and (2) encouraging types of local development, such as regeneration development in specified areas of the LPA's area.

1.2.4 Certificate of lawfulness

Often the dividing line between permitted development and that which requires express permission is unclear. In order to determine whether planning permission is required, the developer can apply for a certificate of lawful use or development, including clarifying the status of existing development.

The application must provide sufficient information to allow the land to be clearly identified and give such details of its planning history as are available. Usually, a local conveyancing search or inspection of the public planning register will provide much useful background information.

Unless the LPA respond within the specified time with a certificate of lawfulness, the applicant may appeal to the SSCLG whose Inspector will review the issues and decide accordingly.

The one drawback to this procedure is that it does draw the LPA's attention to a possible unlawful use in respect of which they might decide to take enforcement action.

1.3 Application for planning permission: nationally significant infrastructure projects

In the case of nationally significant infrastructure projects, as defined in Part 3 of the Planning Act 2008, the Infrastructure Planning Commission is (until its abolition) the appropriate body to receive applications for proposed infrastructure development. The NPSs as well as number of statutory instruments need consideration to ensure that the application is made not just in the correct prescribed form but that there is adherence to the correct principles. The applicable statutory instruments include:

■ the Infrastructure Planning (Applications: Prescribed Forms And Procedures) Regulations 2009

- the Infrastructure Planning (Environmental Impact Assessment) Regulations 2009

- the Conservation of Habitats and Species Regulations 2010

- the Infrastructure Planning (Compulsory Acquisition) Regulations 2010

- the Infrastructure Planning (Examination Procedure) Rules 2010.

Useful information regarding applications and procedure is to be found on the Infrastructure Planning Commission website. Documents which relate to applications which have been made appear on the website and can provide useful examples.

Following the statement in June 2010 that the Commission would be abolished there is currently some uncertainty. The replacement is expected to be a Major Infrastructure Planning Unit in the Planning Inspectorate, controlled by ministers. During the interim, if an application reaches decision stage and the relevant NPS has been designated, the Commission will decide the application; but if the NPS is not designated, the Commission will make a recommendation to the Secretary of State who will make the decision.

1.4 Applications for planning permission: other projects

The legal requirements and procedure for making other planning applications are set out in the Town and Country Planning General Development Procedure Order 1995 (GDPO 1995) as amended from time to time (and not to be confused with GPDO, which is the General Permitted Development Order, discussed earlier). This is a document which should be close to hand at all times when making applications for planning permission.

Applicants must ensure that they are using the latest amended version.

1.4.1 Preliminary matters

1.4.1.1 Planning history

It is frequently worthwhile finding out about the planning history of the site. Earlier applications for planning permission can be checked (e.g. to see whether a similar development proposal has previously been refused, or if any agreements exist that regulate how the site or buildings can be developed) by visiting the LPA and ask to see the Planning Register for the site, which is open for inspection to the public.

1.4.1.2 Consistency with the development plan

It is worth bearing in mind that the development plan is the key document against which the application will be judged.

1.4.1.3 Application for full or outline planning permission?

Outline applications can only be made for the construction of buildings, not any other kind of development.

An outline planning permission gives 'in principle' approval, reserving details such as: layout, scale, appearance, access and landscaping. LPAs do have the power to request detailed information on an aspect of the scheme that the applicant hoped to reserve for later, if the LPA considers that it is necessary to have that information when determining the outline.

For larger building proposals, it is often useful to seek outline approval before committing resources to preparing all the material needed to support a full application. In addition, an outline permission will have the effect of establishing the development value for the land (i.e. it assumes that a development of the type approved in principle is capable of being carried out on the land concerned). It will often be necessary to have reached this stage before finance can be raised to acquire the land and undertake the scheme. Development approved by an outline planning permission cannot be implemented until the reserved matters have been approved by the LPA.

Non-building development can only be the subject of an application for full or detailed planning permission. A full application must include details of access, siting, layout, design, external appearance and landscaping, so far as any of these are relevant to the scheme.

1.4.1.4 Discussions with the LPA

Potential applicants are encouraged (e.g. by Planning Policy Statement 1) to discuss their proposals with planning officers to enable the applicant to align his proposal with the development plan and understand how best to present his application and to ensure that issues of design and of planning can be resolved before the application is submitted. It goes without saying that the LPA does not guarantee any enthusiasm its officers may express; the final decision always resides with the democratically elected members, who have a wide range of discretion. Indeed, it seems that the LPA owes no duty of care at all; although it may form the subject of a complaint to the Ombudsman.

As a result of recent legislation (Local Government Act 2003, section 98), LPAs are empowered to charge for the time spent.

1.4.2 Making the application

Since April 2008 all applications must be made on the standard form prescribed by an amendment which can be located on the Planning Portal website. The information required when making an application is updated from time to time and reference should be made to the planning portal to ensure the latest requirements have been met, for example, as to design and access statements.

LPAs will issue policies in relation to design and access. In respect of design, the statement will set out the design principles and concepts applied. The access statement will deal with access to the development site and ensure that proper thought is given to safe and convenient access to roads and so forth. The statements will demonstrate the design and access thinking to ensure its quality and consistency with the requirements. This

statement will be required both for full and outline planning applications.

For major schemes, professional advice and assistance will usually be needed to complete the forms and provide the bundle of supporting documentation. A site location plan and description of the development is always required, but many LPAs will insist on appropriate detail being submitted, such as technical drawings of how the scheme will look (where the application is for outline planning permission this may not be appropriate).

The correct fee must be paid with each application that requires a fee. Section 303 of the TCPA 1990 provides the power for the SSCLG to make regulations: see Town and Country Planning (Fees for Applications and Deemed Applications) (England) Regulations amended in 2008 and also DCLG Circular 04/08: i issued in April 2008.

1.4.3 Applications by non-owners

It is not necessary to own land to make an application for planning permission. However, an application will not be valid unless it is accompanied by written confirmation that all owners of the land have been formally notified of the application. If the applicant is also the owner (which, in this context, means not just the freeholder, but anyone who is entitled to receive a market rent for the land and a tenant with at least seven years left to run on his lease), then he must sign a certificate that no-one else has an owner's interest in the land. If he is not the 'owner' then he must certify that he has given notice in writing of the application to every person who, on the date 21 days preceding the date of the application, had an 'owner's' interest in the land. Details of the minimum requirements are set out in the GDPO 1995, article 6 and schedule 2 although it is frequently appropriate to advertise more widely to avoid later challenges.

As we shall see later in this chapter, the use of obligations is becoming more widespread; only a person with an appropriate interest in the land may take on such an obligation and this is one area where a non-owner may be at a disadvantage.

1.4.4 The validity of the application

The LPA must acknowledge receipt of the application, and will then decide if it is valid or not. Since April 2008, amended Article 5 of GDPO sets out the requirements for a valid application. DCLG Circular 02/2008 entitled *Standard Application Form and Validation* states that validation should be notified within 3–5 working days for minor applications and 10 working days for major applications. The date of validation is 'day zero' in terms of the timescale available for determining the application. An application that is arguably invalid, and therefore not determined within the statutory period, may apparently still be the subject of an appeal to the Secretary of State (for non-determination). The Secretary of State is entitled to form his own view of the validity of the application.

1.4.5 Consultation

Depending on the nature and size of the development applied for, the LPA is obliged to consult with a wide range of organisations before determining the application. Everyone so consulted may object to, or make representations about, the development proposal. All such comment is a material consideration to which the LPA must have regard when determining the application.

Normally, letters of objection or comment are available to the applicant who may often be able to change elements of the scheme to overcome particular concerns.

1.5 Determination of the planning application
1.5.1 Who determines: calling-in

Ordinarily the planning application will be determined by the LPA. However, section 77 of the TCPA 1990 gives the SSCLG a power to call-in a planning application for his or her own decision, rather than leave it for the LPA to make the decision. The power is not frequently used, generally being limited to cases of much more than local interest. The SSCLG normally becomes aware of such cases by means of the requirement for LPAs to notify the DCLG of cases involving a departure from the development plan or exceeding specified thresholds for different categories of development. Alternatively, other contentious proposals may be brought to the attention of the SSCLG by pressure groups or amenity societies.

In called-in cases, the LPA and the applicant are given the option of an inquiry, in which case, the procedure would be similar to that for a planning appeal, being governed by the same Inquiries Procedure Rules, and the inquiry held before an Inspector appointed by the SSCLG.

Below, we shall assume that the LPA retains the application.

1.5.2 The primacy of the development plan

Section 38(6) of the Planning and Compulsory Purchase Act 2004 (PCPA 2004) provides:

> If regard is to be had to the development plan for the purpose of any determination to be made under the planning Acts the determination must be made in accordance with the plan unless material considerations indicate otherwise.

The phrase 'unless material indications dictate otherwise' means that it may be possible to get permission to carry out a development which does not conform to the development plan, provided there is justification for doing so which is based on valid planning reasoning.

Regard must also be had to government policy in interpreting the development plan. The relevant publication can be viewed on line on the DCLG website or on the government's planning portal.

1.5.3 Planning committees

The democratic input into planning is seen most vividly in the planning committee system. The planning committee will usually consist of a group of the LPA's democratically elected councillors, although in the case of some very significant or controversial applications, the final decision may be made by the full council. There will, however, be rules made by each LPA allowing minor matters to be 'delegated' to planning officers to make 'delegated powers decisions'.

When taking decisions, the planning committee will have access to a report prepared by a planning officer and so will be assisted by professional opinion. The committee is not bound by the officer's recommendation; in some cases, the issues are determined on party political lines. Most planning committee are held in public, and many LPAs allow applicants or objectors to make a brief presentation (a few minutes) of their cases or to participate in the debate.

Where the recommendation is to grant a planning permission but subject to a legal agreement under section 106 of the TCPA 1990 (see below) the Committee will make a resolution to grant planning permission, but the planning permission will not be issued until the legal agreement has been settled. It is important to note that it is only the issue of a signed decision notice that constitutes a planning permission. The resolution of a Committee to grant does not constitute the grant of planning permission itself.

1.5.4 The application process and timescale

On receipt of an application, the administrative section of the LPA will do the initial processing for validity. A Planning Officer will undertake a preliminary review of the submission to assess the adequacy of the information submitted in support of the application. He will also give instructions to the administrative section as to who should be consulted on the application. This process usually takes between one and two weeks to be completed, and is usually referred to as the validation or registration process.

Since August 2005, LPAs have had a discretion to decline to determine an application if it appears to the LPA to be substantially the same as a previous application. Guidance (ODPM Circular 08/2005) has clarified that the intention of the legislation is not to frustrate the submission of improved applications but to avoid the situation where it appears that the applicant is seeking to wear down the LPA.

As a result of recent amendments to the GDPO 1995 there are a variety of time periods for determining planning applications – see the Town and Country Planning (General Development Procedure)(Amendment)(England) Order 2006:

Normal applications: 8 weeks

Major projects: 13 weeks

Projects requiring an Environmental Impact Assessment: 16 weeks.

There is no obligation upon a LPA to make their decision within the time; they may do so at any time. However, a right of appeal exists once the time has expired. LPAs are required to make statistical returns to the DCLG setting out details of the time they have taken to deal with their applications, and many achieve the target for up to 80% of applications received. However, a significant proportion of applications involve complex or contentious proposals. The amount of negotiation, revision and re-consultation can lead to some applications taking many months or even years to be concluded.

What an applicant always has to weigh up after the statutory period has expired is whether there is a good prospect of obtaining planning permission in due course, and whether this is likely to be quicker overall than treating non-determination as a deemed refusal, and submitting an appeal.

Following the validation and acknowledgement of the application, the process of substantive consideration begins. Site notices will be put up, and consultation letters sent out. These will state that interested parties should make any representations about the application to the LPA within 21 days of the date of the notice; there is now a statutory duty upon consultees to respond within 21 days (see section 54 PCPA 2004). The application will then be allocated to a planning officer to be dealt with. The internal organisation and operating procedures of individual authorities vary, but the following would be a typical process. The officer is usually a qualified town planner working in the 'Development Control' section of the planning department. He or she will review the application and decide which other specialist officers in the department need to be consulted, as well as other departments in the LPA. For example, the Highway Authority would be consulted if there are any traffic or transport implications, and a Conservation or Urban Design Officer if the proposals involve a site with a conservation area. Most large redevelopment schemes usually involve consultation with a number of specialist sections or other departments of the council.

Site inspections will be carried out, and the Case Officer will assess whether the proposals conform to relevant development policies. These assessments and internal consultations should usually be complete by the time the 21 day public consultation period has expired (usually about five weeks after submission). At this point, the Case Officer will decide how the application should be dealt with; or whether in more marginal cases, the applicant should be requested to amend the proposals in order to make them more acceptable.

Assuming that the proposals are considered acceptable without amendment, but are too important to be dealt with under 'delegated powers', the Officer will then prepare a report on the application for consideration by the Planning Committee. The report should contain a description of the site and its location, and the application proposals. It should state the relevant planning history of the site, and detail the consultations carried out and responses received. It should then include an appraisal of the proposals in relation to relevant development

plan policies, and any other relevant planning considerations. Finally, it should contain a recommendation as to the decision that should be taken, and any conditions that should be imposed on the permission.

1.6 Conditions and obligations

The grant of planning permission will rarely be unconditional. There may be two types of restriction:

(1) conditions on the planning permission
(2) the requirement for a contribution back to the community, known as an obligation pursuant to a Section 106 Agreement.

Where there is a choice between imposing conditions and entering into a planning obligation, the imposition of a condition is to be preferred – see ODPM Circular 05/2005, paragraph B2.

1.6.1 Conditions

Section 70(1) of the TCPA 1990 provides statutory authority for the LPA to grant planning permission subject to conditions.

Whilst stated in wide terms, the courts have insisted that for validity, a condition must fairly and reasonably relate to the development and not have an ulterior motive beyond the development. Lord Denning put the point like this as early as 1958 in the Pyx Granite case: 'Although the planning authorities are given very wide powers to impose 'such conditions as they think fit', nevertheless the law says that those conditions, to be valid, must fairly and reasonably relate to the permitted development. The planning authority are not at liberty to use their powers for an ulterior motive, however desirable that object may seem to them to be in the public interest.'

It is generally recognised that conditions must be:

(a) imposed for a planning purpose,
(b) must fairly relate to the development permitted, and
(c) must not be so unreasonable that no reasonable authority could have imposed them.

DCLG Circular 11/95 provides further guidance.

In some cases, conditions might apply to other land. Section 72(1)(a) provides a general power where it is in connection with the development – for example, there may be a condition in relation to connection off-site to a main sewer. The 'Grampian principle', after the name of the leading case, is that it is possible to insist on a negative condition off the site, provided that it is properly connected to the development – in that case, the condition was the closure of a road to ensure that access did not harm other development objectives. For example, most larger developments will require the construction of new roads or the upgrading of existing roads which is often achieved using Grampian conditions (although PPG 13, 'Highway Considerations in Development Control', has cautioned against the use of Grampian conditions where this may delay the commencement and jeopardise the permission).

1.6.2 Community infrastructure levy

In previous incarnations of this principle, LPAs could require developers to undertake an obligation to build affordable housing, community facility or make some other contribution to the community. Since 6 April 2010, the primary route for requiring this contribution has been the Community Infrastructure Levy. This was introduced by the Planning Act 2008 but because it remains in its infancy its efficacy is difficult to assess.

1.7 The duration of planning permission

Prior to 1969, planning permissions had indefinite duration. LPAs were granted powers to limit the period by condition. Under section 91 of the TCPA 1990 the normal period was established as five years. By section 51 of PCPA 2004, which amends section 91, however, the normal period is reduced to three years which requires those with planning permission benefit to ensure that commencement is not delayed – whilst it is possible to make a re-application, development plans may readily change meaning that grant will be by no means assured. By amended section 91(1)(b) of the TCPA 1990, LPAs have a discretion to substitute a longer or indeed shorter period where warranted.

It is a question of some difficulty to determine whether or not the development has commenced on time. In one case, it was held that digging a trench for the footings constituted commencement despite the fact that they were immediately back-filled with the soil (in order, apparently, to stop children falling in). In another case, trenches had been dug, but they did not correspond to the development layout, so there was no commencement. It is now established that the developer's intention is not material to the question whether or not development has commenced and what must be shown is that there has been a substantial commencement of the scheme for which planning permission has been granted.

A more intractable and often significant facet of the problem is the so-called 'Whitley principle', named after the leading case in 1990. Planning permission was granted subject to a condition that a number of matters in relation to the scheme be agreed with the LPA in advance. There was difficulty reaching agreement but in order to avoid the expiration of the time period, the developer commenced on site anyway. The Court of Appeal stated that commencement meant commencement in accordance with the conditions. Commencement in breach of condition was not commencement at all and the planning permission was lost. This principle has been applied consistently, but with a modicum of common sense. For example, where the LPA had been aware of the scheme proposed and had not objected, the development was lawful despite the LPA not having formally approved the scheme.

In relation to outline planning permission, the provisions are somewhat different. Under section 92(2) of the TCPA 1990, application for approval of reserved matters must be made

within three years of grant of outline permission; and the commencement must take place within five years of grant of outline permission or if later two years of the last approval received. Section 51 of PCPA 2004 modifies the period; it is now three years and within two years after last approval received but the LPA may vary the time allowed for an application for approval of reserved matters.

Whilst under the pre-2004 legislation, time limits might be extended, that is no longer possible and this adds to the purpose of these changes that once planning permission is granted it must be implemented quickly or be lost. A further piece of legislation that supports this is the completion notice provision in section 94 of TCPA 1990 which provides that the LPA may serve a notice requiring completion within five years (for pre-2004 matters) or three years (post-2004 matters).

1.8 Planning appeals

If the LPA (1) fails to determine the application within the statutory time limit or (2) refuses to grant planning permission or (3) makes a grant subject to conditions which the applicant considers unreasonable, the applicant may appeal under the provision in section 78 of the TCPA 1990. Appeals may also be made in respect of a listed building or conservation area consent application, an application for a Certificate of Lawfulness of an Existing Use or Development or an application for consent to display an advertisement.

Although the appeal is technically to the SSCLG, in practice the appeal is usually handled by an executive agency known as the Planning Inspectorate. Only a very small proportion of appeals are actually decided by the SSCLG.

1.8.1 Procedure

Appeals are made on a form produced by the Planning Inspectorate, with whom the appeal documentation is initially lodged. There are varying time limits for the submission of appeals after the date of the decision; for planning appeals the time limit is six months, for enforcement appeals the date will be the date set for compliance with the enforcement notice.

The appeal forms require details of the applicant, the decision being appealed against, the site and the proposal, and a summary of the grounds of appeal. Copies of the original application particulars must be provided together with the contested decision, if any. Finally, an indication must be given of the type of appeal procedure to be adopted.

There are three options for the method of pursuing the appeal:

(1) written representations only
(2) informal hearing
(3) public inquiry.

Previously the applicant selected his or her preferred method for the application but since 6 April 2009 the Planning Inspectorate is to determine which method is the most suitable.

1.8.1.1 Written representations

The written representations procedure was prior to April 2009 the most popular option and will no doubt prove the most frequently selected by the Planning Inspectorate after April 2009. It is quicker, less costly, and generally considered quite adequate for most minor or non-complex cases. The procedural rules are dealt with under the Town and Country Planning (Appeals) (Written Representations Procedure) (England) Rules 2009.

The procedure is set out in the table at Page 12 of the Planning Inspectorate's 'guide to taking part in planning appeals by written representations'. There are two processes for written applications: one for 'householder appeals' (generally appeals made under section 78 TCPA relating to a single dwelling house) and another for all other appeals. In brief in a 'householder appeal', the LPA has five days from notification from the Planning Inspectorate that an appeal has begun to submit a completed appeals 'questionnaire' and any supporting documents. Thus, the appeal notice bundle and the LPA's appeals questionnaire will be the only representations allowed unless the planning inspectorate orders otherwise.

In respect of all other appeals the LPA has two weeks to respond with a completed appeals 'questionnaire' and also by that time notify interested third parties. The LPA and the appellant can then elect to have the appeal notice and the LPA's appeals 'questionnaire' as the only representations or they can serve further written representations within six weeks. Third parties may also submit their written statements during this period. The LPA and the appellant then have until nine weeks from the start date to provide the Planning Inspectorate with comments on the other parties further written representations. An Inspector from the Planning Inspectorate arranges to inspect the site. He may be accompanied by the parties, but no discussion of the merits of the case is allowed at the site visit. In most cases, the Inspector will then issue his or her decision letter within a few weeks of the site inspection. Overall, the timescale for such appeals is typically between 16 and 20 weeks.

1.8.1.2 Informal hearings

The procedure for informal hearings is set out in the Town and Country Planning (Hearings Procedure) (England) Rules 2000. The procedure is set out in diagrammatic form in Annex 2 of DCLG Circular 05/2000. A hearing is usually arranged within 12 weeks of the parties' agreement to use the procedure. Details are notified to the appellant and to any third party who made representations during the original application process. The hearing arrangements are also publicised locally.

The general aim of the process is to allow cases to be presented orally, in the format of an Inspector-led round table discussion. Written statements of case are required to be submitted to the Inspectorate and copied to the other side at least three weeks prior to the date of the hearing.

At the hearing, the Inspector leads a discussion on the main points at issue. Following this, an accompanied site visit is

usually held. The Inspector's decision letter will then usually follow within a few weeks of the hearing. Overall, the timescale for such appeals is typically between 20 and 25 weeks.

1.8.1.3 Public inquiry

An Inspector is appointed by the Planning Inspectorate to preside over an inquiry, which is held in public, at which the appellant, the council and other interested parties are given the opportunity to present their cases, and to cross-examine the other participants on their cases.

It is usual for the main parties to be legally represented and technical arguments being presented as 'proofs of evidence' by expert witnesses. In the case of major developments, it is not uncommon for public inquiries to last several days, with whole teams of expert witnesses presenting evidence on a range of technical issues.

Detailed procedural requirements for public inquiries are provided in the Town and Country Planning (Inquiries Procedures) (England) Rules 2000, and the Town and Country Planning (Determination by Inspectors) (Inquiries Procedure) (England) Rules 2000. The former apply where the SSCLG is to make a decision after considering a recommendation of the inspector ('recovered cases') whilst the latter deal with the case where the inspector will make the decision on behalf of the SSCLG ('transferred cases'). These rules set out the procedures and requirements for submission of preliminary statements of case, inquiry arrangements and publicity, exchange of proofs of evidence, timetabling and handling of the inquiry itself. It is important to note that the rules are designed to avoid a party being 'surprised' by the submission of evidence not previously signalled, so the procedure obliges the appellant and LPA to exchange copies of their witnesses' evidence three weeks before the inquiry starts.

The decision is usually made by the Inspector a few weeks after the inquiry, and issued in the form of a letter. This letter will summarise the cases presented by each party at the inquiry, the Inspector's findings and conclusions. If the appeal is allowed, the letter will also provide details of any conditions to be imposed. In the few cases where the decision is to be made by the SSCLG, the inquiry Inspector prepares a report of the inquiry for the SSCLG in a similar format to an Inspector's decision letter, but with a recommendation for a decision instead of an actual decision. The SSCLG's letter of decision is then issued subsequently, together with the inspector's report. This process can in some instances take many months after the inquiry to be concluded. Other than in the case of public inquiry appeals to be determined by the SSCLG, the overall timescale for concluding such appeals is typically between 24 and 32 weeks.

1.8.2 Appeal costs

The SSCLG has the power to award costs against one or other of the parties in any planning appeal. Although up until recently no costs were allowed for appeals conducted via written representations only. This power is given by the Local

Government Act 1972 as amended by section 320(2)/section 322 of the TCPA 1990.

It is important to remember that although this power exists, government advice (in DCLG Circular 03/09) is that the basic principle for planning appeals is that each party is expected to bear its own costs, and that an award for costs will only be made where there has been unreasonable behaviour.

Application for an award of costs must be made at the inquiry or hearing, and the inspector will hear representations on the relevant issues from both parties. The decision on the application for costs is contained in a separate decision letter from the main appeal, although both decisions are usually issued together. By way of illustration as to the relative rarity of costs applications, only 4% of written representations, 20% of hearing cases and 25% of inquiry cases resulted in an application for costs, with only about 40% of applications resulting in a costs order.

1.8.3 Challenging appeal decisions

Section 288 of the TCPA 1990 provides the power for an appeal decision to be challenged in the courts. Normally, this can only be done by one of the two principal parties, but in a few cases, it is possible for a third party to demonstrate a sufficiently material interest in order to obtain judicial review.

The time limit for challenges using section 288 is six weeks from the date of the decision. The grounds on which a challenge may be made are principally legal or procedural. In the event that a successful challenge is made, the important point is that this does not mean that the SSCLG's decision is reversed, but that the decision is quashed, and the matter remitted to the SSCLG for reconsideration. It is not, therefore, uncommon for a successful legal challenge to be made, only then for the SSCLG to reconsider the case and come up with the same conclusion as before, having corrected the legal or procedural flaws of the initial decision.

1.8.4 Judicial review

A person who is not the applicant may feel aggrieved by the decision to grant planning permission. It may, in some cases, be possible to seek to have that decision reviewed by judicial review. Speed is required as there is an obligation to make a prompt application.

1.9 Enforcement

Development without permission is, ordinarily, not a criminal offence. The sanctions available are largely civil in nature. However, failing to act in accordance with notices to desist or to reinstate may bring the criminal law into play.

1.9.1 Lapse of time

Sometimes development takes place and no enforcement is carried out, either because the LPA does not get to know or because it is not considered a serious matter.

Time limits are set by the legislation. If development takes place and subsequently the time passes without enforcement action, then the LPA may not subsequently enforce. For operational development the time period is four years and for changes of use the period is ten years. The exception is the case of a change of use to a single dwelling house, where the limit is four years.

1.9.2 Planning contravention notices

Where the LPA suspects that there may have been a contravention, it may serve (pursuant to ss. 171C–171D of the TCPA 1990) a notice, described as a planning contravention notice, requiring the occupier to give information so that the LPA can establish whether there has been a breach. A refusal by the occupier to cooperate may cause the next level of process – an enforcement notice – to be initiated and may adversely affect the recipient's ability to seek compensation in the event that a 'stop notice' is served. Failure to comply with any requirement of a planning contravention notice within a period of 21 days, or the giving of misleading information, is a criminal offence.

1.9.3 Enforcement notices

1.9.3.1 Powers and procedures

By section 172 of the TCPA 1990, a LPA may issue an enforcement notice where it appears to it: '(a) that there has been a breach of planning control; and (b) that it is expedient to issue the notice, having regard to the provisions of the development plan and to any other material consideration'.

The notice may be in respect of:

(1) any development for which there is no planning permission;
(2) the breach of a condition attaching to the planning permission (there is also a separate power under section 187A to issue a 'breach of condition notice').

The notice is to be served on the owner, occupier and any other person who has an interest which, in the LPA's opinion, is materially affected. The notice must state the date upon which it is to take effect; that is, the LPA must give time for compliance.

Strict time limits apply. The notice must be served within 28 days of its issue, that is, from the date when it is made by the LPA. It must also be served 28 days or longer before it is specified to take effect. Different dates may be given for different steps or activities.

The notice must contain a number of prescribed matters, including identifying the breach and what the recipient must do to rectify the breach. This may include:

(a) the alteration or removal of any building or works, (b) the carrying out of any building operation, (c) any activity on the land not to be carried out, (d) the contour of a deposit of refuse or waste materials on land to be modified…
(s. 173(5) of the TCPA 1990).

1.9.3.2 Under-enforcement and the deemed grant of planning permission

By section 173(11), if the notice could have required any buildings to be removed or activity to cease and it does not do so, planning permission is deemed to be granted.

1.9.3.3 The duration of an enforcement notice

Once the notice is served, it continues to have effect and is not discharged by compliance; thus, later contraventions are caught by the notice even though the original contravention was remedied.

1.9.3.4 Failure to comply with an enforcement notice

By section 179 of the PCA 1991, a person who does not comply with the enforcement notice commits a criminal offence and may be charged and tried. Although the practice developed in some areas whereby the person charged would seek planning permission for the development and an adjournment of the criminal proceedings, the courts are now unwilling to adjourn the matter – the offence is the failure to comply and the merits of the planning application are irrelevant.

1.9.3.5 Appealing an enforcement notice

Section 174(1) of the TCPA 1990 provides a right of appeal to the SSCLG. Speed is essential as the appeal must be by notice in writing before the date specified in the notice upon which it is to take effect – there is no power to extend the date. The appeal may be made on a number of grounds set on out in section 174(2): planning permission ought to be granted or the condition ought to be discharged; the matters complained of have not in fact occurred or do not amount to a breach of planning control; the LPA did not have power to enforce (e.g. because the development was sufficiently long-standing); the steps specified exceed what is necessary to remedy the breach; the period allowed for compliance is insufficient. Those grounds can only be raised on an appeal pursuant to section 174 – however, other grounds, such as the alleged nullity of a notice may in some cases be raised, for example, as a defence in criminal proceedings.

An appeal is also deemed to amount to an application for planning permission – section 177(5) of the TCPA 1990.

The applicable procedures are set out in the Town and Country Planning (Enforcement Notices and Appeals) Regulations 2002 to which reference should be made. This sets out a clear and rapid timetable within which the appeal will proceed.

By way of decision, the SSCLG may:

(a) grant planning permission… (b) discharge any condition… (c) determine whether… any existing use of the land was lawful…
(s. 177 TCPA 1990).

The SSCLG may also vary the enforcement notice and this is frequently done.

A further appeal to the High Court is available to either party on a point of law, but requires permission of the court. Again, speed is essential: the appeal must be made within 28 days of the SSCLG decision.

1.9.4 Breach of condition notice

Section 187A provides an alternative route for enforcement in the case of breaches of condition. Although there is no mechanism in the legislation for challenging the validity of a breach of condition notice, its invalidity may be raised as a defence in some cases upon prosecution for failure to comply with it.

1.9.5 Stop notices

Enforcement proceedings may take some time. It is useful, therefore, for LPAs to have a power to stop the development from proceeding any further. Section 183(1) of the TCPA 1990 provides:

> Where the local planning authority considers it expedient that any relevant activity should cease before the period of compliance with an enforcement notice, they may, when they serve a copy of the enforcement notice or otherwise, serve a notice (in this Act referred to as a 'stop notice') prohibiting the carrying out of that activity on the land to which the enforcement notice relates.

Section 187(1) of the TCPA 1990 provides that it is a criminal offence to fail to comply with a stop notice.

If the stop notice is quashed on the grounds that planning ought to be granted, the LPA may have to provide compensation to the person adversely affected.

A new power to enable LPAs to issue a 'temporary stop notice' was enacted in the PCPA 2004 – which inserts sections 171E to 171H into the TCPA 1990.

1.9.6 Injunctions

Injunctions issued by the court may sometimes be successfully sought as an aid to planning control.

1.10 Environmental issues in relation to planning
1.10.1 Introduction

Environmental issues generally are dealt with in the chapter *Environmental issues*, but in this section we discuss specifically the application of Environmental Impact Assessment (EIA) to planning applications.

Environmental assessment has been a feature of UK planning law since the 1985 EEC Directive (EIA Directive) was implemented in 1988. The Environmental Impact Assessment (England and Wales) Regulations 1999 provide the basic regime. Schemes authorised under other legislation than the TCPA 1990 (e.g. Highways) are subject to different environmental controls. Regard must also be had to the Strategic Environmental Assessment directive 2001/42/EC 'on the assessment of the effects of certain plans and programmes on the environment' transposed into UK law by the Environmental Assessment of Plans and Programmes Regulations 2004. This requires a formal environmental assessment of certain plans and programmes which are likely to have significant effects on the environment.

Even though only a small number of all applications will need to be supported by an environmental statement, there is a general obligation to have regard to biodiversity and geological conservation: see OPDM Circular 06/2005 which provides administrative guidance on the application of the law relating to planning and nature conservation and *Planning Policy Statement 9: Biodiversity and Geological Conservation* (ODPM, 2005) and the accompanying Good Practice Guide (ODPM, 2006).

The terminology is as follows: an Environmental Impact Assessment (EIA) is the entire process by which decisions are reached as to whether or not a project is environmentally acceptable. The Environmental Statement (ES) is the documentation submitted by the developer in relation to his application for planning permission; the required content of an ES is set out in Schedule 4 of the Regulations, including measures to mitigate or offset adverse impacts.

1.10.2 The Environmental Impact Assessment (England and Wales) Regulations 1999

The Regulations distinguish three categories of development project: those in Schedule 1, those in Schedule 2 generally and those specifically in paragraph 13 of Schedule 2.

Those in Schedule 1 always require an ES to accompany the application for planning permission. The list comprises what may be described as traditional 'bad neighbour' projects, such as oil refineries, nuclear power stations, iron and steel smelters, asbestos factories, chemical processing plants, long-distance railways and airports, motorways and express roads and other major roads (more than 10 kilometres long), new inland waterways, ports and trading piers, waste incinerators, ground water extraction, gas, oil, chemical and water pipelines, sewage treatment plants above a specified capacity, dams, intensive poultry or pig farms above a certain size, pulp and paper plants, quarries and opencast mines and petrol and chemical stores above a certain capacity.

These types of development always require an ES, and planning permission for them will not be granted unless they have been subject to a full EIA of which the applicant's ES forms part.

Schedule 2 lists 12 kinds of project, including developments relating to agriculture, the extractive industry, the energy, chemical and mineral industries, metal processing, food and rubber industries, textile, leather and paper industries, infrastructure and tourism and leisure projects. Schedule 2 is designed to include smaller or lower-scale versions. These projects are generally less environmentally damaging or are of smaller scale. For these projects, an ES may or may not

be required depending on whether it meets the criteria set out in terms of thresholds and its proximity to sensitive areas.

The third category is set out in paragraph 13 of Schedule 2 and comprises any development involving a change to or extension of a Schedule 1 project, or to a Schedule 2 project (whether or not the original project was itself subject to EIA), where that extension or change would bring the base scheme within Schedule 1 or 2.

1.10.3 Assessment procedure

When it is clear that the project falls within Schedule 1, or meets the thresholds/criteria for a Schedule 2 project and is to be located in a sensitive area, then an ES must be provided with the application. The LPA and the SSCLG can insist on an ES being submitted for such projects and can request further environmental material if they consider the ES is inadequate.

For Schedule 2 projects it is often unclear whether an ES is required. The developer may request a 'screening opinion' by the LPA to decide the matter. Some proposed developments within Schedule 2 could be carried out as permitted development; but if the LPA issues a screening opinion that an EIA is needed, then permitted development rights are withdrawn and a formal planning application, supported by an ES, must be made. Since 2008, if a planning application is made by a developer and is in the opinion of the LPA a schedule 1 or 2 development, has not been the subject of a screening opinion and does not have an ES accompanying it, the planning application itself will be treated as a request for a screening opinion.

The developer may appeal against a positive screening opinion to the SSCLG, who, after considering the available material, will issue a screening direction, either upholding or dismissing the opinion of the LPA.

If the project does require an EIA, what should the developer's ES contain? For larger schemes it is likely that the developer will already have instructed environmental consultants to advise, and to prepare the initial submission of material where a screening opinion has been sought. However, the Regulations helpfully allow the developer to request a formal statement from the LPA on what the ES should contain. That is called a scoping opinion, and as with the screening opinion, an appeal can be made to the SSCLG, who can issue a scoping direction.

Every planning application that falls within the Regulations is called an 'EIA application'. The LPA has up to 16 weeks to determine such an application. That is largely due to the need to assess the environmental implications of the scheme, and to determine whether the ES addresses them all appropriately. In addition, wider consultation on the scheme is necessary, and any body that is believed to hold environmental information relevant to the environmental effects of the project may be requested (by either the developer or the LPA) to release that information.

Note that an ES is a publicly available document, so should not therefore contain information which the developer wishes to keep confidential.

1.10.4 Other types of scheme

There are types of development which either do not require planning permission or can be permitted under powers other than the TCPA 1990. Examples include: afforestation schemes, land drainage, railways and tramways, harbours and highways. These may require separate environmental assessment, and the Regulations relating to such projects should be studied carefully. In particular, some highway schemes that do not require an EIA for planning purposes (i.e. are not Schedule 2 projects) may require an environmental assessment under specific regulations.

1.11 Protecting heritage
1.11.1 Introduction

Through various pieces of legislation, statutory protection exists for a wide variety of buildings and structures, ranging from archaeological sites, ancient monuments, historic buildings and gardens, and historic areas of cities, towns and villages.

1.11.2 Archaeology and ancient monuments

The principal legislation governing archaeology and ancient monuments is contained within the Ancient Monuments and Archaeological Areas Act 1979 (AMAAA 1979). Government advice on the subject is given in *Planning Policy Statement 5: Planning for the Historic Environment* (DCLG, 2010) (which replaces *PPG16 – Archaeology and Planning* (DCLG, 1990)). Nationally important sites are scheduled and are described as a 'scheduled monument'. In these cases, the consent of the SSCLG is required before any works are carried out which would affect the monument. However, government policy is that irrespective of whether remains are 'scheduled' or not, there is a presumption in favour of their physical preservation, and the preservation of their settings, when threatened by development.

The AMAAA 1979 also provides for the designation of 'Areas of Archaeological Importance' (AAIs). In such locations, developers are required to give six weeks' notice to the relevant LPA of any proposals to disturb the ground. The relevant authority then has the power to excavate the site for up to four and a half months before development may proceed – that is, there may be a delay of up to six months.

LPAs have a responsibility to include policies for archaeology in their development plans. These usually include policies for designating areas considered likely to be of archaeological potential, and for the protection of sites from the adverse effects of development. Where areas have been defined as likely to have archaeological potential, it is now common practice for LPAs to require an archaeological evaluation to be carried out prior to submission of development proposals which involve excavation.

In some case, it is not practically possible to undertake a physical archaeological investigation at the time of submission of a planning application. In these circumstances, the LPA (or its archaeological adviser) may agree to a 'desktop study' by

an experienced archaeologist at the planning application stage. If this study indicates that the site has real potential for archaeological remains, which are likely to be disturbed or uncovered by the development, then a condition will normally be imposed preventing the development from proceeding until a full field evaluation has been carried out to confirm the potential or otherwise.

English Heritage is the principal consultee in respect of applications affecting sites or areas of archaeological interest. Developers may seek archaeological advice from any one of a number of archaeological consultants and, in some areas, County museums offer an archaeological consultancy service, such as the Museum of London.

In the event that archaeological remains are discovered, the consequences will be dependent on the quality and importance of the find. If the find is not significant, often all that is necessary is for an archaeologist to carry out a detailed survey and record of the find. Finds of more significance might lead to a requirement for preservation in situ, and in some cases, the scheduling of the remains as an ancient monument.

Occasionally, remains are discovered during the course of development. If the remains are of significance, the SSCLG has the power to schedule the remains. This means that development will at the very least be delayed until Scheduled Monument Consent is granted. At worst, it could lead to the revocation of the planning permission, in which case, there is provision for compensation.

1.11.3 Listed buildings

The principal legislation governing listed buildings and conservation areas is the Planning (Listed Buildings and Conservation Areas) Act 1990 (P(LBCA)A Act 1990'). Government policy guidance on the subject is given in *Planning Policy Statement 5: Planning for the Historic Environment* (DCLG, 2010) (which replaces *PPG15 – Planning and the Historic Environment* (DCLG, 1994)).

The term building is broadly defined; Jodrell Bank telescope is listed which demonstrates the scope for listing.

The expression 'listed' derives from the fact that a list of Buildings of Special Architectural or Historic Interest is maintained by the Secretary of State for Culture, Media and Sport (SSCMS). Once a building is listed, any development – inside or outside – requires listed building consent.

The building may be classified either as Grade I (of exceptional interest and importance to the nation's heritage) or Grade II (which constitute the majority of listed buildings). A Grade II* listing is also kept to identify the most important Grade II buildings. The grading system is important only in terms of the difficulty which a developer will have in obtaining consent or in obtaining a grant for work on the building.

The main criteria for listing are architectural and historic interest, including associations with nationally important figures or events. Listing may be applied to groups of building, such as squares, terraces and so on.

1.11.3.1 The listing process

Anyone may request the SSCMS to consider listing any building. More commonly though, it is LPAs and English Heritage who request listings following surveys of their areas, or special interest groups, such as the Georgian Group, or the Victorian Society, for example.

Although listing normally involves consultation, there is no obligation on the SSCMS to do so. On occasion it may be believed that a building is in urgent need of protection and in such a case, the SSCMS may 'spot list'. Alternatively, by section 3 of the P(LBCA)A 1990 LPAs have the power to serve such notices on buildings considered to be of special architectural or historic interest which are in danger of demolition or unsatisfactory alteration and which provide a six month window in which the SSCMS must decided whether or not to list. An important factor of this particular process is that if the decision is taken not to list the building, the LPA may be liable to pay compensation to the building owner for any loss or damage caused by service of the notice. There are no compensation provisions in respect of the spot listing process.

There is no right of appeal against listing, but it is open to owners or other interested parties to make a case to the SSCMS that a building should not be listed. The decision of the SSCMS on such a request is final and there is no right of appeal against this decision.

If owners are concerned about the risk to a development of their building being listed, they may make an application under section 6 of the P(LBCA)A 1990 to the SCMS for a 'Certificate of Immunity' to avoid the expense of making applications which will falter because of subsequent listing. The certificate prevents listing for five years.

1.11.3.2 The protection

Section 7 of the P(LBCA)A 1990 provides that no 'no person shall execute or cause to be executed any works for the demolition of a listed building or for its alteration or extension in any manner which would affect its character as a building of special architectural or historic interest, unless the works are authorised'. Section 9 provides that a contravention is a criminal offence. A defence requires proof that: (a) the works were urgently necessary, (b) that no other reasonable alternative was available, (c) that he works were the minimum required and (d) that notice was given in writing to the LPA as soon as reasonably practicable.

Note, however, that whilst many listing buildings are churches, many of the provisions of the statute do not apply to them.

1.11.3.3 Applications for listed building consent

When considering work to a listed building a number of factors should be clearly in mind:

(1) if a building is listed, it is listed in its entirety, including everything within its curtilage

(2) any work on the building (whether or not that work would fall within the scope of development under the TCPA 1990 regime) which affects its character requires consent

(3) work to the building which also constitutes development requires planning permission as well as listed building consent.

Applications for listed building consent are submitted to the LPA for the area in which the building is situated. The procedure is set out in section 10 P(LBCA)A 1990 and the Planning (Listed Building and Conservation Areas) Regulations 1990. The process is not dissimilar to an application for planning permission. It includes a requirement for a design and access statement.

1.11.3.4 The grant of consent

There is, obviously, a basic policy presumption in favour of preservation of the building, and all applications must be fully justified against strict criteria set out in PPG15. In summary this means: the presumption becomes stronger the more important the building; the facets of the building which justify its listing are most strongly to be retained. But consent will be granted if the criteria are established; indeed consent to demolish listed buildings is sometimes granted.

Conditions may be made on listed building consent and the LPA must give short reasons.

Although outline consent is not available, the LPA may grant consent subject to a condition reserving to itself a right of approval of subsequent details to be supplied.

1.11.3.5 Appeals

An appeal process is available which closely mirrors the section 78 process.

1.11.3.6 Enforcement

As well as prosecuting for contravention of the regime, LPAs may under section 38 P(LBCA)A 1990 issue a 'listed building enforcement notice'. There is generally no need for a stop notice because an offence is already by that stage being committed.

The notice will specify what is required, including restoring a building to its former state. A notice may be served at any time, even after the sale of the building to a new owner; in that case it will be the new owner who will be required to comply.

1.11.3.7 Repairs notices and compulsory acquisition

Under sections 54–55 of the P(LBCA)A 1990, LPAs have power to carry out urgent works of repair to unoccupied listed buildings, after giving notice to owners, and to recover their costs.

Alternatively, in the case of occupied buildings or non-urgent works, they can serve a 'repairs notice' on the owner in accordance with section 48 of the P(LBCA)A 1990. In the event that the notice is not complied with, the LPA may then begin compulsory purchase proceedings.

1.11.4 Conservation areas

The principle of a conservation area designation is that not just isolated building but the character of the entire area is to be protected. The legislation covering conservation areas is also the Planning (Listed Buildings and Conservation Areas) Act 1990. Likewise, government policy advice for conservation areas is also found in *Planning Policy Statement 5 (PPS5): Planning for the Historic Environment* (DCLG, 2010) (which replaces *PPG15 – Planning and the Historic Environment* (DCLG, 1994)).

Section 69 of the P(LBC)A 1990 imposes a duty on LPAs to designate areas of special architectural or historic interest, the character or appearance of which it is desirable to preserve or enhance, as conservation areas.

1.11.4.1 Conservation area controls

One of the main effects of conservation area legislation is to establish control over the demolition of unlisted buildings in designated conservation areas. The legislation establishes the requirement to obtain conservation area consent for the demolition of any building (other than a listed building) in a conservation area. Government policy (DCLG, 2010) then takes this further. Although the intention of conservation areas is primarily to protect the character and appearance of areas rather than individual buildings, unlisted buildings which make a positive contribution are subject to a presumption in favour of retention. Furthermore, PPS5 (DCLG, 2010) indicates that proposals to demolish such buildings should be considered against the same broad criteria as proposals to demolish listed buildings.

The inference of this is that in conservation areas, all buildings other than those few which detract from the area's quality, or at least make no contribution to its character, are to be treated as though they were listed buildings in the event of demolition being proposed.

This policy statement has given rise to a degree of controversy and debate in planning circles, but has largely been supported by LPAs, many of whom contain conservation policies in their development plans which strengthen and reinforce the government line.

Conservation area controls do not extend to alterations and additions to buildings, nor to internal alterations. To this extent, they fall short of applying the equivalent of listed building controls to all buildings in conservation areas. Where, however, an alteration proposed to a building is so extensive that it would result in the demolition of a substantial part of it, conservation area consent may be required.

1.11.4.2 Designation of conservation areas

Proposals to designate conservation areas are subject to public consultation and local publicity, but there is no legal obligation

to notify owners of proposals for designation. Nor is there any right of appeal against designation.

Section 72 of the P(LBC)A 1990 imposes a duty upon LPAs to pay special attention to the desirability of preserving or enhancing the character or appearance of conservation areas. This requirement is to be applied in the exercise of all the LPAs' planning functions in its area.

1.11.4.3 Effect of designation on permitted development rights

Some permitted development rights are either removed or altered by conservation area status. Examples are stone-cladding of dwellings, insertion of dormer windows into roof slopes and erection of satellite dishes. Also, the size of automatically permitted extensions to dwellings and industrial buildings is reduced.

Other permitted development rights in conservation areas may be removed or reduced by the LPA through the use of directions under Article 4 of the GPDO 1995, subject to approval by the SSCLG.

1.11.4.4 Trees in conservation areas

All trees in conservation areas (subject to certain specified exemptions) are subject to a requirement to give six weeks' notice to the LPA prior to being cut down, lopped or topped. This is because trees are often considered to be important features in the townscape, and the notice period gives the LPA an opportunity to consider serving a Tree Preservation Order. Penalties for failure to comply are similar to those for tree preservation order contraventions, namely a fine or imprisonment.

1.11.4.5 Application procedures

All applications for conservation area consent are made to the relevant LPA, on the Authority's prescribed form. Applications for conservation area consents would rarely be entertained unless accompanied by a planning application for a replacement building. Outline planning applications for replacement buildings are unlikely to be accepted, as a detailed proposal is usually essential in order for the LPA to assess whether the proposal will result in the enhancement or preservation of the character or appearance of the area.

The procedure is similar to that for a listed building consent application, with the exception that there are no statutory obligations for notification of the applications to central government agencies. Many LPAs, however, have established conservation area advisory committees, whose views and advice are sought on applications in conservation areas.

Rights of appeal to the SSCLG exist in respect of non-determination, refusal, or the imposition of unreasonable conditions, adopting procedures almost identical to those for planning and listed building consent applications.

1.12 Trees and hedges

Construction frequently involves cutting down trees or hedge-rows. Due to constraints of space, this will be dealt with only in the briefest outline.

1.12.1 Trees

Cutting down trees does not appear to be within the definition of development and hence not subject to development control. However, there are two forms of protection:

(1) by section 198 of the TCPA 1990 the LPA may make a tree preservation order which specifies the trees affected
(2) trees in a conservation area are protected.

The term tree is not defined and there has been some debate as to what is and is not caught by the definition. Lord Denning once remarked that a tree ought to be something over seven or eight inches in diameter, but other judges have said that the term should bear its natural meaning and judged on a case by case basis.

It is a criminal offence to destroy (or to lop it so that it is likely to be destroyed) a tree which enjoys the protection of a preservation order. The offence is one of strict liability; it is important therefore to check that a tree is not protected before destroying it.

In May 2009, the government published updated guidance (DCLG, 2000 and DCLG, 2009 Addendum) on tree preservation orders and tree protection within the existing legal framework.

1.12.2 Hedgerows

Some hedgerows are also protected. The primary legislation is to be found in section 97 of the Environmental Protection Act 1995 and the Hedgerows Regulations 1997 came into force in June 1997. The scope of the protection extends to hedgerows 'growing in or adjacent to any common land, protected land or land used for agriculture, forestry or the breeding or keeping of horses, ponies and donkey, if the hedgerow has a continuous length of 20 m or more or meets another hedgerow at each end.' Before removing a protected hedgerow, a person must serve a 'hedgerow removal notice' on the LPA. The LPA will issue a 'hedgerow retention notice' if it is satisfied that the hedgerow is an important hedgerow.

Contravention of a number of the regulations constitute criminal offences.

References

DCLG (1990) *Planning Policy Guidance 16 (PPG16): Archaeology and Planning.* HMSO, London, UK. Available for download from: http://webarchive.nationalarchives.gov.uk and www.communities. gov.uk/publications/planningandbuilding/ppg16 [Note this publication has been replaced by DCLG, 2010]